Tidal Current Tables 2019 Atlantic Coast of North America

North Wind Publishing

Brewer, Maine, USA

North Wind Publishing
P.O. Box 3655
Brewer, ME 04915
northwindpublishing.com
info@northwindpublishing.com

Printed in the United States of America.

ISBN-13: 978-0-9995143-6-8

Tidal Current Tables 2019

Atlantic Coast of North America

Issued 2018

SOURCES OF ADDITIONAL INFORMATION

THE NATIONAL OCEAN SERVICE IS NO LONGER PRINTING AND DISTRIBUTING THE TIDE AND TIDAL CURRENT TABLES

Tide and Tidal current data continue to be updated, generated and published by the NOAA/ National Ocean Service; however, the printing and distribution in book-form is now done by several private companies working from information provided by NOS.

NOS now offers two vehicles for obtaining predictions. First, the complete set of Tables as camera-ready page-images will be available on CD-ROM. The CD-ROM vehicle is primarily intended for use by federal or private printers who wish to print in book-form the full set of Tables for distribution to resellers and the general public. Second, for domestic tide stations, predictions are available on the NOS, Center for Operational Oceanographic Products and Services (CO-OPS), website, (http://tidesandcurrents.noaa.gov/).

In addition to predictions, the website provides updated information on the status of the Tables as they are finalized each year. Notices concerning the most recent Table updates and publication cut-off dates are included.

For the names of companies printing and distributing the Tables, please call or write to:

National Ocean Service
Oceanographic Division, N/OPS3
1305 East-West Highway
Silver Spring, MD 20910
(301) 713-2815, fax (301) 713-4500

A list of authorized sales agents is published in the Nautical Chart Catalogs or may be obtained on request from the National Ocean Service.

TECHNICAL ASSISTANCE:

Technical questions relating to **tide and current predictions,** as well as requests for **special predictions**, should be addressed to:

National Ocean Service
Oceanographic Division, N/OPS3
1305 East-West Highway
Silver Spring, MD 20910
(301) 713-2815

Technical questions relating to **actual tide observations, tidal datums, and other information necessary** for **engineering projects** should be addressed to:

National Ocean Service
Oceanographic Division, N/OPS3
1305 East-West Highway
Silver Spring, MD 20910
(301) 713-2815

Technical questions relating to *other publications and nautical charts* should be addressed to:

National Ocean Service
Navigation Services Division
1315 East-West Highway
Silver Spring, MD 20910
(888) 990-NOAA (6622)

SOURCES OF ADDITIONAL INFORMATION

WEBSITES

Center for Operational Oceanographic Products and Services
(PORTS® * Predictions * Observations * Bench Marks * Tides Online * Great Lakes Online)
http://tidesandcurrents.noaa.gov

Marine Chart Division - http://www.nauticalcharts.noaa.gov

Office for Coastal Management - http://www.coast.noaa.gov

Ocean Predictions Center - http://www.opc.ncep.noaa.gov

National Center for Environmental Information - https://www.ncei.noaa.gov

National Centers for Environmental Predictions - http://www.ncep.noaa.gov

National Climatic Data Center - http://www.ncdc.noaa.gov

National Data Buoy Center - http://www.ndbc.noaa.gov

National Geodetic Survey - http://www.ngs.noaa.gov

National Geophysical Data Center - http://www.ngdc.noaa.gov

National Ocean Service - http://www.oceanservice.noaa.gov

National Oceanic and Atmospheric Administration - http://www.noaa.gov

National Oceanographic Data Center - http://www.nodc.noaa.gov

National Weather Service - http://www.weather.gov

U.S. Coast Guard - http://www.uscg.mil

U.S. Geological Survey - http://www.usgs.gov

U.S. Naval Observatory - http://www.usno.navy.mil

U.S. Naval Oceanographic Office - http://www.usno.navy.mil/NAVO

CORRECTIONS:

Corrections to this publication, after the date of printing, may appear in the Notice to Mariners. They may also appear in the Local Notice to Mariners, published weekly, by the various United States Coast Guard Districts.

CONTENTS

IMPORTANT NOTICES

Daylight-saving time is not used in this publication. All daily tidal current predictions and predictions compiled by the use of Table 2 data are based on the standard time meridian indicated for each location. Predicted times may be converted to daylight-saving times, where necessary, by adding 1 hour to these data. In converting times from the Astronomical Data page on the inside back cover, it should be remembered that daylight saving time is based on a meridian 15° east of the normal standard meridian for a particular place.

NOS, in partnership with other agencies and institutions, has established a series of Physical Oceanographic Real Time Systems (PORTS®) in selected areas. These PORTS® sites provide constantly updated information on tide and tidal current conditions, water temperature, and weather conditions. This information is updated every six minutes. PORTS® sites are currently in operation at several major harbors with future sites to be added. The information is accessible through a computer data connection or by a voice response system at the following numbers:

PORTS® SITES	VOICE ACCESS	INTERNET ACCESS
CAPE COD	888-714-2776	www.tidesandcurrents.noaa.gov
CHARLESTON HARBOR	855-216-2137	"
CHERRY POINT	888-817-7794	"
CHESAPEAKE BAY	866-CH-PORTS (866-247-6787)	"
CORPUS CHRISTI	866-728-1897	"
CUYAHOGA	800-376-1192	"
DELAWARE RIVER & BAY	866-30-PORTS (866-307-6787)	"
HOUSTON/GALVESTON	866-HG-PORTS (866-447-6787)	"
HUMBOLDT BAY	855-876-5015	"
JACKSONVILLE	855-901-1549	"
LAKE CHARLES	888-817-7692	"
LOS ANGELES/ LONG BEACH	Not Available	"
LOWER COLUMBIA RIVER	888-53-PORTS (888-537-6787)	"
LOWER MISSISSIPPI RIVER	888-817-7767	"
MATAGORDA BAY	888-524-9765	"
MIAMI	888-270-6145	"
MOBILE BAY	877-84-PORTS (877-847-6787)	"
MORGAN CITY	888-312-4113	"
NARRAGANSETT BAY	866-75-PORTS (866-757-6787)	"
NEW HAVEN	888-80-PORTS (888-807-6787)	"
NEW LONDON	855-626-0509	"
NEW YORK/NEW JERSEY	866-21-PORTS (866-217-6787)	"
PASCAGOULA	888-257-1857	"
PORT EVERGLADES	866-213-5269	"
PORT FOURCHON	855-687-2084	"
PORT OF ANCHORAGE	866-AK-PORTS (866-257-6787)	"
SABINE NECHES	888-257-1859	"
SAN FRANCISCO BAY	866-SB-PORTS (866-727-6787)	"
SAVANNAH	855-907-3136	"
SOO LOCKS	301-713-9596	"
TACOMA	888-60-PORTS (888-607-6787)	"
TAMPA BAY	866-TB-PORTS (866-827-6787)	"
TOLEDO	888-547-9131	"

IMPORTANT NOTICES

PUBLISHED CAUTIONARY NOTICES

Published in Local Notice to Mariners and United States Coast Pilot Notices

UPDATE TO THE 2012 EDITION OF THE NOS TIDAL CURRENT TABLES

The NOAA National Ocean Service's Center for Operational Oceanographic Products and Services (CO-OPS) is updating the tidal current predictions published for the Long Island Sound within the 2012 Tidal Current Tables – Atlantic Coast of North America. Reference stations in this area have been updated with new data; historic secondary stations have been updated; and a number of new stations have been added.

(Issued: October 1, 2011)

OBSERVED TIDAL CONDITIONS DIFFER FROM TIDAL PREDICTIONS IN THE HUDSON RIVER

The observed tides along the Hudson River have been reported to differ significantly from the Published tide predictions; particularly in the northern section of the river from Newburgh to Albany, New York. Based on limited reports and comparisons to USGS stream gauges, it appears that high tides are occurring approximately 1 hour earlier than predicted.

NOAA has no information on what may be causing the difference between predictions and observations. This could be the result of natural changes (shoaling, erosion, etc) or artificial changes (dredging, construction, etc.) in the Hudson River. Based on preliminary evidence, this does not appear to be a temporary condition and may indicate a long term change in the tidal conditions of the Hudson River.

NOAA does not have any water level stations operating along the length of the Hudson River, with the nearest operating station being located at The Battery, New York. Without observational data in the area, the extent of the difference between predictions and observations cannot be confirmed; neither can the areas affected by this change. Resources are not available for the installation and operation of water level stations along the Hudson River.

Mariners operating in this area are urged to use caution.

(Issued: May 24, 2010)

CHANGES TO 2008 EDITIONS OF THE NOS TIDAL CURRENT TABLES

Three new tidal current reference stations have been added to the National Ocean Service tidal Current Tables for 2008. Table 2 "time" and "velocity" correction factors at secondary stations which are affected by these changes have been updated based on the new reference station data.

Tidal Current Tables - 2008 - Atlantic Coast of North America
1. Bucksport, Penobscot Bay, Maine (new)
2. George Washington Bridge, Hudson River (new)
3. Kingston-Rhinecliff, Bridge, Hudson River (new)

(Issued October 1, 2006)

TIDAL CURRENT PREDICTIONS INSIDE U.S. ESTUARIES

At present there are several U.S. estuaries with operational Physical Oceanographic Real Time Systems (PORTS) installed. PORTS systems are presently being installed in several additional estuaries. Over the next ten years there are projected to be twenty or more additional systems installed. In the past, the tidal current reference station has always been located at the entrance to each estuary. All tidal current secondary stations both inside and outside (along the coast) have been referred to the reference station at the entrance to the estuary. This will no longer be the case in estuaries with an operational PORTS system.

Estuaries with an operational PORTS system will have at least two reference stations. One will be the historic station at the entrance to the estuary. All secondary stations along the coast will continue to be referred to this station. The second tidal current reference station will be the primary PORTS station within the estuary. All secondary locations within the estuary itself will be referred to this location. Depending on the circulation dynamics of the estuary, daily tidal current predictions may be provided for one or more additional stations within the estuary.

(Issued October 1, 1999)

ARANSAS PASS – CORPUS CHRISTI BAY, TX

IMPORTANT NOTICES

The Aransas-Corpus Christi Pilots have reported that published tidal current predictions for Aransas Pass deviate from observations by as much as two (2) hours. The published predictions must be used with extreme caution. The Pilots should be consulted for critical transits. Tidal Current predictions of the National Ocean Service (NOS) are derived from analysis of observed data at tidal harmonic frequencies which in turn are based on predictable astronomic positions of the moon and sun. The problem in manyareas of the Gulf of Mexico, including the south Texas coast, is that localized meteorological conditions can significantly effect and alter the times of maximum flood and ebb currents. Real-time observation and reporting systems, such as the Physical Oceanographic Real Time System (PORTS) installed in the Galveston-Houston area, are the only means of providing accurate tidal current data for areas such as this.

(Issued July 17, 1997)

BISCAYNE BAY/PORT OF MIAMI, FL

The Biscayne Bay Pilots report that recent dredging and construction by the US Corps of Engineers (COE) supporting Miami port expansion has significantly effected the currents in Miami Harbor. Both flood and ebb currents should be expected to be stronger than indicated in official published predictions. The actual times for maximum and slack currents should be expected to deviate from the published predictions. Funding to support a survey to obtain new data for more accurate tidal current predictions is not available at this time. Installation of a Physical Oceanographic Real Time System (PORTS), like the one in operation in Tampa Bay, would be the best solution for long term marine safety.

(Issued July 17, 1997)

CHARLESTON HARBOR, SC

The US Army Corps of Engineers (CEO) is planning dredging and construction projects for Charleston Harbor in 1996-1997. Such projects in the past in other areas have resulted in dramatic changes in the observed tidal currents of those areas. Once dredging and/or construction operations commence, the Tidal Current predictions for this region should be considered questionable and potentially dangerous to rely upon. Tide predictions will also be affected but to a lesser degree. Funding for a real time system to monitor the Tidal Currents and a resurvey of the area after COE operations are complete is presently not available. Therefore, once COE operations begin and until such time as a real-time system is installed or a resurvey of the area conducted, the National Oceanic and Atmospheric Administration, National Ocean Service will be unable to provide accurate Tidal Current predictions necessary for marine safety and navigation in this area.

(Issued June 5, 1996)

CHESAPEAKE & DELAWARE CANAL AND BALTIMORE HARBOR CONNECTING CHANNELS

The US Army Corps of Engineers (COE) is planning a project involving the Chesapeake & Delaware Canal (C&D) and the channels in the upper Chesapeake Bay connecting the canal to Baltimore, MD in 1996-1997. Such projects in the past in other areas have resulted in dramatic changes in the observed tidal currents of those areas. Once the project begins, the Tidal Current predictions for the C&D Canal and the channels connecting the canal to Baltimore should be considered questionable and potentially dangerous to rely upon. Tide predictions will be affected but to a lesser degree. Funding for a real-time system to monitor the Tidal Currents and a resurvey of these areas after COE operations are complete is presently not available. Therefore, once COE operations begin and until such time as a real-time system is installed or a resurvey of the area conducted, the National Oceanic and Atmospheric Administration, National Ocean Service will be unable to provide accurate Tidal Current predictions necessary for marine safety and navigation in this area.

(Issued June 5, 1996)

ST. AUGUSTINE, FL – ATLANTIC INTRACOASTAL WATERWAY

The US Coast Guard (USCG) has reported a problem involving the Tidal Currents in the Atlantic Intracoastal Waterway (AICW) in the St. Augustine, FL area. The specific location is the Bridge of Lions over the waterway. Numerous accidents have occurred at this site which are related to the currents in the waterway. There is no National Ocean Service (NOS) Tidal Current Station at or near the Bridge of Lions. Thus the NOS cannot, at this time, make Tidal Current predictions for this location. The USCG states that the cause of the accidents is loss of maneuverability (control) as a vessel passes under the

IMPORTANT NOTICES

bridge. The loss of maneuverability results in the vessel striking the bridge supports. The USCG states in part:

"The affect of a 'fair' tide on a navigating vessel is to reduce the vessel's ability to maneuver. When a vessel is proceeding with a current (fair tide), less water flows across the vessel's rudders. This condition has the affect of reducing the vessel's maneuverability for a given speed over ground (all other things being equal).

The Bridge of Lions is a difficult bridge to navigate, even under ideal conditions. This circa 1926 Bascule bridge has a horizontal clearance of only 76' verses the 90' horizontal clearance of most of the other bridges on this section of the AICW."

In addition, according to the US Coast Pilot, Vol 4, Chapter 12, Tidal Currents in excess of 2 knots often run at right angles to the bridge opening. The Coast Pilot advises mariners to transit the bridge at minimal Tidal Current conditions. Funding for real-time monitoring of the Tidal Currents or a survey to obtain Tidal Current observations upon which to base Tidal Current predictions for this location is not presently available. A consortium of local, state, and federal officials in conjunction with the private sector and commercial shipping interests are presently studying various options to provide accurate Tidal Current predictions necessary for marine safety and navigation at this location.

(Issued June 5, 1996)

WILMINGTON AND CAPE FEAR RIVER, NC

The US Army Corps of Engineers (COE) is due to begin dredging operations in the Wilmington and Cape Fear River area in 1997. The plans call for the deepening of the channel approaching Wilmington and extending up the Cape Fear River. Such actions in the past in other areas have resulted in dramatic changes in the observed tidal currents of those areas. Once dredging operations commence, the Tidal Current predictions for this region should be considered questionable at best and potentially dangerous to rely upon. Tide predictions will also be affected but to a lesser degree. Funding for a real-time system to monitor the Tidal Currents during the project and a resurvey of the area after COE operations are complete is presently not available. Therefore, once COE operations begin and until such time as a real-time system is installed or a resurvey of the area conducted, the National Oceanic and Atmospheric Administration, National Ocean Service will be unable to provide accurate Tidal Current predictions necessary for marine safety and navigation in this area.

(Issued June 5, 1996)

HAMPTON ROADS, VA

Tidal currents in Hampton Roads and Elizabeth River have been significantly altered by dredging and construction of a new bridge/tunnel. Recent dredging by the U.S. Army Corps of Engineers has deepened the channels by 10 feet to a depth of 50 feet. Pilots and officials at the Norfolk Naval Base report hazardous conditions including significantly higher than predicted maximum current velocities, and significant deviation in the predicted times of maximum current. Mariners should exercise EXTREME CAUTION and DISCRETION in the use of published NOS tidal current predictions for this area. Funding for a Quality Assurance study and a full scale resurvey of the area is presently not available.

(Issued March 24, 1992)

CHINCOTEAGUE CHANNEL, VA

United States Coast Guard (USCG) Personnel at the Chincoteague Coast Guard Station, VA report that the times of high and low water computed from differences in Table 2 of the East Coast Tide Tables are frequently off by as much as an hour. The channel is subject to shoaling and is frequently dredged. Exercise caution in using Table 2 Tide differences for this area.

(Issued May 17, 1991)

INTRODUCTION

Current tables for the use of mariners have been published by the National Ocean Service (formerly the Coast and Geodetic Survey) since 1890. Tables for the Atlantic coast first appeared as a part of the tide tables and consisted of brief directions for obtaining the times of the current for a few locations from the times of high and low waters. Daily predictions of slack water for five stations were given for the year 1916, and by 1923 the tables had so expanded that they were then issued as a separate publication entitled Current Tables, Atlantic Coast. A companion volume, Current Tables, Pacific Coast, was also issued that year. In 1930 the predictions for the Atlantic coast were extended to include the times and velocities of maximum current.

In the preparation of these tables, all available observations were used. In some cases, however, the observations were insufficient for obtaining final results, and as further information becomes available it will be included in subsequent editions. All persons using these tables are invited to send information or suggestions for increasing their usefulness to the National Ocean Service, Oceanographic Division, 1305 East-West Highway, N/OPS3, Silver Spring, Maryland 20910, U.S.A. The data for lightship stations are based on observations obtained through the cooperation of the U.S. Coast Guard. By cooperative arrangements, full predictions for Bay of Fundy Entrance (Grand Manan Channel) were furnished by the Canadian Hydrographic Service.

Daily predicted times of slack water and predicted times and velocities of maximum current (flood and ebb) are presented in table 1 for a number of reference stations. Similar predictions for many other locations may be obtained by applying the correction factors listed in Table 2 to the predictions of the appropriate reference station. The speed of a current at times between slack water and maximum current may be approximated by the use of table 3. The duration of weak current near the time of slack water may be computed by the use of Table 4.

LIST OF REFERENCE STATIONS

Station Name	Page	Updated	Data Series
Aransas Pass (between jetties), Texas.....................	188	1995	1 Month (4/9/1990-5/7/1990)
Baltimore Harbor Approach, Maryland.....................	96	1965	29 Days Begining 8/14/1963
Bath Iron Works, Kennebec River...........................	16	2017	1 Month (6/20-8/1/2015)
Bay of Fundy Entrance (Grand Manan Channel)......	4		
Bergen Point Reach (Bayonne Bridge), New York ...	72	1999	4 Months (1/1/1998-4/30/1998)
Bolivar Roads, Galveston Bay, Texas	184	2000	453 Days (5/22/1997-9/9/1998)
Boston Harbor (Deer Island Light), Massachusetts ..	28	2013	2 Months (5/14/2011-7/1/2011)
Brandywine Shoal Light, Delaware Bay...................	80	2004	1 Month (11/22/2002-12/23/2002)
Bucksport, Penobscot Bay, Maine	12	2008	1 Months (7/14/2006-8/22/2006)
Calcasieu Pass, Louisiana....................................	172	2016	5 months (9/18/2009-2/28/2010)
Cape Cod Canal (RR. Bridge), Massachusetts	36	2014	3 Months (6/19/2009-9/4/2009)
Charleston Harbor (off Ft. Sumter), South Carolina..	112	1997	2 Months (5/26/1987-7/28/1987)
Chesapeake & Delaware Canal (Chesapeake City).	100	2016	5 months (1/1/2009-6/1/2009)
Chesapeake Bay Entrance, Virginia	92	2016	5 months (8/27/2009-1/13/2010)
Delaware Bay Entrance	76	2016	1 month (7/13/2000-8/16/2000)
Estes Head, Eastport, Maine	8	2000	16 Months (5/22/1997-9/9/1998)
Fort Pierce Inlet Entrance, Florida	128	2011	2 Months (11/14/2008-1/11/2009)
Galveston Bay Entrance (between jetties), Texas	180	1970	58 Days Beginning 4/5/1935
George Washington Bridge, Hudson River..............	64	2008	3 Months (8/14/2006-11/01/2006)
Hell Gate (off Mill Rock), East River, New York........	56	1970	35 Days (1932)
Johns Pass Entrance, Florida	160	2013	1 Month (11/15/2011-12/13/2011)
Key West, Florida..	144	2014	3 Months (1/26/2013-4/10/2013)
Kingston-Rhinecliff Bridge, Hudson River................	68	2008	3 Months (8/14/2006-11/01/2006)
Lake Worth Inlet Entrance, Florida	132	2011	1 Month (12/17/2008-1/19/2009)
Miami Harbor Entrance, Florida	140	2011	4 Months (11/15/2008-3/18/2009)
Mobile Bay Entrance, Alabama..............................	168	1944	29 Days (1935)
Old Tampa Bay Entrance (Port Tampa), Florida	156	2016	5 months (3/1/2009-8/26/2009)
Philadelphia (Penns Landing), Delaware River	88	2004	1 Month (3/25/2003-4/25/2003)
Pollock Rip Channel, Massachusetts.......................	44	1965	2 Years (1934-1936)
Port Everglades Entrance, Florida	136	2011	4 Months (11/15/2008-3/18/3009)
Portland Harbor Entrance	20	2016	2 months (5/10/2014-7/30/2014)
Portsmouth Harbor Entrance, N.H.	24	1953	15 Days beginning 9/16/1953
Quonset Point, Narragansett Bay, Rhode Island	40	2003	1 Year (7/1/2000-6/29/2001)
Reedy Point, Delaware Bay	84	2018	6 months (4-9/2011)
Sabine Pass, Texas...	176	2016	5 months (5/5/2010-11/5/2010)
Savannah River Entrance, Georgia	116	1999	2 Months (5/7/1997-7/20/1997)
Southport, Cape Fear River, North Carolina.............	104	2018	2 months (3/17/2016 - 5/11/2016)
St. Andrew Bay Entrance, Florida	164	2010	2 Months (1/11/2008-3/6/2008)
St. Johns River Entrance, Florida	124	2000	3 Months (4/16/1998-7/21/1998)
St. Marys River Entrance, Georgia	120	2013	1 Month (11/3/2011-12/27/2011)
Tampa Bay (Sunshine Skyway Bridge), Florida	152	2016	5 months (3/11/2009-8/23/2009)
Tampa Bay Entrance (Egmont Channel), Florida.....	148	1994	13 Months (8/20/1990-9/25/1991)
The Narrows, New York Harbor, New York	60	2003	6 Months (10/19/2001-4/30/2002)
The Race, Long Island Sound	48	2012	4 Months (4/28/2010-9/2/2010)
Throgs Neck Bridge, Long Island Sound, New York.	52	2012	3 Months (5/27/2010-9/1/2010)
Vieques Passage, Puerto Rico	192	1967	15 Days Beginning 4/8/1965
Wilmington (USS North Carolina), North Carolina	108	2018	1 month (5/9/2016 - 6/16/2016)
Woods Hole, The Strait, Massachusetts..................	32	2011	2 Months (6/3/2009-8/20/2009)

TABLE 1.— DAILY CURRENT PREDICTIONS

EXPLANATION OF TABLE

This table gives the predicted times of slack water and the predicted times and speeds of maximum current (flood and ebb) for each day of the year at a number of stations on the Atlantic coast of North America. The times are given in hours and minutes and the speeds in knots.

Time.— The kind of time used for the predictions at each reference station is indicated by the time meridian at the bottom of each page. **Daylight-saving time is not used in this publication.** If daylight-saving time is required, add one (1) hour to the predicted time.

Slack water and maximum current.— The columns headed "Slack" contain the predicted times at which there is no current; or, in other words, the times at which the current has stopped setting in a given direction and is about to begin to set in the opposite direction. Offshore, where the current is rotary, slack water denotes the time of minimum current. Beginning with the slack water before flood, the current increases in speed until the strength or maximum speed of the flood current is reached; it then decreases until the following slack water, or slack before ebb. The ebb current then begins, increases to a maximum speed, and then decreases to the next slack. The predicted times and speeds of maximum current are given in the columns headed "Maximum." Flood speeds are marked with an "F," the ebb speeds with an "E." An entry in the "Slack" column will be slack, flood begins if the maximum current which follows it is marked "F." Otherwise the entry will be slack, ebb begins.

Direction of set.— The terms flood and ebb do not in all cases clearly indicate the direction of the current, the approximate direction toward which the currents flow are given at the top of each page to distinguish the two streams.

Number of slacks and strengths.— There are usually four slacks and four maximums each day. If one is missing in a given day, it will occur soon after midnight as the first slack or maximum of the following day. At some stations where the diurnal inequality is large, there may be on certain days a continuous flood or ebb current with varying speed throughout half the day giving only two slacks and two maximums on that particular day.

Current and tide.— It is important to note that the predicted slacks and strengths given in this table refer to the horizontal motion of the water and not to the vertical rise and fall of the tide. The relation of current to tide is not constant, but varies from place to place, and the time of slack water does not generally coincide with the time of high or low water, nor does the time of maximum speed of the current usually coincide with the time of most rapid change in the vertical height of the tide. At stations located on a tidal river or bay the time of slack water may differ from 1 to 3 hours from the time of high or low water. The times of high and low waters are given in theTide Tables published by the National Ocean Service.

Variations from predictions.— In using this table, bear in mind that actual times of slack or maximum occasionally differ from the predicted times by as much as half an hour and in rare instances the difference may be as much as an hour. Comparisons of predicted with observed times of slack water indicate that more than 90 percent of the slack waters occurred within half an hour of the predicted times. To make sure, therefore, of getting the full advantage of a favorable current or slack water, the navigator should reach the entrance or strait at least half an hour before the predicted time of the desired condition of current. Currents are frequently disturbed by wind or variations in river discharge. On days when the current is affected by such disturbing influences, the times and speeds will differ from those given in the table, but local knowledge will enable one to make proper allowance for these effects.

TABLE 1.—DAILY CURRENT PREDICTIONS

Typical current curves.— The variations in the tidal current from day to day and from place to place are illustrated on the opposite page by the current curves for representative ports along the Atlantic and Gulf Coasts of the United States. Flood current is represented by the solid line curve above the zero speed (slack water) line and the ebb current by the broken line curve below the slack water line. The curves show clearly that the currents along the Atlantic coast are semi-diurnal (two floods and two ebbs in a day) in character with their principal variations following changes in the Moon's distance and phase. In the Gulf of Mexico, however, the currents are diurnal in character. Because the dominant factor is the change in the Moon's declination, the currents in the Gulf tend to become semi-diurnal when the Moon is near the Equator. By reference to the curves, it will be noted that with this diurnal type of current there are times when the current may be erratic (marked with an asterisk), or one flood or ebb current of the day may be quite weak. Therefore, in using the predictions of the current, it is essential to carefully note the speeds as well as the times.

TYPICAL CURRENT CURVES FOR REFERENCE STATIONS
(Flood: Solid Line, Ebb: Broken Line)

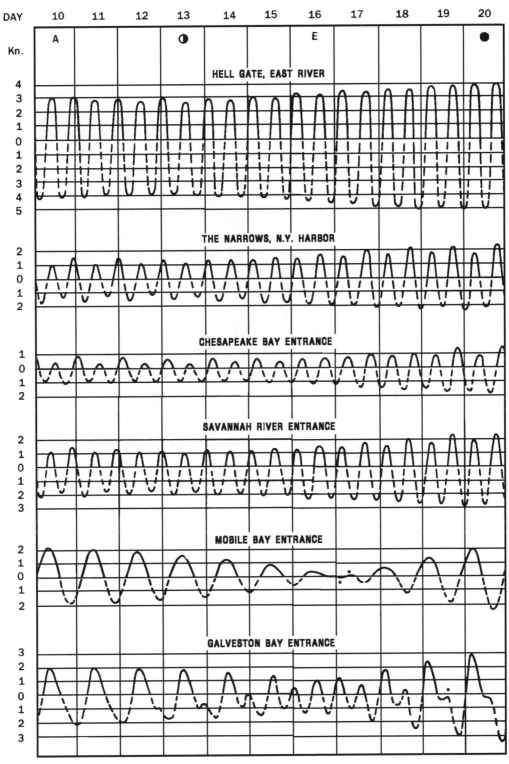

*Current weak and variable.
A discussion of these curves is given on the preceding page.

Lunar data: A—moon in apogee
◑—last quarter
E—moon on equator
●—new moon

Bay of Fundy Entrance (Grand Manan Channel), 2019

F–Flood, Dir. 032° True   E–Ebb, Dir. 212° True

January

Day	Slack (h m)	Maximum (h m)	knots
1 Tu	0118	0429	2.1F
	0757	1110	2.1E
	1411	1714	1.9F
	2038	2337	1.7E
2 W	0222	0535	2.1F
	0858	1211	2.1E
	1513	1820	2.0F
	2143		
3 Th		0038	1.8E
	0324	0635	2.1F
	0953	1306	2.3E
	1609	1917	2.1F
	2239		
4 F		0133	1.9E
	0419	0728	2.2F
	1042	1356	2.4E
	1658	2005	2.3F
	2328		
5 Sa ●		0222	2.0E
	0509	0814	2.2F
	1125	1440	2.4E
	1741	2047	2.4F
6 Su	0011	0306	2.0E
	0553	0854	2.3F
	1204	1521	2.5E
	1820	2124	2.5F
7 M	0049	0346	2.1E
	0633	0931	2.3F
	1240	1558	2.5E
	1856	2159	2.6F
8 Tu	0123	0423	2.1E
	0711	1007	2.3F
	1314	1632	2.4E
	1930	2232	2.6F
9 W	0156	0458	2.1E
	0747	1042	2.3F
	1348	1706	2.4E
	2004	2306	2.6F
10 Th	0228	0533	2.1E
	0824	1117	2.3F
	1422	1740	2.3E
	2038	2341	2.6F
11 F	0301	0608	2.1E
	0902	1155	2.2F
	1459	1816	2.1E
	2114		
12 Sa		0018	2.5F
	0337	0647	2.0E
	0944	1236	2.2F
	1541	1856	2.0E
	2154		
13 Su		0059	2.4F
	0418	0730	1.9E
	1030	1322	2.2F
	1628	1942	1.8E
	2238		
14 M ☽		0145	2.3F
	0505	0820	1.9E
	1122	1415	1.9F
	1725	2037	1.6E
	2330		
15 Tu		0238	2.1F
	0559	0919	1.8E
	1222	1516	1.8F
	1832	2142	1.5E
16 W	0030	0339	2.0F
	0701	1024	1.9E
	1327	1625	1.8F
	1947	2252	1.5E
17 Th	0137	0447	2.0F
	0807	1130	2.0E
	1434	1736	2.0F
	2059		
18 F		0001	1.7E
	0247	0556	2.2F
	0911	1232	2.3E
	1536	1841	2.3F
	2204		
19 Sa		0105	2.0E
	0352	0659	2.4F
	1010	1330	2.6E
	1633	1939	2.7F
	2300		
20 Su		0201	2.3E
	0451	0755	2.7F
	1104	1422	2.9E
	1724	2031	3.1F
	2350		
21 M ○		0253	2.6E
	0544	0846	3.0F
	1154	1511	3.2E
	1812	2118	3.4F
22 Tu	0037	0341	2.9E
	0634	0934	3.2F
	1242	1557	3.3E
	1858	2203	3.6F
23 W	0122	0427	3.1E
	0721	1020	3.3F
	1328	1642	3.4E
	1942	2246	3.7F
24 Th	0205	0511	3.2E
	0808	1105	3.3F
	1413	1727	3.3E
	2025	2329	3.6F
25 F	0249	0556	3.1E
	0854	1149	3.1F
	1459	1812	3.0E
	2109		
26 Sa		0013	3.4F
	0333	0642	2.9E
	0941	1235	2.9F
	1547	1858	2.7E
	2153		
27 Su ◐		0057	3.1F
	0419	0730	2.6E
	1030	1323	2.5F
	1638	1948	2.3E
	2240		
28 M		0144	2.7F
	0508	0823	2.3E
	1123	1416	2.2F
	1736	2044	1.9E
	2332		
29 Tu		0236	2.2F
	0603	0921	2.0E
	1222	1516	1.8F
	1845	2148	1.5E
30 W	0031	0337	1.8E
	0706	1026	1.8E
	1329	1629	1.6F
	2005	2300	1.3E
31 Th	0139	0448	1.6F
	0816	1135	1.7E
	1438	1748	1.6F
	2124		

February

Day	Slack (h m)	Maximum (h m)	knots
1 F		0013	1.3E
	0253	0603	1.5F
	0923	1241	1.8E
	1543	1858	1.7F
	2229		
2 Sa		0117	1.4E
	0400	0709	1.6F
	1021	1337	1.9E
	1637	1952	2.0F
	2320		
3 Su		0210	1.6E
	0456	0759	1.8F
	1109	1424	2.1E
	1722	2034	2.2F
	2359		
4 M ●		0254	1.9E
	0541	0841	2.0F
	1150	1504	2.3E
	1800	2109	2.5F
5 Tu	0034	0332	2.1E
	0620	0917	2.2F
	1225	1540	2.4E
	1835	2141	2.7F
6 W	0104	0405	2.3E
	0655	0951	2.4F
	1257	1612	2.5E
	1907	2211	2.8F
7 Th	0132	0437	2.4E
	0729	1023	2.5F
	1329	1643	2.6E
	1938	2242	3.0F
8 F	0200	0508	2.5E
	0803	1057	2.6F
	1402	1715	2.6E
	2011	2315	3.0F
9 Sa	0230	0540	2.6E
	0838	1132	2.7F
	1437	1748	2.5E
	2044	2349	3.0F
10 Su	0303	0614	2.5E
	0916	1210	2.6F
	1515	1824	2.3E
	2121		
11 M		0027	2.9F
	0340	0652	2.5E
	0957	1252	2.5F
	1558	1905	2.1E
	2202		
12 Tu ◐		0109	2.7F
	0422	0737	2.3E
	1045	1340	2.3F
	1649	1955	1.8E
	2250		
13 W		0158	2.4F
	0512	0832	2.1E
	1141	1437	2.0F
	1753	2058	1.6E
	2349		
14 Th		0257	2.1F
	0614	0939	1.9E
	1248	1546	1.9F
	1912	2217	1.4E
15 F	0102	0409	1.9E
	0728	1056	1.9E
	1402	1706	1.9F
	2038	2339	1.5E
16 Sa	0223	0530	1.9F
	0846	1211	2.1E
	1514	1824	2.2F
	2152		
17 Su		0052	1.8E
	0339	0645	2.2F
	0956	1316	2.5E
	1616	1927	2.6F
	2251		
18 M		0152	2.3E
	0443	0747	2.5F
	1055	1411	2.9E
	1710	2020	3.1F
	2341		
19 Tu ○		0243	2.8E
	0537	0838	2.9F
	1146	1459	3.2E
	1758	2106	3.5F
20 W	0025	0329	3.1E
	0625	0925	3.2F
	1232	1544	3.4E
	1842	2149	3.7F
21 Th	0107	0412	3.4E
	0709	1008	3.4F
	1316	1627	3.5E
	1923	2229	3.8F
22 F	0146	0453	3.5E
	0752	1049	3.5F
	1358	1708	3.4E
	2003	2308	3.8F
23 Sa	0225	0534	3.4E
	0833	1129	3.3F
	1439	1748	3.1E
	2043	2346	3.5F
24 Su	0304	0615	3.1E
	0915	1210	3.0F
	1522	1830	2.7E
	2123		
25 M		0025	3.1F
	0343	0657	2.8E
	0959	1252	2.6F
	1607	1913	2.2E
	2204		
26 Tu ○		0106	2.6F
	0425	0742	2.3E
	1045	1337	2.2F
	1658	2003	1.7E
	2249		
27 W		0151	2.1F
	0512	0835	1.9E
	1139	1431	1.7F
	1803	2105	1.2E
	2344		
28 Th		0245	1.6F
	0611	0941	1.5E
	1244	1541	1.4F
	1933	2225	0.9E

March

Day	Slack (h m)	Maximum (h m)	knots
1 F	0056	0358	1.2F
	0730	1101	1.3E
	1401	1715	1.3F
	2110	2352	0.9E
2 Sa	0226	0533	1.1F
	0856	1217	1.4E
	1516	1841	1.4F
	2219		
3 Su		0103	1.1E
	0345	0654	1.3F
	1003	1318	1.6E
	1614	1936	1.8F
	2306		
4 M		0155	1.5E
	0442	0746	1.6F
	1053	1404	1.9E
	1659	2014	2.1F
	2340		
5 Tu		0235	1.8E
	0525	0825	1.9F
	1131	1442	2.2E
	1735	2046	2.5F
6 W ●	0009	0309	2.2E
	0600	0857	2.2F
	1204	1515	2.4E
	1808	2115	2.8F
7 Th	0035	0339	2.5E
	0633	0928	2.5F
	1235	1546	2.6E
	1838	2144	3.0F
8 F	0101	0409	2.7E
	0704	0959	2.8F
	1306	1616	2.8E
	1909	2214	3.2F
9 Sa	0129	0438	2.9E
	0737	1032	3.0F
	1338	1646	2.8E
	1941	2246	3.3F
10 Su	0158	0509	3.0E
	0811	1106	3.0F
	1412	1719	2.8E
	2015	2320	3.3F
11 M	0230	0542	3.0E
	0847	1143	3.0F
	1449	1754	2.6E
	2051	2357	3.2F
12 Tu	0306	0619	2.8E
	0928	1224	2.8F
	1532	1835	2.3E
	2132		
13 W		0038	2.9F
	0348	0703	2.6E
	1014	1311	2.5F
	1622	1924	1.9E
	2220		
14 Th ◐		0126	2.5F
	0437	0757	2.2E
	1109	1407	2.2F
	1726	2029	1.6E
	2320		
15 F		0226	2.0F
	0539	0907	1.9E
	1217	1518	1.9F
	1850	2154	1.4E
16 Sa	0039	0343	1.7F
	0701	1033	1.8E
	1337	1645	1.9F
	2024	2325	1.5E
17 Su	0210	0514	1.7F
	0830	1154	2.0E
	1454	1809	2.2F
	2140		
18 M		0039	1.9E
	0330	0635	2.1F
	0945	1301	2.4E
	1559	1914	2.7F
	2237		
19 Tu		0138	2.4E
	0432	0736	2.5F
	1044	1355	2.8E
	1652	2005	3.2F
	2324		
20 W ○		0227	2.9E
	0524	0825	3.0F
	1133	1443	3.2E
	1739	2048	3.6F
21 Th	0006	0311	3.3E
	0609	0909	3.3F
	1217	1525	3.4E
	1821	2128	3.8F
22 F	0045	0352	3.6E
	0651	0949	3.5F
	1259	1606	3.5E
	1900	2206	3.9F
23 Sa	0122	0430	3.6E
	0730	1028	3.5F
	1338	1644	3.3E
	1938	2242	3.7F
24 Su	0157	0508	3.5E
	0809	1105	3.4F
	1417	1723	3.0E
	2015	2318	3.4F
25 M	0233	0545	3.2E
	0848	1143	3.0F
	1456	1801	2.6E
	2052		
26 Tu	0308	0624	2.8E
	0928	1221	2.6F
	1538	1841	2.1E
	2130		
27 W		0031	2.5F
	0345	0705	2.3E
	1010	1303	2.1F
	1625	1927	1.5E
	2212		
28 Th		0112	1.9F
	0426	0753	1.7E
	1059	1352	1.6F
	1726	2026	1.0E
	2303		
29 F		0201	1.4F
	0519	0858	1.3E
	1201	1457	1.2F
	1902	2153	0.7E
30 Sa	0017	0311	0.9F
	0641	1025	1.1E
	1321	1635	1.1F
	2049	2328	0.7E
31 Su	0158	0459	0.8F
	0825	1148	1.2E
	1440	1812	1.3F
	2154		

Time meridian 60° W. 0000 is midnight. 1200 is noon. Times are not adjusted for Daylight Saving Time.

4

Bay of Fundy Entrance (Grand Manan Channel), 2019

F–Flood, Dir. 032° True   E–Ebb, Dir. 212° True

April

Day	Slack (h m)	Maximum (h m / knots)
1 M	0323, 0938, 1540, 2235	0039 1.1E, 0630 1.1F, 1249 1.4E, 1906 1.7F
2 Tu	0417, 1027, 1625, 2306	0127 1.5E, 0720 1.5F, 1334 1.8E, 1942 2.1F
3 W	0457, 1104, 1701, 2333	0205 1.9E, 0757 1.9F, 1411 2.1E, 2013 2.5F
4 Th	0531, 1136, 1734, 2359	0237 2.3E, 0829 2.3F, 1444 2.4E, 2042 2.8F
5 F ●	0603, 1208, 1806	0307 2.7E, 0859 2.7F, 1515 2.7E, 2112 3.2F
6 Sa	0027, 0635, 1239, 1839	0337 3.0E, 0932 3.0F, 1546 2.8E, 2144 3.4F
7 Su	0056, 0709, 1313, 1912	0407 3.2E, 1005 3.2F, 1618 2.9E, 2217 3.5F
8 M	0127, 0744, 1348, 1948	0439 3.2E, 1041 3.3F, 1652 2.9E, 2253 3.4F
9 Tu	0201, 0822, 1427, 2026	0514 3.2E, 1119 3.2F, 1730 2.7E, 2331 3.2F
10 W	0239, 0903, 1511, 2109	0553 3.0E, 1201 3.0F, 1813 2.4E
11 Th	0322, 0950, 1604, 2200	0014 2.9F, 0639 2.7E, 1249 2.7F, 1905 2.0E
12 F ◑	0413, 1047, 1710, 2305	0104 2.5F, 0735 2.3E, 1346 2.3F, 2014 1.6E
13 Sa	0519, 1156, 1836	0207 2.0F, 0848 1.9E, 1459 2.0F, 2141 1.4E
14 Su	0645, 1315, 2006	0327 1.7F, 1015 1.8E, 1626 2.0F, 2308 1.6E
15 M	0157, 0815, 1431, 2118	0459 1.7F, 1135 2.0E, 1748 2.3F
16 Tu	0314, 0929, 1535, 2213	0020 2.1E, 0618 2.1F, 1240 2.4E, 1851 2.7F
17 W	0414, 1026, 1628, 2259	0116 2.6E, 0717 2.6F, 1334 2.8E, 1941 3.2F
18 Th	0503, 1115, 1715, 2340	0204 3.0E, 0806 3.0F, 1420 3.1E, 2024 3.5F
19 F ○	0547, 1158, 1756	0247 3.4E, 0848 3.3F, 1503 3.3E, 2104 3.6F
20 Sa	0019, 0628, 1239, 1836	0327 3.5E, 0927 3.4F, 1543 3.2E, 2141 3.6F
21 Su	0055, 0707, 1317, 1913	0405 3.5E, 1005 3.4F, 1621 3.1E, 2216 3.5F
22 M	0129, 0744, 1356, 1949	0442 3.3E, 1041 3.2F, 1658 2.8E, 2251 3.2F
23 Tu	0203, 0822, 1434, 2026	0518 3.0E, 1117 2.9F, 1736 2.4E, 2326 2.8F
24 W	0237, 0859, 1514, 2103	0555 2.6E, 1155 2.5F, 1815 1.9E
25 Th	0312, 0940, 1559, 2144	0002 2.3F, 0634 2.1E, 1235 2.1F, 1859 1.4E
26 F ◐	0351, 1026, 1657, 2235	0042 1.8F, 0720 1.7E, 1321 1.7F, 1958 1.0E
27 Sa	0440, 1123, 1821, 2347	0129 1.3F, 0821 1.2E, 1420 1.3F, 2119 0.7E
28 Su	0556, 1234, 1957	0236 0.9F, 0943 1.0E, 1543 1.1F, 2247 0.8E
29 M	0120, 0738, 1349, 2103	0411 0.8F, 1103 1.1E, 1712 1.3F, 2355 1.1E
30 Tu	0240, 0855, 1451, 2146	0541 1.0F, 1206 1.3E, 1813 1.6F

May

Day	Slack (h m)	Maximum (h m / knots)
1 W	0336, 0947, 1539, 2219	0044 1.5E, 0637 1.4F, 1253 1.6E, 1855 2.0F
2 Th	0418, 1027, 1620, 2250	0123 1.9E, 0718 1.9F, 1333 2.0E, 1931 2.4F
3 F	0455, 1104, 1657, 2321	0158 2.3E, 0754 2.3F, 1408 2.3E, 2006 2.8F
4 Sa ●	0531, 1138, 1734, 2352	0231 2.7E, 0829 2.7F, 1443 2.6E, 2040 3.1F
5 Su	0606, 1214, 1810	0304 3.0E, 0904 3.1F, 1518 2.8E, 2115 3.3F
6 M	0025, 0642, 1250, 1847	0339 3.2E, 0941 3.3F, 1554 2.9E, 2152 3.4F
7 Tu	0100, 0720, 1330, 1927	0414 3.3E, 1019 3.3F, 1632 2.8E, 2231 3.4F
8 W	0138, 0801, 1412, 2009	0453 3.2E, 1059 3.3F, 1714 2.7E, 2313 3.2F
9 Th	0219, 0845, 1459, 2057	0536 3.0E, 1144 3.1F, 1801 2.4E, 2359 2.9F
10 F	0306, 0934, 1554, 2152	0625 2.7E, 1234 2.8F, 1857 2.1E
11 Sa ◑	0400, 1030, 1659, 2258	0052 2.4F, 0723 2.4E, 1332 2.5F, 2006 1.8E
12 Su	0508, 1136, 1818	0155 2.1F, 0834 2.1E, 1442 2.2F, 2125 1.7E
13 M	0015, 0630, 1249, 1937	0313 1.8F, 0953 2.0E, 1601 2.2F, 2243 1.9E
14 Tu	0136, 0753, 1401, 2045	0437 1.9F, 1108 2.1E, 1717 2.4F, 2350 2.2E
15 W	0248, 0904, 1504, 2141	0552 2.2F, 1212 2.3E, 1820 2.7F
16 Th	0347, 1003, 1559, 2229	0047 2.6E, 0651 2.5F, 1307 2.6E, 1912 3.0F
17 F	0438, 1053, 1647, 2312	0137 2.9E, 0741 2.8F, 1355 2.8E, 1957 3.2F
18 Sa ○	0523, 1138, 1731, 2352	0221 3.2E, 0825 3.1F, 1439 2.9E, 2038 3.3F
19 Su	0604, 1220, 1812	0302 3.3E, 0905 3.2F, 1521 2.9E, 2116 3.2F
20 M	0029, 0644, 1259, 1851	0341 3.2E, 0943 3.1F, 1559 2.7E, 2153 3.1F
21 Tu	0104, 0722, 1339, 1928	0419 3.1E, 1020 3.0F, 1639 2.5E, 2228 2.8F
22 W	0139, 0759, 1417, 2006	0456 2.8E, 1057 2.8F, 1718 2.1E, 2304 2.5F
23 Th	0213, 0837, 1457, 2045	0533 2.4E, 1134 2.5F, 1758 1.8E, 2341 2.1F
24 F	0249, 0916, 1541, 2127	0612 2.1E, 1213 2.1F, 1842 1.4E
25 Sa	0328, 0958, 1631, 2217	0021 1.8F, 0656 1.7E, 1257 1.8F, 1935 1.2E
26 Su ◐	0415, 1047, 1732, 2318	0108 1.4F, 0748 1.4E, 1348 1.6F, 2039 1.0E
27 M	0518, 1144, 1842	0206 1.2F, 0853 1.2E, 1450 1.4F, 2149 1.0E
28 Tu	0031, 0637, 1248, 1947	0318 1.1F, 1004 1.1E, 1559 1.5F, 2254 1.2E
29 W	0142, 0755, 1350, 2039	0435 1.2F, 1108 1.3E, 1705 1.6F, 2348 1.5E
30 Th	0242, 0856, 1446, 2124	0540 1.5F, 1202 1.5E, 1759 2.0F
31 F	0332, 0946, 1535, 2204	0035 1.9E, 0632 1.9F, 1250 1.8E, 1846 2.3F

June

Day	Slack (h m)	Maximum (h m / knots)
1 Sa	0417, 1030, 1620, 2242	0117 2.3E, 0717 2.3F, 1333 2.1E, 1929 2.6F
2 Su	0458, 1112, 1703, 2321	0157 2.7E, 0759 2.7F, 1414 2.4E, 2010 2.9F
3 M ●	0539, 1153, 1746, 2359	0236 3.0E, 0840 3.0F, 1455 2.6E, 2051 3.2F
4 Tu	0620, 1234, 1829	0316 3.2E, 0921 3.2F, 1537 2.7E, 2133 3.3F
5 W	0040, 0702, 1318, 1914	0357 3.3E, 1003 3.3F, 1620 2.8E, 2216 3.2F
6 Th	0123, 0746, 1403, 2001	0440 3.2E, 1047 3.3F, 1706 2.7E, 2301 3.1F
7 F	0208, 0832, 1452, 2051	0526 3.1E, 1133 3.2F, 1756 2.5E, 2350 2.9F
8 Sa	0257, 0921, 1545, 2146	0616 2.8E, 1223 3.0F, 1851 2.3E
9 Su	0352, 1014, 1645, 2247	0043 2.6F, 0713 2.5E, 1318 2.8F, 1953 2.2E
10 M ◐	0455, 1113, 1751, 2355	0143 2.3F, 0816 2.3E, 1420 2.5F, 2100 2.1E
11 Tu	0607, 1217, 1859	0250 2.1F, 0924 2.1E, 1527 2.4F, 2209 2.1E
12 W	0106, 0723, 1324, 2005	0404 2.0F, 1033 2.0E, 1637 2.4F, 2314 2.2E
13 Th	0214, 0834, 1428, 2104	0516 2.1F, 1138 2.1E, 1742 2.4F
14 F	0315, 0937, 1527, 2157	0014 2.4E, 0620 2.3F, 1237 2.2E, 1839 2.6F
15 Sa	0410, 1032, 1620, 2244	0107 2.7E, 0715 2.5F, 1330 2.3E, 1929 2.7F
16 Su	0459, 1121, 1708, 2327	0156 2.8E, 0803 2.7F, 1419 2.4E, 2015 2.7F
17 M ○	0543, 1206, 1752	0240 2.9E, 0846 2.8F, 1504 2.4E, 2056 2.7F
18 Tu	0624, 1248, 1834	0322 2.9E, 0926 2.8F, 1546 2.4E, 2135 2.6F
19 W	0045, 0703, 1327, 1914	0402 2.8E, 1004 2.7F, 1626 2.2E, 2212 2.5F
20 Th	0122, 0740, 1405, 1953	0440 2.6E, 1041 2.7F, 1705 2.1E, 2249 2.3F
21 F	0157, 0817, 1442, 2032	0517 2.4E, 1117 2.5F, 1744 1.9E, 2326 2.1F
22 Sa	0232, 0853, 1520, 2112	0554 2.1E, 1154 2.3F, 1824 1.7E
23 Su	0310, 0931, 1559, 2156	0004 1.9F, 0632 1.9E, 1232 2.2F, 1907 1.6E
24 M	0352, 1012, 1643, 2245	0047 1.7F, 0715 1.7E, 1315 2.0F, 1954 1.5E
25 Tu ◐	0442, 1057, 1733, 2341	0135 1.6F, 0804 1.5E, 1403 1.9F, 2048 1.4E
26 W	0542, 1150, 1829	0230 1.5F, 0901 1.3E, 1458 1.8F, 2147 1.5E
27 Th	0042, 0650, 1248, 1927	0333 1.4F, 1004 1.3E, 1559 1.8F, 2246 1.6E
28 F	0145, 0800, 1350, 2024	0440 1.6F, 1107 1.4E, 1701 1.9F, 2344 1.9E
29 Sa	0245, 0904, 1450, 2118	0544 1.8F, 1207 1.6E, 1801 2.1F
30 Su	0339, 1000, 1547, 2208	0037 2.2E, 0641 2.2F, 1301 1.9E, 1855 2.4F

Time meridian 60° W. 0000 is midnight. 1200 is noon. Times are not adjusted for Daylight Saving Time.

Bay of Fundy Entrance (Grand Manan Channel), 2019

F–Flood, Dir. 032° True   E–Ebb, Dir. 212° True

July

Day	Slack (h m)	Maximum (h m / knots)
1 M	0430, 1051, 1640, 2256	0127 2.5E, 0733 2.5F, 1352 2.2E, 1946 2.7F
2 Tu ●	0518, 1139, 1731, 2342	0214 2.8E, 0821 2.9F, 1440 2.4E, 2034 2.9F
3 W	0604, 1225, 1819	0300 3.0E, 0907 3.2F, 1527 2.7E, 2121 3.1F
4 Th	0028, 0649, 1310, 1907	0346 3.2E, 0952 3.4F, 1614 2.8E, 2207 3.2F
5 F	0114, 0734, 1356, 1955	0431 3.3E, 1037 3.5F, 1701 2.9E, 2254 3.2F
6 Sa	0201, 0819, 1442, 2044	0517 3.2E, 1123 3.4F, 1748 2.9E, 2341 3.0F
7 Su	0249, 0905, 1530, 2135	0605 3.0E, 1209 3.3F, 1838 2.8E
8 M	0340, 0954, 1621, 2229	0031 2.8F, 0656 2.8E, 1258 3.1F, 1931 2.6E
9 Tu ◗	0436, 1045, 1716, 2326	0123 2.6F, 0750 2.5E, 1350 2.8F, 2028 2.4E
10 W	0537, 1141, 1815	0221 2.3F, 0849 2.2E, 1447 2.5F, 2129 2.2E
11 Th	0029, 0646, 1242, 1918	0325 2.1F, 0954 1.9E, 1551 2.2F, 2233 2.1E
12 F	0135, 0800, 1347, 2023	0435 1.9F, 1101 1.8E, 1658 2.1F, 2338 2.1E
13 Sa	0241, 0912, 1453, 2124	0547 2.0F, 1208 1.7E, 1805 2.0F
14 Su	0343, 1016, 1556, 2220	0039 2.2E, 0651 2.1F, 1310 1.8E, 1905 2.1F
15 M	0437, 1110, 1651, 2309	0134 2.3E, 0747 2.3F, 1404 1.9E, 1957 2.2F
16 Tu ○	0525, 1158, 1740, 2353	0224 2.4E, 0833 2.5F, 1453 2.1E, 2043 2.3F
17 W	0607, 1239, 1824	0308 2.5E, 0914 2.6F, 1536 2.1E, 2123 2.3F
18 Th	0032, 0646, 1316, 1903	0348 2.5E, 0951 2.7F, 1615 2.2E, 2159 2.4F
19 F	0108, 0721, 1349, 1940	0424 2.5E, 1025 2.7F, 1651 2.2E, 2234 2.4F
20 Sa	0142, 0755, 1420, 2016	0458 2.4E, 1057 2.7F, 1725 2.2E, 2309 2.3F
21 Su	0215, 0827, 1451, 2052	0531 2.3E, 1130 2.7F, 1758 2.1E, 2344 2.3F
22 M	0249, 0901, 1523, 2129	0605 2.2E, 1204 2.6F, 1833 2.1E
23 Tu	0326, 0936, 1559, 2210	0021 2.2F, 0640 2.0E, 1241 2.5F, 1911 2.0E
24 W ○	0407, 1015, 1639, 2257	0102 2.1F, 0719 1.8E, 1321 2.3F, 1954 1.9E
25 Th	0457, 1100, 1727, 2351	0149 1.9F, 0807 1.6E, 1408 2.1F, 2046 1.8E
26 F	0557, 1154, 1823	0243 1.8F, 0905 1.4E, 1503 2.0F, 2147 1.7E
27 Sa	0053, 0709, 1259, 1929	0348 1.7F, 1015 1.3E, 1609 1.8F, 2255 1.8E
28 Su	0200, 0828, 1412, 2038	0501 1.8F, 1129 1.4E, 1721 1.9F
29 M	0307, 0939, 1523, 2143	0003 2.0E, 0612 2.0F, 1238 1.6E, 1830 2.1F
30 Tu	0408, 1039, 1626, 2240	0105 2.3E, 0715 2.4F, 1338 2.0E, 1931 2.4F
31 W ●	0501, 1130, 1722, 2332	0159 2.7E, 0809 2.8F, 1432 2.4E, 2025 2.7F

August

Day	Slack (h m)	Maximum (h m / knots)
1 Th	0550, 1217, 1813	0250 3.0E, 0857 3.2F, 1520 2.8E, 2114 3.0F
2 F	0021, 0636, 1301, 1900	0336 3.2E, 0942 3.5F, 1605 3.1E, 2159 3.3F
3 Sa	0106, 0720, 1343, 1946	0421 3.4E, 1025 3.7F, 1649 3.2E, 2244 3.4F
4 Su	0151, 0802, 1425, 2031	0504 3.4E, 1107 3.7F, 1733 3.3E, 2327 3.3F
5 M	0236, 0845, 1508, 2116	0548 3.2E, 1149 3.6F, 1817 3.1E
6 Tu	0322, 0928, 1551, 2203	0011 3.1F, 0633 2.9E, 1232 3.3F, 1903 2.9E
7 W ◗	0410, 1013, 1638, 2254	0058 2.8F, 0720 2.6E, 1317 2.9F, 1952 2.6E
8 Th	0504, 1102, 1729, 2350	0147 2.4F, 0812 2.1E, 1406 2.5F, 2047 2.2E
9 F	0608, 1158, 1829	0244 2.0F, 0913 1.7E, 1503 2.0F, 2151 1.9E
10 Sa	0054, 0727, 1305, 1940	0352 1.7F, 1025 1.4E, 1612 1.7F, 2302 1.7E
11 Su	0206, 0853, 1423, 2055	0514 1.6F, 1144 1.3E, 1733 1.5F
12 M	0317, 1008, 1539, 2202	0014 1.8E, 0634 1.7F, 1256 1.4E, 1849 1.6F
13 Tu	0419, 1105, 1642, 2256	0117 1.9E, 0736 2.0F, 1355 1.6E, 1948 1.8F
14 W	0508, 1149, 1731, 2340	0210 2.1E, 0823 2.2F, 1442 1.9E, 2033 2.0F
15 Th ○	0549, 1225, 1812	0253 2.3E, 0901 2.5F, 1522 2.1E, 2110 2.2F
16 F	0018, 0625, 1256, 1848	0330 2.4E, 0933 2.7F, 1557 2.3E, 2144 2.4F
17 Sa	0051, 0657, 1324, 1920	0403 2.5E, 1003 2.8F, 1628 2.5E, 2215 2.5F
18 Su	0122, 0727, 1351, 1952	0434 2.6E, 1032 2.9F, 1657 2.5E, 2246 2.6F
19 M	0152, 0757, 1418, 2025	0503 2.5E, 1101 3.0F, 1727 2.6E, 2318 2.7F
20 Tu	0223, 0828, 1447, 2059	0533 2.5E, 1133 3.0F, 1757 2.6E, 2352 2.6F
21 W	0257, 0901, 1519, 2136	0605 2.3E, 1207 2.9F, 1831 2.5E
22 Th	0336, 0938, 1556, 2219	0030 2.5F, 0641 2.1E, 1244 2.7F, 1910 2.3E
23 F ○	0421, 1020, 1640, 2309	0113 2.3F, 0724 1.8E, 1328 2.4F, 1957 2.1E
24 Sa	0517, 1112, 1735	0204 2.0F, 0820 1.5E, 1421 2.1F, 2059 1.8E
25 Su	0011, 0631, 1220, 1845	0308 1.8F, 0935 1.3E, 1528 1.8F, 2217 1.7E
26 M	0125, 0802, 1345, 2009	0427 1.7F, 1103 1.3E, 1651 1.7F, 2338 1.9E
27 Tu	0241, 0925, 1508, 2126	0551 1.9F, 1224 1.6E, 1814 1.9F
28 W	0349, 1028, 1618, 2230	0049 2.2E, 0702 2.4F, 1328 2.0E, 1922 2.3F
29 Th	0446, 1119, 1714, 2323	0147 2.6E, 0757 2.9F, 1421 2.6E, 2016 2.7F
30 F ●	0535, 1203, 1803	0237 3.0E, 0844 3.3F, 1508 3.0E, 2103 3.1F
31 Sa	0010, 0619, 1244, 1847	0322 3.3E, 0927 3.7F, 1550 3.4E, 2146 3.4F

September

Day	Slack (h m)	Maximum (h m / knots)
1 Su	0054, 0701, 1324, 1930	0404 3.5E, 1007 3.9F, 1631 3.6E, 2227 3.6F
2 M	0136, 0741, 1402, 2011	0445 3.5E, 1046 3.9F, 1711 3.6E, 2307 3.5F
3 Tu	0217, 0820, 1440, 2052	0525 3.3E, 1124 3.7F, 1751 3.4E, 2348 3.3F
4 W	0259, 0900, 1519, 2135	0606 3.0E, 1203 3.4F, 1832 3.1E
5 Th	0343, 0941, 1600, 2221	0029 2.9F, 0649 2.5E, 1244 2.9F, 1916 2.6E
6 F	0432, 1025, 1645, 2312	0114 2.5F, 0737 1.9E, 1327 2.4F, 2007 2.1E
7 Sa	0533, 1118, 1741	0205 2.0F, 0835 1.4E, 1426 1.8F, 2110 1.7E
8 Su	0014, 0657, 1227, 1857	0310 1.5F, 0953 1.0E, 1527 1.3F, 2230 1.4E
9 M	0131, 0841, 1358, 2030	0442 1.3F, 1048 0.9E, 1705 1.1F, 2353 1.4E
10 Tu	0252, 0959, 1527, 2147	0620 1.4F, 1243 1.1E, 1838 1.2F
11 W	0357, 1052, 1630, 2241	0059 1.6E, 0723 1.8F, 1341 1.5E, 1936 1.5F
12 Th	0446, 1129, 1715, 2323	0151 1.9E, 0805 2.1F, 1424 1.9E, 2017 1.9F
13 F	0524, 1159, 1751, 2356	0231 2.2E, 0837 2.4F, 1459 2.2E, 2050 2.2F
14 Sa ○	0557, 1226, 1823	0305 2.4E, 0906 2.7F, 1529 2.5E, 2119 2.5F
15 Su	0027, 0627, 1251, 1853	0335 2.6E, 0933 3.0F, 1557 2.7E, 2148 2.7F
16 M	0055, 0656, 1316, 1923	0404 2.7E, 1001 3.1F, 1625 2.9E, 2218 2.9F
17 Tu	0125, 0725, 1342, 1955	0432 2.7E, 1030 3.2F, 1653 2.9E, 2250 3.0F
18 W	0156, 0756, 1411, 2028	0502 2.7E, 1101 3.3F, 1723 2.9E, 2324 2.9F
19 Th	0230, 0830, 1444, 2105	0534 2.5E, 1135 3.1F, 1757 2.8E
20 F ◗	0308, 0907, 1521, 2147	0001 2.8F, 0610 2.3E, 1213 2.9F, 1835 2.6E
21 Sa	0354, 0950, 1605, 2238	0044 2.5F, 0654 2.0E, 1257 2.5F, 1923 2.2E
22 Su	0451, 1045, 1701, 2341	0135 2.2F, 0751 1.6E, 1351 2.2F, 2027 1.9E
23 M	0608, 1158, 1817	0240 1.9F, 0912 1.3E, 1502 1.7F, 2151 1.7E
24 Tu	0058, 0745, 1330, 1951	0404 1.8F, 1048 1.3E, 1634 1.6F, 2320 1.8E
25 W	0220, 0909, 1458, 2114	0534 2.0F, 1210 1.7E, 1802 1.8F
26 Th	0329, 1011, 1606, 2217	0032 2.2E, 0645 2.5F, 1312 2.2E, 1909 2.3F
27 F	0426, 1059, 1659, 2309	0130 2.6E, 0739 3.0F, 1403 2.8E, 2001 2.8F
28 Sa ●	0514, 1142, 1746, 2354	0219 3.1E, 0825 3.4F, 1448 3.3E, 2046 3.3F
29 Su	0557, 1221, 1828	0302 3.4E, 0906 3.8F, 1529 3.6E, 2127 3.5F
30 M	0036, 0638, 1259, 1908	0343 3.5E, 0944 3.9F, 1608 3.7E, 2206 3.6F

Time meridian 60° W. 0000 is midnight. 1200 is noon. Times are not adjusted for Daylight Saving Time.

Bay of Fundy Entrance (Grand Manan Channel), 2019

F–Flood, Dir. 032° True   E–Ebb, Dir. 212° True

October

Day	Slack h m	Max h m	knots
1 Tu	0117	0423	3.4E
	0717	1021	3.9F
	1335	1646	3.6E
	1948	2245	3.5F
2 W	0156	0501	3.2E
	0755	1058	3.6F
	1411	1724	3.4E
	2027	2323	3.3F
3 Th	0236	0540	2.8E
	0833	1135	3.2F
	1448	1803	3.0E
	2107		
4 F		0002	2.9F
	0318	0621	2.3E
	0912	1213	2.7F
	1526	1844	2.5E
	2150		
5 Sa ◐		0044	2.4F
	0405	0707	1.7E
	0954	1254	2.1F
	1608	1932	2.0E
	2239		
6 Su		0132	1.9F
	0504	0805	1.2E
	1045	1342	1.6F
	1659	2034	1.5E
	2338		
7 M		0235	1.4F
	0632	0926	0.8E
	1156	1450	1.1F
	1816	2158	1.2E
8 Tu	0055	0407	1.2F
	0820	1102	0.8E
	1335	1634	0.8F
	2002	2325	1.2E
9 W	0218	0551	1.3F
	0935	1219	1.1E
	1506	1815	1.0F
	2123		
10 Th		0031	1.4E
	0323	0652	1.7F
	1021	1312	1.5E
	1605	1910	1.4F
	2215		
11 F		0120	1.7E
	0411	0731	2.0F
	1054	1352	1.9E
	1646	1947	1.8F
	2254		
12 Sa		0159	2.0E
	0448	0802	2.4F
	1122	1425	2.2E
	1720	2018	2.2F
	2326		
13 Su ○		0232	2.3E
	0521	0830	2.7F
	1144	1454	2.6E
	1751	2048	2.5F
	2356		
14 M		0302	2.5E
	0552	0858	3.0F
	1213	1523	2.8E
	1822	2118	2.8F
15 Tu	0026	0332	2.7E
	0623	0928	3.2F
	1240	1552	3.0E
	1853	2149	3.0F
16 W	0057	0402	2.7E
	0654	0959	3.3F
	1309	1622	3.1E
	1926	2223	3.1F
17 Th	0130	0434	2.7E
	0728	1033	3.3F
	1341	1654	3.1E
	2001	2259	3.1F
18 F	0207	0509	2.6E
	0804	1109	3.2F
	1416	1730	3.0E
	2040	2338	3.0F
19 Sa	0248	0549	2.3E
	0845	1150	2.9F
	1456	1812	2.7E
	2124		
20 Su		0023	2.7F
	0336	0637	2.0E
	0932	1237	2.5F
	1543	1903	2.3E
	2217		
21 M ○		0116	2.4F
	0437	0739	1.6E
	1032	1334	2.1F
	1643	2010	2.0E
	2320		
22 Tu		0223	2.1F
	0555	0901	1.4E
	1149	1448	1.7F
	1803	2134	1.8E
23 W	0036	0345	1.9F
	0726	1031	1.5E
	1318	1619	1.7F
	1935	2259	1.9E
24 Th	0155	0510	2.2F
	0844	1147	1.9E
	1440	1743	2.0F
	2055		
25 F		0008	2.2E
	0303	0619	2.6F
	0943	1247	2.4E
	1544	1848	2.4F
	2157		
26 Sa		0106	2.6E
	0359	0713	3.0F
	1032	1338	2.9E
	1637	1940	2.9F
	2249		
27 Su ●		0155	3.0E
	0448	0759	3.4F
	1115	1422	3.3E
	1723	2024	3.2F
	2334		
28 M		0239	3.2E
	0532	0840	3.6F
	1155	1504	3.5E
	1805	2105	3.4F
29 Tu	0017	0320	3.3E
	0613	0919	3.7F
	1232	1543	3.6E
	1845	2144	3.5F
30 W	0057	0400	3.2E
	0653	0956	3.6F
	1309	1622	3.5E
	1925	2223	3.4F
31 Th	0137	0439	2.9E
	0731	1033	3.3F
	1345	1659	3.2E
	2003	2301	3.1F

November

Day	Slack h m	Max h m	knots
1 F	0217	0519	2.5E
	0810	1110	2.9F
	1421	1739	2.8E
	2043	2339	2.7F
2 Sa	0259	0601	2.1E
	0849	1148	2.5F
	1459	1820	2.3E
	2125		
3 Su		0021	2.3F
	0346	0647	1.6E
	0933	1229	2.0F
	1540	1906	1.9E
	2211		
4 M ◐		0107	1.9F
	0443	0744	1.2E
	1024	1317	1.5F
	1629	2005	1.4E
	2306		
5 Tu		0205	1.5F
	0600	0859	0.9E
	1133	1420	1.0F
	1741	2121	1.1E
6 W	0013	0321	1.3F
	0731	1023	0.9E
	1259	1549	0.9F
	1917	2241	1.1E
7 Th	0126	0449	1.3F
	0842	1134	1.1E
	1421	1721	1.0F
	2038	2346	1.3E
8 F	0231	0555	1.6F
	0929	1227	1.4E
	1520	1822	1.3F
	2133		
9 Sa		0036	1.5E
	0321	0640	1.9F
	1005	1308	1.8E
	1604	1904	1.7F
	2215		
10 Su		0117	1.8E
	0403	0716	2.2F
	1036	1343	2.2E
	1641	1940	2.1F
	2251		
11 M		0153	2.1E
	0440	0749	2.6F
	1105	1416	2.5E
	1715	2013	2.5F
	2324		
12 Tu ○		0227	2.3E
	0516	0823	2.9F
	1135	1448	2.8E
	1749	2047	2.8F
	2358		
13 W		0301	2.5E
	0551	0857	3.1F
	1207	1521	3.0E
	1824	2123	3.1F
14 Th	0033	0336	2.6E
	0628	0932	3.2F
	1240	1555	3.1E
	1901	2159	3.2F
15 F	0111	0413	2.7E
	0706	1010	3.2F
	1317	1632	3.1E
	1940	2239	3.2F
16 Sa	0151	0453	2.6E
	0748	1051	3.1F
	1357	1713	3.0E
	2022	2322	3.1F
17 Su	0236	0538	2.4E
	0833	1136	2.9F
	1441	1759	2.7E
	2109		
18 M		0010	2.8F
	0328	0631	2.1E
	0926	1226	2.5F
	1532	1854	2.4E
	2202		
19 Tu ◑		0104	2.6F
	0428	0734	1.9E
	1027	1325	2.2F
	1634	1959	2.1E
	2303		
20 W		0208	2.3F
	0540	0848	1.8E
	1140	1436	1.9F
	1750	2114	2.0E
21 Th	0012	0321	2.2F
	0657	1005	1.9E
	1258	1556	1.9F
	1913	2230	2.0E
22 F	0123	0437	2.3F
	0808	1115	2.1E
	1412	1714	2.1F
	2028	2337	2.2E
23 Sa	0229	0544	2.6F
	0908	1215	2.5E
	1515	1819	2.4F
	2131		
24 Su		0036	2.5E
	0328	0641	2.9F
	0959	1308	2.8E
	1610	1913	2.7F
	2226		
25 M		0128	2.7E
	0420	0730	3.1F
	1045	1355	3.1E
	1658	2000	3.0F
	2314		
26 Tu ●		0215	2.8E
	0507	0815	3.2F
	1128	1439	3.3E
	1742	2044	3.2F
	2359		
27 W		0259	2.9E
	0551	0856	3.2F
	1208	1521	3.3E
	1824	2125	3.2F
28 Th	0041	0342	2.8E
	0632	0935	3.1F
	1247	1601	3.2E
	1904	2204	3.1F
29 F	0123	0423	2.6E
	0713	1014	2.9F
	1324	1641	2.9E
	1944	2243	2.9F
30 Sa	0204	0505	2.3E
	0754	1052	2.6F
	1402	1721	2.6E
	2024	2322	2.6F

December

Day	Slack h m	Max h m	knots
1 Su	0247	0548	2.0E
	0835	1131	2.3F
	1440	1802	2.2E
	2104		
2 M		0003	2.3F
	0331	0633	1.6E
	0919	1212	1.9F
	1521	1846	1.9E
	2147		
3 Tu		0046	2.0F
	0421	0724	1.4E
	1008	1258	1.5F
	1608	1937	1.5E
	2233		
4 W ◐		0135	1.7F
	0517	0823	1.2E
	1105	1352	1.3F
	1705	2036	1.3E
	2326		
5 Th		0231	1.5F
	0620	0927	1.1E
	1211	1457	1.1F
	1817	2141	1.1E
6 F	0025	0335	1.5F
	0723	1030	1.2E
	1319	1609	1.1F
	1932	2244	1.2E
7 Sa	0125	0438	1.6F
	0817	1126	1.4E
	1420	1716	1.3F
	2036	2340	1.3E
8 Su	0221	0535	1.8F
	0902	1214	1.7E
	1512	1811	1.6F
	2128		
9 M		0030	1.6E
	0312	0624	2.0F
	0943	1257	2.1E
	1557	1857	2.0F
	2213		
10 Tu		0114	1.8E
	0359	0708	2.3F
	1022	1338	2.4E
	1639	1940	2.4F
	2255		
11 W		0156	2.1E
	0443	0750	2.6F
	1101	1417	2.7E
	1720	2021	2.7F
	2336		
12 Th ○		0237	2.3E
	0526	0831	2.8F
	1140	1457	2.9E
	1801	2102	3.0F
13 F	0017	0318	2.5E
	0609	0913	3.0F
	1220	1537	3.1E
	1842	2144	3.2F
14 Sa	0059	0401	2.6E
	0654	0956	3.1F
	1302	1619	3.1E
	1925	2227	3.2F
15 Su	0143	0446	2.6E
	0740	1040	3.0F
	1346	1704	3.0E
	2009	2312	3.2F
16 M	0230	0534	2.6E
	0829	1128	2.9F
	1434	1752	2.9E
	2057	2359	3.1F
17 Tu	0320	0626	2.5E
	0921	1218	2.7F
	1526	1845	2.7E
	2147		
18 W		0051	2.9F
	0415	0723	2.3E
	1019	1314	2.5F
	1624	1943	2.4E
	2242		
19 Th ◑		0148	2.7F
	0515	0825	2.2E
	1121	1416	2.2F
	1730	2047	2.2E
	2342		
20 F		0250	2.5F
	0619	0931	2.2E
	1228	1525	2.1F
	1842	2154	2.1E
21 Sa	0046	0356	2.4F
	0725	1036	2.2E
	1336	1636	2.1F
	1955	2301	2.1E
22 Su	0151	0503	2.4F
	0827	1139	2.4E
	1441	1745	2.2F
	2103		
23 M		0004	2.1E
	0253	0606	2.5F
	0925	1237	2.6E
	1540	1845	2.4F
	2204		
24 Tu		0102	2.2E
	0351	0702	2.6F
	1017	1330	2.7E
	1633	1939	2.6F
	2258		
25 W		0155	2.3E
	0445	0752	2.7F
	1105	1419	2.9E
	1722	2027	2.8F
	2347		
26 Th ●		0244	2.4E
	0534	0838	2.7F
	1149	1504	2.9E
	1806	2111	2.9F
27 F	0032	0330	2.4E
	0619	0921	2.7F
	1231	1547	2.8E
	1848	2152	2.9F
28 Sa	0115	0413	2.3E
	0702	1001	2.6F
	1310	1628	2.7E
	1928	2230	2.8F
29 Su	0155	0455	2.2E
	0744	1040	2.4F
	1349	1707	2.5E
	2006	2308	2.6F
30 M	0233	0535	2.1E
	0824	1118	2.2F
	1426	1745	2.3E
	2043	2344	2.5F
31 Tu	0311	0615	1.9E
	0904	1156	2.0F
	1503	1824	2.0E
	2120		

Time meridian 60° W. 0000 is midnight. 1200 is noon. Times are not adjusted for Daylight Saving Time.

Estes Head, Eastport, Maine, 2019

F—Flood, Dir. 263° True   E—Ebb, Dir. 088° True

January

Day	Slack	Maximum	knots
1 Tu	0123	0507	2.4E
	0735	1116	2.7E
	1357	1736	2.4F
	2006	2343	2.5E
2 W	0218	0601	2.4F
	0830	1211	2.7E
	1452	1830	2.4F
	2101		
3 Th		0038	2.5E
	0311	0652	2.5F
	0921	1302	2.8E
	1543	1919	2.4F
	2152		
4 F		0127	2.5E
	0400	0741	2.4F
	1008	1350	2.8E
	1631	2007	2.4F
	2238		
5 Sa ●		0214	2.4E
	0447	0827	2.4F
	1051	1434	2.7E
	1716	2053	2.3F
	2320		
6 Su		0257	2.3E
	0530	0912	2.3F
	1132	1516	2.6E
	1758	2137	2.2F
7 M	0000	0339	2.3E
	0612	0955	2.2F
	1212	1557	2.5E
	1839	2220	2.2F
8 Tu	0039	0418	2.2E
	0653	1034	2.1F
	1252	1635	2.4E
	1919	2257	2.0F
9 W	0118	0454	2.1E
	0733	0959	2.0F
	1333	1711	2.3E
	1959	2220	2.0F
10 Th	0159	0529	2.0E
	0815	1032	2.0F
	1415	1745	2.2E
	2040	2255	2.0F
11 F	0242	0603	2.0E
	0858	1112	2.0F
	1459	1818	2.1E
	2122	2336	2.0F
12 Sa	0326	0639	1.9E
	0943	1156	2.0F
	1545	1852	2.0E
	2207		
13 Su		0021	2.0F
	0413	0720	1.9E
	1031	1243	1.9F
	1633	1935	1.9E
	2253		
14 M ◐		0109	2.0F
	0502	0813	1.9E
	1122	1334	1.9F
	1724	2031	1.9E
	2344		
15 Tu		0201	2.0F
	0553	0911	2.0E
	1216	1427	1.9F
	1818	2132	1.9E
16 W	0037	0255	2.0F
	0647	1010	2.1E
	1312	1523	1.9F
	1914	2235	2.0E
17 Th	0132	0350	2.1F
	0741	1111	2.3E
	1407	1620	2.0F
	2010	2338	2.1E
18 F	0226	0447	2.2F
	0835	1209	2.5E
	1502	1720	2.2F
	2106		
19 Sa		0036	2.3E
	0321	0546	2.4F
	0929	1304	2.8E
	1556	1823	2.4F
	2201		
20 Su		0130	2.5E
	0414	0645	2.5F
	1022	1356	3.0E
	1649	1923	2.5F
	2255		
21 M ○		0223	2.7E
	0508	0741	2.7F
	1115	1448	3.2E
	1741	2022	2.7F
	2349		
22 Tu		0316	2.9E
	0600	0837	2.8F
	1208	1541	3.3E
	1833	2125	2.8F
23 W	0041	0409	3.0E
	0653	0936	2.8F
	1301	1634	3.3E
	1925	2235	2.8F
24 Th	0133	0503	3.0E
	0746	1041	2.8F
	1354	1727	3.2E
	2017	2337	2.8F
25 F	0226	0556	3.0E
	0841	1156	2.7F
	1448	1822	3.1E
	2110		
26 Sa		0040	2.6F
	0319	0652	2.9E
	0937	1309	2.5F
	1543	1919	2.8E
	2204		
27 Su ◑		0144	2.5F
	0414	0752	2.8E
	1034	1415	2.4F
	1640	2020	2.6E
	2300		
28 M		0246	2.4F
	0511	0852	2.6E
	1133	1516	2.3F
	1739	2120	2.4E
	2357		
29 Tu		0344	2.3F
	0609	0952	2.6E
	1233	1615	2.2F
	1839	2221	2.3E
30 W	0056	0441	2.3F
	0707	1051	2.5E
	1332	1711	2.2F
	1940	2320	2.3E
31 Th	0153	0537	2.3F
	0804	1147	2.5E
	1428	1806	2.2F
	2037		

February

Day	Slack	Maximum	knots
1 F		0015	2.3E
	0247	0629	2.3F
	0856	1240	2.6E
	1520	1856	2.3F
	2128		
2 Sa		0106	2.3E
	0337	0718	2.3F
	0944	1327	2.6E
	1608	1944	2.3F
	2215		
3 Su		0152	2.3E
	0424	0804	2.3F
	1028	1411	2.6E
	1653	2030	2.3F
	2257		
4 M ●		0234	2.3E
	0507	0849	2.3F
	1110	1453	2.6E
	1735	2114	2.3F
	2337		
5 Tu		0314	2.3E
	0549	0931	2.3F
	1150	1532	2.6E
	1815	2155	2.2F
6 W	0015	0352	2.3E
	0629	1011	2.2F
	1229	1609	2.5E
	1853	2233	2.1F
7 Th	0053	0427	2.2E
	0708	0941	2.1F
	1308	1643	2.4E
	1931	2155	2.1F
8 F	0132	0500	2.2E
	0748	1006	2.1F
	1348	1714	2.3E
	2009	2227	2.1F
9 Sa	0212	0530	2.1E
	0828	1044	2.1F
	1429	1740	2.2E
	2048	2306	2.2F
10 Su	0253	0556	2.1E
	0910	1125	2.1F
	1512	1801	2.1E
	2130	2348	2.2F
11 M	0337	0624	2.1E
	0955	1210	2.1F
	1557	1834	2.0E
	2214		
12 Tu ◑		0034	2.2F
	0425	0708	2.0E
	1044	1259	2.0F
	1647	1924	1.9E
	2304		
13 W		0125	2.1F
	0516	0811	2.0E
	1138	1352	2.0F
	1742	2032	1.9E
	2359		
14 Th		0219	2.1F
	0611	0924	2.1E
	1237	1449	2.0F
	1841	2154	1.9E
15 F	0058	0317	2.1F
	0709	1036	2.3E
	1337	1549	2.1F
	1941	2308	2.1E
16 Sa	0158	0417	2.2F
	0807	1142	2.5E
	1435	1653	2.2F
	2041		
17 Su		0013	2.3E
	0256	0522	2.4F
	0905	1242	2.8E
	1533	1808	2.4F
	2139		
18 M		0111	2.6E
	0353	0633	2.6F
	1002	1338	3.1E
	1628	1948	2.6F
	2235		
19 Tu ○		0205	2.9E
	0448	0751	2.8F
	1057	1431	3.3E
	1721	2044	2.8F
	2329		
20 W		0258	3.1E
	0542	0857	2.9F
	1150	1524	3.4E
	1813	2137	2.9F
21 Th	0021	0351	3.2E
	0635	0956	3.0F
	1243	1616	3.4E
	1903	2230	2.9F
22 F	0111	0443	3.2E
	0727	1051	2.9F
	1334	1708	3.2E
	1954	2322	2.8F
23 Sa	0202	0535	3.1E
	0820	1146	2.7F
	1426	1800	3.0E
	2045		
24 Su		0016	2.7F
	0254	0628	3.0E
	0914	1245	2.5F
	1519	1854	2.7E
	2138		
25 M		0116	2.5F
	0346	0724	2.7E
	1008	1348	2.3F
	1613	1953	2.5E
	2232		
26 Tu ○		0217	2.3F
	0440	0823	2.5E
	1105	1449	2.1F
	1709	2053	2.2E
	2328		
27 W		0317	2.1F
	0536	0923	2.4E
	1203	1547	2.0F
	1808	2153	2.1E
28 Th	0026	0414	2.1F
	0634	1022	2.3E
	1302	1644	2.0F
	1909	2252	2.1E

March

Day	Slack	Maximum	knots
1 F	0124	0509	2.1F
	0732	1119	2.3E
	1358	1739	2.1F
	2007	2349	2.1E
2 Sa	0219	0603	2.1F
	0826	1213	2.4E
	1451	1830	2.2F
	2059		
3 Su		0040	2.2E
	0310	0652	2.2F
	0916	1301	2.5E
	1540	1918	2.3F
	2147		
4 M		0125	2.3E
	0358	0739	2.3F
	1002	1345	2.6E
	1626	2003	2.3F
	2229		
5 Tu		0207	2.4E
	0442	0823	2.4F
	1045	1426	2.6E
	1708	2047	2.3F
	2310		
6 W ●		0246	2.4E
	0524	0906	2.3F
	1126	1505	2.6E
	1748	2128	2.3F
	2348		
7 Th		0324	2.4E
	0604	0945	2.3F
	1205	1541	2.5E
	1826	2204	2.2F
8 F	0026	0359	2.4E
	0643	0921	2.1F
	1243	1615	2.4E
	1902	2127	2.2F
9 Sa	0104	0431	2.3E
	0721	0939	2.2F
	1321	1645	2.3E
	1939	2158	2.2F
10 Su	0142	0500	2.3E
	0759	1016	2.2F
	1401	1708	2.2E
	2017	2236	2.3F
11 M	0223	0524	2.3E
	0840	1057	2.2F
	1442	1729	2.2E
	2057	2318	2.3F
12 Tu ◑	0306	0551	2.2E
	0924	1141	2.2F
	1528	1802	2.1E
	2142		
13 W		0004	2.3F
	0352	0634	2.2E
	1013	1231	2.2F
	1618	1851	2.0E
	2233		
14 Th ◑		0055	2.2F
	0444	0735	2.1E
	1109	1324	2.1F
	1714	2003	1.9E
	2330		
15 F		0151	2.1F
	0541	0857	2.2E
	1209	1422	2.0F
	1815	2134	1.9E
16 Sa	0032	0251	2.1F
	0642	1013	2.3E
	1312	1525	2.1F
	1919	2249	2.1E
17 Su	0136	0355	2.2F
	0744	1122	2.5E
	1413	1635	2.2F
	2020	2355	2.4E
18 M	0236	0509	2.3F
	0845	1224	2.8E
	1512	1846	2.4F
	2119		
19 Tu		0054	2.7E
	0335	0706	2.6F
	0943	1320	3.1E
	1607	1940	2.7F
	2215		
20 W ○		0148	3.0E
	0430	0801	2.8F
	1039	1413	3.3E
	1700	2031	2.9F
	2308		
21 Th		0240	3.2E
	0524	0853	3.0F
	1132	1505	3.3E
	1751	2121	3.0F
	2359		
22 F		0331	3.3E
	0616	0945	3.0F
	1223	1556	3.3E
	1841	2211	2.9F
23 Sa	0048	0422	3.3E
	0706	1036	2.9F
	1313	1646	3.1E
	1929	2300	2.8F
24 Su	0136	0512	3.1E
	0757	1126	2.7F
	1402	1736	2.9E
	2019	2350	2.6F
25 M	0225	0602	2.9E
	0848	1219	2.4F
	1452	1828	2.6E
	2109		
26 Tu		0046	2.3F
	0315	0655	2.6E
	0940	1318	2.2F
	1543	1923	2.3E
	2201		
27 W ◑		0146	2.1F
	0406	0752	2.4E
	1033	1419	2.0F
	1636	2022	2.0E
	2256		
28 Th		0246	1.9F
	0500	0850	2.2E
	1129	1517	1.9F
	1733	2122	1.9E
	2353		
29 F		0344	1.9F
	0556	0949	2.1E
	1227	1614	1.9F
	1832	2220	1.9E
30 Sa	0051	0439	1.9F
	0654	1046	2.2E
	1324	1708	1.9F
	1930	2316	2.0E
31 Su	0147	0533	2.0F
	0751	1140	2.3E
	1418	1800	2.1F
	2023		

Time meridian 75° W. 0000 is midnight. 1200 is noon. Times are not adjusted for Daylight Saving Time.

Estes Head, Eastport, Maine, 2019

F–Flood, Dir. 263° True   E–Ebb, Dir. 088° True

April

Day	Slack h m	Maximum h m	knots
1 M		0008	2.1E
	0239	0623	2.1F
	0843	1229	2.4E
	1507	1849	2.2F
	2112		
2 Tu		0054	2.3E
	0328	0711	2.3F
	0931	1314	2.5E
	1553	1934	2.3F
	2156		
3 W		0136	2.4E
	0413	0755	2.4F
	1016	1355	2.6E
	1636	2017	2.4F
	2238		
4 Th		0215	2.5E
	0456	0837	2.4F
	1058	1434	2.6E
	1717	2057	2.3F
	2318		
5 F ●		0253	2.5E
	0536	0916	2.3F
	1138	1510	2.5E
	1755	2131	2.3F
	2357		
6 Sa		0328	2.5E
	0615	0848	2.2F
	1216	1545	2.4E
	1833	2056	2.3F
7 Su	0035	0402	2.5E
	0654	0912	2.3F
	1255	1617	2.3E
	1910	2129	2.3F
8 M	0114	0433	2.4E
	0733	0950	2.3F
	1335	1645	2.3E
	1949	2209	2.4F
9 Tu	0155	0502	2.4E
	0814	1032	2.3F
	1418	1712	2.2E
	2031	2253	2.4F
10 W	0239	0534	2.4E
	0900	1117	2.3F
	1505	1748	2.1E
	2118	2340	2.3F
11 Th	0327	0620	2.3E
	0951	1207	2.2F
	1557	1842	2.0E
	2211		
12 F ◑		0031	2.2F
	0421	0727	2.2E
	1047	1301	2.1F
	1655	2007	2.0E
	2310		
13 Sa		0128	2.2F
	0519	0847	2.3E
	1148	1402	2.1F
	1757	2126	2.0E
14 Su	0014	0231	2.1F
	0622	0959	2.4E
	1252	1509	2.1F
	1900	2235	2.2E
15 M	0118	0341	2.2F
	0726	1105	2.6E
	1353	1732	2.2F
	2002	2339	2.5E
16 Tu	0219	0559	2.4F
	0827	1207	2.8E
	1451	1832	2.5F
	2100		
17 W		0037	2.8E
	0318	0656	2.6F
	0926	1303	3.0E
	1546	1924	2.8F
	2155		
18 Th		0130	3.1E
	0413	0748	2.8F
	1021	1355	3.2E
	1639	2014	2.9F
	2247		
19 F ○		0221	3.3E
	0506	0838	2.9F
	1113	1446	3.2E
	1729	2102	2.9F
	2336		
20 Sa		0311	3.3E
	0556	0928	2.9F
	1203	1536	3.1E
	1817	2151	2.8F
21 Su	0024	0400	3.2E
	0645	1017	2.7F
	1250	1625	2.9E
	1904	2238	2.6F
22 M	0110	0448	3.0E
	0733	1105	2.5F
	1337	1713	2.6E
	1952	2326	2.4F
23 Tu	0156	0536	2.8E
	0821	1154	2.3F
	1424	1801	2.4E
	2040		
24 W		0015	2.2F
	0243	0625	2.5E
	0910	1247	2.1F
	1512	1852	2.1E
	2130		
25 Th		0112	1.9F
	0331	0717	2.3E
	1001	1346	1.9F
	1603	1948	1.9E
	2222		
26 F ◑		0212	1.8F
	0423	0813	2.1E
	1053	1444	1.8F
	1656	2045	1.8E
	2317		
27 Sa		0310	1.7F
	0517	0910	2.0E
	1149	1540	1.8F
	1751	2142	1.8E
28 Su	0013	0405	1.8F
	0614	1006	2.0E
	1245	1634	1.9F
	1848	2236	1.9E
29 M	0110	0459	1.9F
	0711	1100	2.1E
	1339	1726	2.0F
	1942	2328	2.1E
30 Tu	0203	0550	2.0F
	0805	1151	2.2E
	1429	1815	2.1F
	2032		

May

Day	Slack h m	Maximum h m	knots
1 W		0016	2.3E
	0253	0639	2.2F
	0855	1238	2.4E
	1516	1901	2.2F
	2119		
2 Th		0100	2.4E
	0340	0724	2.3F
	0941	1320	2.4E
	1600	1944	2.3F
	2203		
3 F		0141	2.5E
	0424	0806	2.3F
	1025	1400	2.5E
	1643	2023	2.3F
	2246		
4 Sa ●		0220	2.6E
	0507	0843	2.2F
	1108	1438	2.5E
	1723	2047	2.3F
	2327		
5 Su		0257	2.6E
	0547	0814	2.2F
	1149	1515	2.4E
	1803	2026	2.3F
6 M	0007	0334	2.6E
	0628	0846	2.3F
	1230	1551	2.4E
	1843	2103	2.4F
7 Tu	0048	0410	2.6E
	0709	0926	2.4F
	1313	1628	2.3E
	1925	2146	2.4F
8 W	0131	0448	2.6E
	0753	1011	2.4F
	1359	1707	2.3E
	2010	2231	2.4F
9 Th	0217	0530	2.5E
	0841	1058	2.4F
	1448	1754	2.2E
	2100	2320	2.4F
10 F	0308	0622	2.5E
	0934	1149	2.3F
	1542	1855	2.1E
	2155		
11 Sa ◑		0013	2.3F
	0403	0728	2.4E
	1031	1245	2.2F
	1640	2006	2.1E
	2255		
12 Su		0112	2.2F
	0503	0838	2.4E
	1131	1348	2.1F
	1740	2115	2.2E
	2358		
13 M		0219	2.1F
	0605	0945	2.5E
	1233	1511	2.1F
	1842	2220	2.4E
14 Tu	0102	0442	2.2F
	0709	1049	2.6E
	1333	1717	2.3F
	1943	2322	2.7E
15 W	0203	0545	2.4F
	0810	1150	2.8E
	1431	1814	2.6F
	2041		
16 Th		0020	2.9E
	0301	0641	2.6F
	0908	1246	2.9E
	1525	1906	2.7F
	2135		
17 F		0113	3.1E
	0355	0733	2.7F
	1003	1338	3.0E
	1617	1956	2.8F
	2226		
18 Sa ○		0203	3.2E
	0447	0822	2.8F
	1054	1428	2.9E
	1707	2044	2.8F
	2314		
19 Su		0252	3.1E
	0536	0911	2.7F
	1142	1516	2.8E
	1754	2132	2.6F
20 M	0000	0340	3.0E
	0623	0959	2.6F
	1228	1604	2.6E
	1840	2218	2.5F
21 Tu	0044	0426	2.8E
	0709	1045	2.4F
	1312	1650	2.4E
	1926	2303	2.3F
22 W	0128	0511	2.6E
	0754	1131	2.2F
	1356	1735	2.2E
	2012	2347	2.0F
23 Th	0212	0555	2.4E
	0840	1217	2.0F
	1442	1821	2.0E
	2059	2322	1.9F
24 F	0258	0642	2.2E
	0928	1157	1.8F
	1529	1910	1.9E
	2148		
25 Sa		0003	1.7F
	0347	0733	2.1E
	1017	1257	1.7F
	1619	2003	1.8E
	2239		
26 Su ◑		0057	1.6F
	0438	0826	2.0E
	1109	1501	1.7F
	1711	2057	1.8E
	2333		
27 M		0326	1.7F
	0533	0920	2.0E
	1202	1554	1.8F
	1805	2150	1.9E
28 Tu	0029	0420	1.7F
	0628	1013	2.0E
	1255	1646	1.9F
	1858	2242	2.0E
29 W	0123	0513	1.8F
	0722	1106	2.1E
	1346	1737	2.0F
	1950	2333	2.2E
30 Th	0215	0603	2.0F
	0814	1156	2.2E
	1435	1825	2.1F
	2040		
31 F		0021	2.3E
	0304	0650	2.1F
	0904	1242	2.3E
	1522	1908	2.2F
	2126		

June

Day	Slack h m	Maximum h m	knots
1 Sa		0104	2.5E
	0350	0732	2.1F
	0951	1325	2.3E
	1607	1945	2.2F
	2212		
2 Su		0146	2.6E
	0435	0807	2.2F
	1037	1406	2.4E
	1651	1922	2.3F
	2256		
3 M ●		0227	2.7E
	0519	0744	2.3F
	1122	1447	2.4E
	1734	1958	2.4F
	2340		
4 Tu		0308	2.7E
	0603	0823	2.4F
	1207	1530	2.4E
	1818	2040	2.5F
5 W	0024	0351	2.8E
	0648	0907	2.5F
	1253	1614	2.5E
	1904	2126	2.5F
6 Th	0110	0436	2.8E
	0735	0954	2.5F
	1342	1702	2.4E
	1953	2215	2.5F
7 F	0200	0525	2.8E
	0825	1044	2.5F
	1433	1753	2.4E
	2045	2306	2.5F
8 Sa	0252	0619	2.7E
	0918	1137	2.4F
	1527	1852	2.4E
	2141		
9 Su		0000	2.4F
	0348	0720	2.6E
	1014	1233	2.3F
	1624	1956	2.4E
	2240		
10 M ◑		0100	2.2F
	0447	0825	2.6E
	1113	1343	2.2F
	1723	2100	2.5E
	2342		
11 Tu		0319	2.2F
	0549	0929	2.6E
	1213	1557	2.3F
	1824	2203	2.6E
12 W	0045	0427	2.3F
	0651	1031	2.6E
	1312	1658	2.4F
	1924	2303	2.7E
13 Th	0146	0527	2.4F
	0753	1131	2.7E
	1410	1754	2.5F
	2021		
14 F		0002	2.9E
	0243	0623	2.5F
	0851	1228	2.7E
	1505	1847	2.6F
	2115		
15 Sa		0056	3.0E
	0338	0715	2.5F
	0946	1321	2.7E
	1557	1937	2.6F
	2206		
16 Su		0146	3.0E
	0429	0805	2.6F
	1036	1411	2.7E
	1646	2026	2.6F
	2254		
17 M ○		0234	3.0E
	0517	0853	2.5F
	1123	1458	2.6E
	1733	2113	2.5F
	2338		
18 Tu		0320	2.8E
	0602	0940	2.4F
	1207	1544	2.4E
	1818	2159	2.3F
19 W	0020	0404	2.7E
	0646	1025	2.3F
	1248	1628	2.3E
	1901	2242	2.2F
20 Th	0102	0446	2.5E
	0729	1108	2.1F
	1330	1709	2.2E
	1944	2322	2.0F
21 F	0144	0527	2.4E
	0812	1148	2.0F
	1412	1749	2.0E
	2028	2250	1.9F
22 Sa	0227	0607	2.2E
	0856	1115	1.9F
	1457	1831	1.9E
	2114	2329	1.9F
23 Su	0313	0650	2.1E
	0941	1155	1.9F
	1543	1916	1.9E
	2202		
24 M		0014	1.8F
	0402	0737	2.0E
	1029	1241	1.8F
	1631	2006	1.8E
	2253		
25 Tu ◑		0103	1.7F
	0452	0828	1.9E
	1118	1332	1.8F
	1722	2058	1.9E
	2346		
26 W		0157	1.7F
	0545	0921	1.9E
	1209	1426	1.8F
	1815	2151	1.9E
27 Th	0040	0253	1.7F
	0639	1014	1.9E
	1301	1520	1.8F
	1907	2244	2.1E
28 F	0133	0348	1.7F
	0732	1107	2.0E
	1352	1614	1.9F
	1959	2336	2.2E
29 Sa	0225	0457	1.8F
	0825	1200	2.1E
	1442	1708	2.0F
	2049		
30 Su		0026	2.4E
	0315	0557	2.0F
	0916	1249	2.2E
	1531	1800	2.2F
	2138		

Time meridian 75° W. 0000 is midnight. 1200 is noon. Times are not adjusted for Daylight Saving Time.

Estes Head, Eastport, Maine, 2019

F–Flood, Dir. 263° True   E–Ebb, Dir. 088° True

July

Day	Slack h m	Maximum h m	knots
1 M		0113	2.5E
	0403	0631	2.1F
	1006	1335	2.3E
	1620	1847	2.3F
	2226		
2 Tu ●		0159	2.7E
	0451	0717	2.3F
	1056	1422	2.5E
	1708	1934	2.5F
	2314		
3 W		0245	2.9E
	0539	0803	2.5F
	1145	1510	2.6E
	1756	2021	2.6F
4 Th	0003	0333	3.0E
	0628	0852	2.6F
	1234	1559	2.7E
	1845	2111	2.7F
5 F	0052	0423	3.0E
	0717	0943	2.6F
	1325	1650	2.7E
	1936	2202	2.7F
6 Sa	0143	0514	3.0E
	0808	1035	2.6F
	1416	1742	2.7E
	2029	2256	2.6F
7 Su	0236	0607	3.0E
	0901	1128	2.6F
	1510	1838	2.7E
	2125	2351	2.5F
8 M	0332	0705	2.8E
	0956	1228	2.4F
	1606	1939	2.7E
	2223		
9 Tu ◐		0059	2.3F
	0430	0807	2.7E
	1052	1433	2.4F
	1703	2041	2.7E
	2324		
10 W		0305	2.3F
	0530	0909	2.6E
	1151	1537	2.4F
	1802	2143	2.7E
11 Th	0025	0408	2.3F
	0632	1011	2.5E
	1250	1636	2.4F
	1902	2243	2.7E
12 F	0126	0507	2.3F
	0734	1112	2.5E
	1348	1734	2.4F
	2001	2342	2.8E
13 Sa	0224	0604	2.4F
	0833	1211	2.5E
	1444	1828	2.5F
	2056		
14 Su		0038	2.8E
	0319	0656	2.4F
	0929	1304	2.5E
	1537	1919	2.5F
	2147		
15 M		0128	2.8E
	0410	0746	2.4F
	1019	1354	2.5E
	1627	2007	2.4F
	2234		
16 Tu ○		0215	2.8E
	0457	0833	2.4F
	1104	1440	2.4E
	1713	2053	2.4F
	2317		
17 W		0300	2.7E
	0541	0919	2.3F
	1146	1523	2.4E
	1756	2138	2.3F
	2358		
18 Th		0342	2.6E
	0623	1003	2.3F
	1225	1604	2.3E
	1838	2220	2.2F
19 F	0038	0422	2.5E
	0704	1044	2.2F
	1304	1643	2.2E
	1919	2257	2.1F
20 Sa	0118	0459	2.4E
	0744	1119	2.0F
	1344	1719	2.1E
	2000	2223	2.0F
21 Su	0159	0535	2.3E
	0824	1044	2.0F
	1425	1754	2.1E
	2042	2258	2.0F
22 M	0242	0609	2.2E
	0906	1121	2.0F
	1508	1829	2.0E
	2127	2340	2.0F
23 Tu	0327	0644	2.0E
	0949	1203	2.0F
	1554	1909	1.9E
	2213		
24 W ○		0025	1.9F
	0414	0724	1.9E
	1035	1250	2.0F
	1642	1958	1.9E
	2303		
25 Th		0114	1.8F
	0504	0815	1.8E
	1124	1340	1.9F
	1732	2053	1.9E
	2356		
26 F		0206	1.8F
	0556	0913	1.8E
	1216	1433	1.9F
	1826	2151	2.0E
27 Sa	0051	0300	1.8F
	0652	1014	1.8E
	1310	1527	2.0F
	1920	2250	2.1E
28 Su	0146	0356	1.9F
	0748	1116	1.9E
	1405	1623	2.0F
	2014	2348	2.3E
29 M	0240	0455	2.0F
	0843	1215	2.1E
	1459	1721	2.2F
	2107		
30 Tu	0333	0042	2.5E
	0938	0556	2.2F
	1552	1308	2.3E
	2159	1819	2.4F
31 W ●	0426	0134	2.8E
	1031	0656	2.4F
	1644	1359	2.6E
	2251	1915	2.6F

August

Day	Slack h m	Maximum h m	knots
1 Th	0517	0224	3.0E
	1123	0751	2.6F
	1735	1450	2.8E
	2343	2007	2.7F
2 F	0607	0315	3.2E
	1215	0844	2.7F
	1827	1542	2.9E
		2101	2.8F
3 Sa	0034	0406	3.2E
	0657	0939	2.8F
	1305	1633	3.0E
	1919	2156	2.8F
4 Su	0126	0458	3.2E
	0748	1033	2.8F
	1357	1726	3.0E
	2012	2252	2.8F
5 M	0219	0550	3.1E
	0840	1130	2.7F
	1449	1820	3.0E
	2107	2352	2.6F
6 Tu	0313	0646	2.9E
	0934	1258	2.6F
	1543	1918	2.9E
	2203		
7 W ◐		0135	2.4F
	0409	0746	2.7E
	1029	1411	2.4F
	1639	2019	2.7E
	2302		
8 Th		0244	2.3F
	0508	0848	2.5E
	1127	1514	2.3F
	1738	2120	2.6E
9 F	0002	0346	2.2F
	0609	0950	2.4E
	1226	1613	2.3F
	1838	2221	2.6E
10 Sa	0103	0445	2.2F
	0712	1052	2.3E
	1326	1711	2.3F
	1938	2321	2.6E
11 Su	0203	0542	2.2F
	0813	1151	2.3E
	1423	1806	2.3F
	2034		
12 M	0258	0017	2.6E
	0909	0635	2.3F
	1517	1245	2.4E
	2126	1857	2.3F
13 Tu	0348	0108	2.7E
	0959	0724	2.3F
	1606	1334	2.4E
	2213	1945	2.4F
14 W	0435	0154	2.7E
	1043	0811	2.4F
	1651	1418	2.4E
	2255	2031	2.4F
15 Th ○	0518	0237	2.7E
	1123	0855	2.4F
	1734	1459	2.4E
	2335	2114	2.3F
16 F	0559	0318	2.6E
	1200	0938	2.3F
	1814	1538	2.4E
		2156	2.3F
17 Sa	0014	0356	2.5E
	0638	1018	2.2F
	1237	1615	2.3E
	1853	2232	2.2F
18 Su	0053	0431	2.4E
	0716	1049	2.1F
	1315	1648	2.3E
	1932	2156	2.1F
19 M	0132	0503	2.3E
	0753	1014	2.1F
	1354	1720	2.2E
	2012	2229	2.1F
20 Tu ◑	0212	0532	2.2E
	0832	1049	2.2F
	1435	1748	2.1E
	2053	2308	2.1F
21 W	0254	0555	2.1E
	0912	1130	2.2F
	1518	1814	2.1E
	2137	2351	2.1F
22 Th	0338	0619	2.0E
	0955	1214	2.1F
	1604	1849	2.0E
	2224		
23 F ○		0038	2.0F
	0426	0700	1.9E
	1043	1302	2.1F
	1653	1943	2.0E
	2316		
24 Sa		0129	1.9F
	0519	0759	1.8E
	1136	1355	2.0F
	1747	2055	2.0E
25 Su	0012	0224	1.9F
	0616	0922	1.8E
	1233	1451	2.0F
	1844	2207	2.1E
26 M	0111	0322	1.9F
	0715	1038	1.9E
	1332	1549	2.1F
	1942	2314	2.3E
27 Tu	0210	0423	2.0F
	0815	1146	2.1E
	1431	1651	2.2F
	2039		
28 W	0306	0016	2.6E
	0912	0530	2.2F
	1527	1334	2.4E
	2135	1757	2.4F
29 Th	0401	0111	2.9E
	1008	0648	2.5F
	1622	1339	2.7E
	2230	1904	2.6F
30 F ●	0454	0203	3.1E
	1101	0802	2.7F
	1715	1430	3.0E
	2323	2005	2.8F
31 Sa	0546	0255	3.3E
	1153	0856	2.9F
	1808	1522	3.2E
		2105	2.9F

September

Day	Slack h m	Maximum h m	knots
1 Su	0015	0347	3.4E
	0636	0949	2.9F
	1244	1614	3.3E
	1900	2205	3.0F
2 M	0107	0439	3.3E
	0726	1041	2.9F
	1334	1706	3.2E
	1952	2304	2.9F
3 Tu	0159	0531	3.1E
	0817	1136	2.8F
	1426	1758	3.1E
	2046		
4 W	0252	0006	2.7F
	0910	0625	2.9E
	1518	1239	2.6F
	2141	1854	2.9E
5 Th ◑		0114	2.4F
	0346	0723	2.6E
	1004	1346	2.4F
	1613	1954	2.7E
	2237		
6 F		0220	2.2F
	0443	0824	2.4E
	1101	1449	2.2F
	1710	2055	2.5E
	2336		
7 Sa		0321	2.1F
	0543	0927	2.2E
	1200	1549	2.1F
	1809	2156	2.4E
8 Su	0037	0420	2.1F
	0646	1028	2.1E
	1301	1646	2.1F
	1910	2256	2.4E
9 M	0136	0516	2.1F
	0747	1146	2.2E
	1359	1741	2.2F
	2008	2352	2.4E
10 Tu	0231	0609	2.2F
	0843	1221	2.3E
	1452	1833	2.2F
	2100		
11 W	0322	0043	2.5E
	0932	0659	2.3F
	1541	1309	2.4E
	2147	1920	2.3F
12 Th	0408	0129	2.6E
	1015	0745	2.4F
	1626	1352	2.4E
	2230	2005	2.4F
13 F ○	0451	0211	2.6E
	1054	0828	2.4F
	1708	1432	2.5E
	2311	2048	2.4F
14 Sa	0531	0250	2.6E
	1132	0910	2.4F
	1749	1509	2.5E
	2349	2129	2.3F
15 Su	0610	0327	2.5E
	1210	0949	2.3F
	1827	1545	2.5E
		2205	2.2F
16 M	0027	0402	2.4E
	0647	1016	2.2F
	1247	1619	2.4E
	1905	2129	2.2F
17 Tu	0105	0434	2.3E
	0723	0943	2.2F
	1325	1649	2.3E
	1944	2200	2.2F
18 W	0144	0500	2.2E
	0800	1019	2.2F
	1404	1714	2.2E
	2023	2239	2.2F
19 Th	0225	0519	2.1E
	0839	1059	2.2F
	1446	1737	2.2E
	2105	2321	2.2F
20 F ◐	0308	0543	2.0E
	0922	1143	2.2F
	1531	1810	2.1E
	2152		
21 Sa	0356	0007	2.1F
	1009	0624	1.9E
	1620	1231	2.1F
	2243	1900	2.1E
22 Su	0449	0058	2.0F
	1103	0722	1.8E
	1714	1324	2.1F
	2341	2014	2.0E
23 M	0547	0154	2.0F
	1203	0851	1.8E
	1813	1422	2.1F
		2136	2.1E
24 Tu	0042	0255	2.0F
	0649	1013	2.0E
	1306	1523	2.1F
	1915	2248	2.3E
25 W	0143	0358	2.1F
	0750	1123	2.2E
	1407	1628	2.2F
	2015	2352	2.6E
26 Th	0242	0511	2.3F
	0849	1224	2.6E
	1506	1746	2.4F
	2113		
27 F	0338	0050	2.9E
	0945	0706	2.6F
	1602	1319	2.9E
	2209	1924	2.7F
28 Sa ●	0431	0144	3.2E
	1039	0757	2.8F
	1656	1411	3.2E
	2304	2017	2.9F
29 Su	0523	0236	3.3E
	1131	0847	2.9F
	1748	1502	3.3E
	2356	2110	3.0F
30 M	0613	0327	3.3E
	1221	0937	3.0F
	1840	1553	3.4E
		2203	3.0F

Estes Head, Eastport, Maine, 2019

F–Flood, Dir. 263° True   E–Ebb, Dir. 088° True

October

Day	Slack (h m)	Maximum (h m)	knots
1 Tu	0047	0419	3.2E
	0703	1028	2.9F
	1310	1645	3.3E
	1931	2256	2.8F
2 W	0137	0510	3.0E
	0753	1120	2.7F
	1400	1736	3.1E
	2023	2351	2.6F
3 Th	0229	0602	2.7E
	0845	1216	2.5F
	1451	1829	2.8E
	2116		
4 F		0051	2.4E
	0321	0658	2.5E
	0938	1319	2.2F
	1544	1927	2.6E
	2210		
5 Sa		0154	2.1F
	0416	0758	2.2E
	1033	1422	2.1F
	1639	2027	2.4E
	2307		
6 Su		0254	2.0F
	0513	0859	2.1E
	1131	1521	2.0F
	1736	2127	2.3E
7 M	0005	0352	2.0F
	0613	0959	2.0E
	1230	1618	2.0F
	1835	2225	2.2E
8 Tu	0103	0447	2.0F
	0712	1056	2.1E
	1328	1712	2.0F
	1933	2321	2.3E
9 W	0159	0540	2.1F
	0807	1149	2.2E
	1422	1804	2.1F
	2026		
10 Th		0012	2.4E
	0249	0629	2.2F
	0856	1237	2.3E
	1511	1852	2.3F
	2115		
11 F		0058	2.5E
	0336	0715	2.3F
	0940	1320	2.5E
	1557	1937	2.4F
	2200		
12 Sa		0140	2.6E
	0419	0759	2.4F
	1022	1400	2.5E
	1640	2020	2.4F
	2242		
13 Su		0219	2.6E
	0500	0840	2.4F
	1102	1438	2.6E
	1721	2101	2.3F
	2322		
14 M		0257	2.5E
	0539	0918	2.3F
	1140	1515	2.5E
	1800	2137	2.2F
15 Tu	0001	0332	2.4E
	0617	0851	2.2F
	1219	1549	2.5E
	1839	2100	2.2F
16 W	0039	0405	2.3E
	0654	0914	2.2F
	1257	1621	2.4E
	1917	2133	2.2F
17 Th	0118	0434	2.2E
	0732	0951	2.3F
	1337	1650	2.3E
	1957	2213	2.2F
18 F	0159	0458	2.1E
	0811	1032	2.3F
	1418	1716	2.3E
	2039	2256	2.2F
19 Sa	0244	0525	2.0E
	0855	1117	2.3F
	1504	1752	2.2E
	2126	2343	2.2F
20 Su	0333	0608	2.0E
	0945	1205	2.2F
	1554	1844	2.2E
	2219		
21 M		0034	2.1F
	0427	0713	1.9E
	1040	1259	2.1F
	1649	2001	2.2E
	2317		
22 Tu		0131	2.1F
	0525	0843	1.9E
	1141	1358	2.1F
	1750	2119	2.2E
23 W	0018	0233	2.1F
	0627	0957	2.1E
	1245	1502	2.1F
	1852	2228	2.4E
24 Th	0120	0340	2.2F
	0728	1103	2.4E
	1347	1613	2.2F
	1954	2332	2.7E
25 F	0219	0553	2.3F
	0827	1204	2.7E
	1446	1820	2.5F
	2053		
26 Sa		0031	2.9E
	0315	0651	2.6F
	0923	1259	3.0E
	1543	1916	2.7F
	2150		
27 Su		0125	3.1E
	0409	0742	2.8F
	1017	1352	3.2E
	1637	2008	2.9F
	2244		
28 M		0217	3.2E
	0501	0831	2.9F
	1108	1443	3.3E
	1729	2059	2.9F
	2336		
29 Tu		0308	3.1E
	0551	0921	2.9F
	1158	1534	3.3E
	1820	2150	2.9F
30 W	0026	0359	3.0E
	0640	1012	2.8F
	1247	1624	3.2E
	1910	2241	2.7F
31 Th	0115	0450	2.8E
	0729	1102	2.6F
	1335	1714	3.0E
	1959	2332	2.5F

November

Day	Slack (h m)	Maximum (h m)	knots
1 F	0204	0540	2.6E
	0819	1154	2.3F
	1424	1804	2.7E
	2050		
2 Sa		0026	2.2F
	0254	0632	2.3E
	0910	1251	2.1F
	1514	1858	2.5E
	2141		
3 Su		0125	2.0F
	0346	0728	2.1E
	1003	1351	1.9F
	1605	1954	2.3E
	2235		
4 M		0223	1.9F
	0439	0827	2.0E
	1058	1449	1.8F
	1659	2052	2.1E
	2329		
5 Tu		0319	1.9F
	0534	0923	1.9E
	1155	1545	1.8F
	1755	2147	2.1E
6 W	0025	0413	1.9F
	0630	1018	2.0E
	1251	1638	1.9F
	1852	2242	2.1E
7 Th	0119	0505	2.0F
	0724	1110	2.1E
	1345	1730	2.0F
	1946	2333	2.2E
8 F	0211	0555	2.1F
	0815	1200	2.3E
	1436	1820	2.2F
	2037		
9 Sa		0021	2.3E
	0258	0643	2.3F
	0902	1245	2.4E
	1523	1906	2.3F
	2125		
10 Su		0105	2.4E
	0343	0727	2.3F
	0946	1327	2.5E
	1608	1950	2.3F
	2209		
11 M		0146	2.4E
	0426	0809	2.3F
	1029	1406	2.6E
	1651	2031	2.3F
	2252		
12 Tu		0225	2.4E
	0507	0846	2.3F
	1110	1444	2.6E
	1732	2107	2.2F
	2333		
13 W		0302	2.4E
	0547	0816	2.2F
	1150	1521	2.5E
	1812	2033	2.2F
14 Th	0014	0339	2.3E
	0626	0846	2.3F
	1231	1557	2.5E
	1853	2108	2.2F
15 F	0055	0414	2.2E
	0706	0926	2.3F
	1312	1632	2.5E
	1934	2150	2.3F
16 Sa	0138	0449	2.2E
	0749	1009	2.3F
	1355	1708	2.4E
	2019	2235	2.3F
17 Su	0225	0527	2.1E
	0835	1056	2.3F
	1442	1750	2.4E
	2107	2323	2.3F
18 M	0315	0616	2.1E
	0927	1146	2.3F
	1534	1846	2.4E
	2200		
19 Tu		0015	2.2F
	0409	0723	2.1E
	1023	1240	2.2F
	1630	1955	2.3E
	2258		
20 W		0113	2.2F
	0507	0835	2.1E
	1124	1340	2.2F
	1730	2105	2.4E
	2357		
21 Th		0216	2.2F
	0607	0941	2.3E
	1226	1447	2.2F
	1833	2210	2.5E
22 F	0058	0330	2.2F
	0708	1045	2.5E
	1329	1703	2.3F
	1935	2313	2.6E
23 Sa	0157	0538	2.4F
	0807	1145	2.8E
	1428	1807	2.5F
	2035		
24 Su	0253	0634	2.6F
	0903	1242	3.0E
	1525	1903	2.7F
	2132		
25 M	0348	0726	2.8F
	0956	1334	3.2E
	1619	1954	2.8F
	2226		
26 Tu	0440	0816	2.8F
	1048	1425	3.2E
	1711	2045	2.8F
	2318		
27 W	0530	0906	2.7F
	1137	1515	3.2E
	1801	2135	2.7F
28 Th	0007	0341	2.8E
	0619	0956	2.6F
	1224	1605	3.0E
	1849	2225	2.5F
29 F	0054	0430	2.6E
	0706	1044	2.4F
	1310	1652	2.8E
	1936	2313	2.4F
30 Sa	0140	0518	2.4E
	0754	1132	2.2F
	1356	1739	2.6E
	2023		

December

Day	Slack (h m)	Maximum (h m)	knots
1 Su		0001	2.2F
	0227	0605	2.2F
	0842	1221	2.0F
	1443	1827	2.4E
	2111		
2 M		0052	2.0F
	0314	0655	2.0E
	0932	1315	1.9F
	1531	1917	2.2E
	2200		
3 Tu		0147	1.9F
	0403	0747	1.9E
	1023	1411	1.8F
	1621	2010	2.1E
	2251		
4 W		0241	1.8F
	0454	0840	1.9E
	1115	1507	1.7F
	1714	2103	2.0E
	2343		
5 Th		0334	1.8F
	0546	0933	1.9E
	1210	1600	1.8F
	1808	2156	2.0E
6 F	0036	0426	1.9F
	0639	1025	2.0E
	1304	1653	1.9F
	1903	2248	2.1E
7 Sa	0128	0517	2.0F
	0731	1116	2.2E
	1357	1744	2.0F
	1956	2339	2.1E
8 Su	0217	0607	2.1F
	0821	1205	2.3E
	1447	1833	2.0F
	2046		
9 M		0027	2.2E
	0305	0653	2.2F
	0909	1250	2.4E
	1534	1919	2.1F
	2134		
10 Tu		0111	2.3E
	0350	0736	2.2F
	0955	1333	2.5E
	1620	2001	2.1F
	2220		
11 W		0153	2.3E
	0435	0812	2.2F
	1039	1413	2.6E
	1703	2036	2.1F
	2305		
12 Th		0234	2.3E
	0518	0745	2.2F
	1123	1454	2.6E
	1746	2008	2.2F
	2349		
13 F		0314	2.3E
	0601	0822	2.2F
	1206	1534	2.6E
	1829	2047	2.3F
14 Sa	0034	0356	2.3E
	0644	0904	2.3F
	1250	1616	2.7E
	1914	2131	2.4F
15 Su	0119	0439	2.3E
	0730	0950	2.4F
	1336	1700	2.7E
	2000	2219	2.4F
16 M	0208	0525	2.3E
	0818	1039	2.5F
	1425	1747	2.6E
	2050	2308	2.4F
17 Tu	0259	0617	2.3E
	0911	1130	2.4F
	1518	1842	2.6E
	2143		
18 W		0000	2.4F
	0352	0717	2.3E
	1007	1225	2.3F
	1614	1945	2.5E
	2239		
19 Th		0058	2.3F
	0449	0821	2.4E
	1107	1326	2.2F
	1713	2049	2.5E
	2337		
20 F		0204	2.2F
	0547	0924	2.5E
	1209	1445	2.2F
	1814	2153	2.5E
21 Sa	0037	0418	2.3F
	0647	1026	2.6E
	1311	1651	2.3F
	1917	2255	2.6E
22 Su	0136	0520	2.4F
	0747	1127	2.8E
	1411	1752	2.4F
	2017	2356	2.6E
23 M	0233	0618	2.5F
	0844	1225	2.9E
	1508	1848	2.5F
	2115		
24 Tu		0052	2.7E
	0328	0711	2.6F
	0938	1319	3.0E
	1602	1940	2.6F
	2210		
25 W		0145	2.7E
	0421	0801	2.6F
	1030	1409	3.0E
	1654	2030	2.6F
	2301		
26 Th		0235	2.7E
	0511	0850	2.6F
	1118	1458	3.0E
	1742	2119	2.5F
	2349		
27 F		0324	2.6E
	0559	0939	2.5F
	1203	1545	2.9E
	1828	2206	2.4F
28 Sa	0033	0410	2.5E
	0644	1025	2.3F
	1247	1630	2.7E
	1912	2252	2.3F
29 Su	0115	0455	2.3E
	0729	1109	2.2F
	1329	1713	2.5E
	1956	2335	2.1F
30 M	0158	0537	2.2E
	0813	1150	2.0F
	1413	1755	2.4E
	2040		
31 Tu		0017	2.0F
	0241	0619	2.1E
	0859	1121	1.9F
	1457	1838	2.2E
	2125	2346	1.9F

Time meridian 75° W.   0000 is midnight.   1200 is noon.   Times are not adjusted for Daylight Saving Time.

Buecksport, Penobscot Bay, Maine, 2019

F–Flood, Dir. 292° True   E–Ebb, Dir. 113° True

January

Day	Slack (h m)	Maximum (h m)	knots
1 Tu	0120	0422	2.7F
	0654	1042	2.6E
	1407	1650	2.6F
	1929	2307	2.4E
2 W	0219	0515	2.7F
	0754	1135	2.6E
	1504	1743	2.5F
	2034		
3 Th		0000	2.3E
	0312	0606	2.6F
	0843	1227	2.6E
	1556	1834	2.5F
	2121		
4 F		0051	2.3E
	0401	0657	2.6F
	0924	1317	2.5E
	1644	1924	2.5F
	2158		
5 Sa ●		0140	2.2E
	0445	0745	2.6F
	1003	1403	2.5E
	1726	2011	2.5F
	2234		
6 Su		0226	2.2E
	0526	0832	2.5F
	1042	1449	2.4E
	1804	2058	2.4F
	2312		
7 M		0311	2.1E
	0603	0919	2.4F
	1123	1534	2.3E
	1838	2146	2.3F
	2352		
8 Tu		0357	2.0E
	0639	1007	2.3F
	1205	1620	2.2E
	1911	2234	2.2F
9 W	0033	0444	1.9E
	0716	1056	2.1F
	1247	1706	2.1E
	1947	2322	2.1F
10 Th	0115	0529	1.8E
	0756	1144	2.0F
	1331	1750	2.0E
	2026		
11 F		0010	2.1F
	0159	0614	1.7E
	0841	1232	1.9F
	1416	1836	1.8E
	2110		
12 Sa		0058	2.0F
	0244	0406	1.0E
		0451	0.9E
		0702	1.6E
	0930	1322†	1.8F
13 Su		0148	1.9F
	0332	0454	1.0E
		0547	1.0E
		0755	1.6E
	1021	1413†	1.8F
14 M ☽		0239	1.8F
	0422	0543	1.1E
		0640	1.0E
		0848	1.6E
	1114	1505†	1.8F
15 Tu		0329	1.9F
	0512	0940	1.7E
	1208	1556	1.8F
	1738	1856	1.0E
		1952†	0.9E
16 W	0024	0420	1.9F
	0605	1029	1.9E
	1305	1647	1.9F
	1834	2252	1.8E
17 Th	0119	0510	2.1F
	0700	1119	2.1E
	1403	1739	2.1F
	1931	2344	1.9E
18 F	0214	0602	2.2F
	0755	1211	2.3E
	1458	1831	2.3F
	2027		
19 Sa		0036	2.0E
	0307	0653	2.3F
	0849	1302	2.5E
	1550	1921	2.6F
	2121		
20 Su		0127	2.3E
	0400	0742	2.7F
	0942	1352	2.7E
	1642	2010	2.8F
	2214		
21 M ○		0216	2.5E
	0453	0831	2.9F
	1035	1441	2.9E
	1734	2059	2.9F
	2308		
22 Tu		0306	2.6E
	0545	0921	3.0F
	1128	1532	3.0E
	1824	2149	3.0F
23 W	0001	0358	2.7E
	0638	1013	3.0F
	1221	1623	3.0E
	1913	2241	3.1F
24 Th	0053	0450	2.8E
	0731	1105	3.0F
	1313	1715	3.0E
	2004	2333	3.1F
25 F	0144	0541	2.8E
	0827	1157	3.0F
	1406	1806	2.9E
	2058		
26 Sa		0024	3.0F
	0237	0633	2.7E
	0926	1250	2.9F
	1500	1859	2.7E
	2155		
27 Su		0116	2.9F
	0331	0729	2.6E
	1029	1343	2.7F
	1555	1956	2.5E
	2252		
28 M		0209	2.8F
	0425	0827	2.5E
	1132	1437	2.6F
	1651	2054	2.4E
	2351		
29 Tu		0303	2.6F
	0521	0924	2.5E
	1238	1531	2.5F
	1751	2149	2.3E
30 W	0053	0356	2.5F
	0619	1017	2.4E
	1344	1624	2.4F
	1858	2242	2.2E
31 Th	0155	0448	2.5F
	0721	1109	2.4E
	1445	1716	2.3F
	2018	2334	2.1E

February

Day	Slack (h m)	Maximum (h m)	knots
1 F	0253	0540	2.4F
	0818	1202	2.3E
	1538	1808	2.3F
	2109		
2 Sa		0027	2.1E
	0343	0631	2.4F
	0901	1253	2.3E
	1626	1858	2.4F
	2138		
3 Su		0116	2.1E
	0428	0720	2.4F
	0940	1340	2.3E
	1708	1946	2.4F
	2210		
4 M ●		0202	2.1E
	0508	0807	2.4F
	1018	1425	2.3E
	1744	2033	2.4F
	2246		
5 Tu		0247	2.1E
	0543	0854	2.4F
	1059	1509	2.3E
	1815	2119	2.3F
	2325		
6 W		0331	2.0E
	0617	0941	2.3F
	1140	1554	2.2E
	1846	2207	2.3F
7 Th	0006	0416	2.0E
	0652	1029	2.2F
	1222	1638	2.1E
	1918	2254	2.2F
8 F	0047	0501	1.9E
	0730	1117	2.1F
	1305	1722	2.0E
	1954	2342	2.1F
9 Sa	0129	0545	1.8E
	0810	1204	1.9F
	1348	1807	1.9E
	2033		
10 Su		0029	2.0F
	0214	0630	1.8E
	0856	1252	1.9F
	1434	1604	1.3E
		1655†	1.2E
11 M		0117	1.9F
	0300	0719	1.7E
	0945	1342	1.8F
	1523	1638	1.3E
		1753†	1.1E
12 Tu ◖		0207	1.8F
	0348	0517	1.3E
		0617	1.2E
		0813	1.7E
	1037	1434†	1.8F
13 W		0259	1.8F
	0439	0606	1.3E
		0706	1.1E
		0907	1.7E
	1132	1527†	1.8F
14 Th		0350	1.9F
	0533	0700	1.2E
		0747	1.1E
		0959	1.9E
	1231	1619†	1.9F
15 F	0046	0442	2.1F
	0630	1051	2.1E
	1332	1711	2.1F
	1903	2316	1.9E
16 Sa	0146	0535	2.3F
	0729	1144	2.3E
	1432	1804	2.4F
	2003		
17 Su		0010	2.1E
	0244	0627	2.5F
	0826	1237	2.5E
	1529	1856	2.6F
	2059		
18 M		0103	2.4E
	0341	0718	2.8F
	0922	1329	2.8E
	1622	1946	2.9F
	2154		
19 Tu ○		0154	2.6E
	0436	0808	3.0F
	1016	1419	3.0E
	1714	2035	3.1F
	2248		
20 W		0244	2.8E
	0530	0857	3.2F
	1110	1509	3.1E
	1804	2124	3.2F
	2341		
21 Th		0335	2.9E
	0622	0949	3.2F
	1203	1600	3.1E
	1852	2216	3.2F
22 F	0032	0426	3.0E
	0714	1041	3.2F
	1255	1651	3.0E
	1941	2307	3.2F
23 Sa	0121	0517	3.0E
	0807	1133	3.1F
	1345	1742	2.9E
	2032	2358	3.0F
24 Su	0211	0608	2.8E
	0903	1224	2.9F
	1436	1833	2.7E
	2126		
25 M		0049	2.9F
	0302	0701	2.6E
	1003	1316	2.7F
	1528	1928	2.4E
	2223		
26 Tu ○		0142	2.7F
	0353	0757	2.5E
	1105	1410	2.5F
	1622	2025	2.2E
	2321		
27 W		0235	2.5F
	0446	0855	2.3E
	1208	1504	2.3F
	1717	2122	2.1E
28 Th	0023	0328	2.3F
	0541	0950	2.2E
	1316	1557	2.2F
	1817	2215	2.0E

March

Day	Slack (h m)	Maximum (h m)	knots
1 F	0128	0421	2.3F
	0640	1042	2.2E
	1419	1649	2.2F
	1930	2307	1.9E
2 Sa	0229	0513	2.2F
	0741	1134	2.2E
	1513	1741	2.2F
	2040	2359	1.9E
3 Su	0321	0604	2.2F
	0832	1226	2.2E
	1600	1832	2.2F
	2108		
4 M		0050	2.0E
	0406	0654	2.3F
	0913	1314	2.2E
	1641	1920	2.3F
	2141		
5 Tu		0137	2.0E
	0445	0742	2.4F
	0953	1359	2.2E
	1716	2006	2.4F
	2218		
6 W ●		0221	2.1E
	0520	0828	2.4F
	1033	1443	2.2E
	1747	2052	2.4F
	2257		
7 Th		0304	2.1E
	0554	0914	2.3F
	1115	1526	2.2E
	1817	2138	2.3F
	2338		
8 F		0348	2.1E
	0629	1001	2.3F
	1157	1610	2.1E
	1849	2226	2.2F
9 Sa	0019	0433	2.0E
	0704	1049	2.2F
	1239	1655	2.0E
	1923	2313	2.1F
10 Su	0101	0517	2.0E
	0743	1137	2.1F
	1323	1739	1.9E
	2001		
11 M		0000	2.0F
	0144	0318	1.3E
		0357	1.3E
		0601	1.9E
	0826	1224†	2.0F
12 Tu ◖		0047	1.9F
	0230	0404	1.4E
		0454	1.3E
		0648	1.8E
	0915	1314†	1.9F
13 W		0137	1.9F
	0319	0453	1.4E
		0549	1.3E
		0740	1.8E
	1008	1406†	1.8F
14 Th ◖		0230	1.9F
	0411	0543	1.4E
		0639	1.3E
		0837	1.8E
	1104	1459†	1.8F
15 F		0323	1.9F
	0506	0932	1.9E
	1204	1552	2.0F
	1739	1900	1.0E
		1942†	0.9E
16 Sa	0021	0416	2.1F
	0604	1025	2.1E
	1307	1645	2.2F
	1839	2252	2.0E
17 Su	0125	0509	2.3F
	0705	1119	2.4E
	1410	1738	2.4F
	1941	2346	2.2E
18 M	0227	0602	2.6F
	0806	1213	2.6E
	1508	1831	2.7F
	2039		
19 Tu		0040	2.5E
	0325	0655	2.9F
	0903	1306	2.9E
	1602	1921	3.0F
	2134		
20 W ○		0132	2.8E
	0421	0745	3.1F
	0958	1357	3.0E
	1653	2010	3.2F
	2227		
21 Th		0222	3.0E
	0515	0834	3.1F
	1052	1446	3.1E
	1742	2059	3.3F
	2318		
22 F		0311	3.1E
	0606	0924	3.2F
	1144	1536	3.2E
	1830	2150	3.2F
23 Sa	0008	0402	3.1E
	0656	1016	3.2F
	1234	1627	2.9E
	1917	2241	3.1F
24 Su	0056	0453	3.0E
	0746	1108	3.0F
	1322	1717	2.8E
	2005	2332	3.0F
25 M	0143	0543	2.8E
	0838	1159	2.8F
	1410	1808	2.5E
	2056		
26 Tu		0022	2.7F
	0230	0633	2.6E
	0935	1250	2.6F
	1459	1900	2.3E
	2152		
27 W		0114	2.5F
	0320	0727	2.3E
	1034	1342	2.4F
	1550	1956	2.0E
	2249		
28 Th		0207	2.3F
	0410	0825	2.2E
	1135	1436	2.2F
	1642	2053	1.9E
	2350		
29 F		0300	2.2F
	0503	0921	2.1E
	1239	1528	2.1F
	1737	2148	1.8E
30 Sa	0054	0353	2.1F
	0558	1013	2.0E
	1343	1620	2.1F
	1835	2239	1.8E
31 Su	0158	0444	2.1F
	0656	1104	2.0E
	1438	1712	2.1F
	1936	2330	1.9E

Time meridian 75° W. 0000 is midnight. 1200 is noon. Times are not adjusted for Daylight Saving Time.
† See page 196 for the remaining currents on this day.

Bucksport, Penobscot Bay, Maine, 2019

F–Flood, Dir. 292° True   E–Ebb, Dir. 113° True

April

Day	Slack h m	Maximum h m	knots
1 M	0251	0536	2.1E
	0752	1155	2.1E
	1524	1803	2.2F
	2025		
2 Tu		0020	2.0E
	0336	0626	2.2F
	0840	1244	2.1E
	1603	1852	2.3F
	2106		
3 W		0108	2.0E
	0415	0715	2.3F
	0923	1331	2.2E
	1638	1939	2.3F
	2146		
4 Th		0153	2.1E
	0452	0801	2.4F
	1005	1415	2.2E
	1711	2024	2.4F
	2226		
5 F ●		0236	2.2E
	0528	0847	2.4F
	1047	1458	2.2E
	1744	2110	2.3F
	2308		
6 Sa		0320	2.2E
	0603	0934	2.3F
	1131	1542	2.1E
	1818	2157	2.3F
	2350		
7 Su		0404	2.1E
	0640	1022	2.2F
	1214	1627	2.0E
	1854	2244	2.2F
8 M	0033	0449	2.1E
	0719	1110	2.2F
	1259	1712	1.9E
	1933	2332	2.1F
9 Tu	0117	0534	2.0E
	0802	1158	2.1F
	1345	1516	1.3E
		1556	1.2E
		1758†	1.8E
10 W		0020	2.0F
	0204	0621	2.0E
	0851	1247	2.0F
	1433	1604	1.3E
		1650†	1.2E
11 Th		0110	2.0F
	0254	0713	1.9E
	0945	1339	2.0F
	1525	1655	1.2E
		1742†	1.2E
12 F ◐		0203	2.0F
	0347	0810	2.0E
	1043	1433	2.1F
	1620	2040	1.7E
	2301		
13 Sa		0257	2.1F
	0443	0908	2.1E
	1143	1527	2.2F
	1718	2136	1.9E
14 Su	0003	0351	2.2F
	0543	1002	2.3E
	1246	1619	2.4F
	1819	2229	2.1E
15 M	0109	0444	2.4F
	0644	1055	2.4E
	1349	1712	2.6F
	1921	2323	2.4E
16 Tu	0212	0538	2.7F
	0747	1149	2.6E
	1447	1805	2.8F
	2020		
17 W		0017	2.6E
	0311	0631	2.9F
	0846	1243	2.8E
	1540	1857	3.0F
	2114		
18 Th		0110	2.9E
	0407	0722	3.1F
	0940	1334	2.9E
	1631	1946	3.2F
	2205		
19 F ○		0200	3.0E
	0500	0811	3.2F
	1033	1424	2.9E
	1720	2035	3.2F
	2255		
20 Sa		0248	3.1E
	0550	0901	3.2F
	1123	1513	2.9E
	1807	2124	3.1F
	2342		
21 Su		0338	3.0E
	0638	0951	3.1F
	1211	1603	2.7E
	1853	2215	3.0F
22 M	0028	0428	2.9E
	0725	1042	2.9F
	1258	1653	2.6E
	1938	2305	2.8F
23 Tu	0113	0517	2.7E
	0813	1133	2.7F
	1343	1742	2.3E
	2027	2356	2.6F
24 W	0159	0607	2.5E
	0905	1223	2.5F
	1429	1832	2.1E
	2119		
25 Th		0046	2.4F
	0246	0658	2.2E
	1001	1314	2.3F
	1517	1925	1.9E
	2215		
26 F ◐		0138	2.2F
	0335	0753	2.0E
	1057	1406	2.1F
	1607	2022	1.8E
	2313		
27 Sa		0231	2.0F
	0426	0849	1.9E
	1154	1459	2.0F
	1659	2117	1.7E
28 Su	0012	0323	2.0F
	0519	0942	1.9E
	1253	1551	2.0F
	1752	2208	1.8E
29 M	0114	0415	2.0F
	0613	1032	1.9E
	1348	1641	2.1F
	1848	2258	1.9E
30 Tu	0210	0506	2.0F
	0709	1122	2.0E
	1436	1732	2.1F
	1941	2347	1.9E

May

Day	Slack h m	Maximum h m	knots
1 W	0257	0557	2.1E
	0802	1211	2.0E
	1516	1822	2.2F
	2028		
2 Th		0036	2.0E
	0339	0646	2.2F
	0850	1259	2.0E
	1554	1910	2.3F
	2111		
3 F		0123	2.1E
	0419	0734	2.3F
	0934	1345	2.1E
	1631	1956	2.4F
	2154		
4 Sa ●		0207	2.2E
	0457	0820	2.4F
	1019	1429	2.1E
	1708	2041	2.4F
	2237		
5 Su		0251	2.3E
	0536	0906	2.4F
	1104	1513	2.1E
	1747	2128	2.3F
	2322		
6 M		0336	2.3E
	0616	0954	2.3F
	1149	1600	2.0E
	1826	2216	2.2F
7 Tu	0007	0422	2.3E
	0657	1044	2.3F
	1236	1647	2.0E
	1908	2305	2.2F
8 W	0053	0510	2.2E
	0742	1133	2.3F
	1324	1734	1.9E
	1955	2355	2.2F
9 Th	0142	0558	2.2E
	0832	1223	2.2F
	1414	1824	1.9E
	2047		
10 F		0045	2.2F
	0233	0649	2.2E
	0927	1314	2.2F
	1507	1917	1.9E
	2145		
11 Sa ◐		0138	2.2F
	0327	0745	2.2E
	1026	1408	2.3F
	1602	2016	2.0E
	2246		
12 Su		0232	2.3F
	0424	0844	2.3E
	1125	1502	2.4F
	1700	2113	2.1E
	2350		
13 M		0327	2.4F
	0524	0939	2.4E
	1226	1555	2.5F
	1800	2207	2.3E
14 Tu	0055	0420	2.6F
	0625	1033	2.5E
	1327	1647	2.7F
	1901	2300	2.5E
15 W	0159	0513	2.7F
	0728	1126	2.6E
	1425	1740	2.9F
	2000	2354	2.7E
16 Th	0258	0607	2.9F
	0828	1220	2.7E
	1518	1832	3.0F
	2054		
17 F		0047	2.9E
	0353	0659	3.0F
	0923	1312	2.7E
	1609	1922	3.1F
	2143		
18 Sa ○		0138	3.0E
	0445	0748	3.0F
	1013	1401	2.7E
	1658	2011	3.1F
	2231		
19 Su		0226	3.0E
	0535	0837	3.0F
	1102	1450	2.6E
	1745	2059	3.0F
	2316		
20 M		0314	2.9E
	0621	0926	2.9F
	1148	1539	2.5E
	1830	2149	2.8F
21 Tu	0001	0404	2.7E
	0705	1017	2.7F
	1232	1628	2.3E
	1913	2239	2.6F
22 W	0045	0452	2.6E
	0749	1107	2.5F
	1315	1717	2.2E
	1958	2329	2.4F
23 Th	0128	0541	2.4E
	0836	1157	2.4F
	1359	1805	2.0E
	2046		
24 F		0019	2.2F
	0214	0629	2.2E
	0925	1246	2.2F
	1445	1855	1.8E
	2139		
25 Sa		0109	2.1F
	0301	0720	2.0E
	1017	1337	2.1F
	1533	1949	1.7E
	2233		
26 Su ◑		0201	2.0F
	0351	0815	1.9E
	1108	1429	2.0F
	1623	2044	1.7E
	2328		
27 M		0253	1.9F
	0442	0909	1.8E
	1158	1520	2.0F
	1714	1816	0.5E
		1855†	0.5E
28 Tu	0024	0345	1.9F
	0534	0959	1.8E
	1249	1610	2.0F
	1806	2225	1.8E
29 W	0120	0435	2.0F
	0628	1048	1.9E
	1339	1700	2.1F
	1858	2313	1.9E
30 Th	0212	0526	2.0F
		1137	1.9E
	1426	1750	2.1F
	1949		
31 F		0003	2.0E
	0259	0617	2.1F
	0814	1226	1.9E
	1509	1840	2.2F
	2036		

June

Day	Slack h m	Maximum h m	knots
1 Sa		0051	2.1E
	0343	0706	2.3F
	0902	1314	2.0E
	1551	1927	2.3F
	2122		
2 Su		0138	2.2E
	0426	0753	2.4F
	0950	1400	2.0E
	1634	2013	2.4F
	2208		
3 M ●		0223	2.3E
	0509	0840	2.4F
	1037	1446	2.1E
	1717	2100	2.4F
	2255		
4 Tu		0309	2.4E
	0553	0928	2.4F
	1125	1533	2.1E
	1802	2149	2.4F
	2343		
5 W		0357	2.4E
	0638	1017	2.4F
	1215	1622	2.1E
	1848	2239	2.4F
6 Th	0032	0446	2.5E
	0724	1108	2.5F
	1304	1712	2.1E
	1937	2330	2.4F
7 F	0122	0536	2.5E
	0815	1159	2.5F
	1355	1802	2.2E
	2031		
8 Sa		0021	2.4F
	0215	0627	2.5E
	0910	1250	2.5F
	1449	1855	2.2E
	2130		
9 Su		0113	2.5F
	0310	0721	2.4E
	1008	1342	2.6F
	1545	1952	2.2E
	2232		
10 M ◐		0208	2.5F
	0407	0819	2.4E
	1106	1436	2.6F
	1642	2050	2.3E
	2336		
11 Tu		0302	2.6F
	0505	0916	2.5E
	1205	1530	2.7F
	1740	2145	2.5E
12 W	0041	0356	2.6F
	0606	1010	2.5E
	1305	1622	2.8F
	1840	2238	2.6E
13 Th	0145	0449	2.7F
	0709	1103	2.5E
	1404	1714	2.8F
	1940	2331	2.7E
14 F	0246	0542	2.8F
	0812	1156	2.5E
	1459	1807	2.9F
	2034		
15 Sa		0024	2.8E
	0341	0635	2.8F
	0906	1249	2.5E
	1550	1858	2.9F
	2122		
16 Su		0116	2.8E
	0432	0725	2.8F
	0955	1340	2.5E
	1639	1947	2.9F
	2207		
17 M ○		0204	2.8E
	0521	0814	2.8F
	1041	1428	2.4E
	1726	2035	2.8F
	2251		
18 Tu		0252	2.7E
	0605	0902	2.7F
	1124	1515	2.3E
	1809	2123	2.6F
	2334		
19 W		0339	2.6E
	0646	0951	2.5F
	1206	1604	2.2E
	1850	2213	2.4F
20 Th	0017	0427	2.4E
	0726	1041	2.4F
	1247	1652	2.1E
	1931	2303	2.3F
21 F	0100	0514	2.3E
	0806	1130	2.3F
	1329	1738	1.9E
	2014	2352	2.2F
22 Sa	0144	0601	2.1E
	0849	1218	2.2F
	1413	1826	1.8E
	2102		
23 Su		0041	2.0F
	0229	0649	1.9E
	0935	1307	2.1F
	1500	1915	1.7E
	2153		
24 M		0131	1.9F
	0317	0740	1.8E
	1022	1358	2.0F
	1548	1703	0.8E
		1740†	0.7E
25 Tu		0222	1.9F
	0407	0834	1.7E
	1109	1449	1.9F
	1637	2102	1.7E
	2337		
26 W		0314	1.8F
	0458	0612	0.8E
		0702	0.8E
		0925	1.7E
	1158	1539†	2.0F
27 Th	0031	0404	1.9F
	0550	0703	0.8E
		0748	0.7E
		1014	1.7E
	1247	1629†	2.0F
28 F	0126	0455	1.9F
	0645	1103	1.8E
	1338	1719	2.1F
	1911	2329	2.0E
29 Sa	0218	0546	2.0F
	0739	1153	1.8E
	1427	1809	2.2F
	2002		
30 Su		0019	2.1E
	0307	0637	2.2F
	0831	1243	1.9E
	1515	1859	2.3F
	2052		

Time meridian 75° W. 0000 is midnight. 1200 is noon. Times are not adjusted for Daylight Saving Time.
† See page 196 for the remaining currents on this day.

Buucksport, Penobscot Bay, Maine, 2019

F–Flood, Dir. 292° True   E–Ebb, Dir. 113° True

July

Day	Slack	Maximum	knots
1 M	0355, 0922, 1602, 2141	0109 / 0726 / 1332 / 1947	2.3E / 2.3F / 2.0E / 2.4F
2 Tu ●	0443, 1012, 1650, 2230	0156 / 0813 / 1419 / 2034	2.4E / 2.5F / 2.1E / 2.5F
3 W	0531, 1103, 1739, 2321	0243 / 0902 / 1507 / 2123	2.5E / 2.6F / 2.2E / 2.6F
4 Th	0618, 1154, 1829	0332 / 0951 / 1557 / 2214	2.6E / 2.6F / 2.3E / 2.6F
5 F	0013, 0707, 1245, 1920	0423 / 1043 / 1648 / 2306	2.7E / 2.7F / 2.4E / 2.7F
6 Sa	0105, 0757, 1337, 2015	0513 / 1134 / 1739 / 2357	2.7E / 2.8F / 2.5E / 2.7F
7 Su	0157, 0851, 1430, 2114	0604 / 1225 / 1831	2.7E / 2.8F / 2.5E
8 M	0252, 0947, 1525, 2216	0049 / 0657 / 1317 / 1927	2.7F / 2.6E / 2.8F / 2.5E
9 Tu ☽	0348, 1045, 1621, 2319	0143 / 0754 / 1410 / 2025	2.7F / 2.5E / 2.8F / 2.5E
10 W	0446, 1143, 1718	0238 / 0852 / 1504 / 2122	2.7F / 2.5E / 2.8F / 2.6E
11 Th	0024, 0545, 1243, 1817	0332 / 0947 / 1557 / 2215	2.6F / 2.5E / 2.8F / 2.6E
12 F	0129, 0649, 1343, 1918	0425 / 1040 / 1649 / 2308	2.6F / 2.4E / 2.7F / 2.6E
13 Sa	0232, 0756, 1441, 2015	0518 / 1133 / 1742	2.6F / 2.4E / 2.7F
14 Su	0328, 0854, 1534, 2103	0001 / 0610 / 1227 / 1834	2.6E / 2.6F / 2.3E / 2.7F
15 M	0420, 0940, 1624, 2146	0054 / 0701 / 1318 / 1923	2.6E / 2.6F / 2.3E / 2.7F
16 Tu ○	0507, 1020, 1709, 2228	0143 / 0750 / 1406 / 2011	2.6E / 2.6F / 2.2E / 2.6F
17 W	0549, 1059, 1750, 2309	0229 / 0837 / 1452 / 2058	2.5E / 2.5F / 2.2E / 2.5F
18 Th	0627, 1138, 1828, 2350	0315 / 0925 / 1538 / 2147	2.4E / 2.4F / 2.1E / 2.4F
19 F	0701, 1219, 1905	0401 / 1013 / 1625 / 2236	2.3E / 2.3F / 2.0E / 2.3F
20 Sa	0032, 0736, 1300, 1944	0447 / 1102 / 1711 / 2324	2.2E / 2.2F / 1.9E / 2.1F
21 Su	0115, 0813, 1342, 2027	0533 / 1150 / 1756	2.1E / 2.1F / 1.8E
22 M	0159, 0855, 1426, 2114	0012 / 0618 / 1238 / 1843	2.0F / 1.9E / 2.0F / 1.7E
23 Tu	0245, 0939	0101 / 0411 / 0450 / 0706 / 1326†	1.9F / 1.1E / 1.0E / 1.8E / 2.0F
24 W ○	0334, 1025	0151 / 0457 / 0549 / 0758 / 1417†	1.8F / 1.1E / 1.0E / 1.7E / 1.9F
25 Th	0424, 1113	0243 / 0544 / 0643 / 0851 / 1508†	1.8F / 1.0E / 0.9E / 1.6E / 1.9F
26 F	0516, 1203, 1742	0334 / 0942 / 1558 / 1902 / 1949†	1.8F / 1.6E / 1.9F / 1.0E / 0.9E
27 Sa	0043, 0610, 1256, 1836	0425 / 1032 / 1648 / 2258	1.9F / 1.7E / 2.0F / 1.9E
28 Su	0140, 0706, 1350, 1930	0517 / 1122 / 1740 / 2349	2.0F / 1.8E / 2.1F / 2.1E
29 M	0235, 0802, 1444, 2024	0608 / 1214 / 1831	2.2F / 1.9E / 2.3F
30 Tu	0327, 0856, 1536, 2116	0040 / 0659 / 1305 / 1920	2.3E / 2.4F / 2.1E / 2.5F
31 W ●	0418, 0948, 1628, 2209	0130 / 0748 / 1354 / 2009	2.5E / 2.6F / 2.3E / 2.7F

August

Day	Slack	Maximum	knots
1 Th	0508, 1040, 1720, 2301	0219 / 0836 / 1443 / 2058	2.7E / 2.8F / 2.4E / 2.8F
2 F	0558, 1133, 1811, 2354	0308 / 0926 / 1533 / 2148	2.8E / 2.9F / 2.6E / 2.9F
3 Sa	0646, 1225, 1903	0358 / 1017 / 1624 / 2241	2.9E / 3.0F / 2.7E / 3.0F
4 Su	0047, 0736, 1317, 1957	0450 / 1108 / 1716 / 2333	2.9E / 3.0F / 2.8E / 3.0F
5 M	0139, 0828, 1409, 2055	0541 / 1159 / 1807	2.9E / 3.0F / 2.8E
6 Tu	0232, 0923, 1502, 2157	0025 / 0633 / 1251 / 1901	2.9F / 2.7E / 2.9F / 2.7E
7 W ☽	0327, 1021, 1557, 2259	0118 / 0728 / 1344 / 1958	2.8F / 2.6E / 2.8F / 2.6E
8 Th	0424, 1119, 1652	0212 / 0826 / 1438 / 2057	2.7F / 2.4E / 2.7F / 2.6E
9 F	0004, 0523, 1220, 1750	0306 / 0923 / 1531 / 2152	2.6F / 2.3E / 2.6F / 2.5E
10 Sa	0111, 0626, 1324, 1852	0400 / 1017 / 1624 / 2245	2.5F / 2.3E / 2.6F / 2.5E
11 Su	0215, 0743, 1425, 1955	0452 / 1110 / 1716 / 2338	2.4F / 2.2E / 2.5F / 2.4E
12 M	0312, 0850, 1520, 2047	0545 / 1203 / 1809	2.4F / 2.2E / 2.5F
13 Tu	0403, 0931, 1609, 2127	0030 / 0636 / 1255 / 1859	2.4E / 2.4F / 2.2E / 2.5F
14 W	0449, 1000, 1652, 2205	0120 / 0725 / 1342 / 1947	2.4E / 2.5F / 2.2E / 2.5F
15 Th ○	0529, 1033, 1731, 2244	0206 / 0812 / 1428 / 2033	2.4E / 2.5F / 2.1E / 2.5F
16 F	0603, 1110, 1806, 2324	0250 / 0858 / 1512 / 2120	2.3E / 2.4F / 2.1E / 2.4F
17 Sa	0633, 1149, 1840	0334 / 0946 / 1557 / 2208	2.3E / 2.3F / 2.0E / 2.3F
18 Su	0005, 0705, 1230, 1916	0419 / 1033 / 1642 / 2256	2.2E / 2.2F / 2.0E / 2.2F
19 M	0047, 0739, 1311, 1955	0504 / 1121 / 1727 / 2344	2.0E / 2.1F / 1.9E / 2.0F
20 Tu	0130, 0817, 1354, 2038	0548 / 1208 / 1811	1.9E / 2.0F / 1.8E
21 W	0215, 0859, 1439	0032 / 0634 / 1256 / 1607 / 1655†	1.9F / 1.7E / 1.9F / 1.2E / 1.1E
22 Th	0303, 0945, 1527	0121 / 0723 / 1346 / 1654 / 1752†	1.8F / 1.6E / 1.8F / 1.2E / 1.1E
23 F ○	0352, 1035	0213 / 0516 / 0622 / 0817 / 1437†	1.8F / 1.2E / 1.0E / 1.5E / 1.8F
24 Sa	0445, 1126	0305 / 0605 / 0712 / 0912 / 1529†	1.8F / 1.1E / 0.9E / 1.5E / 1.8F
25 Su	0007, 0539, 1222	0357 / 0657 / 0754 / 1003 / 1620†	1.8F / 1.0E / 0.9E / 1.6E / 1.9F
26 M	0107, 0637, 1320, 1902	0448 / 1054 / 1712 / 2320	2.0F / 1.8E / 2.1F / 2.1E
27 Tu	0206, 0735, 1418, 1959	0541 / 1146 / 1804	2.2F / 1.9E / 2.3F
28 W	0302, 0832, 1514, 2055	0013 / 0632 / 1239 / 1855	2.4E / 2.4F / 2.2E / 2.6F
29 Th	0354, 0926, 1608, 2148	0105 / 0722 / 1330 / 1945	2.6E / 2.7F / 2.5E / 2.9F
30 F ●	0445, 1019, 1702, 2242	0155 / 0812 / 1419 / 2033	2.8E / 2.9F / 2.7E / 3.0F
31 Sa	0535, 1111, 1754, 2335	0244 / 0900 / 1509 / 2124	3.0E / 3.1F / 2.9E / 3.1F

September

Day	Slack	Maximum	knots
1 Su	0624, 1203, 1846	0334 / 0950 / 1600 / 2215	3.0E / 3.1F / 3.0E / 3.1F
2 M	0027, 0713, 1254, 1938	0425 / 1042 / 1652 / 2308	3.0E / 3.1F / 3.0E / 3.1F
3 Tu	0119, 0803, 1344, 2034	0517 / 1133 / 1743	2.9E / 3.1F / 2.9E
4 W	0211, 0857, 1436, 2134	0000 / 0608 / 1225 / 1835	3.0F / 2.7E / 3.0F / 2.8E
5 Th ☽	0304, 0955, 1529, 2236	0052 / 0702 / 1317 / 1931	2.8F / 2.5E / 2.8F / 2.6E
6 F	0359, 1055, 1623, 2341	0146 / 0759 / 1411 / 2030	2.6F / 2.3E / 2.6F / 2.4E
7 Sa	0456, 1157, 1720	0240 / 0858 / 1505 / 2127	2.5F / 2.2E / 2.5F / 2.4E
8 Su	0048, 0558, 1303, 1821	0334 / 0953 / 1558 / 2220	2.4F / 2.1E / 2.4F / 2.3E
9 M	0153, 0722, 1407, 1928	0426 / 1046 / 1650 / 2312	2.3F / 2.1E / 2.3F / 2.3E
10 Tu	0250, 0838, 1502, 2025	0518 / 1138 / 1742	2.3F / 2.1E / 2.3F
11 W	0340, 0913, 1550, 2104	0004 / 0610 / 1229 / 1833	2.3E / 2.3F / 2.1E / 2.4F
12 Th	0423, 0932, 1631, 2140	0054 / 0659 / 1317 / 1921	2.3E / 2.4F / 2.1E / 2.4F
13 F ○	0500, 1003, 1707, 2218	0140 / 0746 / 1402 / 2008	2.3E / 2.4F / 2.2E / 2.4F
14 Sa	0532, 1040, 1741, 2257	0223 / 0831 / 1445 / 2053	2.3E / 2.4F / 2.2E / 2.4F
15 Su	0602, 1119, 1814, 2338	0307 / 0917 / 1529 / 2140	2.2E / 2.3F / 2.1E / 2.3F
16 M	0633, 1159, 1849	0351 / 1004 / 1613 / 2228	2.1E / 2.2F / 2.1E / 2.2F
17 Tu	0020, 0706, 1241, 1926	0435 / 1052 / 1658 / 2316	2.0E / 2.1F / 2.0E / 2.1F
18 W	0103, 0743, 1323, 2008	0520 / 1139 / 1742	1.9E / 2.0F / 1.9E
19 Th	0147, 0824	0004 / 0315 / 0405 / 0604 / 1227†	2.0F / 1.2E / 1.1E / 1.7E / 1.9F
20 F ☾	0234, 0910	0053 / 0401 / 0501 / 0652 / 1316†	1.8F / 1.2E / 1.1E / 1.6E / 1.8F
21 Sa	0324, 1002	0144 / 0450 / 0556 / 0746 / 1408†	1.8F / 1.2E / 1.1E / 1.5E / 1.8F
22 Su	0417, 1057	0237 / 0539 / 0646 / 0842 / 1501†	1.8F / 1.1E / 1.0E / 1.5E / 1.8F
23 M	0513, 1155, 1737	0329 / 0937 / 1553 / 1905 / 1942†	1.9F / 1.6E / 2.0F / 1.1E / 1.1E
24 Tu	0039, 0611, 1256, 1836	0421 / 1029 / 1645 / 2254	2.1F / 1.8E / 2.2F / 2.2E
25 W	0140, 0711, 1358, 1937	0514 / 1121 / 1738 / 2347	2.3F / 2.1E / 2.4F / 2.4E
26 Th	0238, 0810, 1456, 2035	0606 / 1214 / 1830	2.6F / 2.4E / 2.7F
27 F	0331, 0905, 1551, 2129	0040 / 0657 / 1306 / 1921	2.7E / 2.8F / 2.6E / 3.0F
28 Sa ●	0422, 0957, 1645, 2223	0131 / 0746 / 1356 / 2010	2.9E / 3.1F / 2.9E / 3.2F
29 Su	0512, 1049, 1737, 2316	0221 / 0835 / 1445 / 2100	3.0E / 3.2F / 3.1E / 3.2F
30 M	0601, 1140, 1828	0310 / 0924 / 1536 / 2151	3.0E / 3.2F / 3.1E / 3.2F

Time meridian 75° W. 0000 is midnight. 1200 is noon. Times are not adjusted for Daylight Saving Time.
† See page 196 for the remaining currents on this day.

14

Bucksport, Penobscot Bay, Maine, 2019

F–Flood, Dir. 292° True   E–Ebb, Dir. 113° True

October

Date	Slack h m	Maximum h m	knots
1 Tu	0007	0401	3.0E
	0649	1015	3.2F
	1229	1627	3.1E
	1919	2243	3.1F
2 W	0057	0453	2.8E
	0738	1107	3.0F
	1318	1718	2.9E
	2012	2335	3.0F
3 Th	0147	0544	2.6E
	0830	1159	2.9F
	1407	1810	2.7E
	2109		
4 F		0027	2.8E
	0238	0636	2.4E
	0927	1251	2.7F
	1458	1903	2.5E
	2210		
5 Sa ☽		0119	2.5E
	0331	0732	2.2F
	1028	1344	2.4F
	1551	2001	2.3F
	2313		
6 Su		0213	2.4E
	0426	0830	2.0F
	1130	1438	2.3F
	1646	2059	2.2E
7 M	0018	0307	2.2F
	0523	0927	2.0E
	1236	1531	2.2F
	1743	2153	2.1E
8 Tu	0122	0359	2.2F
	0627	1019	2.0E
	1341	1623	2.2F
	1843	2244	2.1E
9 W	0219	0450	2.2F
	0744	1110	2.0E
	1436	1714	2.2F
	1943	2334	2.1E
10 Th	0307	0541	2.2F
	0823	1200	2.0E
	1523	1805	2.3F
	2030		
11 F		0024	2.2E
	0348	0631	2.3F
	0855	1248	2.1E
	1603	1854	2.3F
	2110		
12 Sa		0111	2.2E
	0423	0718	2.4F
	0930	1334	2.2E
	1639	1941	2.4F
	2149		
13 Su ○		0155	2.2E
	0455	0804	2.4F
	1008	1417	2.2E
	1714	2027	2.4F
	2229		
14 M		0238	2.2E
	0527	0849	2.4F
	1048	1500	2.2E
	1748	2113	2.3F
	2311		
15 Tu		0322	2.1E
	0601	0935	2.3F
	1130	1544	2.1E
	1824	2200	2.2F
	2354		
16 W		0407	2.0E
	0635	1023	2.1F
	1212	1629	2.1E
	1901	2249	2.1F
17 Th	0037	0452	1.8E
	0713	1111	2.0F
	1255	1714	2.0E
	1942	2337	2.0F
18 F	0122	0250	1.2E
		0337	1.1E
		0538	1.7E
	0754	1159	1.9F
	1341	1515†	1.4E
19 Sa		0026	1.9F
	0210	0625	1.6E
	0842	1248	1.9F
	1429	1604	1.4E
		1656†	1.4E
20 Su		0117	1.9F
	0300	0717	1.6E
	0935	1340	1.8F
	1521	1655	1.4E
		1747†	1.3E
21 M ○		0209	1.9F
	0354	0518	1.1E
		0613	1.0E
		0815	1.6E
	1034	1433†	1.9F
22 Tu		0303	2.0F
	0450	0612	1.0E
		0655	1.0E
		0912	1.7E
	1134	1527†	2.1F
23 W	0015	0355	2.2F
	0549	1005	2.0E
	1237	1620	2.3F
	1814	2230	2.3E
24 Th	0116	0447	2.4F
	0649	1057	2.3E
	1341	1712	2.5F
	1915	2323	2.5E
25 F	0214	0540	2.7F
	0749	1150	2.5E
	1440	1805	2.8F
	2015		
26 Sa		0016	2.7E
	0308	0632	2.9F
	0844	1243	2.8E
	1536	1857	3.0F
	2111		
27 Su ●		0108	2.8E
	0359	0722	3.1F
	0936	1333	3.0E
	1629	1947	3.2F
	2204		
28 M		0158	2.9E
	0449	0810	3.2F
	1026	1423	3.1E
	1721	2036	3.2F
	2256		
29 Tu		0247	2.9E
	0538	0859	3.2F
	1116	1512	3.1E
	1811	2126	3.2F
	2346		
30 W		0337	2.8E
	0626	0950	3.1F
	1204	1603	3.0E
	1900	2218	3.0F
31 Th	0035	0429	2.7E
	0714	1041	2.9F
	1252	1654	2.9E
	1950	2310	2.8F

November

Date	Slack h m	Maximum h m	knots
1 F	0123	0520	2.5E
	0804	1133	2.7F
	1339	1745	2.7E
	2043		
2 Sa		0001	2.6F
	0211	0610	2.3E
	0858	1224	2.5F
	1427	1836	2.4E
	2140		
3 Su		0052	2.4F
	0301	0703	2.0E
	0957	1316	2.3F
	1518	1930	2.2E
	2240		
4 M ○		0145	2.3F
	0352	0800	1.9E
	1057	1409	2.1F
	1610	2028	2.0E
	2339		
5 Tu		0238	2.2F
	0445	0857	1.8E
	1159	1502	2.1F
	1703	2123	2.0E
6 W	0038	0330	2.1F
	0539	0949	1.9E
	1302	1554	2.1F
	1758	2213	2.0E
7 Th	0134	0420	2.1F
	0634	1039	1.9E
	1359	1645	2.1F
	1854	2302	2.0E
8 F	0222	0510	2.2F
	0727	1128	2.0E
	1447	1736	2.2F
	1947	2351	2.0E
9 Sa	0303	0600	2.2F
	0813	1217	2.1E
	1529	1826	2.2F
	2034		
10 Su		0040	2.1E
	0340	0649	2.3F
	0855	1304	2.2E
	1607	1914	2.3F
	2118		
11 M		0126	2.1E
	0416	0736	2.4F
	0936	1348	2.2E
	1644	2000	2.4F
	2200		
12 Tu ○		0210	2.1E
	0452	0821	2.4F
	1018	1432	2.2E
	1722	2046	2.3F
	2244		
13 W		0254	2.0E
	0529	0907	2.3F
	1101	1516	2.2E
	1759	2133	2.3F
	2328		
14 Th		0339	2.0E
	0608	0955	2.2F
	1145	1602	2.2E
	1839	2222	2.2F
15 F	0014	0426	1.9E
	0648	1044	2.1F
	1230	1649	2.1E
	1921	2311	2.2F
16 Sa	0100	0513	1.8E
	0731	1133	2.1F
	1317	1736	2.1E
	2007		
17 Su		0001	2.1F
	0148	0318	1.2E
		0355	1.2E
		0601	1.8E
	0820	1222†	2.0F
18 M		0051	2.1F
	0239	0652	1.8E
	0915	1314	2.0F
	1459	1918	2.0E
	2155		
19 Tu ○		0143	2.1F
	0334	0748	1.8E
	1015	1407	2.1F
	1555	2016	2.1E
	2253		
20 W		0236	2.2F
	0430	0846	2.0E
	1117	1501	2.2F
	1653	2113	2.2E
	2352		
21 Th		0330	2.4F
	0528	0941	2.2E
	1220	1555	2.4F
	1753	2206	2.4E
22 F	0052	0422	2.6F
	0628	1034	2.4E
	1325	1648	2.6F
	1855	2259	2.5E
23 Sa	0151	0514	2.8F
	0727	1127	2.6E
	1426	1741	2.8F
	1956	2352	2.6E
24 Su	0246	0606	2.9F
	0824	1220	2.8E
	1522	1834	3.0F
	2053		
25 M		0045	2.7E
	0338	0657	3.1F
	0915	1312	3.0E
	1616	1924	3.1F
	2146		
26 Tu ●		0136	2.8E
	0429	0747	3.1F
	1005	1402	3.1E
	1707	2014	3.1F
	2237		
27 W		0226	2.7E
	0518	0836	3.1F
	1053	1450	3.0E
	1756	2103	3.0F
	2326		
28 Th		0315	2.6E
	0606	0925	3.0F
	1140	1540	2.9E
	1843	2153	2.9F
29 F	0013	0405	2.5E
	0652	1016	2.8F
	1226	1630	2.7E
	1929	2244	2.7F
30 Sa	0058	0455	2.3E
	0739	1107	2.6F
	1311	1720	2.5E
	2017	2335	2.5F

December

Date	Slack h m	Maximum h m	knots
1 Su	0143	0545	2.2E
	0828	1157	2.4F
	1357	1809	2.3E
	2108		
2 M		0025	2.4F
	0229	0634	2.0E
	0922	1248	2.2F
	1444	1859	2.1E
	2200		
3 Tu		0115	2.2F
	0317	0727	1.8E
	1018	1339	2.1F
	1533	1953	2.0E
	2253		
4 W		0207	2.1F
	0406	0823	1.8E
	1114	1432	2.0F
	1624	2048	1.9E
	2344		
5 Th		0259	2.1F
	0457	0916	1.8E
	1211	1524	2.0F
	1716	2140	1.9E
6 F	0035	0349	2.1F
	0548	1006	1.9E
	1308	1614	2.0F
	1810	2229	1.9E
7 Sa	0126	0439	2.1F
	0640	1055	1.9E
	1402	1705	2.0F
	1904	2317	1.9E
8 Su	0212	0529	2.1F
	0731	1143	2.0E
	1449	1756	2.1F
	1956		
9 M		0007	1.9E
	0256	0619	2.2F
	0819	1232	2.1E
	1532	1845	2.2F
	2045		
10 Tu		0056	1.9E
	0337	0707	2.3F
	0904	1320	2.2E
	1613	1933	2.3F
	2131		
11 W		0142	2.0E
	0418	0754	2.3F
	0949	1405	2.3E
	1654	2020	2.4F
	2217		
12 Th ○		0227	2.0E
	0500	0840	2.3F
	1034	1450	2.3E
	1736	2107	2.4F
	2304		
13 F		0313	2.0E
	0542	0927	2.3F
	1121	1536	2.3E
	1818	2155	2.3F
	2352		
14 Sa		0400	2.0E
	0626	1017	2.3F
	1208	1624	2.4E
	1902	2246	2.3F
15 Su	0040	0449	2.0E
	0712	1107	2.3F
	1257	1713	2.4E
	1948	2335	2.4F
16 M	0129	0538	2.0E
	0802	1157	2.3F
	1347	1802	2.3E
	2040		
17 Tu		0025	2.4F
	0220	0628	2.1E
	0857	1248	2.3F
	1440	1853	2.3E
	2135		
18 W ○		0117	2.4F
	0314	0722	2.1E
	0958	1341	2.4F
	1536	1949	2.3E
	2232		
19 Th		0210	2.5F
	0410	0820	2.2E
	1100	1436	2.4F
	1633	2047	2.3E
	2330		
20 F		0303	2.6F
	0507	0917	2.4E
	1204	1530	2.5F
	1732	2143	2.4E
21 Sa	0029	0356	2.7F
	0605	1011	2.5E
	1309	1623	2.6F
	1834	2236	2.5E
22 Su	0129	0449	2.8F
	0705	1104	2.7E
	1412	1717	2.7F
	1938	2329	2.5E
23 M	0227	0541	2.9F
	0804	1158	2.8E
	1511	1810	2.8F
	2037		
24 Tu		0023	2.5E
	0321	0634	2.9F
	0857	1251	2.9E
	1605	1902	2.9F
	2131		
25 W		0116	2.6E
	0413	0724	3.0F
	0946	1341	2.9E
	1656	1951	2.9F
	2220		
26 Th ●		0205	2.5E
	0503	0813	2.9F
	1032	1430	2.8E
	1744	2040	2.8F
	2307		
27 F		0254	2.5E
	0550	0901	2.8F
	1118	1518	2.7E
	1828	2129	2.7F
	2351		
28 Sa		0342	2.4E
	0633	0951	2.6F
	1202	1606	2.6E
	1909	2219	2.6F
29 Su	0032	0431	2.2E
	0716	1041	2.5F
	1244	1654	2.4E
	1950	2308	2.4F
30 M	0114	0518	2.1E
	0759	1130	2.3F
	1328	1741	2.3E
	2033	2357	2.3F
31 Tu	0157	0605	2.0E
	0845	1219	2.2F
	1412	1828	2.1E
	2118		

Time meridian 75° W. 0000 is midnight. 1200 is noon. Times are not adjusted for Daylight Saving Time.
† See page 196 for the remaining currents on this day.

Bath Iron Works, Kennebec River, 2019

F–Flood, Dir. 001° True   E–Ebb, Dir. 178° True

January

Day	Slack	Maximum	knots
1 Tu	0331	0649	2.0F
	0938	1238	2.1E
	1616	1940	1.8F
	2208		
2 W		0053	1.9E
	0423	0751	2.0F
	1033	1338	2.2E
	1712	2041	1.8F
	2303		
3 Th		0146	1.9E
	0512	0846	2.0F
	1124	1431	2.2E
	1805	2135	1.8F
	2355		
4 F		0235	1.9E
	0600	0934	2.0F
	1212	1517	2.2E
	1854	2223	1.8F
5 Sa ●	0043	0320	1.9E
	0646	1011	1.9F
	1258	1557	2.2E
	1941	2307	1.8F
6 Su	0129	0402	1.8E
	0732	1031	1.9F
	1342	1634	2.1E
	2026	2345	1.7F
7 M	0213	0442	1.8E
	0816	1057	1.9F
	1424	1710	2.1E
	2108		
8 Tu		0011	1.7F
	0256	0522	1.8E
	0900	1133	1.9F
	1505	1747	2.0E
	2149		
9 W		0024	1.6F
	0336	0602	1.8E
	0943	1213	1.9F
	1545	1825	2.0E
	2229		
10 Th		0054	1.7F
	0416	0643	1.8E
	1027	1256	1.9F
	1624	1905	2.0E
	2309		
11 F		0132	1.7F
	0456	0725	1.8E
	1112	1341	1.8F
	1705	1945	1.9E
	2348		
12 Sa		0213	1.8F
	0537	0808	1.8E
	1200	1427	1.8F
	1747	2028	1.9E
13 Su	0028	0256	1.9F
	0620	0854	1.8E
	1251	1515	1.7F
	1833	2113	1.9E
14 M ◑	0110	0342	1.9F
	0706	0942	1.8E
	1345	1606	1.7F
	1923	2203	1.8E
15 Tu	0154	0431	2.0F
	0755	1035	1.9E
	1440	1700	1.6F
	2018	2257	1.8E
16 W	0242	0522	2.0F
	0848	1129	2.0E
	1537	1756	1.6F
	2117	2352	1.8E
17 Th	0332	0615	2.1F
	0942	1224	2.1E
	1633	1853	1.7F
	2216		
18 F		0047	1.9E
	0425	0709	2.2F
	1036	1318	2.3E
	1728	1953	1.8F
	2313		
19 Sa		0141	2.0E
	0518	0804	2.3F
	1130	1411	2.4E
	1822	2055	1.9F
20 Su	0008	0235	2.1E
	0612	0901	2.3F
	1224	1504	2.5E
	1915	2154	2.0F
21 M ○	0102	0329	2.2E
	0708	0958	2.4F
	1318	1557	2.6E
	2007	2250	2.1F
22 Tu	0155	0421	2.3E
	0804	1053	2.5F
	1411	1649	2.6E
	2058	2343	2.2F
23 W	0247	0514	2.4E
	0900	1149	2.5F
	1505	1741	2.6E
	2149		
24 Th		0036	2.2F
	0339	0607	2.4E
	0957	1245	2.4F
	1559	1835	2.5E
	2240		
25 F		0128	2.2F
	0431	0702	2.4E
	1055	1341	2.3F
	1654	1929	2.4E
	2331		
26 Sa		0219	2.2F
	0525	0758	2.3E
	1154	1438	2.1F
	1749	2023	2.2E
27 Su ◐	0022	0310	2.1F
	0620	0855	2.2E
	1254	1539	1.9F
	1846	2120	2.0E
28 M	0115	0405	2.0F
	0716	0957	2.0E
	1355	1654	1.7F
	1945	2221	1.8E
29 Tu	0208	0507	1.9F
	0813	1107	2.0E
	1455	1814	1.6F
	2044	2326	1.7E
30 W	0301	0616	1.8F
	0911	1220	1.9E
	1554	1921	1.6F
	2143		
31 Th		0029	1.7E
	0354	0724	1.8F
	1007	1325	2.0E
	1650	2021	1.6F
	2239		

February

Day	Slack	Maximum	knots
1 F		0125	1.7E
	0445	0823	1.8F
	1059	1418	2.0E
	1741	2114	1.7F
	2331		
2 Sa		0214	1.7E
	0534	0911	1.8F
	1147	1501	2.0E
	1829	2201	1.7F
3 Su	0018	0258	1.8E
	0620	0944	1.8F
	1232	1536	2.1E
	1913	2240	1.7F
4 M ●	0102	0337	1.8E
	0705	0955	1.8F
	1314	1607	2.1E
	1955	2309	1.7F
5 Tu	0143	0414	1.8E
	0748	1025	1.9F
	1354	1639	2.1E
	2034	2316	1.7F
6 W	0222	0451	1.9E
	0830	1102	1.9F
	1433	1713	2.1E
	2112	2340	1.8F
7 Th	0300	0529	1.9E
	0912	1143	2.0F
	1511	1750	2.1E
	2149		
8 F		0015	1.9F
	0338	0608	2.0E
	0955	1226	2.0F
	1549	1828	2.1E
	2225		
9 Sa		0055	2.0F
	0416	0649	2.0E
	1039	1311	1.9F
	1629	1909	2.1E
	2302		
10 Su		0138	2.0F
	0456	0732	2.0E
	1126	1358	1.9F
	1711	1952	2.0E
	2341		
11 M		0222	2.1F
	0539	0817	2.1E
	1218	1447	1.8F
	1758	2038	2.0E
12 Tu ◑	0024	0309	2.1F
	0626	0906	2.0E
	1313	1538	1.7F
	1850	2129	1.9E
13 W	0113	0359	2.1F
	0718	0959	2.0E
	1412	1634	1.6F
	1950	2225	1.8E
14 Th	0207	0453	2.1F
	0815	1057	2.0E
	1512	1733	1.6F
	2053	2325	1.8E
15 F	0305	0549	2.1F
	0915	1157	2.1E
	1612	1834	1.7F
	2156		
16 Sa		0025	1.9E
	0405	0647	2.1F
	1015	1256	2.2E
	1709	1938	1.8F
	2256		
17 Su		0123	2.0E
	0504	0747	2.2F
	1114	1354	2.4E
	1803	2045	1.9F
	2352		
18 M		0220	2.2E
	0601	0848	2.3F
	1210	1450	2.5E
	1856	2146	2.1F
19 Tu ○	0045	0314	2.3E
	0657	0948	2.4F
	1304	1543	2.6E
	1947	2239	2.2F
20 W	0136	0407	2.4E
	0753	1045	2.5F
	1358	1634	2.6E
	2036	2329	2.3F
21 Th	0227	0458	2.5E
	0848	1140	2.5F
	1450	1725	2.5E
	2125		
22 F		0018	2.3F
	0317	0550	2.5E
	0943	1234	2.4F
	1542	1816	2.4E
	2213		
23 Sa		0106	2.3F
	0408	0643	2.4E
	1038	1329	2.2F
	1635	1908	2.3E
	2302		
24 Su		0154	2.2F
	0500	0736	2.3E
	1135	1425	2.0F
	1728	2000	2.1E
	2352		
25 M		0241	2.1F
	0553	0831	2.2E
	1233	1524	1.8F
	1823	2054	1.9E
26 Tu ◐	0044	0330	1.9F
	0648	0930	2.0E
	1332	1639	1.6F
	1921	2152	1.7E
27 W	0138	0424	1.7F
	0745	1039	1.8E
	1431	1755	1.5F
	2019	2257	1.6E
28 Th	0232	0529	1.6F
	0842	1200	1.8E
	1529	1859	1.5F
	2118		

March

Day	Slack	Maximum	knots
1 F		0004	1.5E
	0327	0649	1.6F
	0938	1308	1.8E
	1623	1956	1.5F
	2213		
2 Sa		0102	1.6E
	0419	0751	1.6F
	1031	1358	1.9E
	1713	2047	1.6F
	2303		
3 Su		0150	1.6E
	0507	0836	1.6F
	1119	1436	1.9E
	1757	2130	1.6F
	2348		
4 M		0231	1.7E
	0553	0847	1.7F
	1203	1504	2.0E
	1839	2203	1.6F
5 Tu	0030	0307	1.8E
	0637	0915	1.8F
	1244	1533	2.0E
	1918	2209	1.7F
6 W ●	0108	0343	1.9E
	0719	0952	1.9F
	1322	1604	2.1E
	1955	2226	1.8F
7 Th	0146	0418	2.0E
	0801	1032	2.0F
	1400	1638	2.1E
	2031	2300	1.9F
8 F	0222	0455	2.1E
	0843	1114	2.0F
	1438	1714	2.2E
	2106	2339	2.1F
9 Sa	0259	0534	2.2E
	0925	1158	2.0F
	1516	1753	2.2E
	2141		
10 Su		0020	2.2F
	0338	0615	2.3E
	1009	1246	2.0F
	1557	1835	2.2E
	2218		
11 M		0105	2.2F
	0418	0659	2.3E
	1057	1332	1.9F
	1641	1920	2.1E
	2259		
12 Tu ◑		0151	2.2F
	0503	0746	2.2E
	1149	1422	1.8F
	1731	2009	2.0E
	2346		
13 W		0240	2.2F
	0552	0835	2.2E
	1247	1515	1.7F
	1827	2101	1.9E
14 Th ◑	0041	0332	2.1F
	0648	0930	2.1E
	1348	1612	1.7F
	1929	2159	1.8E
15 F	0142	0428	2.0F
	0749	1030	2.1E
	1450	1713	1.6F
	2034	2302	1.8E
16 Sa	0247	0527	2.0F
	0853	1135	2.1E
	1551	1818	1.7F
	2138		
17 Su		0006	1.9E
	0351	0629	2.1F
	0957	1238	2.2E
	1649	1926	1.8F
	2238		
18 M		0108	2.0E
	0452	0733	2.2F
	1058	1339	2.3E
	1742	2035	2.0F
	2333		
19 Tu		0206	2.2E
	0550	0840	2.3F
	1155	1435	2.4E
	1833	2134	2.2F
20 W ○	0025	0300	2.4E
	0645	0943	2.4F
	1249	1528	2.5E
	1923	2225	2.3F
21 Th	0116	0352	2.6E
	0740	1039	2.5F
	1341	1618	2.5E
	2011	2311	2.4F
22 F	0206	0442	2.6E
	0834	1133	2.4F
	1433	1706	2.5E
	2058	2356	2.4F
23 Sa	0255	0532	2.6E
	0927	1226	2.3F
	1523	1755	2.3E
	2145		
24 Su		0041	2.3F
	0345	0623	2.5E
	1021	1320	2.1F
	1614	1845	2.2E
	2233		
25 M		0126	2.1F
	0435	0714	2.3E
	1116	1414	1.9F
	1707	1936	2.0E
	2323		
26 Tu		0210	2.0F
	0526	0807	2.1E
	1212	1512	1.7F
	1800	2028	1.8E
27 W ◐	0015	0255	1.8F
	0620	0903	1.9E
	1308	1620	1.5F
	1856	2124	1.6E
28 Th	0109	0343	1.6F
	0715	1007	1.7E
	1404	1729	1.4F
	1953	2227	1.5E
29 F	0203	0435	1.5F
	0810	1129	1.7E
	1459	1829	1.4F
	2049	2334	1.4E
30 Sa	0258	0530	1.4F
	0906	1237	1.7E
	1550	1923	1.4F
	2142		
31 Su		0032	1.5E
	0349	0622	1.4F
	0958	1321	1.7E
	1637	2009	1.5F
	2230		

Time meridian 75° W. 0000 is midnight. 1200 is noon. Times are not adjusted for Daylight Saving Time.

Bath Iron Works, Kennebec River, 2019

F—Flood, Dir. 001° True   E—Ebb, Dir. 178° True

April

Day	Slack h m	Maximum h m	knots
1 M		0117	1.6E
	0438	0708	1.5F
	1046	1352	1.8E
	1720	2044	1.5F
	2314		
2 Tu		0156	1.7E
	0523	0752	1.6F
	1129	1421	1.9E
	1759	2044	1.6F
	2354		
3 W		0232	1.9E
	0607	0835	1.7F
	1209	1452	2.0E
	1837	2108	1.8F
4 Th	0031	0308	2.0E
	0650	0918	1.9F
	1248	1526	2.1E
	1912	2144	2.0F
5 F ●	0108	0344	2.2E
	0732	1002	2.0F
	1326	1602	2.1E
	1948	2223	2.1F
6 Sa	0145	0422	2.3E
	0815	1045	2.0F
	1406	1640	2.2E
	2023	2305	2.2F
7 Su	0224	0502	2.4E
	0858	1131	2.0F
	1447	1721	2.2E
	2100	2349	2.3F
8 M	0304	0545	2.4E
	0944	1219	2.0F
	1531	1806	2.2E
	2140		
9 Tu		0035	2.3F
	0347	0630	2.4E
	1033	1308	2.0F
	1619	1853	2.1E
	2226		
10 W		0124	2.3F
	0434	0719	2.4E
	1127	1400	1.9F
	1712	1944	2.0E
	2318		
11 Th		0215	2.2F
	0526	0810	2.3E
	1226	1455	1.8F
	1810	2039	1.9E
12 F ◐	0019	0309	2.1F
	0625	0906	2.2E
	1327	1554	1.7F
	1912	2138	1.8E
13 Sa	0126	0407	2.0F
	0729	1008	2.1E
	1429	1657	1.7F
	2016	2243	1.8E
14 Su	0233	0510	2.0F
	0835	1115	2.1E
	1529	1804	1.8F
	2119	2350	1.9E
15 M	0337	0615	2.0F
	0940	1222	2.2E
	1625	1913	1.9F
	2218		
16 Tu		0053	2.1E
	0439	0724	2.1F
	1041	1323	2.3E
	1718	2019	2.1F
	2313		
17 W		0151	2.3E
	0536	0835	2.2F
	1138	1419	2.4E
	1808	2117	2.3F
18 Th	0004	0246	2.5E
	0632	0940	2.3F
	1232	1510	2.4E
	1856	2206	2.4F
19 F ○	0055	0337	2.6E
	0726	1035	2.3F
	1323	1558	2.4E
	1943	2251	2.4F
20 Sa	0144	0425	2.6E
	0819	1128	2.3F
	1413	1645	2.3E
	2030	2334	2.3F
21 Su	0232	0513	2.5E
	0911	1219	2.2F
	1504	1733	2.2E
	2117		
22 M		0016	2.2F
	0321	0602	2.4E
	1003	1312	2.0F
	1554	1822	2.0E
	2205		
23 Tu		0057	2.0F
	0410	0652	2.2E
	1056	1404	1.8F
	1645	1912	1.8E
	2255		
24 W		0139	1.9F
	0500	0743	2.0E
	1148	1456	1.6F
	1737	2003	1.7E
	2347		
25 Th		0221	1.7F
	0550	0835	1.9E
	1241	1552	1.5F
	1830	2056	1.5E
26 F ◑	0039	0306	1.6F
	0643	0931	1.7E
	1333	1650	1.4F
	1923	2153	1.4E
27 Sa	0133	0353	1.5F
	0735	1034	1.6E
	1423	1744	1.3F
	2015	2253	1.4E
28 Su	0225	0444	1.4F
	0828	1136	1.6E
	1511	1824	1.3F
	2105	2349	1.5E
29 M	0316	0534	1.4F
	0918	1221	1.6E
	1556	1830	1.4F
	2151		
30 Tu		0035	1.6E
	0405	0623	1.5F
	1006	1258	1.7E
	1637	1902	1.5F
	2234		

May

Day	Slack h m	Maximum h m	knots
1 W		0115	1.7E
	0452	0711	1.6F
	1050	1333	1.8E
	1716	1941	1.7F
	2315		
2 Th		0153	1.9E
	0537	0758	1.7F
	1132	1410	2.0E
	1753	2023	1.9F
	2353		
3 F		0232	2.1E
	0621	0846	1.8F
	1213	1448	2.0E
	1829	2106	2.1F
4 Sa ●	0032	0311	2.3E
	0705	0933	1.9F
	1254	1528	2.1E
	1906	2149	2.3F
5 Su	0111	0351	2.4E
	0749	1019	2.0F
	1337	1610	2.2E
	1945	2234	2.4F
6 M	0152	0433	2.5E
	0835	1107	2.0F
	1422	1654	2.2E
	2027	2321	2.4F
7 Tu	0236	0518	2.6E
	0923	1157	2.0F
	1510	1741	2.2E
	2112		
8 W		0010	2.4F
	0322	0605	2.5E
	1014	1249	2.0F
	1601	1831	2.1E
	2203		
9 Th		0101	2.3F
	0413	0656	2.5E
	1109	1343	1.9F
	1656	1924	2.0E
	2301		
10 F		0155	2.2F
	0508	0750	2.4E
	1207	1439	1.9F
	1754	2020	2.0E
11 Sa ◐	0005	0251	2.1F
	0608	0847	2.3E
	1307	1537	1.9F
	1855	2120	1.9E
12 Su	0112	0350	2.1F
	0712	0949	2.2E
	1406	1640	1.9F
	1956	2225	1.9E
13 M	0218	0454	2.0F
	0817	1056	2.1E
	1503	1746	1.9F
	2057	2332	2.0E
14 Tu	0322	0602	2.0F
	0921	1203	2.1E
	1558	1853	2.0F
	2155		
15 W		0036	2.2E
	0423	0717	2.1F
	1022	1304	2.2E
	1650	1958	2.2F
	2250		
16 Th		0135	2.4E
	0521	0832	2.1F
	1119	1359	2.2E
	1740	2056	2.3F
	2343		
17 F		0230	2.5E
	0617	0935	2.2F
	1212	1450	2.2E
	1828	2147	2.3F
18 Sa ○	0033	0321	2.5E
	0710	1029	2.2F
	1304	1538	2.2E
	1916	2232	2.3F
19 Su	0122	0409	2.5E
	0803	1120	2.1F
	1354	1625	2.1E
	2004	2313	2.2F
20 M	0210	0456	2.4E
	0854	1211	2.0F
	1443	1712	2.0E
	2052	2352	2.1F
21 Tu	0258	0543	2.3E
	0944	1300	1.9F
	1532	1759	1.9E
	2140		
22 W		0029	2.0F
	0345	0630	2.2E
	1033	1347	1.8F
	1621	1848	1.8E
	2228		
23 Th		0108	1.8F
	0432	0718	2.0E
	1122	1430	1.6F
	1710	1936	1.6E
	2318		
24 F		0149	1.7F
	0520	0805	1.9E
	1210	1503	1.5F
	1759	2025	1.5E
25 Sa	0008	0232	1.6F
	0608	0852	1.7E
	1257	1529	1.4F
	1847	2114	1.5E
26 Su ◑	0059	0317	1.5F
	0656	0941	1.6E
	1343	1604	1.4F
	1934	2205	1.5E
27 M	0150	0404	1.5F
	0745	1031	1.6E
	1427	1645	1.4F
	2021	2257	1.5E
28 Tu	0240	0454	1.5F
	0834	1119	1.6E
	1510	1729	1.5F
	2107	2346	1.6E
29 W	0330	0544	1.5F
	0922	1204	1.7E
	1551	1813	1.7F
	2151		
30 Th		0031	1.8E
	0419	0634	1.6F
	1009	1247	1.8E
	1631	1858	1.9F
	2234		
31 F		0113	2.0E
	0507	0724	1.6F
	1054	1329	1.9E
	1710	1944	2.0F
	2316		

June

Day	Slack h m	Maximum h m	knots
1 Sa		0156	2.1E
	0553	0815	1.7F
	1140	1413	2.0E
	1750	2032	2.2F
	2358		
2 Su		0239	2.3E
	0640	0906	1.8F
	1226	1457	2.1E
	1831	2120	2.3F
3 M	0041	0323	2.5E
	0727	0957	1.9F
	1313	1543	2.1E
	1915	2208	2.4F
4 Tu	0126	0408	2.6E
	0816	1048	2.0F
	1402	1631	2.2E
	2002	2258	2.4F
5 W	0214	0456	2.6E
	0906	1139	2.0F
	1453	1720	2.2E
	2054	2349	2.4F
6 Th	0304	0545	2.6E
	0958	1233	2.0F
	1545	1812	2.2E
	2149		
7 F		0042	2.4F
	0357	0638	2.5E
	1052	1327	2.0F
	1640	1906	2.1E
	2249		
8 Sa		0138	2.3F
	0453	0733	2.4E
	1147	1423	2.0F
	1736	2003	2.1E
	2352		
9 Su		0234	2.2F
	0553	0830	2.3E
	1244	1519	2.0F
	1834	2102	2.1E
10 M ◐	0057	0334	2.1F
	0654	0930	2.2E
	1340	1619	2.0F
	1933	2205	2.1E
11 Tu	0201	0438	2.0F
	0757	1034	2.1E
	1435	1723	2.0F
	2033	2312	2.1E
12 W	0305	0550	1.9F
	0900	1140	2.1E
	1530	1828	2.1F
	2131		
13 Th		0018	2.2E
	0406	0711	1.9F
	1001	1242	2.1E
	1622	1934	2.1F
	2228		
14 F		0120	2.3E
	0505	0825	2.0F
	1058	1338	2.1E
	1713	2035	2.2F
	2321		
15 Sa		0216	2.4E
	0601	0925	2.0F
	1152	1430	2.1E
	1803	2129	2.2F
16 Su		0308	2.4E
	0654	1019	2.0F
	1244	1520	2.0E
	1851	2216	2.2F
17 M ○	0101	0356	2.4E
	0745	1108	2.0F
	1333	1606	2.0E
	1940	2257	2.1F
18 Tu	0149	0440	2.3E
	0834	1156	1.9F
	1422	1651	1.9E
	2027	2330	2.0F
19 W	0235	0524	2.2E
	0921	1240	1.8F
	1509	1736	1.8E
	2114		
20 Th		0001	1.9F
	0320	0607	2.1E
	1006	1320	1.7F
	1554	1822	1.8E
	2200		
21 F		0037	1.8F
	0404	0649	2.0E
	1051	1346	1.6F
	1639	1906	1.7E
	2247		
22 Sa		0116	1.7F
	0448	0731	1.9E
	1134	1405	1.6F
	1723	1950	1.6E
	2334		
23 Su		0158	1.7F
	0531	0812	1.8E
	1217	1438	1.6F
	1806	2034	1.6E
24 M	0022	0242	1.6F
	0615	0855	1.7E
	1259	1517	1.6F
	1850	2119	1.6E
25 Tu ◑	0112	0329	1.6F
	0700	0939	1.7E
	1340	1600	1.6F
	1934	2207	1.6E
26 W	0203	0418	1.5F
	0747	1027	1.7E
	1422	1646	1.7F
	2020	2257	1.7E
27 Th	0255	0509	1.5F
	0837	1116	1.7E
	1504	1733	1.8F
	2107	2347	1.8E
28 F	0347	0601	1.5F
	0928	1205	1.7E
	1547	1821	2.0F
	2154		
29 Sa		0035	2.0E
	0438	0653	1.6F
	1020	1254	1.8E
	1632	1911	2.1F
	2242		
30 Su		0123	2.1E
	0528	0748	1.7F
	1111	1342	1.9E
	1717	2002	2.2F
	2329		

Time meridian 75° W. 0000 is midnight. 1200 is noon. Times are not adjusted for Daylight Saving Time.

Bath Iron Works, Kennebec River, 2019

F–Flood, Dir. 001° True   E–Ebb, Dir. 178° True

July

Day	Slack	Maximum	knots
1 M		0211 0345	2.3E
	0618 0843		1.8F
	1202 1432		2.0E
	1804 2054		2.3F
2 Tu ●	0017 0259		2.5E
	0708 0938		1.9F
	1253 1521		2.1E
	1854 2147		2.4F
3 W	0106 0348		2.6E
	0758 1032		2.0F
	1345 1611		2.2E
	1947 2239		2.4F
4 Th	0157 0437		2.6E
	0849 1125		2.1F
	1436 1702		2.3E
	2042 2332		2.4F
5 F	0250 0528		2.6E
	0940 1218		2.1F
	1528 1755		2.3E
	2138		
6 Sa	0027		2.4F
	0344 0621		2.6E
	1032 1312		2.2F
	1621 1849		2.3E
	2237		
7 Su ☽	0123		2.3F
	0439 0716		2.5E
	1125 1405		2.2F
	1716 1945		2.3E
	2338		
8 M	0219		2.2F
	0537 0811		2.3E
	1218 1459		2.1F
	1812 2042		2.2E
9 Tu ☽	0040 0318		2.1F
	0636 0909		2.2E
	1312 1555		2.1F
	1909 2143		2.1E
10 W	0143 0423		1.9F
	0736 1010		2.0E
	1406 1655		2.0F
	2008 2250		2.1E
11 Th	0246 0541		1.8F
	0838 1115		1.9E
	1501 1801		2.0F
	2107 2359		2.1E
12 F	0348 0704		1.8F
	0939 1219		1.9E
	1555 1911		2.0F
	2205		
13 Sa	0106		2.2E
	0447 0812		1.8F
	1037 1318		1.9E
	1648 2017		2.0F
	2300		
14 Su	0206		2.2E
	0543 0911		1.9F
	1132 1413		1.9E
	1739 2114		2.0F
	2351		
15 M	0259		2.2E
	0635 1003		1.9F
	1223 1503		1.9E
	1828 2202		2.0F
16 Tu ○	0040 0345		2.2E
	0724 1050		1.9F
	1311 1548		1.9E
	1916 2241		2.0F
17 W	0126 0424		2.2E
	0810 1134		1.9F
	1357 1630		1.9E
	2002 2305		1.9F
18 Th	0210 0502		2.2E
	0853 1211		1.8F
	1441 1711		1.9E
	2047 2330		1.9F
19 F	0253 0539		2.1E
	0935 1236		1.7F
	1523 1751		1.8E
	2131		
20 Sa	0004		1.9F
	0334 0616		2.0E
	1015 1249		1.7F
	1603 1832		1.8E
	2215		
21 Su	0044		1.8F
	0414 0654		2.0E
	1054 1319		1.7F
	1643 1913		1.8E
	2259		
22 M	0126		1.8F
	0454 0733		1.9E
	1132 1356		1.7F
	1723 1954		1.8E
	2346		
23 Tu	0210		1.7F
	0534 0813		1.9E
	1211 1437		1.8F
	1804 2037		1.8E
24 W ☾	0035 0256		1.7F
	0617 0856		1.8E
	1251 1521		1.9F
	1848 2123		1.8E
25 Th	0126 0345		1.6F
	0704 0943		1.7E
	1334 1608		1.9F
	1934 2213		1.8E
26 F	0220 0437		1.5F
	0756 1034		1.7E
	1420 1658		1.9F
	2024 2306		1.9E
27 Sa	0316 0531		1.5F
	0852 1128		1.7E
	1509 1749		2.0F
	2117		
28 Su	0000		2.0E
	0411 0627		1.6F
	0951 1223		1.8E
	1600 1842		2.1F
	2211		
29 M	0053		2.1E
	0504 0725		1.6F
	1048 1317		1.9E
	1653 1937		2.2F
	2305		
30 Tu	0146		2.3E
	0557 0824		1.8F
	1143 1410		2.0E
	1747 2033		2.3F
	2358		
31 W ●	0238		2.4E
	0648 0923		1.9F
	1235 1503		2.2E
	1841 2129		2.4F

August

Day	Slack	Maximum	knots
1 Th	0050 0330		2.6E
	0739 1018		2.1F
	1327 1555		2.3E
	1935 2225		2.4F
2 F	0143 0421		2.6E
	0829 1110		2.2F
	1418 1646		2.4E
	2031 2319		2.5F
3 Sa	0236 0512		2.6E
	0919 1202		2.3F
	1509 1738		2.4E
	2127		
4 Su	0014		2.5F
	0329 0604		2.6E
	1009 1253		2.3F
	1601 1831		2.4E
	2224		
5 M	0109		2.4F
	0423 0657		2.5E
	1059 1344		2.3F
	1653 1926		2.4E
	2322		
6 Tu	0205		2.2F
	0519 0751		2.3E
	1150 1435		2.2F
	1748 2021		2.3E
7 W ☾	0023 0303		2.0F
	0616 0846		2.1E
	1243 1527		2.1F
	1844 2120		2.2E
8 Th	0125 0409		1.8F
	0715 0945		1.9E
	1338 1625		2.0F
	1942 2226		2.0E
9 F	0227 0534		1.7F
	0815 1050		1.8E
	1433 1733		1.9F
	2042 2342		2.0E
10 Sa	0328 0651		1.7F
	0917 1158		1.7E
	1530 1851		1.8F
	2141		
11 Su	0057		2.0E
	0427 0755		1.7F
	1016 1301		1.7E
	1624 2000		1.8F
	2237		
12 M	0200		2.0E
	0521 0852		1.8F
	1110 1357		1.8E
	1716 2057		1.9F
	2329		
13 Tu	0250		2.1E
	0611 0942		1.8F
	1200 1445		1.8E
	1805 2143		1.9F
14 W	0017 0329		2.1E
	0657 1026		1.8F
	1246 1527		1.9E
	1851 2217		1.9F
15 Th ○	0101 0402		2.1E
	0739 1104		1.8F
	1329 1605		1.9E
	1936 2231		1.9F
16 F	0143 0433		2.1E
	0819 1128		1.8F
	1409 1642		1.9E
	2019 2256		1.9F
17 Sa	0222 0505		2.1E
	0858 1136		1.8F
	1447 1718		2.0E
	2101 2332		1.9F
18 Su	0301 0539		2.1E
	0934 1202		1.8F
	1525 1756		2.0E
	2143		
19 M	0012		1.9F
	0339 0615		2.0E
	1010 1238		1.9F
	1602 1835		2.0E
	2226		
20 Tu	0054		1.9F
	0417 0654		2.0E
	1046 1319		2.0F
	1640 1916		2.0E
	2311		
21 W	0139		1.8F
	0456 0735		2.0E
	1123 1401		2.0F
	1720 1959		2.0E
22 Th	0000 0226		1.7F
	0540 0819		1.9E
	1204 1447		2.0F
	1804 2045		2.0E
23 F ◑	0053 0315		1.6F
	0629 0907		1.8E
	1250 1535		2.0F
	1853 2135		2.0E
24 Sa	0149 0409		1.6F
	0724 1000		1.7E
	1342 1627		2.0F
	1947 2230		1.9E
25 Su	0247 0505		1.5F
	0825 1058		1.7E
	1439 1722		2.0F
	2046 2329		2.0E
26 M	0345 0604		1.6F
	0927 1158		1.8E
	1538 1818		2.0F
	2146		
27 Tu	0028		2.1E
	0442 0705		1.7F
	1028 1256		1.9E
	1637 1917		2.1F
	2245		
28 W	0125		2.3E
	0535 0808		1.8F
	1124 1352		2.1E
	1733 2016		2.2F
	2341		
29 Th	0221		2.4E
	0627 0909		2.0F
	1216 1447		2.3E
	1829 2116		2.4F
30 F ●	0036 0314		2.5E
	0717 1004		2.2F
	1308 1539		2.4E
	1924 2213		2.5F
31 Sa	0129 0405		2.6E
	0806 1054		2.3F
	1358 1630		2.5E
	2019 2308		2.5F

September

Day	Slack	Maximum	knots
1 Su	0221 0455		2.6E
	0851 1143		2.4F
	1448 1721		2.6E
	2114		
2 M	0002		2.4F
	0313 0546		2.5E
	0943 1232		2.4F
	1539 1813		2.6E
	2209		
3 Tu	0057		2.3F
	0406 0637		2.4E
	1032 1320		2.3F
	1630 1906		2.5E
	2306		
4 W	0153		2.1F
	0500 0730		2.2E
	1122 1410		2.2F
	1724 2000		2.3E
5 Th	0005 0252		1.9F
	0556 0824		2.0E
	1215 1500		2.0F
	1819 2058		2.1E
6 F	0105 0402		1.7F
	0653 0921		1.8E
	1311 1555		1.8F
	1917 2203		1.9E
7 Sa	0206 0523		1.6F
	0753 1026		1.6E
	1408 1703		1.7F
	2016 2325		1.8E
8 Su	0305 0632		1.6F
	0854 1138		1.6E
	1505 1830		1.6F
	2115		
9 M	0047		1.8E
	0402 0733		1.6F
	0952 1244		1.6E
	1600 1938		1.6F
	2212		
10 Tu	0145		1.9E
	0454 0827		1.7F
	1045 1338		1.7E
	1652 2032		1.7F
	2303		
11 W	0228		1.9E
	0540 0914		1.7F
	1132 1422		1.8E
	1739 2115		1.7F
	2349		
12 Th	0301		2.0E
	0623 0954		1.7F
	1215 1500		1.9E
	1824 2137		1.8F
13 F ○	0031 0328		2.0E
	0703 1021		1.8F
	1255 1534		2.0E
	1907 2149		1.8F
14 Sa	0111 0356		2.1E
	0740 1024		1.8F
	1333 1608		2.0E
	1949 2221		1.9F
15 Su	0149 0427		2.1E
	0816 1047		1.9F
	1410 1643		2.1E
	2030 2259		1.9F
16 M	0227 0501		2.1E
	0855 1122		2.0F
	1446 1720		2.2E
	2112 2341		1.9F
17 Tu	0304 0538		2.1E
	0926 1201		2.1F
	1522 1759		2.2E
	2155		
18 W	0025		1.9F
	0343 0618		2.1E
	1001 1244		2.1F
	1601 1841		2.2E
	2241		
19 Th	0111		1.9F
	0424 0701		2.0E
	1039 1329		2.2F
	1642 1925		2.2E
	2330		
20 F ◐	0159		1.8F
	0510 0747		1.9E
	1123 1416		2.1F
	1728 2012		2.1E
21 Sa	0023 0250		1.7F
	0602 0837		1.8E
	1214 1507		2.1F
	1820 2104		2.1E
22 Su	0121 0345		1.6F
	0701 0932		1.8E
	1314 1601		2.0F
	1918 2201		2.0E
23 M	0221 0443		1.6F
	0803 1033		1.7E
	1417 1658		2.0F
	2021 2303		2.0E
24 Tu	0321 0545		1.7F
	0907 1136		1.8E
	1521 1758		2.0F
	2125		
25 W	0006		2.1E
	0418 0648		1.8F
	1007 1237		2.0E
	1622 1900		2.1F
	2227		
26 Th	0107		2.2E
	0512 0751		1.9F
	1103 1335		2.2E
	1720 2003		2.2F
	2325		
27 F	0203		2.4E
	0603 0852		2.1F
	1156 1430		2.4E
	1816 2106		2.3F
28 Sa ●	0019 0257		2.5E
	0652 0946		2.3F
	1247 1523		2.6E
	1911 2204		2.4F
29 Su	0112 0348		2.5E
	0740 1035		2.4F
	1337 1613		2.7E
	2006 2259		2.4F
30 M	0204 0437		2.5E
	0828 1122		2.4F
	1426 1703		2.7E
	2100 2354		2.3F

Time meridian 75° W. 0000 is midnight. 1200 is noon. Times are not adjusted for Daylight Saving Time.

Bath Iron Works, Kennebec River, 2019

F–Flood, Dir. 001° True   E–Ebb, Dir. 178° True

October

Day	Slack (h m)	Maximum (h m)	knots		Day	Slack (h m)	Maximum (h m)	knots
1 Tu	0256	0526	2.4E		16 W	0232	0505	2.1E
	0916	1209	2.4F			0843	1128	2.2F
	1517	1754	2.6E			1446	1727	2.4E
	2155					2128	2358	1.9F
2 W		0049	2.2F		17 Th	0313	0547	2.1E
	0348	0616	2.3E			0921	1213	2.3F
	1005	1257	2.3F			1527	1810	2.4E
	1608	1846	2.4E			2215		
	2250							
3 Th		0146	2.0F		18 F		0046	1.9F
	0441	0708	2.1E			0358	0632	2.0E
	1056	1345	2.1F			1004	1300	2.2F
	1700	1940	2.2E			1611	1856	2.3E
	2347					2305		
4 F		0246	1.8F		19 Sa		0137	1.8F
	0536	0802	1.9E			0448	0721	2.0E
	1150	1434	1.9F			1053	1350	2.2F
	1754	2036	2.0E			1700	1946	2.3E
						2359		
5 Sa	0045	0353	1.7F		20 Su		0229	1.8F
	0632	0859	1.7E			0543	0813	1.9E
	1246	1526	1.7F			1150	1443	2.1F
	1851	2139	1.8E			1755	2039	2.2E
6 Su	0142	0504	1.6F		21 M	0058	0324	1.7F
	0730	1003	1.6E			0642	0909	1.8E
	1343	1626	1.6F			1254	1539	2.0F
	1948	2301	1.7E			1856	2137	2.1E
7 M	0238	0607	1.5F		22 Tu	0157	0423	1.7F
	0827	1114	1.5E			0744	1011	1.8E
	1439	1751	1.5F			1400	1638	2.0F
	2046					2000	2240	2.1E
8 Tu		0022	1.7E		23 W	0256	0525	1.8F
	0331	0703	1.5F			0846	1116	1.9E
	0923	1219	1.6E			1505	1740	2.0F
	1533	1901	1.5F			2105	2346	2.1E
	2141							
9 W		0112	1.8E		24 Th	0353	0629	1.9F
	0419	0753	1.6F			0945	1219	2.1E
	1014	1309	1.6E			1607	1845	2.1F
	1623	1950	1.5F			2208		
	2231							
10 Th		0148	1.8E		25 F		0047	2.2E
	0503	0836	1.6F			0446	0731	2.1F
	1059	1349	1.8E			1042	1318	2.3E
	1710	2009	1.6F			1706	1951	2.2F
	2316					2307		
11 F		0217	1.9E		26 Sa		0145	2.3E
	0544	0905	1.6F			0537	0832	2.2F
	1140	1424	1.9E			1135	1414	2.5E
	1754	2031	1.7F			1803	2059	2.3F
	2357							
12 Sa		0245	1.9E		27 Su	0002	0238	2.4E
	0622	0904	1.7F			0626	0927	2.3F
	1219	1459	2.0E			1226	1506	2.6E
	1837	2108	1.8F			1858	2200	2.3F
13 Su	0036	0316	2.0E		28 M	0055	0329	2.4E
	0657	0930	1.9F			0714	1016	2.4F
	1255	1533	2.1E			1316	1557	2.7E
	1919	2147	1.9F			1952	2256	2.3F
14 M	0114	0349	2.0E		29 Tu	0147	0417	2.4E
	0733	1006	2.0F			0802	1102	2.4F
	1332	1609	2.2E			1406	1646	2.6E
	2002	2229	1.9F			2046	2351	2.2F
15 Tu	0153	0426	2.1E		30 W	0238	0506	2.3E
	0808	1046	2.2F			0851	1148	2.3F
	1408	1647	2.3E			1456	1736	2.5E
	2044	2312	1.9F			2140		
					31 Th		0046	2.1F
						0330	0556	2.1E
						0941	1235	2.2F
						1546	1827	2.4E
						2233		

November

Day	Slack (h m)	Maximum (h m)	knots		Day	Slack (h m)	Maximum (h m)	knots
1 F		0142	1.9F		16 Sa		0025	1.9F
	0422	0648	1.9E			0338	0608	2.1E
	1032	1322	2.0F			0939	1236	2.3F
	1637	1920	2.2E			1548	1832	2.5E
	2327					2244		
2 Sa		0238	1.8F		17 Su		0117	1.9F
	0515	0742	1.8E			0430	0659	2.0E
	1125	1409	1.8F			1033	1329	2.2F
	1730	2015	2.0E			1640	1924	2.4E
						2338		
3 Su	0020	0335	1.6F		18 M		0211	1.9F
	0609	0836	1.6E			0525	0753	2.0E
	1220	1456	1.7F			1134	1423	2.2F
	1823	2112	1.8E			1737	2018	2.3E
4 M	0113	0433	1.5F		19 Tu	0035	0306	1.9F
	0703	0935	1.5E			0623	0849	2.0E
	1315	1545	1.5F			1238	1519	2.1F
	1917	2217	1.7E			1838	2116	2.2E
5 Tu	0204	0530	1.5F		20 W	0132	0403	1.9F
	0756	1037	1.5E			0722	0950	2.0E
	1409	1636	1.4F			1344	1619	2.0F
	2011	2326	1.7E			1941	2219	2.1E
6 W	0253	0619	1.4F		21 Th	0229	0504	1.9F
	0847	1137	1.5E			0823	1055	2.0E
	1501	1727	1.4F			1449	1723	2.0F
	2103					2045	2324	2.1E
7 Th		0015	1.7E		22 F	0325	0606	2.0F
	0339	0658	1.5F			0922	1159	2.2E
	0936	1226	1.6E			1551	1831	2.0F
	1551	1814	1.4F			2148		
	2152							
8 F		0051	1.7E		23 Sa		0026	2.2E
	0421	0701	1.5F			0418	0708	2.1F
	1020	1306	1.7E			1019	1300	2.3E
	1638	1859	1.5F			1651	1943	2.1F
	2237					2247		
9 Sa		0124	1.8E		24 Su		0124	2.2E
	0500	0728	1.7F			0509	0810	2.2F
	1101	1344	1.9E			1113	1357	2.5E
	1723	1944	1.6F			1748	2057	2.1F
	2319					2343		
10 Su		0159	1.8E		25 M		0218	2.2E
	0538	0806	1.8F			0559	0908	2.3F
	1140	1420	2.0E			1205	1451	2.5E
	1807	2029	1.7F			1844	2159	2.2F
11 M	0000	0235	1.9E		26 Tu	0037	0310	2.2E
	0614	0847	2.0F			0649	1000	2.3F
	1218	1457	2.2E			1256	1542	2.6E
	1851	2115	1.8F			1938	2254	2.2F
12 Tu	0040	0313	2.0E		27 W	0129	0359	2.2E
	0650	0929	2.1F			0738	1047	2.3F
	1256	1536	2.3E			1346	1632	2.5E
	1935	2201	1.8F			2031	2347	2.1F
13 W	0121	0353	2.1E		28 Th	0220	0448	2.1E
	0728	1013	2.3F			0828	1133	2.2F
	1335	1616	2.4E			1436	1721	2.4E
	2019	2247	1.9F			2123		
14 Th	0204	0435	2.1E		29 F		0039	2.0F
	0807	1059	2.3F			0311	0538	2.0E
	1416	1658	2.5E			0919	1217	2.1F
	2105	2335	1.9F			1525	1811	2.3E
						2213		
15 F	0250	0520	2.1E		30 Sa		0130	1.9F
	0851	1146	2.3F			0401	0628	1.9E
	1500	1744	2.5E			1009	1300	1.9F
	2153					1614	1901	2.1E
						2303		

December

Day	Slack (h m)	Maximum (h m)	knots		Day	Slack (h m)	Maximum (h m)	knots
1 Su		0218	1.8F		16 M		0059	2.0F
	0451	0719	1.8E			0412	0639	2.2E
	1100	1342	1.8F			1019	1310	2.3F
	1703	1951	2.0E			1624	1905	2.5E
	2352					2316		
2 M		0303	1.6F		17 Tu		0152	2.1F
	0541	0810	1.7E			0506	0734	2.1E
	1151	1423	1.7F			1119	1405	2.2F
	1752	2039	1.8E			1720	1959	2.4E
3 Tu	0039	0341	1.5F		18 W	0011	0246	2.1F
	0630	0900	1.6E			0602	0830	2.1E
	1243	1506	1.5F			1223	1502	2.1F
	1842	2128	1.7E			1820	2056	2.3E
4 W	0126	0405	1.5F		19 Th	0106	0342	2.0F
	0718	0952	1.5E			0659	0929	2.1E
	1334	1552	1.5F			1327	1602	2.0F
	1931	2219	1.6E			1922	2156	2.2E
5 Th	0210	0436	1.5F		20 F	0201	0440	2.0F
	0806	1044	1.5E			0758	1033	2.1E
	1425	1639	1.4F			1431	1707	2.0F
	2019	2307	1.6E			2025	2300	2.1E
6 F	0253	0515	1.5F		21 Sa	0256	0541	2.1F
	0852	1134	1.6E			0857	1139	2.2E
	1515	1728	1.4F			1534	1819	1.9F
	2107	2352	1.6E			2127		
7 Sa	0335	0556	1.6F		22 Su		0004	2.0E
	0936	1219	1.7E			0350	0644	2.1F
	1604	1817	1.5F			0956	1243	2.3E
	2154					1636	1942	1.9F
						2228		
8 Su		0034	1.7E		23 M		0104	2.0E
	0415	0639	1.8F			0444	0750	2.2F
	1019	1300	1.9E			1052	1343	2.4E
	1652	1905	1.5F			1734	2054	2.0F
	2240					2325		
9 M		0115	1.8E		24 Tu		0200	2.1E
	0454	0724	1.9F			0536	0854	2.2F
	1101	1341	2.0E			1146	1440	2.4E
	1739	1955	1.6F			1829	2153	2.0F
	2324							
10 Tu		0157	1.8E		25 W	0019	0254	2.1E
	0533	0810	2.1F			0627	0950	2.2F
	1142	1423	2.2E			1237	1532	2.4E
	1824	2045	1.7F			1923	2245	2.1F
11 W	0009	0240	1.9E		26 Th	0111	0344	2.0E
	0613	0857	2.2F			0718	1039	2.2F
	1223	1505	2.3E			1327	1621	2.4E
	1910	2135	1.8F			2014	2335	2.0F
12 Th	0054	0324	2.0E		27 F	0201	0432	2.0E
	0655	0945	2.2F			0808	1123	2.1F
	1306	1549	2.4E			1416	1707	2.3E
	1957	2225	1.9F			2102		
13 F	0141	0410	2.1E		28 Sa		0023	2.0F
	0741	1034	2.3F			0249	0519	1.9E
	1352	1634	2.5E			0857	1201	2.0F
	2044	2315	2.0F			1503	1752	2.2E
						2149		
14 Sa	0230	0457	2.1E		29 Su		0107	1.9F
	0830	1124	2.4F			0336	0606	1.9E
	1440	1722	2.6E			0945	1235	1.9F
	2133					1549	1837	2.1E
						2234		
15 Su		0006	2.0F		30 M		0146	1.8F
	0320	0547	2.2E			0422	0652	1.8E
	0923	1216	2.4F			1032	1310	1.8F
	1530	1812	2.5E			1634	1920	2.0E
	2224					2318		
					31 Tu		0211	1.7F
						0507	0737	1.7E
						1120	1348	1.7F
						1719	2001	1.9E

Time meridian 75° W. 0000 is midnight. 1200 is noon. Times are not adjusted for Daylight Saving Time.

Portland Harbor Entrance 2019

F–Flood, Dir. 310° True   E–Ebb, Dir. 138° True

January

Day	Slack (h m)	Maximum (h m)	knots
1 Tu	0144	0359	0.6F
	0734	1038	1.1E
	1427	1639	0.6F
	2013	2301	1.0E
2 W	0241	0455	0.6F
	0832	1134	1.1E
	1523	1738	0.6F
	2110	2355	1.0E
3 Th	0334	0548	0.6F
	0925	1226	1.1E
	1615	1830	0.6F
	2201		
4 F		0045	1.0E
	0423	0636	0.6F
	1012	1315	1.1E
	1703	1916	0.6F
	2247		
5 Sa ●		0131	1.0E
	0506	0720	0.6F
	1054	1400	1.1E
	1748	1959	0.6F
	2330		
6 Su		0215	1.0E
	0546	0802	0.6F
	1133	1444	1.1E
	1833	2042	0.6F
7 M	0011	0258	1.0E
	0626	0844	0.6F
	1208	1526	1.1E
	1917	2127	0.6F
8 Tu	0053	0342	0.9E
	0708	0930	0.6F
	1244	1609	1.1E
	2003	2214	0.6F
9 W	0136	0426	0.9E
	0755	1019	0.6F
	1322	1652	1.1E
	2048	2303	0.6F
10 Th	0218	0512	0.9E
	0847	1110	0.6F
	1402	1736	1.1E
	2132	2350	0.6F
11 F	0258	0559	0.9E
	0941	1201	0.6F
	1444	1822	1.0E
	2214		
12 Sa		0035	0.7F
	0336	0646	0.9E
	1034	1251	0.6F
	1527	1908	1.0E
	2255		
13 Su		0119	0.7F
	0412	0735	0.9E
	1123	1339	0.6F
	1613	1957	1.0E
	2337		
14 M ◑		0202	0.7F
	0449	0824	0.9E
	1211	1427	0.6F
	1704	2048	0.9E
15 Tu	0021	0247	0.7F
	0530	0914	1.0E
	1259	1517	0.6F
	1801	2140	0.9E
16 W	0108	0335	0.6F
	0616	1006	1.1E
	1348	1609	0.6F
	1903	2233	1.0E
17 Th	0158	0426	0.7F
	0710	1058	1.1E
	1438	1703	0.7F
	2006	2325	1.0E
18 F	0247	0517	0.7F
	0807	1150	1.2E
	1529	1756	0.7F
	2103		
19 Sa		0017	1.1E
	0335	0609	0.8F
	0904	1242	1.3E
	1619	1848	0.8F
	2157		
20 Su		0107	1.2E
	0421	0659	0.9F
	0958	1333	1.4E
	1709	1938	0.8F
	2249		
21 M ○		0158	1.2E
	0508	0749	0.9F
	1052	1424	1.4E
	1759	2029	0.9F
	2342		
22 Tu		0248	1.2E
	0558	0840	0.9F
	1147	1515	1.5E
	1850	2121	0.9F
23 W	0036	0340	1.3E
	0652	0934	0.9F
	1244	1606	1.4E
	1943	2216	0.8F
24 Th	0131	0432	1.3E
	0752	1032	0.9F
	1342	1658	1.4E
	2038	2311	0.8F
25 F	0226	0525	1.2E
	0857	1132	0.8F
	1441	1751	1.3E
	2134		
26 Sa		0005	0.8F
	0319	0620	1.2E
	1002	1230	0.8F
	1540	1845	1.2E
	2230		
27 Su ◐		0057	0.8F
	0412	0716	1.2E
	1105	1325	0.7F
	1639	1941	1.1E
	2326		
28 M		0147	0.7F
	0506	0814	1.1E
	1205	1418	0.6F
	1739	2039	1.0E
29 Tu	0022	0236	0.6F
	0603	0912	1.0E
	1304	1511	0.6F
	1842	2136	0.9E
30 W	0119	0328	0.6F
	0704	1011	1.0E
	1403	1607	0.5F
	1944	2233	0.9E
31 Th	0216	0422	0.5F
	0805	1108	1.0E
	1501	1706	0.5F
	2042	2327	0.9E

February

Day	Slack (h m)	Maximum (h m)	knots
1 F	0310	0517	0.5F
	0901	1203	1.0E
	1555	1802	0.5F
	2135		
2 Sa		0018	0.9E
	0358	0608	0.5F
	0949	1252	1.1E
	1644	1852	0.5F
	2222		
3 Su		0105	0.9E
	0441	0654	0.6F
	1030	1337	1.1E
	1728	1936	0.6F
	2305		
4 M ●		0149	0.9E
	0521	0737	0.6F
	1107	1419	1.2E
	1809	2017	0.6F
	2345		
5 Tu		0233	1.0E
	0601	0820	0.7F
	1141	1500	1.2E
	1848	2100	0.6F
6 W	0024	0316	1.0E
	0642	0904	0.7F
	1216	1540	1.2E
	1927	2143	0.7F
7 Th	0102	0359	1.0E
	0727	0952	0.6F
	1253	1622	1.2E
	2007	2228	0.7F
8 F	0139	0442	1.0E
	0815	1041	0.6F
	1333	1704	1.1E
	2047	2314	0.7F
9 Sa	0215	0526	1.0E
	0904	1132	0.6F
	1416	1748	1.1E
	2127	2358	0.7F
10 Su	0249	0611	1.0E
	0952	1220	0.6F
	1500	1834	1.0E
	2209		
11 M	0324	0657	1.0E
	0043		0.7F
	1038	1308	0.6F
	1545	1922	1.0E
	2253		
12 Tu ◐		0127	0.7F
	0401	0746	1.0E
	1125	1355	0.6F
	1633	2013	1.0E
	2339		
13 W	0054	0213	0.7F
	0444	0838	1.0E
	1215	1444	0.6F
	1727	2107	1.0E
14 Th	0030	0302	0.6F
	0535	0933	1.0E
	1311	1537	0.6F
	1828	2202	1.0E
15 F	0123	0354	0.7F
	0636	1029	1.1E
	1410	1634	0.7F
	1936	2258	1.0E
16 Sa	0218	0450	0.7F
	0745	1126	1.2E
	1509	1732	0.7F
	2042	2353	1.1E
17 Su	0312	0547	0.8F
	0851	1221	1.3E
	1604	1828	0.8F
	2142		
18 M		0046	1.2E
	0404	0641	0.9F
	0951	1315	1.4E
	1655	1921	0.8F
	2237		
19 Tu ○		0139	1.2E
	0456	0734	0.9F
	1047	1407	1.4E
	1744	2012	0.9F
	2329		
20 W		0231	1.3E
	0549	0826	0.9F
	1142	1457	1.5E
	1832	2102	0.9F
21 Th	0020	0322	1.3E
	0643	0920	0.9F
	1238	1547	1.4E
	1922	2153	0.9F
22 F	0112	0413	1.3E
	0741	1016	0.9F
	1334	1638	1.3E
	2014	2245	0.8F
23 Sa	0203	0504	1.3E
	0841	1113	0.8F
	1430	1729	1.2E
	2109	2338	0.8F
24 Su	0253	0557	1.2E
	0942	1209	0.7F
	1524	1821	1.1E
	2205		
25 M		0029	0.7F
	0344	0650	1.1E
	1042	1301	0.7F
	1618	1915	1.0E
	2302		
26 Tu ○		0118	0.6F
	0436	0746	1.0E
	1140	1351	0.6F
	1713	2010	0.9E
	2359		
27 W		0207	0.6F
	0531	0844	1.0E
	1239	1442	0.5F
	1810	2107	0.9E
28 Th	0054	0257	0.5F
	0633	0943	0.9E
	1339	1536	0.5F
	1911	2203	0.8E

March

Day	Slack (h m)	Maximum (h m)	knots
1 F	0149	0350	0.5F
	0735	1042	0.9E
	1438	1633	0.4F
	2012	2258	0.8E
2 Sa	0242	0445	0.5F
	0831	1137	0.9E
	1532	1732	0.4F
	2107	2350	0.8E
3 Su	0331	0538	0.6F
	0919	1226	1.0E
	1620	1825	0.5F
	2155		
4 M		0038	0.9E
	0415	0627	0.6F
	1001	1310	1.1E
	1701	1909	0.6F
	2237		
5 Tu		0123	0.9E
	0457	0712	0.6F
	1038	1350	1.2E
	1738	1949	0.7F
	2315		
6 W ●		0206	1.0E
	0538	0756	0.7F
	1113	1430	1.2E
	1813	2029	0.7F
	2349		
7 Th		0248	1.0E
	0618	0840	0.7F
	1148	1510	1.2E
	1848	2109	0.7F
8 F	0022	0329	1.1E
	0659	0925	0.7F
	1226	1551	1.2E
	1924	2151	0.7F
9 Sa	0054	0411	1.1E
	0741	1013	0.7F
	1307	1633	1.1E
	2002	2235	0.7F
10 Su	0127	0453	1.1E
	0824	1100	0.7F
	1349	1717	1.1E
	2043	2321	0.7F
11 M	0202	0537	1.1E
	0908	1149	0.7F
	1433	1802	1.1E
	2126		
12 Tu		0007	0.7F
	0240	0623	1.1E
	0954	1237	0.7F
	1518	1851	1.0E
	2213		
13 W	0322	0054	0.7F
	0322	0712	1.1E
	1045	1326	0.7F
	1606	1942	1.0E
	2303		
14 Th ◐		0142	0.7F
	0410	0806	1.1E
	1141	1416	0.7F
	1700	2037	1.0E
	2356		
15 F		0233	0.7F
	0507	0904	1.1E
	1244	1511	0.7F
	1803	2135	1.0E
16 Sa	0054	0328	0.7F
	0614	1005	1.1E
	1348	1610	0.7F
	1916	2234	1.0E
17 Su	0155	0427	0.7F
	0730	1104	1.2E
	1450	1711	0.7F
	2026	2332	1.1E
18 M	0255	0527	0.8F
	0841	1202	1.3E
	1546	1809	0.8F
	2127		
19 Tu		0028	1.2E
	0353	0625	0.9F
	0944	1256	1.4E
	1637	1903	0.8F
	2222		
20 W ○		0121	1.3E
	0447	0720	0.9F
	1041	1348	1.4E
	1724	1952	0.9F
	2312		
21 Th		0213	1.4E
	0540	0812	0.9F
	1135	1438	1.4E
	1811	2039	0.9F
22 F	0000	0303	1.4E
	0632	0904	0.9F
	1228	1527	1.4E
	1858	2127	0.8F
23 Sa	0048	0352	1.4E
	0726	0957	0.9F
	1321	1616	1.3E
	1949	2217	0.8F
24 Su	0136	0441	1.3E
	0822	1050	0.8F
	1413	1706	1.2E
	2044	2308	0.7F
25 M	0225	0531	1.2E
	0919	1144	0.7F
	1504	1756	1.1E
	2141		
26 Tu		0000	0.6F
	0315	0623	1.1E
	1018	1235	0.6F
	1554	1848	1.0E
	2238		
27 W ◐		0050	0.5F
	0405	0717	1.0E
	1117	1325	0.6F
	1644	1941	0.9E
	2333		
28 Th		0138	0.5F
	0458	0814	0.9E
	1215	1414	0.5F
	1738	2036	0.8E
29 F	0027	0227	0.5F
	0555	0913	0.9E
	1313	1506	0.4F
	1839	2132	0.8E
30 Sa	0120	0318	0.4F
	0655	1011	0.9E
	1410	1602	0.4F
	1940	2228	0.8E
31 Su	0213	0412	0.4F
	0752	1104	0.9E
	1501	1659	0.4F
	2036	2321	0.8E

Time meridian 75° W. 0000 is midnight. 1200 is noon. Times are not adjusted for Daylight Saving Time.

Portland Harbor Entrance 2019

F–Flood, Dir. 310° True   E–Ebb, Dir. 138° True

April

Day	Slack	Maximum	knots	Day	Slack	Maximum	knots
1 M	0304	0507	0.5F	16 Tu	0243	0510	0.8F
	0843	1153	1.0E		0831	1141	1.3E
	1546	1751	0.5F		1523	1747	0.8F
	2123				2109		
2 Tu		0010	0.9E	17 W		0009	1.2E
	0351	0600	0.6F		0343	0611	0.8F
	0927	1237	1.1E		0935	1236	1.3E
	1625	1836	0.6F		1614	1841	0.8F
	2204				2202		
3 W		0055	1.0E	18 Th		0103	1.3E
	0434	0647	0.6F		0437	0706	0.9F
	1007	1318	1.1E		1032	1328	1.3E
	1701	1916	0.7F		1702	1929	0.9F
	2238				2251		
4 Th		0137	1.1E	19 F		0154	1.4E
	0514	0731	0.7F		0528	0757	0.9F
	1045	1359	1.2E		1124	1418	1.3E
	1735	1955	0.8F		1749	2015	0.9F
	2308				2337		
5 F		0218	1.1E	20 Sa		0242	1.4E
	0552	0814	0.7F		0618	0846	0.9F
	1122	1439	1.2E		1215	1506	1.3E
	1808	2034	0.8F		1836	2101	0.8F
	2337						
6 Sa		0258	1.2E	21 Su	0023	0330	1.3E
	0628	0857	0.8F		0708	0935	0.8F
	1200	1520	1.2E		1304	1554	1.2E
	1843	2115	0.8F		1926	2148	0.7F
7 Su	0007	0339	1.2E	22 M	0110	0418	1.2E
	0705	0942	0.8F		0801	1025	0.7F
	1240	1603	1.1E		1353	1641	1.1E
	1921	2158	0.7F		2019	2238	0.6F
8 M	0042	0421	1.2E	23 Tu	0158	0507	1.1E
	0745	1029	0.8F		0857	1117	0.6F
	1323	1647	1.1E		1441	1730	1.0E
	2002	2245	0.7F		2115	2330	0.5F
9 Tu	0121	0505	1.2E	24 W	0246	0557	1.0E
	0829	1118	0.7F		0955	1209	0.6F
	1408	1733	1.1E		1528	1819	0.9E
	2048	2334	0.7F		2210		
10 W	0205	0553	1.2E	25 Th		0020	0.5F
	0920	1209	0.7F		0333	0649	0.9E
	1455	1822	1.1E		1054	1259	0.5F
	2138				1617	1911	0.8E
					2304		
11 Th		0024	0.7F	26 F		0109	0.5F
	0254	0644	1.1E		0420	0744	0.9E
	1017	1300	0.7F		1150	1349	0.5F
	1546	1915	1.0E		1710	2005	0.8E
	2232				2356		
12 F		0116	0.7F	27 Sa		0158	0.5F
	0348	0741	1.1E		0509	0840	0.9E
	1119	1354	0.7F		1243	1439	0.5F
	1642	2012	1.0E		1806	2101	0.7E
	2330						
13 Sa		0209	0.7F	28 Su	0049	0248	0.4F
	0449	0841	1.1E		0604	0935	0.9E
	1224	1449	0.7F		1333	1530	0.5F
	1748	2112	1.0E		1904	2156	0.8E
14 Su	0033	0306	0.7F	29 M	0143	0341	0.4F
	0600	0942	1.2E		0702	1027	0.9E
	1327	1548	0.7F		1421	1622	0.5F
	1900	2212	1.0E		1957	2249	0.8E
15 M	0139	0407	0.7F	30 Tu	0236	0436	0.5F
	0718	1043	1.2E		0759	1115	1.0E
	1427	1649	0.7F		1504	1712	0.6F
	2009	2312	1.1E		2043	2338	0.9E

May

Day	Slack	Maximum	knots	Day	Slack	Maximum	knots
1 W	0324	0530	0.5F	16 Th	0330	0554	0.8F
	0850	1201	1.0E		0922	1215	1.2E
	1545	1758	0.7F		1550	1816	0.8F
	2121				2140		
2 Th		0023	1.0E	17 F		0043	1.3E
	0408	0619	0.6F		0424	0650	0.8F
	0935	1244	1.1E		1018	1307	1.2E
	1622	1840	0.7F		1640	1905	0.8F
	2154				2229		
3 F		0106	1.1E	18 Sa		0133	1.4E
	0447	0704	0.7F		0514	0740	0.8F
	1016	1327	1.1E		1109	1357	1.2E
	1657	1920	0.8F		1728	1951	0.8F
	2224				2316		
4 Sa		0146	1.2E	19 Su		0222	1.3E
	0522	0746	0.8F		0602	0826	0.8F
	1054	1409	1.1E		1157	1444	1.2E
	1732	2000	0.8F		1815	2035	0.7F
	2254						
5 Su		0227	1.2E	20 M	0002	0309	1.3E
	0557	0828	0.8F		0650	0912	0.7F
	1133	1451	1.2E		1243	1530	1.1E
	1807	2041	0.8F		1903	2121	0.6F
	2327						
6 M		0309	1.3E	21 Tu	0047	0355	1.2E
	0633	0912	0.8F		0741	1000	0.7F
	1213	1534	1.1E		1329	1616	1.0E
	1845	2125	0.8F		1952	2209	0.6F
7 Tu	0006	0353	1.3E	22 W	0132	0443	1.1E
	0714	0959	0.8F		0836	1051	0.6F
	1257	1620	1.1E		1416	1703	0.9E
	1927	2213	0.7F		2044	2259	0.5F
8 W	0051	0439	1.2E	23 Th	0216	0531	1.0E
	0802	1051	0.8F		0933	1143	0.5F
	1345	1707	1.1E		1504	1751	0.8E
	2014	2304	0.7F		2137	2350	0.5F
9 Th	0141	0529	1.2E	24 F	0259	0621	1.0E
	0858	1145	0.8F		1028	1234	0.5F
	1437	1758	1.1E		1552	1841	0.8E
	2108	2359	0.7F		2231		
10 F	0236	0622	1.2E	25 Sa		0040	0.5F
	0959	1239	0.7F		0341	0712	0.9E
	1532	1852	1.1E		1118	1322	0.5F
	2208				1641	1934	0.8E
					2325		
11 Sa		0054	0.7F	26 Su		0129	0.5F
	0334	0719	1.2E		0424	0803	0.9E
	1102	1334	0.7F		1206	1409	0.5F
	1631	1950	1.0E		1730	2028	0.8E
	2312						
12 Su		0150	0.7F	27 M	0018	0219	0.5F
	0437	0819	1.2E		0513	0855	0.9E
	1203	1429	0.7F		1251	1455	0.6F
	1735	2051	1.1E		1819	2122	0.8E
13 M	0019	0248	0.7F	28 Tu	0112	0310	0.5F
	0548	0920	1.2E		0609	0946	0.9E
	1303	1526	0.7F		1335	1543	0.6F
	1843	2152	1.1E		1907	2213	0.9E
14 Tu	0126	0349	0.7F	29 W	0204	0404	0.5F
	0706	1021	1.2E		0711	1036	0.9E
	1401	1624	0.7F		1419	1631	0.6F
	1948	2252	1.2E		1951	2302	0.9E
15 W	0230	0453	0.8F	30 Th	0253	0457	0.5F
	0818	1119	1.2E		0809	1124	1.0E
	1457	1722	0.8F		1502	1718	0.7F
	2047	2349	1.3E		2031	2348	1.0E
				31 F	0336	0548	0.6F
					0900	1210	1.0E
					1543	1804	0.7F
					2108		

June

Day	Slack	Maximum	knots	Day	Slack	Maximum	knots
1 Sa		0032	1.1E	16 Su		0113	1.3E
	0415	0634	0.7F		0458	0720	0.7F
	0944	1255	1.1E		1050	1335	1.1E
	1621	1847	0.7F		1708	1927	0.7F
	2142				2258		
2 Su		0115	1.2E	17 M		0202	1.2E
	0452	0718	0.8F		0546	0805	0.7F
	1025	1339	1.1E		1136	1421	1.1E
	1658	1929	0.8F		1754	2011	0.7F
	2218				2343		
3 M		0158	1.3E	18 Tu		0248	1.2E
	0528	0801	0.8F		0634	0849	0.7F
	1106	1423	1.1E		1221	1506	1.0E
	1735	2012	0.8F		1838	2054	0.6F
	2257						
4 Tu		0242	1.3E	19 W	0025	0334	1.2E
	0608	0846	0.8F		0723	0936	0.6F
	1149	1508	1.2E		1306	1551	1.0E
	1814	2057	0.8F		1923	2140	0.6F
	2341						
5 W		0329	1.3E	20 Th	0105	0419	1.1E
	0653	0935	0.8F		0814	1025	0.6F
	1236	1555	1.1E		1352	1637	0.9E
	1858	2146	0.8F		2011	2229	0.5F
6 Th	0031	0417	1.3E	21 F	0145	0504	1.1E
	0745	1028	0.8F		0905	1116	0.5F
	1328	1644	1.1E		1438	1723	0.8E
	1948	2240	0.8F		2103	2320	0.5F
7 F	0126	0509	1.3E	22 Sa	0224	0551	1.0E
	0843	1124	0.8F		0954	1205	0.6F
	1423	1736	1.1E		1523	1812	0.8E
	2047	2337	0.8F		2158		
8 Sa	0224	0602	1.3E	23 Su		0011	0.5F
	0943	1220	0.8F		0304	0638	1.0E
	1520	1831	1.1E		1040	1251	0.6F
	2152				1606	1902	0.8E
					2252		
9 Su		0035	0.8F	24 M		0101	0.5F
	0324	0658	1.3E		0346	0726	1.0E
	1042	1314	0.8F		1123	1335	0.6F
	1618	1929	1.1E		1646	1953	0.8E
	2259				2345		
10 M		0132	0.8F	25 Tu		0150	0.5F
	0428	0757	1.2E		0432	0815	0.9E
	1139	1407	0.8F		1205	1419	0.6F
	1718	2030	1.1E		1726	2044	0.9E
11 Tu	0006	0230	0.8F	26 W	0036	0239	0.5F
	0537	0857	1.2E		0524	0906	0.9E
	1237	1501	0.8F		1249	1504	0.6F
	1820	2130	1.2E		1808	2134	0.9E
12 W	0111	0330	0.7F	27 Th	0126	0330	0.5F
	0651	0957	1.1E		0622	0957	0.9E
	1334	1557	0.7F		1334	1551	0.6F
	1922	2230	1.2E		1851	2223	1.0E
13 Th	0214	0432	0.7F	28 F	0214	0422	0.6F
	0802	1056	1.1E		0723	1047	0.9E
	1432	1654	0.7F		1420	1640	0.6F
	2023	2327	1.2E		1937	2312	1.0E
14 F	0313	0534	0.7F	29 Sa	0300	0514	0.6F
	0905	1152	1.1E		0820	1136	1.0E
	1528	1749	0.7F		1505	1728	0.7F
	2119				2022	2359	1.1E
15 Sa		0022	1.3E	30 Su	0343	0603	0.7F
	0408	0631	0.7F		0910	1224	1.0E
	1000	1245	1.1E		1547	1815	0.7F
	1620	1841	0.7F		2107		
	2210						

Portland Harbor Entrance 2019

F–Flood, Dir. 310° True   E–Ebb, Dir. 138° True

July

Day	Slack	Maximum	knots
1 M		0046	1.2E
	0424	0651	0.7F
	0957	1310	1.1E
	1627	1901	0.8F
	2151		
2 Tu ●		0132	1.3E
	0506	0737	0.8F
	1042	1357	1.1E
	1707	1946	0.8F
	2237		
3 W		0220	1.3E
	0550	0824	0.8F
	1129	1445	1.2E
	1749	2034	0.9F
	2326		
4 Th		0308	1.4E
	0638	0914	0.8F
	1220	1533	1.2E
	1837	2125	0.9F
5 F	0019	0358	1.4E
	0730	1007	0.8F
	1314	1624	1.2E
	1931	2220	0.8F
6 Sa	0116	0450	1.4E
	0825	1103	0.8F
	1410	1717	1.2E
	2033	2319	0.8F
7 Su	0216	0543	1.3E
	0922	1158	0.8F
	1505	1811	1.2E
	2139		
8 M		0017	0.8F
	0316	0638	1.3E
	1018	1252	0.8F
	1559	1908	1.2E
	2246		
9 Tu ☽		0115	0.8F
	0419	0734	1.2E
	1115	1343	0.8F
	1655	2007	1.2E
	2350		
10 W		0211	0.8F
	0524	0833	1.1E
	1212	1435	0.7F
	1753	2106	1.1E
11 Th	0053	0309	0.7F
	0633	0933	1.1E
	1310	1529	0.7F
	1856	2206	1.1E
12 F	0154	0408	0.6F
	0740	1031	1.0E
	1410	1625	0.6F
	1959	2305	1.1E
13 Sa	0254	0509	0.6F
	0842	1128	1.0E
	1507	1723	0.6F
	2059		
14 Su		0001	1.1E
	0351	0608	0.6F
	0938	1222	1.0E
	1600	1816	0.6F
	2153		
15 M		0054	1.1E
	0443	0700	0.6F
	1028	1311	1.0E
	1648	1904	0.6F
	2240		
16 Tu ○		0143	1.2E
	0531	0745	0.7F
	1115	1358	1.0E
	1731	1947	0.6F
	2322		
17 W		0228	1.2E
	0617	0828	0.6F
	1159	1442	1.0E
	1812	2029	0.6F
18 Th	0000	0311	1.2E
	0701	0912	0.6F
	1242	1526	0.9E
	1855	2113	0.6F
19 F	0037	0353	1.2E
	0746	0957	0.6F
	1325	1610	0.9E
	1941	2201	0.6F
20 Sa	0113	0436	1.1E
	0830	1044	0.6F
	1406	1655	0.9E
	2031	2251	0.6F
21 Su	0152	0519	1.1E
	0914	1131	0.6F
	1445	1741	0.9E
	2125	2342	0.6F
22 M	0232	0604	1.1E
	0956	1216	0.6F
	1522	1828	0.9E
	2217		
23 Tu		0032	0.6F
	0315	0650	1.0E
	1038	1300	0.7F
	1557	1915	0.9E
	2307		
24 W ○		0120	0.6F
	0359	0738	1.0E
	1120	1343	0.7F
	1632	2004	0.9E
	2355		
25 Th		0208	0.6F
	0446	0828	0.9E
	1204	1427	0.6F
	1710	2054	0.9E
26 F	0043	0256	0.6F
	0539	0919	0.9E
	1251	1514	0.6F
	1755	2145	1.0E
27 Sa	0132	0347	0.6F
	0637	1011	0.9E
	1340	1604	0.6F
	1847	2237	1.0E
28 Su	0222	0440	0.6F
	0739	1103	0.9E
	1429	1655	0.6F
	1943	2329	1.1E
29 M	0313	0534	0.6F
	0838	1154	1.0E
	1516	1747	0.7F
	2040		
30 Tu		0020	1.2E
	0401	0626	0.7F
	0932	1245	1.1E
	1600	1837	0.8F
	2133		
31 W ●		0110	1.3E
	0449	0716	0.8F
	1024	1334	1.1E
	1645	1926	0.9F
	2225		

August

Day	Slack	Maximum	knots
1 Th		0200	1.4E
	0535	0805	0.8F
	1114	1424	1.2E
	1732	2015	0.9F
	2318		
2 F		0250	1.4E
	0623	0854	0.9F
	1206	1514	1.2E
	1823	2107	0.9F
3 Sa	0012	0340	1.4E
	0712	0946	0.9F
	1258	1605	1.3E
	1919	2203	0.9F
4 Su	0110	0430	1.4E
	0804	1040	0.9F
	1351	1657	1.3E
	2021	2301	0.9F
5 M	0209	0522	1.3E
	0858	1134	0.8F
	1443	1750	1.3E
	2125		
6 Tu		0000	0.8F
	0308	0616	1.3E
	0954	1227	0.8F
	1536	1845	1.2E
	2228		
7 W ☽		0056	0.8F
	0407	0711	1.2E
	1052	1318	0.8F
	1629	1942	1.2E
	2330		
8 Th		0150	0.7F
	0507	0809	1.1E
	1150	1409	0.7F
	1727	2041	1.1E
9 F	0031	0244	0.6F
	0610	0907	1.0E
	1249	1501	0.6F
	1831	2142	1.0E
10 Sa	0133	0341	0.6F
	0714	1006	0.9E
	1349	1557	0.6F
	1938	2242	1.0E
11 Su	0235	0441	0.5F
	0817	1103	0.9E
	1446	1655	0.5F
	2039	2340	1.0E
12 M	0333	0543	0.5F
	0914	1157	0.9E
	1539	1750	0.5F
	2133		
13 Tu		0034	1.1E
	0426	0638	0.5F
	1006	1247	0.9E
	1625	1839	0.6F
	2218		
14 W		0121	1.1E
	0512	0723	0.6F
	1052	1334	0.9E
	1708	1923	0.6F
	2257		
15 Th ○		0204	1.2E
	0554	0804	0.6F
	1134	1418	1.0E
	1748	2005	0.6F
	2333		
16 F		0245	1.2E
	0633	0844	0.6F
	1213	1500	1.0E
	1830	2048	0.7F
17 Sa	0008	0325	1.2E
	0711	0925	0.7F
	1250	1543	1.0E
	1913	2134	0.6F
18 Su	0044	0406	1.2E
	0750	1009	0.7F
	1325	1625	1.0E
	2000	2223	0.6F
19 M	0123	0447	1.1E
	0830	1053	0.7F
	1400	1709	1.0E
	2048	2312	0.6F
20 Tu	0204	0531	1.1E
	0911	1138	0.7F
	1433	1753	1.0E
	2137		
21 W		0002	0.6F
	0246	0615	1.0E
	0953	1223	0.7F
	1507	1838	1.0E
	2224		
22 Th		0049	0.6F
	0329	0702	1.0E
	1037	1308	0.7F
	1543	1925	1.0E
	2310		
23 F ○		0136	0.6F
	0413	0752	0.9E
	1123	1353	0.6F
	1623	2016	1.0E
	2359		
24 Sa		0224	0.6F
	0502	0844	0.9E
	1211	1440	0.6F
	1711	2109	1.0E
25 Su	0052	0315	0.6F
	0559	0938	0.9E
	1302	1531	0.6F
	1808	2205	1.0E
26 M	0149	0410	0.6F
	0705	1033	0.9E
	1355	1626	0.7F
	1914	2301	1.1E
27 Tu	0247	0507	0.6F
	0812	1128	1.0E
	1448	1721	0.7F
	2020	2356	1.2E
28 W	0341	0603	0.7F
	0913	1221	1.1E
	1540	1816	0.8F
	2120		
29 Th		0049	1.3E
	0430	0656	0.8F
	1008	1314	1.2E
	1630	1908	0.9F
	2217		
30 F ●		0140	1.4E
	0517	0745	0.9F
	1059	1405	1.3E
	1721	2000	1.0F
	2311		
31 Sa		0231	1.5E
	0603	0834	0.9F
	1148	1455	1.3E
	1813	2052	1.0F

September

Day	Slack	Maximum	knots
1 Su	0006	0320	1.4E
	0650	0923	0.9F
	1237	1545	1.4E
	1908	2146	0.9F
2 M	0103	0410	1.4E
	0740	1014	0.9F
	1327	1636	1.4E
	2007	2243	0.9F
3 Tu	0159	0501	1.3E
	0834	1107	0.8F
	1418	1728	1.3E
	2107	2340	0.8F
4 W	0255	0554	1.2E
	0931	1200	0.7F
	1510	1821	1.2E
	2208		
5 Th ☽		0035	0.8F
	0350	0647	1.1E
	1031	1252	0.7F
	1604	1917	1.1E
	2309		
6 F		0127	0.7F
	0446	0743	1.0E
	1130	1343	0.6F
	1702	2016	1.0E
7 Sa	0011	0219	0.6F
	0544	0841	0.9E
	1228	1435	0.5F
	1806	2117	0.9E
8 Su	0113	0314	0.5F
	0647	0939	0.9E
	1326	1528	0.5F
	1912	2218	0.9E
9 M	0214	0412	0.4F
	0750	1037	0.8E
	1422	1625	0.5F
	2013	2317	0.9E
10 Tu	0312	0514	0.4F
	0849	1132	0.8E
	1514	1721	0.5F
	2105		
11 W		0009	1.0E
	0402	0610	0.5F
	0941	1222	0.9E
	1601	1812	0.5F
	2149		
12 Th		0054	1.1E
	0445	0655	0.6F
	1025	1308	0.9E
	1645	1858	0.6F
	2228		
13 F ○		0135	1.1E
	0522	0734	0.6F
	1103	1351	1.0E
	1726	1941	0.7F
	2304		
14 Sa		0215	1.2E
	0558	0812	0.7F
	1137	1433	1.0E
	1806	2024	0.7F
	2340		
15 Su		0254	1.2E
	0633	0851	0.7F
	1208	1513	1.1E
	1846	2108	0.7F
16 M		0335	1.2E
	0708	0932	0.7F
	1239	1554	1.1E
	1927	2154	0.7F
17 Tu	0055	0416	1.1E
	0746	1015	0.7F
	1311	1636	1.1E
	2010	2241	0.7F
18 W	0136	0459	1.1E
	0827	1100	0.7F
	1345	1719	1.1E
	2054	2330	0.7F
19 Th	0218	0543	1.0E
	0910	1147	0.7F
	1422	1803	1.1E
	2139		
20 F		0018	0.7F
	0300	0630	1.0E
	0956	1234	0.6F
	1503	1851	1.0E
	2228		
21 Sa		0106	0.7F
	0345	0720	1.0E
	1044	1321	0.6F
	1548	1943	1.0E
	2322		
22 Su		0155	0.6F
	0434	0813	0.9E
	1134	1410	0.6F
	1639	2039	1.0E
23 M	0021	0247	0.6F
	0532	0909	0.9E
	1229	1503	0.6F
	1740	2138	1.1E
24 Tu	0122	0343	0.6F
	0640	1007	1.0E
	1327	1600	0.7F
	1851	2237	1.1E
25 W	0222	0442	0.7F
	0752	1104	1.0E
	1427	1659	0.7F
	2004	2334	1.2E
26 Th	0317	0540	0.7F
	0855	1200	1.1E
	1525	1757	0.8F
	2110		
27 F		0028	1.3E
	0408	0634	0.8F
	0950	1254	1.3E
	1619	1853	0.9F
	2209		
28 Sa ●		0120	1.4E
	0455	0723	0.9F
	1039	1345	1.4E
	1711	1945	1.0F
	2305		
29 Su		0211	1.4E
	0540	0811	0.9F
	1127	1435	1.4E
	1803	2037	1.0F
	2359		
30 M		0301	1.4E
	0627	0858	0.9F
	1214	1525	1.4E
	1855	2129	0.9F

Time meridian 75° W. 0000 is midnight. 1200 is noon. Times are not adjusted for Daylight Saving Time.

Portland Harbor Entrance 2019

F—Flood, Dir. 310° True   E—Ebb, Dir. 138° True

October

Day	Slack h m	Max h m	knots
1 Tu	0052	0350	1.3E
	0717	0948	0.8F
	1303	1615	1.4E
	1950	2223	0.9F
2 W	0146	0440	1.2E
	0812	1040	0.7F
	1354	1705	1.3E
	2048	2317	0.8F
3 Th	0239	0531	1.1E
	0910	1134	0.7F
	1447	1757	1.2E
	2148		
4 F		0012	0.7F
	0331	0623	1.0E
	1010	1227	0.6F
	1541	1852	1.0E
	2250		
5 Sa ◐		0104	0.6F
	0423	0717	0.9E
	1108	1318	0.5F
	1637	1950	1.0E
	2351		
6 Su		0155	0.5F
	0519	0813	0.8E
	1205	1408	0.5F
	1736	2050	0.9E
7 M	0050	0248	0.5F
	0620	0911	0.8E
	1300	1459	0.4F
	1837	2150	0.9E
8 Tu	0148	0343	0.4F
	0723	1009	0.8E
	1355	1553	0.4F
	1935	2245	0.9E
9 W	0241	0440	0.4F
	0820	1103	0.8E
	1448	1649	0.5F
	2028	2335	1.0E
10 Th	0327	0533	0.5F
	0909	1154	0.9E
	1537	1742	0.5F
	2115		
11 F		0021	1.0E
	0408	0618	0.6F
	0950	1240	1.0E
	1621	1831	0.6F
	2157		
12 Sa		0103	1.1E
	0445	0659	0.7F
	1025	1322	1.0E
	1702	1915	0.7F
	2236		
13 Su O		0143	1.1E
	0520	0737	0.7F
	1056	1402	1.1E
	1740	1958	0.7F
	2312		
14 M		0223	1.1E
	0554	0816	0.8F
	1124	1442	1.2E
	1817	2040	0.7F
	2349		
15 Tu		0304	1.1E
	0629	0856	0.8F
	1153	1523	1.2E
	1854	2124	0.7F
16 W	0027	0346	1.1E
	0706	0939	0.7F
	1226	1604	1.2E
	1932	2210	0.7F
17 Th	0107	0429	1.1E
	0746	1025	0.7F
	1303	1647	1.1E
	2015	2258	0.7F
18 F	0149	0513	1.1E
	0830	1113	0.7F
	1345	1733	1.1E
	2103	2348	0.7F
19 Sa	0234	0601	1.0E
	0917	1202	0.7F
	1432	1822	1.1E
	2157		
20 Su		0039	0.7F
	0322	0651	1.0E
	1008	1253	0.7F
	1522	1915	1.1E
	2255		
21 M O		0131	0.7F
	0415	0746	1.0E
	1103	1345	0.7F
	1617	2013	1.1E
	2355		
22 Tu		0224	0.7F
	0515	0844	1.0E
	1203	1439	0.7F
	1721	2112	1.1E
23 W	0056	0320	0.7F
	0622	0943	1.0E
	1307	1538	0.7F
	1835	2212	1.2E
24 Th	0154	0417	0.7F
	0731	1042	1.1E
	1411	1639	0.8F
	1951	2311	1.2E
25 F	0250	0515	0.8F
	0833	1139	1.2E
	1512	1740	0.8F
	2059		
26 Sa		0006	1.3E
	0342	0609	0.8F
	0928	1234	1.3E
	1607	1837	0.9F
	2200		
27 Su ●		0100	1.3E
	0431	0700	0.9F
	1018	1326	1.4E
	1659	1930	0.9F
	2255		
28 M		0151	1.3E
	0519	0747	0.9F
	1105	1416	1.5E
	1750	2020	0.9F
	2347		
29 Tu		0240	1.3E
	0607	0834	0.8F
	1153	1505	1.4E
	1840	2110	0.9F
30 W	0038	0329	1.2E
	0657	0922	0.8F
	1242	1554	1.3E
	1933	2201	0.8F
31 Th	0128	0418	1.2E
	0750	1013	0.7F
	1333	1643	1.2E
	2030	2254	0.7F

November

Day	Slack h m	Max h m	knots
1 F	0219	0507	1.1E
	0847	1107	0.6F
	1426	1735	1.1E
	2130	2348	0.6F
2 Sa	0310	0558	1.0E
	0945	1200	0.5F
	1517	1828	1.0E
	2231		
3 Su		0041	0.5F
	0402	0650	0.9E
	1042	1251	0.5F
	1607	1923	0.9E
	2328		
4 M ◐		0132	0.5F
	0456	0745	0.8E
	1137	1340	0.5F
	1657	2019	0.9E
5 Tu	0022	0221	0.5F
	0552	0841	0.7E
	1232	1429	0.4F
	1750	2114	0.9E
6 W	0113	0311	0.5F
	0648	0937	0.8E
	1326	1521	0.4F
	1846	2207	0.9E
7 Th	0200	0401	0.5F
	0741	1031	0.8E
	1419	1616	0.4F
	1943	2257	0.9E
8 F	0245	0451	0.5F
	0827	1121	0.9E
	1509	1711	0.5F
	2036	2343	1.0E
9 Sa	0327	0538	0.6F
	0907	1207	1.0E
	1554	1801	0.6F
	2123		
10 Su		0028	1.0E
	0406	0621	0.7F
	0941	1249	1.1E
	1634	1847	0.7F
	2205		
11 M		0110	1.1E
	0443	0702	0.7F
	1012	1330	1.2E
	1711	1930	0.7F
	2243		
12 Tu O		0152	1.1E
	0518	0743	0.8F
	1041	1411	1.2E
	1747	2012	0.8F
	2320		
13 W		0234	1.1E
	0554	0823	0.8F
	1113	1452	1.2E
	1822	2055	0.8F
	2358		
14 Th		0316	1.1E
	0630	0906	0.7F
	1149	1535	1.2E
	1901	2140	0.8F
15 F	0039	0400	1.1E
	0709	0952	0.7F
	1231	1620	1.2E
	1946	2229	0.7F
16 Sa	0124	0446	1.1E
	0753	1042	0.7F
	1318	1707	1.2E
	2037	2322	0.7F
17 Su	0213	0535	1.0E
	0843	1134	0.7F
	1409	1758	1.2E
	2134		
18 M		0016	0.7F
	0306	0626	1.0E
	0939	1228	0.7F
	1504	1852	1.2E
	2233		
19 Tu O		0109	0.7F
	0401	0722	1.0E
	1041	1323	0.7F
	1602	1949	1.2E
	2331		
20 W		0202	0.7F
	0500	0820	1.0E
	1145	1419	0.7F
	1707	2048	1.2E
21 Th	0028	0255	0.7F
	0603	0920	1.1E
	1251	1518	0.7F
	1821	2148	1.2E
22 F	0125	0351	0.8F
	0707	1020	1.2E
	1356	1619	0.8F
	1938	2247	1.2E
23 Sa	0222	0448	0.8F
	0808	1118	1.3E
	1457	1722	0.8F
	2047	2344	1.2E
24 Su	0317	0543	0.8F
	0905	1213	1.3E
	1553	1820	0.8F
	2147		
25 M		0039	1.2E
	0410	0636	0.8F
	0957	1306	1.4E
	1646	1913	0.9F
	2241		
26 Tu ●		0130	1.2E
	0500	0725	0.8F
	1048	1356	1.4E
	1736	2002	0.9F
	2332		
27 W		0220	1.2E
	0549	0812	0.8F
	1137	1446	1.3E
	1826	2050	0.8F
28 Th	0020	0308	1.2E
	0638	0859	0.7F
	1226	1534	1.3E
	1918	2139	0.7F
29 F	0109	0355	1.1E
	0728	0948	0.6F
	1315	1623	1.2E
	2013	2231	0.6F
30 Sa	0159	0443	1.0E
	0709	1039	0.6F
	1403	1712	1.1E
	2111	2325	0.6F

December

Day	Slack h m	Max h m	knots
1 Su	0249	0532	0.9F
	0917	1131	0.5F
	1448	1802	1.0E
	2207		
2 M		0017	0.5F
	0339	0623	0.8E
	1013	1222	0.5F
	1532	1852	1.0E
	2259		
3 Tu		0106	0.5F
	0429	0715	0.8E
	1108	1311	0.5F
	1614	1944	0.9E
	2346		
4 W ◐		0151	0.5F
	0517	0809	0.8E
	1201	1400	0.5F
	1700	2035	0.9E
5 Th	0031	0236	0.6F
	0604	0902	0.8E
	1254	1451	0.5F
	1754	2126	0.9E
6 F	0116	0322	0.6F
	0650	0954	0.9E
	1346	1543	0.5F
	1854	2216	0.9E
7 Sa	0200	0409	0.6F
	0734	1044	0.9E
	1436	1637	0.5F
	1953	2305	0.9E
8 Su	0244	0457	0.6F
	0815	1130	1.0E
	1522	1729	0.6F
	2045	2352	1.0E
9 M	0327	0544	0.7F
	0854	1215	1.1E
	1603	1817	0.6F
	2131		
10 Tu		0037	1.0E
	0407	0629	0.7F
	0930	1259	1.1E
	1641	1901	0.7F
	2211		
11 W		0121	1.1E
	0445	0712	0.7F
	1005	1341	1.2E
	1718	1944	0.8F
	2250		
12 Th O		0205	1.1E
	0521	0754	0.8F
	1042	1425	1.2E
	1756	2028	0.8F
	2331		
13 F		0249	1.1E
	0558	0837	0.8F
	1123	1510	1.3E
	1838	2114	0.8F
14 Sa	0015	0334	1.1E
	0638	0924	0.8F
	1208	1556	1.3E
	1925	2205	0.8F
15 Su	0104	0422	1.1E
	0724	1015	0.8F
	1259	1645	1.3E
	2017	2259	0.8F
16 M	0157	0512	1.1E
	0818	1110	0.8F
	1354	1736	1.3E
	2113	2353	0.8F
17 Tu	0251	0604	1.1E
	0919	1207	0.8F
	1451	1830	1.3E
	2209		
18 W O		0046	0.8F
	0345	0700	1.1E
	1024	1304	0.8F
	1552	1926	1.2E
	2305		
19 Th		0138	0.8F
	0440	0758	1.1E
	1130	1400	0.8F
	1657	2024	1.2E
20 F	0001	0230	0.8F
	0538	0857	1.2E
	1234	1458	0.8F
	1809	2124	1.1E
21 Sa	0058	0324	0.8F
	0640	0957	1.2E
	1338	1559	0.7F
	1922	2224	1.1E
22 Su	0157	0420	0.7F
	0743	1055	1.3E
	1439	1701	0.7F
	2030	2322	1.1E
23 M	0255	0518	0.7F
	0844	1152	1.3E
	1538	1801	0.8F
	2130		
24 Tu		0017	1.1E
	0351	0613	0.7F
	0941	1247	1.3E
	1632	1855	0.8F
	2224		
25 W		0110	1.1E
	0443	0704	0.7F
	1034	1339	1.3E
	1723	1945	0.7F
	2314		
26 Th ●		0159	1.1E
	0531	0752	0.7F
	1123	1428	1.3E
	1813	2032	0.7F
27 F	0002	0246	1.1E
	0618	0837	0.7F
	1210	1515	1.2E
	1903	2119	0.6F
28 Sa	0049	0333	1.0E
	0704	0923	0.6F
	1253	1601	1.2E
	1954	2208	0.6F
29 Su	0137	0419	0.9E
	0753	1011	0.6F
	1335	1647	1.1E
	2045	2258	0.6F
30 M	0225	0506	0.9E
	0846	1102	0.5F
	1415	1733	1.1E
	2135	2347	0.6F
31 Tu	0310	0554	0.8E
	0941	1153	0.5F
	1455	1820	1.0E
	2221		

Time meridian 75° W. 0000 is midnight. 1200 is noon. Times are not adjusted for Daylight Saving Time.

Portsmouth Harbor Entrance, N.H., 2019

F–Flood, Dir. 342° True   E–Ebb, Dir. 194° True

January

Day	Slack h m	Max h m	knots	Day	Slack h m	Max h m	knots
1 Tu	0233	0436	1.1F	16 W	0209	0415	1.1F
	0854	1124	1.5E		0811	1051	1.5E
	1514	1721	1.0F		1451	1648	1.0F
	2126	2347	1.4E		2049	2316	1.3E
2 W	0326	0531	1.1F	17 Th	0257	0505	1.1F
	0948	1226	1.5E		0901	1143	1.5E
	1611	2005	1.0F		1543	1740	1.0F
	2222				2144		
3 Th		0044	1.4E	18 F		0008	1.4E
	0418	0624	1.1F		0345	0555	1.2F
	1039	1335	1.6E		0952	1236	1.6E
	1705	2058	1.0F		1634	1832	1.1F
	2314				2238		
4 F		0138	1.4E	19 Sa		0101	1.4E
	0509	0715	1.1F		0435	0646	1.3F
	1129	1504	1.6E		1044	1329	1.7E
	1755	2144	1.0F		1724	1925	1.1F
					2330		
5 Sa ●	0004	0227	1.4E	20 Su		0154	1.5E
	0558	0805	1.2F		0524	0738	1.3F
	1217	1502	1.6E		1137	1422	1.8E
	1844	2222	1.0F		1815	2017	1.2F
6 Su	0052	0311	1.4E	21 M ○	0022	0246	1.6E
	0646	0853	1.2F		0616	0830	1.4F
	1303	1538	1.6E		1230	1514	1.9E
	1930	2151	1.0F		1905	2109	1.2F
7 M	0138	0353	1.4E	22 Tu	0114	0338	1.6E
	0734	0939	1.2F		0708	0923	1.4F
	1347	1617	1.6E		1324	1605	1.9E
	2016	2226	1.0F		1956	2201	1.3F
8 Tu	0222	0435	1.4E	23 W	0205	0429	1.7E
	0821	1024	1.2F		0803	1016	1.4F
	1430	1658	1.5E		1417	1657	1.9E
	2100	2305	1.0F		2047	2252	1.3F
9 W	0306	0519	1.3E	24 Th	0257	0521	1.6E
	0908	1110	1.1F		0858	1110	1.4F
	1511	1740	1.5E		1512	1749	1.8E
	2144	2346	1.1F		2138	2344	1.3F
10 Th	0349	0603	1.3E	25 F	0349	0615	1.6E
	0955	1156	1.1F		0956	1204	1.3F
	1553	1825	1.5E		1609	1843	1.7E
	2227				2231		
11 F		0028	1.1F	26 Sa		0035	1.3F
	0431	0649	1.3E		0444	0709	1.6E
	1043	1242	1.1F		1054	1259	1.2F
	1637	1910	1.4E		1707	1937	1.6E
	2311				2324		
12 Sa		0110	1.1F	27 Su ◐		0126	1.2F
	0514	0735	1.3E		0539	0804	1.5E
	1130	1328	1.0F		1154	1354	1.1F
	1722	1956	1.4E		1807	2031	1.5E
	2354						
13 Su		0154	1.0F	28 M	0017	0218	1.2F
	0557	0822	1.3E		0635	0901	1.5E
	1219	1415	1.0F		1254	1451	1.0F
	1809	2044	1.4E		1907	2127	1.4E
14 M ◐	0038	0239	1.0F	29 Tu	0111	0311	1.1F
	0640	0910	1.3E		0731	0959	1.5E
	1309	1504	1.0F		1353	1553	0.9F
	1900	2133	1.3E		2005	2224	1.3E
15 Tu	0123	0326	1.1F	30 W	0206	0407	1.1F
	0725	1000	1.4E		0827	1100	1.4E
	1400	1556	0.9F		1452	1701	0.9F
	1954	2224	1.3E			1755	0.9F
					1846†		0.9F
				31 Th	0300	0502	1.1F
					0922	1205	1.4E
					1548	1946	0.9F
					2157		

February

Day	Slack h m	Max h m	knots	Day	Slack h m	Max h m	knots
1 F		0017	1.3E	16 Sa	0318	0528	1.2F
	0353	0556	1.1F		0927	1211	1.6E
	1014	1408	1.5E		1609	1807	1.0F
	1641	2037	1.0F		2215		
	2249						
2 Sa		0111	1.3E	17 Su		0037	1.4E
	0445	0648	1.1F		0412	0622	1.3F
	1104	1457	1.5E		1026	1306	1.7E
	1730	2122	1.0F		1701	1901	1.1F
	2337				2310		
3 Su		0200	1.3E	18 M		0131	1.5E
	0534	0739	1.1F		0506	0716	1.3F
	1151	1435	1.5E		1122	1401	1.8E
	1817	2155	1.0F		1753	1955	1.2F
4 M ●	0024	0243	1.3E	19 Tu ○	0003	0226	1.6E
	0622	0827	1.1F		0600	0811	1.4F
	1236	1509	1.5E		1218	1454	1.8E
	1902	2117	1.0F		1844	2048	1.2F
5 Tu	0108	0324	1.4E	20 W	0055	0318	1.7E
	0708	0913	1.1F		0654	0905	1.4F
	1319	1547	1.5E		1312	1546	1.9E
	1945	2152	1.0F		1934	2140	1.3F
6 W	0151	0406	1.4E	21 Th	0145	0410	1.7E
	0754	0957	1.1F		0749	0959	1.4F
	1401	1627	1.5E		1406	1638	1.8E
	2028	2231	1.1F		2024	2231	1.3F
7 Th	0232	0448	1.4E	22 F	0236	0502	1.7E
	0839	1042	1.1F		0844	1053	1.3F
	1441	1709	1.5E		1500	1729	1.8E
	2109	2311	1.1F		2115	2321	1.3F
8 F	0312	0531	1.4E	23 Sa	0327	0554	1.7E
	0924	1127	1.1F		0940	1147	1.3F
	1521	1753	1.5E		1554	1821	1.7E
	2150	2353	1.1F		2206		
9 Sa	0350	0616	1.4E	24 Su		0011	1.3F
	1009	1212	1.1F		0419	0648	1.6E
	1603	1838	1.5E		1037	1241	1.2F
	2232				1650	1914	1.6E
					2258		
10 Su		0035	1.1F	25 M		0101	1.2F
	0429	0702	1.4E		0512	0741	1.6E
	1055	1258	1.1F		1134	1335	1.1F
	1646	1925	1.4E		1747	2007	1.5E
	2314				2351		
11 M		0119	1.1F	26 Tu ◑		0151	1.2F
	0508	0749	1.4E		0608	0836	1.5E
	1143	1345	1.1F		1232	1430	1.0F
	1734	2013	1.4E		1844	2101	1.3E
	2357						
12 Tu ◐		0204	1.1F	27 W	0045	0243	1.1F
	0550	0838	1.4E		0703	0932	1.4E
	1233	1433	1.0F		1330	1529	0.9F
	1826	2103	1.4E		1941	2157	1.3E
13 W	0043	0252	1.1F	28 Th	0140	0337	1.0F
	0637	0929	1.4E		0759	1032	1.4E
	1325	1525	1.0F		1427	1657	0.8F
	1922	2155	1.3E		2036	2253	1.2E
14 Th	0132	0342	1.1F				
	0730	1022	1.5E				
	1420	1618	1.0F				
	2020	2248	1.3E				
15 F	0224	0435	1.2F				
	0828	1116	1.5E				
	1515	1713	1.0F				
	2118	2342	1.4E				

March

Day	Slack h m	Max h m	knots	Day	Slack h m	Max h m	knots
1 F	0235	0433	1.0F	16 Sa	0157	0408	1.2F
	0854	1252	1.4E		0803	1051	1.6E
	1522	1920	0.9F		1448	1647	0.9F
	2130	2348	1.2E		2056	2318	1.4E
2 Sa	0329	0529	1.0F	17 Su	0256	0504	1.2F
	0947	1347	1.4E		0908	1148	1.6E
	1613	2009	0.9F		1544	1743	1.1F
	2220				2154		
3 Su		0040	1.2E	18 M		0015	1.5E
	0420	0621	1.0F		0354	0600	1.2F
	1036	1317	1.4E		1010	1244	1.7E
	1701	2050	0.9F		1638	1838	1.1F
	2308				2249		
4 M		0128	1.3E	19 Tu		0111	1.5E
	0509	0711	1.0F		0451	0657	1.3F
	1123	1355	1.4E		1108	1341	1.7E
	1747	2001	1.0F		1730	1933	1.2F
	2353				2343		
5 Tu		0212	1.3E	20 W ○		0206	1.6E
	0557	0759	1.1F		0546	0754	1.3F
	1208	1434	1.4E		1204	1435	1.8E
	1830	2037	1.0F		1821	2026	1.2F
6 W ●	0036	0253	1.4E	21 Th	0034	0300	1.7E
	0642	0845	1.1F		0640	0845	1.3F
	1250	1514	1.5E		1259	1527	1.8E
	1912	2115	1.1F		1911	2118	1.3F
7 Th	0117	0335	1.4E	22 F	0124	0351	1.8E
	0726	0929	1.1F		0734	0944	1.3F
	1331	1555	1.5E		1352	1618	1.8E
	1952	2155	1.1F		2000	2207	1.3F
8 F	0155	0417	1.5E	23 Sa	0214	0442	1.8E
	0810	1013	1.2F		0829	1038	1.3F
	1411	1638	1.5E		1445	1708	1.7E
	2032	2235	1.2F		2050	2256	1.3F
9 Sa	0232	0500	1.5E	24 Su	0303	0533	1.7E
	0853	1057	1.2F		0923	1131	1.2F
	1451	1722	1.5E		1537	1759	1.6E
	2112	2317	1.2F		2141	2346	1.3F
10 Su	0307	0544	1.5E	25 M	0353	0625	1.7E
	0936	1142	1.2F		1018	1224	1.2F
	1532	1808	1.5E		1631	1850	1.5E
	2152				2232		
11 M		0001	1.2F	26 Tu		0035	1.2F
	0342	0631	1.5E		0446	0717	1.6E
	1021	1229	1.2F		1113	1316	1.1F
	1616	1855	1.5E		1725	1942	1.4E
	2234				2325		
12 Tu		0046	1.2F	27 W ◐		0125	1.1F
	0420	0719	1.5E		0539	0810	1.5E
	1109	1316	1.1F		1209	1408	1.0F
	1704	1944	1.4E		1820	2034	1.3E
	2318						
13 W		0132	1.2F	28 Th	0019	0216	1.1F
	0504	0808	1.5E		0634	0903	1.4E
	1200	1405	1.1F		1304	1503	0.9F
	1757	2035	1.4E		1915	2128	1.2E
14 Th ◐	0007	0221	1.2F	29 F	0114	0309	1.0F
	0557	0900	1.5E		0729	0958	1.4E
	1254	1456	1.0F		1359	1601	0.8F
	1855	2128	1.4E			1708	0.8F
					1753†		0.8F
15 F	0100	0313	1.2F	30 Sa	0209	0404	0.9F
	0658	0955	1.5E		0824	1053	1.3E
	1351	1551	1.0F		1451	1701	0.8F
	1955	2223	1.4E			1748	0.8F
					1845†		0.8F
				31 Su	0303	0459	0.9F
					0916	1144	1.3E
					1542	1752	0.9F
					2150		

Time meridian 75° W. 0000 is midnight. 1200 is noon. Times are not adjusted for Daylight Saving Time.
If three consecutive entries are marked (F) the middle one is not a true maximum but an intermediate value to show the current pattern.
† See page 196 for the remaining currents on this day.

Portsmouth Harbor Entrance, N.H., 2019

F–Flood, Dir. 342° True   E–Ebb, Dir. 194° True

April

Day	Slack	Maximum	knots
1 M		0005	1.2E
	0355	0552	0.9F
	1006	1230	1.3E
	1628	1835	0.9F
	2236		
2 Tu		0052	1.2E
	0444	0642	1.0F
	1052	1315	1.3E
	1713	1916	1.0F
	2320		
3 W		0137	1.3E
	0530	0730	1.0F
	1137	1358	1.4E
	1755	1957	1.0F
4 Th	0001	0221	1.4E
	0614	0815	1.1F
	1219	1441	1.4E
	1835	2038	1.1F
5 F ●	0040	0303	1.5E
	0657	0900	1.1F
	1301	1524	1.5E
	1915	2119	1.2F
6 Sa	0117	0346	1.6E
	0740	0944	1.2F
	1342	1607	1.5E
	1954	2201	1.2F
7 Su	0152	0429	1.6E
	0822	1028	1.2F
	1423	1652	1.5E
	2033	2244	1.2F
8 M	0226	0514	1.7E
	0905	1114	1.2F
	1505	1739	1.5E
	2114	2329	1.3F
9 Tu	0302	0602	1.7E
	0951	1201	1.2F
	1549	1827	1.5E
	2157		
10 W		0015	1.3F
	0342	0651	1.7E
	1040	1249	1.2F
	1639	1917	1.4E
	2244		
11 Th		0104	1.3F
	0430	0742	1.6E
	1132	1339	1.1F
	1734	2009	1.4E
	2337		
12 F ◐		0154	1.2F
	0529	0835	1.6E
	1228	1431	1.1F
	1833	2103	1.4E
13 Sa	0035	0247	1.2F
	0635	0930	1.6E
	1325	1525	1.1F
	1934	2159	1.4E
14 Su	0136	0343	1.2F
	0744	1028	1.6E
	1423	1622	1.1F
	2035	2256	1.4E
15 M	0237	0442	1.2F
	0851	1126	1.6E
	1519	1720	1.1F
	2133	2354	1.5E
16 Tu	0338	0541	1.2F
	0954	1223	1.6E
	1614	1816	1.1F
	2228		
17 W		0051	1.6E
	0436	0639	1.2F
	1053	1320	1.7E
	1706	1910	1.2F
	2321		
18 Th		0147	1.7E
	0531	0738	1.2F
	1149	1415	1.7E
	1756	2003	1.3F
19 F ○	0012	0242	1.7E
	0626	0835	1.2F
	1243	1508	1.7E
	1846	2054	1.3F
20 Sa	0102	0333	1.8E
	0719	0931	1.3F
	1336	1558	1.7E
	1936	2143	1.3F
21 Su	0151	0423	1.8E
	0812	1023	1.2F
	1427	1647	1.6E
	2025	2232	1.3F
22 M	0239	0512	1.7E
	0905	1115	1.2F
	1518	1736	1.5E
	2115	2320	1.2F
23 Tu	0328	0602	1.7E
	0958	1206	1.1F
	1609	1826	1.4E
	2207		
24 W		0009	1.2F
	0419	0652	1.6E
	1050	1255	1.0F
	1701	1916	1.3E
	2259		
25 Th		0059	1.1F
	0511	0742	1.5E
	1143	1344	1.0F
	1754	2006	1.2E
	2353		
26 F ◑		0149	1.0F
	0604	0832	1.4E
	1235	1434	0.9F
	1846	2057	1.2E
27 Sa	0047	0240	0.9F
	0657	0922	1.3E
	1327	1525	0.9F
	1937	2149	1.2E
28 Su	0141	0333	0.9F
	0750	1013	1.2E
	1417	1617	0.9F
	2028	2240	1.2E
29 M	0235	0428	0.9F
	0841	1102	1.2E
	1506	1707	0.9F
	2116	2329	1.2E
30 Tu	0326	0520	0.9F
	0931	1150	1.3E
	1552	1752	0.9F
	2201		

May

Day	Slack	Maximum	knots
1 W		0016	1.2E
	0415	0610	0.9F
	1018	1236	1.3E
	1636	1835	1.0F
	2244		
2 Th		0102	1.3E
	0501	0657	1.0F
	1103	1322	1.4E
	1717	1918	1.1F
	2324		
3 F		0147	1.4E
	0545	0744	1.0F
	1147	1408	1.4E
	1758	2001	1.1F
4 Sa ●	0002	0232	1.5E
	0628	0829	1.1F
	1230	1453	1.5E
	1837	2044	1.2F
5 Su	0038	0316	1.6E
	0710	0915	1.2F
	1313	1538	1.5E
	1917	2128	1.3F
6 M	0114	0401	1.7E
	0753	1000	1.2F
	1356	1624	1.5E
	1957	2213	1.3F
7 Tu	0151	0447	1.8E
	0838	1047	1.2F
	1440	1712	1.5E
	2040	2259	1.3F
8 W	0231	0535	1.8E
	0925	1135	1.2F
	1527	1801	1.5E
	2126	2348	1.3F
9 Th	0317	0626	1.8E
	1015	1224	1.2F
	1618	1852	1.5E
	2218		
10 F		0038	1.3F
	0410	0718	1.7E
	1108	1315	1.2F
	1714	1945	1.5E
	2315		
11 Sa ◐		0130	1.3F
	0512	0812	1.7E
	1204	1407	1.1F
	1813	2040	1.4E
12 Su	0015	0224	1.2F
	0620	0908	1.6E
	1300	1502	1.1F
	1913	2137	1.4E
13 M	0117	0321	1.2F
	0728	1005	1.6E
	1358	1558	1.1F
	2013	2235	1.5E
14 Tu	0220	0421	1.1F
	0834	1104	1.6E
	1454	1656	1.1F
	2111	2333	1.5E
15 W	0321	0522	1.1F
	0936	1202	1.6E
	1549	1752	1.2F
	2206		
16 Th		0031	1.6E
	0420	0623	1.1F
	1036	1259	1.6E
	1641	1846	1.2F
	2259		
17 F		0129	1.7E
	0516	0723	1.1F
	1132	1355	1.6E
	1732	1939	1.2F
	2350		
18 Sa ○		0224	1.7E
	0610	0823	1.2F
	1225	1448	1.6E
	1822	2030	1.3F
19 Su	0040	0316	1.8E
	0702	0920	1.2F
	1317	1537	1.6E
	1911	2119	1.3F
20 M	0128	0404	1.8E
	0754	1011	1.1F
	1407	1624	1.5E
	2001	2207	1.3F
21 Tu	0216	0451	1.7E
	0845	1059	1.1F
	1456	1712	1.4E
	2051	2255	1.2F
22 W	0304	0538	1.6E
	0935	1146	1.1F
	1545	1800	1.4E
	2142	2344	1.2F
23 Th	0353	0625	1.6E
	1025	1232	1.0F
	1635	1848	1.3E
	2233		
24 F		0033	1.1F
	0442	0712	1.5E
	1115	1317	1.0F
	1724	1936	1.2E
	2326		
25 Sa ◑		0122	1.0F
	0532	0759	1.4E
	1204	1402	0.9F
	1814	2025	1.2E
26 Su ◐	0019	0211	0.9F
	0623	0847	1.3E
	1253	1449	0.9F
	1903	2114	1.2E
27 M	0111	0302	0.9F
	0713	0935	1.3E
	1341	1537	0.9F
	1951	2203	1.2E
28 Tu	0204	0354	0.9F
	0804	1024	1.2E
	1428	1625	0.9F
	2038	2252	1.2E
29 W	0255	0446	0.9F
	0853	1112	1.2E
	1513	1711	1.0F
	2122	2339	1.3E
30 Th	0343	0536	0.9F
	0942	1200	1.3E
	1557	1756	1.0F
	2205		
31 F		0027	1.4E
	0430	0624	0.9F
	1029	1248	1.3E
	1639	1841	1.1F
	2245		

June

Day	Slack	Maximum	knots
1 Sa		0114	1.5E
	0514	0712	1.0F
	1115	1336	1.4E
	1720	1926	1.2F
	2324		
2 Su		0201	1.6E
	0558	0759	1.1F
	1201	1423	1.4E
	1801	2011	1.2F
3 M ●	0003	0248	1.7E
	0642	0846	1.1F
	1246	1511	1.5E
	1842	2057	1.3F
4 Tu	0043	0335	1.8E
	0727	0933	1.2F
	1331	1558	1.5E
	1926	2145	1.4F
5 W	0126	0423	1.8E
	0814	1021	1.2F
	1418	1647	1.5E
	2012	2233	1.4F
6 Th	0212	0512	1.8E
	0902	1110	1.2F
	1507	1737	1.5E
	2103	2323	1.4F
7 F	0302	0603	1.8E
	0953	1201	1.2F
	1559	1829	1.5E
	2157		
8 Sa		0015	1.3F
	0358	0656	1.8E
	1046	1252	1.2F
	1654	1923	1.5E
	2256		
9 Su		0109	1.3F
	0500	0750	1.7E
	1141	1344	1.2F
	1752	2018	1.5E
	2357		
10 M ◐		0204	1.2F
	0606	0846	1.6E
	1236	1438	1.2F
	1851	2115	1.5E
11 Tu	0100	0301	1.1F
	0712	0943	1.6E
	1332	1534	1.1F
	1950	2213	1.5E
12 W	0202	0401	1.1F
	0816	1041	1.5E
	1428	1631	1.1F
	2047	2313	1.5E
13 Th	0304	0504	1.0F
	0918	1139	1.5E
	1523	1727	1.2F
	2143		
14 F		0012	1.6E
	0403	0607	1.0F
	1016	1237	1.5E
	1616	1821	1.2F
	2237		
15 Sa		0111	1.6E
	0459	0711	1.0F
	1112	1334	1.5E
	1708	1914	1.2F
	2328		
16 Su		0209	1.7E
	0552	0821	1.1F
	1205	1427	1.5E
	1758	2006	1.2F
17 M ○	0018	0300	1.7E
	0644	1017	1.1F
	1256	1516	1.5E
	1848	2056	1.2F
18 Tu	0106	0346	1.7E
	0734	1003	1.1F
	1344	1602	1.4E
	1937	2144	1.2F
19 W	0154	0429	1.7E
	0823	1041	1.1F
	1432	1647	1.4E
	2027	2231	1.2F
20 Th	0240	0512	1.6E
	0910	1122	1.1F
	1518	1732	1.4E
	2116	2319	1.1F
21 F	0326	0556	1.5E
	0957	1204	1.0F
	1605	1818	1.3E
	2207		
22 Sa		0007	1.1F
	0412	0641	1.5E
	1044	1246	1.0F
	1652	1905	1.3E
	2257		
23 Su		0054	1.0F
	0459	0726	1.4E
	1130	1329	1.0F
	1738	1951	1.2E
	2348		
24 M		0142	1.0F
	0546	0812	1.3E
	1216	1413	1.0F
	1825	2038	1.2E
25 Tu ◑	0039	0230	0.9F
	0635	0859	1.3E
	1302	1458	1.0F
	1911	2126	1.2E
26 W	0129	0320	0.9F
	0724	0947	1.3E
	1347	1545	1.0F
	1955	2215	1.2E
27 Th	0220	0411	0.9F
	0815	1037	1.3E
	1433	1632	1.0F
	2040	2304	1.3E
28 F	0309	0501	0.9F
	0905	1126	1.3E
	1518	1719	1.1F
	2123	2353	1.4E
29 Sa	0357	0551	0.9F
	0955	1215	1.3E
	1602	1806	1.1F
	2206		
30 Su		0042	1.5E
	0444	0640	1.0F
	1044	1305	1.4E
	1645	1853	1.2F
	2250		

Time meridian 75° W. 0000 is midnight. 1200 is noon. Times are not adjusted for Daylight Saving Time.
If three consecutive entries are marked (F) the middle one is not a true maximum but an intermediate value to show the current pattern.

Portsmouth Harbor Entrance, N.H., 2019

F–Flood, Dir. 342° True   E–Ebb, Dir. 194° True

July

Day	Slack (h m)	Maximum (h m)	knots
1 M		0132	1.6E
	0530	0729	1.1F
	1133	1355	1.4E
	1729	1941	1.3F
	2334		
2 Tu ●		0221	1.7E
	0616	0819	1.1F
	1220	1445	1.5E
	1814	2030	1.3F
3 W	0020	0311	1.8E
	0703	0908	1.2F
	1309	1534	1.6E
	1901	2120	1.4F
4 Th	0109	0400	1.9E
	0751	0957	1.2F
	1357	1624	1.6E
	1952	2210	1.4F
5 F	0159	0450	1.9E
	0841	1047	1.3F
	1447	1715	1.6E
	2045	2302	1.4F
6 Sa	0252	0542	1.9E
	0931	1138	1.3F
	1539	1808	1.6E
	2141	2355	1.4F
7 Su	0349	0635	1.8E
	1024	1230	1.3F
	1633	1902	1.6E
	2240		
8 M		0049	1.3F
	0449	0729	1.7E
	1117	1322	1.2F
	1730	1957	1.6E
	2340		
9 Tu ◑		0144	1.2F
	0551	0824	1.6E
	1212	1414	1.2F
	1828	2053	1.5E
10 W	0042	0241	1.1F
	0655	0920	1.5E
	1307	1508	1.1F
	1926	2151	1.5E
11 Th	0144	0341	1.0F
	0757	1018	1.5E
	1402	1604	1.1F
	2023	2251	1.5E
12 F	0245	0445	1.0F
	0858	1117	1.4E
	1458	1701	1.1F
	2119	2352	1.5E
13 Sa	0344	0552	1.0F
	0956	1215	1.4E
	1552	1756	1.1F
	2214		
14 Su		0054	1.6E
	0439	0834	1.0F
	1050	1312	1.4E
	1644	1850	1.1F
	2306		
15 M		0200	1.6E
	0532	0925	1.1F
	1142	1406	1.4E
	1735	1942	1.2F
	2356		
16 Tu ○		0250	1.6E
	0622	1009	1.1F
	1232	1454	1.4E
	1825	2033	1.2F
17 W	0044	0327	1.6E
	0710	1043	1.0F
	1319	1538	1.4E
	1914	2121	1.2F
18 Th	0130	0404	1.6E
	0757	1015	1.0F
	1405	1620	1.4E
	2003	2208	1.2F
19 F	0215	0444	1.6E
	0842	1051	1.1F
	1449	1703	1.4E
	2051	2254	1.1F
20 Sa	0258	0526	1.5E
	0926	1131	1.1F
	1532	1747	1.4E
	2139	2340	1.1F
21 Su	0341	0609	1.5E
	1010	1212	1.1F
	1616	1832	1.3E
	2227		
22 M		0026	1.1F
	0425	0653	1.4E
	1054	1254	1.1F
	1659	1918	1.3E
	2315		
23 Tu		0112	1.0F
	0510	0739	1.4E
	1138	1337	1.1F
	1742	2004	1.3E
24 W ◐	0004	0158	1.0F
	0557	0825	1.3E
	1222	1421	1.0F
	1825	2051	1.3E
25 Th	0053	0246	0.9F
	0646	0913	1.3E
	1307	1507	1.0F
	1908	2140	1.3E
26 F	0143	0336	0.9F
	0737	1003	1.3E
	1352	1555	1.0F
	1954	2230	1.4E
27 Sa	0233	0428	0.9F
	0830	1054	1.3E
	1439	1644	1.1F
	2041	2321	1.4E
28 Su	0324	0519	0.9F
	0923	1145	1.3E
	1526	1734	1.1F
	2130		
29 M		0012	1.5E
	0414	0610	1.0F
	1015	1237	1.4E
	1614	1824	1.2F
	2221		
30 Tu		0105	1.6E
	0503	0701	1.1F
	1107	1329	1.4E
	1702	1914	1.3F
	2312		
31 W ●		0157	1.7E
	0551	0753	1.1F
	1157	1421	1.5E
	1752	2006	1.3F

August

Day	Slack (h m)	Maximum (h m)	knots
1 Th	0004	0249	1.8E
	0640	0844	1.2F
	1247	1512	1.6E
	1843	2058	1.4F
2 F	0056	0339	1.9E
	0729	0934	1.3F
	1337	1603	1.7E
	1935	2150	1.4F
3 Sa	0149	0430	1.9E
	0819	1025	1.3F
	1427	1654	1.7E
	2030	2243	1.4F
4 Su	0243	0522	1.9E
	0909	1116	1.3F
	1518	1747	1.7E
	2126	2337	1.4F
5 M	0338	0615	1.8E
	1000	1207	1.3F
	1611	1841	1.7E
	2224		
6 Tu		0031	1.3F
	0436	0708	1.7E
	1053	1258	1.3F
	1706	1935	1.6E
	2323		
7 W ◑		0126	1.2F
	0536	0802	1.6E
	1147	1349	1.2F
	1803	2031	1.6E
8 Th	0023	0222	1.1F
	0636	0857	1.5E
	1242	1442	1.2F
	1900	2128	1.5E
9 F	0124	0321	1.0F
	0737	0955	1.4E
	1337	1537	1.1F
	1958	2228	1.5E
10 Sa	0224	0426	0.9F
	0836	1053	1.3E
	1433	1634	1.1F
	2055	2331	1.5E
11 Su	0322	0557	0.9F
	0933	1151	1.3E
	1529	1731	1.1F
	2150		
12 M		0139	1.5E
	0417	0816	1.0F
	1026	1249	1.3E
	1622	1826	1.1F
	2243		
13 Tu		0234	1.5E
	0509	0905	1.0F
	1117	1343	1.3E
	1713	1919	1.1F
	2332		
14 W		0319	1.5E
	0557	0946	1.0F
	1205	1430	1.4E
	1802	2010	1.1F
15 Th ○	0020	0301	1.5E
	0643	0918	1.0F
	1251	1512	1.4E
	1851	2058	1.1F
16 F	0105	0335	1.5E
	0727	0940	1.0F
	1334	1552	1.4E
	1938	2143	1.1F
17 Sa	0148	0413	1.5E
	0810	1016	1.1F
	1416	1633	1.4E
	2024	2227	1.1F
18 Su	0229	0454	1.5E
	0852	1055	1.1F
	1457	1715	1.4E
	2109	2312	1.1F
19 M	0310	0536	1.5E
	0934	1136	1.1F
	1536	1759	1.4E
	2155	2356	1.1F
20 Tu	0352	0621	1.5E
	1016	1218	1.1F
	1615	1844	1.4E
	2241		
21 W		0041	1.1F
	0435	0706	1.4E
	1058	1301	1.1F
	1654	1930	1.4E
	2328		
22 Th		0127	1.0F
	0521	0753	1.4E
	1141	1346	1.1F
	1735	2017	1.4E
23 F ○	0016	0214	1.0F
	0610	0842	1.3E
	1226	1432	1.1F
	1818	2107	1.4E
24 Sa	0106	0304	1.0F
	0702	0932	1.3E
	1313	1521	1.1F
	1907	2158	1.4E
25 Su	0158	0356	1.0F
	0757	1024	1.3E
	1403	1612	1.1F
	2002	2251	1.5E
26 M	0252	0449	1.0F
	0853	1117	1.3E
	1455	1704	1.1F
	2100	2345	1.5E
27 Tu	0345	0542	1.0F
	0949	1211	1.4E
	1548	1757	1.2F
	2158		
28 W		0039	1.6E
	0436	0635	1.1F
	1043	1305	1.5E
	1641	1851	1.3F
	2254		
29 Th		0134	1.7E
	0527	0728	1.1F
	1135	1359	1.6E
	1734	1945	1.3F
	2349		
30 F ●		0227	1.8E
	0616	0820	1.2F
	1226	1452	1.7E
	1827	2039	1.4F
31 Sa	0044	0319	1.8E
	0706	0912	1.3F
	1316	1543	1.7E
	1921	2132	1.4F

September

Day	Slack (h m)	Maximum (h m)	knots
1 Su	0137	0410	1.9E
	0727	0940	1.3F
	1406	1634	1.8E
	2016	2226	1.4F
2 M	0231	0502	1.8E
	0845	1052	1.3F
	1456	1726	1.8E
	2111	2320	1.3F
3 Tu	0325	0554	1.7E
	0936	1143	1.3F
	1548	1819	1.7E
	2208		
4 W		0014	1.3F
	0421	0646	1.6E
	1029	1233	1.3F
	1641	1913	1.7E
	2305		
5 Th ○		0108	1.2F
	0519	0740	1.5E
	1122	1324	1.2F
	1737	2008	1.6E
6 F	0004	0203	1.1F
	0617	0834	1.4E
	1217	1416	1.1F
	1835	2104	1.5E
7 Sa	0102	0300	1.0F
	0715	0930	1.3E
	1313	1511	1.1F
	1932	2203	1.4E
8 Su	0200	0404	0.9F
		0513	0.9F
		0555	0.9F
	0812	1028	1.2E
	1409	1608†	1.0F
9 M	0257	0657	0.9F
	0907	1126	1.2E
	1505	1705	1.0F
	2125		
10 Tu		0121	1.4E
	0351	0750	0.9F
	1000	1223	1.2E
	1559	1801	1.0F
	2217		
11 W		0213	1.4E
	0441	0836	1.0F
	1049	1316	1.3E
	1650	1854	1.0F
	2306		
12 Th		0256	1.4E
	0527	0911	1.0F
	1136	1400	1.3E
	1739	1945	1.0F
	2352		
13 F ○		0224	1.4E
	0612	0826	1.0F
	1220	1441	1.4E
	1826	2031	1.1F
14 Sa	0036	0302	1.5E
	0654	0902	1.1F
	1301	1521	1.4E
	1911	2116	1.1F
15 Su	0119	0341	1.5E
	0736	0940	1.1F
	1341	1602	1.5E
	1956	2159	1.1F
16 M	0200	0422	1.5E
	0817	1019	1.1F
	1419	1643	1.5E
	2039	2242	1.1F
17 Tu	0240	0505	1.5E
	0857	1100	1.2F
	1455	1727	1.5E
	2123	2326	1.1F
18 W	0321	0549	1.5E
	0937	1143	1.2F
	1530	1812	1.5E
	2207		
19 Th		0011	1.1F
	0403	0635	1.4E
	1018	1227	1.2F
	1606	1858	1.5E
	2253		
20 F		0057	1.1F
	0448	0723	1.4E
	1101	1312	1.2F
	1645	1946	1.5E
	2341		
21 Sa ○		0145	1.1F
	0538	0812	1.4E
	1148	1400	1.1F
	1732	2037	1.5E
22 Su	0033	0234	1.0F
	0632	0904	1.3E
	1238	1450	1.1F
	1828	2130	1.5E
23 M	0126	0326	1.0F
	0729	0957	1.3E
	1332	1543	1.1F
	1931	2224	1.5E
24 Tu	0222	0421	1.0F
	0827	1052	1.3E
	1429	1638	1.1F
	2036	2320	1.6E
25 W	0317	0516	1.0F
	0924	1147	1.4E
	1527	1734	1.2F
	2139		
26 Th		0016	1.6E
	0410	0610	1.1F
	1020	1243	1.5E
	1623	1830	1.2F
	2238		
27 F		0112	1.7E
	0502	0704	1.2F
	1113	1338	1.6E
	1718	1926	1.3F
	2335		
28 Sa ●		0206	1.7E
	0552	0757	1.3F
	1204	1432	1.7E
	1813	2021	1.3F
29 Su	0030	0259	1.8E
	0642	0849	1.3F
	1255	1524	1.8E
	1907	2116	1.3F
30 M	0124	0351	1.8E
	0731	0939	1.3F
	1344	1615	1.8E
	2001	2210	1.3F

Time meridian 75° W. 0000 is midnight. 1200 is noon. Times are not adjusted for Daylight Saving Time.
If three consecutive entries are marked (F) the middle one is not a true maximum but an intermediate value to show the current pattern.
† See page 196 for the remaining currents on this day.

Portsmouth Harbor Entrance, N.H., 2019

F–Flood, Dir. 342° True   E–Ebb, Dir. 194° True

October

Day	Slack	Maximum	knots		Day	Slack	Maximum	knots
1 Tu	0217	0441	1.7E		16 W	0210	0434	1.5E
	0821	1029	1.3F			0819	1026	1.2F
	1434	1706	1.8E			1414	1656	1.6E
	2055	2303	1.3F			2052	2257	1.2F
2 W	0310	0532	1.6E		17 Th	0252	0519	1.5E
	0912	1119	1.3F			0859	1110	1.2F
	1525	1758	1.7E			1448	1741	1.6E
	2151	2357	1.2F			2136	2342	1.2F
3 Th	0404	0624	1.5E		18 F	0334	0606	1.4E
	1004	1209	1.3F			0940	1155	1.2F
	1617	1851	1.7E			1525	1829	1.6E
	2246					2222		
4 F		0050	1.1F		19 Sa		0029	1.1F
	0500	0717	1.4E			0420	0655	1.4E
	1058	1300	1.2F			1025	1242	1.2F
	1712	1944	1.6E			1607	1919	1.6E
	2343					2311		
5 Sa		0144	1.0F		20 Su		0117	1.1F
	0555	0810	1.3E			0511	0745	1.4E
	1153	1351	1.1F			1114	1331	1.2F
	1809	2039	1.5E			1659	2010	1.6E
6 Su	0039	0238	0.9F		21 M	0003	0207	1.1F
	0651	0905	1.3E			0606	0837	1.4E
	1249	1444	1.0F			1209	1423	1.2F
	1905	2135	1.4E			1801	2104	1.6E
7 M	0134	0337	0.9F		22 Tu	0057	0259	1.1F
	0746	1001	1.2E			0704	0932	1.4E
	1345	1540	1.0F			1307	1517	1.2F
	2001	2233	1.3E			1909	2159	1.6E
8 Tu	0228	0457	0.8F		23 W	0153	0354	1.1F
	0839	1057	1.2E			0803	1028	1.4E
	1441	1638	0.9F			1408	1614	1.1F
	2056	2357	1.3E			2016	2256	1.6E
9 W	0320	0557	0.9F		24 Th	0249	0450	1.1F
	0930	1151	1.2E			0901	1125	1.5E
	1535	1734	0.9F			1508	1712	1.2F
	2148					2121	2353	1.6E
10 Th		0018	1.3E		25 F	0344	0546	1.1F
		0101	1.3E			0957	1221	1.5E
		0143	1.3E			1607	1810	1.2F
	0409	0657	0.9F			2222		
	1018	1240†	1.3E					
11 F		0102	1.3E		26 Sa		0050	1.6E
	0454	0702	1.0F			0436	0640	1.2F
	1103	1325	1.3E			1051	1317	1.6E
	1714	1915	1.0F			1703	1908	1.2F
	2322					2319		
12 Sa		0145	1.4E		27 Su		0145	1.7E
	0537	0742	1.0F			0527	0733	1.3F
	1146	1407	1.4E			1143	1413	1.7E
	1759	2002	1.0F		●	1758	2005	1.2F
13 Su ○	0006	0226	1.4E		28 M	0015	0239	1.7E
	0619	0822	1.1F			0617	0825	1.3F
	1226	1449	1.5E			1233	1506	1.8E
	1844	2046	1.1F			1852	2101	1.3F
14 M	0048	0308	1.5E		29 Tu	0109	0331	1.7E
	0659	0903	1.1F			0707	0915	1.3F
	1304	1530	1.5E			1323	1556	1.8E
	1926	2129	1.1F			1946	2156	1.2F
15 Tu	0130	0351	1.5E		30 W	0201	0421	1.6E
	0739	0944	1.2F			0758	1005	1.3F
	1340	1612	1.6E			1413	1647	1.8E
	2009	2212	1.1F			2039	2248	1.2F
					31 Th	0253	0511	1.6E
						0849	1055	1.3F
						1503	1737	1.7E
						2132	2341	1.1F

November

Day	Slack	Maximum	knots		Day	Slack	Maximum	knots
1 F	0345	0602	1.5E		16 Sa	0308	0539	1.5E
	0941	1145	1.2F			0907	1126	1.3F
	1554	1829	1.7E			1456	1803	1.7E
	2226					2154		
2 Sa		0033	1.1F		17 Su		0002	1.2F
	0438	0653	1.4E			0355	0629	1.5E
	1034	1236	1.2F			0954	1215	1.3F
	1647	1920	1.5E			1543	1853	1.7E
	2319					2244		
3 Su		0123	1.0F		18 M		0051	1.2F
	0531	0745	1.3E			0446	0720	1.4E
	1129	1327	1.1F			1048	1306	1.3F
	1742	2012	1.4E			1639	1946	1.7E
						2336		
4 M ◐	0012	0213	0.9F		19 Tu ◐		0142	1.2F
	0624	0837	1.2E			0542	0813	1.4E
	1224	1419	1.0F			1146	1358	1.2F
	1836	2104	1.4E			1743	2040	1.6E
5 Tu	0105	0305	0.9F		20 W	0031	0234	1.1F
	0717	0930	1.2E			0640	0908	1.4E
	1320	1512	0.9F			1246	1454	1.2F
	1930	2156	1.3E			1851	2136	1.6E
6 W	0156	0358	0.9F		21 Th	0126	0329	1.1F
	0808	1023	1.2E			0739	1005	1.5E
	1414	1608	0.9F			1349	1552	1.1F
	2023	2246	1.3E			1958	2233	1.6E
7 Th	0245	0449	0.9F		22 F	0222	0425	1.1F
	0857	1114	1.2E			0838	1103	1.5E
	1508	1703	0.9F			1450	1651	1.1F
	2114	2334	1.2E			2103	2330	1.6E
8 F	0333	0536	0.9F		23 Sa	0317	0521	1.2F
	0944	1202	1.2E			0934	1200	1.6E
	1558	1754	0.9F			1550	1751	1.1F
	2203					2204		
9 Sa		0021	1.3E		24 Su		0027	1.6E
	0418	0619	1.0F			0411	0615	1.2F
	1028	1247	1.3E			1029	1258	1.7E
	1646	1843	0.9F			1648	1851	1.1F
	2249					2302		
10 Su		0106	1.3E		25 M		0124	1.6E
	0501	0702	1.0F			0503	0709	1.3F
	1110	1331	1.4E			1121	1354	1.7E
	1731	1929	1.0F			1743	1951	1.2F
	2334					2358		
11 M		0151	1.4E		26 Tu ●		0219	1.6E
	0542	0744	1.1F			0554	0801	1.3F
	1149	1415	1.5E			1213	1448	1.8E
	1814	2014	1.0F			1836	2049	1.2F
12 Tu ○	0017	0236	1.4E		27 W	0051	0311	1.6E
	0623	0827	1.2F			0645	0853	1.3F
	1226	1459	1.6E			1303	1539	1.8E
	1857	2059	1.1F			1929	2144	1.2F
13 W	0059	0320	1.4E		28 Th	0143	0401	1.5E
	0702	0910	1.2F			0735	0943	1.3F
	1302	1542	1.7E			1353	1628	1.7E
	1939	2143	1.1F			2021	2235	1.1F
14 Th	0142	0405	1.5E		29 F	0234	0449	1.5E
	0742	0954	1.3F			0826	1032	1.3F
	1338	1627	1.7E			1442	1717	1.7E
	2022	2228	1.2F			2112	2325	1.1F
15 F	0224	0451	1.5E		30 Sa	0324	0539	1.4E
	0823	1039	1.3F			0918	1122	1.2F
	1415	1714	1.7E			1532	1805	1.6E
	2107	2314	1.2F			2203		

December

Day	Slack	Maximum	knots		Day	Slack	Maximum	knots
1 Su		0013	1.1F		16 M	0332	0604	1.5E
	0414	0628	1.3E			0931	1151	1.3F
	1010	1212	1.1F			1529	1830	1.8E
	1622	1854	1.5E			2219		
	2253							
2 M		0059	1.0F		17 Tu		0027	1.2F
	0504	0718	1.3E			0424	0657	1.5E
	1104	1302	1.1F			1027	1243	1.3F
	1713	1942	1.4E			1626	1923	1.7E
	2343					2311		
3 Tu		0145	1.0F		18 W ○		0118	1.2F
	0554	0807	1.2E			0519	0750	1.5E
	1158	1352	1.0F			1126	1337	1.3F
	1805	2030	1.4E			1730	2017	1.7E
4 W ◐	0032	0231	0.9F		19 Th ◐		0210	1.2F
	0644	0857	1.2E			0617	0845	1.5E
	1251	1443	0.9F			1228	1432	1.2F
	1856	2118	1.3E			1836	2113	1.6E
5 Th	0121	0318	0.9F		20 F	0100	0303	1.2F
	0733	0946	1.2E			0715	0942	1.5E
	1345	1536	0.9F			1330	1530	1.1F
	1947	2207	1.2E			1941	2210	1.6E
6 F	0208	0406	0.9F		21 Sa	0156	0359	1.2F
	0820	1035	1.2E			0814	1041	1.5E
	1437	1629	0.8F			1432	1631	1.1F
	2038	2255	1.2E			2045	2308	1.5E
7 Sa	0255	0454	1.0F		22 Su	0252	0455	1.2F
	0906	1123	1.2E			0911	1139	1.6E
	1527	1720	0.9F			1533	1733	1.0F
	2127	2342	1.2E			2146		
8 Su	0340	0539	1.0F		23 M		0005	1.5E
	0950	1210	1.3E			0347	0551	1.2F
	1615	1808	0.9F			1007	1238	1.6E
	2215					1631	1836	1.0F
						2244		
9 M		0030	1.3E		24 Tu		0103	1.5E
	0424	0623	1.1F			0440	0645	1.2F
	1032	1256	1.4E			1101	1337	1.7E
	1700	1855	1.0F			1726	1939	1.1F
	2301					2339		
10 Tu		0117	1.3E		25 W		0159	1.5E
	0506	0708	1.1F			0532	0738	1.2F
	1111	1342	1.5E			1153	1433	1.7E
	1744	1942	1.0F			1819	2045	1.1F
	2346							
11 W		0204	1.4E		26 Th ●	0032	0252	1.5E
	0546	0753	1.2F			0623	0831	1.3F
	1150	1429	1.6E			1243	1523	1.7E
	1827	2028	1.1F			1910	2141	1.1F
12 Th ○	0030	0251	1.4E		27 F	0122	0341	1.5E
	0627	0838	1.2F			0714	0922	1.2F
	1228	1515	1.7E			1333	1610	1.7E
	1911	2114	1.1F			2000	2224	1.1F
13 F	0114	0337	1.5E		28 Sa	0211	0428	1.4E
	0709	0924	1.3F			0804	1011	1.2F
	1308	1601	1.8E			1421	1655	1.7E
	1955	2201	1.2F			2049	2305	1.1F
14 Sa	0158	0425	1.5E		29 Su	0259	0514	1.4E
	0753	1012	1.3F			0855	1100	1.2F
	1351	1649	1.8E			1508	1740	1.6E
	2041	2248	1.2F			2137	2347	1.1F
15 Su	0244	0514	1.5E		30 M	0346	0601	1.4E
	0840	1100	1.4F			0946	1148	1.1F
	1437	1739	1.8E			1555	1825	1.5E
	2129	2337	1.2F			2224		
					31 Tu		0030	1.0F
						0433	0648	1.3E
						1037	1237	1.1F
						1643	1910	1.4E
						2311		

Time meridian 75° W. 0000 is midnight. 1200 is noon. Times are not adjusted for Daylight Saving Time.
If three consecutive entries are marked (F) the middle one is not a true maximum but an intermediate value to show the current pattern.
† See page 196 for the remaining currents on this day.

Boston Harbor (Deer Island Light), Massachusetts, 2019

F–Flood, Dir. 264° True   E–Ebb, Dir. 112° True

January

Day	Slack (h m)	Maximum (h m)	knots
1 Tu	0102	0355	1.3F
	0649	1127	1.4E
	1342	1640	1.3F
	1921	2348	1.2E
2 W	0157	0500	1.3F
	0744	1221	1.5E
	1441	1737	1.3F
	2018		
3 Th		0038	1.2E
	0251	0552	1.3F
	0838	1312	1.5E
	1537	1828	1.4F
	2115		
4 F		0128	1.2E
	0344	0640	1.3F
	0931	1406	1.5E
	1629	1918	1.4F
	2207		
5 Sa ●		0221	1.2E
	0433	0730	1.3F
	1019	1457	1.4E
	1716	2011	1.4F
	2253		
6 Su		0309	1.1E
	0519	0821	1.3F
	1102	1542	1.4E
	1800	2100	1.4F
	2335		
7 M		0348	1.1E
	0603	0907	1.3F
	1143	1619	1.3E
	1842	2142	1.3F
8 Tu	0016	0418	1.1E
	0646	0942	1.3F
	1224	1648	1.2E
	1921	2217	1.3F
9 W	0058	0441	1.1E
	0729	1004	1.2F
	1306	1708	1.1E
	1959	2240	1.2F
10 Th	0141	0510	1.1E
	0811	1025	1.1F
	1349	1730	1.1E
	2036	2254	1.1F
11 F	0224	0551	1.1E
	0853	1057	1.1F
	1433	1808	1.0E
	2114	2324	1.1F
12 Sa	0308	0642	1.0E
	0937	1140	1.0F
	1519	1854	1.0E
	2155		
13 Su		0007	1.0F
	0353	0729	1.0E
	1026	1233	0.9F
	1607	1938	1.0E
	2242		
14 M ◑		0057	1.0F
	0442	0813	1.0E
	1121	1327	0.9F
	1701	2021	0.9E
	2335		
15 Tu		0146	1.0F
	0533	0902	1.0E
	1216	1419	0.9F
	1757	2111	0.9E
16 W	0028	0234	1.0F
	0621	1014	1.0E
	1309	1513	1.0F
	1850	2222	0.9E
17 Th	0119	0326	1.1F
	0707	1124	1.1E
	1402	1617	1.0F
	1942	2328	1.0E
18 F	0210	0424	1.2F
	0754	1213	1.2E
	1456	1719	1.2F
	2036		
19 Sa		0018	1.1E
	0304	0520	1.3F
	0844	1303	1.3E
	1550	1810	1.3F
	2131		
20 Su		0111	1.1E
	0357	0612	1.4F
	0937	1402	1.4E
	1642	1900	1.4F
	2223		
21 M ○		0215	1.2E
	0450	0704	1.5F
	1028	1501	1.5E
	1731	1954	1.5F
	2311		
22 Tu		0315	1.3E
	0541	0800	1.6F
	1117	1549	1.6E
	1821	2048	1.6F
	2359		
23 W		0404	1.4E
	0633	0856	1.7F
	1207	1634	1.6E
	1910	2135	1.7F
24 Th	0047	0452	1.4E
	0727	0946	1.7F
	1300	1723	1.5E
	2000	2219	1.7F
25 F	0138	0547	1.4E
	0821	1035	1.6F
	1355	1820	1.4E
	2050	2306	1.6F
26 Sa	0230	0651	1.4E
	0915	1130	1.5F
	1452	1918	1.3E
	2141		
27 Su ☾		0002	1.4F
	0323	0749	1.3E
	1014	1243	1.3F
	1550	2011	1.2E
	2236		
28 M		0113	1.3F
	0420	0848	1.3E
	1117	1402	1.2F
	1654	2110	1.1E
	2336		
29 Tu		0221	1.2F
	0522	0959	1.3E
	1222	1512	1.2F
	1800	2224	1.0E
30 W	0035	0329	1.2F
	0622	1107	1.3E
	1323	1620	1.2F
	1900	2326	1.0E
31 Th	0131	0438	1.2F
	0718	1202	1.4E
	1421	1719	1.2F
	1956		

February

Day	Slack (h m)	Maximum (h m)	knots
1 F		0017	1.1E
	0225	0533	1.2F
	0811	1251	1.4E
	1515	1810	1.3F
	2052		
2 Sa		0104	1.1E
	0318	0621	1.2F
	0904	1340	1.4E
	1606	1858	1.3F
	2144		
3 Su		0152	1.1E
	0408	0708	1.2F
	0953	1430	1.3E
	1650	1947	1.3F
	2229		
4 M ●		0240	1.1E
	0454	0758	1.2F
	1037	1513	1.3E
	1731	2035	1.3F
	2310		
5 Tu		0320	1.1E
	0537	0845	1.2F
	1118	1547	1.3E
	1809	2117	1.3F
	2349		
6 W		0349	1.2E
	0619	0921	1.2F
	1157	1610	1.2E
	1846	2149	1.3F
7 Th	0028	0413	1.2E
	0701	0941	1.2F
	1237	1626	1.2E
	1923	2202	1.3F
8 F	0108	0441	1.2E
	0742	0959	1.2F
	1318	1649	1.1E
	1959	2216	1.3F
9 Sa	0149	0517	1.2E
	0823	1029	1.2F
	1400	1724	1.1E
	2037	2247	1.2F
10 Su	0230	0604	1.1E
	0905	1108	1.1F
	1444	1812	1.0E
	2117	2327	1.2F
11 M	0312	0656	1.0E
	0951	1156	1.0F
	1531	1904	1.0E
	2202		
12 Tu ☾		0015	1.1F
	0356	0744	1.0E
	1044	1252	1.0F
	1624	1952	1.0E
	2254		
13 W		0109	1.1F
	0446	0832	1.0E
	1142	1348	1.0F
	1722	2040	0.9E
	2351		
14 Th		0201	1.1F
	0539	0934	1.0E
	1240	1444	1.0F
	1821	2147	0.9E
15 F	0048	0254	1.1F
	0632	1100	1.1E
	1336	1547	1.1F
	1917	2309	0.9E
16 Sa	0144	0354	1.2F
	0724	1158	1.2E
	1432	1658	1.2F
	2013		
17 Su		0007	1.1E
	0240	0458	1.3F
	0818	1248	1.3E
	1528	1755	1.3F
	2110		
18 M		0101	1.1E
	0337	0555	1.4F
	0915	1345	1.4E
	1621	1845	1.5F
	2204		
19 Tu ○		0204	1.3E
	0433	0650	1.5F
	1011	1444	1.5E
	1711	1939	1.6F
	2254		
20 W		0304	1.4E
	0526	0748	1.6F
	1103	1535	1.6E
	1800	2033	1.7F
	2340		
21 Th		0355	1.5E
	0619	0847	1.7F
	1154	1620	1.6E
	1849	2121	1.7F
22 F	0027	0442	1.5E
	0712	0938	1.7F
	1246	1706	1.5E
	1938	2204	1.7F
23 Sa	0116	0534	1.5E
	0805	1026	1.6F
	1339	1758	1.4E
	2026	2247	1.6F
24 Su	0207	0635	1.4E
	0859	1118	1.5F
	1434	1856	1.3E
	2116	2337	1.4F
25 M	0258	0734	1.4E
	0955	1229	1.3F
	1529	1949	1.1E
	2208		
26 Tu ☽		0044	1.3F
	0352	0830	1.3E
	1056	1348	1.2F
	1629	2043	1.0E
	2306		
27 W		0158	1.1F
	0452	0934	1.2E
	1200	1453	1.1F
	1735	2152	0.9E
28 Th	0006	0304	1.1F
	0554	1043	1.2E
	1301	1558	1.1F
	1837	2301	0.9E

March

Day	Slack (h m)	Maximum (h m)	knots
1 F	0104	0414	1.0F
	0651	1139	1.2E
	1356	1658	1.1F
	1932	2353	1.0E
2 Sa	0159	0513	1.1F
	0743	1226	1.3E
	1448	1749	1.2F
	2024		
3 Su		0037	1.0E
	0251	0601	1.1F
	0834	1310	1.2E
	1536	1834	1.2F
	2115		
4 M		0119	1.0E
	0342	0646	1.1F
	0924	1354	1.2E
	1619	1920	1.3F
	2201		
5 Tu		0202	1.1E
	0428	0731	1.1F
	1009	1435	1.2E
	1657	2005	1.3F
	2242		
6 W ●		0243	1.1E
	0510	0816	1.2F
	1050	1508	1.2E
	1734	2046	1.3F
	2320		
7 Th		0317	1.2E
	0551	0853	1.2F
	1129	1529	1.2E
	1810	2114	1.3F
	2357		
8 F		0345	1.2E
	0631	0911	1.2F
	1207	1551	1.2E
	1846	2121	1.3F
9 Sa	0034	0415	1.3E
	0712	0931	1.3F
	1246	1619	1.2E
	1924	2143	1.4F
10 Su	0113	0449	1.2E
	0753	1003	1.3F
	1328	1652	1.2E
	2003	2216	1.4F
11 M	0151	0530	1.2E
	0836	1041	1.3F
	1412	1735	1.1E
	2044	2255	1.3F
12 Tu	0232	0623	1.1E
	0921	1126	1.2F
	1459	1832	1.0E
	2128	2342	1.3F
13 W	0315	0718	1.1E
	1013	1221	1.1F
	1552	1928	1.0E
	2220		
14 Th ☽		0036	1.2F
	0404	0809	1.1E
	1112	1321	1.1F
	1652	2020	0.9E
	2319		
15 F		0133	1.2F
	0501	0907	1.1E
	1214	1420	1.1F
	1756	2123	0.9E
16 Sa	0022	0229	1.2F
	0601	1036	1.1E
	1313	1523	1.1F
	1856	2253	1.0E
17 Su	0121	0330	1.2F
	0700	1142	1.3E
	1409	1639	1.2F
	1952	2357	1.1E
18 M	0220	0440	1.3F
	0758	1233	1.4E
	1505	1741	1.4F
	2049		
19 Tu		0051	1.2E
	0320	0544	1.4F
	0858	1326	1.5E
	1559	1830	1.5F
	2143		
20 W ○		0150	1.4E
	0417	0641	1.5F
	0957	1425	1.5E
	1649	1922	1.6F
	2234		
21 Th		0251	1.5E
	0511	0740	1.6F
	1050	1518	1.6E
	1738	2016	1.7F
	2320		
22 F		0343	1.6E
	0604	0840	1.7F
	1140	1604	1.6E
	1827	2106	1.7F
23 Sa	0006	0430	1.6E
	0657	0932	1.7F
	1230	1648	1.5E
	1915	2148	1.7F
24 Su	0054	0520	1.6E
	0749	1018	1.6F
	1322	1736	1.3E
	2003	2229	1.6F
25 M	0143	0618	1.5E
	0841	1107	1.4F
	1414	1832	1.2E
	2051	2313	1.4F
26 Tu	0233	0716	1.4E
	0934	1214	1.2F
	1508	1927	1.0E
	2141		
27 W ☽		0012	1.2F
	0325	0810	1.3E
	1031	1330	1.1F
	1604	2017	0.9E
	2236		
28 Th		0134	1.1F
	0421	0906	1.2E
	1133	1432	1.0F
	1707	2114	0.8E
	2336		
29 F		0240	1.0F
	0522	1012	1.1E
	1233	1533	1.0F
	1809	2227	0.8E
30 Sa	0036	0347	0.9F
	0621	1111	1.1E
	1326	1632	1.1F
	1904	2326	0.9E
31 Su	0131	0449	1.0F
	0713	1157	1.1E
	1414	1724	1.1F
	1953		

Boston Harbor (Deer Island Light), Massachusetts, 2019

F–Flood, Dir. 264° True   E–Ebb, Dir. 112° True

April

Day	Slack h m	Max h m	knots
1 M		0007	1.0E
	0222	0539	1.0F
	0802	1236	1.1E
	1459	1808	1.2F
	2040		
2 Tu		0044	1.0E
	0311	0622	1.1F
	0851	1310	1.1E
	1541	1850	1.2F
	2127		
3 W		0118	1.1E
	0358	0702	1.1F
	0938	1339	1.1E
	1620	1929	1.2F
	2209		
4 Th		0156	1.1E
	0441	0740	1.1F
	1020	1409	1.1E
	1657	2004	1.2F
	2248		
5 F ●		0239	1.2E
	0521	0811	1.2F
	1100	1443	1.2E
	1734	2017	1.3F
	2325		
6 Sa		0316	1.3E
	0602	0832	1.2F
	1138	1518	1.2E
	1812	2038	1.3F
7 Su	0001	0351	1.3E
	0642	0903	1.3F
	1217	1552	1.2E
	1851	2112	1.4F
8 M	0036	0425	1.3E
	0725	0939	1.4F
	1258	1628	1.2E
	1932	2149	1.5F
9 Tu	0114	0503	1.2E
	0809	1018	1.4F
	1344	1709	1.1E
	2015	2229	1.5F
10 W	0155	0553	1.2E
	0856	1102	1.3F
	1433	1805	1.0E
	2102	2315	1.4F
11 Th	0240	0655	1.1E
	0948	1155	1.2F
	1527	1908	1.0E
	2153		
12 F ◐		0009	1.3F
	0332	0751	1.1E
	1046	1257	1.2F
	1626	2005	0.9E
	2254		
13 Sa		0109	1.2F
	0432	0849	1.1E
	1149	1359	1.2F
	1731	2108	0.9E
	2359		
14 Su		0209	1.2F
	0537	1010	1.2E
	1249	1502	1.2F
	1833	2238	1.0E
15 M	0102	0312	1.2F
	0641	1123	1.3E
	1346	1618	1.3F
	1930	2344	1.2E
16 Tu	0203	0428	1.3F
	0741	1216	1.4E
	1441	1724	1.4F
	2025		
17 W		0038	1.3F
	0303	0538	1.4F
	0842	1307	1.5E
	1535	1814	1.5F
	2120		
18 Th		0135	1.5F
	0401	0635	1.5F
	0941	1403	1.5E
	1627	1904	1.6F
	2212		
19 F ○		0235	1.6F
	0456	0732	1.6F
	1036	1459	1.5E
	1716	1957	1.7F
	2300		
20 Sa		0329	1.6F
	0548	0832	1.6F
	1125	1547	1.5E
	1804	2049	1.7F
	2346		
21 Su		0417	1.6F
	0640	0924	1.6F
	1213	1631	1.4E
	1852	2134	1.6F
22 M	0032	0506	1.6E
	0732	1010	1.5F
	1303	1716	1.3E
	1940	2213	1.5F
23 Tu	0120	0559	1.5E
	0823	1056	1.4F
	1354	1807	1.1E
	2027	2252	1.4F
24 W	0209	0655	1.3E
	0913	1155	1.2F
	1445	1902	1.0E
	2115	2340	1.2F
25 Th	0258	0746	1.2E
	1004	1307	1.1F
	1538	1949	0.9E
	2206		
26 F ◑		0104	1.0F
	0351	0834	1.1E
	1100	1407	1.0F
	1636	2034	0.8E
	2304		
27 Sa		0214	0.9F
	0448	0928	1.0E
	1157	1504	1.0F
	1735	2131	0.8E
28 Su	0004	0316	0.9F
	0547	1030	1.0E
	1248	1601	1.0F
	1830	2243	0.8E
29 M	0059	0418	0.9F
	0640	1120	1.0E
	1334	1654	1.0F
	1918	2331	0.9E
30 Tu	0150	0511	0.9F
	0729	1156	1.0E
	1416	1739	1.1F
	2004		

May

Day	Slack h m	Max h m	knots
1 W		0007	1.0E
	0238	0554	1.0F
	0816	1221	1.0E
	1458	1817	1.1F
	2049		
2 Th		0038	1.1E
	0324	0630	1.0F
	0902	1242	1.1E
	1540	1847	1.1F
	2133		
3 F		0113	1.1E
	0409	0658	1.1F
	0947	1314	1.1E
	1620	1856	1.2F
	2214		
4 Sa ●		0158	1.2E
	0451	0718	1.1F
	1030	1358	1.1E
	1700	1920	1.3F
	2252		
5 Su		0246	1.2E
	0533	0753	1.2F
	1110	1447	1.2E
	1740	1959	1.4F
	2327		
6 M		0328	1.3E
	0615	0835	1.3F
	1151	1530	1.2E
	1822	2041	1.4F
7 Tu	0003	0406	1.3E
	0700	0916	1.4F
	1233	1610	1.2E
	1905	2124	1.5F
8 W	0042	0444	1.3E
	0746	0958	1.5F
	1320	1652	1.1E
	1952	2207	1.5F
9 Th	0125	0532	1.3E
	0835	1042	1.4F
	1411	1746	1.1E
	2040	2253	1.5F
10 F	0214	0636	1.2E
	0926	1133	1.3F
	1505	1854	1.0E
	2133	2346	1.4F
11 Sa ◐	0309	0736	1.2E
	1022	1234	1.3F
	1603	1954	1.0E
	2233		
12 Su		0048	1.3F
	0410	0832	1.2E
	1123	1338	1.2F
	1706	2055	1.0E
	2340		
13 M		0152	1.3F
	0518	0943	1.2E
	1224	1441	1.3F
	1808	2219	1.1E
14 Tu	0045	0258	1.3F
	0624	1101	1.3E
	1321	1553	1.3F
	1906	2329	1.3E
15 W	0146	0420	1.3F
	0725	1157	1.4E
	1416	1704	1.4F
	2001		
16 Th		0024	1.4E
	0246	0532	1.4F
	0825	1248	1.4E
	1511	1757	1.5F
	2056		
17 F		0119	1.5E
	0344	0627	1.5F
	0925	1342	1.4E
	1604	1846	1.6F
	2150		
18 Sa ○		0218	1.6E
	0440	0722	1.5F
	1020	1439	1.4E
	1654	1938	1.6F
	2240		
19 Su		0314	1.6E
	0532	0820	1.6F
	1110	1530	1.4E
	1742	2033	1.6F
	2326		
20 M		0403	1.6E
	0623	0913	1.5F
	1157	1615	1.3E
	1830	2120	1.5F
21 Tu	0011	0449	1.6E
	0713	0959	1.5F
	1244	1657	1.2E
	1917	2200	1.5F
22 W	0056	0537	1.4E
	0801	1043	1.4F
	1333	1741	1.1E
	2004	2235	1.3F
23 Th	0144	0628	1.3E
	0848	1132	1.2F
	1422	1830	1.0E
	2050	2313	1.1F
24 F	0231	0716	1.2E
	0934	1236	1.1F
	1511	1916	0.9E
	2138		
25 Sa		0009	1.0F
	0320	0757	1.0E
	1021	1337	1.0F
	1602	1954	0.9E
	2230		
26 Su ◑		0143	0.9F
	0413	0830	0.9E
	1112	1430	0.9F
	1656	2030	0.9E
	2327		
27 M		0240	0.8F
	0509	0900	0.9E
	1202	1522	0.9F
	1750	2117	0.9E
28 Tu	0023	0339	0.8F
	0604	0950	0.8E
	1248	1616	0.9F
	1840	2235	0.9E
29 W	0114	0437	0.9F
	0653	1053	0.9E
	1332	1703	1.0F
	1925	2327	1.0E
30 Th	0202	0522	0.9F
	0740	1130	1.0E
	1415	1739	1.0F
	2010		
31 F		0004	1.1E
	0249	0556	1.0F
	0826	1203	1.0E
	1459	1750	1.1F
	2054		

June

Day	Slack h m	Max h m	knots
1 Sa		0040	1.1E
	0336	0614	1.1F
	0914	1240	1.1E
	1544	1806	1.2F
	2137		
2 Su		0123	1.2E
	0421	0641	1.2F
	1001	1324	1.1E
	1629	1842	1.3F
	2218		
3 M ●		0217	1.2E
	0506	0721	1.3F
	1045	1419	1.1E
	1712	1926	1.4F
	2256		
4 Tu		0308	1.3E
	0551	0808	1.4F
	1128	1512	1.2E
	1757	2014	1.5F
	2335		
5 W		0351	1.4E
	0637	0856	1.5F
	1213	1557	1.2E
	1843	2102	1.6F
6 Th	0016	0431	1.4E
	0725	0940	1.5F
	1300	1641	1.2E
	1932	2148	1.6F
7 F	0103	0517	1.4E
	0814	1024	1.5F
	1351	1734	1.1E
	2023	2235	1.6F
8 Sa	0155	0618	1.3E
	0905	1113	1.5F
	1444	1841	1.1E
	2117	2328	1.5F
9 Su	0252	0720	1.3E
	0958	1211	1.4F
	1539	1942	1.1E
	2216		
10 M ◐		0030	1.4F
	0353	0815	1.3E
	1057	1316	1.3F
	1639	2042	1.2E
	2321		
11 Tu		0139	1.3F
	0459	0917	1.2E
	1157	1420	1.3F
	1741	2158	1.2E
12 W	0027	0248	1.3F
	0606	1036	1.2E
	1255	1528	1.3F
	1841	2313	1.3E
13 Th	0129	0413	1.3F
	0708	1138	1.3E
	1351	1643	1.4F
	1936		
14 F		0010	1.5E
	0229	0522	1.4F
	0808	1230	1.3E
	1446	1740	1.4F
	2032		
15 Sa		0103	1.5E
	0328	0616	1.5F
	0907	1322	1.3E
	1541	1830	1.5F
	2128		
16 Su		0200	1.6E
	0423	0709	1.5F
	1004	1419	1.3E
	1632	1921	1.5F
	2219		
17 M ○		0256	1.6E
	0515	0805	1.5F
	1054	1512	1.3E
	1721	2016	1.5F
	2306		
18 Tu		0345	1.6E
	0604	0858	1.5F
	1139	1557	1.3E
	1808	2106	1.4F
	2349		
19 W		0429	1.5E
	0651	0944	1.5F
	1224	1636	1.2E
	1855	2147	1.4F
20 Th	0033	0511	1.4E
	0736	1025	1.4F
	1309	1713	1.1E
	1940	2220	1.3F
21 F	0118	0553	1.2E
	0819	1105	1.2F
	1355	1750	1.0E
	2025	2249	1.1F
22 Sa	0204	0633	1.1E
	0859	1151	1.1F
	1440	1831	1.0E
	2110	2324	1.0F
23 Su	0250	0706	1.0E
	0940	1252	1.0F
	1526	1912	1.0E
	2157		
24 M		0015	0.9F
	0338	0731	0.9E
	1023	1345	0.9F
	1615	1950	0.9E
	2248		
25 Tu ◑		0138	0.8F
	0429	0801	0.9E
	1111	1425	0.9F
	1707	2030	0.9E
	2343		
26 W		0215	0.8F
	0523	0837	0.9E
	1200	1427	0.9F
	1758	2120	0.9E
27 Th	0036	0254	0.8F
	0616	0927	0.9E
	1248	1502	0.9F
	1846	2235	1.0E
28 F	0125	0432	0.8F
	0705	1035	0.9E
	1334	1550	0.9F
	1930	2332	1.0E
29 Sa	0214	0508	0.9F
	0753	1131	1.0E
	1422	1642	1.0F
	2014		
30 Su		0015	1.1E
	0303	0535	1.0F
	0843	1215	1.0E
	1511	1728	1.2F
	2059		

Time meridian 75° W. 0000 is midnight. 1200 is noon. Times are not adjusted for Daylight Saving Time.

Boston Harbor (Deer Island Light), Massachusetts, 2019

F–Flood, Dir. 264° True   E–Ebb, Dir. 112° True

July

Day	Slack (h m)	Maximum (h m)	knots
1 M		0058	1.2E
	0353	0612	1.2F
	0934	1301	1.1E
	1600	1813	1.3F
	2144		
2 Tu ●		0151	1.2E
	0441	0656	1.3F
	1023	1358	1.1E
	1648	1859	1.4F
	2228		
3 W		0249	1.3E
	0528	0746	1.4F
	1109	1458	1.2E
	1735	1951	1.5F
	2312		
4 Th		0337	1.4E
	0616	0837	1.5F
	1154	1547	1.2E
	1824	2043	1.6F
	2357		
5 F		0419	1.5E
	0704	0924	1.6F
	1240	1632	1.3E
	1915	2132	1.7F
6 Sa	0046	0504	1.3E
	0754	1008	1.6F
	1330	1723	1.3E
	2007	2220	1.7F
7 Su	0140	0559	1.4E
	0843	1054	1.6F
	1422	1827	1.3E
	2101	2312	1.5F
8 M	0236	0701	1.3E
	0934	1148	1.5F
	1515	1930	1.3E
	2159		
9 Tu ◑		0014	1.4F
	0336	0756	1.3E
	1030	1252	1.4F
	1612	2028	1.3E
	2303		
10 W		0127	1.3F
	0440	0854	1.2E
	1130	1358	1.3F
	1714	2139	1.3E
11 Th	0009	0241	1.3F
	0547	1009	1.1E
	1229	1504	1.3F
	1815	2255	1.3E
12 F	0112	0401	1.3F
	0650	1118	1.2E
	1327	1621	1.3F
	1913	2354	1.4E
13 Sa	0212	0508	1.3F
	0750	1212	1.2E
	1422	1723	1.3F
	2009		
14 Su		0047	1.5E
	0310	0603	1.4F
	0849	1303	1.2E
	1518	1815	1.4F
	2105		
15 M		0141	1.5E
	0406	0654	1.4F
	0946	1357	1.2E
	1611	1904	1.4F
	2158		
16 Tu ○		0235	1.5E
	0456	0746	1.4F
	1036	1450	1.2E
	1700	1957	1.3F
	2245		
17 W		0324	1.5E
	0542	0839	1.4F
	1120	1536	1.1E
	1746	2048	1.3F
	2327		
18 Th		0406	1.4E
	0625	0925	1.4F
	1201	1613	1.2E
	1831	2131	1.3F
19 F	0009	0441	1.3E
	0707	1004	1.4F
	1243	1643	1.2E
	1915	2204	1.3F
20 Sa	0051	0509	1.2E
	0746	1036	1.3F
	1325	1709	1.1E
	1958	2227	1.2F
21 Su	0134	0528	1.1E
	0823	1056	1.2F
	1407	1742	1.1E
	2040	2251	1.1F
22 M	0218	0555	1.0E
	0900	1115	1.1F
	1450	1827	1.1E
	2123	2328	1.0F
23 Tu	0303	0636	1.0E
	0939	1151	1.0F
	1535	1913	1.0E
	2210		
24 W ◐		0017	0.9F
	0350	0719	0.9E
	1023	1238	1.0F
	1622	1956	1.0E
	2302		
25 Th		0112	0.8F
	0442	0801	0.9E
	1113	1327	0.9F
	1713	2040	1.0E
	2357		
26 F		0202	0.9F
	0537	0846	0.9E
	1206	1413	1.0F
	1803	2140	0.9E
27 Sa	0050	0253	0.9F
	0631	0947	0.9E
	1257	1502	1.0F
	1850	2300	1.0E
28 Su	0142	0354	0.9F
	0723	1101	0.9E
	1348	1558	1.0F
	1935	2353	1.1E
29 M	0234	0500	1.1F
	0815	1156	1.0E
	1440	1656	1.2F
	2023		
30 Tu	0326	0549	1.2F
	0909	1245	1.1E
	1534	1748	1.3F
	2114		
31 W ●		0130	1.3E
	0418	0636	1.3F
	1001	1342	1.1E
	1626	1838	1.4F
	2204		

August

Day	Slack (h m)	Maximum (h m)	knots
1 Th		0230	1.4E
	0507	0725	1.5F
	1049	1446	1.2E
	1716	1931	1.5F
	2253		
2 F		0322	1.5E
	0555	0818	1.6F
	1135	1538	1.3E
	1807	2027	1.6F
	2341		
3 Sa		0406	1.5E
	0643	0907	1.7F
	1220	1624	1.4E
	1859	2120	1.7F
4 Su	0031	0450	1.5E
	0732	0952	1.7F
	1308	1713	1.4E
	1952	2208	1.7F
5 M	0125	0540	1.4E
	0821	1036	1.7F
	1359	1813	1.4E
	2046	2258	1.6F
6 Tu	0221	0640	1.4E
	0911	1125	1.5F
	1451	1916	1.4E
	2143	2359	1.4F
7 W ◑	0318	0737	1.2E
	1003	1226	1.4F
	1546	2015	1.3E
	2244		
8 Th		0116	1.3F
	0420	0832	1.1E
	1102	1335	1.3F
	1646	2120	1.3E
	2350		
9 F		0232	1.2F
	0526	0942	1.0E
	1203	1443	1.2F
	1750	2235	1.3E
10 Sa	0053	0345	1.2F
	0632	1057	1.0E
	1303	1600	1.2F
	1850	2336	1.4E
11 Su	0153	0452	1.2F
	0731	1154	1.1E
	1359	1706	1.2F
	1946		
12 M		0028	1.4E
	0250	0546	1.3F
	0829	1243	1.1E
	1455	1758	1.3F
	2041		
13 Tu		0118	1.4E
	0344	0635	1.3F
	0925	1333	1.1E
	1549	1847	1.3F
	2134		
14 W		0209	1.4E
	0432	0724	1.4F
	1014	1424	1.2E
	1638	1936	1.3F
	2222		
15 Th ○		0257	1.4E
	0515	0814	1.4F
	1056	1509	1.2E
	1723	2027	1.3F
	2304		
16 F		0337	1.3E
	0555	0900	1.4F
	1135	1545	1.2E
	1806	2110	1.3F
	2343		
17 Sa		0407	1.3E
	0633	0938	1.4F
	1213	1613	1.2E
	1848	2143	1.3F
18 Su	0023	0425	1.2E
	0709	1004	1.3F
	1252	1636	1.2E
	1929	2202	1.2F
19 M	0104	0440	1.1E
	0745	1013	1.3F
	1333	1704	1.2E
	2010	2222	1.2F
20 Tu	0146	0508	1.1E
	0822	1035	1.2F
	1413	1745	1.1E
	2051	2255	1.1F
21 W	0229	0549	1.0E
	0900	1109	1.2F
	1455	1835	1.1E
	2135	2338	1.0F
22 Th	0314	0641	1.0E
	0942	1153	1.1F
	1538	1925	1.0E
	2224		
23 F ◐		0030	0.9F
	0404	0730	0.9E
	1030	1245	1.0F
	1626	2011	1.0E
	2320		
24 Sa		0126	0.9F
	0501	0818	0.9E
	1126	1337	1.0F
	1718	2103	1.0E
25 Su	0018	0220	0.9F
	0600	0913	0.9E
	1224	1429	1.1F
	1810	2223	1.0E
26 M	0113	0318	1.0F
	0656	1035	0.9E
	1319	1525	1.1F
	1901	2332	1.1E
27 Tu	0207	0427	1.1F
	0750	1141	1.0E
	1414	1628	1.2F
	1953		
28 W		0021	1.2E
	0301	0529	1.2F
	0845	1233	1.1E
	1511	1728	1.3F
	2048		
29 Th		0111	1.4E
	0354	0617	1.4F
	0939	1329	1.2E
	1606	1822	1.4F
	2144		
30 F ●		0209	1.4E
	0444	0706	1.5F
	1028	1432	1.3E
	1659	1917	1.6F
	2237		
31 Sa		0305	1.5E
	0533	0759	1.6F
	1114	1526	1.4E
	1751	2015	1.7F
	2327		

September

Day	Slack (h m)	Maximum (h m)	knots
1 Su		0351	1.6E
	0621	0850	1.7F
	1159	1614	1.5E
	1844	2110	1.7F
2 M	0017	0435	1.5E
	0709	0935	1.8F
	1246	1702	1.5E
	1937	2158	1.7F
3 Tu	0110	0522	1.4E
	0758	1018	1.7F
	1336	1759	1.5E
	2031	2247	1.6F
4 W	0204	0619	1.3E
	0847	1104	1.6F
	1428	1902	1.4E
	2126	2345	1.4F
5 Th ◑	0300	0719	1.2E
	0939	1200	1.4F
	1522	2001	1.3E
	2225		
6 F		0107	1.2F
	0359	0813	1.1E
	1035	1312	1.2F
	1620	2101	1.3E
	2329		
7 Sa		0220	1.1F
	0504	0916	1.0E
	1137	1425	1.1F
	1723	2212	1.2E
	2347		
8 Su	0033	0326	1.1F
	0611	1032	0.9E
	1238	1538	1.1F
	1825	2315	1.3E
9 M	0132	0431	1.2F
	0711	1132	1.0E
	1336	1646	1.1F
	1921		
10 Tu		0006	1.3E
	0226	0526	1.2F
	0805	1221	1.1E
	1431	1740	1.2F
	2014		
11 W		0052	1.3E
	0316	0614	1.3F
	0857	1305	1.1E
	1524	1827	1.2F
	2106		
12 Th		0138	1.3E
	0402	0659	1.3F
	0945	1351	1.1E
	1613	1913	1.2F
	2154		
13 F ○		0222	1.2E
	0443	0745	1.3F
	1026	1436	1.2E
	1657	2000	1.2F
	2236		
14 Sa		0301	1.2E
	0520	0830	1.3F
	1105	1513	1.2E
	1738	2044	1.2F
	2316		
15 Su		0327	1.2E
	0556	0907	1.3F
	1142	1541	1.2E
	1819	2117	1.2F
	2354		
16 M		0344	1.2E
	0632	0927	1.3F
	1219	1607	1.3E
	1859	2133	1.2F
17 Tu	0033	0406	1.2E
	0709	0935	1.3F
	1257	1636	1.2E
	1940	2154	1.2F
18 W	0113	0436	1.2E
	0747	1002	1.3F
	1336	1711	1.2E
	2021	2227	1.2F
19 Th	0157	0514	1.1E
	0826	1037	1.3F
	1416	1759	1.1E
	2104	2307	1.1F
20 F ◐	0242	0605	1.0E
	0908	1120	1.2F
	1457	1855	1.0E
	2152	2357	1.1F
21 Sa	0332	0704	1.0E
	0956	1210	1.2F
	1543	1946	1.0E
	2247		
22 Su		0055	1.0F
	0429	0756	0.9E
	1052	1306	1.1F
	1636	2037	1.1E
	2347		
23 M		0153	1.0F
	0531	0851	0.9E
	1154	1402	1.1F
	1735	2148	1.0E
24 Tu	0046	0251	1.1F
	0631	1010	0.9E
	1254	1500	1.1F
	1833	2309	1.2E
25 W	0141	0358	1.1F
	0726	1127	1.0E
	1352	1605	1.2F
	1930		
26 Th		0003	1.3E
	0235	0507	1.3F
	0820	1221	1.2E
	1451	1712	1.3F
	2028		
27 F		0052	1.4E
	0329	0559	1.4F
	0914	1315	1.3E
	1548	1810	1.5F
	2126		
28 Sa ●		0147	1.5E
	0421	0647	1.6F
	1005	1416	1.4E
	1643	1905	1.6F
	2222		
29 Su		0245	1.5E
	0510	0739	1.7F
	1053	1514	1.5E
	1736	2005	1.7F
	2313		
30 M		0335	1.5E
	0558	0832	1.7F
	1139	1603	1.6E
	1829	2102	1.7F

Time meridian 75° W. 0000 is midnight. 1200 is noon. Times are not adjusted for Daylight Saving Time.

Boston Harbor (Deer Island Light), Massachusetts, 2019

F–Flood, Dir. 264° True   E–Ebb, Dir. 112° True

October

Day	Slack (h m)	Maximum (h m)	knots
1 Tu	0003	0420	1.5E
	0647	0920	1.7F
	1225	1651	1.6E
	1922	2151	1.7F
2 W	0054	0506	1.4E
	0736	1002	1.7F
	1314	1746	1.5E
	2015	2238	1.5F
3 Th	0147	0600	1.3E
	0825	1045	1.5F
	1406	1847	1.4E
	2108	2334	1.4F
4 F	0242	0700	1.1E
	0915	1136	1.3F
	1458	1944	1.3E
	2204		
5 Sa		0053	1.2F
	0338	0755	1.0E
	1009	1249	1.2F
	1554	2040	1.2E
	2305		
6 Su		0203	1.1F
	0440	0850	0.9E
	1110	1408	1.0F
	1655	2143	1.2E
7 M	0007	0304	1.1F
	0546	1000	0.9E
	1213	1516	1.0F
	1758	2247	1.2E
8 Tu	0104	0406	1.1F
	0644	1105	0.9E
	1311	1622	1.0F
	1854	2339	1.2E
9 W	0155	0501	1.2F
	0735	1154	1.0E
	1405	1718	1.1F
	1945		
10 Th		0022	1.2E
	0242	0549	1.2F
	0823	1235	1.1E
	1456	1804	1.1F
	2034		
11 F		0100	1.1E
	0325	0632	1.2F
	0909	1313	1.1E
	1544	1847	1.1F
	2122		
12 Sa		0135	1.1E
	0406	0713	1.2F
	0953	1352	1.2E
	1628	1930	1.2F
	2206		
13 Su		0206	1.1E
	0443	0753	1.2F
	1033	1432	1.2E
	1709	2011	1.2F
	2246		
14 M		0233	1.1E
	0520	0825	1.2F
	1110	1508	1.2E
	1749	2043	1.2F
	2325		
15 Tu		0304	1.2E
	0557	0834	1.3F
	1146	1540	1.3E
	1829	2100	1.2F
16 W	0003	0337	1.2E
	0635	0859	1.3F
	1223	1612	1.3E
	1910	2127	1.3F
17 Th	0044	0412	1.2E
	0715	0933	1.4F
	1300	1646	1.2E
	1953	2202	1.3F
18 F	0127	0450	1.1E
	0757	1010	1.4F
	1339	1729	1.2E
	2037	2242	1.3F
19 Sa	0215	0538	1.0E
	0841	1053	1.4F
	1421	1827	1.1E
	2125	2330	1.2F
20 Su	0305	0641	1.0E
	0929	1142	1.3F
	1509	1925	1.1E
	2218		
21 M		0027	1.1F
	0401	0740	0.9E
	1025	1240	1.2F
	1603	2017	1.1E
	2318		
22 Tu		0128	1.1F
	0502	0835	0.9E
	1129	1340	1.2F
	1706	2119	1.1E
23 W	0018	0227	1.2F
	0604	0948	1.0E
	1233	1439	1.2F
	1810	2243	1.2E
24 Th	0115	0331	1.2F
	0700	1111	1.1E
	1333	1546	1.3F
	1911	2344	1.3E
25 F	0210	0443	1.3F
	0754	1208	1.3E
	1432	1700	1.4F
	2010		
26 Sa		0034	1.4E
	0304	0540	1.5F
	0848	1301	1.4E
	1531	1801	1.5F
	2109		
27 Su		0127	1.4E
	0357	0629	1.6F
	0941	1400	1.5E
	1627	1857	1.6F
	2206		
28 M		0225	1.5E
	0448	0720	1.6F
	1031	1500	1.6E
	1721	1957	1.6F
	2258		
29 Tu		0319	1.5E
	0537	0814	1.7F
	1119	1552	1.7E
	1813	2055	1.6F
	2348		
30 W		0406	1.4E
	0626	0905	1.7F
	1206	1640	1.6E
	1906	2145	1.6F
31 Th	0038	0451	1.3E
	0715	0949	1.6F
	1254	1732	1.6E
	1958	2231	1.5F

November

Day	Slack (h m)	Maximum (h m)	knots
1 F	0130	0542	1.2E
	0804	1030	1.5F
	1344	1829	1.4E
	2049	2323	1.3F
2 Sa	0223	0639	1.1E
	0854	1115	1.3F
	1435	1924	1.3E
	2141		
3 Su		0033	1.2F
	0317	0733	1.0E
	0945	1222	1.1F
	1528	2015	1.2E
	2236		
4 M		0140	1.1F
	0413	0822	0.9E
	1042	1348	1.0F
	1625	2107	1.1E
	2333		
5 Tu		0238	1.0F
	0513	0917	0.9E
	1143	1450	0.9F
	1725	2207	1.0E
6 W	0028	0335	1.0F
	0610	1026	0.9E
	1241	1553	0.9F
	1822	2303	1.0E
7 Th	0116	0431	1.1F
	0700	1120	1.0E
	1334	1651	1.0F
	1912	2346	1.0E
8 F	0201	0520	1.1F
	0745	1201	1.0E
	1423	1738	1.0F
	1959		
9 Sa		0018	1.0E
	0243	0602	1.1F
	0830	1234	1.1E
	1510	1819	1.1F
	2046		
10 Su		0039	1.0E
	0324	0638	1.2F
	0915	1306	1.1E
	1555	1857	1.1F
	2132		
11 M		0101	1.1E
	0405	0705	1.2F
	0958	1345	1.2E
	1638	1929	1.1F
	2216		
12 Tu		0139	1.1E
	0445	0714	1.2F
	1037	1432	1.2E
	1719	1954	1.2F
	2256		
13 W		0226	1.1E
	0524	0744	1.3F
	1114	1514	1.2E
	1800	2025	1.2F
	2337		
14 Th		0312	1.2E
	0605	0824	1.3F
	1150	1551	1.3E
	1842	2102	1.3F
15 F	0018	0353	1.2E
	0647	0905	1.4F
	1226	1627	1.3E
	1927	2140	1.4F
16 Sa	0102	0433	1.1E
	0731	0947	1.5F
	1307	1707	1.2E
	2013	2221	1.4F
17 Su	0150	0520	1.1E
	0818	1030	1.5F
	1352	1802	1.2E
	2101	2307	1.3F
18 M	0241	0622	1.0E
	0908	1119	1.4F
	1443	1904	1.2E
	2153		
19 Tu		0001	1.3F
	0335	0725	1.0E
	1004	1217	1.3F
	1539	1959	1.2E
	2250		
20 W		0103	1.2F
	0433	0821	1.0E
	1107	1320	1.3F
	1643	2055	1.2E
	2351		
21 Th		0204	1.3F
	0535	0927	1.1E
	1212	1423	1.3F
	1750	2214	1.2E
22 F	0049	0305	1.3F
	0633	1052	1.2E
	1314	1531	1.3F
	1853	2323	1.3E
23 Sa	0144	0416	1.4F
	0728	1153	1.3E
	1414	1652	1.4F
	1952		
24 Su		0016	1.3E
	0239	0521	1.5F
	0822	1247	1.5E
	1514	1755	1.5F
	2052		
25 M		0108	1.4E
	0333	0612	1.5F
	0918	1345	1.6E
	1611	1850	1.5F
	2151		
26 Tu		0206	1.4E
	0426	0703	1.6F
	1011	1445	1.6E
	1706	1948	1.6F
	2244		
27 W		0303	1.4E
	0516	0759	1.7F
	1100	1552	1.7E
	1758	2046	1.6F
	2334		
28 Th		0352	1.4E
	0606	0853	1.6F
	1147	1636	1.6E
	1849	2136	1.6F
29 F	0022	0437	1.3E
	0655	0938	1.5F
	1234	1714	1.5E
	1939	2221	1.5F
30 Sa	0112	0523	1.2E
	0744	1018	1.4F
	1323	1806	1.4E
	2028	2308	1.3F

December

Day	Slack (h m)	Maximum (h m)	knots
1 Su	0203	0615	1.1E
	0832	1058	1.3F
	1412	1857	1.3E
	2114		
2 M		0006	1.2F
	0252	0706	1.0E
	0921	1152	1.1F
	1501	1943	1.1E
	2202		
3 Tu		0111	1.1F
	0342	0750	1.0E
	1012	1320	0.9F
	1553	2024	1.0E
	2252		
4 W		0207	1.0F
	0435	0829	0.9E
	1109	1421	0.9F
	1649	2102	0.9E
	2343		
5 Th		0258	1.0F
	0529	0915	0.9E
	1206	1518	0.9F
	1745	2151	0.8E
6 F	0032	0353	1.0F
	0620	1028	0.9E
	1259	1617	0.9F
	1836	2249	0.9E
7 Sa	0116	0445	1.0F
	0707	1121	1.0E
	1347	1708	0.9F
	1924	2323	0.9E
8 Su	0159	0528	1.0F
	0752	1158	1.0E
	1434	1750	1.0F
	2010	2351	1.0E
9 M	0243	0559	1.1F
	0837	1231	1.1E
	1521	1823	1.0F
	2058		
10 Tu		0024	1.0E
	0327	0605	1.1F
	0921	1308	1.1E
	1606	1845	1.1F
	2145		
11 W		0104	1.1E
	0411	0629	1.2F
	1003	1357	1.2E
	1650	1911	1.2F
	2230		
12 Th		0155	1.1E
	0455	0708	1.3F
	1042	1449	1.2E
	1733	1953	1.3F
	2313		
13 F		0251	1.1E
	0538	0753	1.4F
	1120	1533	1.3E
	1817	2037	1.4F
	2356		
14 Sa		0338	1.2E
	0623	0841	1.5F
	1159	1611	1.3E
	1903	2120	1.5F
15 Su	0040	0420	1.2E
	0710	0926	1.5F
	1241	1651	1.3E
	1950	2202	1.5F
16 M	0128	0506	1.2E
	0759	1012	1.6F
	1330	1741	1.3E
	2038	2247	1.5F
17 Tu	0218	0605	1.1E
	0850	1100	1.5F
	1423	1843	1.3E
	2128	2338	1.4F
18 W	0309	0709	1.1E
	0945	1157	1.4F
	1521	1940	1.2E
	2223		
19 Th		0038	1.3F
	0405	0806	1.1E
	1047	1302	1.3F
	1623	2034	1.2E
	2322		
20 F		0140	1.3F
	0505	0909	1.2E
	1153	1408	1.3F
	1731	2143	1.2E
21 Sa	0022	0241	1.3F
	0606	1033	1.2E
	1256	1520	1.3F
	1835	2302	1.2E
22 Su	0119	0350	1.3F
	0703	1139	1.4E
	1357	1644	1.3F
	1935		
23 M		0000	1.3E
	0215	0503	1.4F
	0759	1234	1.5E
	1457	1747	1.4F
	2036		
24 Tu		0052	1.3E
	0310	0558	1.5F
	0856	1330	1.6E
	1555	1840	1.5F
	2136		
25 W		0148	1.3E
	0405	0650	1.5F
	0952	1429	1.6E
	1650	1936	1.5F
	2230		
26 Th		0246	1.3E
	0457	0745	1.5F
	1043	1523	1.6E
	1741	2032	1.5F
	2319		
27 F		0337	1.3E
	0547	0840	1.5F
	1129	1609	1.6E
	1830	2123	1.5F
28 Sa	0006	0421	1.3E
	0635	0928	1.4F
	1214	1653	1.5E
	1917	2206	1.5F
29 Su	0052	0502	1.2E
	0723	1008	1.4F
	1300	1737	1.4E
	2001	2248	1.4F
30 M	0138	0544	1.1E
	0810	1043	1.2F
	1346	1821	1.2E
	2043	2331	1.2F
31 Tu	0223	0629	1.1E
	0855	1121	1.1F
	1433	1902	1.1E
	2125		

Time meridian 75° W. 0000 is midnight. 1200 is noon. Times are not adjusted for Daylight Saving Time.

Woods Hole, The Strait, Massachusetts, 2019

F–Flood, Dir. 079° True   E–Ebb, Dir. 267° True

January

Day	Slack	Maximum	knots
1 Tu	0018	0426	2.3F
	0629	0946	2.7E
	1257	1700	2.3F
	1858	2153	2.5E
2 W	0111	0525	2.3F
	0724	1045	2.9E
	1352	1759	2.4F
	1955	2256	2.6E
3 Th	0201	0621	2.3F
	0816	1133	3.0E
	1443	1853	2.5F
	2048	2343	2.6E
4 F	0250	0711	2.3F
	0905	1216	3.0E
	1532	1942	2.6F
	2138		
5 Sa ●		0023	2.6E
	0337	0757	2.3F
	0951	1243	3.0E
	1618	2028	2.5F
	2225		
6 Su		0054	2.6E
	0422	0839	2.1F
	1036	1305	3.0E
	1702	2113	2.4F
	2311		
7 M		0127	2.6E
	0506	0916	2.0F
	1119	1338	3.0E
	1744	2158	2.2F
	2355		
8 Tu		0203	2.6E
	0550	0824	1.9F
	1202	1415	3.0E
	1825	2240	2.0F
9 W	0038	0241	2.6E
	0633	0901	1.9F
	1244	1455	3.0E
	1905	2158	1.8F
10 Th	0120	0322	2.6E
	0717	0945	1.9F
	1325	1536	2.9E
	1946	2228	1.8F
11 F	0202	0404	2.6E
	0803	1033	1.8F
	1406	1619	2.9E
	2028	2308	1.8F
12 Sa	0244	0447	2.6E
	0852	1122	1.8F
	1449	1704	2.9E
	2112	2349	1.9F
13 Su	0326	0532	2.6E
	0944	1210	1.8F
	1534	1750	2.8E
	2157		
14 M ◐		0031	1.9F
	0410	0620	2.6E
	1035	1258	1.8F
	1623	1840	2.7E
	2244		
15 Tu		0116	2.0F
	0456	0710	2.6E
	1127	1349	1.9F
	1717	1933	2.7E
	2331		
16 W		0203	2.1F
	0546	0805	2.7E
	1218	1442	1.9F
	1815	2029	2.7E
17 Th	0020	0253	2.1F
	0639	0900	2.9E
	1310	1537	2.0F
	1915	2125	2.8E
18 F	0111	0345	2.2F
	0734	0955	3.2E
	1402	1635	2.1F
	2012	2220	3.0E
19 Sa	0203	0439	2.3F
	0827	1048	3.4E
	1453	1738	2.3F
	2106	2314	3.2E
20 Su	0255	0537	2.4F
	0920	1140	3.6E
	1545	1845	2.4F
	2159		
21 M ○		0007	3.4E
	0348	0636	2.5F
	1012	1233	3.8E
	1636	1946	2.6F
	2252		
22 Tu		0101	3.5E
	0442	0734	2.6F
	1105	1325	3.9E
	1728	2044	2.6F
	2344		
23 W		0153	3.6E
	0536	0829	2.6F
	1159	1416	3.9E
	1819	2151	2.6F
24 Th	0037	0244	3.6E
	0632	0931	2.7F
	1252	1507	3.8E
	1911	2304	2.6F
25 F	0129	0335	3.5E
	0729	1048	2.4F
	1346	1558	3.6E
	2005		
26 Sa		0004	2.5F
	0222	0427	3.3E
	0830	1212	2.3F
	1441	1650	3.3E
	2102		
27 Su ◑		0100	2.5F
	0315	0520	3.1E
	0934	1324	2.2F
	1537	1742	3.0E
	2200		
28 M		0159	2.3F
	0410	0614	2.8E
	1037	1433	2.1F
	1635	1838	2.6E
	2257		
29 Tu		0301	2.2F
	0505	0714	2.6E
	1138	1537	2.1F
	1734	1941	2.4E
	2351		
30 W		0402	2.1F
	0601	0938	2.6E
	1235	1638	2.2F
	1834	2156	2.3E
31 Th	0044	0500	2.1F
	0656	1034	2.7E
	1329	1736	2.2F
	1931	2249	2.4E

February

Day	Slack	Maximum	knots
1 F	0136	0556	2.1F
	0749	1122	2.7E
	1420	1830	2.3F
	2024	2336	2.5E
2 Sa	0225	0648	2.1F
	0839	1205	2.8E
	1508	1919	2.4F
	2113		
3 Su		0017	2.5E
	0311	0733	2.1F
	0925	1238	2.8E
	1552	2004	2.4F
	2158		
4 M ●		0038	2.5E
	0356	0812	2.1F
	1008	1236	2.8E
	1634	2046	2.3F
	2242		
5 Tu		0100	2.6E
	0439	0730	2.0F
	1050	1308	2.9E
	1713	2124	2.1F
	2324		
6 W		0133	2.7E
	0521	0753	2.0F
	1131	1345	3.0E
	1751	2039	2.0F
7 Th	0005	0211	2.8E
	0602	0830	2.1F
	1212	1424	3.1E
	1828	2102	2.0F
8 F	0045	0250	2.8E
	0643	0912	2.1F
	1251	1505	3.1E
	1905	2140	2.0F
9 Sa	0124	0332	2.9E
	0725	0958	2.0F
	1331	1549	3.2E
	1943	2223	2.0F
10 Su	0204	0415	2.9E
	0811	1048	2.0F
	1414	1634	3.1E
	2024	2309	2.0F
11 M	0245	0500	2.9E
	0902	1139	2.0F
	1500	1721	3.0E
	2110	2355	2.1F
12 Tu ◑	0328	0548	2.9E
	0956	1229	2.0F
	1551	1810	2.9E
	2202		
13 W		0043	2.1F
	0417	0638	2.9E
	1053	1322	1.9F
	1648	1903	2.8E
	2256		
14 Th		0133	2.1F
	0510	0733	2.9E
	1149	1418	2.0F
	1749	2001	2.8E
	2352		
15 F		0227	2.1F
	0609	0831	3.0E
	1245	1517	2.0F
	1852	2100	2.8E
16 Sa	0048	0323	2.2F
	0710	0930	3.2E
	1341	1620	2.1F
	1952	2158	3.0E
17 Su	0145	0422	2.3F
	0808	1026	3.4E
	1435	1734	2.3F
	2048	2254	3.2E
18 M	0241	0525	2.4F
	0904	1121	3.6E
	1528	1907	2.5F
	2141	2349	3.4E
19 Tu ○	0336	0632	2.5F
	0957	1215	3.7E
	1620	2003	2.7F
	2233		
20 W		0043	3.5E
	0430	0735	2.6F
	1050	1308	3.8E
	1710	2055	2.7F
	2325		
21 Th		0135	3.6E
	0523	0832	2.6F
	1143	1358	3.8E
	1800	2152	2.7F
22 F	0016	0226	3.6E
	0617	0941	2.5F
	1235	1448	3.7E
	1850	2251	2.6F
23 Sa	0107	0315	3.5E
	0712	1108	2.4F
	1328	1537	3.5E
	1941	2347	2.5F
24 Su	0158	0405	3.3E
	0810	1212	2.3F
	1421	1627	3.2E
	2035		
25 M		0041	2.4F
	0250	0456	3.1E
	0911	1312	2.2F
	1516	1718	2.8E
	2132		
26 Tu ○		0137	2.2F
	0342	0547	2.8E
	1013	1414	2.1F
	1612	1811	2.5E
	2229		
27 W ◑		0237	2.0F
	0436	0641	2.5E
	1113	1515	2.0F
	1709	1910	2.2E
	2325		
28 Th		0337	1.9F
	0531	0757	2.3E
	1210	1614	2.0F
	1807	2141	2.1E

March

Day	Slack	Maximum	knots
1 F	0019	0434	1.9F
	0627	1016	2.4E
	1303	1710	2.1F
	1904	2233	2.3E
2 Sa	0110	0529	1.9F
	0721	1103	2.5E
	1353	1804	2.1F
	1956	2318	2.3E
3 Su	0159	0620	1.9F
	0810	1145	2.6E
	1439	1852	2.2F
	2044	2357	2.4E
4 M	0244	0705	2.0F
	0856	1211	2.6E
	1521	1936	2.2F
	2128		
5 Tu		0004	2.5E
	0328	0740	2.0F
	0939	1159	2.7E
	1601	2014	2.1F
	2210		
6 W ●		0025	2.6E
	0409	0648	2.0F
	1020	1234	2.9E
	1638	2038	2.0F
	2250		
7 Th		0100	2.8E
	0450	0722	2.1F
	1059	1313	3.1E
	1714	1950	2.1F
	2329		
8 F		0139	2.9E
	0530	0800	2.2F
	1139	1354	3.2E
	1749	2022	2.1F
9 Sa	0008	0219	3.1E
	0610	0841	2.2F
	1219	1436	3.3E
	1825	2100	2.2F
10 Su	0046	0300	3.2E
	0650	0926	2.2F
	1300	1519	3.3E
	1901	2143	2.2F
11 M	0125	0344	3.2E
	0734	1017	2.1F
	1345	1605	3.3E
	1942	2232	2.2F
12 Tu ◑	0206	0431	3.2E
	0824	1111	2.1F
	1433	1654	3.2E
	2030	2323	2.2F
13 W	0252	0519	3.2E
	0921	1205	2.0F
	1527	1744	3.1E
	2127		
14 Th ◐		0015	2.1F
	0345	0610	3.1E
	1022	1300	2.0F
	1626	1838	2.9E
	2229		
15 F		0109	2.1F
	0443	0705	3.0E
	1123	1359	2.0F
	1728	1936	2.8E
	2331		
16 Sa		0206	2.1F
	0546	0805	3.0E
	1223	1503	2.1F
	1831	2038	2.8E
17 Su	0032	0307	2.2F
	0650	0907	3.1E
	1321	1612	2.2F
	1931	2139	3.0E
18 M	0131	0411	2.3F
	0751	1007	3.3E
	1417	1804	2.4F
	2028	2237	3.2E
19 Tu	0228	0523	2.4F
	0847	1103	3.5E
	1510	1908	2.6F
	2121	2333	3.4E
20 W ○	0323	0702	2.6F
	0941	1158	3.6E
	1600	1959	2.8F
	2213		
21 Th		0027	3.6E
	0417	0804	2.7F
	1033	1251	3.7E
	1650	2047	2.8F
	2303		
22 F		0118	3.6E
	0509	0859	2.7F
	1125	1340	3.7E
	1738	2138	2.7F
	2353		
23 Sa		0207	3.6E
	0601	1000	2.6F
	1217	1429	3.5E
	1826	2233	2.6F
24 Su	0043	0254	3.5E
	0654	1102	2.5F
	1308	1516	3.3E
	1915	2328	2.4F
25 M	0132	0342	3.3E
	0748	1159	2.4F
	1400	1605	3.0E
	2007		
26 Tu		0021	2.2F
	0223	0430	3.0E
	0846	1255	2.2F
	1453	1654	2.7E
	2104		
27 W ◑		0114	2.0F
	0314	0519	2.7E
	0947	1352	2.1F
	1548	1745	2.4E
	2202		
28 Th		0211	1.8F
	0407	0609	2.4E
	1045	1450	2.0F
	1643	1840	2.1E
	2259		
29 F		0308	1.7F
	0500	0705	2.2E
		0812	2.1F
		0856	2.1E
	1140	1546†	1.9F
30 Sa		0404	1.7F
	0555	0953	2.2E
	1232	1640	1.9F
	1833	2212	2.1E
31 Su	0042	0457	1.7F
	0648	1039	2.3E
	1320	1733	1.9F
	1924	2255	2.3E

Time meridian 75° W.   0000 is midnight.   1200 is noon.   Times are not adjusted for Daylight Saving Time.
If three or more consecutive entries are marked (F) or (E) the middle ones are not true maximums but intermediate values to show the current pattern.
† See page 196 for the remaining currents on this day.

Woods Hole, The Strait, Massachusetts, 2019

F–Flood, Dir. 079° True   E–Ebb, Dir. 267° True

April

Day	Slack (h m)	Maximum (h m)	knots
1 M	0130	0546	1.7F
	0738	1116	2.4E
	1404	1821	2.0F
	2011	2328	2.3E
2 Tu	0215	0457	1.7F
	0824	1044	2.5E
	1445	1903	1.9F
	2055	2314	2.5E
3 W	0258	0527	1.9F
	0907	1119	2.7E
	1523	1936	1.9F
	2135	2347	2.7E
4 Th	0339	0609	2.0F
	0947	1159	2.9E
	1559	1835	2.0F
	2214		
5 F ●		0026	2.9E
	0419	0651	2.2F
	1027	1240	3.1E
	1635	1909	2.2F
	2252		
6 Sa		0106	3.1E
	0459	0732	2.3F
	1108	1323	3.3E
	1710	1946	2.3F
	2330		
7 Su		0148	3.3E
	0538	0814	2.3F
	1150	1407	3.4E
	1747	2025	2.3F
8 M	0009	0231	3.4E
	0620	0859	2.3F
	1234	1452	3.4E
	1826	2109	2.3F
9 Tu	0050	0316	3.5E
	0704	0950	2.3F
	1322	1540	3.4E
	1909	2159	2.3F
10 W	0134	0404	3.5E
	0754	1047	2.2F
	1413	1629	3.3E
	2000	2255	2.2F
11 Th	0225	0453	3.4E
	0853	1145	2.1F
	1508	1721	3.1E
	2102	2352	2.1F
12 F ◐	0321	0545	3.3E
	0957	1244	2.1F
	1607	1815	3.0E
	2209		
13 Sa		0050	2.1F
	0422	0641	3.1E
	1101	1345	2.1F
	1708	1913	2.9E
	2315		
14 Su		0151	2.1F
	0526	0741	3.0E
	1202	1453	2.1F
	1810	2016	2.9E
15 M	0017	0257	2.2F
	0631	0846	3.0E
	1300	1620	2.3F
	1910	2120	3.0E
16 Tu	0117	0407	2.2F
	0732	0948	3.2E
	1355	1754	2.5F
	2007	2220	3.2E
17 W	0215	0611	2.4F
	0830	1046	3.3E
	1448	1853	2.7F
	2100	2317	3.4E
18 Th	0309	0714	2.6F
	0924	1141	3.4E
	1538	1944	2.8F
	2151		
19 F ○		0010	3.5E
	0402	0806	2.8F
	1016	1233	3.5E
	1627	2031	2.8F
	2241		
20 Sa		0100	3.6E
	0454	0857	2.8F
	1107	1322	3.4E
	1714	2120	2.7F
	2330		
21 Su		0148	3.5E
	0545	0951	2.7F
	1158	1409	3.3E
	1802	2213	2.5F
22 M	0018	0233	3.4E
	0635	1048	2.5F
	1249	1456	3.1E
	1850	2307	2.2F
23 Tu	0107	0318	3.2E
	0726	1142	2.4F
	1339	1543	2.8E
	1941	2359	2.0F
24 W	0155	0404	2.9E
	0820	1235	2.2F
	1430	1630	2.6E
	2035		
25 Th		0049	1.8F
	0245	0450	2.7E
	0917	1327	2.1F
	1522	1719	2.3E
	2133		
26 F ◑		0140	1.7F
	0336	0538	2.4E
	1014	1421	1.9F
	1614	1810	2.1E
	2229		
27 Sa		0233	1.6F
	0427	0628	2.2E
	1107	1514	1.8F
	1706	1904	2.0E
		2012†	1.9E
28 Su		0157	1.5F
	0519	0722	2.1E
	1156	1605	1.8F
	1757	2144	2.0E
29 M	0011	0232	1.5F
	0611	0820	2.1E
		0917	2.0E
		1005	2.1E
	1241	1655†	1.7F
30 Tu	0058	0317	1.6F
	0701	0914	2.2E
	1324	1741	1.7F
	1934	2155	2.3E

May

Day	Slack (h m)	Maximum (h m)	knots
1 W	0144	0401	1.7F
	0748	0958	2.4E
	1404	1629	1.7F
	2018	2230	2.5E
2 Th	0227	0447	1.9F
	0832	1041	2.7E
	1442	1708	1.9F
	2058	2310	2.7E
3 F	0308	0533	2.0F
	0914	1124	2.9E
	1519	1749	2.1F
	2137	2351	3.0E
4 Sa ●	0349	0620	2.2F
	0956	1209	3.1E
	1556	1831	2.2F
	2216		
5 Su		0034	3.3E
	0429	0705	2.3F
	1040	1254	3.3E
	1634	1913	2.4F
	2255		
6 M		0119	3.5E
	0511	0750	2.4F
	1125	1341	3.4E
	1714	1956	2.4F
	2337		
7 Tu		0204	3.6E
	0554	0837	2.4F
	1213	1428	3.5E
	1757	2042	2.4F
8 W	0022	0251	3.7E
	0640	0929	2.4F
	1303	1517	3.4E
	1845	2134	2.3F
9 Th	0111	0340	3.7E
	0732	1022	2.3F
	1355	1607	3.4E
	1940	2233	2.2F
10 F	0205	0431	3.6E
	0831	1131	2.2F
	1451	1700	3.2E
	2044	2335	2.2F
11 Sa ◐	0303	0523	3.4E
	0935	1232	2.2F
	1549	1754	3.1E
	2153		
12 Su		0037	2.1F
	0404	0619	3.2E
	1039	1335	2.2F
	1648	1852	2.9E
	2259		
13 M		0140	2.1F
	0507	0718	3.0E
	1140	1448	2.3F
	1748	1955	2.9E
14 Tu	0002	0250	2.1F
	0611	0823	3.0E
	1237	1623	2.4F
	1848	2101	3.0E
15 W	0102	0445	2.2F
	0712	0929	3.0E
	1332	1735	2.5F
	1945	2205	3.2E
16 Th	0200	0604	2.5F
	0810	1029	3.1E
	1424	1834	2.7F
	2038	2302	3.3E
17 F	0255	0703	2.7F
	0905	1124	3.2E
	1514	1926	2.7F
	2129	2355	3.4E
18 Sa ○	0347	0755	2.8F
	0957	1216	3.2E
	1603	2014	2.7F
	2217		
19 Su		0044	3.4E
	0438	0845	2.8F
	1048	1305	3.1E
	1651	2102	2.5F
	2306		
20 M		0129	3.4E
	0527	0936	2.7F
	1138	1351	3.0E
	1738	2152	2.3F
	2353		
21 Tu		0212	3.3E
	0615	1029	2.5F
	1228	1435	2.9E
	1826	2244	2.1F
22 W		0254	3.1E
	0704	1121	2.4F
	1317	1520	2.7E
	1915	2333	1.9F
23 Th	0128	0337	2.9E
	0753	1211	2.2F
	1405	1606	2.5E
	2006		
24 F		0019	1.7F
	0215	0422	2.0F
	0845	1259	2.0F
	1454	1652	2.3E
	2100		1.6F
25 Sa	0303	0507	2.5E
	0937	1347	1.8F
	1542	1738	2.2E
	2155		
26 Su ◑		0025	1.5F
	0352	0553	2.3E
	1028	1434	1.7F
	1631	1826	2.1E
	2247		
27 M		0106	1.5F
	0440	0641	2.2E
	1114	1357	1.6F
	1719	1917	2.0E
	2337		
28 Tu		0150	1.6F
	0530	0733	2.2E
	1158	1422	1.6F
	1807	2012	2.1E
29 W	0024	0237	1.6F
	0619	0826	2.3E
	1240	1501	1.7F
	1853	2103	2.3E
30 Th	0110	0324	1.7F
	0709	0917	2.4E
	1321	1542	1.8F
	1938	2149	2.5E
31 F	0154	0412	1.9F
	0756	1005	2.6E
	1401	1625	2.0F
	2020	2234	2.8E

June

Day	Slack (h m)	Maximum (h m)	knots
1 Sa	0237	0501	2.0F
	0843	1052	2.9E
	1441	1710	2.1F
	2101	2319	3.1E
2 Su	0320	0551	2.2F
	0929	1139	3.1E
	1522	1757	2.3F
	2143		
3 M ●		0005	3.4E
	0403	0642	2.3F
	1015	1227	3.3E
	1604	1845	2.4F
	2226		
4 Tu		0052	3.6E
	0447	0731	2.4F
	1104	1316	3.4E
	1649	1932	2.5F
	2312		
5 W		0140	3.8E
	0533	0820	2.5F
	1154	1406	3.5E
	1737	2021	2.5F
6 Th	0001	0228	3.9E
	0622	0913	2.4F
	1245	1456	3.5E
	1828	2115	2.4F
7 F	0054	0318	3.8E
	0715	1015	2.4F
	1338	1547	3.4E
	1925	2217	2.3F
8 Sa	0149	0410	3.7E
	0812	1121	2.4F
	1433	1640	3.3E
	2028	2323	2.2F
9 Su	0246	0503	3.5E
	0914	1223	2.3F
	1529	1734	3.2E
	2136		
10 M ◐		0026	2.2F
	0346	0558	3.3E
	1017	1327	2.3F
	1627	1830	3.0E
	2243		
11 Tu		0132	2.1F
	0447	0656	3.0E
	1116	1447	2.3F
	1725	1932	2.9E
	2346		
12 W		0304	2.1F
	0549	0759	2.9E
	1212	1607	2.4F
	1824	2040	2.9E
13 Th	0046	0443	2.2F
	0651	0907	2.8E
	1307	1714	2.4F
	1921	2151	3.0E
14 F	0144	0549	2.4F
	0750	1013	2.9E
	1400	1814	2.5F
	2015	2253	3.2E
15 Sa	0239	0647	2.6F
	0845	1110	2.9E
	1450	1908	2.6F
	2106	2345	3.2E
16 Su	0331	0739	2.7F
	0938	1203	2.9E
	1540	1957	2.5F
	2154		
17 M ○		0031	3.2E
	0420	0828	2.7F
	1028	1252	2.9E
	1628	2043	2.4F
	2242		
18 Tu		0112	3.2E
	0508	0917	2.7F
	1117	1335	2.8E
	1715	2130	2.2F
	2329		
19 W		0151	3.1E
	0554	1007	2.5F
	1205	1416	2.8E
	1802	2217	2.0F
20 Th	0014	0230	3.0E
	0639	1056	2.3F
	1251	1457	2.7E
	1848	2301	1.9F
21 F	0100	0310	2.9E
	0724	1142	2.1F
	1337	1539	2.6E
	1935	2218	1.7F
22 Sa	0144	0352	2.8E
	0810	1225	1.9F
	1422	1621	2.4E
	2025	2301	1.7F
23 Su	0229	0435	2.7E
	0857	1301	1.8F
	1507	1705	2.4E
	2117	2345	1.7F
24 M	0314	0519	2.6E
	0944	1222	1.7F
	1552	1750	2.3E
	2209		
25 Tu ◑		0028	1.7F
	0400	0605	2.5E
	1029	1255	1.7F
	1637	1837	2.2E
	2259		
26 W		0114	1.7F
	0447	0654	2.4E
	1113	1335	1.8F
	1723	1927	2.3E
	2347		
27 Th		0201	1.7F
	0537	0745	2.4E
	1156	1418	1.8F
	1809	2019	2.4E
28 F	0035	0250	1.8F
	0629	0839	2.5E
	1239	1503	1.9F
	1856	2111	2.6E
29 Sa	0121	0340	1.9F
	0722	0931	2.6E
	1322	1550	2.1F
	1943	2200	2.9E
30 Su	0208	0432	2.0F
	0814	1022	2.8E
	1407	1638	2.2F
	2029	2249	3.2E

Time meridian 75° W. 0000 is midnight. 1200 is noon. Times are not adjusted for Daylight Saving Time.
If three or more consecutive entries are marked (F) or (E) the middle ones are not true maximums but intermediate values to show the current pattern.
† See page 196 for the remaining currents on this day.

Woods Hole, The Strait, Massachusetts, 2019

F–Flood, Dir. 079° True   E–Ebb, Dir. 267° True

July

Day	Slack	Maximum	knots
1 M	0254	0526	2.1F
	0904	1112	3.0E
	1453	1729	2.3F
	2115	2338	3.5E
2 Tu ●	0340	0623	2.3F
	0954	1203	3.2E
	1540	1822	2.4F
	2203		
3 W		0028	3.7E
	0427	0717	2.4F
	1044	1254	3.4E
	1630	1915	2.5F
	2253		
4 Th		0118	3.9E
	0516	0808	2.5F
	1135	1345	3.5E
	1721	2007	2.6F
	2345		
5 F		0208	3.9E
	0606	0903	2.5F
	1227	1436	3.6E
	1815	2102	2.5F
6 Sa	0039	0259	3.9E
	0658	1005	2.5F
	1320	1527	3.5E
	1911	2205	2.4F
7 Su	0133	0350	3.8E
	0753	1113	2.5F
	1413	1620	3.4E
	2012	2313	2.3F
8 M	0229	0443	3.6E
	0851	1217	2.4F
	1508	1713	3.3E
	2118		
9 Tu ☽		0020	2.2F
	0327	0536	3.3E
	0952	1320	2.4F
	1604	1808	3.1E
	2225		
10 W		0136	2.1F
	0427	0632	3.0E
	1051	1437	2.3F
	1701	1907	2.9E
	2328		
11 Th		0317	2.1F
	0527	0733	2.7E
	1147	1549	2.3F
	1759	2016	2.8E
12 F	0028	0428	2.2F
	0629	0844	2.6E
	1242	1653	2.3F
	1856	2201	2.8E
13 Sa	0126	0531	2.4F
	0729	1008	2.6E
	1336	1753	2.3F
	1951	2304	3.0E
14 Su	0221	0628	2.5F
	0825	1115	2.6E
	1428	1848	2.4F
	2042	2354	3.0E
15 M	0312	0720	2.6F
	0917	1206	2.7E
	1517	1937	2.4F
	2131		
16 Tu ○		0036	3.0E
	0400	0809	2.7F
	1006	1248	2.7E
	1605	2022	2.3F
	2218		
17 W		0101	3.0E
	0446	0855	2.6F
	1053	1321	2.7E
	1651	2104	2.2F
	2303		
18 Th		0129	3.0E
	0529	0941	2.4F
	1138	1354	2.7E
	1735	2143	2.0F
	2347		
19 F		0204	3.0E
	0611	1026	2.2F
	1223	1430	2.7E
	1819	2056	1.9F
20 Sa	0030	0242	3.0E
	0651	1108	2.0F
	1305	1509	2.7E
	1903	2134	1.9F
21 Su	0112	0322	2.9E
	0732	1032	1.8F
	1348	1549	2.6E
	1949	2219	1.8F
22 M	0154	0403	2.9E
	0813	1055	1.8F
	1429	1631	2.6E
	2037	2307	1.8F
23 Tu	0236	0447	2.8E
	0856	1133	1.8F
	1511	1715	2.5E
	2127	2353	1.8F
24 W ☽	0320	0532	2.7E
	0941	1213	1.9F
	1554	1800	2.5E
	2219		
25 Th		0040	1.8F
	0407	0619	2.6E
	1027	1256	1.9F
	1638	1848	2.5E
	2310		
26 F		0128	1.8F
	0458	0710	2.5E
	1113	1341	1.9F
	1725	1941	2.5E
27 Sa	0000	0219	1.8F
	0553	0805	2.5E
	1200	1429	2.0F
	1815	2036	2.7E
28 Su	0050	0312	1.9F
	0651	0901	2.6E
	1249	1520	2.1F
	1909	2130	2.9E
29 M	0140	0407	2.0F
	0747	0955	2.8E
	1340	1612	2.2F
	2002	2222	3.2E
30 Tu	0230	0506	2.1F
	0842	1049	3.0E
	1431	1708	2.3F
	2054	2314	3.5E
31 W ●	0320	0608	2.3F
	0934	1141	3.3E
	1523	1806	2.4F
	2145		

August

Day	Slack	Maximum	knots
1 Th		0007	3.7E
	0409	0708	2.5F
	1025	1234	3.4E
	1614	1903	2.6F
	2237		
2 F		0059	3.9E
	0459	0802	2.6F
	1116	1326	3.6E
	1707	1957	2.6F
	2330		
3 Sa		0150	4.0E
	0549	0855	2.6F
	1208	1417	3.7E
	1801	2053	2.6F
4 Su	0023	0240	3.9E
	0640	0956	2.6F
	1300	1508	3.6E
	1857	2156	2.5F
5 M	0117	0331	3.8E
	0732	1107	2.5F
	1352	1559	3.5E
	1956	2310	2.3F
6 Tu	0212	0422	3.5E
	0827	1211	2.5F
	1445	1651	3.3E
	2059		
7 W ☽		0029	2.2F
	0308	0514	3.2E
	0926	1313	2.3F
	1540	1745	3.1E
	2205		
8 Th		0152	2.1F
	0406	0609	2.9E
	1025	1422	2.2F
	1636	1841	2.8E
	2308		
9 F		0305	2.1F
	0506	0708	2.5E
	1123	1529	2.1F
	1733	1946	2.6E
10 Sa	0008	0409	2.2F
	0606	0820	2.3E
	1219	1632	2.1F
	1830	2207	2.6E
11 Su	0106	0510	2.3F
	0706	1024	2.4E
	1314	1731	2.2F
	1926	2259	2.8E
12 M	0200	0606	2.4F
	0802	1116	2.5E
	1406	1826	2.2F
	2018	2347	2.8E
13 Tu	0250	0658	2.5F
	0853	1202	2.6E
	1454	1914	2.3F
	2107		
14 W		0029	2.9E
	0336	0745	2.5F
	0941	1242	2.6E
	1540	1958	2.2F
	2152		
15 Th ○		0052	2.9E
	0419	0829	2.5F
	1025	1303	2.7E
	1624	2035	2.2F
	2236		
16 F		0101	2.9E
	0459	0911	2.3F
	1109	1326	2.7E
	1707	2000	2.0F
	2318		
17 Sa		0134	3.0E
	0538	0949	2.1F
	1150	1400	2.8E
	1749	2022	2.1F
	2359		
18 Su		0211	3.0E
	0615	0857	2.0F
	1231	1437	2.8E
	1830	2059	2.0F
19 M	0039	0250	3.1E
	0652	0926	1.9F
	1310	1516	2.8E
	1912	2142	2.0F
20 Tu	0119	0332	3.1E
	0729	1005	1.9F
	1349	1558	2.8E
	1957	2230	1.9F
21 W	0200	0415	3.0E
	0809	1049	2.0F
	1429	1641	2.8E
	2045	2319	1.9F
22 Th	0244	0501	2.9E
	0853	1134	2.0F
	1510	1727	2.8E
	2137		
23 F ○		0009	1.9F
	0332	0548	2.8E
	0942	1221	2.0F
	1555	1815	2.8E
	2232		
24 Sa		0059	1.9F
	0425	0639	2.7E
	1034	1309	2.0F
	1645	1907	2.7E
	2326		
25 Su		0152	1.9F
	0523	0735	2.6E
	1128	1401	2.0F
	1741	2004	2.8E
26 M	0021	0249	1.9F
	0624	0833	2.7E
	1224	1456	2.1F
	1840	2102	3.0E
27 Tu	0115	0347	2.0F
	0724	0931	2.8E
	1319	1552	2.2F
	1939	2159	3.2E
28 W	0208	0450	2.2F
	0820	1027	3.1E
	1414	1652	2.3F
	2035	2253	3.5E
29 Th	0300	0600	2.3F
	0913	1122	3.3E
	1508	1754	2.5F
	2129	2347	3.7E
30 F ●	0351	0709	2.5F
	1005	1215	3.5E
	1601	1857	2.6F
	2222		
31 Sa	0440	0802	2.7F
	1056	1308	3.7E
	1654	1953	2.7F
	2314		

September

Day	Slack	Maximum	knots
1 Su		0131	3.9E
	0530	0851	2.7F
	1147	1358	3.7E
	1747	2049	2.6F
2 M	0007	0221	3.8E
	0619	0950	2.6F
	1238	1448	3.7E
	1842	2158	2.5F
3 Tu	0100	0311	3.7E
	0709	1101	2.5F
	1329	1538	3.5E
	1938	2330	2.4F
4 W	0153	0401	3.4E
	0803	1202	2.4F
	1421	1629	3.3E
	2039		
5 Th ☽		0038	2.3F
	0248	0453	3.1E
	0900	1301	2.2F
	1515	1720	3.0E
	2143		
6 F		0143	2.2F
	0345	0546	2.7E
	1001	1405	2.1F
	1609	1814	2.7E
	2246		
7 Sa		0247	2.1F
	0443	0642	2.4E
	1100	1508	2.0F
	1706	1914	2.4E
	2345		
8 Su		0348	2.1F
	0542	0754	2.2E
	1157	1608	1.9F
	1803	2152	2.4E
9 M	0041	0445	2.2F
	0641	1012	2.3E
	1251	1706	2.0F
	1859	2243	2.6E
10 Tu	0134	0541	2.3F
	0736	1100	2.4E
	1341	1759	2.0F
	1952	2328	2.7E
11 W	0222	0632	2.3F
	0826	1144	2.5E
	1429	1848	2.1F
	2040		
12 Th		0007	2.7E
	0306	0719	2.3F
	0912	1221	2.6E
	1513	1930	2.1F
	2124		
13 F ○		0007	2.7E
	0346	0800	2.3F
	0955	1229	2.7E
	1556	2002	2.1F
	2206		
14 Sa		0025	2.8E
	0424	0836	2.1F
	1035	1252	2.8E
	1637	1918	2.1F
	2247		
15 Su		0101	3.0E
	0501	0748	2.0F
	1115	1326	2.9E
	1718	1950	2.2F
	2327		
16 M		0139	3.1E
	0537	0809	2.1F
	1154	1404	3.0E
	1758	2027	2.2F
17 Tu	0007	0219	3.2E
	0612	0843	2.1F
	1232	1444	3.1E
	1838	2109	2.1F
18 W	0047	0302	3.2E
	0648	0923	2.1F
	1309	1526	3.1E
	1920	2157	2.1F
19 Th	0129	0346	3.2E
	0726	1009	2.1F
	1348	1610	3.1E
	2006	2248	2.0F
20 F	0215	0433	3.1E
	0810	1059	2.1F
	1430	1657	3.1E
	2058	2341	2.0F
21 Sa ○	0305	0521	3.0E
	0903	1150	2.0F
	1518	1746	3.0E
	2157		
22 Su		0035	2.0F
	0400	0613	2.8E
	1002	1243	2.0F
	1613	1838	3.0E
	2256		
23 M		0130	2.0F
	0459	0708	2.7E
	1103	1338	2.1F
	1714	1936	2.9E
	2354		
24 Tu		0229	2.0F
	0600	0808	2.7E
	1203	1436	2.1F
	1817	2036	3.0E
25 W	0051	0331	2.1F
	0701	0909	2.9E
	1302	1537	2.2F
	1919	2136	3.2E
26 Th	0146	0437	2.2F
	0758	1007	3.1E
	1359	1640	2.3F
	2017	2233	3.4E
27 F	0239	0607	2.4F
	0852	1103	3.4E
	1454	1750	2.5F
	2112	2328	3.6E
28 Sa ●	0330	0716	2.6F
	0944	1157	3.6E
	1547	1904	2.6F
	2205		
29 Su		0021	3.7E
	0419	0805	2.7F
	1035	1249	3.7E
	1640	2007	2.7F
	2258		
30 M		0113	3.7E
	0508	0851	2.7F
	1125	1340	3.7E
	1733	2111	2.7F
	2350		

Time meridian 75° W. 0000 is midnight. 1200 is noon. Times are not adjusted for Daylight Saving Time.
If three or more consecutive entries are marked (F) or (E) the middle ones are not true maximums but intermediate values to show the current pattern.

Woods Hole, The Strait, Massachusetts, 2019

F–Flood, Dir. 079° True   E–Ebb, Dir. 267° True

October

Date	Slack (h m)	Max (h m)	knots
1 Tu		0202	3.6E
	0557	0947	2.6F
	1215	1428	3.7E
	1826	2226	2.5F
2 W	0042	0251	3.5E
	0647	1051	2.4F
	1306	1517	3.5E
	1921	2330	2.4F
3 Th	0135	0341	3.2E
	0739	1150	2.3F
	1357	1606	3.2E
	2018		
4 F		0028	2.3F
	0229	0431	2.9E
	0836	1246	2.1F
	1449	1655	2.9E
	2120		
5 Sa ◑		0126	2.2F
	0324	0523	2.6E
	0936	1344	1.9F
	1542	1746	2.6E
	2221		
6 Su		0225	2.1F
	0420	0618	2.3E
	1036	1444	1.8F
	1637	1841	2.3E
	2319		
7 M		0322	2.1F
	0516	0757	2.0E
	1132	1541	1.8F
	1733	1957	2.2E
8 Tu	0012	0417	2.1F
	0611	0951	2.2E
	1225	1636	1.8F
	1828	2220	2.4E
9 W	0102	0511	2.1F
	0705	1038	2.4E
	1314	1728	1.9F
	1920	2302	2.4E
10 Th	0147	0601	2.1F
	0754	1119	2.5E
	1400	1816	1.9F
	2009	2333	2.5E
11 F	0230	0648	2.1F
	0839	1150	2.5E
	1444	1856	1.9F
	2053	2312	2.6E
12 Sa	0309	0727	2.0F
	0921	1142	2.6E
	1526	1805	2.0F
	2134	2346	2.8E
13 Su ○	0346	0657	1.9F
	1000	1214	2.8E
	1607	1841	2.1F
	2215		
14 M		0026	2.9E
	0422	0655	2.0F
	1038	1252	3.0E
	1647	1919	2.2F
	2255		
15 Tu		0107	3.1E
	0457	0729	2.2F
	1116	1331	3.1E
	1726	1958	2.2F
	2336		
16 W		0149	3.2E
	0533	0807	2.2F
	1153	1413	3.3E
	1806	2041	2.2F
17 Th	0019	0233	3.3E
	0610	0848	2.2F
	1232	1456	3.4E
	1848	2128	2.2F
18 F	0103	0319	3.3E
	0651	0935	2.2F
	1313	1542	3.4E
	1933	2221	2.1F
19 Sa	0151	0407	3.2E
	0737	1028	2.1F
	1359	1630	3.4E
	2026	2318	2.1F
20 Su	0243	0457	3.1E
	0833	1125	2.1F
	1451	1720	3.3E
	2127		
21 M ◐		0015	2.1F
	0339	0549	3.0E
	0938	1222	2.1F
	1550	1813	3.2E
	2229		
22 Tu		0112	2.1F
	0438	0645	2.9E
	1043	1320	2.1F
	1652	1910	3.1E
	2330		
23 W		0212	2.1F
	0538	0744	2.9E
	1146	1421	2.1F
	1756	2012	3.0E
24 Th	0027	0316	2.2F
	0638	0847	3.0E
	1246	1525	2.2F
	1859	2115	3.1E
25 F	0123	0427	2.3F
	0736	0948	3.2E
	1344	1634	2.3F
	1959	2213	3.3E
26 Sa	0216	0608	2.5F
	0831	1045	3.4E
	1440	1827	2.5F
	2055	2309	3.4E
27 Su ●	0307	0708	2.7F
	0923	1139	3.6E
	1534	1932	2.7F
	2148		
28 M		0003	3.5E
	0357	0758	2.7F
	1013	1231	3.7E
	1627	2026	2.7F
	2241		
29 Tu		0054	3.5E
	0446	0846	2.7F
	1103	1321	3.7E
	1719	2121	2.7F
	2333		
30 W		0144	3.4E
	0535	0939	2.5F
	1153	1409	3.6E
	1811	2220	2.6F
31 Th	0025	0232	3.2E
	0625	1037	2.3F
	1242	1455	3.4E
	1903	2317	2.5F

November

Date	Slack (h m)	Max (h m)	knots
1 F	0117	0321	3.0E
	0717	1133	2.1F
	1332	1542	3.1E
	1957		
2 Sa		0011	2.4F
	0208	0410	2.7E
	0812	1227	2.0F
	1423	1630	2.9E
	2054		
3 Su		0105	2.2F
	0301	0500	2.5E
	0910	1319	1.8F
	1515	1719	2.6E
	2152		
4 M ◑		0159	2.1F
	0353	0551	2.2E
	1009	1413	1.7F
	1607	1809	2.3E
	2247		
5 Tu		0252	2.0F
	0446	0647	2.1E
	1103	1507	1.7F
	1700	1903	2.2E
		2015†	2.1E
6 W		0345	1.9F
	0538	0924	2.1E
	1154	1558	1.6F
	1753	2004	2.1E
		2045†	2.1E
7 Th	0024	0436	1.9F
	0629	1011	2.2E
	1243	1647	1.6F
	1844	2105	2.2E
8 F	0108	0525	1.8F
	0718	1049	2.3E
	1329	1554	1.7F
	1933	2148	2.3E
9 Sa	0149	0609	1.8F
	0802	1028	2.4E
	1413	1635	1.8F
	2018	2228	2.5E
10 Su	0228	0454	1.8F
	0844	1058	2.6E
	1455	1720	1.9F
	2101	2309	2.7E
11 M	0306	0532	1.9F
	0923	1136	2.8E
	1536	1805	2.0F
	2143	2352	2.9E
12 Tu ○	0343	0613	2.1F
	1004	1217	3.1E
	1617	1849	2.2F
	2225		
13 W		0036	3.1E
	0420	0654	2.2F
	1039	1300	3.3E
	1657	1933	2.3F
	2309		
14 Th		0121	3.2E
	0459	0736	2.3F
	1118	1344	3.5E
	1738	2017	2.3F
	2354		
15 F		0207	3.3E
	0539	0820	2.3F
	1201	1429	3.6E
	1821	2105	2.3F
16 Sa	0041	0254	3.3E
	0624	0908	2.3F
	1246	1517	3.6E
	1908	2159	2.3F
17 Su	0131	0344	3.3E
	0714	1004	2.2F
	1337	1606	3.6E
	2001	2259	2.2F
18 M	0224	0435	3.2E
	0812	1104	2.2F
	1432	1657	3.5E
	2102	2358	2.2F
19 Tu ◑	0319	0527	3.1E
	0918	1205	2.2F
	1531	1751	3.3E
	2204		
20 W		0056	2.2F
	0417	0622	3.0E
	1025	1305	2.2F
	1633	1847	3.2E
	2305		
21 Th		0156	2.3F
	0515	0721	3.0E
	1129	1408	2.2F
	1736	1948	3.1E
22 F	0003	0301	2.3F
	0615	0825	3.0E
	1230	1517	2.2F
	1839	2052	3.0E
23 Sa	0058	0422	2.4F
	0713	0928	3.1E
	1329	1709	2.3F
	1939	2153	3.1E
24 Su	0152	0554	2.5F
	0808	1027	3.3E
	1425	1830	2.5F
	2036	2251	3.2E
25 M	0244	0654	2.6F
	0901	1122	3.4E
	1520	1927	2.7F
	2131	2345	3.2E
26 Tu ●	0335	0746	2.6F
	0951	1214	3.5E
	1613	2019	2.8F
	2223		
27 W		0038	3.2E
	0425	0835	2.6F
	1041	1304	3.5E
	1704	2111	2.8F
	2315		
28 Th		0128	3.1E
	0515	0926	2.4F
	1130	1350	3.4E
	1754	2205	2.7F
29 F	0006	0215	3.0E
	0604	1019	2.3F
	1219	1435	3.3E
	1843	2258	2.5F
30 Sa	0056	0302	2.8E
	0655	1112	2.1F
	1308	1519	3.1E
	1933	2350	2.4F

December

Date	Slack (h m)	Max (h m)	knots
1 Su	0145	0348	2.7E
	0746	1202	1.9F
	1356	1605	2.9E
	2025		
2 M		0039	2.2F
	0235	0435	2.5E
	0840	1248	1.8F
	1445	1650	2.6E
	2118		
3 Tu		0128	2.1F
	0324	0522	2.3E
	0936	1331	1.6F
	1534	1737	2.4E
	2209		
4 W ◑		0217	1.9F
	0413	0610	2.2E
	1030	1302	1.6F
	1624	1824	2.3E
	2257		
5 Th		0305	1.7F
	0501	0701	2.1E
	1120	1341	1.6F
	1713	1915	2.2E
	2342		
6 F		0256	1.6F
		0349	1.6F
	0550	0756	1.6F
	1209	1424†	1.6F
7 Sa	0025	0247	1.7F
	0637	0850	2.2E
	1255	1510	1.6F
	1853	2100	2.3E
8 Su	0106	0326	1.7F
	0722	0936	2.4E
	1341	1556	1.7F
	1942	2148	2.4E
9 M	0147	0407	1.9F
	0805	1018	2.6E
	1424	1643	1.8F
	2028	2234	2.6E
10 Tu	0227	0450	2.0F
	0846	1101	2.9E
	1506	1733	2.0F
	2113	2320	2.8E
11 W	0307	0536	2.1F
	0926	1145	3.2E
	1548	1822	2.1F
	2158		
12 Th ○		0007	3.0E
	0347	0623	2.3F
	1007	1231	3.4E
	1631	1910	2.3F
	2244		
13 F		0055	3.2E
	0430	0710	2.4F
	1050	1318	3.6E
	1714	1957	2.4F
	2332		
14 Sa		0143	3.3E
	0515	0758	2.4F
	1137	1406	3.7E
	1800	2046	2.4F
15 Su	0021	0232	3.4E
	0604	0848	2.4F
	1227	1454	3.8E
	1848	2141	2.4F
16 M	0112	0322	3.4E
	0656	0945	2.3F
	1319	1544	3.8E
	1941	2242	2.4F
17 Tu	0204	0413	3.4E
	0754	1048	2.3F
	1415	1636	3.7E
	2039	2343	2.4F
18 W ○	0259	0506	3.3E
	0859	1150	2.2F
	1513	1729	3.5E
	2140		
19 Th		0040	2.4F
	0355	0600	3.2E
	1007	1252	2.2F
	1613	1825	3.2E
	2240		
20 F		0139	2.3F
	0452	0658	3.1E
	1111	1358	2.2F
	1715	1924	3.0E
	2338		
21 Sa		0246	2.3F
	0551	0801	3.0E
	1213	1528	2.1F
	1818	2028	2.9E
22 Su	0034	0423	2.3F
	0649	0908	3.0E
	1313	1713	2.3F
	1919	2134	2.9E
23 M	0129	0538	2.4F
	0746	1012	3.2E
	1411	1818	2.5F
	2018	2235	2.9E
24 Tu	0223	0639	2.5F
	0839	1110	3.2E
	1505	1914	2.7F
	2113	2332	2.9E
25 W	0314	0732	2.5F
	0930	1203	3.3E
	1558	2005	2.8F
	2205		
26 Th ●		0027	2.9E
	0405	0820	2.5F
	1020	1251	3.3E
	1647	2055	2.8F
	2255		
27 F		0116	2.9E
	0455	0908	2.4F
	1108	1334	3.2E
	1735	2145	2.7F
	2345		
28 Sa		0200	2.9E
	0543	0957	2.2F
	1155	1415	3.2E
	1821	2235	2.5F
29 Su	0032	0242	2.8E
	0630	1045	2.1F
	1242	1455	3.0E
	1907	2324	2.4F
30 M	0119	0324	2.7E
	0718	1130	1.9F
	1328	1537	2.9E
	1952		
31 Tu		0010	2.2F
	0205	0407	2.5E
	0807	1203	1.8F
	1413	1620	2.8E
	2039		

Time meridian 75° W. 0000 is midnight. 1200 is noon. Times are not adjusted for Daylight Saving Time.
If three or more consecutive entries are marked (F) or (E) the middle ones are not true maximums but intermediate values to show the current pattern.
† See page 196 for the remaining currents on this day.

Cape Cod Canal (RR. Bridge), Massachusetts, 2019

F–Flood, Dir. 070° True   E–Ebb, Dir. 250° True

January

Day	Slack	Maximum	knots	Day	Slack	Maximum	knots
1 Tu		0315	4.1F	16 W		0109	4.3F
	0541	0821	4.7E		0458	0722	4.5E
	1153	1556	4.2F		1115	1342	4.1F
	1814	2100	4.3E		1732	1950	4.5E
					2330		
2 W	0012	0413	4.2F	17 Th		0200	4.5F
	0635	0937	4.8E		0549	0815	4.8E
	1247	1654	4.4F		1207	1435	4.3F
	1911	2216	4.4E		1828	2047	4.7E
3 Th	0105	0505	4.3F	18 F	0023	0253	4.7F
	0726	1036	5.0E		0641	0910	5.2E
	1339	1747	4.7F		1259	1531	4.6F
	2006	2311	4.6E		1925	2144	5.0E
4 F	0156	0552	4.3F	19 Sa	0117	0348	4.9F
	0816	1123	5.2E		0734	1005	5.6E
	1429	1836	4.8F		1351	1628	4.9F
	2057	2359	4.7E		2020	2240	5.3E
5 Sa ●	0247	0635	4.3F	20 Su	0211	0442	5.1F
	0904	1203	5.2E		0828	1059	6.0E
	1517	1924	4.8F		1443	1722	5.2F
	2145				2113	2334	5.6E
6 Su		0045	4.7E	21 M ○	0304	0535	5.2F
	0335	0705	4.2F		0922	1152	6.2E
	0951	1240	5.1E		1535	1816	5.3F
	1603	2010	4.6F		2206		
	2232						
7 M		0127	4.7E	22 Tu		0027	5.8E
	0422	0654	4.1F		0357	0628	5.3F
	1036	1315	5.0E		1015	1245	6.3E
	1648	2052	4.4F		1627	1909	5.3F
	2317				2258		
8 Tu		0202	4.5E	23 W		0120	5.8E
	0508	0731	4.0F		0449	0721	5.2F
	1120	1351	4.8E		1109	1338	6.3E
	1731	2017	4.1F		1719	2002	5.2F
					2351		
9 W	0001	0232	4.3E	24 Th		0212	5.8E
	0552	0812	4.0F		0541	0814	5.1F
	1204	1429	4.7E		1204	1431	6.1E
	1814	2042	3.9F		1811	2054	5.0F
10 Th	0044	0303	4.1E	25 F	0043	0303	5.6E
	0636	0853	3.9F		0635	0908	4.8F
	1247	1507	4.5E		1259	1523	5.8E
	1856	2119	3.9F		1904	2146	4.7F
11 F	0125	0338	4.0E	26 Sa	0136	0354	5.4E
	0720	0936	3.8F		0731	1003	4.4F
	1329	1547	4.4E		1355	1615	5.3E
	1937	2200	3.8F		1959	2240	4.4F
12 Sa	0206	0416	3.9E	27 Su ☽	0229	0447	5.1E
	0803	1021	3.7F		0829	1105	4.1F
	1412	1629	4.4E		1453	1710	4.8E
	2018	2244	3.8F		2055	2341	4.1F
13 Su	0246	0457	3.9E	28 M	0322	0542	4.8E
	0848	1109	3.7F		0929	1322	3.9F
	1456	1715	4.3E		1552	1810	4.4E
	2102	2331	3.9F		2152		
14 M ☾	0327	0542	4.0E	29 Tu		0051	3.9F
	0935	1159	3.7F		0417	0642	4.5E
	1544	1804	4.3E		1029	1434	3.9F
	2148				1652	1918	4.0E
					2250		
15 Tu		0020	4.1F	30 W		0245	3.8F
	0411	0631	4.2E		0512	0750	4.4E
	1024	1250	3.9F		1128	1537	4.1F
	1636	1856	4.4E		1752	2053	4.0E
	2238				2347		
				31 Th		0348	3.8F
					0607	0921	4.5E
					1224	1634	4.3F
					1850	2207	4.2E

February

Day	Slack	Maximum	knots	Day	Slack	Maximum	knots
1 F	0042	0443	3.9F	16 Sa	0002	0230	4.6F
	0701	1026	4.7E		0618	0845	5.2E
	1316	1727	4.5F		1237	1511	4.6F
	1944	2301	4.4E		1906	2124	4.9E
2 Sa	0135	0533	4.0F	17 Su	0059	0328	4.7F
	0752	1115	4.8E		0716	0944	5.5E
	1406	1815	4.7F		1333	1613	4.8F
	2034	2348	4.6E		2002	2223	5.3E
3 Su	0225	0617	4.1F	18 M	0155	0426	4.7F
	0841	1154	4.9E		0813	1042	5.9E
	1453	1901	4.7F		1427	1712	5.0F
	2121				2056	2318	5.6E
4 M ●		0031	4.6E	19 Tu ○	0249	0522	5.1F
	0312	0651	4.1F		0908	1136	6.1E
	0926	1221	4.8E		1520	1807	5.2F
	1538	1943	4.5F		2148		
	2205						
5 Tu		0106	4.6E	20 W		0011	5.8E
	0357	0629	4.1F		0341	0615	5.2F
	1010	1247	4.8E		1001	1229	6.2E
	1620	2017	4.3F		1611	1858	5.2F
	2247				2239		
6 W		0128	4.4E	21 Th		0103	5.9E
	0439	0702	4.2F		0432	0707	5.2F
	1051	1319	4.8E		1054	1322	6.2E
	1700	1931	4.1F		1701	1947	5.1F
	2327				2329		
7 Th		0152	4.4E	22 F		0153	5.9E
	0520	0740	4.2F		0523	0759	5.1F
	1131	1355	4.8E		1147	1414	6.0E
	1739	2003	4.2F		1750	2033	4.9F
8 F	0006	0223	4.3E	23 Sa	0019	0243	5.7E
	0600	0820	4.2F		0615	0850	4.8F
	1211	1433	4.8E		1241	1504	5.6E
	1816	2041	4.2F		1841	2119	4.7F
9 Sa	0043	0259	4.4E	24 Su	0110	0332	5.5E
	0639	0902	4.2F		0709	0943	4.4F
	1251	1514	4.9E		1336	1555	5.2E
	1854	2122	4.3F		1933	2208	4.3F
10 Su	0121	0338	4.5E	25 M	0201	0421	5.1E
	0719	0946	4.1F		0805	1042	4.0F
	1333	1556	4.8E		1432	1648	4.6E
	1933	2206	4.3F		2028	2301	4.0F
11 M	0159	0421	4.6E	26 Tu ☽	0253	0514	4.7E
	0802	1033	4.1F		0903	1311	3.8F
	1418	1643	4.8E		1530	1747	4.1E
	2016	2254	4.3F		2126		
12 Tu ☾	0241	0507	4.7E	27 W		0002	3.7F
	0849	1125	4.1F		0348	0612	4.4E
	1509	1733	4.7E		1003	1414	3.8F
	2105	2345	4.4F		1629	1858	3.8E
					2225		
13 W	0328	0557	4.7E	28 Th		0220	3.5F
	0943	1219	4.1F		0444	0718	4.1E
	1606	1827	4.6E		1102	1515	4.0F
	2202				1729	2045	3.8E
					2324		
14 Th		0039	4.4F				
	0421	0650	4.8E				
	1041	1314	4.2F				
	1706	1924	4.6E				
	2302						
15 F		0133	4.5F				
	0519	0747	5.0E				
	1139	1411	4.4F				
	1807	2023	4.7E				

March

Day	Slack	Maximum	knots	Day	Slack	Maximum	knots
1 F		0323	3.6F	16 Sa		0111	4.4F
	0541	0907	4.1E		0457	0722	5.0E
	1159	1611	4.2F		1117	1352	4.4F
	1826	2152	4.0E		1747	2002	4.7E
					2344		
2 Sa	0020	0420	3.7F	17 Su		0210	4.4F
	0635	1012	4.3E		0600	0824	5.1E
	1251	1703	4.3F		1218	1456	4.5F
	1919	2245	4.3E		1847	2105	4.9E
3 Su	0112	0510	3.9F	18 M	0043	0311	4.6F
	0727	1100	4.5E		0700	0926	5.4E
	1341	1750	4.4F		1316	1604	4.7F
	2008	2330	4.5E		1943	2207	5.3E
4 M	0201	0552	4.0F	19 Tu	0139	0413	4.8F
	0815	1136	4.6E		0758	1027	5.7E
	1426	1833	4.4F		1410	1711	5.0F
	2053				2037	2303	5.6E
5 Tu		0008	4.5E	20 W ○	0233	0512	5.0F
	0246	0615	4.0F		0853	1122	5.9E
	0859	1150	4.6E		1502	1804	5.1F
	1509	1909	4.2F		2128	2354	5.8E
	2134						
6 W ●		0030	4.4E	21 Th	0324	0605	5.2F
	0328	0556	4.1F		0946	1214	6.0E
	0940	1211	4.7E		1552	1847	5.2F
	1549	1823	4.2F		2217		
	2212						
7 Th		0042	4.4E	22 F		0044	5.9E
	0408	0629	4.3F		0414	0655	5.1F
	1019	1243	4.8E		1037	1306	6.0E
	1626	1850	4.3F		1640	1927	5.1F
	2249				2305		
8 F		0109	4.5E	23 Sa		0133	5.9E
	0445	0707	4.4F		0504	0745	5.0F
	1057	1320	5.0E		1129	1356	5.7E
	1701	1926	4.5F		1728	2008	4.8F
	2324				2354		
9 Sa		0144	4.7E	24 Su		0221	5.8E
	0522	0747	4.5F		0554	0833	4.7F
	1135	1400	5.1E		1222	1446	5.4E
	1736	2005	4.7F		1817	2051	4.6F
10 Su	0000	0223	4.9E	25 M	0043	0308	5.5E
	0559	0829	4.6F		0646	0924	4.3F
	1216	1442	5.2E		1316	1536	4.9E
	1813	2048	4.7F		1908	2137	4.2F
11 M	0037	0304	5.1E	26 Tu	0133	0356	5.1E
	0638	0914	4.6F		0740	1146	4.0F
	1300	1527	5.2E		1411	1628	4.4E
	1853	2133	4.7F		2003	2229	3.8F
12 Tu	0117	0348	5.2E	27 W ☽	0225	0447	4.7E
	0721	1002	4.5F		0837	1253	3.9F
	1349	1615	5.1E		1508	1727	4.0E
	1939	2222	4.6F		2101	2328	3.5F
13 W	0203	0436	5.2E	28 Th	0320	0542	4.2E
	0812	1055	4.4F		0936	1352	3.8F
	1443	1706	4.9E		1605	1843	3.7E
	2034	2316	4.5F		2201		
14 Th ☾	0255	0528	5.1E	29 F		0155	3.3F
	0909	1152	4.3F		0416	0645	3.9E
	1542	1802	4.8E		1034	1449	3.9F
	2136				1703	2027	3.7E
					2300		
15 F		0012	4.4F	30 Sa		0256	3.4F
	0354	0624	5.1E		0513	0844	3.8E
	1013	1251	4.3F		1131	1544	4.0F
	1645	1901	4.7E		1758	2130	3.9E
	2241				2355		
				31 Su		0352	3.5F
					0607	0949	3.9E
					1223	1634	4.1F
					1849	2221	4.1E

Time meridian 75° W. 0000 is midnight. 1200 is noon. Times are not adjusted for Daylight Saving Time.

Cape Cod Canal (RR. Bridge), Massachusetts, 2019

F–Flood, Dir. 070° True   E–Ebb, Dir. 250° True

April

Day	Slack (h m)	Maximum (h m)	knots
1 M	0046	0440	3.6F
	0658	1034	4.1E
	1310	1719	4.1F
	1936	2304	4.2E
2 Tu	0132	0518	3.7F
	0744	1100	4.2E
	1354	1757	4.0F
	2019	2333	4.2E
3 W	0215	0449	3.9F
	0827	1102	4.4E
	1435	1713	4.0F
	2057	2334	4.3E
4 Th	0256	0519	4.1F
	0907	1131	4.6E
	1512	1737	4.3F
	2134	2356	4.5E
5 F ●	0333	0555	4.4F
	0945	1207	4.9E
	1548	1812	4.6F
	2208		
6 Sa		0029	4.8E
	0410	0634	4.6F
	1023	1246	5.2E
	1623	1851	4.8F
	2242		
7 Su		0108	5.2E
	0446	0716	4.8F
	1103	1329	5.3E
	1659	1932	5.0F
	2318		
8 M		0150	5.4E
	0523	0800	4.9F
	1146	1414	5.5E
	1738	2017	5.1F
	2358		
9 Tu		0234	5.6E
	0604	0846	4.9F
	1234	1502	5.5E
	1822	2104	5.0F
10 W	0043	0321	5.7E
	0650	0936	4.8F
	1327	1551	5.3E
	1914	2155	4.8F
11 Th	0135	0410	5.6E
	0744	1030	4.6F
	1423	1644	5.1E
	2012	2251	4.6F
12 F ☽	0232	0504	5.4E
	0845	1129	4.5F
	1523	1740	4.9E
	2116	2350	4.4F
13 Sa	0334	0601	5.2E
	0951	1231	4.4F
	1625	1840	4.7E
	2223		
14 Su		0051	4.3F
	0439	0702	5.0E
	1057	1335	4.4F
	1727	1943	4.7E
	2326		
15 M		0153	4.4F
	0543	0805	5.1E
	1159	1444	4.4F
	1826	2047	4.9E

Day	Slack (h m)	Maximum (h m)	knots
16 Tu	0026	0257	4.5F
	0644	0909	5.2E
	1256	1617	4.7F
	1922	2150	5.2E
17 W	0121	0405	4.7F
	0741	1012	5.5E
	1350	1727	4.9F
	2015	2246	5.6E
18 Th	0214	0511	4.9F
	0836	1108	5.7E
	1441	1809	5.0F
	2105	2337	5.8E
19 F ○	0306	0607	5.0F
	0929	1159	5.7E
	1529	1832	5.0F
	2153		
20 Sa		0025	5.9E
	0355	0656	5.0F
	1020	1249	5.6E
	1617	1902	4.9F
	2240		
21 Su		0112	5.9E
	0444	0741	4.8F
	1111	1339	5.4E
	1705	1941	4.7F
	2328		
22 M		0159	5.7E
	0533	0826	4.6F
	1203	1429	5.1E
	1754	2024	4.4F
23 Tu	0016	0245	5.4E
	0624	0914	4.3F
	1256	1519	4.7E
	1846	2111	4.0F
24 W	0107	0332	5.0E
	0716	1129	4.0F
	1350	1610	4.3E
	1940	2202	3.7F
25 Th	0159	0420	4.6E
	0811	1230	3.9F
	1444	1707	3.9E
	2037	2300	3.4F
26 F ☽	0252	0512	4.1E
	0907	1325	3.8F
	1538	1820	3.6E
	2135		
27 Sa		0007	3.2F
	0347	0609	3.8E
	1004	1419	3.7F
	1633	1957	3.6E
	2232		
28 Su		0221	3.2F
	0442	0711	3.6E
	1058	1510	3.7F
	1725	2100	3.6E
	2326		
29 M		0313	3.2F
	0534	0905	3.5E
	1149	1558	3.7F
	1814	2150	3.7E
30 Tu	0014	0257	3.3F
	0623	0910	3.7E
	1234	1639	3.6F
	1858	2227	3.8E

May

Day	Slack (h m)	Maximum (h m)	knots
1 W	0059	0324	3.5F
	0709	0939	3.9E
	1316	1546	3.7F
	1939	2220	3.9E
2 Th	0141	0403	3.8F
	0751	1014	4.2E
	1356	1619	4.0F
	2017	2241	4.3E
3 F	0220	0442	4.1F
	0832	1052	4.6E
	1433	1657	4.4F
	2052	2315	4.7E
4 Sa ●	0258	0522	4.5F
	0912	1133	5.0E
	1510	1737	4.8F
	2128	2353	5.2E
5 Su	0335	0604	4.8F
	0953	1216	5.3E
	1548	1819	5.1F
	2205		
6 M		0036	5.6E
	0414	0648	5.1F
	1037	1302	5.5E
	1628	1903	5.2F
	2244		
7 Tu		0121	5.9E
	0454	0734	5.2F
	1123	1350	5.6E
	1712	1951	5.2F
	2329		
8 W		0208	6.0E
	0539	0822	5.2F
	1214	1440	5.6E
	1801	2040	5.1F
9 Th	0019	0257	6.0E
	0629	0914	5.0F
	1309	1531	5.5E
	1855	2133	4.9F
10 F	0115	0349	5.9E
	0725	1009	4.8F
	1406	1624	5.3E
	1955	2230	4.6F
11 Sa ☽	0214	0443	5.6E
	0827	1109	4.6F
	1505	1721	5.0E
	2059	2330	4.4F
12 Su	0317	0541	5.3E
	0932	1214	4.4F
	1605	1820	4.8E
	2204		
13 M		0034	4.3F
	0421	0642	5.1E
	1037	1320	4.4F
	1705	1922	4.8E
	2307		
14 Tu		0138	4.3F
	0524	0745	5.0E
	1137	1433	4.4F
	1803	2027	4.9E
15 W	0006	0246	4.3F
	0625	0851	5.0E
	1234	1619	4.6F
	1858	2131	5.2E

Day	Slack (h m)	Maximum (h m)	knots
16 Th	0102	0437	4.5F
	0723	0956	5.1E
	1327	1714	4.7F
	1951	2229	5.5E
17 F	0155	0543	4.8F
	0818	1054	5.3E
	1417	1759	4.8F
	2040	2319	5.7E
18 Sa ○	0246	0638	4.9F
	0911	1146	5.3E
	1507	1822	4.7F
	2128		
19 Su		0006	5.8E
	0336	0731	4.9F
	1003	1236	5.2E
	1555	1839	4.6F
	2216		
20 M		0052	5.7E
	0424	0823	4.8F
	1053	1326	5.1E
	1643	1918	4.5F
	2303		
21 Tu		0138	5.5E
	0513	0915	4.6F
	1144	1416	4.9E
	1733	2001	4.2F
	2352		
22 W		0224	5.3E
	0602	1009	4.4F
	1235	1505	4.6E
	1824	2048	3.9F
23 Th	0042	0309	4.9E
	0652	1106	4.1F
	1326	1553	4.3E
	1917	2137	3.7F
24 F	0132	0355	4.5E
	0744	1201	3.9F
	1417	1642	4.0E
	2011	2230	3.4F
25 Sa	0224	0442	4.1E
	0836	1253	3.7F
	1508	1735	3.6E
	2105	2326	3.2F
26 Su ☽	0315	0531	3.8E
	0929	1341	3.5F
	1558	1830	3.4E
	2159		
27 M		0020	3.1F
	0406	0621	3.6E
	1020	1425	3.4F
	1646	1918	3.3E
	2250		
28 Tu		0107	3.2F
	0455	0710	3.5E
	1108	1333	3.3F
	1732	1956	3.4E
	2337		
29 W		0152	3.3F
	0543	0758	3.6E
	1153	1411	3.5F
	1815	2035	3.6E
30 Th	0022	0236	3.5F
	0629	0845	3.8E
	1234	1453	3.8F
	1855	2115	3.9E
31 F	0104	0321	3.8F
	0714	0931	4.2E
	1314	1536	4.2F
	1934	2156	4.4E

June

Day	Slack (h m)	Maximum (h m)	knots
1 Sa	0144	0406	4.2F
	0758	1017	4.6E
	1354	1621	4.6F
	2012	2238	5.0E
2 Su	0224	0452	4.6F
	0842	1103	5.0E
	1436	1705	4.9F
	2052	2322	5.5E
3 M ●	0305	0537	4.9F
	0928	1149	5.3E
	1519	1751	5.2F
	2134		
4 Tu		0008	5.9E
	0347	0624	5.2F
	1015	1238	5.6E
	1604	1839	5.3F
	2219		
5 W		0056	6.1E
	0432	0712	5.3F
	1105	1328	5.7E
	1652	1929	5.3F
	2309		
6 Th		0146	6.2E
	0520	0803	5.3F
	1157	1420	5.7E
	1744	2020	5.2F
7 F	0002	0238	6.2E
	0613	0856	5.2F
	1252	1512	5.6E
	1839	2114	5.0F
8 Sa	0100	0330	6.0E
	0709	0951	4.9F
	1348	1605	5.4E
	1938	2211	4.7F
9 Su	0159	0424	5.7E
	0809	1051	4.6F
	1445	1701	5.2E
	2040	2311	4.4F
10 M ◐	0300	0521	5.4E
	0911	1155	4.4F
	1543	1759	5.0E
	2143		
11 Tu		0015	4.2F
	0402	0621	5.0E
	1013	1301	4.3F
	1641	1900	4.8E
	2245		
12 W		0122	4.1F
	0504	0724	4.8E
	1113	1412	4.3F
	1738	2003	4.9E
	2345		
13 Th		0322	4.2F
	0605	0831	4.7E
	1209	1559	4.4F
	1833	2109	5.0E
14 F	0042	0440	4.4F
	0704	0942	4.7E
	1303	1656	4.5F
	1925	2212	5.2E
15 Sa	0135	0538	4.7F
	0800	1045	4.8E
	1354	1745	4.5F
	2016	2304	5.4E

Day	Slack (h m)	Maximum (h m)	knots
16 Su	0227	0631	4.9F
	0854	1139	4.9E
	1445	1828	4.5F
	2105	2351	5.5E
17 M ○	0316	0722	4.9F
	0945	1229	5.0E
	1534	1834	4.4F
	2153		
18 Tu		0035	5.5E
	0404	0811	4.9F
	1034	1318	4.9E
	1623	1902	4.3F
	2240		
19 W		0120	5.3E
	0452	0859	4.7F
	1123	1406	4.8E
	1712	1943	4.1F
	2328		
20 Th		0204	5.1E
	0539	0947	4.4F
	1212	1450	4.6E
	1802	2027	4.0F
21 F	0016	0247	4.9E
	0626	1035	4.1F
	1300	1531	4.3E
	1851	2112	3.8F
22 Sa	0105	0328	4.6E
	0714	0957	3.8F
	1347	1609	4.0E
	1941	2158	3.6F
23 Su	0152	0410	4.3E
	0802	1032	3.6F
	1433	1648	3.7E
	2030	2246	3.4F
24 M	0239	0453	4.0E
	0850	1115	3.5F
	1518	1729	3.5E
	2119	2334	3.3F
25 Tu ◐	0326	0538	3.8E
	0936	1158	3.4F
	1602	1811	3.4E
	2208		
26 W		0022	3.3F
	0413	0624	3.7E
	1022	1242	3.5F
	1645	1855	3.5E
	2255		
27 Th		0109	3.4F
	0501	0713	3.7E
	1107	1326	3.7F
	1727	1941	3.8E
	2341		
28 F		0156	3.6F
	0549	0802	3.9E
	1151	1412	4.0F
	1810	2028	4.1E
29 Sa	0025	0244	3.8F
	0638	0854	4.2E
	1235	1500	4.3F
	1852	2117	4.6E
30 Su	0109	0334	4.2F
	0727	0945	4.6E
	1321	1549	4.6F
	1937	2206	5.2E

Time meridian 75° W. 0000 is midnight. 1200 is noon. Times are not adjusted for Daylight Saving Time.

Cape Cod Canal (RR. Bridge), Massachusetts, 2019

F–Flood, Dir. 070° True   E–Ebb, Dir. 250° True

July

Day	Slack	Maximum	knots
1 M	0153	0424	4.6F
	0816	1036	5.0E
	1408	1639	4.9F
	2023	2255	5.7E
2 Tu ●	0239	0514	5.0F
	0906	1127	5.4E
	1456	1728	5.2F
	2111	2344	6.0E
3 W	0326	0604	5.3F
	0956	1218	5.6E
	1546	1819	5.4F
	2202		
4 Th		0035	6.3E
	0415	0654	5.4F
	1048	1309	5.8E
	1637	1910	5.4F
	2254		
5 F		0127	6.4E
	0505	0746	5.4F
	1140	1402	5.8E
	1729	2003	5.3F
	2348		
6 Sa		0220	6.3E
	0558	0839	5.2F
	1234	1454	5.8E
	1823	2056	5.1F
7 Su	0045	0313	6.1E
	0653	0933	5.0F
	1328	1546	5.6E
	1920	2152	4.8F
8 M	0143	0406	5.8E
	0750	1030	4.7F
	1423	1639	5.3E
	2019	2251	4.4F
9 Tu ◐	0242	0501	5.3E
	0848	1131	4.4F
	1518	1735	5.0E
	2120	2356	4.1F
10 W	0342	0600	4.9E
	0948	1234	4.2F
	1614	1834	4.8E
	2222		
11 Th		0110	4.0F
	0444	0702	4.5E
	1047	1338	4.1F
	1711	1937	4.7E
	2323		
12 F		0322	4.1F
	0545	0812	4.3E
	1144	1536	4.0F
	1806	2046	4.7E
13 Sa	0020	0427	4.3F
	0645	0935	4.3E
	1239	1637	4.1F
	1900	2158	4.9E
14 Su	0114	0523	4.6F
	0741	1044	4.5E
	1333	1730	4.2F
	1952	2256	5.1E
15 M	0206	0615	4.8F
	0835	1137	4.7E
	1425	1818	4.3F
	2043	2343	5.2E
16 Tu ○	0256	0704	4.9F
	0925	1225	4.8E
	1515	1902	4.3F
	2131		
17 W		0025	5.2E
	0343	0751	4.9F
	1013	1311	4.9E
	1603	1935	4.2F
	2218		
18 Th		0105	5.2E
	0429	0836	4.7F
	1059	1353	4.8E
	1650	1925	4.2F
	2304		
19 F		0143	5.0E
	0514	0917	4.4F
	1144	1428	4.6E
	1736	2002	4.1F
	2349		
20 Sa		0220	4.9E
	0558	0842	4.1F
	1228	1458	4.4E
	1821	2042	4.0F
21 Su	0034	0257	4.7E
	0641	0909	4.0F
	1311	1530	4.2E
	1906	2123	3.8F
22 M	0117	0335	4.5E
	0724	0946	3.8F
	1353	1605	4.0E
	1951	2207	3.6F
23 Tu	0200	0416	4.3E
	0806	1028	3.8F
	1433	1643	3.9E
	2036	2253	3.5F
24 W ◐	0244	0459	4.1E
	0849	1113	3.8F
	1513	1725	3.8E
	2122	2341	3.5F
25 Th	0330	0545	4.0E
	0933	1200	3.8F
	1555	1811	3.9E
	2209		
26 F		0030	3.6F
	0420	0635	4.0E
	1021	1248	4.0F
	1639	1859	4.1E
	2258		
27 Sa		0120	3.7F
	0512	0727	4.1E
	1110	1337	4.1F
	1727	1951	4.4E
	2347		
28 Su		0212	4.0F
	0606	0822	4.3E
	1202	1429	4.4F
	1817	2044	4.8E
29 M	0037	0306	4.3F
	0701	0918	4.6E
	1254	1522	4.6F
	1909	2138	5.2E
30 Tu	0127	0401	4.6F
	0754	1014	5.0E
	1346	1616	4.9F
	2002	2232	5.7E
31 W ●	0218	0455	5.0E
	0847	1107	5.4E
	1438	1709	5.2F
	2054	2325	6.1E

August

Day	Slack	Maximum	knots
1 Th	0309	0547	5.3F
	0939	1159	5.7E
	1530	1802	5.4F
	2147		
2 F		0017	6.3E
	0359	0639	5.4F
	1030	1251	5.9E
	1621	1854	5.4F
	2240		
3 Sa		0110	6.4E
	0450	0731	5.4F
	1121	1343	6.0E
	1712	1946	5.3F
	2334		
4 Su		0203	6.3E
	0542	0822	5.2F
	1213	1435	5.9E
	1805	2039	5.1F
5 M	0029	0255	6.1E
	0634	0913	5.0F
	1306	1525	5.7E
	1900	2133	4.8F
6 Tu	0125	0347	5.7E
	0728	1005	4.7F
	1358	1617	5.4E
	1957	2230	4.4F
7 W ◐	0223	0441	5.2E
	0823	1101	4.3F
	1452	1710	5.1E
	2057	2335	4.0F
8 Th	0322	0538	4.6E
	0922	1200	4.0F
	1547	1807	4.7E
	2158		
9 F		0158	3.9F
	0423	0641	4.2E
	1021	1304	3.8F
	1643	1909	4.5E
	2259		
10 Sa		0308	4.0F
	0525	0757	4.0E
	1121	1517	3.7F
	1740	2022	4.4E
	2357		
11 Su		0409	4.2F
	0624	0935	4.1E
	1218	1619	3.9F
	1836	2154	4.6E
12 M	0052	0504	4.5F
	0721	1037	4.4E
	1312	1713	4.1F
	1930	2252	4.8E
13 Tu	0144	0555	4.7F
	0813	1128	4.7E
	1404	1800	4.2F
	2021	2337	5.0E
14 W	0233	0642	4.8F
	0902	1213	4.8E
	1453	1843	4.3F
	2109		
15 Th ○		0015	5.0E
	0320	0726	4.8F
	0947	1254	4.8E
	1540	1916	4.3F
	2154		
16 F		0045	5.0E
	0404	0807	4.6F
	1031	1328	4.7E
	1624	1859	4.2F
	2237		
17 Sa		0114	4.9E
	0446	0834	4.3F
	1112	1351	4.6E
	1706	1931	4.2F
	2319		
18 Su		0147	4.9E
	0526	0755	4.2F
	1152	1417	4.5E
	1748	2008	4.2F
19 M	0000	0223	4.8E
	0605	0828	4.2F
	1231	1449	4.4E
	1828	2048	4.1F
20 Tu	0041	0301	4.7E
	0643	0907	4.2F
	1309	1524	4.3E
	1908	2130	4.0F
21 W	0122	0341	4.6E
	0721	0948	4.2F
	1346	1604	4.4E
	1950	2215	3.9F
22 Th	0205	0425	4.5E
	0802	1034	4.1F
	1425	1647	4.4E
	2034	2303	3.8F
23 F ○	0252	0512	4.4E
	0847	1123	4.1F
	1508	1734	4.4E
	2123	2355	3.8F
24 Sa	0344	0603	4.3E
	0939	1214	4.1F
	1557	1825	4.5E
	2217		
25 Su		0049	3.9F
	0441	0658	4.3E
	1037	1308	4.2F
	1651	1919	4.7E
	2314		
26 M		0144	4.1F
	0540	0755	4.4E
	1135	1403	4.4F
	1749	2016	4.9E
27 Tu	0010	0242	4.3F
	0638	0855	4.7E
	1232	1500	4.6F
	1848	2115	5.3E
28 W	0105	0341	4.6F
	0734	0953	5.1E
	1328	1557	4.9F
	1944	2213	5.7E
29 Th	0159	0439	5.0F
	0828	1049	5.5E
	1421	1653	5.2F
	2039	2308	6.1E
30 F ●	0252	0534	5.2F
	0919	1142	5.8E
	1513	1747	5.4F
	2133		
31 Sa		0001	6.3E
	0343	0625	5.4F
	1010	1233	6.0E
	1604	1839	5.4F
	2225		

September

Day	Slack	Maximum	knots
1 Su		0054	6.3E
	0433	0714	5.4F
	1100	1324	6.1E
	1655	1930	5.3F
	2318		
2 M		0146	6.2E
	0522	0802	5.2F
	1150	1414	6.0E
	1746	2022	5.1F
3 Tu	0012	0237	5.9E
	0612	0849	4.9F
	1241	1504	5.8E
	1839	2114	4.7F
4 W	0108	0328	5.5E
	0704	0938	4.6F
	1332	1553	5.4E
	1935	2209	4.3F
5 Th ◐	0204	0420	4.9E
	0759	1030	4.1F
	1425	1645	5.0E
	2033	2318	3.9F
6 F	0302	0517	4.4E
	0857	1128	3.8F
	1519	1740	4.6E
	2133		
7 Sa		0146	3.9F
	0402	0622	3.9E
	0958	1236	3.5F
	1616	1842	4.3E
	2234		
8 Su		0248	4.0F
	0503	0754	3.8E
	1059	1457	3.5F
	1715	2001	4.1E
	2333		
9 M		0347	4.2F
	0601	0924	4.0E
	1157	1557	3.7F
	1812	2144	4.3E
10 Tu	0028	0441	4.4F
	0657	1022	4.3E
	1251	1650	4.0F
	1906	2239	4.5E
11 W	0120	0530	4.6F
	0747	1110	4.6E
	1341	1737	4.1F
	1957	2322	4.7E
12 Th	0208	0615	4.6F
	0834	1153	4.8E
	1429	1817	4.2F
	2043	2355	4.8E
13 F ○	0252	0656	4.6F
	0918	1228	4.7E
	1513	1836	4.2F
	2126		
14 Sa		0012	4.8E
	0334	0727	4.7F
	0958	1247	4.6E
	1555	1824	4.3F
	2207		
15 Su		0037	4.8E
	0413	0643	4.3F
	1036	1305	4.6E
	1634	1857	4.3F
	2247		
16 M		0110	4.9E
	0450	0713	4.4F
	1113	1334	4.6E
	1712	1934	4.4F
	2325		
17 Tu		0147	4.9E
	0526	0750	4.5F
	1148	1409	4.7E
	1749	2014	4.4F
18 W	0005	0227	4.9E
	0601	0830	4.5F
	1223	1447	4.8E
	1827	2056	4.3F
19 Th	0047	0310	4.9E
	0639	0913	4.5F
	1301	1529	4.9E
	1906	2142	4.3F
20 F ◐	0132	0355	4.8E
	0721	1000	4.4F
	1342	1614	5.0E
	1951	2231	4.2F
21 Sa	0222	0443	4.7E
	0811	1051	4.3F
	1430	1703	4.9E
	2043	2325	4.1F
22 Su	0317	0536	4.6E
	0908	1146	4.3F
	1525	1756	4.9E
	2143		
23 M		0023	4.2F
	0416	0633	4.5E
	1011	1243	4.3F
	1625	1853	4.9E
	2246		
24 Tu		0121	4.3F
	0517	0732	4.6E
	1114	1341	4.4F
	1728	1953	5.0E
	2347		
25 W		0221	4.4F
	0616	0833	4.8E
	1213	1440	4.6F
	1829	2054	5.3E
26 Th	0045	0324	4.7F
	0713	0934	5.2E
	1310	1541	4.8F
	1928	2155	5.6E
27 F	0140	0425	4.9F
	0807	1031	5.6E
	1404	1639	5.1F
	2024	2252	5.9E
28 Sa ●	0233	0521	5.2F
	0859	1124	5.9E
	1456	1734	5.3F
	2117	2345	6.1E
29 Su	0323	0609	5.3F
	0948	1214	6.1E
	1547	1825	5.3F
	2210		
30 M		0037	6.1E
	0412	0654	5.2F
	1037	1304	6.1E
	1637	1916	5.2F
	2302		

Time meridian 75° W. 0000 is midnight. 1200 is noon. Times are not adjusted for Daylight Saving Time.

Cape Cod Canal (RR. Bridge), Massachusetts, 2019

F–Flood, Dir. 070° True   E–Ebb, Dir. 250° True

October

Day	Slack	Maximum	knots
1 Tu		0128	5.9E
	0501	0739	5.0F
	1126	1353	6.0E
	1727	2006	4.9F
	2356		
2 W		0219	5.6E
	0550	0824	4.8F
	1215	1441	5.8E
	1819	2057	4.6F
3 Th	0050	0310	5.2E
	0642	0911	4.4F
	1306	1530	5.4E
	1913	2151	4.2F
4 F	0146	0402	4.7E
	0737	1002	4.0F
	1359	1620	4.9E
	2009		
5 Sa ◑		0025	3.9F
	0242	0459	4.2E
	0835	1100	3.6F
	1454	1714	4.5E
	2108		
6 Su		0127	3.9F
	0340	0606	3.8E
	0935	1216	3.3F
	1551	1815	4.1E
	2208		
7 M		0224	4.0F
	0438	0749	3.8E
	1036	1433	3.4F
	1649	1936	3.9E
	2306		
8 Tu		0320	4.1F
	0535	0903	4.0E
	1133	1531	3.6F
	1746	2122	4.0E
9 W	0001	0412	4.2E
	0628	0959	4.2E
	1226	1623	3.8F
	1839	2215	4.2E
10 Th	0051	0500	4.3F
	0717	1046	4.4E
	1315	1708	4.0F
	1928	2256	4.4E
11 F	0137	0543	4.3F
	0802	1126	4.5E
	1400	1743	4.0F
	2013	2317	4.5E
12 Sa	0220	0616	4.2F
	0843	1150	4.5E
	1442	1720	4.1F
	2055	2329	4.6E
13 Su ○	0259	0531	4.2F
	0921	1155	4.5E
	1522	1747	4.2F
	2135	2358	4.7E
14 M	0336	0559	4.4F
	0957	1220	4.7E
	1600	1822	4.4F
	2213		
15 Tu		0034	4.8E
	0412	0635	4.6F
	1031	1254	4.9E
	1636	1901	4.5F
	2252		
16 W		0114	5.0E
	0447	0715	4.7F
	1105	1333	5.1E
	1712	1942	4.6F
	2333		
17 Th		0156	5.1E
	0524	0757	4.8F
	1141	1415	5.3E
	1749	2026	4.7F
18 F	0017	0242	5.1E
	0605	0843	4.8F
	1222	1459	5.4E
	1831	2113	4.6F
19 Sa	0105	0329	5.1E
	0651	0932	4.7F
	1309	1547	5.4E
	1919	2204	4.5F
20 Su	0158	0419	5.0E
	0745	1024	4.5F
	1403	1638	5.3E
	2015	2300	4.4F
21 M ○	0254	0513	4.9E
	0845	1122	4.4F
	1502	1732	5.2E
	2118		
22 Tu		0000	4.4F
	0354	0610	4.8E
	0950	1222	4.4F
	1605	1831	5.1E
	2223		
23 W		0101	4.4F
	0455	0710	4.8E
	1054	1322	4.4F
	1709	1932	5.1E
	2326		
24 Th		0203	4.5F
	0554	0812	4.9E
	1154	1423	4.5F
	1811	2035	5.2E
25 F	0025	0307	4.6F
	0651	0914	5.2E
	1251	1525	4.7F
	1910	2137	5.4E
26 Sa	0120	0411	4.8F
	0745	1012	5.5E
	1345	1628	4.9F
	2007	2235	5.7E
27 Su ●	0212	0506	5.0F
	0836	1105	5.8E
	1438	1726	5.1F
	2101	2329	5.8E
28 M	0302	0550	5.1F
	0925	1155	6.0E
	1529	1819	5.1F
	2154		
29 Tu		0021	5.7E
	0351	0632	5.0F
	1013	1243	6.0E
	1618	1909	5.0F
	2246		
30 W		0112	5.5E
	0440	0715	4.8F
	1102	1332	5.9E
	1708	1959	4.7F
	2339		
31 Th		0204	5.2E
	0529	0800	4.5F
	1151	1420	5.6E
	1759	2051	4.4F

November

Day	Slack	Maximum	knots
1 F	0032	0255	4.9E
	0621	0848	4.2F
	1242	1508	5.3E
	1851	2302	4.2F
2 Sa	0126	0347	4.5E
	0716	0939	3.8F
	1335	1558	4.8E
	1945		
3 Su		0005	4.1F
	0221	0442	4.2E
	0813	1037	3.5F
	1429	1650	4.4E
	2042		
4 M ◑		0102	4.0F
	0315	0548	3.9E
	0911	1305	3.4F
	1524	1747	4.0E
	2139		
5 Tu		0156	3.9F
	0410	0724	3.8E
	1009	1402	3.4F
	1620	1853	3.8E
	2235		
6 W		0248	3.9F
	0503	0833	3.8E
	1105	1456	3.5F
	1715	2042	3.7E
	2328		
7 Th		0338	3.9F
	0555	0929	4.0E
	1156	1547	3.5F
	1806	2138	3.8E
8 F	0017	0424	3.9F
	0642	1016	4.1E
	1244	1630	3.6F
	1854	2206	3.9E
9 Sa	0101	0501	3.8F
	0725	1048	4.1E
	1328	1602	3.7F
	1939	2213	4.1E
10 Su	0142	0410	3.9F
	0804	1043	4.2E
	1409	1634	3.9F
	2021	2244	4.3E
11 M	0221	0443	4.2F
	0841	1106	4.5E
	1448	1710	4.2F
	2102	2320	4.6E
12 Tu ○	0258	0521	4.5F
	0911	1139	4.8E
	1525	1749	4.5F
	2142		
13 W		0000	4.8E
	0335	0601	4.7F
	0951	1218	5.2E
	1602	1830	4.7F
	2223		
14 Th		0043	5.0E
	0413	0644	4.9F
	1028	1301	5.5E
	1639	1914	4.9F
	2306		
15 F		0129	5.2E
	0454	0729	5.0F
	1108	1346	5.7E
	1720	2000	5.0F
	2353		
16 Sa		0217	5.3E
	0539	0817	5.0F
	1154	1434	5.8E
	1805	2050	5.0F
17 Su	0044	0307	5.4E
	0629	0908	4.9F
	1247	1524	5.8E
	1857	2142	4.8F
18 M	0138	0358	5.3E
	0725	1002	4.7F
	1344	1616	5.7E
	1954	2238	4.7F
19 Tu ○	0234	0452	5.1E
	0826	1100	4.5F
	1444	1711	5.5E
	2057	2339	4.5F
20 W	0333	0549	5.0E
	0929	1201	4.4F
	1546	1810	5.3E
	2201		
21 Th		0042	4.5F
	0432	0648	4.9E
	1033	1303	4.4F
	1650	1911	5.1E
	2303		
22 F		0143	4.5F
	0530	0749	5.0E
	1134	1405	4.4F
	1752	2014	5.1E
23 Sa	0002	0246	4.6F
	0627	0852	5.2E
	1232	1512	4.5F
	1852	2118	5.1E
24 Su	0057	0351	4.7F
	0721	0952	5.4E
	1327	1641	4.7F
	1950	2220	5.2E
25 M	0149	0450	4.7F
	0812	1047	5.7E
	1419	1803	4.8F
	2045	2316	5.3E
26 Tu ●	0240	0533	4.7F
	0902	1137	5.8E
	1511	1902	4.9F
	2138		
27 W		0008	5.3E
	0330	0613	4.7F
	0951	1225	5.8E
	1600	1958	4.9F
	2230		
28 Th		0100	5.2E
	0420	0655	4.5F
	1039	1313	5.7E
	1649	2052	4.8F
	2321		
29 F		0152	5.0E
	0510	0741	4.3F
	1129	1401	5.5E
	1739	2146	4.6F
30 Sa	0013	0243	4.8E
	0601	0829	4.1F
	1219	1449	5.2E
	1829	2242	4.3F

December

Day	Slack	Maximum	knots
1 Su	0104	0333	4.5E
	0654	0919	3.8F
	1311	1536	4.8E
	1921	2338	4.1F
2 M	0156	0424	4.3E
	0749	1013	3.6F
	1403	1625	4.4E
	2014		
3 Tu		0032	4.0F
	0247	0519	4.0E
	0843	1113	3.4F
	1455	1715	4.1E
	2107		
4 W ◑		0122	3.8F
	0337	0624	3.7E
	0938	1217	3.3F
	1547	1807	3.8E
	2200		
5 Th		0209	3.6F
	0427	0744	3.6E
	1031	1304	3.2F
	1639	1859	3.6E
	2250		
6 F		0252	3.5F
	0515	0843	3.5E
	1121	1345	3.2F
	1729	1948	3.6E
	2337		
7 Sa		0201	3.5F
	0600	0844	3.5E
	1208	1426	3.3F
	1817	2035	3.6E
8 Su	0021	0239	3.6F
	0642	0908	3.7E
	1252	1509	3.5F
	1902	2119	3.8E
9 M	0102	0320	3.9F
	0722	0944	4.1E
	1333	1552	3.8F
	1946	2203	4.1E
10 Tu	0142	0403	4.2F
	0759	1023	4.5E
	1412	1636	4.2F
	2029	2246	4.5E
11 W	0222	0447	4.5F
	0837	1104	5.0E
	1451	1719	4.5F
	2113	2331	4.8E
12 Th ○	0303	0531	4.8F
	0917	1147	5.5E
	1531	1804	4.9F
	2157		
13 F		0017	5.2E
	0346	0617	5.1F
	0959	1234	5.8E
	1613	1850	5.1F
	2243		
14 Sa		0105	5.4E
	0431	0706	5.2F
	1045	1322	6.0E
	1658	1939	5.2F
	2332		
15 Su		0155	5.6E
	0519	0756	5.2F
	1135	1413	6.1E
	1746	2029	5.2F
16 M		0246	5.6E
	0611	0848	5.1F
	1230	1504	6.1E
	1839	2122	5.1F
17 Tu	0118	0338	5.6E
	0707	0942	4.9F
	1327	1557	6.0E
	1936	2218	4.9F
18 W ○	0214	0431	5.4E
	0806	1040	4.7F
	1427	1652	5.7E
	2037	2318	4.7F
19 Th ◑	0310	0527	5.2E
	0908	1141	4.5F
	1528	1749	5.3E
	2138		
20 F		0019	4.5F
	0408	0625	5.0E
	1011	1244	4.3F
	1630	1850	5.0E
	2239		
21 Sa		0120	4.4F
	0505	0725	5.0E
	1112	1349	4.2F
	1733	1953	4.8E
	2338		
22 Su		0220	4.4F
	0602	0828	5.0E
	1211	1553	4.3F
	1834	2100	4.7E
23 M	0034	0328	4.3F
	0656	0931	5.2E
	1307	1707	4.5F
	1933	2208	4.8E
24 Tu	0128	0507	4.4F
	0749	1030	5.4E
	1401	1805	4.8F
	2028	2309	4.9E
25 W	0220	0558	4.4F
	0840	1122	5.5E
	1452	1858	4.9F
	2121		
26 Th ●		0003	5.0E
	0311	0639	4.4F
	0930	1210	5.5E
	1542	1949	5.0F
	2212		
27 F ○		0054	5.0E
	0401	0649	4.3F
	1019	1258	5.5E
	1630	2039	4.9F
	2302		
28 Sa		0145	4.9E
	0451	0730	4.3F
	1107	1345	5.3E
	1718	2127	4.7F
	2350		
29 Su		0232	4.8E
	0540	0814	4.1F
	1156	1430	5.1E
	1806	2215	4.4F
30 M	0039	0316	4.6E
	0630	0858	4.0F
	1246	1514	4.8E
	1854	2304	4.1F
31 Tu	0127	0357	4.4E
	0721	0944	3.8F
	1334	1557	4.5E
	1943	2352	3.8F

Time meridian 75° W. 0000 is midnight. 1200 is noon. Times are not adjusted for Daylight Saving Time.

Quonset Point, Narragansett Bay, Rhode Island, 2019

F–Flood, Dir. 021° True   E–Ebb, Dir. 200° True

January

Day	Slack (h m)	Maximum (h m)	knots
1 Tu		0143	0.3F
	0356	0649	0.4E
	1128	1412	0.3F
	1624	1911	0.4E
	2234		
2 W		0238	0.3F
	0458	0746	0.5E
	1206	1512	0.3F
	1721	2003	0.4E
	2308		
3 Th		0338	0.3F
	0553	0836	0.5E
	1229	1609	0.3F
	1812	2052	0.5E
	2347		
4 F		0432	0.3F
	0641	0924	0.5E
	1250	1656	0.3F
	1858	2139	0.5E
5 Sa ●	0029	0516	0.3F
	0725	1010	0.5E
	1322	1737	0.3F
	1941	2225	0.5E
6 Su	0112	0553	0.3F
	0807	1055	0.5E
	1402	1814	0.3F
	2023	2309	0.5E
7 M	0158	0629	0.3F
	0847	1138	0.5E
	1445	1852	0.3F
	2106	2354	0.5E
8 Tu	0245	0707	0.3F
	0927	1222	0.5E
		1933	*
9 W		0039	0.4E
		0750	*
		1306	0.5E
		2018	*
10 Th		0125	0.4E
		0838	*
		1348	0.4E
		2104	*
11 F		0207	0.4E
		0926	*
		1424	0.4E
		2148	*
12 Sa		0243	0.3E
		1014	*
		1456	0.3E
		2232	*
13 Su		0315	0.3E
		1103	*
		1529	0.3E
		2319	*
14 M ◑		0350	0.3E
		1153	*
		1609	0.3E
15 Tu		0007	*
		0438	0.3E
		1242	*
		1706	0.3E
16 W		0053	*
		0604	0.3E
	1134	1330	*
	1710	1825	0.3E
17 Th		0143	*
		0720	0.3E
		1425	*
		1927	0.4E
18 F		0243	*
		0808	0.4E
		1528	*
		2018	0.4E
	2323		
19 Sa		0350	0.3F
	0603	0855	0.4E
	1228	1627	0.3F
	1827	2108	0.5E
20 Su	0011	0447	0.3F
	0656	0942	0.5E
	1315	1719	0.3F
	1919	2157	0.5E
21 M ○	0100	0537	0.4F
	0747	1030	0.5E
	1405	1808	0.4F
	2011	2247	0.5E
22 Tu	0150	0627	0.4F
	0838	1118	0.5E
	1456	1900	0.4F
	2104	2336	0.6E
23 W	0243	0721	0.4F
	0931	1207	0.5E
	1542	1955	0.4F
	2157		
24 Th		0028	0.5E
	0335	0819	0.5F
	1023	1258	0.5E
	1623	2052	0.3F
	2250		
25 F		0122	0.5E
	0427	0917	0.3F
	1117	1350	*
	1704	2147	0.3F
	2345		
26 Sa		0216	0.5E
		0620	*
		0711	*
		1014	*
	1212	1441†	0.5E
27 Su ◐	0040	0308	0.5E
		0702	*
		0758	*
		1110	0.3F
	1306	1530†	0.4E
28 M	0136	0402	0.4E
	0936	1205	0.3F
	1400	1624	0.4E
	2109		
29 Tu		0030	0.3F
	0232	0507	0.4E
	1034	1258	0.3F
	1455	1733	0.3E
	2133		
30 W		0122	0.3F
	0331	0624	0.4E
		1349	*
		1845	0.4E
	2209		
31 Th		0215	0.3F
	0433	0726	0.4E
		1444	*
		1942	0.4E
	2248		

February

Day	Slack (h m)	Maximum (h m)	knots
1 F		0313	0.3F
	0530	0817	0.4E
		1542	*
		2032	0.4E
	2329		
2 Sa		0408	0.3F
	0619	0904	0.5E
	1229	1631	0.3F
	1835	2119	0.5E
3 Su	0010	0451	0.3F
	0701	0949	0.5E
	1259	1711	0.3F
	1917	2205	0.5E
4 M ●	0053	0526	0.3F
	0740	1033	0.5E
	1337	1745	0.3F
	1958	2249	0.5E
5 Tu	0138	0558	0.3F
	0818	1114	0.5E
	1417	1818	0.3F
	2037	2331	0.5E
6 W	0225	0632	0.3F
	0855	1153	0.5E
	1456	1853	0.3F
	2115		
7 Th		0012	0.5E
	0310	0711	0.3F
	0933	1232	0.5E
		1933	*
8 F		0052	0.4E
		0758	*
		1309	0.4E
		2018	*
9 Sa		0131	0.4E
		0850	*
		1345	0.4E
		2106	*
10 Su		0206	0.4E
		0941	*
		1420	0.4E
		1901	*
		2002†	*
11 M		0240	0.4E
		1032	*
		1457	0.4E
		1948	*
		2041†	*
12 Tu ◐		0318	0.3E
		1124	*
		1538	0.3E
		2339	*
13 W		0402	0.3E
		1216	*
		1630	0.3E
14 Th		0032	*
		0505	0.3E
		1308	*
		1741	0.3E
15 F		0124	*
		0638	0.3E
		1402	*
		1858	0.4E
	2212		
16 Sa		0222	0.3F
	0441	0744	0.4E
	1134	1504	0.3F
	1710	1957	0.4E
	2306		
17 Su		0328	0.3F
	0545	0835	0.4E
	1219	1606	0.3F
	1810	2049	0.5E
	2356		
18 M		0429	0.4F
	0640	0925	0.5E
	1304	1701	0.4F
	1903	2140	0.5E
19 Tu ○	0046	0521	0.4F
	0731	1013	0.5E
	1350	1750	0.3F
	1955	2231	0.6E
20 W	0138	0611	0.4F
	0822	1100	0.6E
	1435	1840	0.4F
	2046	2320	0.6E
21 Th	0232	0703	0.4F
	0913	1148	0.6E
	1515	1933	0.4F
	2138		
22 F		0010	0.6E
	0325	0759	0.4F
	1004	1237	0.5E
	1553	2029	0.4F
	2230		
23 Sa		0103	0.5E
	0415	0857	0.3F
	1056	1328	0.5E
	1630	2124	0.3F
	2322		
24 Su		0156	0.5E
		0557	*
		0651	*
		0953	0.3F
	1148	1418†	0.4E
25 M	0017	0248	0.4E
		0633	*
		0744	*
		1049	0.3F
	1241	1507†	0.4E
26 Tu ◑	0112	0339	0.4E
		0720	*
		0830	*
		1144	*
		1558†	0.4E
27 W		0009	0.3F
	0207	0439	0.3E
		0822	*
		0910	*
		1236†	*
28 Th		0100	*
		0555	0.3E
		1325	*
		1818	0.3E

March

Day	Slack (h m)	Maximum (h m)	knots
1 F		0150	*
		0704	0.3E
		1415	*
		1921	0.4E
2 Sa		0241	*
		0757	0.4E
		1509	*
		2013	0.4E
3 Su		0335	*
		0843	0.4E
		1601	*
		2100	0.4E
	2354		
4 M		0421	0.3F
	0633	0927	0.5E
	1233	1642	0.3F
	1852	2144	0.5E
5 Tu	0036	0457	0.3F
	0711	1008	0.5E
	1307	1715	0.3F
	1930	2227	0.5E
6 W ●	0119	0529	0.3F
	0747	1047	0.5E
	1344	1745	0.3F
	2006	2306	0.5E
7 Th	0204	0602	0.3F
	0824	1123	0.5E
	1422	1817	0.3F
	2041	2342	0.5E
8 F	0248	0640	0.3F
	0901	1156	0.5E
	1458	1852	0.3F
	2117		
9 Sa		0017	0.5E
	0331	0725	0.3F
	0940	1231	0.4E
		1935	*
10 Su		0053	0.4E
		0818	*
		1307	0.4E
		1804	*
		1858†	*
11 M		0130	0.4E
		0911	*
		1348	0.4E
		1831	*
		1947†	*
12 Tu ◐		0210	0.4E
		1005	*
		1430	0.4E
		1912	*
		2025†	*
13 W		0252	0.4E
		1059	*
		1515	0.4E
		2009	*
		2057†	*
14 Th ◑		0339	0.4E
		1154	*
		1606	0.4E
15 F		0013	*
		0438	0.3E
		1248	*
		1711	0.4E
	2047		
16 Sa		0107	0.3F
		0604	0.3E
	1036	1342	0.3F
	1544	1832	0.4E
	2154		
17 Su		0203	0.3F
	0420	0721	0.4E
	1125	1441	0.3F
	1651	1937	0.4E
	2253		
18 M		0307	0.3F
	0526	0816	0.5E
	1207	1544	0.3F
	1752	2032	0.5E
	2346		
19 Tu		0410	0.4F
	0622	0906	0.5E
	1245	1640	0.3F
	1846	2124	0.6E
20 W ○	0037	0504	0.4F
	0714	0954	0.6E
	1324	1731	0.4F
	1937	2214	0.6E
21 Th	0129	0554	0.4F
	0804	1040	0.6E
	1402	1819	0.4F
	2027	2303	0.6E
22 F	0222	0644	0.4F
	0854	1127	0.6E
	1441	1910	0.4F
	2117	2352	0.6E
23 Sa	0314	0738	0.4F
	0943	1214	0.5E
	1520	2005	0.3F
	2208		
24 Su		0043	0.5E
	0401	0835	0.3F
	1033	1304	0.5E
		1717	*
		1802†	*
25 M		0135	0.5E
	0445	0930	0.3F
	1122	1354	0.4E
		1748	*
		1907†	*
26 Tu		0227	0.4E
		0609	*
		0727	*
		1025	*
		1444†	0.4E
27 W ◑		0317	0.4E
		0652	*
		0814	*
		1119	*
		1533†	0.3E
28 Th		0411	0.3E
		0747	*
		0855	*
		1211	*
		1630†	0.3E
29 F		0035	*
		0521	0.3E
		1258	*
		1747	0.3E
30 Sa		0121	*
		0637	0.3E
		1343	*
		1859	0.3E
31 Su		0204	*
		0733	0.4E
		1429	*
		1953	0.4E

Time meridian 75° W. 0000 is midnight. 1200 is noon. Times are not adjusted for Daylight Saving Time.

* Current weak and variable.

† See page 196 for the remaining currents on this day.

Quonset Point, Narragansett Bay, Rhode Island, 2019

F–Flood, Dir. 021° True   E–Ebb, Dir. 200° True

April (Days 1–15)

Date	Slack (h m)	Maximum (h m)	knots
1 M		0251	*
		0819	0.4E
		1518	*
		2039	0.4E
2 Tu		0341	*
		0901	0.4E
		1604	*
		2122	0.4E
3 W	0019	0423	0.3F
	0640	0940	0.5E
	1234	1640	0.3F
	1859	2202	0.5E
4 Th	0100	0500	0.3F
	0716	1017	0.5E
	1308	1713	0.3F
	1933	2239	0.5E
5 F ●	0142	0536	0.3F
	0753	1050	0.5E
	1344	1746	0.3F
	2007	2312	0.5E
6 Sa	0224	0615	0.3F
	0830	1122	0.5E
	1422	1821	0.3F
	2044	2344	0.5E
7 Su	0305	0658	0.3F
	0910	1156	0.5E
	1500	1903	0.3F
	2124		
8 M		0019	0.5E
	0344	0750	0.3F
	0953	1235	0.5E
	1959		
9 Tu		0100	0.4E
		0846	*
		1320	0.5E
		1807	*
		1921†	*
10 W		0145	0.4E
		0941	*
		1407	0.4E
		1845	*
		1959†	*
11 Th		0232	0.4E
		1037	*
		1456	0.4E
		2257	*
12 F ◑		0322	0.4E
	0716	1133	0.3F
	1322	1547	0.4E
	1908	2354	0.3F
13 Sa	0151	0419	0.4E
	0915	1229	0.3F
	1422	1649	0.4E
	2027		
14 Su		0049	0.3F
	0253	0536	0.4E
	1022	1322	0.3F
	1525	1808	0.4E
	2140		
15 M		0145	0.3F
	0359	0657	0.4E
	1108	1419	0.3F
	1631	1919	0.5E
	2244		

April (Days 16–30)

Date	Slack (h m)	Maximum (h m)	knots
16 Tu		0245	0.3F
	0505	0754	0.5E
	1145	1520	0.4F
	1732	2015	0.5E
	2339		
17 W		0349	0.4F
	0603	0844	0.5E
	1217	1618	0.4F
	1827	2107	0.6E
18 Th	0030	0446	0.4F
	0655	0932	0.6E
	1251	1710	0.4F
	1918	2157	0.6E
19 F ○	0121	0536	0.4F
	0744	1019	0.6E
	1328	1758	0.4F
	2007	2245	0.6E
20 Sa	0212	0625	0.4F
	0832	1105	0.5E
	1407	1847	0.4F
	2056	2333	0.6E
21 Su	0300	0716	0.3F
	0920	1151	0.5E
	1449	1940	0.3F
	2146		
22 M		0022	0.5E
	0343	0810	0.3F
	1007	1240	0.5E
	1532	2035	0.3F
	2235		
23 Tu		0114	0.5E
		0519	*
		0602	*
		0905	*
		1331†	0.4E
24 W		0206	0.4E
		0550	*
		0705	*
		0957	*
		1421†	0.4E
25 Th		0255	0.4E
		0631	*
		0753	*
		1049	*
		1510†	0.3E
26 F ◑		0344	0.3E
		0723	*
		0833	*
		1140	*
		1602†	0.3E
27 Sa		0003	*
		0442	0.3E
		1226	*
		1710	0.3E
28 Su		0046	*
		0559	0.3E
		1307	*
		1831	0.3E
29 M		0125	*
		0703	0.3E
		1346	*
		1930	0.3E
30 Tu		0205	*
		0751	0.3E
		1426	*
		2017	0.4E

May (Days 1–15)

Date	Slack (h m)	Maximum (h m)	knots
1 W		0252	*
		0832	0.4E
		1512	*
		2058	0.4E
2 Th		0345	*
		0909	0.4E
		1600	*
		2135	0.4E
3 F	0040	0431	0.3F
	0644	0943	0.4E
	1232	1642	0.3F
	1859	2209	0.4E
4 Sa ●	0118	0512	0.3F
	0722	1015	0.4E
	1309	1720	0.3F
	1936	2240	0.5E
5 Su	0158	0552	0.3F
	0801	1049	0.5E
	1348	1759	0.3F
	2016	2313	0.5E
6 M	0238	0636	0.3F
	0844	1127	0.5E
	1430	1843	0.3F
	2100	2351	0.5E
7 Tu	0319	0727	0.3F
	0929	1209	0.5E
	1513	1938	0.3F
	2149		
8 W		0035	0.5E
	0400	0824	0.3F
	1019	1256	0.5E
		1748	*
		1847†	*
9 Th		0124	0.5E
	0445	0921	0.3F
	1112	1347	0.5E
		1824	*
		1929†	*
10 F		0215	0.5E
	0538	1017	0.3F
	1208	1438	0.5E
		1911	*
		2004†	*
11 Sa ◑	0035	0307	0.4E
	0653	1114	0.3F
	1306	1531	0.4E
	1846	2336	0.3F
12 Su	0134	0402	0.4E
	0856	1209	0.3F
	1405	1630	0.4E
	2010		
13 M		0031	0.3F
	0234	0509	0.4E
	1000	1302	0.3F
	1506	1744	0.4E
	2134		
14 Tu		0126	0.3F
	0337	0629	0.4E
	1043	1356	0.4F
	1609	1859	0.5E
	2244		
15 W		0224	0.3F
	0442	0731	0.5E
	1116	1455	0.4F
	1711	1957	0.5E
	2339		

May (Days 16–31)

Date	Slack (h m)	Maximum (h m)	knots
16 Th		0327	0.4F
	0542	0822	0.5E
	1146	1556	0.4F
	1807	2049	0.6E
17 F	0027	0426	0.4F
	0634	0910	0.5E
	1220	1650	0.4F
	1858	2139	0.6E
18 Sa ○	0113	0517	0.4F
	0723	0958	0.5E
	1257	1738	0.4F
	1947	2227	0.6E
19 Su	0158	0604	0.4F
	0809	1044	0.5E
	1339	1825	0.4F
	2035	2314	0.6E
20 M	0241	0652	0.3F
	0855	1130	0.5E
	1423	1914	0.3F
	2123		
21 Tu		0002	0.5E
	0321	0742	0.3F
	0942	1217	0.5E
	1509	2006	0.3F
	2211		
22 W		0051	0.5E
		0835	*
		1308	0.4E
		1716	*
		1818†	*
23 Th		0142	0.4E
		0539	*
		0636	*
		0926	*
		1359†	0.4E
24 F		0231	0.4E
		0617	*
		0727	*
		1015	*
		1448†	0.4E
25 Sa		0317	0.4E
		0705	*
		0807	*
		1102	*
		1535†	0.3E
26 Su ◑		0403	0.3E
		1147	*
		1629	0.3E
27 M		0006	*
		0503	0.3E
		1227	*
		1750	0.3E
28 Tu		0046	*
		0620	0.3E
		1304	*
		1901	0.3E
29 W		0126	*
		0716	0.3E
		1340	*
		1950	0.3E
30 Th		0211	*
		0758	0.3E
		1422	*
		2030	0.4E
31 F		0304	*
		0833	0.4E
		1516	*
		2105	0.4E

June (Days 1–15)

Date	Slack (h m)	Maximum (h m)	knots
1 Sa		0400	*
		0906	0.4E
		1611	*
		2137	0.4E
2 Su	0054	0448	0.3F
	0652	0942	0.4E
	1237	1658	0.3F
	1910	2210	0.4E
3 M ●	0132	0532	0.3F
	0735	1020	0.5E
	1319	1742	0.3F
	1954	2247	0.5E
4 Tu	0214	0617	0.3F
	0821	1102	0.5E
	1404	1828	0.3F
	2042	2329	0.5E
5 W	0258	0707	0.3F
	0909	1147	0.5E
	1451	1922	0.3F
	2132		
6 Th		0015	0.5E
	0343	0804	0.3F
	1001	1236	0.5E
	1538	2023	0.3F
	2225		
7 F		0106	0.5E
	0430	0901	0.3F
	1055	1329	0.5E
		1807	*
		1855†	*
8 Sa		0159	0.5E
	0521	0958	0.3F
	1152	1422	0.5E
	1721	2219	0.3F
9 Su	0018	0251	0.5E
	0626	1053	0.3F
	1249	1514	0.5E
	1827	2317	0.3F
10 M ◑	0116	0343	0.5E
	0814	1149	0.3F
	1347	1611	0.4E
	1957		
11 Tu		0013	0.3F
	0215	0444	0.4E
	0929	1242	0.3F
	1445	1720	0.4E
	2144		
12 W		0108	0.3F
	0315	0558	0.4E
	1012	1335	0.4F
	1547	1837	0.4E
	2254		
13 Th		0204	0.3F
	0418	0706	0.4E
	1044	1431	0.4F
	1649	1939	0.5E
	2346		
14 F		0305	0.3F
	0519	0800	0.5E
	1117	1533	0.4F
	1747	2031	0.5E
15 Sa	0029	0406	0.3F
	0612	0849	0.5E
	1153	1630	0.4F
	1839	2120	0.6E

June (Days 16–30)

Date	Slack (h m)	Maximum (h m)	knots
16 Su	0105	0458	0.3F
	0700	0936	0.5E
	1232	1719	0.4F
	1928	2208	0.6E
17 M ○	0139	0544	0.3F
	0746	1023	0.5E
	1315	1803	0.4F
	2014	2255	0.5E
18 Tu	0217	0627	0.3F
	0831	1109	0.5E
	1401	1847	0.3F
	2059	2341	0.5E
19 W	0256	0712	0.3F
	0916	1156	0.5E
	1448	1933	0.3F
	2143		
20 Th		0028	0.5E
		0800	*
		1244	0.5E
		2021	*
21 F		0116	0.5E
		0849	*
		1335	0.4E
		1745	*
		1842†	*
22 Sa		0203	0.4E
		0611	*
		0655	*
		0935	*
		1423†	0.4E
23 Su		0246	0.4E
		0651	*
		0740	*
		1019	*
		1507†	0.3E
24 M		0325	0.3E
		1102	*
		1548	0.3E
	2325		
25 Tu ◑		0403	0.3E
		1143	*
		1637	0.3E
26 W		0010	*
		0452	0.3E
		1224	*
		1810	
27 Th		0053	*
		0614	0.3E
		1303	*
		1915	0.3E
28 F		0138	*
		0712	0.3E
		1345	*
		1957	0.3E
29 Sa		0229	*
		0752	0.3E
		1439	*
		2031	0.4E
30 Su		0328	*
		0831	0.4E
		1543	*
		2106	0.4E

Time meridian 75° W. 0000 is midnight. 1200 is noon. Times are not adjusted for Daylight Saving Time.
* Current weak and variable.
† See page 196 for the remaining currents on this day.

Quonset Point, Narragansett Bay, Rhode Island, 2019

F–Flood, Dir. 021° True   E–Ebb, Dir. 200° True

July

Day	Slack (h m)	Maximum (h m)	knots
1 M	0030	0424	0.3F
	0625	0911	0.4E
	1211	1639	0.3F
	1849	2144	0.4E
2 Tu ●	0109	0513	0.3F
	0713	0955	0.5E
	1256	1727	0.3F
	1937	2226	0.5E
3 W	0154	0559	0.3F
	0801	1041	0.5E
	1343	1814	0.3F
	2026	2310	0.5E
4 Th	0241	0649	0.3F
	0852	1128	0.5E
	1432	1907	0.3F
	2117	2357	0.5E
5 F	0329	0744	0.3F
	0945	1218	0.5E
	1523	2005	0.3F
	2210		
6 Sa		0048	0.5E
	0414	0841	0.3F
	1039	1311	0.5E
	1613	2104	0.3F
	2304		
7 Su		0141	0.5E
	0501	0937	0.3F
	1134	1405	0.5E
	1706	2201	0.3F
8 M	0000	0233	0.5E
	0553	1033	0.3F
	1230	1458	0.5E
	1810	2258	0.3F
9 Tu ◐	0057	0324	0.5E
	0700	1128	0.3F
	1327	1552	0.5E
	1955	2355	0.3F
10 W	0154	0418	0.4E
	0836	1222	0.3F
	1424	1655	0.4E
	2202		
11 Th		0050	0.3F
	0252	0526	0.4E
	0938	1315	0.3F
	1524	1813	0.4E
	2302		
12 F		0144	0.3F
	0353	0639	0.4E
	1016	1410	0.3F
	1627	1919	0.4E
	2351		
13 Sa		0242	0.3F
	0454	0737	0.4E
	1053	1510	0.3F
	1728	2013	0.5E
14 Su	0029	0343	0.3F
	0549	0828	0.5E
	1131	1609	0.3F
	1821	2102	0.5E
15 M	0053	0437	0.3F
	0638	0916	0.5E
	1212	1659	0.4F
	1908	2149	0.5E
16 Tu ○	0116	0521	0.3F
	0723	1004	0.5E
	1255	1740	0.3F
	1951	2235	0.5E
17 W	0149	0601	0.3F
	0807	1050	0.5E
	1340	1819	0.3F
	2033	2319	0.5E
18 Th	0228	0640	0.3F
	0850	1135	0.5E
	1427	1857	0.3F
	2113		
19 F		0003	0.5E
	0308	0721	0.3F
	0933	1221	0.5E
	1514	1939	0.3F
	2153		
20 Sa		0047	0.5E
		0805	*
		1308	0.4E
		2024	*
21 Su		0131	0.5E
		0849	*
		1354	0.4E
		2111	*
22 M		0212	0.4E
		0932	*
		1435	0.4E
		2158	*
23 Tu		0247	0.4E
		0714	*
		0802	*
		1015	*
		1509†	0.3E
24 W ◐		0319	0.3E
		1100	*
		1541	0.3E
		2335	*
25 Th		0355	0.3E
		1147	*
		1621	0.3E
26 F		0022	*
		0442	0.3E
		1233	*
		1734	*
27 Sa		0110	*
		0557	0.3E
		1320	*
		1911	0.3E
28 Su		0200	*
		0708	0.3E
		1413	*
		1956	0.3E
29 M		0258	*
		0759	0.4E
		1518	*
		2037	0.4E
30 Tu	0011	0400	0.3F
	0601	0846	0.4E
	1150	1620	0.3F
	1830	2121	0.4E
31 W ●	0052	0453	0.3F
	0653	0934	0.5E
	1237	1711	0.3F
	1920	2206	0.5E

August

Day	Slack (h m)	Maximum (h m)	knots
1 Th	0137	0542	0.3F
	0744	1022	0.5E
	1326	1759	0.4F
	2010	2252	0.5E
2 F	0224	0631	0.4F
	0835	1111	0.5E
	1417	1850	0.4F
	2101	2339	0.5E
3 Sa	0310	0724	0.4F
	0928	1200	0.6E
	1509	1947	0.4F
	2153		
4 Su		0029	0.5E
	0353	0820	0.4F
	1020	1253	0.6E
	1601	2045	0.3F
	2247		
5 M		0121	0.5E
	0435	0916	0.3F
	1114	1347	0.5E
	1653	2143	0.3F
	2341		
6 Tu		0213	0.5E
		0622	*
		0709	*
		1012	0.3F
	1209	1440†	0.5E
7 W ◐	0037	0303	0.5E
		0703	*
		0759	*
		1107	0.3F
	1306	1532†	0.4E
8 Th	0132	0354	0.4E
		0758	*
		0844	*
		1203	0.3F
	1403	1631†	0.4E
9 F		0032	0.3F
	0228	0455	0.4E
	0856	1257	0.3F
	1502	1746	0.4E
	2300		
10 Sa		0124	0.3F
	0326	0611	0.4E
	1000	1350	0.3F
	1605	1858	0.4E
	2346		
11 Su		0219	0.3F
	0427	0716	0.4E
	1037	1447	0.3F
	1707	1954	0.4E
12 M	0019	0317	0.3F
	0525	0809	0.4E
	1116	1546	0.3F
	1759	2042	0.5E
13 Tu	0033	0412	0.3F
	0616	0857	0.5E
	1156	1635	0.3F
	1845	2129	0.5E
14 W	0048	0457	0.3F
	0701	0944	0.5E
	1237	1715	0.3F
	1925	2213	0.5E
15 Th ○	0119	0534	0.3F
	0743	1030	0.5E
	1321	1749	0.3F
	2004	2255	0.5E
16 F	0157	0608	0.3F
	0824	1114	0.5E
	1407	1822	0.3F
	2042	2336	0.5E
17 Sa	0236	0641	0.3F
	0903	1156	0.5E
	1454	1859	0.3F
	2120		
18 Su		0016	0.5E
	0315	0718	0.3F
	0941	1239	0.5E
		1942	*
19 M		0056	0.4E
		0759	*
		1320	0.4E
		2031	*
20 Tu		0134	0.4E
		0616	*
		0700	*
		0846	*
		1358†	0.4E
21 W		0209	0.4E
		0643	*
		0751	*
		0933	*
		1431†	0.4E
22 Th		0244	0.4E
		0724	*
		0832	*
		1022	*
		1504†	0.3E
23 F ◐		0321	0.3E
		0819	*
		0907	*
		1115	*
		1542†	0.3E
24 Sa		0405	0.3E
		1208	*
		1632	0.3E
25 Su		0045	*
		0505	0.3E
		1259	*
		1759	0.3E
26 M		0136	*
		0627	0.3E
		1352	*
		1921	0.3E
27 Tu		0233	*
		0732	0.4E
	1043	1454	0.3F
	1714	2012	0.4E
	2354		
28 W		0335	0.3F
	0541	0825	0.5E
	1134	1559	0.3F
	1811	2100	0.5E
29 Th	0035	0433	0.3F
	0636	0915	0.5E
	1223	1654	0.4F
	1903	2147	0.5E
30 F ●	0117	0523	0.4F
	0727	1005	0.6E
	1313	1744	0.4F
	1953	2234	0.6E
31 Sa	0201	0612	0.4F
	0818	1054	0.6E
	1405	1834	0.4F
	2044	2321	0.6E

September

Day	Slack (h m)	Maximum (h m)	knots
1 Su	0245	0703	0.4F
	0909	1143	0.6E
	1458	1928	0.4F
	2136		
2 M		0009	0.5E
	0326	0758	0.4F
	1001	1235	0.6E
	1550	2026	0.3F
	2228		
3 Tu		0059	0.5E
	0406	0855	0.3F
	1054	1328	0.5E
	1640	2124	0.3F
	2321		
4 W		0151	0.5E
		0555	*
		0656	*
		0951	0.3F
	1148	1421†	0.5E
5 Th ◐		0014	0.4E
		0632	*
		0749	*
		1047	0.3F
	1244	1513†	0.4E
6 F	0109	0331	0.4E
		0720	*
		0836	*
		1144	0.3F
	1341	1608†	0.4E
7 Sa		0012	0.3F
		0427	0.3E
		0822	*
		0918	*
		1237†	0.3F
8 Su		0103	*
		0541	0.3E
	1026	1328	0.3F
	1539	1834	0.3E
9 M		0154	*
		0653	0.3E
	1040	1420	0.3E
	1640	1933	0.4E
10 Tu		0247	*
		0749	0.4E
	1105	1515	0.3F
	1733	2021	0.4E
	2335		
11 W		0342	*
		0838	0.4E
	1141	1606	0.3F
	1817	2106	0.5E
12 Th	0018	0428	0.3F
	0637	0925	0.5E
	1221	1646	0.3F
	1857	2149	0.5E
13 F ○	0048	0504	0.3F
	0717	1009	0.5E
	1303	1720	0.3F
	1934	2229	0.5E
14 Sa	0124	0535	0.3F
	0754	1051	0.5E
	1347	1752	0.3F
	2011	2308	0.5E
15 Su	0202	0605	0.3F
	0829	1130	0.5E
	1432	1826	0.3F
	2048	2344	0.5E
16 M	0240	0636	0.3F
	0904	1208	0.5E
	1516	1907	0.3F
	2126		
17 Tu		0020	0.4E
		0713	*
		1244	0.4E
		1956	*
18 W		0056	0.4E
		0555	*
		0639	*
		0802	*
		1320†	0.4E
19 Th		0133	0.4E
		0617	*
		0734	*
		0858	*
		1356†	0.4E
20 F		0213	0.4E
		0652	*
		0813	*
		0953	*
		1435†	0.4E
21 Sa ○		0254	0.4E
		0740	*
		0847	*
		1049	*
		1516†	0.3E
22 Su		0340	0.4E
		1146	*
		1606	0.3E
23 M		0022	*
		0436	0.3E
		1240	*
		1716	0.3E
24 Tu		0114	*
		0553	0.4E
	0925	1333	0.4F
	1543	1847	0.4E
	2255		
25 W		0209	0.3F
	0416	0708	0.4E
	1026	1432	0.3F
	1651	1948	0.4E
	2335		
26 Th		0310	0.3F
	0521	0806	0.5E
	1121	1536	0.3F
	1751	2038	0.5E
27 F	0013	0410	0.4F
	0617	0858	0.5E
	1212	1635	0.4F
	1845	2126	0.5E
28 Sa ●	0052	0503	0.4F
	0709	0948	0.6E
	1302	1727	0.4F
	1936	2214	0.6E
29 Su	0133	0552	0.4F
	0759	1037	0.6E
	1355	1817	0.4F
	2026	2301	0.6E
30 M	0214	0642	0.4F
	0850	1126	0.6E
	1449	1909	0.4F
	2117	2348	0.5E

Time meridian 75° W. 0000 is midnight. 1200 is noon. Times are not adjusted for Daylight Saving Time.
* Current weak and variable.
† See page 196 for the remaining currents on this day.

Quonset Point, Narragansett Bay, Rhode Island, 2019

F–Flood, Dir. 021° True   E–Ebb, Dir. 200° True

October

Day	Slack (h m)	Maximum (h m)	knots
1 Tu	0256	0735	0.4F
	0941	1216	0.6E
	1539	2006	0.3F
	2207		
2 W		0037	0.5E
	0338	0833	0.3F
	1033	1309	0.5E
	1626	2103	0.3F
	2258		
3 Th		0128	0.5E
	0531		*
	0638		*
		0930	0.3F
	1127	1402†	0.5E
4 F	0220	0608	0.4E
	0733		*
		1026	0.3F
	1222	1454†	0.4E
5 Sa ◑		0310	0.4E
	0652		*
	0820		*
	1122		*
		1545†	0.4E
6 Su		0403	0.3E
	0747		*
	0903		*
	1215		*
		1646	0.3E
7 M	0040		*
		0510	0.3E
	1303		*
		1803	0.3E
8 Tu	0126		*
		0629	0.3E
	1349		*
		1907	0.3E
9 W	0213		*
		0729	0.4E
	1436		*
		1957	0.4E
10 Th	0302		*
		0819	0.4E
	1526		*
		2041	0.4E
11 F	0350		*
		0904	0.4E
	1611		*
		2122	0.5E
12 Sa	0015	0429	0.3F
	0647	0946	0.5E
	1245	1649	0.3F
	1904	2201	0.5E
13 Su ○	0050	0502	0.3F
	0721	1026	0.5E
	1326	1724	0.3F
	1940	2238	0.5E
14 M	0127	0532	0.3F
	0755	1102	0.5E
	1409	1800	0.3F
	2017	2312	0.5E
15 Tu	0205	0604	0.3F
	0830	1136	0.5E
	1451	1840	0.3F
	2056	2345	0.4E
16 W	0244	0640	0.3F
	0908	1209	0.4E
	1531	1927	0.3F
	2136		
17 Th		0021	0.4E
	0729		*
	1245		*
	2021		*
18 F		0102	0.4E
	0554		*
	0706		*
	0831		*
		1326†	0.4E
19 Sa		0146	0.4E
	0627		*
	0746		*
	0930		*
		1411†	0.4E
20 Su		0233	0.4E
	0712		*
	0820		*
	1027		*
		1457†	0.4E
21 M ◐		0321	0.4E
	1125		*
		1547	0.4E
	2009		
22 Tu		0001	0.3F
	0151	0415	0.4E
	0750	1220	0.3F
	1419	1650	0.4E
	2136		
23 W		0054	0.3F
	0251	0526	0.4E
	0906	1314	0.3F
	1521	1814	0.4E
	2229		
24 Th		0147	0.3F
	0355	0645	0.4E
	1014	1411	0.3F
	1628	1923	0.4E
	2310		
25 F		0245	0.3F
	0500	0747	0.5E
	1112	1514	0.3F
	1730	2016	0.5E
	2347		
26 Sa		0346	0.4F
	0558	0840	0.5E
	1204	1616	0.4F
	1826	2105	0.5E
27 Su ●	0024	0443	0.4F
	0650	0931	0.6E
	1255	1710	0.4F
	1917	2153	0.6E
28 M	0103	0533	0.4F
	0741	1020	0.6E
	1347	1759	0.4F
	2007	2240	0.6E
29 Tu	0144	0622	0.4F
	0831	1109	0.6E
	1440	1850	0.4F
	2056	2327	0.5E
30 W	0228	0714	0.4F
	0922	1158	0.6E
	1528	1944	0.3F
	2145		
31 Th		0015	0.5E
	0313	0810	0.3F
	1013	1249	0.5E
	1610	2041	0.3F
	2234		

November

Day	Slack (h m)	Maximum (h m)	knots
1 F		0106	0.5E
	0512		*
	0614		*
		0907	0.3F
	1105	1342†	0.5E
2 Sa		0158	0.4E
	0548		*
	0713		*
		1001	0.3F
	1157	1433†	0.4E
3 Su		0249	0.4E
	0630		*
	0800		*
	1054		*
		1522†	0.4E
4 M ◑		0340	0.3E
	0721		*
	0842		*
	1146		*
		1615†	0.3E
5 Tu	0010		*
		0439	0.3E
	1232		*
		1722	0.3E
6 W	0054		*
		0558	0.3E
	1314		*
		1834	0.3E
7 Th	0134		*
		0706	0.3E
	1354		*
		1928	0.3E
8 F	0213		*
		0757	0.4E
	1438		*
		2013	0.4E
9 Sa	0257		*
		0841	0.4E
	1529		*
		2053	0.4E
10 Su	0344		*
		0922	0.4E
	1616		*
		2131	0.4E
11 M		0426	*
		0959	0.4E
	1305	1657	0.3F
	1909	2206	0.4E
12 Tu ○	0053	0504	0.3F
	0723	1033	0.5E
	1345	1736	0.3F
	1947	2239	0.4E
13 W	0132	0541	0.3F
	0800	1105	0.5E
	1426	1816	0.3F
	2026	2313	0.5E
14 Th	0213	0620	0.3F
	0841	1138	0.5E
	1506	1903	0.3F
	2109	2352	0.5E
15 F	0255	0709	0.3F
	0926	1217	0.4E
	1545	1957	0.3F
	2155		
16 Sa		0035	0.5E
	0809		*
		1302	0.4E
	2053		
17 Su		0123	0.5E
	0608		*
	0713		*
	0910		*
		1351†	0.4E
18 M		0213	0.5E
	0649		*
	0749		*
		1007	0.3F
	1203	1440†	0.4E
19 Tu ◐	0035	0303	0.4E
	0611	1105	*
	1301	1531	0.4E
	1929	2339	0.3F
20 W	0133	0357	0.4E
	0727	1201	0.3F
	1400	1628	0.4E
	2058		
21 Th		0033	0.3F
	0232	0502	0.4E
	0851	1256	0.3F
	1500	1743	0.4E
	2157		
22 F		0126	0.3F
	0334	0621	0.4E
	1007	1351	0.3F
	1605	1857	0.4E
	2241		
23 Sa		0221	0.4F
	0437	0728	0.5E
	1109	1452	0.3F
	1709	1953	0.5E
	2319		
24 Su		0322	0.4F
	0538	0822	0.5E
	1202	1556	0.4F
	1806	2044	0.5E
	2357		
25 M		0422	0.4F
	0632	0913	0.6E
	1251	1652	0.4F
	1858	2132	0.5E
26 Tu ●	0036	0514	0.4F
	0723	1003	0.6E
	1340	1742	0.4F
	1946	2220	0.5E
27 W	0118	0603	0.4F
	0813	1051	0.6E
	1430	1830	0.4F
	2034	2307	0.5E
28 Th	0203	0652	0.4F
	0902	1139	0.5E
	1513	1920	0.3F
	2121	2355	0.5E
29 F	0250	0745	0.3F
	0951	1228	0.5E
	1550	2014	0.3F
	2209		
30 Sa		0044	0.5E
	0501		*
	0540		*
		0839	0.3F
	1040	1319†	0.5E

December

Day	Slack (h m)	Maximum (h m)	knots
1 Su		0136	0.4E
	0534		*
	0647		*
	0931		*
		1410†	0.4E
2 M		0227	0.4E
	0613		*
	0737		*
	1021		*
		1457†	0.4E
3 Tu		0316	0.3E
	0700		*
	0818		*
	1109		*
		1543†	0.3E
4 W ◑		0407	0.3E
	0802		*
	0850		*
	1154		*
		1635	0.3E
5 Th	0016		*
		0516	0.3E
	1236		*
		1746	0.3E
6 F	0053		*
		0635	0.3E
	1315		*
		1853	0.3E
7 Sa	0128		*
		0732	0.3E
	1356		*
		1942	0.3E
8 Su	0205		*
		0816	0.4E
	1445		*
		2022	0.3E
9 M	0253		*
		0855	0.4E
	1540		*
		2058	0.4E
10 Tu	0350		*
		0931	0.4E
	1630		*
		2132	0.4E
11 W	0439		*
		1003	0.4E
	1320	1714	0.3F
	1918	2208	0.4E
12 Th ○	0103	0522	0.3F
	0736	1036	0.4E
	1400	1756	0.3F
	2000	2246	0.5E
13 F	0146	0605	0.3F
	0820	1112	0.5E
	1442	1842	0.3F
	2046	2327	0.5E
14 Sa	0231	0653	0.3F
	0908	1154	0.5E
	1524	1935	0.3F
	2135		
15 Su		0012	0.5E
	0317	0751	0.3F
	0958	1240	0.5E
	1607	2032	0.3F
	2227		
16 M		0102	0.5E
	0404	0850	0.3F
	1050	1331	0.5E
	1652	2127	0.3F
	2321		
17 Tu		0155	0.5E
	0454	0948	0.3F
	1145	1423	0.5E
	1744	2222	0.3F
18 W ◐	0017	0247	0.5E
	0552	1045	0.3F
	1243	1513	0.5E
	1850	2318	0.3F
19 Th	0115	0339	0.5E
	0707	1142	0.3F
	1341	1607	0.4E
	2011		
20 F		0012	0.3F
	0212	0440	0.4E
	0843	1238	0.3F
	1440	1713	0.4E
	2120		
21 Sa		0105	0.3F
	0312	0556	0.4E
	1013	1333	0.3F
	1542	1829	0.4E
	2211		
22 Su		0200	0.4F
	0415	0708	0.5E
	1117	1431	0.3F
	1646	1931	0.5E
	2253		
23 M		0300	0.4F
	0518	0805	0.5E
	1208	1535	0.3F
	1745	2023	0.5E
	2333		
24 Tu		0402	0.4F
	0614	0856	0.5E
	1253	1633	0.4F
	1837	2112	0.5E
25 W	0014	0456	0.4F
	0706	0945	0.6E
	1335	1723	0.4F
	1925	2200	0.5E
26 Th ●	0057	0544	0.4F
	0754	1033	0.6E
	1412	1808	0.3F
	2011	2248	0.5E
27 F	0142	0629	0.4F
	0841	1120	0.5E
	1447	1854	0.3F
	2058	2335	0.5E
28 Sa	0230	0716	0.3F
	0927	1206	0.5E
	1522	1943	0.3F
	2144		
29 Su		0023	0.5E
	0316	0805	0.3F
	1011	1254	0.5E
	2033		*
30 M		0113	0.4E
	0854		*
		1343	0.4E
	2120		*
31 Tu		0204	0.4E
	0602		*
	0708		*
	0941		*
		1428†	0.4E

Time meridian 75° W. 0000 is midnight. 1200 is noon. Times are not adjusted for Daylight Saving Time.
* Current weak and variable.
† See page 196 for the remaining currents on this day.

Pollock Rip Channel, Massachusetts, 2019

F–Flood, Dir. 035° True   E–Ebb, Dir. 225° True

January

Day	Slack (h m)	Maximum (h m)	knots
1 Tu		0237	2.0F
	0533	0831	1.7E
	1136	1511	2.1F
	1808	2104	1.6E
2 W	0003	0336	2.0F
	0628	0930	1.8E
	1232	1607	2.2F
	1906	2204	1.6E
3 Th	0101	0430	2.0F
	0720	1023	1.8E
	1324	1659	2.2F
	1959	2256	1.7E
4 F	0153	0520	2.0F
	0808	1109	1.8E
	1410	1746	2.3F
	2047	2342	1.7E
5 Sa ●	0240	0605	1.9F
	0852	1151	1.8E
	1453	1829	2.3F
	2131		
6 Su		0023	1.7E
	0322	0646	1.9F
	0934	1228	1.8E
	1532	1909	2.2F
	2212		
7 M		0100	1.6E
	0401	0724	1.8F
	1014	1303	1.8E
	1609	1945	2.2F
	2252		
8 Tu		0134	1.6E
	0439	0759	1.8F
	1054	1338	1.8E
	1646	2019	2.1F
	2330		
9 W		0209	1.7E
	0517	0834	1.8F
	1134	1416	1.8E
	1724	2053	2.1F
10 Th	0010	0247	1.7E
	0556	0909	1.7F
	1217	1456	1.7E
	1804	2129	2.0F
11 F	0052	0327	1.7E
	0638	0949	1.7F
	1302	1539	1.7E
	1847	2209	2.0F
12 Sa	0135	0411	1.7E
	0722	1032	1.7F
	1350	1626	1.6E
	1933	2254	1.9F
13 Su	0221	0457	1.7E
	0809	1121	1.7F
	1441	1716	1.6E
	2022	2342	1.8F
14 M ◗	0310	0546	1.6E
	0859	1213	1.7F
	1535	1808	1.5E
	2115		
15 Tu		0035	1.8F
	0400	0637	1.6E
	0951	1309	1.7F
	1630	1903	1.5E
	2210		
16 W		0130	1.7F
	0452	0730	1.6E
	1043	1405	1.7F
	1726	1959	1.5E
	2306		
17 Th		0226	1.7F
	0543	0823	1.6E
	1136	1502	1.8F
	1821	2055	1.5E
18 F	0003	0321	1.7F
	0634	0916	1.7E
	1228	1555	2.0F
	1914	2149	1.6E
19 Sa	0058	0414	1.8F
	0724	1007	1.7E
	1319	1646	2.1F
	2006	2242	1.7E
20 Su	0150	0505	1.9F
	0813	1058	1.9E
	1409	1735	2.2F
	2056	2333	1.8E
21 M ○	0242	0554	1.9F
	0902	1148	2.0E
	1458	1824	2.4F
	2145		
22 Tu		0023	1.9E
	0332	0643	2.0F
	0952	1238	2.1E
	1548	1913	2.4F
	2234		
23 W		0113	2.0E
	0422	0734	2.1F
	1042	1329	2.2E
	1639	2003	2.5F
	2324		
24 Th		0204	2.0E
	0514	0826	2.1F
	1135	1421	2.1E
	1732	2056	2.4F
25 F	0016	0256	2.0E
	0607	0921	2.1F
	1231	1515	2.0E
	1826	2152	2.3F
26 Sa	0110	0351	1.9E
	0702	1021	2.0F
	1329	1613	1.9E
	1924	2252	2.2F
27 Su ◑	0206	0449	1.8E
	0801	1126	1.9F
	1431	1715	1.7E
	2025	2357	2.0F
28 M	0304	0551	1.7E
	0902	1234	1.9F
	1536	1822	1.6E
	2130		
29 Tu		0105	1.9F
	0404	0656	1.6E
	1005	1342	1.9F
	1641	1933	1.5E
	2235		
30 W		0211	1.9F
	0504	0803	1.6E
	1108	1446	2.0F
	1745	2042	1.5E
	2340		
31 Th		0313	1.9F
	0603	0905	1.6E
	1207	1545	2.1F
	1845	2144	1.5E

February

Day	Slack (h m)	Maximum (h m)	knots
1 F	0039	0409	1.9F
	0657	1001	1.7E
	1301	1638	2.2F
	1938	2237	1.6E
2 Sa	0133	0459	1.9F
	0746	1050	1.7E
	1349	1725	2.2F
	2026	2324	1.6E
3 Su	0220	0545	1.9F
	0831	1132	1.7E
	1432	1808	2.2F
	2109		
4 M ●		0003	1.6E
	0301	0626	1.9F
	0913	1208	1.8E
	1510	1847	2.2F
	2148		
5 Tu		0038	1.7E
	0338	0702	1.9F
	0952	1242	1.8E
	1547	1921	2.2F
	2225		
6 W		0109	1.7E
	0414	0734	1.9F
	1029	1314	1.8E
	1622	1952	2.2F
	2301		
7 Th		0141	1.8E
	0448	0805	1.9F
	1107	1349	1.8E
	1657	2021	2.2F
	2338		
8 F		0215	1.8E
	0524	0836	1.9F
	1146	1426	1.9E
	1734	2053	2.1F
9 Sa	0016	0252	1.8E
	0601	0910	1.9F
	1228	1506	1.8E
	1813	2129	2.0F
10 Su	0056	0332	1.8E
	0641	0949	1.9F
	1313	1550	1.8E
	1855	2209	2.0F
11 M	0140	0416	1.7E
	0725	1033	1.8F
	1402	1637	1.7E
	1942	2255	1.8F
12 Tu ◑	0227	0504	1.7E
	0812	1123	1.8F
	1455	1729	1.6E
	2034	2346	1.7F
13 W	0318	0555	1.6E
	0905	1220	1.7F
	1553	1824	1.5E
	2131		
14 Th		0044	1.6F
	0413	0650	1.6E
	1002	1322	1.7F
	1653	1924	1.4E
	2233		
15 F		0148	1.6F
	0510	0749	1.6E
	1101	1428	1.8F
	1753	2026	1.4E
	2336		
16 Sa		0254	1.6F
	0607	0848	1.6E
	1201	1532	1.9F
	1851	2127	1.6E
17 Su	0037	0356	1.7F
	0702	0946	1.8E
	1258	1630	2.1F
	1946	2225	1.7E
18 M	0133	0452	1.8F
	0756	1042	1.9E
	1352	1723	2.3F
	2038	2318	1.8E
19 Tu ○	0226	0544	2.0F
	0847	1134	2.0E
	1445	1813	2.4F
	2127		
20 W		0009	2.0E
	0317	0634	2.1F
	0937	1225	2.2E
	1535	1901	2.5F
	2215		
21 Th		0058	2.1E
	0406	0722	2.2F
	1028	1315	2.2E
	1625	1950	2.5F
	2304		
22 F		0146	2.1E
	0455	0812	2.2F
	1119	1405	2.2E
	1716	2039	2.4F
	2353		
23 Sa		0235	2.1E
	0545	0903	2.2F
	1212	1457	2.1E
	1808	2131	2.3F
24 Su	0044	0326	2.0E
	0637	0958	2.1F
	1308	1551	1.9E
	1902	2227	2.1F
25 M	0137	0420	1.8E
	0731	1059	2.0F
	1407	1650	1.7E
	2000	2329	1.9F
26 Tu ◐	0234	0519	1.7E
	0830	1205	1.9F
	1509	1754	1.6E
	2103		
27 W		0036	1.8F
	0333	0623	1.6E
	0932	1313	1.9F
	1614	1904	1.4E
	2208		
28 Th		0144	1.7F
	0435	0731	1.5E
	1036	1418	1.9F
	1718	2014	1.4E
	2313		

March

Day	Slack (h m)	Maximum (h m)	knots
1 F		0247	1.7F
	0535	0836	1.5E
	1137	1518	2.0F
	1818	2118	1.5E
2 Sa	0014	0344	1.8F
	0630	0934	1.6E
	1232	1611	2.1F
	1911	2211	1.5E
3 Su	0107	0434	1.9F
	0721	1024	1.6E
	1321	1659	2.2F
	1958	2257	1.6E
4 M	0153	0519	1.9F
	0807	1106	1.7E
	1405	1741	2.2F
	2040	2335	1.7E
5 Tu	0234	0559	2.0F
	0848	1143	1.8E
	1444	1818	2.2F
	2118		
6 W ●		0009	1.7E
	0310	0635	2.0F
	0926	1216	1.8E
	1520	1851	2.2F
	2154		
7 Th		0039	1.8E
	0344	0705	2.0F
	1003	1248	1.9E
	1554	1920	2.2F
	2229		
8 F		0109	1.9E
	0417	0734	2.0F
	1040	1321	1.9E
	1628	1948	2.2F
	2304		
9 Sa		0142	1.9E
	0450	0802	2.0F
	1117	1357	1.9E
	1704	2018	2.1F
	2340		
10 Su		0218	1.9E
	0525	0835	2.0F
	1157	1436	1.9E
	1742	2053	2.0F
11 M	0019	0257	1.9E
	0603	0913	2.0F
	1241	1518	1.8E
	1823	2132	1.9F
12 Tu	0101	0340	1.8E
	0645	0956	1.9F
	1329	1605	1.7E
	1910	2218	1.8F
13 W	0148	0428	1.7E
	0733	1046	1.9F
	1423	1657	1.6E
	2002	2310	1.7F
14 Th ◗	0242	0520	1.6E
	0827	1144	1.8F
	1522	1754	1.5E
	2103		
15 F		0012	1.6F
	0340	0618	1.5E
	0928	1251	1.8F
	1626	1857	1.4E
	2209		
16 Sa		0122	1.5F
	0443	0721	1.5E
	1033	1404	1.8F
	1730	2004	1.5E
	2316		
17 Su		0236	1.6F
	0545	0826	1.6E
	1138	1514	1.9F
	1830	2109	1.6E
18 M	0019	0343	1.7F
	0644	0929	1.7E
	1240	1615	2.1F
	1926	2209	1.7E
19 Tu	0117	0441	1.9F
	0740	1028	1.9E
	1337	1709	2.3F
	2018	2303	1.9E
20 W ○	0210	0533	2.1F
	0832	1121	2.0E
	1430	1759	2.4F
	2107	2353	2.0E
21 Th	0300	0621	2.2F
	0923	1212	2.1E
	1520	1847	2.4F
	2154		
22 F		0040	2.1E
	0347	0708	2.3F
	1012	1300	2.2E
	1609	1933	2.4F
	2241		
23 Sa		0126	2.1E
	0434	0755	2.3F
	1102	1348	2.1E
	1658	2020	2.3F
	2328		
24 Su		0212	2.0E
	0521	0843	2.3F
	1153	1437	2.0E
	1748	2109	2.2F
25 M	0017	0300	1.9E
	0610	0936	2.2F
	1246	1529	1.8E
	1840	2202	2.0F
26 Tu	0108	0351	1.8E
	0702	1032	2.1F
	1343	1624	1.7E
	1935	2301	1.8F
27 W ◑	0203	0447	1.6E
	0758	1135	1.9F
	1443	1726	1.5E
	2036		
28 Th		0006	1.7F
	0302	0548	1.5E
	0858	1241	1.9F
	1545	1833	1.4E
	2139		
29 F ◗		0113	1.6F
	0403	0654	1.4E
	1000	1346	1.9F
	1646	1941	1.4E
	2242		
30 Sa		0216	1.7F
	0503	0800	1.4E
	1101	1445	2.0F
	1744	2042	1.4E
	2341		
31 Su		0312	1.7F
	0559	0859	1.5E
	1157	1538	2.0F
	1836	2135	1.5E

Time meridian 75° W. 0000 is midnight. 1200 is noon. Times are not adjusted for Daylight Saving Time.

Pollock Rip Channel, Massachusetts, 2019

F–Flood, Dir. 035° True   E–Ebb, Dir. 225° True

April

Day	Slack (h m)	Maximum (h m)	knots
1 M	0034	0403	1.8F
	0651	0949	1.6E
	1247	1625	2.1F
	1923	2221	1.6E
2 Tu	0120	0447	1.9F
	0737	1033	1.7E
	1332	1707	2.2F
	2005	2259	1.7E
3 W	0200	0527	2.0F
	0819	1110	1.8E
	1412	1744	2.2F
	2043	2333	1.8E
4 Th	0237	0602	2.1F
	0858	1144	1.8E
	1449	1817	2.2F
	2120		
5 F ●		0004	1.9E
	0310	0633	2.1F
	0935	1217	1.9E
	1524	1846	2.1F
	2155		
6 Sa		0035	1.9E
	0343	0701	2.1F
	1012	1252	1.9E
	1559	1914	2.1F
	2230		
7 Su		0109	1.9E
	0417	0730	2.1F
	1050	1328	1.9E
	1635	1945	2.1F
	2306		
8 M		0145	1.9E
	0452	0804	2.1F
	1130	1408	1.9E
	1714	2021	2.0F
	2345		
9 Tu		0226	1.9E
	0530	0842	2.1F
	1214	1451	1.8E
	1757	2102	1.9F
10 W	0029	0310	1.9E
	0613	0927	2.0F
	1303	1539	1.7E
	1845	2150	1.8F
11 Th	0118	0359	1.8E
	0703	1019	2.0F
	1359	1633	1.6E
	1940	2245	1.6F
12 F ◐	0214	0454	1.6E
	0800	1120	1.9F
	1500	1732	1.5E
	2043	2351	1.5F
13 Sa	0316	0554	1.6E
	0904	1230	1.8F
	1604	1837	1.5E
	2151		
14 Su		0107	1.5F
	0422	0701	1.5E
	1012	1347	1.9F
	1708	1946	1.5E
	2259		
15 M		0223	1.6F
	0527	0809	1.6E
	1120	1458	2.0F
	1809	2052	1.6E
16 Tu	0003	0330	1.8F
	0628	0914	1.7E
	1223	1559	2.1F
	1905	2152	1.8E
17 W	0100	0427	2.0F
	0725	1014	1.9E
	1321	1653	2.3F
	1957	2246	1.9E
18 Th	0152	0519	2.2F
	0818	1108	2.0E
	1414	1743	2.3F
	2045	2335	2.0E
19 F ○	0241	0607	2.3F
	0908	1158	2.0E
	1505	1830	2.3F
	2132		
20 Sa		0020	2.1E
	0327	0653	2.4F
	0957	1245	2.0E
	1553	1916	2.3F
	2218		
21 Su		0105	2.0E
	0412	0739	2.3F
	1046	1332	2.0E
	1640	2001	2.1F
	2304		
22 M		0149	2.0E
	0458	0826	2.3F
	1135	1419	1.9E
	1728	2048	2.0F
	2351		
23 Tu		0235	1.9E
	0544	0915	2.2F
	1226	1507	1.7E
	1818	2139	1.8F
24 W	0040	0323	1.7E
	0633	1007	2.0F
	1319	1600	1.6E
	1910	2234	1.7F
25 Th	0133	0415	1.6E
	0726	1105	1.9F
	1415	1656	1.5E
	2007	2335	1.6F
26 F ◑	0229	0512	1.5E
	0822	1206	1.9F
	1512	1757	1.4E
	2106		
27 Sa		0038	1.6F
	0328	0614	1.4E
	0921	1307	1.9F
	1609	1859	1.4E
	2206		
28 Su		0138	1.6F
	0427	0716	1.4E
	1019	1404	1.9F
	1704	1958	1.5E
	2302		
29 M		0234	1.7F
	0523	0814	1.5E
	1115	1457	2.0F
	1755	2050	1.6E
	2354		
30 Tu		0324	1.8F
	0614	0906	1.6E
	1206	1544	2.0F
	1842	2136	1.7E

May

Day	Slack (h m)	Maximum (h m)	knots
1 W	0040	0409	1.9F
	0702	0951	1.6E
	1252	1627	2.1F
	1925	2216	1.8E
2 Th	0121	0450	2.0F
	0746	1032	1.7E
	1335	1705	2.1F
	2005	2252	1.8E
3 F	0159	0526	2.1F
	0827	1109	1.8E
	1414	1739	2.1F
	2043	2327	1.9E
4 Sa ●	0235	0558	2.1F
	0906	1145	1.8E
	1452	1811	2.0F
	2120		
5 Su		0001	1.9E
	0310	0629	2.1F
	0945	1222	1.9E
	1530	1842	2.0F
	2157		
6 M		0037	2.0E
	0345	0701	2.2F
	1025	1301	1.9E
	1609	1916	2.0F
	2235		
7 Tu		0116	2.0E
	0422	0738	2.2F
	1107	1343	1.9E
	1650	1955	1.9F
	2316		
8 W		0159	1.9E
	0504	0819	2.2F
	1153	1429	1.8E
	1736	2039	1.8F
9 Th	0002	0245	1.9E
	0550	0907	2.1F
	1244	1519	1.8E
	1827	2130	1.7F
10 F	0054	0337	1.8E
	0642	1002	2.1F
	1340	1614	1.7E
	1925	2229	1.6F
11 Sa ◐	0153	0433	1.7E
	0741	1105	2.0F
	1441	1715	1.6E
	2028	2338	1.6F
12 Su	0257	0536	1.6E
	0846	1216	1.9F
	1544	1820	1.6E
	2135		
13 M		0055	1.6F
	0403	0643	1.6E
	0954	1330	2.0F
	1646	1928	1.6E
	2242		
14 Tu		0208	1.7F
	0509	0752	1.6E
	1102	1439	2.0F
	1746	2034	1.7E
	2344		
15 W		0313	1.9F
	0611	0859	1.7E
	1205	1540	2.1F
	1842	2134	1.8E
16 Th	0041	0411	2.1F
	0709	0959	1.8E
	1304	1636	2.2F
	1934	2227	1.9E
17 F	0133	0504	2.2F
	0803	1054	1.9E
	1358	1727	2.2F
	2023	2316	2.0E
18 Sa ○	0222	0553	2.3F
	0854	1144	1.9E
	1449	1814	2.2F
	2110		
19 Su		0002	2.0E
	0308	0640	2.3F
	0943	1231	1.9E
	1536	1900	2.1F
	2156		
20 M		0045	1.9E
	0352	0725	2.3F
	1031	1317	1.8E
	1623	1945	2.0F
	2241		
21 Tu		0128	1.9E
	0436	0810	2.2F
	1118	1401	1.7E
	1709	2030	1.8F
	2326		
22 W		0211	1.8E
	0520	0855	2.1F
	1206	1447	1.6E
	1756	2116	1.7F
23 Th	0013	0257	1.7E
	0606	0942	2.1F
	1255	1534	1.6E
	1845	2206	1.6F
24 F	0103	0345	1.6E
	0655	1033	2.0F
	1345	1625	1.5E
	1936	2300	1.6F
25 Sa ◑	0156	0437	1.5E
	0746	1126	1.9F
	1437	1718	1.5E
	2030	2356	1.6F
26 Su ◑	0251	0532	1.5E
	0840	1221	1.9F
	1529	1813	1.5E
	2124		
27 M		0053	1.6F
	0347	0628	1.5E
	0935	1316	1.9F
	1621	1907	1.5E
	2218		
28 Tu		0148	1.7F
	0442	0724	1.5E
	1029	1408	1.9F
	1711	1959	1.6E
	2308		
29 W		0239	1.8F
	0534	0817	1.5E
	1121	1457	1.9F
	1758	2046	1.7E
	2356		
30 Th		0326	1.9F
	0624	0906	1.6E
	1210	1542	1.9F
	1843	2130	1.7E
31 F	0040	0408	2.0F
	0710	0951	1.6E
	1256	1623	1.9F
	1926	2210	1.8E

June

Day	Slack (h m)	Maximum (h m)	knots
1 Sa	0121	0447	2.0F
	0754	1033	1.7E
	1339	1700	1.9F
	2007	2249	1.8E
2 Su	0159	0523	2.1F
	0837	1114	1.7E
	1421	1736	1.9F
	2046	2328	1.9E
3 M ●	0238	0559	2.1F
	0919	1155	1.8E
	1502	1812	1.9F
	2126		
4 Tu		0008	1.9E
	0317	0636	2.2F
	1002	1237	1.8E
	1545	1852	1.9F
	2208		
5 W		0051	2.0E
	0358	0717	2.2F
	1047	1323	1.9E
	1630	1935	1.9F
	2253		
6 Th		0136	2.0E
	0443	0802	2.2F
	1135	1411	1.8E
	1719	2023	1.8F
	2342		
7 F		0226	1.9E
	0533	0853	2.2F
	1227	1502	1.8E
	1812	2117	1.8F
8 Sa	0036	0319	1.9E
	0627	0949	2.2F
	1322	1558	1.8E
	1910	2218	1.7F
9 Su	0135	0417	1.9E
	0726	1052	2.1F
	1421	1658	1.7E
	2012	2326	1.7F
10 M ◐	0239	0519	1.7E
	0830	1201	2.0F
	1522	1802	1.7E
	2117		
11 Tu		0039	1.8F
	0344	0626	1.7E
	0936	1312	2.0F
	1623	1908	1.7E
	2221		
12 W		0150	1.9F
	0450	0735	1.7E
	1043	1419	2.0F
	1722	2013	1.7E
	2323		
13 Th		0255	2.0F
	0553	0842	1.7E
	1147	1521	2.1F
	1819	2114	1.8E
14 F	0020	0354	2.1F
	0652	0945	1.7E
	1247	1618	2.1F
	1913	2209	1.8E
15 Sa	0114	0448	2.2F
	0748	1042	1.7E
	1342	1711	2.1F
	2003	2300	1.9E
16 Su	0204	0539	2.3F
	0840	1133	1.7E
	1434	1800	2.0F
	2050	2346	1.9E
17 M ○	0251	0626	2.3F
	0929	1220	1.7E
	1521	1846	1.9F
	2136		
18 Tu		0029	1.8E
	0334	0711	2.3F
	1015	1303	1.7E
	1606	1929	1.9F
	2220		
19 W		0110	1.8E
	0417	0754	2.2F
	1100	1345	1.6E
	1649	2011	1.8F
	2303		
20 Th		0150	1.7E
	0458	0835	2.1F
	1143	1425	1.6E
	1732	2053	1.7F
	2348		
21 F		0231	1.7E
	0540	0916	2.1F
	1227	1507	1.6E
	1816	2136	1.7F
22 Sa	0034	0315	1.7E
	0624	0958	2.0F
	1312	1551	1.6E
	1902	2221	1.7F
23 Su	0122	0401	1.6E
	0710	1043	2.0F
	1359	1637	1.6E
	1950	2309	1.6F
24 M	0213	0451	1.6E
	0759	1131	1.9F
	1447	1726	1.6E
	2039		
25 Tu ◑		0001	1.7F
	0305	0542	1.5E
	0850	1222	1.9F
	1536	1816	1.6E
	2130		
26 W		0054	1.7F
	0359	0635	1.5E
	0942	1313	1.8F
	1625	1906	1.6E
	2220		
27 Th		0146	1.7F
	0452	0728	1.5E
	1035	1404	1.8F
	1714	1956	1.6E
	2310		
28 F		0237	1.8F
	0544	0820	1.5E
	1126	1453	1.8F
	1802	2044	1.7E
	2357		
29 Sa		0324	1.9F
	0634	0910	1.6E
	1217	1539	1.8F
	1848	2130	1.7E
30 Su	0042	0409	2.0F
	0722	0958	1.6E
	1305	1623	1.8F
	1932	2215	1.8E

Time meridian 75° W. 0000 is midnight. 1200 is noon. Times are not adjusted for Daylight Saving Time.

Pollock Rip Channel, Massachusetts, 2019

F–Flood, Dir. 035° True   E–Ebb, Dir. 225° True

July

Day	Slack h m	Maximum h m	knots		Day	Slack h m	Maximum h m	knots
1 M	0126	0452	2.0F		**16** Tu ○	0234	0611	2.3F
	0809	1044	1.7E			0913	1207	1.7E
	1352	1706	1.8F			1505	1830	1.9F
	2016	2259	1.9E			2117		
2 Tu ●	0209	0533	2.1F		**17** W		0014	1.8E
	0855	1130	1.7E			0317	0654	2.2F
	1438	1748	1.9F			0957	1248	1.6E
	2100	2344	1.9E			1548	1912	1.9F
						2159		
3 W	0253	0616	2.2F		**18** Th		0052	1.8E
	0941	1217	1.8E			0357	0734	2.2F
	1525	1833	1.9F			1038	1324	1.6E
	2146					1627	1950	1.8F
						2240		
4 Th		0030	2.0E		**19** F		0128	1.8E
	0339	0701	2.3F			0435	0811	2.2F
	1028	1304	1.9E			1117	1400	1.7E
	1613	1919	1.9F			1705	2026	1.8F
	2233					2321		
5 F		0118	2.0E		**20** Sa		0205	1.7E
	0427	0749	2.3F			0513	0846	2.1F
	1117	1354	1.9E			1157	1436	1.7E
	1703	2010	1.9F			1744	2102	1.8F
	2324							
6 Sa		0209	2.0E		**21** Su	0003	0244	1.7E
	0518	0840	2.3F			0553	0921	2.1F
	1209	1446	1.9E			1237	1515	1.7E
	1756	2104	1.9F			1825	2140	1.8F
7 Su	0019	0303	2.0E		**22** M	0047	0326	1.7E
	0612	0936	2.3F			0634	0959	2.0F
	1302	1541	1.9E			1320	1556	1.7E
	1852	2204	1.9F			1908	2221	1.7F
8 M	0117	0400	1.9E		**23** Tu	0134	0411	1.7E
	0710	1036	2.2F			0719	1041	1.9F
	1359	1639	1.8E			1404	1641	1.7E
	1952	2309	1.9F			1953	2307	1.7F
9 Tu ◐	0219	0501	1.8E		**24** W ◑	0224	0459	1.6E
	0812	1142	2.1F			0806	1128	1.9F
	1458	1740	1.8E			1451	1728	1.6E
	2054					2041	2357	1.7F
10 W		0019	1.9F		**25** Th	0316	0550	1.5E
	0324	0607	1.7E			0857	1218	1.8F
	0917	1250	2.0F			1541	1818	1.6E
	1558	1845	1.7E			2132		
	2157							
11 Th		0129	1.9F		**26** F		0051	1.7F
	0429	0716	1.6E			0411	0643	1.5E
	1023	1358	2.0F			0951	1311	1.7F
	1658	1951	1.7E			1631	1910	1.6E
	2300					2223		
12 F		0235	2.0F		**27** Sa		0146	1.7F
	0534	0826	1.6E			0506	0738	1.5E
	1128	1502	2.0F			1046	1406	1.7F
	1756	2054	1.7E			1722	2002	1.6E
						2315		
13 Sa	0000	0336	2.1F		**28** Su		0241	1.8F
	0636	0931	1.6E			0600	0833	1.5E
	1230	1601	2.0F			1141	1500	1.7F
	1852	2153	1.8E			1813	2054	1.7E
14 Su	0056	0432	2.2F		**29** M	0006	0334	1.9F
	0733	1029	1.6E			0653	0927	1.5E
	1327	1655	2.0F			1235	1553	1.7F
	1944	2245	1.8E			1902	2145	1.7E
15 M	0147	0524	2.2F		**30** Tu	0056	0425	2.0F
	0825	1121	1.7E			0744	1019	1.6E
	1419	1745	1.9F			1327	1642	1.8F
	2032	2332	1.8E			1951	2235	1.8E
					31 W ●	0145	0513	2.2F
						0833	1109	1.7E
						1417	1730	1.9F
						2039	2324	2.0E

August

Day	Slack h m	Maximum h m	knots		Day	Slack h m	Maximum h m	knots
1 Th	0234	0559	2.3F		**16** F		0031	1.8E
	0921	1158	1.9E			0334	0709	2.2F
	1506	1818	2.0F			1010	1258	1.7E
	2127					1600	1924	1.9F
						2216		
2 F		0013	2.1E		**17** Sa		0104	1.8E
	0323	0647	2.4F			0409	0742	2.2F
	1009	1247	2.0E			1047	1329	1.7E
	1555	1906	2.0F			1635	1956	1.9F
	2216					2254		
3 Sa		0102	2.1E		**18** Su		0137	1.8E
	0412	0735	2.4F			0445	0812	2.1F
	1057	1336	2.0E			1123	1402	1.8E
	1645	1956	2.1F			1710	2026	1.9F
	2307					2333		
4 Su		0153	2.1E		**19** M		0213	1.8E
	0503	0825	2.4F			0521	0843	2.1F
	1147	1427	2.0E			1201	1438	1.8E
	1736	2049	2.1F			1747	2059	1.9F
5 M	0001	0246	2.1E		**20** Tu	0014	0252	1.8E
	0556	0918	2.3F			0559	0917	2.0F
	1239	1519	2.0E			1240	1517	1.8E
	1830	2145	2.1F			1826	2137	1.9F
6 Tu	0058	0341	2.0E		**21** W	0058	0334	1.7E
	0653	1016	2.2F			0641	0956	1.9F
	1334	1615	1.9E			1323	1559	1.7E
	1927	2248	2.0F			1908	2219	1.8F
7 W ◐	0158	0441	1.8E		**22** Th	0145	0420	1.7E
	0752	1120	2.1F			0726	1039	1.8F
	1432	1715	1.8E			1409	1645	1.7E
	2028	2356	2.0F			1954	2307	1.8F
8 Th	0302	0546	1.7E		**23** F ◑	0237	0510	1.6E
	0856	1228	1.9F			0817	1129	1.7F
	1532	1820	1.7E			1458	1735	1.6E
	2131					2045		
9 F		0107	2.0F		**24** Sa		0001	1.7F
	0408	0656	1.6E			0333	0604	1.5E
	1003	1338	1.9F			0912	1225	1.6F
	1633	1927	1.6E			1552	1829	1.6E
	2235					2140		
10 Sa		0215	2.0F		**25** Su		0101	1.7F
	0514	0808	1.5E			0431	0702	1.4E
	1110	1443	1.9F			1011	1326	1.6F
	1734	2034	1.6E			1647	1925	1.5E
	2338					2237		
11 Su		0317	2.1F		**26** M		0204	1.8F
	0617	0916	1.5E			0530	0802	1.4E
	1213	1543	1.9F			1112	1429	1.6F
	1832	2135	1.7E			1743	2023	1.6E
						2335		
12 M	0036	0414	2.2F		**27** Tu		0306	1.9F
	0715	1014	1.6E			0626	0901	1.5E
	1310	1637	1.9F			1211	1529	1.7F
	1925	2229	1.7E			1838	2120	1.7E
13 Tu	0128	0505	2.2F		**28** W	0031	0402	2.0F
	0806	1105	1.6E			0720	0957	1.6E
	1401	1726	1.9F			1306	1624	1.8F
	2013	2315	1.7E			1930	2214	1.8E
14 W	0214	0551	2.3F		**29** Th	0125	0455	2.2F
	0851	1148	1.7E			0811	1050	1.8E
	1445	1810	1.9F			1358	1715	1.9F
	2057	2355	1.8E			2021	2306	2.0E
15 Th ○	0256	0632	2.3F		**30** F ○	0216	0543	2.3F
	0932	1225	1.7E			0859	1140	1.9E
	1524	1849	1.9F			1448	1804	2.1F
	2137					2110	2356	2.1E
					31 Sa	0307	0631	2.4F
						0947	1228	2.0E
						1536	1851	2.2F
						2200		

September

Day	Slack h m	Maximum h m	knots		Day	Slack h m	Maximum h m	knots
1 Su		0046	2.2E		**16** M		0108	1.9E
	0356	0718	2.5F			0415	0737	2.1F
	1035	1316	2.1E			1048	1327	1.9E
	1625	1940	2.3F			1635	1951	2.0F
	2250					2303		
2 M		0136	2.2E		**17** Tu		0142	1.9E
	0447	0807	2.4F			0450	0806	2.1F
	1123	1405	2.1E			1124	1402	1.9E
	1714	2031	2.3F			1709	2022	2.0F
	2343					2342		
3 Tu		0227	2.1E		**18** W		0220	1.8E
	0538	0858	2.3F			0527	0838	2.0F
	1214	1456	2.0E			1202	1440	1.8E
	1806	2125	2.2F			1746	2058	2.0F
4 W	0038	0321	2.0E		**19** Th	0025	0301	1.8E
	0633	0954	2.1F			0607	0916	1.9F
	1307	1549	1.9E			1243	1517	1.7E
	1901	2225	2.1F			1827	2139	1.9F
5 Th ○	0137	0419	1.8E		**20** F	0111	0346	1.7E
	0731	1057	2.0F			0652	0959	1.8F
	1404	1648	1.7E			1329	1607	1.7E
	2000	2332	2.0F			1913	2226	1.8F
6 F	0240	0524	1.6E		**21** Sa ○	0203	0437	1.6E
	0835	1205	1.8F			0743	1050	1.7F
	1505	1752	1.6E			1420	1658	1.6E
	2103					2004	2322	1.8F
7 Sa		0043	1.9F		**22** Su	0300	0532	1.5E
	0346	0635	1.5E			0840	1148	1.5F
	0942	1316	1.7F			1517	1754	1.5E
	1608	1902	1.5E			2103		
	2208							
8 Su		0151	2.0F		**23** M		0025	1.7F
	0452	0748	1.5E			0401	0632	1.4E
	1049	1422	1.8F			0943	1255	1.5F
	1710	2011	1.5E			1617	1855	1.5E
	2312					2205		
9 M		0254	2.0F		**24** Tu		0134	1.8F
	0554	0855	1.5E			0503	0736	1.4E
	1152	1522	1.8F			1048	1406	1.5F
	1809	2113	1.6E			1718	1958	1.6E
						2309		
10 Tu	0011	0350	2.1F		**25** W		0242	1.9F
	0650	0952	1.6E			0602	0839	1.5E
	1248	1615	1.9F			1150	1511	1.7F
	1902	2206	1.7E			1817	2059	1.7E
11 W	0103	0439	2.2F		**26** Th	0010	0343	2.0F
	0739	1040	1.7E			0657	0938	1.7E
	1336	1702	2.0F			1247	1609	1.9F
	1950	2251	1.7E			1912	2157	1.8E
12 Th	0149	0524	2.3F		**27** F	0106	0437	2.2F
	0823	1121	1.7E			0748	1031	1.9E
	1418	1744	2.0F			1340	1701	2.1F
	2032	2330	1.8E			2004	2250	2.0E
13 F ○	0229	0603	2.3F		**28** Sa ●	0159	0527	2.3F
	0902	1156	1.8E			0837	1121	2.0E
	1455	1821	2.0F			1429	1749	2.2F
	2112					2054	2341	2.1E
14 Sa		0004	1.8E		**29** Su	0250	0614	2.4F
	0306	0638	2.2F			0924	1208	2.1E
	0938	1226	1.8E			1516	1836	2.3F
	1530	1854	2.0F			2144		
	2149							
15 Su		0036	1.8E		**30** M		0030	2.2E
	0341	0709	2.2F			0340	0701	2.4F
	1013	1256	1.8E			1011	1255	2.1E
	1602	1923	2.0F			1603	1924	2.4F
	2226					2234		

Time meridian 75° W. 0000 is midnight. 1200 is noon. Times are not adjusted for Daylight Saving Time.

Pollock Rip Channel, Massachusetts, 2019

F–Flood, Dir. 035° True   E–Ebb, Dir. 225° True

October

Day	Slack (h m)	Maximum (h m)	knots
1 Tu		0119	2.2E
	0429	0748	2.3F
	1059	1342	2.1E
	1651	2013	2.3F
	2325		
2 W		0209	2.1E
	0520	0838	2.2F
	1148	1431	2.0E
	1741	2105	2.2F
3 Th	0019	0301	1.9E
	0613	0933	2.0F
	1241	1523	1.8E
	1834	2203	2.1F
4 F	0117	0358	1.7E
	0710	1034	1.8F
	1337	1620	1.7E
	1931	2308	2.0F
5 Sa ☽	0218	0501	1.6E
	0812	1141	1.7F
	1437	1723	1.5E
	2033		
6 Su		0016	1.9F
	0321	0610	1.4E
	0917	1250	1.6F
	1540	1832	1.5E
	2138		
7 M		0123	1.9F
	0424	0721	1.4E
	1023	1355	1.7F
	1642	1941	1.5E
	2241		
8 Tu		0224	2.0F
	0524	0825	1.5E
	1124	1453	1.8F
	1741	2042	1.5E
	2339		
9 W		0319	2.1F
	0617	0919	1.6E
	1217	1545	1.9F
	1834	2135	1.6E
10 Th	0031	0407	2.2F
	0705	1006	1.7E
	1304	1631	2.0F
	1921	2220	1.7E
11 F	0117	0451	2.2F
	0748	1046	1.8E
	1345	1712	2.1F
	2004	2258	1.8E
12 Sa	0158	0530	2.2F
	0827	1120	1.8E
	1422	1749	2.1F
	2043	2333	1.8E
13 Su ○	0235	0604	2.2F
	0903	1151	1.9E
	1456	1821	2.1F
	2121		
14 M		0005	1.9E
	0310	0634	2.1F
	0939	1221	1.9E
	1529	1850	2.1F
	2158		
15 Tu		0038	1.9E
	0345	0702	2.1F
	1013	1253	1.9E
	1601	1918	2.1F
	2235		
16 W		0113	1.9E
	0420	0731	2.0F
	1049	1328	1.9E
	1635	1949	2.1F
	2314		
17 Th		0150	1.8E
	0457	0804	1.9F
	1127	1407	1.9E
	1712	2025	2.1F
	2357		
18 F		0232	1.8E
	0538	0843	1.8F
	1208	1449	1.8E
	1753	2107	2.0F
19 Sa	0043	0318	1.7E
	0624	0928	1.7F
	1255	1536	1.7E
	1839	2156	1.9F
20 Su	0136	0409	1.6E
	0716	1020	1.6F
	1348	1628	1.6E
	1933	2253	1.9F
21 M ○	0234	0506	1.5E
	0816	1122	1.5F
	1448	1727	1.5E
	2034	2358	1.8F
22 Tu	0336	0608	1.5E
	0921	1232	1.5F
	1552	1830	1.5E
	2140		
23 W		0110	1.8F
	0438	0713	1.5E
	1027	1347	1.6F
	1656	1936	1.6E
	2246		
24 Th		0221	1.9F
	0537	0818	1.6E
	1130	1454	1.8F
	1757	2040	1.7E
	2349		
25 F		0324	2.1F
	0633	0918	1.8E
	1228	1553	2.0F
	1854	2140	1.8E
26 Sa	0048	0419	2.2F
	0725	1012	1.9E
	1321	1646	2.1F
	1948	2235	2.0E
27 Su ●	0143	0510	2.3F
	0815	1102	2.0E
	1410	1735	2.3F
	2039	2326	2.1E
28 M	0234	0558	2.3F
	0902	1149	2.1E
	1457	1823	2.4F
	2129		
29 Tu		0015	2.1E
	0324	0645	2.3F
	0949	1236	2.1E
	1544	1910	2.4F
	2219		
30 W		0104	2.0E
	0413	0732	2.2F
	1036	1322	2.0E
	1631	1958	2.3F
	2309		
31 Th		0152	1.9E
	0502	0821	2.0F
	1124	1409	1.9E
	1719	2048	2.2F

November

Day	Slack (h m)	Maximum (h m)	knots
1 F	0002	0243	1.8E
	0554	0913	1.9F
	1215	1459	1.8E
	1809	2143	2.1F
2 Sa	0056	0337	1.6E
	0648	1011	1.7F
	1310	1553	1.6E
	1903	2242	2.0F
3 Su	0153	0436	1.5E
	0747	1113	1.6F
	1408	1652	1.5E
	2001	2345	1.9F
4 M ☽	0252	0539	1.4E
	0848	1218	1.6F
	1508	1755	1.4E
	2102		
5 Tu		0048	1.9F
	0350	0643	1.4E
	0949	1320	1.6F
	1608	1900	1.4E
	2202		
6 W		0146	2.0F
	0446	0743	1.5E
	1046	1417	1.7F
	1706	2000	1.5E
	2259		
7 Th		0240	2.0F
	0538	0837	1.6E
	1139	1509	1.9F
	1759	2053	1.6E
	2351		
8 F		0329	2.1F
	0625	0923	1.7E
	1226	1555	2.0F
	1847	2140	1.6E
9 Sa	0038	0413	2.1F
	0709	1004	1.8E
	1308	1637	2.1F
	1931	2221	1.7E
10 Su	0122	0453	2.1F
	0750	1041	1.8E
	1346	1715	2.1F
	2013	2258	1.8E
11 M	0201	0528	2.1F
	0828	1114	1.9E
	1422	1748	2.1F
	2052	2333	1.8E
12 Tu ○	0239	0600	2.0F
	0904	1147	1.9E
	1456	1819	2.1F
	2131		
13 W		0009	1.8E
	0316	0630	2.0F
	0941	1222	1.9E
	1530	1849	2.2F
	2210		
14 Th		0046	1.8E
	0353	0702	1.9F
	1018	1259	1.9E
	1606	1922	2.2F
	2250		
15 F		0125	1.8E
	0432	0737	1.9F
	1057	1339	1.9E
	1644	2000	2.1F
	2334		
16 Sa		0208	1.8E
	0515	0818	1.8F
	1140	1423	1.9E
	1727	2044	2.1F
17 Su	0021	0255	1.7E
	0603	0905	1.7F
	1229	1511	1.8E
	1815	2134	2.0F
18 M	0114	0347	1.7E
	0656	0959	1.6F
	1323	1605	1.7E
	1910	2232	2.0F
19 Tu ☽	0211	0444	1.6E
	0756	1102	1.6F
	1425	1704	1.6E
	2011	2337	1.9F
20 W	0311	0546	1.6E
	0900	1213	1.6F
	1529	1808	1.6E
	2118		
21 Th		0049	1.9F
	0413	0651	1.6E
	1006	1327	1.7F
	1635	1915	1.6E
	2225		
22 F		0159	2.0F
	0513	0756	1.7E
	1109	1436	1.8F
	1738	2021	1.7E
	2330		
23 Sa		0304	2.0F
	0610	0857	1.8E
	1207	1537	2.0F
	1837	2124	1.8E
24 Su	0030	0402	2.1F
	0703	0953	1.9E
	1302	1632	2.2F
	1933	2221	1.9E
25 M	0127	0455	2.2F
	0754	1045	2.0E
	1353	1723	2.3F
	2026	2315	1.9E
26 Tu ●	0220	0545	2.2F
	0843	1133	2.0E
	1441	1812	2.4F
	2117		
27 W		0004	1.9E
	0310	0633	2.1F
	0930	1220	2.0E
	1527	1859	2.4F
	2206		
28 Th		0052	1.9E
	0359	0720	2.0F
	1016	1305	1.9E
	1613	1946	2.3F
	2255		
29 F		0139	1.8E
	0447	0807	1.9F
	1103	1350	1.9E
	1659	2033	2.2F
	2344		
30 Sa		0227	1.7E
	0535	0855	1.8F
	1152	1437	1.8E
	1746	2122	2.1F

December

Day	Slack (h m)	Maximum (h m)	knots
1 Su	0034	0315	1.6E
	0625	0946	1.7F
	1243	1526	1.6E
	1836	2214	2.0F
2 M	0125	0407	1.5E
	0717	1041	1.6F
	1336	1618	1.6E
	1927	2308	2.0F
3 Tu ○	0217	0501	1.5E
	0811	1138	1.6F
	1432	1714	1.5E
	2022		
4 W		0004	1.9F
	0310	0556	1.5E
	0906	1236	1.6F
	1528	1812	1.5E
	2117		
5 Th		0100	1.9F
	0402	0651	1.5E
	1001	1332	1.7F
	1624	1909	1.5E
	2212		
6 F		0153	1.9F
	0453	0744	1.6E
	1053	1424	1.8F
	1718	2003	1.5E
	2306		
7 Sa		0243	1.9F
	0542	0833	1.7E
	1141	1513	1.9F
	1809	2054	1.5E
	2356		
8 Su		0330	1.9F
	0628	0918	1.7E
	1226	1558	2.0F
	1856	2140	1.6E
9 M	0043	0413	1.9F
	0711	0959	1.8E
	1308	1638	2.0F
	1941	2222	1.7E
10 Tu	0127	0452	1.9F
	0752	1038	1.8E
	1347	1715	2.1F
	2024	2302	1.7E
11 W ●	0208	0527	1.9F
	0832	1115	1.9E
	1425	1750	2.1F
	2105	2341	1.7E
12 Th ○	0249	0602	1.9F
	0911	1153	1.9E
	1502	1824	2.2F
	2147		
13 F		0022	1.8E
	0329	0637	1.9F
	0951	1233	1.9E
	1541	1901	2.2F
	2229		
14 Sa		0104	1.8E
	0411	0716	1.9F
	1033	1316	2.0E
	1623	1942	2.2F
	2314		
15 Su		0148	1.8E
	0456	0759	1.8F
	1118	1402	2.0E
	1708	2027	2.2F
16 M		0236	1.8E
	0545	0848	1.8F
	1208	1451	1.9E
	1758	2118	2.2F
17 Tu	0053	0328	1.8E
	0638	0942	1.8F
	1303	1545	1.8E
	1852	2214	2.1F
18 W ○	0148	0424	1.7E
	0736	1044	1.7F
	1403	1643	1.8E
	1952	2317	2.0F
19 Th ☽	0247	0524	1.7E
	0838	1153	1.7F
	1507	1747	1.7E
	2057		
20 F		0026	2.0F
	0347	0627	1.7E
	0942	1306	1.8F
	1613	1854	1.6E
	2204		
21 Sa		0137	2.0F
	0447	0733	1.7E
	1046	1416	1.9F
	1718	2003	1.6E
	2310		
22 Su		0245	2.0F
	0546	0837	1.7E
	1147	1521	2.0F
	1821	2109	1.7E
23 M	0014	0346	2.0F
	0643	0937	1.8E
	1244	1619	2.2F
	1920	2211	1.7E
24 Tu	0113	0443	2.0F
	0736	1032	1.9E
	1337	1713	2.3F
	2014	2307	1.8E
25 W	0208	0535	2.0F
	0826	1122	1.9E
	1427	1803	2.3F
	2106	2357	1.8E
26 Th ●	0259	0623	2.0F
	0914	1208	1.9E
	1514	1850	2.3F
	2154		
27 F ○		0044	1.8E
	0346	0709	1.9F
	0959	1252	1.9E
	1558	1934	2.3F
	2240		
28 Sa		0127	1.7E
	0431	0753	1.9F
	1044	1334	1.8E
	1641	2017	2.2F
	2325		
29 Su		0209	1.7E
	0515	0836	1.8F
	1129	1416	1.8E
	1724	2059	2.2F
30 M	0009	0251	1.7E
	0559	0919	1.8F
	1215	1459	1.7E
	1807	2142	2.1F
31 Tu	0054	0334	1.6E
	0644	1004	1.7F
	1303	1544	1.6E
	1853	2227	2.0F

Time meridian 75° W. 0000 is midnight. 1200 is noon. Times are not adjusted for Daylight Saving Time.

The Race, Long Island Sound, 2019

F–Flood, Dir. 291° True   E–Ebb, Dir. 106° True

January

Day	Slack	Maximum	knots	Day	Slack	Maximum	knots
1 Tu	0151	0459	3.4F	**16** W	0044	0337	3.1F
	0752	1111	4.5E		0642	1000	4.1E
	1441	1743	3.2F		1336	1615	2.7F
	2031	2337	3.8E		1917	2223	3.6E
2 W	0246	0555	3.5F	**17** Th	0139	0433	3.2F
	0846	1205	4.6E		0739	1056	4.4E
	1535	1838	3.3F		1431	1715	3.0F
	2125				2017	2320	3.9E
3 Th		0029	3.8E	**18** F	0235	0530	3.5F
	0338	0646	3.5F		0836	1150	4.8E
	0935	1254	4.7E		1524	1814	3.3F
	1624	1927	3.3F		2115		
	2214						
4 F		0116	3.9E	**19** Sa		0015	4.2E
	0426	0731	3.5F		0330	0627	3.8F
	1021	1338	4.6E		0931	1244	5.1E
	1708	2010	3.4F		1617	1910	3.7F
	2258				2210		
5 Sa		0159	3.9E	**20** Su		0109	4.5E
	0512	0813	3.4F		0425	0723	4.1F
	1103	1419	4.5E		1025	1419	5.4E
	1750	2049	3.4F		1709	2004	4.0F
	2338				2303		
6 Su		0239	3.9E	**21** M		0203	4.8E
	0555	0850	3.3F		0519	0816	4.3F
	1142	1457	4.4E		1119	1429	5.5E
	1828	2124	3.3F		1800	2055	4.2F
					2356		
7 M	0016	0318	3.9E	**22** Tu		0256	5.0E
	0636	0926	3.2F		0614	0909	4.3F
	1220	1533	4.2E		1212	1522	5.5E
	1905	2158	3.2F		1850	2147	4.3F
8 Tu	0053	0355	3.8E	**23** W	0048	0350	5.1E
	0716	1000	3.1F		0709	1003	4.2F
	1256	1609	4.1E		1305	1615	5.4E
	1940	2230	3.2F		1942	2239	4.3F
9 W	0129	0432	3.8E	**24** Th	0142	0444	5.1E
	0755	1036	3.0F		0806	1058	4.0F
	1332	1645	3.9E		1400	1709	5.1E
	2016	2304	3.1F		2034	2333	4.2F
10 Th	0206	0510	3.8E	**25** F	0236	0540	5.0E
	0836	1114	2.8F		0905	1157	3.7F
	1410	1722	3.8E		1457	1804	4.7E
	2052	2341	3.0F		2129		
11 F	0244	0550	3.8E	**26** Sa		0030	3.9F
	0919	1155	2.7F		0331	0637	4.7E
	1451	1802	3.6E		1007	1300	3.4F
	2130				1557	1903	4.3E
					2227		
12 Sa		0021	3.0F	**27** Su		0129	3.7F
	0324	0633	3.7E		0429	0738	4.5E
	1005	1241	2.6F		1112	1407	3.1F
	1535	1846	3.5E		1659	2005	3.9E
	2212				2327		
13 Su		0105	2.9F	**28** M		0231	3.4F
	0408	0719	3.7E		0528	0842	4.3E
	1054	1329	2.5F		1218	1514	2.9F
	1624	1935	3.4E		1804	2111	3.6E
	2259						
14 M		0152	2.9F	**29** Tu	0028	0333	3.2F
	0455	0810	3.8E		0628	0948	4.2E
	1147	1422	2.5F		1321	1621	2.9F
	1718	2028	3.3E		1909	2217	3.5E
	2350						
15 Tu		0243	3.0F	**30** W	0128	0434	3.1F
	0547	0904	3.9E		0727	1051	4.2E
	1241	1517	2.6F		1420	1722	2.9F
	1816	2125	3.4E		2009	2317	3.5E
				31 Th	0225	0532	3.1F
					0823	1146	4.2E
					1514	1817	3.0F
					2103		

February

Day	Slack	Maximum	knots	Day	Slack	Maximum	knots
1 F		0010	3.6E	**16** Sa	0214	0508	3.5F
	0318	0624	3.1F		0815	1129	4.7E
	0913	1235	4.3E		1502	1753	3.3F
	1602	1905	3.1F		2053	2356	4.3E
	2151						
2 Sa		0056	3.7E	**17** Su	0312	0609	3.8F
	0406	0711	3.2F		0913	1225	5.0E
	0959	1318	4.3E		1556	1852	3.7F
	1645	1947	3.2F		2150		
	2233						
3 Su		0137	3.8E	**18** M		0051	4.7E
	0451	0751	3.2F		0409	0707	4.1F
	1040	1356	4.2E		1009	1319	5.3E
	1724	2024	3.3F		1648	1946	4.1F
	2311				2244		
4 M		0214	3.9E	**19** Tu		0145	5.1E
	0532	0827	3.2F		0504	0802	4.3F
	1118	1431	4.2E		1103	1412	5.5E
	1800	2057	3.3F	O	1739	2037	4.4F
	2347				2336		
5 Tu		0250	4.0E	**20** W		0238	5.3E
	0611	0901	3.2F		0559	0855	4.4F
	1154	1505	4.1E		1156	1504	5.5E
	1835	2127	3.3F		1829	2127	4.5F
6 W	0021	0325	4.0E	**21** Th	0028	0331	5.4E
	0648	0933	3.2F		0653	0948	4.3F
	1229	1538	4.1E		1249	1556	5.3E
	1908	2158	3.3F		1919	2217	4.5F
7 Th	0055	0400	4.1E	**22** F	0119	0424	5.3E
	0725	1007	3.1F		0748	1041	4.1F
	1304	1613	4.0E		1342	1648	5.0E
	1941	2230	3.3F		2010	2308	4.2F
8 F	0130	0437	4.1E	**23** Sa	0211	0517	5.1E
	0804	1043	3.1F		0845	1137	3.8F
	1341	1650	3.9E		1437	1742	4.6E
	2015	2305	3.3F		2103		
9 Sa	0207	0516	4.1E	**24** Su		0002	3.9F
	0844	1123	3.0F		0304	0612	4.8E
	1420	1730	3.8E		0944	1237	3.4F
	2052	2344	3.2F		1534	1838	4.2E
					2200		
10 Su	0247	0557	4.1E	**25** M		0059	3.5F
	0928	1207	2.8F		0400	0710	4.4E
	1504	1813	3.7E		1046	1341	3.0F
	2133				1634	1938	3.7E
					2300		
11 M		0028	3.1F	**26** Tu		0200	3.2F
	0330	0643	4.0E		0457	0813	4.1E
	1016	1255	2.7F		1150	1447	2.8F
	1552	1901	3.6E	O	1737	2043	3.4E
	2221						
12 Tu		0116	3.1F	**27** W	0002	0303	2.9F
	0419	0734	4.0E		0557	0919	3.9E
	1109	1348	2.6F		1253	1552	2.7F
	1646	1956	3.5E		1840	2150	3.3E
	2314						
13 W		0209	3.0F	**28** Th	0103	0406	2.8F
	0513	0830	4.0E		0658	1024	3.8E
	1207	1446	2.6F		1352	1653	2.7F
	1746	2055	3.5E		1940	2251	3.3E
14 Th	0013	0306	3.1F				
	0612	0929	4.1E				
	1306	1547	2.7F				
	1849	2157	3.6E				
15 F	0114	0406	3.2F				
	0713	1030	4.3E				
	1405	1650	3.0F				
	1953	2257	3.9E				

March

Day	Slack	Maximum	knots	Day	Slack	Maximum	knots
1 F	0202	0505	2.8F	**16** Sa	0056	0347	3.2F
	0755	1121	3.8E		0654	1009	4.2E
	1446	1748	2.8F		1343	1632	3.0F
	2033	2344	3.4E		1934	2239	4.0E
2 Sa	0254	0558	2.8F	**17** Su	0159	0452	3.4F
	0846	1209	3.9E		0758	1110	4.5E
	1533	1835	2.9F		1441	1736	3.4F
	2120				2035	2339	4.5E
3 Su		0029	3.6E	**18** M	0259	0556	3.7F
	0342	0644	2.9F		0858	1207	4.9E
	0932	1251	3.9E		1535	1834	3.8F
	1615	1916	3.0F		2132		
	2201						
4 M		0108	3.8E	**19** Tu		0035	4.9E
	0425	0724	3.0F		0356	0655	4.0F
	1013	1327	4.0E		0955	1302	5.1E
	1652	1952	3.2F		1627	1928	4.2F
	2238				2225		
5 Tu		0144	3.9E	**20** W		0128	5.3E
	0505	0800	3.2F		0451	0750	4.3F
	1050	1400	4.0E		1048	1354	5.3E
	1727	2024	3.3F	O	1717	2018	4.4F
	2313				2316		
6 W		0218	4.1E	**21** Th		0220	5.5E
	0543	0833	3.2F		0544	0841	4.4F
	1126	1433	4.1E		1140	1445	5.3E
	1801	2054	3.4F		1806	2106	4.5F
	2347						
7 Th		0252	4.3E	**22** F	0005	0311	5.6E
	0619	0905	3.3F		0637	0932	4.3F
	1201	1507	4.1E		1232	1536	5.1E
	1833	2124	3.4F		1855	2154	4.4F
8 F	0021	0328	4.4E	**23** Sa	0055	0402	5.4E
	0656	0939	3.3F		0729	1023	4.1F
	1237	1543	4.1E		1323	1627	4.8E
	1907	2157	3.5F		1945	2243	4.2F
9 Sa	0056	0405	4.4E	**24** Su	0144	0454	5.2E
	0733	1015	3.3F		0823	1116	3.7F
	1315	1621	4.1E		1416	1719	4.4E
	1941	2232	3.5F		2037	2334	3.8F
10 Su	0134	0444	4.5E	**25** M	0235	0546	4.8E
	0813	1055	3.2F		0918	1212	3.3F
	1355	1702	4.0E		1510	1812	4.0E
	2020	2312	3.4F		2133		
11 M	0214	0527	4.4E	**26** Tu		0028	3.3F
	0856	1139	3.1F		0328	0641	4.3E
	1439	1746	3.8E		1017	1311	2.9F
	2103	2357	3.3F		1607	1910	3.6E
					2231		
12 Tu	0259	0614	4.3E	**27** W		0127	2.9F
	0945	1228	2.9F		0424	0739	3.9E
	1528	1836	3.7E		1117	1414	2.7F
	2153				1705	2011	3.3E
					2333		
13 W		0047	3.2F	**28** Th		0228	2.6F
	0350	0705	4.1E		0522	0842	3.6E
	1040	1322	2.8F		1218	1516	2.5F
	1623	1931	3.6E		1805	2115	3.1E
	2249						
14 Th		0143	3.1F	**29** F	0034	0330	2.5F
	0447	0803	4.1E		0621	0946	3.4E
	1140	1422	2.7F		1316	1615	2.5F
	1724	2032	3.6E		1902	2216	3.2E
	2352						
15 F		0243	3.1F	**30** Sa	0132	0428	2.4F
	0549	0905	4.1E		0718	1044	3.4E
	1242	1526	2.8F		1408	1708	2.6F
	1829	2136	3.7E		1954	2308	3.3E
				31 Su	0224	0521	2.5F
					0810	1132	3.5E
					1454	1755	2.7F
					2041	2353	3.5E

Time meridian 75° W. 0000 is midnight. 1200 is noon. Times are not adjusted for Daylight Saving Time.

The Race, Long Island Sound, 2019

F–Flood, Dir. 291° True   E–Ebb, Dir. 106° True

April

April 1–15

Day	Slack	Maximum	knots
1 M	0311	0608	2.7F
	0857	1213	3.6E
	1535	1836	2.9F
	2122		
2 Tu		0031	3.8E
	0354	0649	2.9F
	0939	1249	3.7E
	1613	1912	3.1F
	2200		
3 W		0107	4.0E
	0434	0726	3.1F
	1018	1324	3.8E
	1649	1945	3.3F
	2235		
4 Th		0143	4.3E
	0512	0801	3.2F
	1056	1359	4.0E
	1724	2017	3.4F
	2311		
5 F ●		0219	4.5E
	0549	0836	3.4F
	1133	1435	4.1E
	1758	2050	3.5F
	2347		
6 Sa		0256	4.7E
	0626	0912	3.5F
	1211	1513	4.1E
	1834	2125	3.6F
7 Su	0024	0335	4.7E
	0705	0950	3.5F
	1251	1554	4.1E
	1912	2204	3.6F
8 M	0104	0417	4.7E
	0746	1031	3.4F
	1334	1638	4.1E
	1953	2246	3.5F
9 Tu	0147	0501	4.6E
	0831	1117	3.3F
	1420	1724	4.0E
	2040	2333	3.4F
10 W	0235	0550	4.5E
	0921	1207	3.1F
	1511	1816	3.8E
	2133		
11 Th		0025	3.2F
	0328	0644	4.3E
	1018	1303	2.9F
	1607	1913	3.7E
	2233		
12 F ◐		0124	3.1F
	0428	0743	4.1E
	1119	1405	2.9F
	1709	2015	3.7E
	2338		
13 Sa		0227	3.0F
	0532	0846	4.1E
	1222	1511	3.0F
	1813	2120	3.9E
14 Su	0044	0334	3.1F
	0638	0951	4.2E
	1323	1617	3.2F
	1917	2224	4.2E
15 M	0148	0441	3.3F
	0743	1053	4.4E
	1420	1719	3.5F
	2017	2324	4.6E

April 16–30

Day	Slack	Maximum	knots
16 Tu	0248	0545	3.6F
	0844	1151	4.7E
	1514	1817	3.9F
	2113		
17 W		0020	5.0E
	0345	0644	3.9F
	0941	1245	4.9E
	1606	1910	4.2F
	2205		
18 Th		0112	5.3E
	0438	0738	4.1F
	1034	1337	5.0E
	1656	1959	4.4F
	2255		
19 F ○		0203	5.5E
	0530	0829	4.2F
	1125	1427	5.0E
	1745	2046	4.4F
	2343		
20 Sa		0252	5.5E
	0621	0918	4.1F
	1215	1516	4.8E
	1833	2132	4.2F
21 Su	0031	0341	5.4E
	0711	1006	3.9F
	1304	1606	4.6E
	1922	2218	4.0F
22 M	0118	0430	5.0E
	0801	1055	3.6F
	1354	1655	4.2E
	2013	2306	3.6F
23 Tu	0206	0519	4.6E
	0852	1146	3.3F
	1445	1746	3.9E
	2106	2357	3.1F
24 W	0256	0610	4.2E
	0945	1239	2.9F
	1536	1839	3.5E
	2202		
25 Th		0050	2.7F
	0347	0702	3.7E
	1040	1335	2.6F
	1629	1934	3.2E
	2300		
26 F ◑		0147	2.4F
	0441	0758	3.4E
	1136	1431	2.5F
	1723	2032	3.1E
	2359		
27 Sa		0245	2.3F
	0536	0856	3.1E
	1230	1526	2.4F
	1816	2129	3.1E
28 Su	0055	0341	2.2F
	0632	0952	3.1E
	1320	1616	2.4F
	1907	2221	3.3E
29 M	0147	0434	2.3F
	0725	1042	3.1E
	1406	1703	2.6F
	1954	2307	3.5E
30 Tu	0234	0523	2.5F
	0814	1125	3.3E
	1449	1745	2.8F
	2036	2348	3.8E

May

May 1–15

Day	Slack	Maximum	knots
1 W	0318	0607	2.7F
	0900	1206	3.5E
	1529	1824	3.0F
	2117		
2 Th		0027	4.1E
	0359	0648	3.0F
	0942	1245	3.7E
	1607	1902	3.2F
	2156		
3 F		0106	4.4E
	0439	0728	3.2F
	1024	1324	3.9E
	1645	1939	3.4F
	2235		
4 Sa ●		0145	4.7E
	0518	0806	3.4F
	1105	1404	4.1E
	1724	2017	3.6F
	2314		
5 Su		0226	4.9E
	0558	0846	3.6F
	1146	1446	4.2E
	1804	2056	3.7F
	2356		
6 M		0308	5.0E
	0640	0927	3.6F
	1229	1530	4.2E
	1846	2139	3.7F
7 Tu	0039	0353	5.0E
	0724	1011	3.6F
	1315	1617	4.2E
	1932	2224	3.7F
8 W	0126	0440	4.8E
	0811	1059	3.5F
	1404	1706	4.2E
	2022	2314	3.5F
9 Th	0217	0531	4.7E
	0903	1152	3.3F
	1457	1800	4.1E
	2118		
10 F		0009	3.3F
	0312	0626	4.4E
	0959	1249	3.2F
	1554	1858	4.0E
	2220		
11 Sa ◐		0109	3.1F
	0413	0725	4.2E
	1100	1352	3.1F
	1655	2000	4.0E
	2327		
12 Su		0215	3.1F
	0517	0829	4.1E
	1201	1457	3.2F
	1758	2105	4.1E
13 M	0033	0323	3.1F
	0623	0934	4.1E
	1302	1601	3.4F
	1900	2209	4.4E
14 Tu	0137	0431	3.2F
	0729	1037	4.2E
	1359	1702	3.6F
	2000	2309	4.7E
15 W	0237	0535	3.5F
	0830	1135	4.4E
	1454	1759	3.9F
	2055		

May 16–31

Day	Slack	Maximum	knots
16 Th		0005	5.0E
	0333	0634	3.7F
	0927	1230	4.5E
	1546	1852	4.1F
	2147		
17 F		0057	5.3E
	0426	0728	3.9F
	1020	1321	4.6E
	1636	1941	4.1F
	2236		
18 Sa ○		0147	5.4E
	0517	0817	3.9F
	1111	1410	4.6E
	1725	2027	4.1F
	2323		
19 Su		0235	5.3E
	0605	0904	3.9F
	1159	1458	4.5E
	1813	2112	4.0F
20 M	0009	0321	5.1E
	0652	0949	3.8F
	1246	1546	4.3E
	1901	2156	3.7F
21 Tu	0054	0407	4.8E
	0739	1034	3.5F
	1332	1632	4.1E
	1950	2240	3.4F
22 W	0139	0453	4.4E
	0825	1119	3.2F
	1418	1719	3.8E
	2039	2326	3.0F
23 Th	0224	0538	4.0E
	0912	1205	2.9F
	1504	1806	3.5E
	2130		
24 F		0013	2.7F
	0310	0624	3.7E
	1000	1252	2.7F
	1551	1855	3.3E
	2223		
25 Sa		0103	2.4F
	0358	0712	3.3E
	1049	1341	2.5F
	1638	1945	3.2E
	2318		
26 Su ◑		0154	2.2F
	0448	0802	3.1E
	1138	1429	2.5F
	1726	2037	3.2E
27 M	0012	0247	2.1F
	0540	0854	3.0E
	1227	1517	2.5F
	1815	2128	3.3E
28 Tu	0103	0339	2.2F
	0633	0945	3.0E
	1313	1603	2.6F
	1902	2216	3.5E
29 W	0152	0430	2.3F
	0725	1034	3.1E
	1358	1649	2.7F
	1948	2302	3.8E
30 Th	0238	0520	2.6F
	0816	1125	3.3E
	1442	1734	3.0F
	2033	2346	4.1E
31 F	0322	0607	2.8F
	0904	1205	3.6E
	1525	1819	3.2F
	2117		

June

June 1–15

Day	Slack	Maximum	knots
1 Sa		0030	4.5E
	0405	0653	3.1F
	0951	1250	3.8E
	1608	1902	3.5F
	2201		
2 Su		0113	4.8E
	0448	0737	3.4F
	1036	1335	4.1E
	1652	1946	3.7F
	2246		
3 M ●		0158	5.0E
	0532	0822	3.6F
	1122	1421	4.3E
	1737	2031	3.8F
	2331		
4 Tu		0244	5.1E
	0617	0907	3.7F
	1209	1509	4.4E
	1824	2117	3.9F
5 W	0019	0332	5.2E
	0704	0954	3.8F
	1258	1558	4.4E
	1914	2206	3.8F
6 Th	0109	0422	5.1E
	0753	1044	3.7F
	1349	1650	4.4E
	2007	2258	3.7F
7 F	0202	0515	4.9E
	0845	1137	3.6F
	1443	1745	4.4E
	2105	2355	3.5F
8 Sa	0258	0610	4.6E
	0941	1235	3.5F
	1540	1843	4.3E
	2208		
9 Su		0056	3.3F
	0358	0708	4.4E
	1040	1337	3.4F
	1639	1944	4.3E
	2314		
10 M ◐		0203	3.1F
	0502	0811	4.1E
	1140	1440	3.4F
	1740	2048	4.3E
11 Tu	0020	0312	3.1F
	0608	0916	4.0E
	1240	1543	3.5F
	1842	2153	4.5E
12 W	0125	0420	3.1F
	0714	1020	4.0E
	1338	1644	3.6F
	1941	2254	4.7E
13 Th	0225	0525	3.3F
	0816	1120	4.1E
	1434	1742	3.7F
	2036	2351	4.9E
14 F	0322	0624	3.5F
	0914	1215	4.2E
	1528	1836	3.8F
	2129		
15 Sa		0043	5.0E
	0414	0717	3.6F
	1007	1307	4.2E
	1619	1926	3.9F
	2218		

June 16–30

Day	Slack	Maximum	knots
16 Su		0132	5.1E
	0503	0806	3.7F
	1056	1355	4.2E
	1708	2012	3.8F
	2304		
17 M ○		0219	5.0E
	0550	0850	3.7F
	1142	1441	4.2E
	1756	2055	3.7F
	2348		
18 Tu		0303	4.8E
	0634	0932	3.6F
	1225	1526	4.1E
	1841	2136	3.5F
19 W	0031	0345	4.6E
	0716	1012	3.4F
	1308	1609	4.0E
	1926	2216	3.3F
20 Th	0112	0426	4.3E
	0757	1051	3.2F
	1349	1651	3.8E
	2012	2256	3.0F
21 F	0153	0506	4.0E
	0838	1129	3.1F
	1430	1733	3.7E
	2057	2337	2.7F
22 Sa	0233	0547	3.7E
	0920	1209	2.9F
	1511	1815	3.5E
	2145		
23 Su		0020	2.5F
	0316	0628	3.4E
	1002	1251	2.7F
	1553	1900	3.4E
	2234		
24 M		0107	2.3F
	0401	0713	3.2E
	1046	1334	2.7F
	1637	1946	3.4E
	2324		
25 Tu ◑		0156	2.2F
	0449	0801	3.1E
	1132	1420	2.6F
	1722	2035	3.4E
26 W	0016	0247	2.2F
	0541	0852	3.0E
	1219	1508	2.7F
	1811	2126	3.6E
27 Th	0106	0339	2.3F
	0636	0945	3.1E
	1308	1557	2.8F
	1900	2217	3.8E
28 F	0156	0433	2.5F
	0732	1037	3.3E
	1357	1648	3.0F
	1951	2307	4.1E
29 Sa	0244	0527	2.8F
	0826	1128	3.5E
	1446	1739	3.2F
	2041	2356	4.5E
30 Su	0332	0619	3.1F
	0919	1219	3.9E
	1535	1830	3.5F
	2131		

Time meridian 75° W. 0000 is midnight. 1200 is noon. Times are not adjusted for Daylight Saving Time.

The Race, Long Island Sound, 2019

F–Flood, Dir. 291° True   E–Ebb, Dir. 106° True

July

Day	Slack (h m)	Maximum (h m)	knots
1 M		0045	4.8E
	0420	0710	3.4F
	1009	1308	4.2E
	1624	1920	3.8F
	2221		
2 Tu ●		0133	5.1E
	0507	0759	3.7F
	1059	1358	4.4E
	1714	2009	4.0F
	2311		
3 W		0223	5.3E
	0555	0848	3.9F
	1149	1448	4.6E
	1805	2059	4.1F
4 Th	0001	0313	5.3E
	0644	0937	4.0F
	1239	1540	4.8E
	1857	2150	4.1F
5 F	0053	0405	5.3E
	0734	1028	4.0F
	1332	1633	4.8E
	1952	2243	3.9F
6 Sa	0146	0457	5.1E
	0826	1121	4.0F
	1425	1728	4.8E
	2050	2340	3.7F
7 Su	0243	0552	4.8E
	0920	1217	3.8F
	1521	1825	4.6E
	2152		
8 M		0042	3.4F
	0342	0650	4.5E
	1017	1317	3.7F
	1619	1925	4.5E
	2257		
9 Tu ◐		0148	3.2F
	0445	0751	4.1E
	1117	1419	3.6F
	1719	2029	4.4E
10 W	0004	0257	3.1F
	0550	0857	3.9E
	1218	1522	3.5F
	1820	2134	4.4E
11 Th	0109	0406	3.0F
	0657	1002	3.8E
	1318	1625	3.4F
	1920	2238	4.5E
12 F	0211	0511	3.1F
	0800	1105	3.8E
	1417	1725	3.5F
	2018	2337	4.6E
13 Sa	0308	0611	3.2F
	0859	1202	3.9E
	1512	1820	3.5F
	2112		
14 Su		0030	4.7E
	0400	0704	3.4F
	0951	1253	4.0E
	1604	1911	3.6F
	2201		
15 M		0118	4.7E
	0448	0751	3.4F
	1039	1340	4.0E
	1652	1956	3.6F
	2247		
16 Tu ○		0203	4.7E
	0532	0833	3.5F
	1122	1424	4.1E
	1738	2037	3.5F
	2329		
17 W		0244	4.6E
	0613	0912	3.5F
	1202	1504	4.1E
	1821	2115	3.4F
18 Th	0008	0322	4.4E
	0651	0947	3.4F
	1240	1543	4.0E
	1903	2151	3.2F
19 F	0046	0358	4.2E
	0728	1020	3.3F
	1317	1621	4.0E
	1943	2226	3.1F
20 Sa	0123	0434	4.0E
	0804	1054	3.2F
	1354	1658	3.9E
	2024	2303	2.9F
21 Su	0200	0511	3.8E
	0840	1128	3.1F
	1431	1737	3.8E
	2106	2342	2.7F
22 M	0239	0549	3.6E
	0917	1206	3.0F
	1509	1818	3.7E
	2151		
23 Tu		0025	2.6F
	0320	0631	3.4E
	0958	1248	2.9F
	1551	1901	3.7E
	2238		
24 W ◐		0112	2.4F
	0406	0716	3.3E
	1042	1333	2.8F
	1635	1949	3.7E
	2328		
25 Th		0202	2.4F
	0457	0807	3.2E
	1131	1422	2.8F
	1725	2041	3.7E
26 F	0021	0255	2.4F
	0553	0902	3.2E
	1223	1514	2.9F
	1818	2136	3.9E
27 Sa	0115	0352	2.5F
	0652	1000	3.3E
	1318	1609	3.0F
	1914	2232	4.1E
28 Su	0209	0450	2.7F
	0752	1056	3.6E
	1413	1706	3.2F
	2011	2326	4.4E
29 M	0302	0549	3.1F
	0849	1151	3.9E
	1507	1802	3.5F
	2106		
30 Tu		0019	4.8E
	0353	0645	3.4F
	0944	1244	4.3E
	1601	1857	3.8F
	2200		
31 W ●		0111	5.1E
	0444	0738	3.8F
	1037	1337	4.7E
	1654	1950	4.1F
	2252		

August

Day	Slack (h m)	Maximum (h m)	knots
1 Th		0203	5.3E
	0533	0828	4.1F
	1128	1429	5.0E
	1747	2042	4.3F
	2344		
2 F		0254	5.5E
	0623	0918	4.3F
	1220	1521	5.1E
	1841	2134	4.3F
3 Sa	0037	0346	5.4E
	0712	1009	4.3F
	1312	1615	5.2E
	1936	2228	4.2F
4 Su	0130	0439	5.2E
	0803	1101	4.3F
	1404	1709	5.1E
	2033	2324	3.9F
5 M	0226	0533	4.9E
	0857	1155	4.1F
	1459	1805	4.9E
	2133		
6 Tu		0025	3.6F
	0324	0630	4.5E
	0953	1253	3.8F
	1556	1904	4.7E
	2237		
7 W ◐		0130	3.2F
	0426	0730	4.1E
	1053	1355	3.5F
	1655	2007	4.4E
	2343		
8 Th		0239	3.0F
	0531	0836	3.7E
	1156	1459	3.3F
	1756	2113	4.3E
9 F	0049	0348	2.9F
	0637	0943	3.6E
	1258	1604	3.2F
	1858	2220	4.2E
10 Sa	0152	0453	2.9F
	0741	1048	3.6E
	1359	1706	3.2F
	1958	2321	4.3E
11 Su	0250	0553	3.1F
	0839	1146	3.7E
	1455	1803	3.2F
	2053		
12 M		0015	4.3E
	0341	0645	3.2F
	0931	1237	3.8E
	1547	1854	3.3F
	2142		
13 Tu		0102	4.4E
	0427	0731	3.3F
	1016	1322	3.9E
	1634	1938	3.3F
	2227		
14 W		0143	4.4E
	0509	0811	3.4F
	1057	1402	4.0E
	1718	2017	3.3F
	2307		
15 Th ○		0221	4.3E
	0547	0846	3.4F
	1134	1439	4.1E
	1758	2052	3.3F
	2344		
16 F		0255	4.2E
	0622	0918	3.4F
	1210	1514	4.1E
	1837	2125	3.2F
17 Sa	0019	0328	4.1E
	0656	0948	3.4F
	1243	1549	4.1E
	1914	2157	3.2F
18 Su	0054	0402	4.0E
	0729	1018	3.3F
	1317	1624	4.1E
	1952	2231	3.1F
19 M	0129	0437	3.9E
	0802	1051	3.3F
	1352	1701	4.1E
	2030	2309	2.9F
20 Tu	0207	0515	3.8E
	0838	1128	3.2F
	1430	1740	4.0E
	2112	2350	2.8F
21 W	0247	0555	3.6E
	0917	1209	3.1F
	1510	1823	4.0E
	2157		
22 Th		0035	2.7F
	0332	0641	3.5E
	1001	1254	3.0F
	1556	1911	3.9E
	2247		
23 F ○		0125	2.6F
	0422	0732	3.4E
	1052	1345	2.9F
	1647	2004	3.8E
	2342		
24 Sa		0220	2.5F
	0519	0828	3.3E
	1148	1440	2.9F
	1743	2101	3.9E
25 Su	0040	0319	2.6F
	0620	0929	3.4E
	1248	1538	3.0F
	1844	2201	4.1E
26 M	0138	0421	2.8F
	0723	1029	3.7E
	1347	1639	3.2F
	1945	2300	4.4E
27 Tu	0234	0523	3.1F
	0824	1128	4.1E
	1446	1740	3.5F
	2045	2357	4.7E
28 W	0328	0622	3.5F
	0921	1224	4.5E
	1542	1838	3.9F
	2141		
29 Th		0051	5.1E
	0420	0717	3.9F
	1015	1317	4.9E
	1637	1934	4.2F
	2235		
30 F ●		0143	5.3E
	0510	0808	4.3F
	1107	1410	5.3E
	1731	2027	4.4F
	2328		
31 Sa		0235	5.4E
	0600	0858	4.5F
	1158	1502	5.5E
	1824	2119	4.4F

September

Day	Slack (h m)	Maximum (h m)	knots
1 Su	0020	0327	5.4E
	0649	0947	4.5F
	1249	1555	5.5E
	1919	2212	4.3F
2 M	0113	0419	5.2E
	0740	1038	4.4F
	1341	1648	5.4E
	2014	2306	4.0F
3 Tu	0208	0512	4.8E
	0833	1131	4.1F
	1434	1742	5.1E
	2113		
4 W		0005	3.6F
	0305	0608	4.4E
	0929	1228	3.8F
	1530	1840	4.7E
	2214		
5 Th ○		0109	3.2F
	0405	0708	4.0E
	1029	1329	3.4F
	1628	1941	4.3E
	2319		
6 F		0216	3.0F
	0508	0812	3.6E
	1133	1434	3.1F
	1730	2048	4.0E
7 Sa	0024	0324	2.8F
	0613	0921	3.4E
	1237	1540	2.9F
	1833	2156	3.9E
8 Su	0127	0428	2.8F
	0715	1026	3.4E
	1339	1643	2.9F
	1933	2259	3.9E
9 M	0224	0527	2.9F
	0813	1124	3.6E
	1435	1740	2.9F
	2029	2352	4.0E
10 Tu	0314	0618	3.0F
	0903	1214	3.7E
	1526	1830	3.0F
	2118		
11 W		0038	4.0E
	0359	0702	3.1F
	0947	1256	3.9E
	1612	1913	3.1F
	2201		
12 Th		0117	4.0E
	0438	0740	3.2F
	1026	1333	4.1E
	1653	1951	3.2F
	2240		
13 F ○		0151	4.0E
	0515	0813	3.3F
	1101	1408	4.2E
	1732	2025	3.3F
	2317		
14 Sa		0224	4.0E
	0549	0844	3.4F
	1135	1442	4.3E
	1808	2057	3.3F
	2351		
15 Su		0256	4.0E
	0621	0913	3.4F
	1208	1515	4.4E
	1844	2129	3.3F
16 M		0330	4.0E
	0654	0943	3.4F
	1242	1551	4.4E
	1921	2202	3.2F
17 Tu	0102	0406	3.9E
	0728	1017	3.4F
	1317	1628	4.4E
	1958	2239	3.1F
18 W	0139	0445	3.9E
	0804	1054	3.3F
	1355	1708	4.3E
	2038	2320	3.0F
19 Th	0220	0527	3.8E
	0844	1136	3.2F
	1437	1751	4.2E
	2123		
20 F		0006	2.9F
	0306	0613	3.6E
	0930	1223	3.1F
	1524	1840	4.1E
	2214		
21 Sa		0057	2.7F
	0357	0705	3.5E
	1023	1316	3.0F
	1617	1934	4.0E
	2310		
22 Su		0153	2.7F
	0454	0803	3.5E
	1123	1424	2.9F
	1717	2034	3.9E
23 M	0010	0254	2.7F
	0556	0905	3.6E
	1226	1515	3.0F
	1820	2136	4.0E
24 Tu	0111	0357	2.9F
	0700	1008	3.9E
	1329	1619	3.2F
	1924	2238	4.3E
25 W	0209	0500	3.2F
	0802	1108	4.3E
	1429	1722	3.5F
	2026	2336	4.6E
26 Th	0304	0600	3.6F
	0900	1205	4.7E
	1526	1822	3.8F
	2124		
27 F		0031	5.0E
	0356	0656	4.0F
	0954	1259	5.2E
	1622	1919	4.1F
	2219		
28 Sa ●		0124	5.2E
	0447	0747	4.4F
	1046	1351	5.5E
	1715	2012	4.3F
	2312		
29 Su		0216	5.3E
	0537	0837	4.6F
	1136	1443	5.7E
	1808	2104	4.4F
30 M	0004	0307	5.2E
	0627	0925	4.5F
	1226	1534	5.6E
	1901	2155	4.2F

Time meridian 75° W. 0000 is midnight. 1200 is noon. Times are not adjusted for Daylight Saving Time.

The Race, Long Island Sound, 2019

F–Flood, Dir. 291° True   E–Ebb, Dir. 106° True

October

Day	Slack	Maximum
1 Tu	0056, 0717, 1317, 1955	0359 5.0E, 1015 4.4F, 1626 5.4E, 2249 4.0F
2 W	0150, 0810, 1409, 2051	0452 4.7E, 1106 4.0F, 1719 5.1E, 2345 3.6F
3 Th	0245, 0906, 1503, 2149	0546 4.3E, 1202 3.6F, 1815 4.6E
4 F	0342, 1005, 1559, 2251	0045 3.2F, 0644 3.9E, 1301 3.2F, 1914 4.2E
5 Sa	0442, 1108, 1659, 2353	0149 2.9F, 0746 3.5E, 1405 2.8F, 2017 3.8E
6 Su	0543, 1211, 1800	0253 2.7F, 0851 3.3E, 1509 2.6F, 2124 3.6E
7 M	0053, 0642, 1312, 1901	0355 2.7F, 0956 3.3E, 1611 2.6F, 2226 3.5E
8 Tu	0148, 0737, 1408, 1956	0451 2.7F, 1053 3.5E, 1707 2.6F, 2319 3.5E
9 W	0237, 0826, 1458, 2045	0540 2.8F, 1141 3.7E, 1757 2.7F
10 Th	0321, 0909, 1543, 2129	0003 3.6F, 0623 2.9F, 1222 3.9E, 1840 2.9F
11 F	0400, 0948, 1623, 2209	0041 3.7E, 0701 3.1F, 1258 4.1E, 1919 3.0F
12 Sa	0437, 1024, 1702, 2246	0115 3.7E, 0735 3.2F, 1333 4.2E, 1953 3.2F
13 Su	0512, 1058, 1738, 2322	0149 3.8E, 0806 3.3F, 1407 4.4E, 2027 3.3F
14 M	0546, 1132, 1814, 2358	0223 3.9E, 0837 3.4F, 1442 4.5E, 2100 3.3F
15 Tu	0620, 1208, 1851	0259 4.0E, 0911 3.5F, 1519 4.6E, 2136 3.4F
16 W	0036, 0657, 1246, 1930	0338 4.0E, 0947 3.5F, 1559 4.6E, 2214 3.3F
17 Th	0116, 0735, 1326, 2011	0419 4.0E, 1026 3.4F, 1641 4.5E, 2256 3.2F
18 F	0159, 0819, 1411, 2057	0503 3.9E, 1110 3.3F, 1726 4.4E, 2343 3.1F
19 Sa	0246, 0908, 1500, 2149	0551 3.8E, 1159 3.2F, 1816 4.2E
20 Su	0338, 1003, 1556, 2246	0035 3.0F, 0644 3.7E, 1254 3.0F, 1911 4.1E
21 M	0436, 1105, 1656, 2346	0133 2.9F, 0743 3.7E, 1354 3.0F, 2011 4.0E
22 Tu	0538, 1210, 1801	0234 2.9F, 0845 3.8E, 1457 3.0F, 2115 4.0E
23 W	0047, 0641, 1314, 1906	0338 3.1F, 0949 4.1E, 1603 3.2F, 2218 4.2E
24 Th	0145, 0742, 1415, 2009	0440 3.4F, 1050 4.5E, 1708 3.4F, 2317 4.5E
25 F	0240, 0840, 1513, 2108	0540 3.7F, 1147 4.9E, 1809 3.7F
26 Sa	0333, 0934, 1608, 2204	0013 4.7E, 0635 4.1F, 1241 5.3E, 1906 4.0F
27 Su	0425, 1026, 1702, 2257	0106 4.9E, 0727 4.3F, 1333 5.5E, 2000 4.2F
28 M	0515, 1115, 1753, 2349	0158 5.0E, 0817 4.4F, 1424 5.6E, 2051 4.2F
29 Tu	0606, 1205, 1845	0249 4.9E, 0905 4.4F, 1515 5.6E, 2141 4.1F
30 W	0040, 0656, 1254, 1936	0340 4.8E, 0954 4.2F, 1605 5.3E, 2231 3.9F
31 Th	0131, 0748, 1344, 2028	0432 4.5E, 1043 3.8F, 1656 4.9E, 2324 3.5F

November

Day	Slack	Maximum
1 F	0223, 0842, 1435, 2122	0524 4.1E, 1136 3.6F, 1749 4.5E
2 Sa	0317, 0939, 1529, 2218	0019 3.2F, 0618 3.8E, 1231 3.0F, 1843 4.0E
3 Su	0411, 1039, 1624, 2315	0116 2.9F, 0715 3.5E, 1330 2.7F, 1940 3.6E
4 M	0506, 1140, 1721	0214 2.7F, 0814 3.3E, 1430 2.4F, 2040 3.3E
5 Tu	0011, 0601, 1239, 1818	0310 2.6F, 0914 3.3E, 1528 2.3F, 2138 3.2E
6 W	0103, 0653, 1333, 1912	0403 2.6F, 1009 3.4E, 1623 2.3F, 2231 3.2E
7 Th	0152, 0741, 1422, 2003	0451 2.6F, 1057 3.5E, 1714 2.5F, 2316 3.2E
8 F	0236, 0824, 1507, 2049	0534 2.8F, 1139 3.8E, 1759 2.6F, 2357 3.3E
9 Sa	0316, 0905, 1549, 2132	0614 2.9F, 1218 4.0E, 1840 2.8F
10 Su	0355, 0943, 1628, 2212	0035 3.5E, 0651 3.1F, 1255 4.3E, 1918 3.0F
11 M	0433, 1021, 1707, 2252	0112 3.7E, 0727 3.3F, 1332 4.5E, 1955 3.2F
12 Tu	0510, 1059, 1745, 2331	0150 3.8E, 0803 3.4F, 1410 4.7E, 2033 3.4F
13 W	0549, 1138, 1824	0230 4.0E, 0840 3.5F, 1451 4.8E, 2111 3.5F
14 Th	0012, 0629, 1219, 1905	0312 4.0E, 0920 3.6F, 1533 4.8E, 2152 3.5F
15 F	0055, 0712, 1303, 1949	0356 4.1E, 1003 3.5F, 1618 4.8E, 2237 3.4F
16 Sa	0141, 0759, 1351, 2036	0443 4.1E, 1049 3.5F, 1706 4.6E, 2325 3.3F
17 Su	0230, 0850, 1442, 2128	0533 4.0E, 1140 3.3F, 1757 4.4E
18 M	0323, 0948, 1539, 2225	0018 3.2F, 0627 4.0E, 1237 3.2F, 1852 4.3E
19 Tu	0421, 1051, 1640, 2324	0116 3.2F, 0726 4.0E, 1338 3.0F, 1952 4.1E
20 W	0521, 1157, 1744	0217 3.2F, 0828 4.1E, 1443 3.0F, 2055 4.0E
21 Th	0024, 0623, 1301, 1850	0320 3.3F, 0932 4.3E, 1550 3.1F, 2159 4.1E
22 F	0122, 0723, 1403, 1954	0421 3.5F, 1033 4.6E, 1656 3.3F, 2259 4.3E
23 Sa	0219, 0821, 1501, 2054	0521 3.8F, 1131 4.9E, 1759 3.5F, 2356 4.4E
24 Su	0313, 0915, 1556, 2150	0618 4.0F, 1226 5.2E, 1856 3.8F
25 M	0406, 1007, 1649, 2243	0050 4.6E, 0711 4.1F, 1318 5.4E, 1949 3.9F
26 Tu	0457, 1057, 1740, 2334	0142 4.6E, 0801 4.2F, 1408 5.4E, 2039 4.0F
27 W	0548, 1145, 1829	0233 4.6E, 0848 4.1F, 1458 5.3E, 2127 3.9F
28 Th	0023, 0638, 1233, 1917	0323 4.5E, 0935 3.9F, 1546 5.1E, 2214 3.8F
29 F	0112, 0728, 1320, 2005	0412 4.3E, 1022 3.6F, 1634 4.7E, 2302 3.5F
30 Sa	0200, 0819, 1408, 2054	0501 4.1E, 1110 3.3F, 1722 4.3E, 2350 3.2F

December

Day	Slack	Maximum
1 Su	0248, 0912, 1456, 2143	0550 3.8E, 1159 2.9F, 1810 3.9E
2 M	0336, 1006, 1545, 2233	0039 3.0F, 0640 3.6E, 1250 2.6F, 1859 3.5E
3 Tu	0425, 1102, 1635, 2323	0128 2.7F, 0731 3.4E, 1343 2.3F, 1949 3.2E
4 W	0513, 1157, 1727	0217 2.6F, 0824 3.3E, 1436 2.2F, 2041 3.0E
5 Th	0012, 0601, 1250, 1820	0305 2.5F, 0916 3.3E, 1529 2.2F, 2133 2.9E
6 F	0059, 0648, 1340, 1913	0352 2.6F, 1005 3.5E, 1620 2.2F, 2222 3.0E
7 Sa	0145, 0734, 1426, 2003	0437 2.6F, 1051 3.7E, 1709 2.4F, 2308 3.1E
8 Su	0229, 0818, 1510, 2051	0521 2.8F, 1134 3.9E, 1756 2.6F, 2352 3.3E
9 M	0312, 0902, 1553, 2136	0605 3.0F, 1216 4.2E, 1840 2.9F
10 Tu	0354, 0945, 1635, 2221	0035 3.6E, 0648 3.2F, 1258 4.5E, 1923 3.2F
11 W	0437, 1028, 1716, 2305	0118 3.8E, 0730 3.4F, 1341 4.7E, 2006 3.4F
12 Th	0520, 1112, 1759, 2349	0203 4.0E, 0813 3.6F, 1425 4.9E, 2049 3.6F
13 F	0604, 1157, 1843	0248 4.2E, 0857 3.7F, 1510 5.0E, 2133 3.7F
14 Sa	0035, 0651, 1244, 1929	0335 4.3E, 0943 3.8F, 1558 5.0E, 2219 3.7F
15 Su	0123, 0741, 1334, 2017	0424 4.4E, 1032 3.7F, 1647 4.9E, 2309 3.6F
16 M	0214, 0835, 1427, 2109	0516 4.4E, 1124 3.5F, 1739 4.7E
17 Tu	0307, 0934, 1524, 2204	0002 3.6F, 0611 4.4E, 1221 3.3F, 1835 4.4E
18 W	0404, 1037, 1624, 2302	0059 3.5F, 0709 4.3E, 1323 3.2F, 1934 4.2E
19 Th	0503, 1143, 1728	0159 3.5F, 0810 4.3E, 1430 3.1F, 2036 4.0E
20 F	0002, 0604, 1248, 1835	0301 3.5F, 0914 4.4E, 1538 3.0F, 2141 4.0E
21 Sa	0101, 0704, 1351, 1940	0403 3.5F, 1017 4.6E, 1646 3.2F, 2243 4.0E
22 Su	0200, 0803, 1450, 2041	0505 3.6F, 1117 4.8E, 1749 3.3F, 2342 4.1E
23 M	0256, 0859, 1545, 2138	0603 3.8F, 1213 5.0E, 1847 3.5F
24 Tu	0350, 0952, 1637, 2230	0037 4.2E, 0657 3.9F, 1305 5.1E, 1940 3.7F
25 W	0443, 1041, 1726, 2319	0129 4.3E, 0748 3.9F, 1355 5.1E, 2028 3.8F
26 Th	0533, 1128, 1813	0219 4.4E, 0834 3.9F, 1442 5.0E, 2113 3.8F
27 F	0006, 0621, 1214, 1858	0306 4.3E, 0919 3.7F, 1527 4.8E, 2156 3.7F
28 Sa	0050, 0708, 1257, 1941	0352 4.2E, 1001 3.5F, 1611 4.6E, 2237 3.5F
29 Su	0134, 0755, 1340, 2023	0436 4.1E, 1043 3.2F, 1653 4.2E, 2317 3.3F
30 M	0216, 0842, 1422, 2105	0519 3.9E, 1125 2.9F, 1735 3.9E, 2358 3.1F
31 Tu	0258, 0930, 1505, 2148	0603 3.7E, 1209 2.6F, 1817 3.6E

Time meridian 75° W. 0000 is midnight. 1200 is noon. Times are not adjusted for Daylight Saving Time.

Throgs Neck Bridge, Long Island Sound, New York, 2019

F–Flood, Dir. 106° True   E–Ebb, Dir. 262° True

January

Date	Slack (h m)	Max (h m)	knots
1 Tu		0204	1.6F
	0544	0742	0.9E
	1204	1433	1.6F
	1817	2015	0.9E
2 W	0032	0258	1.6F
	0638	0839	0.9E
	1259	1526	1.6F
	1909	2110	1.0E
3 Th	0122	0348	1.6F
	0731	0931	1.0E
	1349	1615	1.6F
	1958	2158	1.0E
4 F	0209	0436	1.6F
	0819	1018	1.0E
	1435	1702	1.6F
	2044	2244	1.0E
5 Sa ●	0252	0523	1.7F
	0905	1104	1.0E
	1518	1748	1.6F
	2128	2330	1.0E
6 Su	0330	0608	1.7F
	0949	1151	1.0E
	1557	1833	1.6F
	2210		
7 M		0016	1.0E
	0406	0653	1.7F
	1031	1240	1.0E
	1633	1917	1.6F
	2251		
8 Tu		0104	1.0E
	0439	0737	1.7F
	1114	1327	1.0E
	1707	2000	1.5F
	2331		
9 W		0150	1.0E
	0512	0821	1.7F
	1157	1414	1.0E
	1740	2044	1.5F
10 Th	0010	0236	1.0E
	0547	0906	1.6F
	1240	1501	1.0E
	1815	2130	1.5F
11 F	0048	0322	1.0E
	0625	0954	1.6F
	1322	1549	1.0E
	1853	2218	1.5F
12 Sa	0126	0410	1.0E
	0707	1044	1.6F
	1405	1637	1.0E
	1934	2308	1.5F
13 Su	0208	0457	1.0E
	0752	1135	1.5F
	1451	1725	1.0E
	2021	2358	1.5F
14 M ☽	0256	0545	1.0E
	0843	1226	1.5F
	1538	1812	1.0E
	2114		
15 Tu		0049	1.5F
	0348	0633	1.0E
	0939	1318	1.5F
	1627	1901	1.0E
	2210		
16 W		0141	1.5F
	0440	0722	0.9E
	1037	1410	1.6F
	1715	1951	1.0E
	2306		
17 Th		0234	1.6F
	0532	0813	0.9E
	1134	1503	1.6F
	1805	2042	1.0E
	2359		
18 F		0326	1.7F
	0623	0903	1.0E
	1233	1555	1.7F
	1855	2131	1.1E
19 Sa	0052	0417	1.7F
	0715	0952	1.0E
	1332	1646	1.7F
	1945	2219	1.1E
20 Su	0145	0508	1.8F
	0806	1041	1.1E
	1431	1738	1.7F
	2035	2307	1.1E
21 M ○	0238	0600	1.9F
	0857	1132	1.1E
	1527	1829	1.8F
	2125	2358	1.1E
22 Tu	0331	0651	1.9F
	0950	1225	1.1E
	1622	1920	1.8F
	2218		
23 W		0052	1.1E
	0426	0743	1.9F
	1047	1321	1.1E
	1718	2011	1.8F
	2316		
24 Th		0146	1.1E
	0523	0834	1.9F
	1150	1416	1.1E
	1813	2103	1.7F
25 F	0017	0240	1.1E
	0622	0928	1.8F
	1255	1511	1.0E
	1910	2157	1.6F
26 Sa	0119	0335	1.0E
	0724	1024	1.7F
	1358	1607	1.0E
	2009	2253	1.6F
27 Su ☽	0222	0431	1.0E
	0831	1121	1.6F
	1501	1703	0.9E
	2112	2348	1.5F
28 M	0325	0526	0.9E
	0940	1217	1.5F
	1601	1757	0.9E
	2214		
29 Tu		0043	1.5F
	0425	0620	0.9E
	1044	1312	1.5F
	1659	1852	0.9E
	2312		
30 W		0137	1.5F
	0523	0716	0.8E
	1142	1407	1.5F
	1753	1948	0.9E
31 Th	0005	0231	1.5F
	0618	0812	0.8E
	1235	1459	1.5F
	1845	2043	0.9E

February

Date	Slack (h m)	Max (h m)	knots
1 F	0055	0321	1.5F
	0709	0906	0.9E
	1324	1548	1.5F
	1933	2133	0.9E
2 Sa	0140	0409	1.6F
	0756	0954	0.9E
	1408	1634	1.5F
	2018	2218	1.0E
3 Su	0220	0454	1.6F
	0840	1039	1.0E
	1448	1719	1.5F
	2059	2302	1.0E
4 M ●	0256	0539	1.7F
	0921	1124	1.0E
	1524	1803	1.6F
	2137	2347	1.1E
5 Tu	0329	0623	1.7F
	1000	1211	1.0E
	1557	1847	1.6F
	2213		
6 W		0032	1.1E
	0401	0707	1.8F
	1038	1258	1.1E
	1629	1930	1.6F
	2247		
7 Th		0118	1.1E
	0435	0751	1.8F
	1116	1344	1.1E
	1702	2013	1.6F
	2320		
8 F		0204	1.1E
	0511	0836	1.7F
	1154	1430	1.1E
	1737	2058	1.6F
	2355		
9 Sa		0249	1.1E
	0550	0922	1.7F
	1232	1516	1.1E
	1815	2145	1.6F
10 Su	0034	0335	1.1E
	0630	1012	1.6F
	1313	1603	1.0E
	1856	2235	1.5F
11 M	0119	0423	1.0E
	0713	1104	1.6F
	1357	1651	1.0E
	1941	2327	1.5F
12 Tu ☽	0209	0511	1.0E
	0759	1156	1.5F
	1448	1740	1.0E
	2032		
13 W		0020	1.5F
	0305	0600	0.9E
	0855	1249	1.5F
	1544	1829	1.0E
	2131		
14 Th		0113	1.5F
	0405	0650	0.9E
	1003	1343	1.5F
	1642	1920	0.9E
	2234		
15 F		0207	1.6F
	0506	0743	0.9E
	1115	1438	1.5F
	1740	2013	1.0E
	2336		
16 Sa		0302	1.6F
	0605	0838	0.9E
	1224	1532	1.6F
	1837	2106	1.0E
17 Su	0036	0355	1.7F
	0702	0931	1.0E
	1329	1625	1.7F
	1932	2156	1.1E
18 M	0135	0447	1.8F
	0757	1022	1.1E
	1427	1717	1.8F
	2024	2246	1.1E
19 Tu ○	0231	0539	1.9F
	0850	1113	1.1E
	1521	1808	1.8F
	2115	2338	1.1E
20 W	0326	0631	1.9F
	0944	1207	1.1E
	1614	1900	1.8F
	2207		
21 Th		0031	1.1E
	0420	0723	1.9F
	1039	1302	1.1E
	1705	1950	1.8F
	2302		
22 F		0125	1.1E
	0516	0814	1.9F
	1138	1356	1.1E
	1757	2040	1.8F
23 Sa	0000	0219	1.1E
	0612	0906	1.8F
	1238	1450	1.0E
	1850	2132	1.7F
24 Su	0100	0312	1.0E
	0710	1000	1.7F
	1338	1544	1.0E
	1945	2226	1.6F
25 M	0202	0407	1.0E
	0810	1055	1.5F
	1438	1639	0.9E
	2044	2322	1.5F
26 Tu ☾	0303	0502	0.9E
	0915	1151	1.5F
	1537	1733	0.9E
	2145		
27 W		0016	1.4F
	0404	0555	0.8E
	1019	1245	1.4F
	1634	1825	0.8E
	2243		
28 Th		0109	1.4F
	0501	0649	0.8E
	1116	1338	1.4F
	1727	1919	0.8E
	2336		

March

Date	Slack (h m)	Max (h m)	knots
1 F		0201	1.4F
	0554	0744	0.8E
	1207	1430	1.4F
	1818	2013	0.8E
2 Sa	0023	0252	1.5F
	0644	0838	0.8E
	1254	1518	1.4F
	1905	2104	0.9E
3 Su	0105	0339	1.5F
	0729	0928	0.9E
	1336	1604	1.5F
	1947	2149	1.0E
4 M	0143	0424	1.6F
	0811	1013	1.0E
	1414	1648	1.5F
	2026	2233	1.1E
5 Tu	0218	0509	1.7F
	0850	1057	1.1E
	1448	1732	1.6F
	2102	2316	1.1E
6 W ●	0251	0553	1.8F
	0927	1141	1.1E
	1519	1815	1.7F
	2134		
7 Th		0000	1.2E
	0325	0638	1.8F
	1001	1227	1.1E
	1551	1859	1.7F
	2203		
8 F		0046	1.2E
	0400	0722	1.8F
	1035	1313	1.2E
	1625	1943	1.7F
	2234		
9 Sa		0131	1.2E
	0437	0807	1.8F
	1108	1358	1.2E
	1702	2028	1.7F
	2311		
10 Su		0216	1.1E
	0516	0853	1.7F
	1146	1443	1.1E
	1741	2115	1.7F
	2354		
11 M		0302	1.1E
	0555	0942	1.6F
	1228	1530	1.1E
	1822	2205	1.6F
12 Tu	0041	0349	1.0E
	0637	1034	1.6F
	1315	1618	1.0E
	1906	2258	1.5F
13 W	0133	0439	0.9E
	0723	1128	1.5F
	1409	1708	1.0E
	1956	2352	1.5F
14 Th ☽	0232	0530	0.9E
	0820	1223	1.4F
	1511	1759	0.9E
	2056		
15 F		0047	1.5F
	0339	0622	0.8E
	0940	1319	1.4F
	1618	1852	0.9E
	2208		
16 Sa		0143	1.5F
	0448	0717	0.9E
	1108	1415	1.5F
	1722	1947	0.9E
	2320		
17 Su		0239	1.6F
	0552	0814	0.9E
	1219	1510	1.6F
	1822	2042	1.0E
18 M	0026	0333	1.7F
	0652	0911	1.0E
	1321	1603	1.7F
	1918	2136	1.1E
19 Tu	0127	0426	1.8F
	0748	1004	1.1E
	1417	1655	1.7F
	2011	2227	1.1E
20 W ○	0224	0519	1.9F
	0841	1055	1.1E
	1508	1747	1.8F
	2101	2318	1.2E
21 Th	0318	0611	2.0F
	0933	1148	1.1E
	1558	1838	1.9F
	2152		
22 F		0010	1.2E
	0411	0702	2.0F
	1027	1242	1.1E
	1647	1928	1.9F
	2246		
23 Sa		0104	1.1E
	0504	0753	1.9F
	1122	1336	1.1E
	1737	2017	1.8F
	2342		
24 Su		0157	1.1E
	0558	0843	1.8F
	1219	1428	1.0E
	1828	2107	1.7F
25 M	0041	0249	1.0E
	0652	0935	1.6F
	1316	1520	1.0E
	1920	2200	1.5F
26 Tu	0141	0342	0.9E
	0747	1028	1.5F
	1414	1613	0.9E
	2014	2253	1.4F
27 W ☾	0240	0436	0.8E
	0847	1123	1.4F
	1511	1706	0.9E
	2112	2347	1.4F
28 Th	0339	0530	0.8E
	0948	1216	1.3F
	1606	1758	0.8E
	2209		
29 F		0039	1.3F
	0434	0622	0.7E
	1043	1307	1.3F
	1658	1849	0.8E
	2259		
30 Sa		0130	1.4F
	0526	0714	0.8E
	1133	1357	1.3F
	1747	1941	0.8E
	2344		
31 Su		0219	1.4F
	0613	0808	0.8E
	1217	1446	1.4F
	1831	2031	0.9E

Time meridian 75° W. 0000 is midnight. 1200 is noon. Times are not adjusted for Daylight Saving Time.

Throgs Neck Bridge, Long Island Sound, New York, 2019

F–Flood, Dir. 106° True   E–Ebb, Dir. 262° True

April

Day	Slack h m	Maximum h m	knots		Day	Slack h m	Maximum h m	knots
1 M	0025 0658 1257 1913	0307 0858 1532 2119	1.5F 0.9E 1.4F 1.0E		**16** Tu	0016 0640 1306 1902	0312 0851 1541 2115	1.8F 1.0E 1.7F 1.1E
2 Tu	0102 0739 1333 1950	0353 0944 1616 2203	1.6F 1.0E 1.5F 1.1E		**17** W	0117 0736 1400 1955	0406 0946 1633 2207	1.9F 1.1E 1.8F 1.1E
3 W	0139 0817 1407 2024	0438 1027 1700 2245	1.7F 1.1E 1.6F 1.2E		**18** Th	0214 0828 1450 2046	0458 1037 1724 2258	1.9F 1.1E 1.8F 1.2E
4 Th	0215 0852 1440 2054	0523 1110 1744 2328	1.8F 1.2E 1.7F 1.2E		**19** F ○	0307 0919 1539 2137	0550 1128 1815 2349	1.9F 1.1E 1.9F 1.2E
5 F ●	0251 0924 1514 2124	0608 1155 1829	1.9F 1.2E 1.8F		**20** Sa	0359 1010 1628 2229	0641 1221 1905	1.9F 1.1E 1.8F
6 Sa	0328 0955 1550 2158	0013 0654 1240 1914	1.2E 1.9F 1.2E 1.8F		**21** Su	0450 1103 1716 2324	0042 0731 1313 1953	1.1E 1.8F 1.1E 1.8F
7 Su	0405 1029 1629 2236	0058 0739 1326 2000	1.2E 1.8F 1.2E 1.8F		**22** M	0541 1158 1805	0135 0819 1405 2042	1.0E 1.7F 1.0E 1.7F
8 M	0444 1107 1709 2321	0144 0826 1412 2047	1.1E 1.8F 1.1E 1.7F		**23** Tu	0021 0631 1253 1853	0226 0909 1455 2132	1.0E 1.6F 1.0E 1.5F
9 Tu	0524 1152 1752	0230 0914 1458 2137	1.1E 1.7F 1.1E 1.6F		**24** W	0118 0721 1347 1942	0318 1000 1547 2224	0.9E 1.4F 0.9E 1.4F
10 W	0010 0608 1243 1837	0318 1007 1548 2231	1.0E 1.5F 1.0E 1.5F		**25** Th	0215 0814 1441 2032	0410 1052 1638 2316	0.8E 1.3F 0.9E 1.3F
11 Th	0105 0658 1341 1928	0409 1102 1640 2327	0.9E 1.5F 1.0E 1.5F		**26** F ◑	0310 0908 1534 2124	0502 1144 1729	0.8E 1.3F 0.8E
12 F ◐	0208 0801 1448 2030	0503 1159 1733	0.9E 1.4F 0.9E		**27** Sa	0403 1002 1624 2213	0007 0553 1234 1818	1.3F 0.8E 1.2F 0.8E
13 Sa	0321 0934 1600 2151	0023 0558 1255 1826	1.5F 0.8E 1.4F 0.9E		**28** Su	0452 1050 1710 2258	0056 0644 1322 1907	1.4F 0.8E 1.3F 0.9E
14 Su	0434 1101 1707 2310	0119 0654 1352 1922	1.6F 0.9E 1.5F 0.9E		**29** M	0539 1132 1753 2340	0145 0734 1410 1957	1.4F 0.8E 1.3F 0.9E
15 M	0540 1208 1807	0216 0753 1448 2020	1.6F 0.9E 1.6F 1.0E		**30** Tu	0622 1211 1833	0234 0825 1457 2046	1.5F 0.9E 1.4F 1.0E

May

Day	Slack h m	Maximum h m	knots		Day	Slack h m	Maximum h m	knots
1 W	0020 0703 1248 1910	0321 0912 1543 2131	1.6F 1.0E 1.6F 1.1E		**16** Th	0105 0720 1340 1939	0345 0926 1611 2147	1.8F 1.0E 1.8F 1.1E
2 Th	0059 0741 1325 1945	0407 0957 1628 2214	1.7F 1.1E 1.7F 1.2E		**17** F	0200 0812 1430 2031	0437 1017 1702 2238	1.9F 1.1E 1.8F 1.1E
3 F	0139 0815 1402 2018	0453 1040 1714 2257	1.8F 1.2E 1.7F 1.2E		**18** Sa ○	0253 0903 1519 2121	0528 1107 1752 2328	1.9F 1.1E 1.8F 1.1E
4 Sa ●	0218 0848 1440 2051	0539 1123 1800 2341	1.8F 1.2E 1.8F 1.2E		**19** Su	0344 0952 1607 2212	0619 1158 1841	1.8F 1.1E 1.8F
5 Su	0257 0920 1519 2128	0626 1208 1847	1.9F 1.2E 1.8F		**20** M	0433 1043 1653 2305	0020 0708 1250 1929	1.1E 1.8F 1.1E 1.7F
6 M	0336 0956 1559 2208	0026 0713 1254 1934	1.1E 1.8F 1.2E 1.8F		**21** Tu	0520 1134 1739 2359	0112 0755 1341 2016	1.0E 1.7F 1.0E 1.6F
7 Tu	0417 1037 1641 2254	0113 0801 1342 2022	1.1E 1.8F 1.1E 1.7F		**22** W	0607 1226 1823	0202 0842 1430 2104	0.9E 1.5F 1.0E 1.5F
8 W	0501 1125 1726 2346	0201 0850 1430 2112	1.0E 1.7F 1.1E 1.7F		**23** Th	0052 0651 1318 1904	0252 0930 1519 2152	0.9E 1.4F 0.9E 1.4F
9 Th	0550 1220 1814	0251 0942 1520 2206	1.0E 1.6F 1.0E 1.6F		**24** F	0144 0735 1408 1945	0343 1020 1608 2243	0.8E 1.3F 0.9E 1.4F
10 F	0045 0647 1322 1908	0344 1038 1613 2303	0.9E 1.5F 0.9E 1.5F		**25** Sa	0236 0820 1456 2029	0433 1109 1658 2333	0.8E 1.3F 0.9E 1.4F
11 Sa ◑	0152 0758 1432 2014	0440 1135 1708	0.9E 1.5F 0.9E		**26** Su ◑	0326 0907 1544 2116	0523 1158 1746	0.8E 1.3F 0.9E
12 Su	0308 0929 1544 2140	0000 0536 1232 1803	1.6F 0.9E 1.5F 0.9E		**27** M	0414 0954 1628 2205	0022 0612 1247 1833	1.4F 0.9E 1.3F 0.9E
13 M	0421 1047 1649 2259	0057 0633 1328 1859	1.6F 0.9E 1.5F 0.9E		**28** Tu	0500 1039 1710 2252	0111 0701 1335 1922	1.5F 0.9E 1.4F 1.0E
14 Tu	0525 1150 1749	0154 0731 1424 1957	1.7F 0.9E 1.6F 1.0E		**29** W	0543 1121 1751 2337	0200 0750 1423 2011	1.5F 1.0E 1.5F 1.0E
15 W	0005 0624 1246 1845	0251 0830 1519 2054	1.7F 1.0E 1.7F 1.1E		**30** Th	0624 1203 1829	0249 0839 1511 2058	1.6F 1.0E 1.6F 1.1E
					31 F	0021 0702 1244 1907	0337 0925 1558 2143	1.7F 1.1E 1.7F 1.1E

June

Day	Slack h m	Maximum h m	knots		Day	Slack h m	Maximum h m	knots
1 Sa	0105 0738 1326 1945	0424 1009 1645 2227	1.8F 1.2E 1.8F 1.1E		**16** Su	0237 0844 1458 2105	0506 1046 1728 2307	1.8F 1.1E 1.8F 1.0E
2 Su	0148 0814 1409 2023	0512 1053 1733 2311	1.8F 1.2E 1.8F 1.1E		**17** M ○	0326 0932 1544 2154	0555 1135 1817 2357	1.7F 1.0E 1.7F 1.0E
3 M	0230 0850 1451 2103	0600 1138 1821 2357	1.8F 1.2E 1.8F 1.1E		**18** Tu	0412 1020 1628 2243	0643 1225 1904	1.7F 1.0E 1.7F
4 Tu	0314 0930 1534 2146	0649 1225 1910	1.8F 1.1E 1.8F		**19** W	0456 1108 1709 2333	0048 0729 1314 1949	1.0E 1.6F 1.0E 1.6F
5 W	0359 1015 1618 2235	0046 0738 1314 1959	1.1E 1.7F 1.1E 1.8F		**20** Th	0538 1156 1747	0137 0814 1402 2034	0.9E 1.5F 1.0E 1.6F
6 Th	0449 1106 1706 2329	0136 0828 1404 2050	1.0E 1.7F 1.1E 1.7F		**21** F	0021 0616 1243 1823	0226 0859 1449 2121	0.9E 1.4F 1.0E 1.5F
7 F	0545 1203 1758	0228 0920 1455 2143	1.0E 1.6F 1.0E 1.7F		**22** Sa	0109 0653 1328 1858	0314 0946 1537 2209	0.9E 1.4F 0.9E 1.5F
8 Sa	0032 0646 1308 1856	0322 1015 1549 2240	1.0E 1.5F 1.0E 1.6F		**23** Su	0156 0728 1412 1936	0402 1034 1625 2258	0.9E 1.3F 0.9E 1.5F
9 Su	0142 0756 1416 2005	0418 1112 1645 2337	0.9E 1.5F 1.0E 1.6F		**24** M	0243 0808 1455 2020	0451 1123 1712 2348	0.9E 1.3F 1.0E 1.5F
10 M ◐	0256 0915 1526 2129	0515 1208 1741	0.9E 1.5F 1.0E		**25** Tu ◑	0330 0853 1539 2111	0539 1211 1759	0.9E 1.4F 1.0E
11 Tu	0405 1026 1630 2245	0035 0612 1304 1837	1.6F 0.9E 1.6F 1.0E		**26** W	0415 0943 1623 2204	0037 0627 1300 1847	1.5F 1.0E 1.4F 1.0E
12 W	0508 1128 1730 2351	0132 0709 1400 1934	1.7F 0.9E 1.6F 1.0E		**27** Th	0459 1032 1706 2255	0127 0715 1350 1936	1.5F 1.0E 1.5F 1.0E
13 Th	0606 1225 1827	0228 0808 1455 2032	1.7F 0.9E 1.7F 1.0E		**28** F	0541 1120 1750 2345	0218 0804 1440 2025	1.6F 1.0E 1.6F 1.0E
14 F	0050 0702 1319 1922	0323 0905 1548 2127	1.7F 1.0E 1.7F 1.0E		**29** Sa	0622 1207 1833	0308 0853 1530 2113	1.6F 1.1E 1.7F 1.0E
15 Sa	0145 0754 1410 2015	0416 0957 1639 2218	1.8F 1.0E 1.8F 1.1E		**30** Su	0033 0703 1254 1917	0357 0939 1619 2159	1.7F 1.1E 1.7F 1.1E

Time meridian 75° W.   0000 is midnight.   1200 is noon.   Times are not adjusted for Daylight Saving Time.

Throgs Neck Bridge, Long Island Sound, New York, 2019

F–Flood, Dir. 106° True   E–Ebb, Dir. 262° True

July

Day	Slack	Maximum	knots
1 M	0122	0446	1.7F
	0745	1024	1.1E
	1341	1708	1.8F
	2000	2244	1.1E
2 Tu ●	0211	0536	1.7F
	0827	1110	1.1E
	1428	1757	1.8F
	2044	2331	1.1E
3 W	0301	0626	1.8F
	0911	1158	1.1E
	1514	1848	1.8F
	2131		
4 Th		0021	1.1E
	0353	0716	1.8F
	0959	1249	1.1E
	1602	1938	1.8F
	2221		
5 F		0114	1.1E
	0447	0806	1.7F
	1051	1340	1.1E
	1653	2028	1.8F
	2319		
6 Sa		0207	1.1E
	0544	0858	1.7F
	1150	1433	1.1E
	1749	2121	1.7F
7 Su	0023	0301	1.0E
	0642	0952	1.6F
	1254	1527	1.0E
	1849	2217	1.7F
8 M	0132	0357	1.0E
	0745	1048	1.6F
	1400	1622	1.0E
	1957	2315	1.6F
9 Tu ◐	0241	0454	1.0E
	0854	1144	1.6F
	1506	1718	1.0E
	2116		
10 W		0012	1.6F
	0347	0550	0.9E
	1003	1240	1.6F
	1611	1814	1.0E
	2230		
11 Th		0109	1.6F
	0449	0646	0.9E
	1106	1336	1.6F
	1712	1911	0.9E
	2334		
12 F		0205	1.6F
	0547	0744	0.9E
	1203	1431	1.6F
	1810	2009	0.9E
13 Sa	0033	0301	1.6F
	0642	0842	0.9E
	1257	1525	1.6F
	1906	2106	0.9E
14 Su	0128	0353	1.6F
	0735	0936	1.0E
	1348	1615	1.7F
	1958	2158	1.0E
15 M	0218	0443	1.6F
	0824	1024	1.0E
	1435	1704	1.7F
	2047	2246	1.0E
16 Tu ○	0305	0530	1.6F
	0910	1111	1.0E
	1519	1751	1.7F
	2133	2334	1.0E
17 W	0348	0617	1.6F
	0955	1158	1.0E
	1558	1837	1.7F
	2218		
18 Th		0022	1.0E
	0427	0701	1.6F
	1038	1246	1.0E
	1635	1921	1.7F
	2302		
19 F		0110	1.0E
	0504	0745	1.6F
	1120	1333	1.0E
	1708	2005	1.7F
	2346		
20 Sa		0157	1.0E
	0537	0828	1.5F
	1202	1418	1.0E
	1741	2049	1.6F
21 Su	0030	0243	1.0E
	0609	0912	1.5F
	1241	1504	1.0E
	1815	2135	1.6F
22 M	0112	0330	1.0E
	0642	0958	1.4F
	1319	1550	1.0E
	1853	2224	1.6F
23 Tu	0155	0418	1.0E
	0720	1047	1.4F
	1359	1638	1.0E
	1935	2314	1.5F
24 W ◑	0239	0506	1.0E
	0802	1137	1.4F
	1442	1726	1.0E
	2022		
25 Th		0004	1.5F
	0324	0553	1.0E
	0852	1227	1.5F
	1532	1813	1.0E
	2116		
26 F		0055	1.5F
	0411	0641	1.0E
	0946	1318	1.5F
	1623	1902	0.9E
	2214		
27 Sa		0147	1.5F
	0458	0730	1.0E
	1042	1410	1.6F
	1714	1952	0.9E
	2311		
28 Su		0240	1.6F
	0545	0821	1.0E
	1135	1502	1.6F
	1804	2043	1.0E
29 M	0008	0331	1.6F
	0633	0910	1.0E
	1227	1554	1.7F
	1854	2132	1.0E
30 Tu	0105	0422	1.7F
	0722	0958	1.1E
	1319	1644	1.8F
	1943	2220	1.0E
31 W ●	0202	0513	1.7F
	0810	1045	1.1E
	1411	1735	1.8F
	2031	2308	1.1E

August

Day	Slack	Maximum	knots
1 Th	0256	0604	1.8F
	0857	1134	1.1E
	1501	1826	1.9F
	2120		
2 F		0000	1.1E
	0349	0655	1.8F
	0946	1225	1.1E
	1552	1917	1.9F
	2213		
3 Sa		0053	1.1E
	0442	0745	1.8F
	1039	1318	1.1E
	1646	2008	1.9F
	2310		
4 Su		0147	1.1E
	0536	0836	1.8F
	1136	1411	1.1E
	1742	2100	1.8F
5 M	0013	0241	1.1E
	0631	0928	1.7F
	1238	1504	1.1E
	1842	2155	1.7F
6 Tu	0118	0336	1.0E
	0728	1023	1.6F
	1342	1600	1.0E
	1947	2251	1.6F
7 W ◐	0223	0432	1.0E
	0831	1120	1.6F
	1448	1656	1.0E
	2100	2349	1.6F
8 Th	0327	0528	0.9E
	0939	1215	1.5F
	1552	1752	0.9E
	2212		
9 F		0045	1.5F
	0428	0623	0.9E
	1042	1311	1.5F
	1654	1848	0.9E
	2316		
10 Sa		0141	1.5F
	0526	0720	0.9E
	1140	1406	1.5F
	1753	1946	0.8E
11 Su	0014	0236	1.5F
	0621	0818	0.9E
	1234	1500	1.6F
	1847	2044	0.8E
12 M	0107	0329	1.5F
	0713	0912	0.9E
	1323	1550	1.6F
	1938	2137	0.9E
13 Tu	0155	0417	1.5F
	0800	1000	1.0E
	1408	1637	1.6F
	2025	2223	0.9E
14 W	0238	0503	1.6F
	0844	1045	1.0E
	1448	1723	1.7F
	2108	2308	1.0E
15 Th ○	0318	0547	1.6F
	0925	1130	1.0E
	1524	1808	1.7F
	2149	2354	1.0E
16 F	0353	0631	1.6F
	1004	1215	1.1E
	1556	1851	1.7F
	2228		
17 Sa		0041	1.1E
	0424	0714	1.6F
	1040	1301	1.1E
	1628	1935	1.8F
	2308		
18 Su		0127	1.1E
	0455	0756	1.6F
	1114	1346	1.1E
	1701	2018	1.7F
	2346		
19 M		0212	1.1E
	0527	0839	1.6F
	1148	1431	1.1E
	1736	2103	1.7F
20 Tu	0024	0257	1.1E
	0601	0925	1.6F
	1223	1516	1.1E
	1815	2151	1.6F
21 W	0103	0344	1.1E
	0646	1013	1.5F
	1304	1604	1.0E
	1855	2241	1.6F
22 Th	0144	0432	1.0E
	0722	1104	1.5F
	1351	1652	1.0E
	1940	2333	1.5F
23 F ◑	0230	0520	1.0E
	0810	1156	1.5F
	1444	1740	0.9E
	2032		
24 Sa		0026	1.5F
	0322	0608	1.0E
	0905	1249	1.5F
	1543	1830	0.9E
	2134		
25 Su		0119	1.5F
	0418	0658	0.9E
	1006	1343	1.5F
	1643	1921	0.9E
	2245		
26 M		0213	1.5F
	0515	0750	1.0E
	1107	1437	1.6F
	1741	2015	0.9E
	2352		
27 Tu		0307	1.6F
	0610	0843	1.0E
	1206	1530	1.7F
	1836	2108	1.0E
28 W	0056	0400	1.6F
	0704	0933	1.0E
	1303	1622	1.8F
	1929	2158	1.0E
29 Th	0155	0451	1.7F
	0755	1022	1.1E
	1359	1713	1.9F
	2021	2248	1.1E
30 F ●	0249	0542	1.8F
	0844	1111	1.1E
	1452	1805	1.9F
	2112	2339	1.1E
31 Sa	0340	0633	1.8F
	0933	1203	1.2E
	1545	1856	2.0F
	2204		

September

Day	Slack	Maximum	knots
1 Su		0033	1.1E
	0431	0724	1.8F
	1025	1256	1.2E
	1639	1947	1.9F
	2300		
2 M		0127	1.1E
	0522	0814	1.8F
	1121	1349	1.1E
	1735	2039	1.9F
3 Tu	0001	0220	1.1E
	0615	0905	1.7F
	1222	1443	1.1E
	1834	2132	1.7F
4 W	0102	0314	1.0E
	0709	0959	1.6F
	1325	1537	1.0E
	1935	2228	1.6F
5 Th ○	0204	0410	1.0E
	0809	1054	1.5F
	1430	1634	0.9E
	2043	2325	1.5F
6 F	0306	0505	0.9E
	0914	1150	1.5F
	1534	1730	0.8E
	2152		
7 Sa		0021	1.4F
	0407	0600	0.9E
	1018	1251	1.4F
	1635	1825	0.8E
	2254		
8 Su		0116	1.4F
	0503	0655	0.8E
	1115	1340	1.4F
	1732	1921	0.8E
	2350		
9 M		0209	1.4F
	0557	0751	0.8E
	1207	1433	1.5F
	1825	2019	0.8E
10 Tu	0040	0301	1.4F
	0647	0845	0.9E
	1253	1522	1.5F
	1913	2111	0.9E
11 W	0125	0348	1.5F
	0732	0933	1.0E
	1335	1608	1.6F
	1958	2157	0.9E
12 Th	0206	0432	1.5F
	0814	1017	1.0E
	1412	1653	1.7F
	2039	2241	1.0E
13 F ○	0241	0516	1.6F
	0852	1059	1.1E
	1446	1737	1.7F
	2117	2324	1.1E
14 Sa	0313	0559	1.6F
	0926	1141	1.1E
	1517	1821	1.8F
	2153		
15 Su		0009	1.1E
	0343	0642	1.7F
	0957	1228	1.2E
	1550	1905	1.8F
	2227		
16 M		0055	1.1E
	0414	0725	1.7F
	1027	1313	1.2E
	1624	1948	1.8F
	2301		
17 Tu		0140	1.2E
	0448	0809	1.7F
	1100	1358	1.1E
	1701	2033	1.8F
	2335		
18 W		0225	1.1E
	0525	0854	1.7F
	1138	1443	1.1E
	1740	2120	1.7F
19 Th	0013	0311	1.1E
	0605	0942	1.6F
	1223	1530	1.0E
	1820	2211	1.6F
20 F ◑	0056	0359	1.0E
	0647	1034	1.5F
	1312	1619	0.9E
	1905	2304	1.5F
21 Sa	0146	0448	1.0E
	0734	1128	1.5F
	1408	1709	0.9E
	1956	2358	1.4F
22 Su	0243	0538	0.9E
	0829	1222	1.5F
	1511	1800	0.8E
	2103		
23 M		0053	1.4F
	0347	0629	0.9E
	0934	1317	1.5F
	1618	1853	0.8E
	2227		
24 Tu		0148	1.5F
	0451	0722	0.9E
	1044	1412	1.6F
	1722	1949	0.9E
	2342		
25 W		0243	1.5F
	0551	0816	1.0E
	1150	1507	1.7F
	1821	2045	1.0E
26 Th	0045	0337	1.6F
	0647	0910	1.0E
	1251	1600	1.8F
	1917	2138	1.0E
27 F	0143	0429	1.7F
	0739	1001	1.1E
	1349	1652	1.9F
	2010	2229	1.1E
28 Sa ●	0235	0520	1.8F
	0830	1050	1.2E
	1444	1744	2.0F
	2101	2319	1.2E
29 Su	0325	0611	1.9F
	0919	1141	1.2E
	1537	1836	2.0F
	2153		
30 M		0012	1.1E
	0415	0701	1.9F
	1011	1234	1.2E
	1631	1927	1.9F
	2248		

Time meridian 75° W. 0000 is midnight. 1200 is noon. Times are not adjusted for Daylight Saving Time.

Throgs Neck Bridge, Long Island Sound, New York, 2019

F–Flood, Dir. 106° True   E–Ebb, Dir. 262° True

October

Day	Slack (h m)	Maximum (h m)	knots
1 Tu		0106	1.1E
	0505	0751	1.8F
	1107	1328	1.1E
	1726	2018	1.8F
	2345		
2 W		0159	1.1E
	0557	0842	1.7F
	1207	1422	1.1E
	1823	2109	1.7F
3 Th	0045	0252	1.0E
	0650	0934	1.6F
	1309	1516	1.0E
	1921	2203	1.6F
4 F	0144	0347	0.9E
	0747	1029	1.5F
	1412	1611	0.9E
	2023	2259	1.4F
5 Sa	0244	0442	0.9E
	0847	1124	1.4F
	1514	1707	0.8E
	2126	2354	1.3F
6 Su	0342	0536	0.8E
	0948	1218	1.4F
	1613	1801	0.8E
	2226		
7 M		0047	1.3F
	0437	0628	0.8E
	1044	1311	1.4F
	1707	1854	0.7E
	2319		
8 Tu		0139	1.3F
	0529	0721	0.8E
	1133	1402	1.4F
	1757	1949	0.8E
9 W	0006	0228	1.3F
	0616	0813	0.9E
	1217	1451	1.5F
	1843	2041	0.9E
10 Th	0048	0315	1.4F
	0659	0902	1.0E
	1256	1537	1.6F
	1926	2128	1.0E
11 F	0126	0400	1.5F
	0739	0946	1.1E
	1332	1622	1.7F
	2006	2211	1.1E
12 Sa	0159	0443	1.6F
	0815	1028	1.1E
	1406	1706	1.8F
	2042	2253	1.1E
13 Su	0231	0526	1.7F
	0847	1111	1.2E
	1440	1750	1.8F
	2116	2337	1.2E
14 M	0302	0610	1.7F
	0917	1155	1.2E
	1514	1835	1.8F
	2147		
15 Tu		0022	1.2E
	0336	0655	1.8F
	0947	1240	1.2E
	1551	1920	1.8F
	2218		
16 W		0107	1.2E
	0413	0740	1.8F
	1022	1326	1.1E
	1629	2005	1.8F
	2253		
17 Th		0153	1.2E
	0452	0826	1.7F
	1103	1412	1.1E
	1708	2052	1.7F
	2334		
18 F		0239	1.1E
	0533	0914	1.7F
	1150	1459	1.0E
	1751	2143	1.6F
19 Sa	0021	0327	1.0E
	0618	1006	1.6F
	1242	1548	0.9E
	1838	2237	1.5F
20 Su	0114	0418	1.0E
	0705	1101	1.5F
	1340	1641	0.9E
	1932	2332	1.4F
21 M	0214	0510	0.9E
	0800	1157	1.5F
	1445	1734	0.9E
	2044		
22 Tu		0028	1.4F
	0323	0602	0.9E
	0908	1252	1.5F
	1558	1828	0.9E
	2215		
23 W		0124	1.5F
	0431	0655	0.9E
	1026	1348	1.6F
	1705	1924	0.9E
	2328		
24 Th		0219	1.5F
	0532	0751	1.0E
	1136	1444	1.7F
	1805	2022	1.0E
25 F	0030	0314	1.7F
	0629	0846	1.0E
	1240	1538	1.8F
	1902	2117	1.0E
26 Sa	0126	0406	1.8F
	0723	0939	1.1E
	1339	1631	1.9F
	1957	2209	1.1E
27 Su	0218	0458	1.8F
	0814	1030	1.2E
	1434	1723	1.9F
	2048	2259	1.1E
28 M	0308	0549	1.9F
	0905	1121	1.2E
	1528	1815	1.9F
	2140	2351	1.1E
29 Tu	0358	0639	1.9F
	0958	1213	1.1E
	1621	1906	1.9F
	2233		
30 W		0045	1.1E
	0448	0729	1.8F
	1053	1308	1.1E
	1715	1956	1.8F
	2328		
31 Th		0138	1.1E
	0539	0819	1.7F
	1152	1401	1.0E
	1809	2046	1.7F

November

Day	Slack (h m)	Maximum (h m)	knots
1 F	0025	0231	1.0E
	0630	0909	1.6F
	1252	1454	0.9E
	1903	2138	1.5F
2 Sa	0122	0323	0.9E
	0722	1002	1.5F
	1351	1548	0.8E
	1957	2231	1.4F
3 Su	0219	0417	0.9E
	0816	1055	1.4F
	1449	1642	0.8E
	2054	2324	1.3F
4 M	0314	0509	0.8E
	0911	1148	1.4F
	1544	1734	0.8E
	2149		
5 Tu		0015	1.3F
	0406	0559	0.8E
	1003	1239	1.4F
	1635	1825	0.8E
	2240		
6 W		0105	1.3F
	0455	0648	0.8E
	1050	1328	1.4F
	1723	1916	0.8E
	2324		
7 Th		0153	1.3F
	0540	0738	0.9E
	1132	1417	1.5F
	1808	2006	0.9E
8 F	0003	0240	1.4F
	0621	0827	1.0E
	1211	1504	1.6F
	1850	2055	1.0E
9 Sa	0039	0326	1.5F
	0700	0913	1.1E
	1249	1550	1.7F
	1930	2140	1.1E
10 Su	0114	0410	1.6F
	0736	0957	1.1E
	1326	1635	1.8F
	2006	2222	1.2E
11 M	0149	0455	1.7F
	0809	1040	1.2E
	1404	1720	1.8F
	2039	2305	1.2E
12 Tu	0225	0540	1.8F
	0841	1123	1.2E
	1443	1806	1.8F
	2110	2350	1.2E
13 W	0303	0626	1.8F
	0915	1208	1.1E
	1521	1853	1.8F
	2143		
14 Th		0036	1.2E
	0342	0713	1.8F
	0953	1255	1.1E
	1601	1940	1.8F
	2220		
15 F		0123	1.1E
	0423	0800	1.8F
	1036	1342	1.0E
	1644	2027	1.7F
	2304		
16 Sa		0210	1.1E
	0506	0849	1.7F
	1124	1431	1.0E
	1730	2118	1.6F
	2354		
17 Su		0259	1.0E
	0552	0941	1.6F
	1218	1521	0.9E
	1821	2212	1.5F
18 M	0050	0350	1.0E
	0641	1036	1.6F
	1318	1615	0.9E
	1920	2308	1.5F
19 Tu	0153	0443	0.9E
	0737	1132	1.5F
	1426	1710	0.9E
	2034		
20 W		0004	1.5F
	0302	0536	0.9E
	0847	1228	1.6F
	1540	1805	0.9E
	2159		
21 Th		0059	1.6F
	0410	0630	0.9E
	1011	1325	1.6F
	1648	1901	0.9E
	2310		
22 F		0155	1.6F
	0512	0726	1.0E
	1124	1422	1.7F
	1749	1959	1.0E
23 Sa	0010	0250	1.7F
	0610	0823	1.0E
	1228	1517	1.8F
	1847	2056	1.0E
24 Su	0106	0344	1.7F
	0706	0918	1.1E
	1328	1610	1.8F
	1942	2149	1.1E
25 M	0200	0435	1.8F
	0800	1010	1.1E
	1424	1703	1.9F
	2034	2240	1.1E
26 Tu	0251	0526	1.8F
	0853	1101	1.1E
	1518	1754	1.9F
	2125	2331	1.1E
27 W	0341	0617	1.8F
	0945	1153	1.1E
	1610	1845	1.8F
	2216		
28 Th		0024	1.1E
	0430	0707	1.8F
	1039	1247	1.0E
	1701	1934	1.7F
	2309		
29 F		0117	1.1E
	0519	0756	1.7F
	1135	1340	1.0E
	1751	2022	1.6F
30 Sa	0003	0208	1.0E
	0607	0844	1.6F
	1231	1432	0.9E
	1839	2111	1.5F

December

Day	Slack (h m)	Maximum (h m)	knots
1 Su	0057	0258	0.9E
	0653	0933	1.5F
	1325	1523	0.9E
	1926	2201	1.4F
2 M	0149	0349	0.9E
	0738	1024	1.4F
	1418	1614	0.8E
	2013	2251	1.3F
3 Tu	0240	0439	0.9E
	0823	1115	1.4F
	1509	1705	0.8E
	2100	2341	1.3F
4 W	0329	0527	0.9E
	0910	1204	1.4F
	1558	1753	0.8E
	2147		
5 Th		0029	1.3F
	0415	0615	0.9E
	0956	1253	1.4F
	1645	1842	0.9E
	2230		
6 F		0116	1.3F
	0458	0702	0.9E
	1041	1342	1.5F
	1729	1931	0.9E
	2310		
7 Sa		0204	1.4F
	0539	0751	1.0E
	1124	1430	1.6F
	1811	2020	1.0E
	2349		
8 Su		0252	1.5F
	0619	0839	1.0E
	1207	1518	1.6F
	1851	2107	1.1E
9 M	0029	0338	1.6F
	0657	0926	1.1E
	1249	1605	1.7F
	1928	2152	1.1E
10 Tu	0109	0425	1.7F
	0734	1010	1.1E
	1332	1652	1.8F
	2003	2235	1.2E
11 W	0151	0512	1.8F
	0811	1054	1.1E
	1415	1739	1.8F
	2037	2319	1.2E
12 Th	0233	0600	1.8F
	0849	1139	1.1E
	1457	1827	1.8F
	2216		
13 F		0005	1.2E
	0316	0648	1.8F
	0930	1226	1.1E
	1541	1916	1.7F
	2155		
14 Sa		0054	1.1E
	0359	0737	1.8F
	1014	1315	1.0E
	1628	2004	1.7F
	2241		
15 Su		0142	1.1E
	0444	0826	1.8F
	1103	1405	1.0E
	1718	2054	1.6F
	2333		
16 M		0232	1.0E
	0532	0917	1.7F
	1159	1457	1.0E
	1812	2147	1.6F
17 Tu	0031	0323	1.0E
	0623	1012	1.6F
	1302	1551	1.0E
	1912	2243	1.5F
18 W	0134	0417	1.0E
	0721	1108	1.6F
	1411	1647	0.9E
	2021	2339	1.5F
19 Th	0242	0512	1.0E
	0832	1205	1.6F
	1523	1742	0.9E
	2139		
20 F		0035	1.5F
	0350	0607	1.0E
	0957	1302	1.6F
	1630	1838	0.9E
	2249		
21 Sa		0131	1.6F
	0453	0702	1.0E
	1111	1359	1.7F
	1732	1935	0.9E
	2350		
22 Su		0226	1.6F
	0553	0800	1.0E
	1216	1455	1.7F
	1830	2034	1.0E
23 M	0047	0321	1.7F
	0651	0858	1.0E
	1316	1550	1.8F
	1925	2129	1.0E
24 Tu	0141	0413	1.8F
	0747	0952	1.1E
	1412	1642	1.8F
	2018	2220	1.1E
25 W	0233	0505	1.8F
	0840	1043	1.1E
	1504	1733	1.7F
	2108	2311	1.1E
26 Th	0322	0555	1.8F
	0931	1134	1.0E
	1554	1823	1.7F
	2158		
27 F		0002	1.0E
	0410	0644	1.8F
	1022	1226	1.0E
	1641	1911	1.7F
	2247		
28 Sa		0053	1.0E
	0455	0731	1.7F
	1113	1318	1.0E
	1727	1957	1.6F
	2337		
29 Su		0143	1.0E
	0538	0817	1.6F
	1204	1408	0.9E
	1809	2042	1.5F
30 M	0026	0231	1.0E
	0618	0903	1.6F
	1254	1456	0.9E
	1848	2128	1.4F
31 Tu	0113	0318	0.9E
	0654	0951	1.5F
	1342	1544	0.9E
	1925	2216	1.4F

Time meridian 75° W. 0000 is midnight. 1200 is noon. Times are not adjusted for Daylight Saving Time.

Hell Gate (off Mill Rock), East River, New York, 2019

F–Flood, Dir. 050° True   E–Ebb, Dir. 230° True

January

Day	Slack (h m)	Maximum (h m)	knots
1 Tu	0015	0318	3.3F
	0607	0926	4.6E
	1249	1551	3.3F
	1838	2152	4.5E
2 W	0108	0412	3.3F
	0701	1021	4.7E
	1341	1642	3.3F
	1929	2242	4.5E
3 Th	0157	0500	3.4F
	0750	1107	4.7E
	1429	1728	3.4F
	2016	2324	4.6E
4 F	0242	0544	3.5F
	0835	1148	4.8E
	1513	1810	3.4F
	2059		
5 Sa ●		0003	4.6E
	0325	0625	3.5F
	0918	1224	4.8E
	1554	1849	3.4F
	2141		
6 Su		0038	4.7E
	0405	0703	3.5F
	0959	1300	4.8E
	1634	1926	3.4F
	2221		
7 M		0114	4.7E
	0445	0740	3.5F
	1040	1335	4.8E
	1713	2003	3.3F
	2301		
8 Tu		0151	4.7E
	0524	0817	3.4F
	1119	1412	4.8E
	1752	2039	3.3F
	2340		
9 W		0229	4.6E
	0603	0855	3.3F
	1159	1451	4.7E
	1832	2117	3.2F
10 Th	0020	0308	4.6E
	0643	0934	3.2F
	1240	1531	4.6E
	1912	2157	3.1F
11 F	0100	0350	4.5E
	0725	1016	3.1F
	1322	1613	4.5E
	1953	2239	3.0F
12 Sa	0143	0434	4.4E
	0809	1101	3.0F
	1407	1659	4.4E
	2037	2325	2.9F
13 Su	0228	0521	4.4E
	0858	1149	2.9F
	1455	1747	4.3E
	2125		
14 M ◑		0014	2.8F
	0318	0612	4.4E
	0952	1242	2.9F
	1548	1839	4.3E
	2216		
15 Tu		0107	2.9F
	0411	0706	4.4E
	1049	1338	2.9F
	1644	1934	4.3E
	2311		
16 W		0203	3.0F
	0508	0803	4.6E
	1147	1436	3.0F
	1742	2031	4.4E
17 Th	0006	0300	3.1F
	0606	0902	4.7E
	1245	1535	3.2F
	1839	2128	4.6E
18 F	0101	0357	3.3F
	0703	0959	4.8E
	1341	1631	3.4F
	1935	2225	4.7E
19 Sa	0156	0453	3.6F
	0759	1056	5.0E
	1434	1726	3.6F
	2029	2320	4.9E
20 Su	0249	0547	3.8F
	0853	1150	5.2E
	1527	1819	3.7F
	2122		
21 M O		0014	5.1E
	0342	0640	3.9F
	0946	1244	5.3E
	1618	1911	3.8F
	2214		
22 Tu		0107	5.2E
	0435	0733	4.0F
	1039	1336	5.3E
	1710	2003	3.9F
	2306		
23 W		0159	5.2E
	0528	0826	4.0F
	1133	1428	5.2E
	1802	2055	3.8F
	2359		
24 Th		0252	5.1E
	0623	0920	3.9F
	1226	1521	5.1E
	1856	2149	3.7F
25 F	0052	0346	5.0E
	0720	1016	3.7F
	1321	1615	4.9E
	1951	2245	3.6F
26 Sa	0147	0442	4.8E
	0819	1115	3.5F
	1418	1712	4.7E
	2048	2344	3.4F
27 Su ◐	0245	0541	4.6E
	0920	1217	3.3F
	1517	1812	4.5E
	2148		
28 M		0046	3.2F
	0344	0645	4.5E
	1023	1322	3.1F
	1617	1917	4.3E
	2248		
29 Tu		0150	3.1F
	0444	0754	4.4E
	1125	1427	3.1F
	1716	2025	4.2E
	2347		
30 W		0252	3.1F
	0542	0901	4.3E
	1223	1526	3.1F
	1813	2128	4.2E
31 Th	0042	0349	3.1F
	0637	0959	4.4E
	1317	1620	3.1F
	1905	2220	4.3E

February

Day	Slack (h m)	Maximum (h m)	knots
1 F	0133	0439	3.2F
	0728	1047	4.5E
	1405	1706	3.2F
	1953	2304	4.4E
2 Sa	0218	0523	3.3F
	0814	1127	4.5E
	1448	1748	3.3F
	2037	2341	4.5E
3 Su	0300	0603	3.4F
	0857	1203	4.6E
	1528	1826	3.3F
	2118		
4 M ●		0015	4.6E
	0340	0640	3.5F
	0938	1236	4.7E
	1607	1901	3.4F
	2157		
5 Tu		0049	4.7E
	0418	0716	3.5F
	1017	1310	4.8E
	1644	1936	3.4F
	2235		
6 W		0125	4.7E
	0455	0751	3.5F
	1056	1346	4.8E
	1720	2010	3.4F
	2313		
7 Th		0201	4.7E
	0532	0827	3.5F
	1134	1422	4.8E
	1756	2046	3.4F
	2350		
8 F		0239	4.7E
	0608	0904	3.4F
	1212	1501	4.7E
	1832	2123	3.3F
9 Sa	0028	0318	4.7E
	0646	0942	3.4F
	1251	1541	4.6E
	1909	2202	3.2F
10 Su	0107	0400	4.6E
	0727	1024	3.2F
	1333	1624	4.5E
	1949	2245	3.1F
11 M	0150	0445	4.6E
	0812	1110	3.1F
	1419	1710	4.4E
	2034	2333	3.1F
12 Tu ◐	0238	0535	4.5E
	0904	1202	3.0F
	1511	1801	4.3E
	2126		
13 W		0026	3.0F
	0334	0630	4.4E
	1004	1300	3.0F
	1609	1858	4.3E
	2225		
14 Th		0126	3.0F
	0436	0729	4.5E
	1109	1402	3.0F
	1712	1958	4.3E
	2329		
15 F		0229	3.2F
	0540	0832	4.5E
	1214	1507	3.2F
	1815	2101	4.5E
16 Sa	0033	0334	3.4F
	0643	0936	4.7E
	1316	1610	3.4F
	1916	2204	4.7E
17 Su	0134	0435	3.6F
	0744	1038	4.9E
	1413	1709	3.6F
	2013	2304	4.9E
18 M	0231	0534	3.8F
	0841	1136	5.1E
	1508	1804	3.8F
	2108		
19 Tu O		0000	5.1E
	0326	0628	4.0F
	0935	1231	5.2E
	1559	1857	4.0F
	2200		
20 W		0054	5.2E
	0419	0721	4.1F
	1028	1323	5.3E
	1650	1948	4.0F
	2251		
21 Th		0146	5.3E
	0512	0813	4.1F
	1120	1414	5.2E
	1740	2038	4.0F
	2342		
22 F		0237	5.2E
	0604	0904	4.0F
	1211	1504	5.1E
	1831	2129	3.9F
23 Sa	0033	0327	5.1E
	0657	0957	3.8F
	1303	1554	4.9E
	1923	2221	3.7F
24 Su	0126	0419	4.9E
	0752	1051	3.6F
	1357	1646	4.6E
	2017	2316	3.4F
25 M	0220	0513	4.6E
	0850	1149	3.3F
	1452	1741	4.4E
	2114		
26 Tu ◑		0015	3.2F
	0317	0612	4.3E
	0950	1251	3.1F
	1550	1842	4.1E
	2214		
27 W		0118	3.0F
	0416	0717	4.1E
	1051	1356	2.9F
	1649	1949	4.0E
	2314		
28 Th		0222	3.0F
	0515	0827	4.1E
	1151	1458	2.9F
	1747	2057	3.9E

March

Day	Slack (h m)	Maximum (h m)	knots
1 F	0011	0322	3.0F
	0612	0931	4.1E
	1245	1553	3.0F
	1840	2153	4.0E
2 Sa	0103	0414	3.1F
	0704	1021	4.2E
	1334	1640	3.1F
	1928	2238	4.2E
3 Su	0150	0459	3.2F
	0751	1101	4.3E
	1418	1722	3.2F
	2012	2314	4.3E
4 M	0232	0538	3.4F
	0834	1136	4.5E
	1457	1758	3.3F
	2053	2348	4.5E
5 Tu	0311	0614	3.5F
	0914	1209	4.6E
	1535	1833	3.5F
	2132		
6 W ●		0022	4.6E
	0348	0649	3.6F
	0953	1242	4.7E
	1611	1906	3.5F
	2209		
7 Th		0057	4.7E
	0424	0723	3.7F
	1031	1317	4.8E
	1646	1940	3.6F
	2245		
8 F		0132	4.8E
	0500	0758	3.7F
	1108	1353	4.8E
	1720	2015	3.6F
	2322		
9 Sa		0210	4.8E
	0535	0834	3.6F
	1146	1431	4.8E
	1754	2051	3.5F
	2358		
10 Su		0249	4.8E
	0612	0912	3.6F
	1224	1510	4.7E
	1829	2130	3.4F
11 M	0037	0330	4.8E
	0652	0954	3.4F
	1305	1553	4.6E
	1908	2212	3.3F
12 Tu	0120	0415	4.7E
	0737	1039	3.3F
	1351	1639	4.5E
	1953	2300	3.2F
13 W	0209	0505	4.6E
	0829	1131	3.2F
	1444	1731	4.3E
	2047	2355	3.2F
14 Th ◑	0307	0601	4.5E
	0931	1231	3.1F
	1544	1829	4.3E
	2151		
15 F		0058	3.1F
	0412	0703	4.4E
	1039	1337	3.1F
	1651	1933	4.3E
	2302		
16 Sa		0206	3.2F
	0521	0810	4.5E
	1149	1446	3.2F
	1757	2041	4.4E
17 Su	0012	0316	3.4F
	0628	0918	4.6E
	1254	1553	3.4F
	1900	2148	4.6E
18 M	0116	0421	3.6F
	0730	1022	4.8E
	1353	1653	3.7F
	1957	2250	4.9E
19 Tu	0215	0520	3.9F
	0827	1122	5.0E
	1447	1748	3.9F
	2052	2347	5.1E
20 W O	0310	0615	4.1F
	0921	1216	5.1E
	1538	1840	4.0F
	2143		
21 Th		0039	5.2E
	0402	0706	4.2F
	1012	1306	5.2E
	1628	1929	4.1F
	2233		
22 F		0129	5.3E
	0453	0756	4.2F
	1102	1355	5.2E
	1716	2018	4.1F
	2322		
23 Sa		0217	5.2E
	0543	0845	4.0F
	1152	1442	5.0E
	1805	2106	3.9F
24 Su	0011	0305	5.1E
	0633	0934	3.8F
	1241	1529	4.8E
	1854	2155	3.7F
25 M	0101	0353	4.8E
	0725	1025	3.6F
	1332	1617	4.5E
	1946	2246	3.4F
26 Tu	0153	0443	4.5E
	0818	1118	3.3F
	1425	1708	4.2E
	2040	2341	3.2F
27 W ◐	0247	0536	4.2E
	0915	1216	3.0F
	1520	1803	4.0E
	2138		
28 Th		0042	3.0F
	0345	0635	4.0E
	1015	1319	2.9F
	1618	1906	3.8E
	2238		
29 F		0146	2.9F
	0443	0741	3.9E
	1114	1422	2.8F
	1715	2012	3.8E
	2336		
30 Sa		0247	2.9F
	0540	0847	3.9E
	1209	1518	2.9F
	1809	2112	3.9E
31 Su	0029	0340	2.9F
	0633	0941	4.0E
	1258	1606	3.0F
	1857	2200	4.0E

Time meridian 75° W. 0000 is midnight. 1200 is noon. Times are not adjusted for Daylight Saving Time.

Hell Gate (off Mill Rock), East River, New York, 2019

F–Flood, Dir. 050° True   E–Ebb, Dir. 230° True

April

Day	Slack (h m)	Maximum (h m)	knots
1 M	0117	0426	3.1F
	0721	1023	4.2E
	1342	1648	3.2F
	1942	2239	4.2E
2 Tu	0159	0506	3.3F
	0804	1100	4.4E
	1423	1725	3.3F
	2022	2315	4.5E
3 W	0239	0543	3.5F
	0845	1135	4.5E
	1501	1800	3.5F
	2101	2350	4.6E
4 Th	0317	0618	3.6F
	0924	1210	4.7E
	1537	1834	3.6F
	2138		
5 F ●		0026	4.8E
	0354	0653	3.7F
	1002	1246	4.8E
	1612	1908	3.6F
	2215		
6 Sa		0103	4.9E
	0430	0729	3.7F
	1040	1324	4.8E
	1646	1944	3.7F
	2252		
7 Su		0142	4.9E
	0507	0806	3.7F
	1118	1402	4.8E
	1721	2022	3.6F
	2330		
8 M		0222	4.9E
	0545	0846	3.6F
	1158	1443	4.7E
	1758	2102	3.6F
9 Tu	0011	0305	4.9E
	0627	0928	3.5F
	1241	1527	4.6E
	1840	2146	3.5F
10 W	0056	0351	4.8E
	0714	1016	3.4F
	1328	1615	4.5E
	1928	2237	3.4F
11 Th	0148	0442	4.6E
	0809	1110	3.2F
	1423	1709	4.4E
	2026	2334	3.2F
12 F ◐	0248	0540	4.5E
	0912	1211	3.1F
	1526	1809	4.3E
	2134		
13 Sa		0039	3.2F
	0355	0643	4.4E
	1022	1319	3.1F
	1633	1915	4.3E
	2247		
14 Su		0151	3.2F
	0505	0752	4.4E
	1131	1430	3.2F
	1739	2025	4.4E
	2358		
15 M		0302	3.4F
	0611	0902	4.6E
	1235	1537	3.5F
	1841	2133	4.6E
16 Tu	0102	0407	3.6F
	0713	1007	4.7E
	1333	1636	3.7F
	1939	2235	4.9E
17 W	0200	0506	3.9F
	0809	1105	4.9E
	1427	1730	3.9F
	2032	2331	5.1E
18 Th	0254	0559	4.0F
	0902	1158	5.0E
	1517	1821	4.0F
	2122		
19 F ○		0022	5.2E
	0345	0648	4.1F
	0952	1247	5.1E
	1606	1908	4.1F
	2211		
20 Sa		0110	5.2E
	0434	0736	4.1F
	1040	1333	5.0E
	1653	1955	4.0F
	2259		
21 Su		0156	5.2E
	0522	0823	3.9F
	1128	1418	4.9E
	1740	2041	3.9F
	2346		
22 M		0241	5.0E
	0610	0910	3.7F
	1215	1502	4.7E
	1827	2128	3.6F
23 Tu	0034	0326	4.8E
	0659	0957	3.5F
	1303	1547	4.5E
	1917	2216	3.4F
24 W	0123	0412	4.5E
	0750	1047	3.2F
	1353	1635	4.2E
	2008	2307	3.1F
25 Th	0214	0501	4.2E
	0843	1140	3.0F
	1445	1725	4.0E
	2103		
26 F ○		0003	2.9F
	0308	0554	4.0E
	0939	1238	2.8F
	1540	1821	3.8E
	2201		
27 Sa		0103	2.8F
	0404	0651	3.9E
	1035	1337	2.8F
	1635	1920	3.8E
	2258		
28 Su		0202	2.8F
	0500	0751	3.9E
	1129	1433	2.8F
	1728	2018	3.9E
	2351		
29 M		0256	2.9F
	0553	0846	4.0E
	1219	1522	2.9F
	1817	2109	4.0E
30 Tu	0040	0344	3.0F
	0641	0934	4.1E
	1304	1605	3.1F
	1902	2154	4.3E

May

Day	Slack (h m)	Maximum (h m)	knots
1 W	0125	0426	3.2F
	0727	1016	4.3E
	1346	1645	3.3F
	1945	2235	4.5E
2 Th	0206	0506	3.4F
	0809	1056	4.5E
	1425	1722	3.4F
	2025	2315	4.7E
3 F	0246	0544	3.5F
	0850	1135	4.7E
	1503	1759	3.5F
	2104	2354	4.8E
4 Sa ●	0325	0622	3.6F
	0930	1214	4.8E
	1540	1836	3.6F
	2143		
5 Su		0034	5.0E
	0404	0700	3.7F
	1010	1254	4.8E
	1617	1915	3.7F
	2223		
6 M		0115	5.0E
	0444	0741	3.7F
	1051	1336	4.8E
	1656	1956	3.7F
	2304		
7 Tu		0158	5.0E
	0526	0823	3.6F
	1133	1420	4.8E
	1737	2040	3.6F
	2349		
8 W		0244	5.0E
	0612	0909	3.5F
	1219	1506	4.7E
	1824	2128	3.5F
9 Th	0037	0333	4.9E
	0703	0959	3.4F
	1310	1557	4.6E
	1917	2221	3.4F
10 F	0132	0426	4.7E
	0800	1055	3.3F
	1407	1653	4.5E
	2019	2321	3.3F
11 Sa ◐	0233	0525	4.6E
	0903	1158	3.2F
	1509	1754	4.4E
	2127		
12 Su		0027	3.2F
	0340	0629	4.5E
	1010	1305	3.2F
	1615	1901	4.4E
	2239		
13 M		0138	3.3F
	0447	0737	4.5E
	1116	1415	3.3F
	1720	2011	4.5E
	2346		
14 Tu		0248	3.4F
	0552	0846	4.6E
	1218	1519	3.5F
	1820	2119	4.7E
15 W	0049	0352	3.6F
	0652	0950	4.7E
	1315	1618	3.6F
	1917	2220	4.9E
16 Th	0145	0449	3.7F
	0748	1047	4.8E
	1407	1711	3.8F
	2010	2314	5.0E
17 F	0238	0541	3.8F
	0840	1138	4.9E
	1457	1800	3.9F
	2059		
18 Sa ○		0003	5.1E
	0328	0629	3.9F
	0929	1226	4.9E
	1545	1847	3.9F
	2147		
19 Su		0049	5.1E
	0416	0716	3.8F
	1016	1310	4.9E
	1631	1932	3.8F
	2234		
20 M		0133	5.1E
	0502	0800	3.7F
	1101	1353	4.8E
	1717	2017	3.7F
	2319		
21 Tu		0216	4.9E
	0548	0845	3.6F
	1147	1435	4.7E
	1803	2101	3.5F
22 W	0005	0258	4.7E
	0635	0929	3.4F
	1232	1518	4.5E
	1849	2146	3.3F
23 Th	0051	0341	4.5E
	0722	1015	3.2F
	1319	1602	4.3E
	1938	2233	3.1F
24 F	0139	0427	4.3E
	0811	1103	3.0F
	1407	1649	4.1E
	2029	2323	2.9F
25 Sa	0228	0515	4.2E
	0902	1154	2.8F
	1458	1739	4.0E
	2122		
26 Su ○		0016	2.8F
	0320	0606	4.1E
	0954	1247	2.8F
	1549	1831	4.0E
	2216		
27 M		0110	2.8F
	0413	0659	4.0E
	1046	1339	2.8F
	1641	1925	4.0E
	2309		
28 Tu		0204	2.8F
	0506	0751	4.1E
	1136	1430	2.8F
	1730	2017	4.1E
	2359		
29 W		0254	2.9F
	0556	0842	4.2E
	1222	1516	3.0F
	1818	2106	4.3E
30 Th	0046	0341	3.1F
	0644	0930	4.3E
	1306	1600	3.2F
	1903	2153	4.5E
31 F	0131	0425	3.3F
	0729	1015	4.5E
	1348	1643	3.3F
	1946	2238	4.7E

June

Day	Slack (h m)	Maximum (h m)	knots
1 Sa	0214	0508	3.4F
	0814	1100	4.6E
	1429	1724	3.5F
	2029	2322	4.9E
2 Su	0257	0551	3.5F
	0857	1143	4.8E
	1510	1807	3.6F
	2113		
3 M ●	0341	0634	3.6F
	0941	1228	4.8E
	1552	1850	3.7F
	2157		
4 Tu		0052	5.1E
	0425	0718	3.6F
	1026	1313	4.9E
	1636	1935	3.7F
	2243		
5 W		0139	5.1E
	0512	0805	3.6F
	1113	1401	4.9E
	1723	2023	3.7F
	2332		
6 Th		0227	5.1E
	0601	0854	3.6F
	1202	1450	4.8E
	1815	2115	3.6F
7 F	0024	0319	5.0E
	0654	0947	3.5F
	1255	1543	4.7E
	1911	2210	3.5F
8 Sa	0120	0413	4.8E
	0751	1044	3.4F
	1352	1640	4.6E
	2013	2310	3.4F
9 Su	0221	0512	4.7E
	0852	1146	3.3F
	1453	1742	4.6E
	2119		
10 M ◐		0016	3.3F
	0324	0615	4.6E
	0956	1251	3.3F
	1556	1848	4.5E
	2227		
11 Tu		0125	3.3F
	0429	0722	4.5E
	1059	1358	3.3F
	1659	1956	4.6E
	2332		
12 W		0232	3.4F
	0532	0829	4.5E
	1159	1501	3.4F
	1759	2103	4.7E
13 Th	0033	0335	3.5F
	0631	0932	4.6E
	1255	1559	3.5F
	1855	2203	4.8E
14 F	0129	0431	3.6F
	0726	1029	4.7E
	1348	1652	3.6F
	1948	2257	4.9E
15 Sa	0221	0523	3.6F
	0817	1119	4.7E
	1437	1741	3.7F
	2037	2345	4.9E
16 Su	0310	0610	3.6F
	0905	1205	4.8E
	1524	1827	3.7F
	2124		
17 M ○		0030	4.9E
	0356	0655	3.6F
	0951	1248	4.8E
	1609	1911	3.7F
	2210		
18 Tu		0007	5.0E
	0441	0738	3.6F
	1035	1328	4.7E
	1654	1953	3.6F
	2254		
19 W		0111	4.9E
	0525	0819	3.5F
	1119	1408	4.6E
	1737	2035	3.5F
	2337		
20 Th		0151	4.8E
	0608	0900	3.3F
	1202	1448	4.5E
	1821	2116	3.3F
21 F		0231	4.7E
	0651	0942	3.2F
	1245	1530	4.4E
	1905	2159	3.2F
22 Sa	0021	0311	4.6E
	0736	1025	3.1F
	1330	1613	4.3E
	1951	2244	3.0F
23 Su	0105	0353	4.5E
	0821	1110	2.9F
	1416	1658	4.2E
	2039	2330	2.9F
24 M	0151	0437	4.3E
	0909	1157	2.8F
	1503	1746	4.2E
	2129		
25 Tu ○		0020	2.9F
	0328	0612	4.2E
	0957	1246	2.8F
	1553	1837	4.2E
	2220		
26 W		0111	2.9F
	0419	0703	4.2E
	1046	1336	2.9F
	1643	1928	4.2E
	2312		
27 Th		0203	2.9F
	0510	0754	4.2E
	1134	1426	3.0F
	1733	2021	4.3E
28 F	0003	0255	3.0F
	0601	0846	4.3E
	1222	1516	3.1F
	1822	2112	4.5E
29 Sa	0053	0345	3.2F
	0651	0936	4.4E
	1309	1605	3.3F
	1911	2203	4.7E
30 Su	0142	0434	3.3F
	0740	1026	4.6E
	1355	1653	3.5F
	2000	2253	4.9E

Time meridian 75° W. 0000 is midnight. 1200 is noon. Times are not adjusted for Daylight Saving Time.

Hell Gate (off Mill Rock), East River, New York, 2019

F–Flood, Dir. 050° True   E–Ebb, Dir. 230° True

July

Days 1–15

Day	Slack h m	Max h m	knots
1 M	0230 / 0829 / 1442 / 2048	0523 / 1116 / 1741 / 2343	3.5F / 4.7E / 3.6F / 5.0E
2 Tu ●	0318 / 0917 / 1530 / 2138	0611 / 1205 / 1830	3.6F / 4.9E / 3.7F
3 W	0406 / 1006 / 1619 / 2228	0032 / 0700 / 1254 / 1919	5.1E / 3.7F / 4.9E / 3.8F
4 Th	0456 / 1056 / 1710 / 2320	0122 / 0749 / 1345 / 2010	5.1E / 3.7F / 5.0E / 3.8F
5 F	0547 / 1148 / 1804	0213 / 0841 / 1437 / 2103	5.1E / 3.7F / 5.0E / 3.8F
6 Sa	0013 / 0640 / 1242 / 1900	0306 / 0934 / 1531 / 2159	5.0E / 3.6F / 4.9E / 3.7F
7 Su	0109 / 0736 / 1338 / 2001	0401 / 1031 / 1627 / 2259	4.9E / 3.5F / 4.8E / 3.5F
8 M	0208 / 0835 / 1437 / 2104	0458 / 1130 / 1727	4.7E / 3.4F / 4.7E
9 Tu ◐	0309 / 0935 / 1538 / 2208	0002 / 0559 / 1233 / 1831	3.4F / 4.6E / 3.4F / 4.6E
10 W	0411 / 1036 / 1639 / 2312	0108 / 0703 / 1338 / 1938	3.3F / 4.5E / 3.3F / 4.5E
11 Th	0512 / 1136 / 1739	0214 / 0810 / 1441 / 2045	3.3F / 4.4E / 3.4F / 4.5E
12 F	0013 / 0611 / 1233 / 1836	0317 / 0914 / 1540 / 2147	3.3F / 4.4E / 3.4F / 4.6E
13 Sa	0109 / 0706 / 1327 / 1929	0413 / 1012 / 1634 / 2242	3.4F / 4.5E / 3.5F / 4.7E
14 Su	0201 / 0757 / 1416 / 2018	0505 / 1102 / 1723 / 2329	3.4F / 4.5E / 3.5F / 4.7E
15 M	0249 / 0844 / 1502 / 2105	0551 / 1146 / 1808	3.5F / 4.6E / 3.6F

Days 16–31

Day	Slack h m	Max h m	knots
16 Tu O	0334 / 0929 / 1546 / 2149	0011 / 0634 / 1226 / 1850	4.7E / 3.5F / 4.6E / 3.6F
17 W	0416 / 1011 / 1628 / 2231	0049 / 0714 / 1304 / 1929	4.7E / 3.5F / 4.6E / 3.6F
18 Th	0457 / 1053 / 1708 / 2312	0126 / 0753 / 1341 / 2008	4.7E / 3.5F / 4.6E / 3.5F
19 F	0536 / 1133 / 1748 / 2353	0203 / 0830 / 1419 / 2046	4.7E / 3.4F / 4.6E / 3.5F
20 Sa	0616 / 1214 / 1828	0241 / 0908 / 1457 / 2125	4.6E / 3.3F / 4.5E / 3.4F
21 Su	0034 / 0655 / 1255 / 1909	0320 / 0947 / 1538 / 2205	4.5E / 3.2F / 4.4E / 3.3F
22 M	0117 / 0736 / 1337 / 1952	0401 / 1028 / 1620 / 2248	4.4E / 3.1F / 4.4E / 3.1F
23 Tu	0200 / 0818 / 1421 / 2037	0444 / 1111 / 1705 / 2334	4.3E / 3.0F / 4.3E / 3.0F
24 W ◑	0247 / 0902 / 1508 / 2127	0530 / 1157 / 1754	4.2E / 3.0F / 4.3E
25 Th	0337 / 0950 / 1559 / 2220	0023 / 0619 / 1247 / 1845	3.0F / 4.2E / 2.9F / 4.3E
26 F	0429 / 1042 / 1652 / 2316	0116 / 0711 / 1340 / 1939	3.0F / 4.2E / 3.0F / 4.3E
27 Sa	0524 / 1135 / 1747	0212 / 0806 / 1436 / 2036	3.0F / 4.2E / 3.1F / 4.4E
28 Su	0013 / 0619 / 1230 / 1843	0309 / 0902 / 1531 / 2132	3.1F / 4.3E / 3.3F / 4.6E
29 M	0109 / 0714 / 1323 / 1937	0404 / 0957 / 1626 / 2228	3.3F / 4.5E / 3.5F / 4.8E
30 Tu	0202 / 0807 / 1417 / 2031	0458 / 1052 / 1720 / 2322	3.5F / 4.7E / 3.7F / 4.9E
31 W ●	0255 / 0859 / 1509 / 2124	0551 / 1146 / 1813	3.7F / 4.9E / 3.9F

August

Days 1–15

Day	Slack h m	Max h m	knots
1 Th	0346 / 0951 / 1602 / 2216	0015 / 0643 / 1238 / 1905	5.1E / 3.8F / 5.0E / 4.0F
2 F	0437 / 1042 / 1654 / 2309	0108 / 0734 / 1330 / 1957	5.2E / 3.9F / 5.1E / 4.0F
3 Sa	0528 / 1134 / 1748	0159 / 0826 / 1423 / 2050	5.1E / 3.9F / 5.1E / 4.0F
4 Su	0002 / 0620 / 1227 / 1843	0251 / 0918 / 1516 / 2145	5.1E / 3.9F / 5.0E / 3.9F
5 M	0057 / 0714 / 1322 / 1941	0345 / 1013 / 1611 / 2242	4.9E / 3.7F / 4.9E / 3.7F
6 Tu	0153 / 0810 / 1419 / 2041	0440 / 1110 / 1708 / 2343	4.7E / 3.6F / 4.7E / 3.5F
7 W ◐	0252 / 0908 / 1518 / 2144	0538 / 1211 / 1810	4.5E / 3.4F / 4.5E
8 Th	0352 / 1009 / 1619 / 2247	0047 / 0641 / 1316 / 1917	3.4F / 4.3E / 3.3F / 4.4E
9 F	0454 / 1110 / 1720 / 2348	0154 / 0749 / 1421 / 2027	3.3F / 4.2E / 3.3F / 4.3E
10 Sa	0553 / 1209 / 1818	0257 / 0857 / 1522 / 2132	3.2F / 4.1E / 3.3F / 4.3E
11 Su	0045 / 0648 / 1303 / 1912	0355 / 0957 / 1617 / 2227	3.3F / 4.2E / 3.4F / 4.4E
12 M	0137 / 0739 / 1352 / 2001	0446 / 1047 / 1705 / 2313	3.3F / 4.3E / 3.5F / 4.4E
13 Tu	0224 / 0825 / 1437 / 2046	0531 / 1128 / 1748 / 2351	3.4F / 4.4E / 3.5F / 4.5E
14 W	0306 / 0908 / 1519 / 2128	0612 / 1204 / 1827	3.5F / 4.5E / 3.6F
15 Th O	0346 / 0948 / 1558 / 2209	0026 / 0649 / 1238 / 1904	4.6E / 3.5F / 4.5E / 3.6F

Days 16–31

Day	Slack h m	Max h m	knots
16 F	0424 / 1027 / 1636 / 2248	0059 / 0724 / 1313 / 1939	4.6E / 3.5F / 4.6E / 3.6F
17 Sa	0501 / 1105 / 1713 / 2326	0134 / 0759 / 1348 / 2015	4.7E / 3.5F / 4.6E / 3.6F
18 Su	0537 / 1143 / 1750	0209 / 0834 / 1425 / 2051	4.6E / 3.5F / 4.6E / 3.6F
19 M	0005 / 0613 / 1221 / 1827	0247 / 0910 / 1504 / 2129	4.6E / 3.4F / 4.6E / 3.5F
20 Tu	0045 / 0649 / 1301 / 1906	0326 / 0948 / 1544 / 2210	4.5E / 3.3F / 4.5E / 3.4F
21 W	0126 / 0727 / 1342 / 1948	0407 / 1029 / 1628 / 2254	4.4E / 3.2F / 4.4E / 3.2F
22 Th	0211 / 0808 / 1429 / 2036	0452 / 1115 / 1715 / 2342	4.3E / 3.1F / 4.3E / 3.1F
23 F O	0300 / 0856 / 1521 / 2132	0540 / 1205 / 1807	4.2E / 3.1F / 4.3E
24 Sa	0355 / 0951 / 1619 / 2233	0036 / 0634 / 1301 / 1904	3.1F / 4.1E / 3.1F / 4.3E
25 Su	0454 / 1053 / 1720 / 2337	0136 / 0732 / 1402 / 2004	3.1F / 4.1E / 3.2F / 4.3E
26 M	0554 / 1156 / 1821	0238 / 0833 / 1504 / 2106	3.2F / 4.2E / 3.3F / 4.5E
27 Tu	0039 / 0653 / 1257 / 1920	0340 / 0934 / 1605 / 2207	3.4F / 4.4E / 3.6F / 4.7E
28 W	0137 / 0749 / 1355 / 2016	0438 / 1033 / 1703 / 2305	3.6F / 4.7E / 3.8F / 4.9E
29 Th	0232 / 0843 / 1451 / 2110	0533 / 1129 / 1758 / 2359	3.8F / 4.9E / 4.0F / 5.0E
30 F ●	0324 / 0935 / 1544 / 2203	0626 / 1223 / 1851	4.0F / 5.1E / 4.1F
31 Sa	0415 / 1026 / 1637 / 2255	0052 / 0717 / 1315 / 1943	5.1E / 4.1F / 5.2E / 4.2F

September

Days 1–15

Day	Slack h m	Max h m	knots
1 Su	0505 / 1117 / 1729 / 2347	0143 / 0808 / 1406 / 2034	5.1E / 4.1F / 5.2E / 4.1F
2 M	0556 / 1209 / 1823	0234 / 0859 / 1458 / 2127	5.1E / 4.0F / 5.1E / 4.0F
3 Tu	0040 / 0648 / 1302 / 1918	0325 / 0951 / 1550 / 2222	4.9E / 3.9F / 4.9E / 3.8F
4 W	0135 / 0742 / 1358 / 2016	0418 / 1047 / 1645 / 2320	4.6E / 3.7F / 4.6E / 3.6F
5 Th ◐	0232 / 0839 / 1456 / 2116	0514 / 1146 / 1745	4.4E / 3.4F / 4.4E
6 F	0331 / 0940 / 1558 / 2219	0023 / 0616 / 1251 / 1851	3.3F / 4.1E / 3.3F / 4.2E
7 Sa	0433 / 1042 / 1659 / 2321	0130 / 0725 / 1358 / 2005	3.2F / 3.9E / 3.2F / 4.0E
8 Su	0533 / 1143 / 1758	0235 / 0837 / 1501 / 2113	3.1F / 3.9E / 3.2F / 4.0E
9 M	0018 / 0628 / 1238 / 1852	0333 / 0938 / 1556 / 2207	3.2F / 4.0E / 3.3F / 4.1E
10 Tu	0109 / 0717 / 1327 / 1940	0423 / 1026 / 1643 / 2250	3.3F / 4.1E / 3.4F / 4.2E
11 W	0155 / 0802 / 1410 / 2024	0507 / 1105 / 1724 / 2325	3.4F / 4.2E / 3.5F / 4.4E
12 Th	0236 / 0843 / 1451 / 2104	0545 / 1138 / 1801 / 2357	3.5F / 4.4E / 3.5F / 4.5E
13 F O	0314 / 0921 / 1528 / 2143	0619 / 1210 / 1836	3.6F / 4.5E / 3.7F
14 Sa	0350 / 0958 / 1605 / 2220	0029 / 0653 / 1243 / 1909	4.6E / 3.5F / 4.6E / 3.7F
15 Su	0425 / 1035 / 1640 / 2258	0103 / 0726 / 1317 / 1944	4.6E / 3.7F / 4.7E / 3.7F

Days 16–30

Day	Slack h m	Max h m	knots
16 M	0459 / 1111 / 1715 / 2335	0137 / 0800 / 1354 / 2019	4.7E / 3.6F / 4.7E / 3.7F
17 Tu	0533 / 1148 / 1751	0214 / 0835 / 1431 / 2056	4.6E / 3.6F / 4.7E / 3.6F
18 W	0013 / 0607 / 1226 / 1829	0253 / 0912 / 1512 / 2136	4.5E / 3.5F / 4.6E / 3.5F
19 Th	0054 / 0644 / 1307 / 1911	0334 / 0953 / 1555 / 2219	4.4E / 3.4F / 4.5E / 3.4F
20 F	0138 / 0725 / 1354 / 1959	0418 / 1039 / 1643 / 2308	4.3E / 3.3F / 4.4E / 3.2F
21 Sa O	0228 / 0815 / 1448 / 2056	0508 / 1131 / 1736	4.2E / 3.2F / 4.3E
22 Su	0325 / 0915 / 1550 / 2201	0004 / 0603 / 1230 / 1835	3.1F / 4.1E / 3.1F / 4.2E
23 M	0428 / 1023 / 1656 / 2310	0107 / 0704 / 1336 / 1939	3.1F / 4.1E / 3.2F / 4.3E
24 Tu	0532 / 1133 / 1801	0214 / 0809 / 1443 / 2045	3.2F / 4.2E / 3.4F / 4.4E
25 W	0016 / 0633 / 1239 / 1903	0319 / 0914 / 1548 / 2148	3.4F / 4.4E / 3.6F / 4.6E
26 Th	0116 / 0730 / 1339 / 2000	0420 / 1016 / 1648 / 2248	3.7F / 4.7E / 3.9F / 4.9E
27 F	0211 / 0824 / 1435 / 2054	0516 / 1114 / 1743 / 2343	3.9F / 5.0E / 4.1F / 5.0E
28 Sa ●	0303 / 0916 / 1528 / 2146	0608 / 1207 / 1835	4.1F / 5.2E / 4.2F
29 Su	0353 / 1006 / 1620 / 2237	0034 / 0658 / 1258 / 1926	5.1E / 4.2F / 5.2E / 4.2F
30 M	0443 / 1056 / 1711 / 2327	0124 / 0747 / 1348 / 2016	5.1E / 4.2F / 5.2E / 4.2F

Time meridian 75° W. 0000 is midnight. 1200 is noon. Times are not adjusted for Daylight Saving Time.

Hell Gate (off Mill Rock), East River, New York, 2019

F–Flood, Dir. 050° True   E–Ebb, Dir. 230° True

October

Day	Slack (h m)	Maximum (h m)	knots
1 Tu		0213	5.0E
	0532	0837	4.1F
	1147	1437	5.1E
	1803	2106	4.0F
2 W	0018	0302	4.8E
	0623	0928	3.9F
	1238	1528	4.9E
	1855	2159	3.8F
3 Th	0111	0353	4.6E
	0716	1021	3.6F
	1332	1620	4.6E
	1951	2255	3.5F
4 F	0206	0446	4.3E
	0812	1119	3.4F
	1429	1716	4.3E
	2049	2356	3.2F
5 Sa ◖	0304	0546	4.0E
	0912	1222	3.2F
	1529	1820	4.0E
	2150		
6 Su		0102	3.1F
	0404	0653	3.8E
	1014	1329	3.0F
	1630	1931	3.9E
	2251		
7 M		0206	3.0F
	0503	0806	3.8E
	1115	1432	3.0F
	1729	2041	3.9E
	2348		
8 Tu		0304	3.0F
	0558	0908	3.9E
	1210	1527	3.1F
	1822	2135	4.0E
9 W	0039	0353	3.1F
	0647	0954	4.0E
	1259	1614	3.3F
	1910	2216	4.1E
10 Th	0124	0435	3.3F
	0730	1032	4.2E
	1342	1654	3.4F
	1953	2251	4.3E
11 F	0204	0512	3.4F
	0811	1105	4.4E
	1422	1730	3.5F
	2033	2323	4.5E
12 Sa	0242	0546	3.5F
	0849	1137	4.6E
	1459	1804	3.6F
	2111	2356	4.6E
13 Su ○	0318	0619	3.6F
	0925	1211	4.7E
	1536	1838	3.7F
	2149		
14 M		0030	4.7E
	0353	0653	3.7F
	1002	1247	4.8E
	1612	1913	3.7F
	2226		
15 Tu		0106	4.7E
	0427	0727	3.7F
	1038	1324	4.8E
	1647	1949	3.7F
	2303		
16 W		0143	4.7E
	0501	0803	3.6F
	1115	1402	4.8E
	1724	2026	3.6F
	2341		
17 Th		0223	4.6E
	0536	0842	3.6F
	1153	1444	4.8E
	1804	2107	3.5F
18 F	0022	0305	4.5E
	0615	0924	3.5F
	1236	1528	4.7E
	1847	2152	3.4F
19 Sa	0107	0351	4.4E
	0659	1011	3.3F
	1325	1617	4.5E
	1938	2243	3.2F
20 Su	0159	0442	4.3E
	0752	1105	3.2F
	1421	1711	4.4E
	2037	2341	3.1F
21 M ○	0258	0539	4.2E
	0857	1207	3.2F
	1525	1812	4.3E
	2144		
22 Tu		0045	3.1F
	0403	0643	4.2E
	1009	1316	3.2F
	1633	1918	4.3E
	2253		
23 W		0154	3.2F
	0508	0750	4.3E
	1121	1426	3.4F
	1740	2026	4.5E
	2359		
24 Th		0301	3.4F
	0611	0857	4.5E
	1227	1532	3.6F
	1842	2131	4.7E
25 F	0058	0402	3.7F
	0709	1000	4.8E
	1327	1632	3.8F
	1940	2231	4.9E
26 Sa	0153	0457	3.9F
	0803	1058	5.0E
	1422	1727	4.0F
	2033	2325	5.0E
27 Su ●	0245	0549	4.1F
	0854	1151	5.2E
	1514	1818	4.1F
	2124		
28 M		0016	5.1E
	0335	0639	4.1F
	0944	1241	5.3E
	1605	1908	4.1F
	2214		
29 Tu		0104	5.1E
	0424	0727	4.1F
	1033	1329	5.2E
	1655	1956	4.0F
	2303		
30 W		0152	5.0E
	0512	0815	4.0F
	1122	1416	5.1E
	1745	2045	3.9F
	2352		
31 Th		0239	4.8E
	0602	0904	3.8F
	1212	1504	4.9E
	1836	2135	3.6F

November

Day	Slack (h m)	Maximum (h m)	knots
1 F	0043	0327	4.6E
	0653	0955	3.5F
	1303	1553	4.6E
	1928	2228	3.4F
2 Sa	0135	0417	4.3E
	0747	1049	3.3F
	1356	1645	4.3E
	2024	2324	3.1F
3 Su	0229	0511	4.0E
	0845	1148	3.0F
	1452	1742	4.1E
	2121		
4 M ◖		0024	2.9F
	0325	0610	3.9E
	0944	1250	2.9F
	1550	1843	3.9E
	2219		
5 Tu		0126	2.8F
	0421	0714	3.8E
	1043	1352	2.9F
	1647	1947	3.9E
	2315		
6 W		0223	2.9F
	0515	0815	3.9E
	1138	1447	2.9F
	1740	2043	4.0E
7 Th	0005	0312	3.0F
	0604	0905	4.0E
	1227	1534	3.1F
	1828	2128	4.1E
8 F	0051	0355	3.1F
	0650	0947	4.2E
	1312	1616	3.2F
	1913	2207	4.3E
9 Sa	0132	0434	3.3F
	0731	1025	4.4E
	1353	1654	3.4F
	1955	2244	4.5E
10 Su	0211	0510	3.4F
	0811	1102	4.6E
	1432	1731	3.5F
	2035	2321	4.6E
11 M	0248	0545	3.5F
	0849	1139	4.8E
	1510	1807	3.6F
	2114	2358	4.7E
12 Tu ○	0324	0621	3.6F
	0927	1217	4.9E
	1548	1844	3.6F
	2152		
13 W		0036	4.8E
	0400	0658	3.6F
	1005	1256	5.0E
	1626	1922	3.6F
	2231		
14 Th		0116	4.8E
	0437	0736	3.6F
	1044	1337	5.0E
	1706	2002	3.6F
	2312		
15 F		0158	4.8E
	0516	0817	3.6F
	1126	1421	4.9E
	1749	2045	3.5F
	2354		
16 Sa		0242	4.7E
	0558	0902	3.5F
	1211	1507	4.9E
	1835	2132	3.4F
17 Su	0041	0330	4.6E
	0647	0952	3.4F
	1302	1557	4.7E
	1928	2224	3.2F
18 M	0134	0422	4.5E
	0744	1048	3.3F
	1359	1653	4.6E
	2028	2323	3.1F
19 Tu ○	0234	0521	4.4E
	0850	1150	3.2F
	1503	1753	4.5E
	2133		
20 W		0027	3.1F
	0338	0625	4.4E
	1001	1259	3.2F
	1610	1859	4.5E
	2240		
21 Th		0135	3.2F
	0443	0732	4.5E
	1111	1409	3.3F
	1717	2007	4.5E
	2343		
22 F		0242	3.4F
	0546	0840	4.7E
	1216	1516	3.5F
	1819	2113	4.7E
23 Sa	0042	0344	3.6F
	0645	0944	4.9E
	1315	1616	3.7F
	1917	2213	4.8E
24 Su	0137	0440	3.8F
	0740	1042	5.0E
	1410	1711	3.8F
	2011	2308	5.0E
25 M	0229	0532	3.9F
	0831	1135	5.2E
	1502	1802	3.9F
	2102	2358	5.0E
26 Tu ●	0319	0621	3.9F
	0921	1224	5.2E
	1552	1851	3.9F
	2150		
27 W		0046	5.0E
	0407	0708	3.9F
	1010	1311	5.2E
	1640	1938	3.8F
	2238		
28 Th		0131	4.9E
	0455	0755	3.8F
	1057	1356	5.1E
	1728	2024	3.7F
	2325		
29 F		0216	4.8E
	0543	0842	3.7F
	1144	1441	4.9E
	1816	2111	3.5F
30 Sa	0012	0301	4.6E
	0632	0929	3.4F
	1232	1526	4.7E
	1905	2159	3.3F

December

Day	Slack (h m)	Maximum (h m)	knots
1 Su	0100	0347	4.4E
	0722	1018	3.2F
	1321	1612	4.5E
	1956	2248	3.0F
2 M	0149	0435	4.2E
	0815	1109	3.0F
	1411	1701	4.3E
	2048	2340	2.9F
3 Tu	0240	0525	4.1E
	0909	1203	2.8F
	1503	1752	4.1E
	2142		
4 W ◖		0034	2.8F
	0332	0618	4.0E
	1004	1259	2.7F
	1556	1846	4.0E
	2234		
5 Th		0128	2.7F
	0424	0713	4.0E
	1058	1353	2.8F
	1649	1940	4.0E
	2325		
6 F		0219	2.8F
	0514	0805	4.1E
	1149	1444	2.8F
	1740	2031	4.1E
7 Sa	0012	0306	2.9F
	0602	0855	4.2E
	1236	1531	3.0F
	1828	2118	4.3E
8 Su	0056	0350	3.1F
	0647	0941	4.4E
	1321	1614	3.1F
	1913	2202	4.4E
9 M	0138	0431	3.2F
	0731	1024	4.6E
	1403	1655	3.3F
	1957	2245	4.6E
10 Tu	0217	0511	3.4F
	0813	1107	4.8E
	1445	1736	3.4F
	2039	2327	4.7E
11 W	0257	0551	3.5F
	0855	1149	5.0E
	1526	1817	3.5F
	2121		
12 Th ○		0009	4.8E
	0337	0632	3.6F
	0937	1232	5.1E
	1608	1859	3.5F
	2203		
13 F		0052	4.9E
	0418	0714	3.6F
	1020	1317	5.1E
	1651	1942	3.6F
	2247		
14 Sa		0137	4.9E
	0501	0759	3.6F
	1105	1403	5.1E
	1737	2028	3.5F
	2333		
15 Su		0224	4.9E
	0548	0847	3.6F
	1153	1451	5.0E
	1826	2117	3.4F
16 M	0022	0314	4.8E
	0640	0938	3.5F
	1246	1542	4.9E
	1919	2209	3.3F
17 Tu	0115	0407	4.7E
	0738	1034	3.4F
	1342	1637	4.8E
	2017	2307	3.2F
18 W ○	0213	0505	4.6E
	0842	1136	3.3F
	1444	1736	4.7E
	2119		
19 Th		0010	3.2F
	0315	0607	4.6E
	0949	1242	3.2F
	1548	1840	4.6E
	2223		
20 F		0116	3.2F
	0419	0714	4.6E
	1057	1352	3.2F
	1653	1947	4.6E
	2326		
21 Sa		0222	3.3F
	0522	0822	4.7E
	1202	1459	3.3F
	1756	2054	4.6E
22 Su	0026	0325	3.4F
	0622	0928	4.8E
	1302	1600	3.5F
	1855	2156	4.7E
23 M	0122	0423	3.6F
	0718	1028	4.9E
	1357	1656	3.6F
	1949	2252	4.8E
24 Tu	0214	0516	3.7F
	0811	1121	5.0E
	1449	1747	3.6F
	2040	2343	4.9E
25 W	0304	0605	3.7F
	0901	1210	5.1E
	1538	1835	3.7F
	2128		
26 Th ●		0029	4.9E
	0352	0652	3.7F
	0949	1255	5.1E
	1624	1920	3.6F
	2214		
27 F		0113	4.9E
	0438	0737	3.7F
	1034	1337	5.0E
	1710	2003	3.5F
	2259		
28 Sa		0154	4.8E
	0523	0820	3.6F
	1119	1418	4.9E
	1754	2046	3.4F
	2343		
29 Su		0235	4.7E
	0608	0902	3.4F
	1203	1458	4.8E
	1838	2128	3.3F
30 M	0026	0316	4.6E
	0653	0945	3.3F
	1247	1539	4.6E
	1923	2210	3.1F
31 Tu	0110	0358	4.4E
	0739	1029	3.1F
	1332	1622	4.4E
	2009	2254	2.9F

Time meridian 75° W. 0000 is midnight. 1200 is noon. Times are not adjusted for Daylight Saving Time.

The Narrows, New York Harbor, New York, 2019

F–Flood, Dir. 336° True   E–Ebb, Dir. 164° True

January

Date	Slack (h m)	Maximum (h m)	knots
1 Tu	0022	0333	1.4F
	0623	0954	1.7E
	1307	1609	1.2F
	1837	2205	1.7E
2 W	0112	0432	1.5F
	0718	1043	1.8E
	1403	1707	1.2F
	1931	2251	1.7E
3 Th	0200	0520	1.6F
	0805	1127	1.8E
	1455	1755	1.3F
	2020	2333	1.7E
4 F	0244	0559	1.6F
	0846	1207	1.8E
	1540	1838	1.3F
	2104		
5 Sa ●		0014	1.6E
	0324	0631	1.6F
	0923	1246	1.8E
	1620	1917	1.2F
	2144		
6 Su		0054	1.6E
	0400	0657	1.5F
	0959	1323	1.8E
	1656	1951	1.1F
	2223		
7 M		0134	1.5E
	0436	0725	1.4F
	1035	1359	1.8E
	1732	2017	1.0F
	2302		
8 Tu		0214	1.5E
	0513	0801	1.4F
	1114	1434	1.8E
	1808	2044	1.0F
	2343		
9 W		0252	1.4E
	0555	0844	1.4F
	1156	1509	1.8E
	1846	2120	1.1F
10 Th	0027	0331	1.5E
	0643	0932	1.4F
	1240	1546	1.8E
	1927	2204	1.2F
11 F	0112	0414	1.5E
	0736	1024	1.4F
	1326	1629	1.8E
	2011	2252	1.3F
12 Sa	0158	0503	1.5E
	0831	1117	1.5F
	1413	1718	1.8E
	2056	2340	1.5F
13 Su	0246	0602	1.6E
	0928	1208	1.5F
	1502	1815	1.9E
	2144		
14 M ◑		0027	1.6F
	0337	0704	1.7E
	1024	1259	1.6F
	1555	1913	1.9E
	2233		
15 Tu		0115	1.8F
	0432	0803	1.8E
	1121	1350	1.6F
	1651	2010	2.0E
	2322		
16 W		0204	1.9F
	0528	0859	2.0E
	1216	1446	1.6F
	1749	2105	2.1E
17 Th	0011	0258	2.0F
	0622	0953	2.2E
	1311	1547	1.7F
	1845	2158	2.2E
18 F	0101	0354	2.1F
	0714	1041	2.4E
	1404	1644	1.8F
	1938	2248	2.2E
19 Sa	0152	0447	2.3F
	0804	1128	2.5E
	1455	1734	1.9F
	2029	2336	2.3E
20 Su	0243	0537	2.3F
	0853	1214	2.5E
	1544	1822	1.9F
	2119		
21 M ○		0025	2.3E
	0333	0625	2.3F
	0942	1303	2.5E
	1631	1911	1.9F
	2209		
22 Tu		0118	2.2E
	0425	0717	2.2F
	1032	1354	2.4E
	1720	2003	1.8F
	2301		
23 W		0211	2.2E
	0520	0812	2.0F
	1125	1444	2.3E
	1812	2059	1.7F
	2357		
24 Th		0305	2.1E
	0619	0912	1.8F
	1220	1535	2.1E
	1908	2200	1.6F
25 F	0054	0400	1.9E
	0725	1018	1.6F
	1317	1630	1.9E
	2008	2306	1.6F
26 Sa	0153	0503	1.8E
	0833	1129	1.5F
	1414	1734	1.8E
	2108		
27 Su ◐		0010	1.6F
	0253	0616	1.6E
	0942	1235	1.4F
	1512	1845	1.7E
	2208		
28 M		0108	1.5F
	0356	0731	1.6E
	1050	1338	1.3F
	1614	1953	1.6E
	2307		
29 Tu		0208	1.5F
	0503	0841	1.6E
	1155	1447	1.2F
	1721	2056	1.6E
30 W	0003	0314	1.4F
	0608	0943	1.7E
	1257	1558	1.2F
	1826	2153	1.6E
31 Th	0057	0418	1.4F
	0705	1036	1.7E
	1357	1658	1.2F
	1925	2243	1.6E

February

Date	Slack (h m)	Maximum (h m)	knots
1 F	0147	0510	1.5F
	0753	1120	1.8E
	1449	1748	1.2F
	2015	2326	1.5E
2 Sa	0233	0552	1.5F
	0834	1158	1.8E
	1533	1832	1.2F
	2057		
3 Su		0005	1.5E
	0313	0627	1.4F
	0908	1232	1.7E
	1607	1909	1.2F
	2132		
4 M ●		0041	1.5E
	0348	0650	1.4F
	0940	1303	1.7E
	1636	1936	1.1F
	2203		
5 Tu		0116	1.5E
	0419	0706	1.4F
	1011	1333	1.7E
	1702	1941	1.1F
	2234		
6 W		0150	1.5E
	0451	0734	1.4F
	1044	1402	1.7E
	1728	1958	1.1F
	2307		
7 Th		0222	1.5E
	0526	0811	1.4F
	1121	1433	1.8E
	1757	2032	1.2F
	2345		
8 F		0255	1.6E
	0607	0855	1.5F
	1202	1507	1.9E
	1833	2114	1.3F
9 Sa	0027	0331	1.7E
	0654	0943	1.5F
	1246	1545	1.9E
	1915	2201	1.5F
10 Su	0113	0412	1.7E
	0747	1034	1.5F
	1332	1629	2.0E
	2001	2252	1.6F
11 M	0200	0501	1.7E
	0843	1128	1.5F
	1420	1720	1.9E
	2051	2344	1.8F
12 Tu ◑	0251	0602	1.8E
	0943	1221	1.5F
	1512	1819	1.9E
	2144		
13 W		0035	1.9F
	0345	0710	1.8E
	1044	1315	1.5F
	1610	1923	1.9E
	2240		
14 Th		0127	1.9F
	0444	0816	1.9E
	1143	1411	1.5F
	1713	2028	1.9E
	2336		
15 F		0222	2.0F
	0545	0918	2.1E
	1241	1514	1.6F
	1815	2129	2.0E
16 Sa	0033	0323	2.0F
	0644	1014	2.3E
	1337	1618	1.7F
	1913	2226	2.1E
17 Su	0129	0424	2.1F
	0740	1104	2.4E
	1430	1713	1.8F
	2008	2318	2.3E
18 M	0225	0519	2.3F
	0832	1153	2.5E
	1519	1803	2.0F
	2059		
19 Tu ○		0009	2.4E
	0320	0611	2.3F
	0923	1242	2.5E
	1606	1851	2.0F
	2150		
20 W		0101	2.4E
	0413	0703	2.3F
	1014	1333	2.5E
	1653	1941	2.0F
	2241		
21 Th		0154	2.4E
	0506	0758	2.1F
	1106	1423	2.4E
	1743	2035	1.9F
	2335		
22 F		0247	2.3E
	0603	0856	1.9F
	1200	1513	2.3E
	1837	2133	1.9F
23 Sa	0031	0340	2.1E
	0705	1000	1.8F
	1256	1606	2.1E
	1936	2237	1.8F
24 Su	0129	0439	1.9E
	0812	1110	1.6F
	1352	1706	1.9E
	2037	2343	1.7F
25 M	0228	0549	1.8E
	0921	1218	1.4F
	1450	1816	1.7E
	2139		
26 Tu ◐		0044	1.6F
	0330	0706	1.7E
	1030	1322	1.3F
	1554	1928	1.6E
	2241		
27 W		0144	1.5F
	0436	0819	1.7E
	1137	1429	1.2F
	1704	2036	1.5E
	2341		
28 Th		0249	1.4F
	0543	0925	1.7E
	1240	1539	1.2F
	1814	2138	1.5E

March

Date	Slack (h m)	Maximum (h m)	knots
1 F	0038	0355	1.4F
	0644	1020	1.7E
	1340	1641	1.2F
	1915	2230	1.5E
2 Sa	0131	0451	1.4F
	0734	1104	1.8E
	1431	1732	1.3F
	2005	2314	1.6E
3 Su	0219	0536	1.4F
	0815	1140	1.8E
	1512	1813	1.3F
	2044	2351	1.6E
4 M	0259	0612	1.4F
	0849	1210	1.7E
	1542	1847	1.2F
	2114		
5 Tu		0024	1.6E
	0332	0636	1.4F
	0919	1237	1.7E
	1606	1907	1.2F
	2140		
6 W ●		0055	1.6E
	0402	0648	1.4F
	0947	1303	1.7E
	1626	1903	1.2F
	2206		
7 Th		0125	1.6E
	0431	0710	1.4F
	1016	1330	1.8E
	1648	1921	1.3F
	2235		
8 F		0153	1.7E
	0502	0743	1.5F
	1049	1359	1.9E
	1715	1954	1.4F
	2308		
9 Sa		0223	1.7E
	0539	0823	1.5F
	1127	1432	1.9E
	1748	2035	1.6F
	2348		
10 Su		0256	1.8E
	0621	0909	1.5F
	1209	1510	2.0E
	1828	2121	1.7F
11 M	0033	0334	1.9E
	0712	0959	1.5F
	1256	1551	2.0E
	1914	2212	1.7F
12 Tu	0121	0418	1.9E
	0808	1053	1.5F
	1345	1638	1.9E
	2006	2305	1.8F
13 W	0211	0511	1.8E
	0909	1149	1.4F
	1438	1735	1.8E
	2103		
14 Th ◑		0000	1.8F
	0305	0619	1.8E
	1013	1245	1.4F
	1537	1843	1.7E
	2204		
15 F		0055	1.8F
	0406	0736	1.8E
	1116	1342	1.4F
	1643	1956	1.7E
	2308		
16 Sa		0153	1.8F
	0512	0847	1.9E
	1215	1445	1.5F
	1749	2106	1.8E
17 Su	0011	0256	1.8F
	0616	0949	2.1E
	1310	1552	1.6F
	1851	2207	2.0E
18 M	0112	0403	2.0F
	0716	1042	2.3E
	1403	1651	1.8F
	1946	2300	2.3E
19 Tu	0210	0503	2.1F
	0811	1131	2.4E
	1452	1741	2.0F
	2038	2351	2.4E
20 W ○	0305	0556	2.2F
	0903	1218	2.5E
	1539	1828	2.1F
	2128		
21 Th		0041	2.5E
	0357	0647	2.2F
	0952	1308	2.5E
	1625	1916	2.2F
	2218		
22 F		0133	2.5E
	0449	0739	2.1F
	1043	1358	2.4E
	1713	2007	2.1F
	2310		
23 Sa		0225	2.4E
	0543	0835	2.0F
	1135	1448	2.3E
	1805	2102	2.0F
24 Su	0005	0317	2.3E
	0642	0936	1.8F
	1230	1539	2.1E
	1902	2203	1.8F
25 M	0102	0412	2.1E
	0747	1046	1.6F
	1327	1636	1.9E
	2003	2310	1.7F
26 Tu	0159	0517	1.8E
	0856	1157	1.4F
	1427	1744	1.7E
	2107		
27 W ◐		0016	1.6F
	0259	0633	1.7E
	1006	1302	1.3F
	1531	1859	1.5E
	2212		
28 Th		0116	1.5F
	0402	0748	1.7E
	1112	1405	1.3F
	1642	2011	1.5E
	2314		
29 F		0218	1.4F
	0508	0855	1.7E
	1213	1511	1.2F
	1752	2114	1.5E
30 Sa	0012	0323	1.3F
	0610	0950	1.7E
	1307	1613	1.3F
	1852	2207	1.6E
31 Su	0106	0422	1.4F
	0702	1034	1.8E
	1355	1703	1.3F
	1939	2251	1.6E

Time meridian 75° W. 0000 is midnight. 1200 is noon. Times are not adjusted for Daylight Saving Time.

The Narrows, New York Harbor, New York, 2019

F–Flood, Dir. 336° True   E–Ebb, Dir. 164° True

April

Day	Slack (h m)	Maximum (h m)	knots
1 M	0153	0508	1.4F
	0745	1108	1.8E
	1433	1743	1.3F
	2016	2327	1.7E
2 Tu	0234	0544	1.4F
	0820	1138	1.8E
	1502	1813	1.3F
	2045	2359	1.7E
3 W	0309	0610	1.5F
	0850	1204	1.8E
	1526	1825	1.3F
	2111		
4 Th		0029	1.8E
	0340	0625	1.5F
	0919	1231	1.8E
	1548	1827	1.4F
	2138		
5 F		0058	1.8E
	0410	0646	1.5F
	0949	1258	1.9E
	1612	1850	1.6F
	2206		
6 Sa		0126	1.9E
	0442	0718	1.5F
	1021	1328	1.9E
	1639	1923	1.7F
	2239		
7 Su		0156	1.9E
	0517	0757	1.5F
	1058	1403	2.0E
	1712	2004	1.8F
	2317		
8 M		0230	1.9E
	0559	0841	1.5F
	1140	1441	2.0E
	1752	2049	1.8F
9 Tu	0001	0307	2.0E
	0648	0931	1.4F
	1228	1522	1.9E
	1838	2139	1.8F
10 W	0049	0349	1.9E
	0744	1026	1.3F
	1319	1608	1.8E
	1931	2234	1.7F
11 Th	0140	0438	1.8E
	0846	1124	1.3F
	1414	1703	1.6E
	2032	2332	1.7F
12 F	0235	0542	1.7E
	0950	1223	1.3F
	1514	1814	1.5E
	2140		
13 Sa		0031	1.6F
	0336	0704	1.7E
	1052	1320	1.3F
	1619	1935	1.5E
	2250		
14 Su		0131	1.6F
	0444	0821	1.7E
	1151	1421	1.4F
	1727	2048	1.7E
	2356		
15 M		0235	1.6F
	0552	0926	1.9E
	1245	1528	1.5F
	1830	2150	1.9E
16 Tu	0058	0345	1.7F
	0654	1020	2.1E
	1336	1630	1.8F
	1926	2244	2.2E
17 W	0156	0448	1.9F
	0749	1108	2.2E
	1425	1720	2.0F
	2018	2333	2.4E
18 Th	0250	0541	2.0F
	0840	1154	2.4E
	1512	1806	2.1F
	2107		
19 F		0021	2.5E
	0341	0629	2.1F
	0929	1242	2.4E
	1558	1851	2.2F
	2155		
20 Sa		0111	2.5E
	0431	0719	2.0F
	1017	1331	2.4E
	1644	1939	2.1F
	2245		
21 Su		0202	2.4E
	0523	0812	1.8F
	1108	1421	2.2E
	1733	2031	2.0F
	2337		
22 M		0253	2.3E
	0620	0912	1.7F
	1203	1512	2.0E
	1827	2128	1.8F
23 Tu	0031	0345	2.1E
	0722	1021	1.5F
	1301	1606	1.8E
	1927	2232	1.6F
24 W	0128	0444	1.9E
	0829	1133	1.4F
	1402	1710	1.6E
	2032	2341	1.5F
25 Th	0224	0554	1.7E
	0936	1237	1.3F
	1504	1824	1.4E
	2137		
26 F		0043	1.4F
	0323	0706	1.7E
	1038	1335	1.3F
	1610	1936	1.4E
	2240		
27 Sa		0140	1.4F
	0424	0810	1.7E
	1134	1433	1.3F
	1715	2038	1.5E
	2338		
28 Su		0239	1.3F
	0524	0904	1.7E
	1222	1530	1.3F
	1811	2131	1.6E
29 M	0030	0337	1.3F
	0617	0949	1.8E
	1305	1621	1.3F
	1858	2215	1.7E
30 Tu	0117	0427	1.4F
	0703	1026	1.8E
	1342	1700	1.4F
	1936	2253	1.8E

May

Day	Slack (h m)	Maximum (h m)	knots
1 W	0200	0505	1.5F
	0741	1058	1.9E
	1414	1726	1.5F
	2009	2327	1.9E
2 Th	0238	0533	1.5F
	0815	1128	1.9E
	1442	1737	1.6F
	2039	2359	2.0E
3 F	0314	0556	1.6F
	0848	1158	2.0E
	1510	1754	1.7F
	2109		
4 Sa		0030	2.0E
	0348	0623	1.6F
	0921	1228	2.0E
	1539	1823	1.8F
	2141		
5 Su		0101	2.0E
	0423	0656	1.6F
	0957	1301	2.0E
	1610	1858	1.9F
	2215		
6 M		0135	2.1E
	0501	0735	1.5F
	1035	1339	2.0E
	1645	1939	1.9F
	2254		
7 Tu		0211	2.0E
	0544	0820	1.5F
	1119	1419	1.9E
	1726	2024	1.8F
	2338		
8 W		0249	2.0E
	0633	0911	1.3F
	1209	1503	1.8E
	1813	2115	1.7F
9 Th	0027	0331	1.9E
	0729	1006	1.3F
	1303	1550	1.6E
	1910	2211	1.6F
10 F	0120	0419	1.8E
	0830	1106	1.2F
	1359	1645	1.5E
	2016	2313	1.5F
11 Sa	0216	0522	1.6E
	0932	1207	1.2F
	1458	1758	1.4E
	2128		
12 Su		0015	1.4F
	0316	0645	1.6E
	1033	1304	1.3F
	1602	1922	1.4E
	2240		
13 M		0115	1.4F
	0423	0802	1.6E
	1129	1402	1.4F
	1709	2035	1.6E
	2347		
14 Tu		0219	1.4F
	0530	0906	1.7E
	1222	1506	1.5F
	1811	2136	1.8E
15 W	0047	0330	1.5F
	0632	1000	1.9E
	1313	1610	1.7F
	1908	2229	2.0E
16 Th	0144	0436	1.6F
	0728	1048	2.1E
	1401	1702	1.9F
	2000	2317	2.2E
17 F	0237	0528	1.7F
	0818	1133	2.2E
	1448	1747	2.0F
	2048		
18 Sa		0003	2.3E
	0327	0615	1.8F
	0906	1218	2.2E
	1533	1829	2.1F
	2135		
19 Su		0051	2.3E
	0416	0702	1.7F
	0954	1306	2.1E
	1618	1913	2.0F
	2221		
20 M		0140	2.3E
	0505	0753	1.6F
	1044	1356	2.0E
	1705	2001	1.9F
	2310		
21 Tu		0229	2.2E
	0558	0850	1.5F
	1138	1447	1.9E
	1755	2054	1.7F
22 W	0001	0318	2.0E
	0657	0955	1.3F
	1235	1538	1.7E
	1852	2153	1.6F
23 Th	0054	0410	1.9E
	0758	1103	1.3F
	1333	1636	1.5E
	1954	2259	1.4F
24 F	0148	0509	1.8E
	0858	1204	1.2F
	1430	1742	1.4E
	2057		
25 Sa		0001	1.4F
	0241	0613	1.7E
	0954	1256	1.3F
	1527	1850	1.4E
	2158		
26 Su		0055	1.4F
	0335	0714	1.7E
	1044	1343	1.3F
	1623	1951	1.5E
	2254		
27 M		0144	1.3F
	0430	0807	1.7E
	1129	1428	1.3F
	1717	2044	1.6E
	2346		
28 Tu		0234	1.3F
	0524	0854	1.8E
	1209	1513	1.3F
	1805	2131	1.7E
29 W	0034	0326	1.4F
	0612	0936	1.8E
	1247	1553	1.4F
	1848	2213	1.9E
30 Th	0119	0413	1.4F
	0656	1000	1.9E
	1323	1623	1.6F
	1928	2251	2.0E
31 F	0203	0451	1.5F
	0737	1051	2.0E
	1358	1652	1.8F
	2005	2327	2.1E

June

Day	Slack (h m)	Maximum (h m)	knots
1 Sa	0245	0525	1.6F
	0817	1126	2.1E
	1434	1723	2.0F
	2041		
2 Su		0002	2.2E
	0325	0600	1.7F
	0856	1201	2.1E
	1509	1758	2.1F
	2117		
3 M		0039	2.2E
	0405	0637	1.7F
	0936	1240	2.1E
	1547	1837	2.1F
	2155		
4 Tu		0117	2.2E
	0447	0719	1.6F
	1019	1321	2.0E
	1626	1920	2.0F
	2237		
5 W		0158	2.2E
	0531	0805	1.5F
	1105	1407	1.9E
	1711	2007	1.9F
	2323		
6 Th		0240	2.1E
	0621	0857	1.4F
	1157	1453	1.7E
	1802	2100	1.7F
7 F	0014	0324	1.9E
	0717	0953	1.3F
	1252	1543	1.6E
	1902	2158	1.5F
8 Sa	0108	0413	1.8E
	0816	1054	1.2F
	1349	1640	1.5E
	2012	2302	1.4F
9 Su	0205	0515	1.6E
	0915	1156	1.3F
	1447	1754	1.4E
	2124		
10 M		0006	1.3F
	0303	0633	1.5E
	1014	1252	1.3F
	1548	1914	1.4E
	2234		
11 Tu		0106	1.3F
	0406	0745	1.5E
	1109	1348	1.4F
	1653	2024	1.5E
	2339		
12 W		0209	1.2F
	0511	0848	1.6E
	1202	1450	1.4F
	1756	2125	1.7E
13 Th	0039	0322	1.3F
	0613	0943	1.7E
	1253	1556	1.6F
	1854	2219	1.8E
14 F	0136	0432	1.3F
	0709	1032	1.9E
	1342	1651	1.7F
	1945	2306	2.0E
15 Sa	0229	0525	1.4F
	0801	1117	1.9E
	1429	1735	1.8F
	2033	2351	2.1E
16 Su	0319	0612	1.5F
	0849	1202	1.9E
	1514	1815	1.9F
	2117		
17 M		0036	2.1E
	0406	0656	1.5F
	0937	1248	1.9E
	1558	1855	1.8F
	2200		
18 Tu		0122	2.1E
	0452	0743	1.4F
	1024	1336	1.8E
	1642	1937	1.7F
	2245		
19 W		0207	2.0E
	0539	0832	1.3F
	1114	1424	1.7E
	1728	2023	1.6F
	2331		
20 Th		0252	1.9E
	0629	0925	1.2F
	1205	1511	1.6E
	1818	2114	1.5F
21 F	0020	0336	1.9E
	0720	1021	1.1F
	1258	1600	1.5E
	1914	2210	1.4F
22 Sa	0109	0423	1.8E
	0812	1114	1.2F
	1348	1654	1.4E
	2013	2308	1.4F
23 Su	0159	0514	1.7E
	0900	1159	1.2F
	1437	1754	1.4E
	2110		
24 M		0000	1.4F
	0247	0610	1.7E
	0946	1236	1.3F
	1526	1854	1.5E
	2205		
25 Tu		0047	1.4F
	0337	0704	1.7E
	1029	1311	1.4F
	1616	1948	1.6E
	2258		
26 W		0132	1.4F
	0428	0754	1.8E
	1111	1350	1.5F
	1708	2040	1.7E
	2348		
27 Th		0220	1.4F
	0520	0843	1.9E
	1153	1433	1.6F
	1758	2128	1.9E
28 F	0038	0313	1.5F
	0611	0930	2.0E
	1235	1522	1.8F
	1845	2213	2.1E
29 Sa	0127	0406	1.5F
	0659	1014	2.1E
	1318	1609	1.9F
	1929	2255	2.2E
30 Su	0214	0454	1.6F
	0746	1056	2.1E
	1401	1654	2.1F
	2012	2336	2.3E

Time meridian 75° W. 0000 is midnight. 1200 is noon. Times are not adjusted for Daylight Saving Time.

The Narrows, New York Harbor, New York, 2019

F–Flood, Dir. 336° True   E–Ebb, Dir. 164° True

July

Date	Slack (h m)	Maximum (h m)	knots
1 M	0301	0537	1.7F
	0832	1138	2.2E
	1444	1736	2.2F
	2054		
2 Tu ●		0017	2.4E
	0345	0620	1.7F
	0917	1222	2.1E
	1528	1819	2.2F
	2137		
3 W		0100	2.3E
	0430	0704	1.7F
	1004	1308	2.1E
	1614	1905	2.1F
	2223		
4 Th		0145	2.3E
	0516	0752	1.6F
	1052	1358	2.0E
	1703	1955	2.0F
	2311		
5 F		0232	2.2E
	0605	0844	1.5F
	1144	1448	1.9E
	1757	2050	1.8F
6 Sa	0004	0319	2.0E
	0659	0940	1.4F
	1240	1539	1.8E
	1859	2150	1.6F
7 Su	0059	0409	1.8E
	0756	1041	1.4F
	1336	1636	1.6E
	2008	2255	1.4F
8 M	0155	0508	1.7E
	0854	1144	1.4F
	1433	1746	1.5E
	2117		
9 Tu ◐		0001	1.3F
	0251	0619	1.6E
	0953	1241	1.4F
	1533	1902	1.5E
	2226		
10 W		0102	1.2F
	0350	0728	1.5E
	1050	1337	1.4F
	1638	2013	1.5E
	2330		
11 Th		0206	1.1F
	0454	0832	1.6E
	1145	1440	1.4F
	1743	2117	1.6E
12 F	0032	0323	1.1F
	0558	0930	1.6E
	1238	1549	1.5F
	1843	2213	1.7E
13 Sa	0131	0433	1.2F
	0658	1022	1.7E
	1329	1648	1.5F
	1935	2301	1.8E
14 Su	0227	0528	1.2F
	0752	1109	1.7E
	1418	1734	1.6F
	2022	2345	1.9E
15 M	0316	0615	1.3F
	0841	1153	1.7E
	1503	1813	1.6F
	2104		
16 Tu ○		0026	1.9E
	0400	0658	1.6F
	0926	1237	1.6E
	1545	1847	1.6F
	2143		
17 W		0107	1.9E
	0440	0738	1.2F
	1009	1320	1.6E
	1625	1920	1.5F
	2223		
18 Th		0146	1.9E
	0518	0815	1.2F
	1051	1403	1.6E
	1705	1957	1.5F
	2303		
19 F		0224	1.8E
	0556	0846	1.1F
	1133	1444	1.5E
	1748	2038	1.4F
	2346		
20 Sa		0301	1.8E
	0636	0918	1.1F
	1217	1524	1.5E
	1835	2124	1.4F
21 Su	0030	0339	1.8E
	0717	0957	1.2F
	1301	1606	1.5E
	1925	2213	1.4F
22 M	0115	0419	1.8E
	0759	1040	1.2F
	1346	1652	1.5E
	2019	2304	1.4F
23 Tu	0200	0505	1.8E
	0842	1126	1.4F
	1432	1747	1.6E
	2113	2354	1.4F
24 W ◐	0247	0558	1.8E
	0927	1211	1.5F
	1520	1846	1.6E
	2208		
25 Th		0043	1.5F
	0336	0654	1.8E
	1014	1256	1.7F
	1612	1944	1.7E
	2303		
26 F		0132	1.5F
	0430	0750	1.9E
	1103	1344	1.8F
	1707	2041	1.9E
	2358		
27 Sa		0225	1.5F
	0527	0845	1.9E
	1152	1435	1.9F
	1801	2134	2.1E
28 Su	0051	0325	1.5F
	0624	0939	2.0E
	1241	1531	2.0F
	1854	2223	2.2E
29 M	0144	0423	1.6F
	0718	1029	2.1E
	1332	1625	2.1F
	1944	2309	2.4E
30 Tu	0234	0515	1.8F
	0809	1117	2.2E
	1422	1716	2.2F
	2032	2354	2.4E
31 W ●	0322	0601	1.9F
	0858	1205	2.2E
	1512	1804	2.3F
	2119		

August

Date	Slack (h m)	Maximum (h m)	knots
1 Th		0040	2.5E
	0408	0647	1.9F
	0946	1254	2.2E
	1603	1853	2.2F
	2208		
2 F		0129	2.4E
	0454	0735	1.8F
	1036	1346	2.2E
	1654	1944	2.1F
	2258		
3 Sa		0217	2.3E
	0542	0826	1.8F
	1127	1437	2.1E
	1749	2040	1.9F
	2350		
4 Su		0305	2.2E
	0634	0921	1.7F
	1222	1529	2.0E
	1850	2140	1.7F
5 M	0045	0355	2.0E
	0730	1021	1.6F
	1319	1624	1.8E
	1956	2245	1.5F
6 Tu	0140	0451	1.8E
	0828	1125	1.5F
	1416	1730	1.7E
	2104	2354	1.4F
7 W ◐	0236	0558	1.7E
	0929	1227	1.5F
	1516	1846	1.6E
	2213		
8 Th		0058	1.3F
	0335	0709	1.6E
	1029	1325	1.5F
	1621	2000	1.5E
	2320		
9 F		0205	1.1F
	0440	0818	1.5E
	1128	1430	1.4F
	1728	2109	1.6E
10 Sa	0025	0320	1.1F
	0550	0922	1.5E
	1226	1541	1.4F
	1832	2209	1.7E
11 Su	0127	0429	1.1F
	0655	1018	1.5E
	1321	1643	1.4F
	1927	2258	1.7E
12 M	0224	0525	1.2F
	0752	1106	1.6E
	1412	1732	1.5F
	2013	2340	1.8E
13 Tu	0312	0612	1.3F
	0839	1149	1.6E
	1457	1812	1.5F
	2053		
14 W		0017	1.8E
	0351	0653	1.3F
	0919	1229	1.6E
	1537	1845	1.5F
	2128		
15 Th ○		0051	1.8E
	0424	0727	1.2F
	0954	1306	1.5E
	1612	1910	1.4F
	2202		
16 F		0123	1.8E
	0452	0750	1.1F
	1026	1342	1.5E
	1645	1933	1.4F
	2236		
17 Sa		0154	1.8E
	0519	0758	1.1F
	1058	1415	1.6E
	1720	2004	1.4F
	2311		
18 Su		0225	1.8E
	0548	0823	1.2F
	1134	1448	1.6E
	1758	2043	1.4F
	2350		
19 M		0257	1.8E
	0620	0859	1.3F
	1213	1522	1.6E
	1842	2128	1.4F
20 Tu	0032	0332	1.9E
	0658	0943	1.4F
	1257	1559	1.7E
	1931	2216	1.4F
21 W	0116	0412	1.9E
	0742	1031	1.5F
	1342	1643	1.7E
	2025	2308	1.4F
22 Th	0202	0459	1.9E
	0830	1122	1.7F
	1430	1739	1.7E
	2123		
23 F ○		0001	1.5F
	0252	0556	1.8E
	0922	1213	1.8F
	1522	1845	1.8E
	2222		
24 Sa		0054	1.5F
	0347	0659	1.8E
	1017	1304	1.8F
	1619	1952	1.9E
	2321		
25 Su		0148	1.5F
	0449	0804	1.8E
	1114	1358	1.9F
	1720	2055	2.0E
26 M	0018	0248	1.5F
	0552	0907	1.9E
	1211	1457	1.9F
	1820	2152	2.2E
27 Tu	0114	0352	1.6F
	0651	1005	2.1E
	1307	1559	2.1F
	1916	2243	2.3E
28 W	0206	0450	1.8F
	0746	1057	2.2E
	1403	1656	2.2F
	2009	2331	2.5E
29 Th	0255	0540	2.0F
	0837	1147	2.4E
	1457	1748	2.3F
	2100		
30 F ●		0018	2.5E
	0342	0626	2.1F
	0926	1237	2.4E
	1549	1838	2.3F
	2149		
31 Sa		0106	2.5E
	0427	0713	2.1F
	1015	1328	2.4E
	1641	1930	2.2F
	2239		

September

Date	Slack (h m)	Maximum (h m)	knots
1 Su		0156	2.4E
	0514	0803	2.0F
	1106	1420	2.4E
	1735	2025	2.0F
	2331		
2 M		0244	2.3E
	0604	0856	1.9F
	1200	1511	2.2E
	1833	2123	1.8F
3 Tu	0025	0334	2.1E
	0659	0955	1.8F
	1256	1605	2.0E
	1937	2229	1.6F
4 W	0120	0428	1.9E
	0759	1100	1.7F
	1354	1708	1.8E
	2046	2341	1.4F
5 Th ◐	0217	0534	1.7E
	0902	1207	1.6F
	1454	1824	1.7E
	2156		
6 F		0049	1.3F
	0319	0649	1.6E
	1007	1309	1.5F
	1559	1943	1.6E
	2306		
7 Sa		0156	1.2F
	0428	0803	1.5E
	1111	1414	1.4F
	1708	2055	1.6E
8 Su	0012	0307	1.2F
	0543	0912	1.5E
	1212	1525	1.4F
	1815	2157	1.7E
9 M	0113	0415	1.2F
	0651	1010	1.5E
	1310	1628	1.4F
	1912	2246	1.8E
10 Tu	0209	0511	1.3F
	0747	1059	1.6E
	1402	1719	1.4F
	1959	2326	1.8E
11 W	0254	0556	1.3F
	0831	1139	1.6E
	1447	1800	1.5F
	2038	2359	1.8E
12 Th	0330	0635	1.3F
	0905	1215	1.6E
	1524	1833	1.4F
	2110		
13 F ○		0028	1.7E
	0357	0704	1.3F
	0933	1247	1.6E
	1556	1854	1.4F
	2139		
14 Sa		0055	1.7E
	0419	0713	1.2F
	0958	1317	1.6E
	1625	1908	1.4F
	2208		
15 Su		0121	1.7E
	0440	0714	1.3F
	1025	1345	1.6E
	1655	1933	1.4F
	2238		
16 M		0148	1.8E
	0503	0740	1.4F
	1055	1414	1.7E
	1728	2008	1.4F
	2312		
17 Tu		0219	1.9E
	0532	0817	1.5F
	1131	1444	1.8E
	1806	2050	1.4F
	2352		
18 W		0253	1.9E
	0608	0900	1.6F
	1213	1518	1.8E
	1853	2137	1.4F
19 Th	0036	0332	1.9E
	0652	0948	1.7F
	1259	1559	1.9E
	1946	2230	1.4F
20 F ◐	0124	0417	1.9E
	0741	1041	1.7F
	1348	1647	1.8E
	2045	2326	1.4F
21 Sa	0216	0510	1.8E
	0837	1136	1.8F
	1441	1749	1.8E
	2147		
22 Su		0022	1.4F
	0313	0615	1.7E
	0938	1231	1.8F
	1538	1904	1.8E
	2249		
23 M		0118	1.4F
	0416	0728	1.7E
	1042	1328	1.8F
	1642	2017	1.9E
	2348		
24 Tu		0217	1.5F
	0523	0839	1.8E
	1146	1428	1.8F
	1748	2122	2.1E
25 W	0043	0321	1.6F
	0625	0942	2.0E
	1247	1534	1.9F
	1849	2217	2.2E
26 Th	0136	0423	1.8F
	0722	1037	2.2E
	1345	1637	2.1F
	1945	2306	2.4E
27 F	0226	0515	2.0F
	0814	1127	2.4E
	1441	1731	2.2F
	2037	2353	2.5E
28 Sa ●	0313	0602	2.2F
	0903	1216	2.5E
	1533	1821	2.3F
	2127		
29 Su		0040	2.5E
	0358	0648	2.2F
	0952	1306	2.6E
	1624	1911	2.2F
	2216		
30 M		0129	2.5E
	0444	0736	2.2F
	1042	1358	2.5E
	1716	2005	2.0F
	2306		

Time meridian 75° W.   0000 is midnight.   1200 is noon.   Times are not adjusted for Daylight Saving Time.

The Narrows, New York Harbor, New York, 2019

F–Flood, Dir. 336° True   E–Ebb, Dir. 164° True

October

Day	Slack (h m)	Maximum (h m)	knots
1 Tu		0219	2.4E
	0534	0828	2.1F
	1135	1449	2.4E
	1813	2103	1.8F
2 W	0000	0310	2.2E
	0628	0926	1.9F
	1231	1543	2.2E
	1916	2209	1.6F
3 Th	0058	0404	2.0E
	0728	1031	1.8F
	1329	1643	1.9E
	2025	2324	1.4F
4 F	0158	0508	1.7E
	0834	1142	1.6F
	1429	1757	1.8E
	2136		
5 Sa ☽		0034	1.4F
	0302	0625	1.5E
	0942	1248	1.5F
	1532	1916	1.7E
	2244		
6 Su		0139	1.3F
	0413	0743	1.5E
	1049	1351	1.4F
	1639	2029	1.7E
	2348		
7 M		0244	1.3F
	0527	0853	1.5E
	1152	1458	1.4F
	1746	2130	1.8E
8 Tu	0046	0349	1.3F
	0633	0951	1.6E
	1249	1601	1.4F
	1845	2219	1.8E
9 W	0137	0445	1.4F
	0726	1039	1.7E
	1341	1654	1.4F
	1932	2258	1.8E
10 Th	0220	0529	1.4F
	0807	1118	1.7E
	1425	1735	1.5F
	2011	2329	1.8E
11 F	0253	0605	1.4F
	0839	1151	1.7E
	1502	1808	1.5F
	2042	2356	1.8E
12 Sa	0319	0629	1.3F
	0905	1221	1.7E
	1534	1829	1.4F
	2110		
13 Su ○		0022	1.8E
	0340	0629	1.4F
	0929	1249	1.8E
	1603	1842	1.4F
	2138		
14 M		0047	1.8E
	0401	0638	1.5F
	0955	1316	1.8E
	1632	1905	1.4F
	2207		
15 Tu		0114	1.8E
	0424	0706	1.6F
	1024	1344	1.8E
	1704	1939	1.4F
	2240		
16 W		0146	1.9E
	0454	0743	1.7F
	1058	1414	1.9E
	1741	2020	1.4F
	2319		
17 Th		0222	1.9E
	0530	0826	1.8F
	1139	1448	1.9E
	1826	2107	1.4F
18 F	0005	0302	1.9E
	0613	0914	1.8F
	1225	1528	1.9E
	1918	2200	1.3F
19 Sa	0056	0346	1.8E
	0704	1007	1.7F
	1315	1614	1.9E
	2017	2257	1.3F
20 Su	0150	0438	1.7E
	0803	1105	1.7F
	1408	1711	1.8E
	2119	2356	1.3F
21 M ◑	0248	0542	1.6E
	0909	1205	1.7F
	1507	1825	1.7E
	2221		
22 Tu		0053	1.4F
	0350	0700	1.6E
	1019	1304	1.6F
	1611	1944	1.8E
	2320		
23 W		0150	1.5F
	0456	0816	1.7E
	1127	1404	1.7F
	1719	2053	1.9E
24 Th	0014	0252	1.6F
	0600	0921	1.9E
	1229	1510	1.7F
	1823	2151	2.1E
25 F	0106	0355	1.8F
	0658	1017	2.2E
	1328	1616	1.9F
	1920	2241	2.2E
26 Sa	0156	0450	2.0F
	0750	1107	2.4E
	1423	1712	2.0F
	2013	2328	2.4E
27 Su ●	0243	0537	2.2F
	0840	1155	2.5E
	1515	1802	2.1F
	2102		
28 M		0014	2.4E
	0330	0623	2.3F
	0929	1244	2.5E
	1606	1851	2.1F
	2151		
29 Tu		0103	2.4E
	0416	0710	2.3F
	1019	1335	2.5E
	1657	1944	1.9F
	2241		
30 W		0154	2.3E
	0505	0801	2.1F
	1110	1427	2.4E
	1753	2042	1.7F
	2336		
31 Th		0246	2.1E
	0558	0857	2.0F
	1205	1520	2.2E
	1854	2148	1.5F

November

Day	Slack (h m)	Maximum (h m)	knots
1 F	0034	0340	1.9E
	0658	1001	1.8F
	1302	1617	2.0E
	2001	2303	1.4F
2 Sa	0137	0442	1.7E
	0804	1113	1.6F
	1400	1724	1.8E
	2109		
3 Su		0013	1.4F
	0240	0557	1.5E
	0913	1221	1.5F
	1500	1840	1.7E
	2214		
4 M ◑		0114	1.4F
	0347	0713	1.5E
	1020	1321	1.4F
	1602	1949	1.7E
	2313		
5 Tu		0212	1.4F
	0455	0821	1.5E
	1121	1421	1.4F
	1705	2048	1.8E
6 W	0006	0311	1.4F
	0557	0918	1.6E
	1216	1521	1.4F
	1803	2137	1.8E
7 Th	0052	0405	1.4F
	0647	1005	1.7E
	1306	1615	1.4F
	1852	2216	1.8E
8 F	0132	0450	1.4F
	0728	1045	1.8E
	1351	1659	1.4F
	1932	2249	1.8E
9 Sa	0205	0524	1.4F
	0802	1119	1.8E
	1431	1733	1.4F
	2006	2319	1.8E
10 Su	0234	0543	1.5F
	0831	1151	1.9E
	1506	1756	1.4F
	2037	2347	1.8E
11 M	0259	0548	1.6F
	0859	1220	1.9E
	1539	1815	1.4F
	2108		
12 Tu ○		0015	1.9E
	0325	0608	1.7F
	0927	1249	1.9E
	1611	1841	1.5F
	2140		
13 W		0045	1.9E
	0353	0639	1.8F
	0958	1319	2.0E
	1646	1916	1.4F
	2216		
14 Th		0120	1.9E
	0426	0717	1.9F
	1034	1352	2.0E
	1724	1958	1.4F
	2257		
15 F		0159	1.8E
	0503	0800	1.8F
	1114	1429	2.0E
	1809	2045	1.3F
	2344		
16 Sa		0241	1.8E
	0548	0849	1.8F
	1201	1509	2.0E
	1900	2138	1.3F
17 Su	0037	0327	1.7E
	0641	0944	1.7F
	1252	1554	1.9E
	1957	2236	1.3F
18 M	0132	0418	1.6E
	0743	1043	1.6F
	1347	1648	1.8E
	2057	2335	1.3F
19 Tu ◐	0229	0521	1.5E
	0852	1145	1.5F
	1445	1758	1.7E
	2157		
20 W		0032	1.3F
	0329	0640	1.5E
	1004	1245	1.5F
	1547	1918	1.7E
	2254		
21 Th		0127	1.4F
	0433	0756	1.6E
	1112	1344	1.5F
	1653	2026	1.7E
	2348		
22 F		0225	1.5F
	0536	0902	1.8E
	1214	1449	1.5F
	1757	2126	1.9E
23 Sa	0039	0327	1.7F
	0635	0959	2.0E
	1312	1556	1.6F
	1855	2217	2.0E
24 Su	0129	0426	1.9F
	0730	1049	2.2E
	1408	1656	1.7F
	1949	2305	2.2E
25 M	0217	0516	2.1F
	0820	1137	2.3E
	1500	1747	1.8F
	2039	2351	2.2E
26 Tu ●	0305	0601	2.2F
	0909	1225	2.4E
	1551	1835	1.8F
	2128		
27 W		0039	2.2E
	0352	0647	2.2F
	0957	1314	2.4E
	1641	1927	1.7F
	2219		
28 Th		0131	2.1E
	0440	0736	2.1F
	1046	1406	2.3E
	1734	2024	1.6F
	2313		
29 F		0224	2.0E
	0531	0830	1.9F
	1138	1457	2.2E
	1832	2128	1.5F
30 Sa	0011	0318	1.8E
	0629	0931	1.7F
	1233	1550	2.0E
	1933	2238	1.4F

December

Day	Slack (h m)	Maximum (h m)	knots
1 Su	0112	0415	1.6E
	0733	1039	1.6F
	1329	1647	1.9E
	2036	2344	1.3F
2 M	0212	0521	1.5E
	0839	1146	1.5F
	1424	1753	1.8E
	2135		
3 Tu		0040	1.4F
	0310	0632	1.5E
	0942	1244	1.4F
	1520	1857	1.7E
	2228		
4 W ◐		0130	1.4F
	0408	0736	1.5E
	1041	1335	1.4F
	1616	1953	1.7E
	2316		
5 Th		0219	1.3F
	0504	0832	1.6E
	1134	1427	1.4F
	1710	2042	1.7E
	2359		
6 F		0307	1.3F
	0555	0921	1.7E
	1224	1520	1.3F
	1800	2125	1.8E
7 Sa	0037	0351	1.4F
	0639	1004	1.8E
	1310	1609	1.4F
	1845	2204	1.8E
8 Su	0113	0425	1.5F
	0718	1042	1.9E
	1354	1649	1.4F
	1925	2239	1.9E
9 M	0147	0446	1.6F
	0754	1117	2.0E
	1435	1720	1.5F
	2003	2313	1.9E
10 Tu	0220	0511	1.8F
	0828	1151	2.1E
	1513	1749	1.5F
	2040	2347	2.0E
11 W	0254	0542	1.9F
	0902	1225	2.1E
	1551	1821	1.5F
	2118		
12 Th ○		0022	2.0E
	0329	0618	2.0F
	0937	1300	2.1E
	1629	1859	1.5F
	2159		
13 F		0102	1.9E
	0407	0658	2.0F
	1016	1337	2.1E
	1710	1942	1.5F
	2242		
14 Sa		0145	1.8E
	0448	0743	1.9F
	1058	1418	2.1E
	1755	2030	1.4F
	2331		
15 Su		0230	1.8E
	0536	0833	1.8F
	1146	1500	2.0E
	1845	2122	1.3F
16 M		0317	1.7E
	0631	0928	1.6F
	1239	1544	1.9E
	1940	2219	1.3F
17 Tu	0118	0408	1.6E
	0735	1028	1.5F
	1334	1636	1.7E
	2037	2318	1.3F
18 W ◐	0214	0509	1.5E
	0844	1131	1.4F
	1429	1741	1.6E
	2134		
19 Th		0015	1.4F
	0311	0625	1.5E
	0954	1231	1.4F
	1528	1856	1.6E
	2230		
20 F		0108	1.4F
	0412	0739	1.5E
	1100	1329	1.3F
	1630	2004	1.6E
	2324		
21 Sa		0203	1.5F
	0516	0846	1.6E
	1202	1431	1.3F
	1734	2104	1.7E
22 Su	0016	0305	1.6F
	0617	0945	1.8E
	1301	1544	1.3F
	1834	2159	1.8E
23 M	0108	0408	1.7F
	0713	1037	2.0E
	1358	1649	1.4F
	1929	2248	1.9E
24 Tu	0158	0502	1.8F
	0804	1124	2.1E
	1451	1742	1.5F
	2022	2335	2.0E
25 W	0247	0548	1.9F
	0852	1211	2.1E
	1541	1830	1.5F
	2112		
26 Th ●		0023	2.0E
	0334	0632	1.9F
	0938	1258	2.2E
	1629	1919	1.5F
	2202		
27 F		0114	1.9E
	0421	0718	1.9F
	1025	1347	2.1E
	1717	2011	1.4F
	2253		
28 Sa		0205	1.8E
	0510	0807	1.7F
	1113	1434	2.1E
	1808	2106	1.3F
	2347		
29 Su		0256	1.7E
	0602	0901	1.6F
	1203	1521	2.0E
	1901	2204	1.3F
30 M	0041	0346	1.6E
	0659	1000	1.5F
	1255	1609	1.9E
	1954	2301	1.3F
31 Tu	0134	0440	1.5E
	0758	1100	1.4F
	1346	1701	1.8E
	2045	2352	1.3F

Time meridian 75° W. 0000 is midnight. 1200 is noon. Times are not adjusted for Daylight Saving Time.

George Washington Bridge, Hudson River, 2019

F–Flood, Dir. 010° True   E–Ebb, Dir. 203° True

January

Day	Slack	Max	knots
1 Tu	0137	0501	2.2F
	0808	1131	2.7F
	1444	1734	1.5F
	2008	2342	2.5E
2 W	0226	0555	2.3F
	0901	1224	2.9F
	1547	1833	1.5F
	2102		
3 Th		0032	2.5E
	0311	0644	2.4F
	0949	1315	3.0F
	1644	1924	1.5F
	2152		
4 F		0120	2.4E
	0355	0729	2.4F
	1034	1403	3.1F
	1734	2012	1.5F
	2240		
5 Sa ●		0205	2.3E
	0436	0811	2.4F
	1117	1448	3.1F
	1818	2059	1.4F
	2327		
6 Su		0249	2.2E
	0517	0853	2.3F
	1157	1530	3.0F
	1857	2147	1.4F
7 M	0012	0330	2.1E
	0557	0936	2.1F
	1235	1609	2.9E
	1931	2235	1.4F
8 Tu	0055	0408	2.0E
	0637	1021	1.9F
	1310	1645	2.8E
	2004	2319	1.4F
9 W	0138	0444	1.8E
	0718	1105	1.7F
	1345	1717	2.6E
	2037		
10 Th		0000	1.4F
	0221	0518	1.7E
	0803	1146	1.5F
	1420	1747	2.4E
	2114		
11 F		0039	1.4F
	0304	0555	1.6E
	0854	1225	1.3F
	1458	1819	2.3E
	2153		
12 Sa		0116	1.4F
	0349	0644	1.5E
	0950	1306	1.2F
	1540	1903	2.2E
	2233		
13 Su		0152	1.4F
	0435	0757	1.6E
	1048	1352	1.2F
	1627	2002	2.1E
	2315		
14 M ☽		0226	1.5F
	0523	0905	1.7E
	1147	1443	1.2F
	1720	2102	2.1E
	2358		
15 Tu		0301	1.7F
	0615	1000	2.0E
	1247	1538	1.2F
	1817	2154	2.1E
16 W	0042	0340	1.9F
	0707	1051	2.3E
	1345	1637	1.2F
	1915	2243	2.2E
17 Th	0127	0426	2.1F
	0759	1143	2.7E
	1442	1735	1.3F
	2010	2334	2.3E
18 F	0215	0517	2.3F
	0850	1235	2.9E
	1537	1829	1.4F
	2103		
19 Sa		0027	2.4E
	0305	0609	2.6F
	0942	1327	3.2E
	1629	1917	1.5F
	2155		
20 Su		0120	2.5E
	0356	0659	2.8F
	1035	1417	3.3E
	1719	2005	1.6F
	2249		
21 M ○		0212	2.7E
	0448	0748	2.8F
	1127	1505	3.4E
	1806	2055	1.7F
	2343		
22 Tu		0304	2.8E
	0540	0840	2.7F
	1218	1552	3.4E
	1853	2153	1.8F
23 W	0038	0355	2.8E
	0633	0940	2.6F
	1308	1639	3.3E
	1942	2253	1.8F
24 Th	0134	0447	2.7E
	0730	1049	2.3F
	1357	1728	3.1E
	2034	2350	1.9F
25 F	0230	0544	2.5E
	0831	1155	2.1F
	1447	1821	2.9E
	2129		
26 Sa		0046	2.0F
	0328	0650	2.3E
	0940	1257	1.8F
	1539	1923	2.6E
	2225		
27 Su ☾		0141	2.0F
	0430	0805	2.2E
	1055	1400	1.6F
	1634	2030	2.4E
	2321		
28 M		0238	2.0F
	0535	0914	2.3E
	1212	1504	1.4F
	1735	2130	2.3E
29 Tu	0014	0335	2.0F
	0642	1015	2.4E
	1328	1610	1.3F
	1840	2225	2.3E
30 W	0107	0434	2.1F
	0744	1110	2.6E
	1438	1715	1.2F
	1943	2317	2.2E
31 Th	0157	0530	2.2F
	0838	1203	2.8E
	1540	1815	1.3F
	2039		

February

Day	Slack	Max	knots
1 F		0007	2.2E
	0244	0622	2.2F
	0926	1253	2.9E
	1632	1906	1.4F
	2129		
2 Sa		0056	2.1E
	0330	0708	2.3F
	1010	1339	2.9E
	1716	1951	1.4F
	2217		
3 Su		0142	2.1E
	0414	0749	2.2F
	1050	1422	2.9E
	1752	2034	1.4F
	2302		
4 M ●		0225	2.1E
	0455	0829	2.1F
	1128	1502	2.9E
	1821	2116	1.5F
	2346		
5 Tu		0305	2.1E
	0535	0908	2.0F
	1203	1537	2.9E
	1848	2158	1.5F
6 W	0028	0342	2.1E
	0614	0946	1.8F
	1237	1609	2.8E
	1915	2238	1.5F
7 Th	0108	0416	2.1E
	0653	1025	1.7F
	1311	1638	2.7E
	1945	2315	1.5F
8 F	0146	0447	2.0E
	0735	1102	1.5F
	1347	1704	2.6E
	2020	2347	1.5F
9 Sa	0225	0519	2.0E
	0822	1139	1.4F
	1425	1734	2.5E
	2058		
10 Su		0015	1.5F
	0304	0557	1.9E
	0915	1219	1.4F
	1507	1813	2.3E
	2141		
11 M		0042	1.6F
	0347	0649	1.9E
	1014	1306	1.3F
	1554	1902	2.1E
	2226		
12 Tu ☽		0115	1.7F
	0436	0807	2.0E
	1116	1402	1.2F
	1646	2006	2.0E
	2314		
13 W		0200	1.8F
	0531	0923	2.2E
	1219	1504	1.2F
	1744	2114	2.0E
14 Th	0004	0253	2.0F
	0631	1024	2.4E
	1322	1608	1.2F
	1845	2215	2.1E
15 F	0056	0352	2.1F
	0732	1121	2.7E
	1422	1713	1.3F
	1946	2313	2.2E
16 Sa	0151	0456	2.3F
	0831	1216	2.9E
	1519	1812	1.4F
	2043		
17 Su		0012	2.4E
	0247	0559	2.5F
	0927	1309	3.2E
	1611	1904	1.6F
	2139		
18 M		0109	2.6E
	0343	0656	2.7F
	1021	1400	3.3E
	1659	1952	1.8F
	2235		
19 Tu ○		0203	2.8E
	0438	0748	2.7F
	1113	1448	3.4E
	1745	2042	1.9F
	2331		
20 W		0256	2.9E
	0532	0841	2.6F
	1203	1535	3.4E
	1830	2135	2.0F
21 Th	0026	0347	3.0E
	0626	0940	2.4F
	1252	1621	3.3E
	1916	2232	2.1F
22 F	0120	0438	2.9E
	0722	1043	2.2F
	1339	1707	3.1E
	2004	2327	2.1F
23 Sa	0213	0531	2.7E
	0822	1144	2.0F
	1426	1755	2.8E
	2056		
24 Su		0021	2.1F
	0307	0631	2.4E
	0929	1243	1.7F
	1516	1852	2.4E
	2150		
25 M		0114	2.0F
	0404	0741	2.3E
	1044	1343	1.4F
	1609	1958	2.1E
	2246		
26 Tu ◑		0210	1.9F
	0505	0851	2.3E
	1203	1446	1.2F
	1708	2103	2.0E
	2341		
27 W		0307	1.9F
	0610	0952	2.3E
	1319	1550	1.1F
	1813	2200	1.9E
28 Th	0036	0406	1.9F
	0714	1047	2.5E
	1426	1654	1.1F
	1919	2253	1.9E

March

Day	Slack	Max	knots
1 F	0130	0504	1.9F
	0810	1139	2.6E
	1521	1753	1.2F
	2017	2344	2.0E
2 Sa	0221	0558	2.0F
	0857	1226	2.7E
	1606	1843	1.3F
	2108		
3 Su		0032	2.0E
	0309	0645	2.0F
	0939	1311	2.7E
	1642	1925	1.5F
	2153		
4 M		0117	2.1E
	0354	0726	2.0F
	1016	1351	2.8E
	1710	2004	1.6F
	2236		
5 Tu		0200	2.2E
	0435	0803	2.0F
	1052	1428	2.8E
	1735	2039	1.6F
	2317		
6 W ●		0239	2.2E
	0514	0837	1.9F
	1127	1502	2.8E
	1800	2113	1.7F
	2356		
7 Th		0315	2.3E
	0552	0910	1.8F
	1202	1532	2.8E
	1828	2145	1.7F
8 F	0033	0347	2.3E
	0630	0942	1.7F
	1239	1600	2.8E
	1858	2211	1.7F
9 Sa	0108	0417	2.4E
	0710	1015	1.6F
	1316	1632	2.7E
	1932	2230	1.7F
10 Su	0144	0449	2.4E
	0756	1054	1.6F
	1356	1700	2.6E
	2010	2256	1.8F
11 M	0223	0526	2.4E
	0848	1141	1.5F
	1439	1738	2.4E
	2053	2335	1.9F
12 Tu ☽	0307	0613	2.3E
	0947	1233	1.3F
	1526	1824	2.2E
	2142		
13 W		0023	1.9F
	0357	0720	2.2E
	1051	1334	1.2F
	1618	1924	2.0E
	2236		
14 Th ◑		0119	2.0F
	0456	0852	2.3E
	1156	1440	1.2F
	1717	2043	1.9E
	2333		
15 F		0222	2.0F
	0602	1001	2.5E
	1300	1547	1.2F
	1822	2157	2.1E
16 Sa	0033	0333	2.1F
	0710	1100	2.7E
	1401	1653	1.3F
	1929	2300	2.3E
17 Su	0134	0446	2.2F
	0813	1156	2.9E
	1456	1755	1.5F
	2030		
18 M		0001	2.5E
	0235	0554	2.4F
	0910	1249	3.1E
	1547	1848	1.8F
	2128		
19 Tu		0059	2.8E
	0335	0653	2.5F
	1004	1340	3.3E
	1635	1937	2.1F
	2224		
20 W ○		0153	3.0E
	0432	0745	2.5F
	1055	1428	3.4E
	1720	2024	2.2F
	2319		
21 Th		0245	3.1E
	0527	0837	2.5F
	1145	1514	3.3E
	1804	2114	2.3F
22 F	0012	0335	3.2E
	0620	0933	2.3F
	1233	1600	3.2E
	1848	2207	2.3F
23 Sa	0103	0425	3.1E
	0715	1033	2.0F
	1319	1644	3.0E
	1933	2301	2.2F
24 Su	0152	0516	2.9E
	0813	1131	1.8F
	1406	1730	2.6E
	2021	2354	2.1F
25 M	0243	0611	2.6E
	0920	1229	1.5F
	1454	1821	2.2E
	2112		
26 Tu		0047	2.0F
	0335	0715	2.3E
	1035	1327	1.3F
	1546	1924	1.9E
	2208		
27 W ◑		0141	1.8F
	0432	0824	2.2E
	1152	1427	1.1F
	1643	2033	1.7E
	2307		
28 Th		0238	1.7F
	0533	0926	2.3E
	1302	1528	1.0F
	1748	2135	1.6E
29 F		0336	1.7F
	0635	1020	2.3E
	1401	1628	1.1F
	1856	2229	1.7E
30 Sa	0104	0434	1.6F
	0732	1109	2.4E
	1447	1724	1.2F
	1955	2319	1.8E
31 Su	0159	0529	1.7F
	0819	1154	2.5E
	1524	1813	1.4F
	2044		

Time meridian 75° W. 0000 is midnight. 1200 is noon. Times are not adjusted for Daylight Saving Time.

George Washington Bridge, Hudson River, 2019

F–Flood, Dir. 010° True   E–Ebb, Dir. 203° True

April

Day	Slack h m	Max h m	knots		Day	Slack h m	Max h m	knots
1 M		0006	1.9E		**16 Tu**	0228	0546	2.2F
	0248	0617	1.7F			0850	1227	3.1E
	0859	1236	2.6E			1520	1830	2.1F
	1553	1853	1.6F			2117		
	2127							
2 Tu		0051	2.1E		**17 W**		0046	2.9E
	0333	0658	1.7F			0329	0645	2.3F
	0936	1314	2.6E			0943	1317	3.2E
	1618	1928	1.7F			1607	1918	2.3F
	2207					2212		
3 W		0132	2.2E		**18 Th**		0140	3.1E
	0413	0733	1.8F			0427	0738	2.3F
	1013	1350	2.7E			1034	1405	3.2E
	1644	1959	1.8F			1652	2005	2.5F
	2244					2305		
4 Th		0210	2.4E		**19 F** ○		0232	3.3E
	0451	0806	1.8F			0522	0829	2.2F
	1050	1423	2.7E			1124	1452	3.1E
	1713	2025	1.9F			1736	2051	2.5F
	2320					2355		
5 F ●		0245	2.5E		**20 Sa**		0321	3.3E
	0529	0836	1.8F			0616	0922	2.1F
	1128	1454	2.7E			1212	1537	3.0E
	1743	2044	1.9F			1819	2141	2.4F
	2355							
6 Sa		0318	2.6E		**21 Su**	0044	0410	3.2E
	0608	0905	1.7F			0709	1020	1.8F
	1208	1524	2.7E			1259	1621	2.7E
	1816	2058	2.0F			1901	2234	2.3F
7 Su	0031	0350	2.7E		**22 M**	0131	0459	3.0E
	0649	0937	1.7F			0807	1118	1.6F
	1248	1555	2.7E			1346	1706	2.4E
	1851	2124	2.1F			1946	2327	2.1F
8 M	0108	0424	2.8E		**23 Tu**	0218	0550	2.7E
	0735	1020	1.6F			0913	1214	1.4F
	1330	1630	2.5E			1434	1753	2.0E
	1929	2204	2.2F			2035		
9 Tu	0149	0503	2.8E		**24 W**		0020	1.9F
	0827	1114	1.5F			0307	0647	2.4E
	1414	1710	2.4E			1024	1309	1.2F
	2014	2253	2.2F			1524	1850	1.6E
						2130		
10 W	0236	0550	2.7E		**25 Th**		0113	1.7F
	0926	1213	1.3F			0357	0751	2.2E
	1502	1756	2.2E			1132	1405	1.1F
	2106	2350	2.1F			1620	2000	1.4E
						2231		
11 Th	0330	0654	2.5E		**26 F** ◑		0208	1.6F
	1030	1316	1.2F			0451	0853	2.2E
	1555	1856	2.0E			1231	1501	1.1F
	2206					1722	2106	1.4E
						2334		
12 F ◐		0053	2.1F		**27 Sa**		0304	1.4F
	0430	0826	2.4E			0547	0947	2.2E
	1135	1423	1.2F			1319	1556	1.2F
	1657	2023	1.9E			1828	2202	1.5E
	2310							
13 Sa		0205	2.0F		**28 Su**	0036	0359	1.4F
	0537	0939	2.6E			0641	1033	2.3E
	1238	1529	1.3F			1357	1647	1.3F
	1806	2145	2.1E			1927	2251	1.7E
14 Su	0017	0322	2.0F		**29 M**	0133	0453	1.4F
	0647	1039	2.7E			0730	1115	2.3E
	1336	1634	1.5F			1428	1734	1.5F
	1916	2249	2.4E			2015	2337	1.9E
15 M	0123	0437	2.1F		**30 Tu**	0223	0541	1.4F
	0752	1134	2.9E			0813	1155	2.4E
	1430	1735	1.8F			1456	1814	1.7F
	2020	2349	2.7E			2056		

May

Day	Slack h m	Max h m	knots		Day	Slack h m	Max h m	knots
1 W		0021	2.1E		**16 Th**		0032	3.0E
	0307	0624	1.5F			0324	0633	2.0F
	0853	1233	2.5E			0920	1253	3.0E
	1524	1848	1.8F			1538	1859	2.5F
	2133					2158		
2 Th		0101	2.3E		**17 F**		0126	3.2E
	0347	0701	1.6F			0424	0726	2.0F
	0932	1309	2.5E			1011	1342	3.0E
	1555	1916	1.9F			1624	1945	2.6F
	2208					2249		
3 F		0139	2.5E		**18 Sa** ○		0217	3.3E
	0426	0734	1.6F			0519	0817	2.0F
	1013	1343	2.6E			1102	1429	2.9E
	1627	1936	2.1F			1708	2030	2.6F
	2243					2338		
4 Sa ●		0215	2.7E		**19 Su**		0306	3.3E
	0506	0805	1.7F			0613	0910	1.8F
	1055	1417	2.6E			1151	1515	2.7E
	1701	1952	2.2F			1750	2117	2.5F
	2319							
5 Su		0251	2.9E		**20 M**	0025	0354	3.2E
	0548	0836	1.7F			0706	1007	1.6F
	1138	1451	2.6E			1239	1559	2.4E
	1737	2014	2.3F			1832	2209	2.3F
	2358							
6 M		0327	3.0E		**21 Tu**	0110	0441	3.1E
	0631	0911	1.7F			0801	1103	1.5F
	1221	1527	2.6E			1326	1643	2.2E
	1815	2048	2.4F			1915	2301	2.1F
7 Tu	0040	0406	3.1E		**22 W**	0154	0528	2.8E
	0718	0958	1.6F			0901	1157	1.3F
	1305	1606	2.5E			1413	1727	1.8E
	1857	2132	2.5F			2001	2353	1.9F
8 W	0125	0448	3.1E		**23 Th**	0238	0617	2.5E
	0810	1058	1.5F			1002	1248	1.2F
	1352	1648	2.4E			1502	1817	1.6E
	1944	2226	2.4F			2054		
9 Th	0215	0536	2.9E		**24 F**		0044	1.7F
	0908	1201	1.4F			0322	0712	2.3E
	1442	1737	2.2E			1057	1339	1.2F
	2039	2329	2.3F			1555	1922	1.4E
						2155		
10 F	0309	0638	2.7E		**25 Sa**		0135	1.5F
	1010	1304	1.3F			0408	0811	2.1E
	1539	1838	2.0E			1144	1429	1.2F
	2144					1652	2031	1.3E
						2259		
11 Sa		0039	2.1E		**26 Su** ◑		0227	1.3F
	0409	0802	2.6E			0455	0904	2.1E
	1112	1408	1.4F			1222	1518	1.3F
	1643	2011	2.0E			1752	2129	1.4E
	2253							
12 Su		0156	2.0F		**27 M**	0001	0319	1.2F
	0514	0915	2.6E			0544	0950	2.1E
	1212	1511	1.5F			1255	1604	1.4F
	1753	2133	2.2E			1849	2219	1.6E
13 M	0004	0313	1.9F		**28 Tu**	0058	0409	1.1F
	0622	1015	2.7E			0634	1031	2.2E
	1308	1613	1.7F			1327	1648	1.5F
	1904	2237	2.5E			1937	2304	1.8E
14 Tu	0114	0426	1.9F		**29 W**	0149	0459	1.2F
	0727	1110	2.9E			0723	1110	2.3E
	1401	1714	2.0F			1400	1727	1.7F
	2008	2336	2.7E			2018	2346	2.1E
15 W	0221	0533	2.0F		**30 Th**	0234	0545	1.3F
	0826	1202	3.0E			0809	1148	2.3E
	1451	1809	2.3F			1434	1801	1.8F
	2105					2055		
					31 F		0028	2.3E
						0318	0626	1.4F
						0854	1226	2.4E
						1509	1828	2.0F
						2131		

June

Day	Slack h m	Max h m	knots		Day	Slack h m	Max h m	knots
1 Sa		0108	2.6E		**16 Su**		0200	3.2E
	0401	0704	1.5F			0517	0805	1.7F
	0939	1305	2.4E			1041	1407	2.6E
	1546	1850	2.2F			1641	2010	2.6F
	2209					2319		
2 Su		0148	2.9E		**17 M** ○		0249	3.3E
	0445	0739	1.6F			0609	0857	1.6F
	1024	1343	2.5E			1131	1453	2.4E
	1624	1915	2.4F			1724	2056	2.4F
	2249							
3 M ●		0228	3.1E		**18 Tu**		0005	0335	3.2E
	0530	0814	1.6F			0659	0950	1.5F
	1110	1423	2.5E			1219	1538	2.3E
	1705	1946	2.6F			1806	2145	2.3F
	2333							
4 Tu		0310	3.2E		**19 W**	0048	0420	3.1E
	0615	0853	1.6F			0748	1044	1.4F
	1156	1504	2.5E			1306	1620	2.1E
	1747	2026	2.7F			1848	2236	2.1F
5 W	0019	0352	3.3E		**20 Th**	0129	0503	2.9E
	0703	0944	1.5F			0835	1134	1.4F
	1243	1547	2.5E			1351	1702	1.8E
	1833	2113	2.6F			1933	2326	1.8F
6 Th	0108	0437	3.1E		**21 F**	0208	0544	2.6E
	0754	1046	1.5F			0921	1221	1.3F
	1333	1634	2.4E			1438	1746	1.6E
	1924	2211	2.5F			2023		
7 F	0159	0526	3.1E		**22 Sa**		0013	1.6F
	0849	1149	1.5F			0246	0627	2.4E
	1426	1725	2.3E			1003	1306	1.3F
	2022	2320	2.3F			1526	1837	1.4E
						2119		
8 Sa	0253	0624	2.8E		**23 Su**		0100	1.4F
	0947	1249	1.5F			0325	0715	2.2E
	1525	1829	2.1E			1041	1350	1.3F
	2128					1616	1943	1.3E
						2219		
9 Su		0034	2.1F		**24 M**		0146	1.2F
	0350	0737	2.7E			0407	0807	2.1E
	1046	1349	1.6F			1117	1433	1.4F
	1629	1959	2.1E			1708	2047	1.4E
	2240					2319		
10 M ◐		0149	1.9F		**25 Tu** ◑		0234	1.1F
	0450	0849	2.6E			0451	0857	2.0E
	1144	1450	1.8F			1153	1515	1.4F
	1739	2118	2.2E			1800	2140	1.6E
	2353							
11 Tu		0300	1.8F		**26 W**	0015	0322	1.0F
	0554	0950	2.7E			0541	0941	2.1E
	1239	1550	2.0F			1230	1554	1.5F
	1849	2222	2.5E			1849	2226	1.8E
12 W	0106	0410	1.7F		**27 Th**	0108	0411	1.1F
	0659	1044	2.8E			0635	1022	2.1E
	1332	1650	2.2F			1308	1630	1.7F
	1954	2320	2.8E			1933	2310	2.1E
13 Th	0215	0517	1.7F		**28 F**	0159	0502	1.1F
	0800	1137	2.8E			0728	1103	2.2E
	1422	1747	2.4F			1347	1704	1.8F
	2050					2015	2354	2.4E
14 F		0016	3.0E		**29 Sa**	0249	0551	1.3F
	0320	0619	1.7F			0819	1145	2.2E
	0856	1229	2.8E			1428	1737	2.1F
	1511	1838	2.5F			2057		
	2143							
15 Sa		0109	3.1E		**30 Su**		0039	2.7E
	0421	0714	1.7F			0338	0635	1.4F
	0949	1319	2.7E			0908	1230	2.3E
	1557	1925	2.6F			1510	1811	2.3F
	2232					2140		

Time meridian 75° W. 0000 is midnight. 1200 is noon. Times are not adjusted for Daylight Saving Time.

George Washington Bridge, Hudson River, 2019

F–Flood, Dir. 010° True   E–Ebb, Dir. 203° True

July

Day	Slack	Maximum	knots
1 M		0124	3.0E
	0426	0717	1.5F
	0955	1316	2.4E
	1554	1849	2.6F
	2226		
2 Tu ●		0210	3.2E
	0513	0757	1.6F
	1044	1401	2.5E
	1640	1929	2.7F
	2315		
3 W		0255	3.3E
	0559	0840	1.6F
	1134	1448	2.6E
	1727	2013	2.8F
4 Th	0005	0340	3.4E
	0646	0932	1.6F
	1225	1535	2.6E
	1817	2104	2.7F
5 F	0055	0426	3.3E
	0734	1032	1.6F
	1317	1625	2.6E
	1911	2206	2.5F
6 Sa	0145	0514	3.2E
	0826	1133	1.7F
	1412	1718	2.5E
	2010	2319	2.3F
7 Su	0236	0606	3.0E
	0920	1230	1.8F
	1511	1822	2.3E
	2116		
8 M		0029	2.0F
	0329	0709	2.7E
	1017	1328	1.9F
	1613	1943	2.2E
	2228		
9 Tu ☽		0137	1.8F
	0425	0820	2.6E
	1114	1426	2.0F
	1720	2100	2.3E
	2343		
10 W		0245	1.6F
	0526	0923	2.6E
	1209	1526	2.1F
	1830	2204	2.5E
11 Th	0057	0353	1.5F
	0631	1020	2.6E
	1303	1625	2.2F
	1935	2302	2.7E
12 F	0210	0500	1.4F
	0735	1114	2.5E
	1355	1724	2.3F
	2033	2358	2.9E
13 Sa	0317	0605	1.5F
	0834	1206	2.5E
	1445	1819	2.4F
	2125		
14 Su		0051	3.0E
	0418	0701	1.5F
	0929	1257	2.4E
	1533	1908	2.5F
	2214		
15 M		0142	3.1E
	0512	0751	1.5F
	1021	1346	2.4E
	1618	1953	2.5F
	2300		
16 Tu ○		0229	3.2E
	0600	0840	1.5F
	1111	1432	2.3E
	1702	2037	2.4F
	2343		
17 W		0314	3.1E
	0642	0929	1.5F
	1158	1516	2.2E
	1745	2122	2.2F
18 Th	0023	0355	3.0E
	0720	1017	1.5F
	1243	1558	2.1E
	1827	2209	2.0F
19 F	0100	0433	2.9E
	0754	1103	1.5F
	1326	1637	2.0E
	1909	2255	1.8F
20 Sa	0135	0508	2.7E
	0827	1146	1.5F
	1409	1715	1.8E
	1954	2339	1.6F
21 Su	0210	0540	2.5E
	0901	1226	1.4F
	1451	1753	1.7E
	2044		
22 M		0021	1.4F
	0246	0611	2.3E
	0937	1304	1.4F
	1535	1839	1.5E
	2138		
23 Tu		0103	1.2F
	0325	0647	2.1E
	1016	1341	1.4F
	1620	1944	1.5E
	2235		
24 W ☽		0147	1.1F
	0408	0738	2.0E
	1056	1416	1.5F
	1706	2050	1.6E
	2332		
25 Th		0234	1.0F
	0458	0839	2.0E
	1138	1450	1.6F
	1755	2144	1.9E
26 F	0030	0325	1.0F
	0553	0933	2.0E
	1221	1525	1.7F
	1846	2233	2.2E
27 Sa	0126	0420	1.1F
	0651	1022	2.0E
	1306	1606	1.9F
	1937	2323	2.4E
28 Su	0222	0517	1.2F
	0748	1111	2.1E
	1353	1653	2.1F
	2027		
29 M		0013	2.7E
	0315	0610	1.3F
	0840	1203	2.2E
	1441	1744	2.4F
	2117		
30 Tu		0103	3.0E
	0406	0658	1.4F
	0932	1255	2.4E
	1531	1834	2.6F
	2208		
31 W ●		0152	3.2E
	0454	0742	1.6F
	1023	1347	2.6E
	1623	1922	2.7F
	2300		

August

Day	Slack	Maximum	knots
1 Th		0239	3.4E
	0540	0827	1.7F
	1116	1437	2.7E
	1714	2010	2.8F
	2351		
2 F		0326	3.4E
	0625	0917	1.8F
	1209	1527	2.8E
	1807	2104	2.6F
3 Sa	0040	0411	3.4E
	0711	1014	1.9F
	1303	1618	2.8E
	1902	2208	2.4F
4 Su	0129	0457	3.2E
	0759	1112	2.0F
	1358	1711	2.7E
	2000	2317	2.2F
5 M	0218	0545	3.0E
	0850	1208	2.0F
	1454	1811	2.5E
	2105		
6 Tu		0021	1.9F
	0308	0642	2.7E
	0946	1304	2.0F
	1554	1924	2.3E
	2217		
7 W ☽		0124	1.7F
	0402	0749	2.5E
	1042	1401	2.0F
	1657	2039	2.3E
	2332		
8 Th		0229	1.4F
	0500	0857	2.3E
	1139	1501	2.0F
	1805	2145	2.4E
9 F	0050	0336	1.3F
	0606	0956	2.3E
	1235	1601	2.1F
	1912	2243	2.6E
10 Sa	0204	0444	1.3F
	0713	1052	2.2E
	1330	1702	2.1F
	2013	2339	2.8E
11 Su	0311	0549	1.3F
	0816	1145	2.2E
	1422	1759	2.2F
	2105		
12 M		0031	2.9E
	0408	0645	1.4F
	0911	1236	2.2E
	1512	1849	2.3F
	2152		
13 Tu		0120	3.0E
	0457	0733	1.5F
	1002	1325	2.2E
	1600	1934	2.3F
	2236		
14 W		0205	3.0E
	0537	0817	1.5F
	1049	1410	2.2E
	1644	2016	2.2F
	2316		
15 Th ○		0247	3.0E
	0610	0900	1.6F
	1144	1453	2.2E
	1727	2058	2.1F
	2353		
16 F		0325	2.9E
	0638	0942	1.6F
	1216	1533	2.2E
	1807	2139	1.9F
17 Sa	0027	0359	2.8E
	0704	1024	1.6F
	1256	1610	2.2E
	1847	2221	1.7F
18 Su	0101	0430	2.7E
	0733	1102	1.6F
	1334	1644	2.1E
	1927	2301	1.5F
19 M	0135	0456	2.6E
	0804	1137	1.6F
	1412	1714	2.0E
	2011	2340	1.4F
20 Tu	0211	0522	2.4E
	0840	1208	1.5F
	1450	1747	1.9E
	2101		
21 W		0019	1.3F
	0250	0555	2.3E
	0920	1235	1.5F
	1531	1830	1.9E
	2156		
22 Th		0100	1.2F
	0334	0637	2.1E
	1004	1301	1.6F
	1615	1937	1.9E
	2256		
23 F ○		0149	1.1F
	0423	0734	1.9E
	1051	1338	1.7F
	1706	2058	2.0E
	2357		
24 Sa		0246	1.1F
	0519	0844	1.9E
	1140	1427	1.8F
	1803	2200	2.2E
25 Su	0058	0346	1.1F
	0620	0948	1.9E
	1231	1523	2.0F
	1903	2256	2.5E
26 M	0157	0448	1.2F
	0721	1047	2.1E
	1325	1624	2.1F
	2002	2350	2.8E
27 Tu	0252	0547	1.3F
	0819	1144	2.3E
	1420	1728	2.3F
	2058		
28 W		0043	3.0E
	0344	0639	1.5F
	0913	1241	2.5E
	1516	1827	2.5F
	2152		
29 Th		0133	3.2E
	0431	0725	1.7F
	1007	1336	2.7E
	1612	1920	2.6F
	2244		
30 F ●		0221	3.3E
	0516	0810	1.9F
	1101	1428	2.9E
	1706	2011	2.6F
	2335		
31 Sa		0307	3.4E
	0600	0858	2.1F
	1155	1519	3.1E
	1800	2105	2.5F

September

Day	Slack	Maximum	knots
1 Su	0023	0352	3.3E
	0644	0952	2.2F
	1249	1610	3.0E
	1854	2206	2.3F
2 M	0111	0437	3.2E
	0730	1048	2.2F
	1342	1701	2.9E
	1951	2309	2.1F
3 Tu	0159	0523	2.9E
	0820	1144	2.2F
	1435	1757	2.7E
	2055		
4 W		0010	1.8F
	0248	0615	2.6E
	0913	1239	2.1F
	1531	1903	2.4E
	2207		
5 Th ☽		0111	1.5F
	0340	0719	2.2E
	1010	1336	2.0F
	1631	2017	2.3E
	2324		
6 F		0214	1.3F
	0438	0830	2.0E
	1109	1435	1.9F
	1736	2123	2.4E
7 Sa	0043	0320	1.2F
	0544	0934	1.9E
	1208	1536	1.9F
	1844	2222	2.5E
8 Su	0155	0426	1.2F
	0654	1031	2.0E
	1306	1638	1.9F
	1946	2316	2.6E
9 M	0256	0529	1.2F
	0759	1124	2.0E
	1402	1737	2.0F
	2039		
10 Tu		0006	2.7E
	0346	0624	1.4F
	0854	1214	2.1E
	1455	1828	2.0F
	2124		
11 W		0053	2.8E
	0426	0709	1.5F
	0941	1302	2.2E
	1544	1913	2.1F
	2204		
12 Th		0135	2.8E
	0458	0749	1.7F
	1025	1347	2.3E
	1628	1953	2.0F
	2242		
13 F ○		0214	2.8E
	0525	0826	1.7F
	1106	1428	2.3E
	1709	2030	1.9F
	2317		
14 Sa		0250	2.8E
	0549	0901	1.8F
	1145	1506	2.4E
	1747	2107	1.8F
	2352		
15 Su		0322	2.8E
	0615	0935	1.8F
	1222	1541	2.4E
	1823	2143	1.7F
16 M	0026	0350	2.7E
	0644	1005	1.7F
	1257	1612	2.4E
	1902	2220	1.6F
17 Tu	0102	0416	2.6E
	0716	1029	1.7F
	1332	1641	2.4E
	1943	2257	1.5F
18 W	0140	0445	2.5E
	0751	1046	1.7F
	1408	1712	2.3E
	2031	2337	1.4F
19 Th	0221	0519	2.3E
	0831	1115	1.8F
	1448	1752	2.3E
	2126		
20 F		0022	1.2F
	0306	0600	2.1E
	0917	1158	1.8F
	1533	1846	2.2E
	2227		
21 Sa ○		0115	1.2F
	0355	0652	1.9E
	1009	1249	1.9F
	1627	2013	2.2E
	2330		
22 Su		0216	1.1F
	0452	0804	1.8E
	1105	1349	1.9F
	1728	2131	2.3E
23 M	0032	0320	1.1F
	0555	0924	1.9E
	1204	1456	2.0F
	1835	2231	2.6E
24 Tu	0131	0423	1.2F
	0700	1030	2.1E
	1305	1608	2.1F
	1940	2327	2.8E
25 W	0226	0524	1.5F
	0802	1131	2.4E
	1406	1719	2.2F
	2039		
26 Th		0020	3.0E
	0316	0618	1.7F
	0859	1229	2.7E
	1506	1822	2.4F
	2133		
27 F		0111	3.2E
	0403	0707	2.0F
	0954	1325	3.0E
	1604	1916	2.5F
	2225		
28 Sa ●		0159	3.3E
	0448	0752	2.2F
	1048	1417	3.2E
	1700	2007	2.5F
	2315		
29 Su		0246	3.3E
	0533	0838	2.4F
	1141	1508	3.3E
	1754	2100	2.3F
30 M	0004	0331	3.2E
	0617	0929	2.4F
	1233	1558	3.2E
	1848	2158	2.1F

Time meridian 75° W. 0000 is midnight. 1200 is noon. Times are not adjusted for Daylight Saving Time.

George Washington Bridge, Hudson River, 2019

F–Flood, Dir. 010° True   E–Ebb, Dir. 203° True

October

Day	Slack h m	Max h m	knots
1 Tu	0052	0416	3.0E
	0702	1024	2.4F
	1324	1649	3.1E
	1944	2300	1.9F
2 W	0140	0502	2.7E
	0749	1120	2.2F
	1415	1742	2.8E
	2047	2359	1.6F
3 Th	0229	0551	2.4E
	0840	1215	2.1F
	1508	1842	2.5E
	2200		
4 F		0059	1.4F
	0321	0650	2.0E
	0937	1312	1.9F
	1603	1952	2.4E
	2317		
5 Sa ◐		0200	1.2F
	0419	0803	1.7E
	1038	1410	1.8F
	1704	2059	2.3E
6 Su	0031	0302	1.1F
	0524	0910	1.7E
	1141	1511	1.7F
	1808	2157	2.4E
7 M	0134	0404	1.2F
	0635	1009	1.7E
	1244	1611	1.7F
	1910	2248	2.5E
8 Tu	0226	0502	1.3F
	0740	1101	1.9E
	1344	1709	1.7F
	2002	2336	2.6E
9 W	0307	0554	1.4F
	0832	1151	2.0E
	1438	1801	1.7F
	2046		
10 Th		0019	2.6E
	0340	0638	1.6F
	0916	1237	2.2E
	1526	1846	1.8F
	2125		
11 F		0100	2.6E
	0407	0715	1.8F
	0956	1320	2.3E
	1609	1925	1.8F
	2201		
12 Sa		0137	2.6E
	0433	0748	1.9F
	1034	1400	2.4E
	1647	2000	1.7F
	2238		
13 Su ○		0211	2.6E
	0500	0817	1.9F
	1110	1437	2.5E
	1724	2033	1.7F
	2315		
14 M		0243	2.6E
	0529	0841	1.9F
	1144	1511	2.6E
	1800	2105	1.6F
	2353		
15 Tu		0312	2.6E
	0600	0856	2.0F
	1219	1542	2.7E
	1838	2138	1.6F
16 W	0032	0341	2.5E
	0633	0911	2.0F
	1254	1613	2.7E
	1920	2216	1.5F
17 Th	0113	0413	2.4E
	0709	0942	2.1F
	1331	1647	2.7E
	2008	2303	1.4F
18 F	0155	0450	2.3E
	0751	1027	2.1F
	1414	1728	2.7E
	2103	2356	1.3F
19 Sa	0241	0533	2.1E
	0839	1119	2.1F
	1503	1820	2.5E
	2203		
20 Su		0053	1.2F
	0332	0624	1.9E
	0935	1219	2.0F
	1558	1939	2.4E
	2306		
21 M ○		0155	1.2F
	0430	0737	1.8E
	1038	1326	2.0F
	1701	2104	2.5E
22 Tu	0006	0258	1.3F
	0535	0908	1.9E
	1144	1441	2.0F
	1809	2207	2.6E
23 W	0103	0400	1.4F
	0643	1018	2.2E
	1251	1557	2.0F
	1916	2302	2.8E
24 Th	0156	0500	1.7F
	0748	1119	2.5E
	1356	1709	2.1F
	2016	2355	2.9E
25 F	0246	0556	2.0F
	0846	1217	2.8E
	1459	1812	2.2F
	2111		
26 Sa		0047	3.1E
	0334	0646	2.3F
	0941	1312	3.1E
	1559	1908	2.2F
	2203		
27 Su ●		0136	3.1E
	0420	0733	2.5F
	1034	1405	3.3E
	1655	1959	2.2F
	2254		
28 M		0224	3.1E
	0505	0819	2.6F
	1126	1455	3.4E
	1749	2051	2.1F
	2344		
29 Tu		0310	3.0E
	0550	0907	2.5F
	1217	1545	3.3E
	1843	2149	1.9F
30 W	0033	0356	2.8E
	0634	1001	2.4F
	1306	1635	3.2E
	1939	2249	1.7F
31 Th	0122	0442	2.5E
	0720	1057	2.3F
	1355	1725	2.9E
	2042	2348	1.5F

November

Day	Slack h m	Max h m	knots
1 F	0212	0529	2.2E
	0809	1153	2.1F
	1444	1821	2.7E
	2153		
2 Sa		0045	1.3F
	0304	0624	1.8E
	0904	1248	1.9F
	1535	1923	2.4E
	2304		
3 Su		0142	1.2F
	0400	0733	1.5E
	1007	1344	1.7F
	1629	2028	2.3E
4 M ◐	0006	0239	1.2F
	0503	0843	1.5E
	1113	1442	1.5F
	1725	2125	2.3E
5 Tu	0058	0335	1.2F
	0611	0943	1.6E
	1220	1539	1.4F
	1822	2215	2.3E
6 W ○	0141	0428	1.4F
	0713	1035	1.8E
	1322	1635	1.4F
	1914	2259	2.4E
7 Th	0215	0517	1.5F
	0804	1123	1.9E
	1417	1727	1.4F
	1959	2340	2.4E
8 F	0244	0600	1.7F
	0846	1208	2.1E
	1503	1813	1.4F
	2040		
9 Sa		0019	2.4E
	0312	0636	1.8F
	0923	1250	2.3E
	1544	1853	1.5F
	2119		
10 Su		0056	2.4E
	0341	0707	2.0F
	0958	1330	2.5E
	1622	1929	1.5F
	2158		
11 M		0131	2.5E
	0412	0732	2.0F
	1033	1406	2.6E
	1659	2001	1.6F
	2239		
12 Tu ○		0204	2.5E
	0445	0750	2.1F
	1107	1441	2.8E
	1737	2033	1.6F
	2321		
13 W		0237	2.5E
	0520	0805	2.2F
	1143	1519	2.9E
	1817	2106	1.5F
14 Th	0004	0311	2.5E
	0556	0831	2.3F
	1222	1551	3.0E
	1901	2145	1.5F
15 F	0047	0347	2.4E
	0636	0909	2.4F
	1304	1629	3.0E
	1949	2238	1.4F
16 Sa	0132	0427	2.3E
	0720	0957	2.4F
	1350	1712	2.9E
	2042	2337	1.3F
17 Su	0220	0512	2.2E
	0811	1055	2.3F
	1441	1803	2.8E
	2140		
18 M		0035	1.3F
	0312	0605	2.0E
	0911	1201	2.1F
	1537	1913	2.6E
	2240		
19 Tu ○		0135	1.4F
	0412	0720	1.9E
	1019	1313	2.0F
	1638	2036	2.5E
	2337		
20 W		0235	1.5F
	0518	0854	2.0E
	1129	1430	1.9F
	1743	2141	2.6E
21 Th	0032	0336	1.7F
	0627	1004	2.3E
	1239	1545	1.8F
	1849	2237	2.8E
22 F	0125	0435	2.0F
	0733	1105	2.6E
	1348	1655	1.9F
	1950	2330	2.9E
23 Sa	0216	0533	2.2F
	0833	1202	2.9E
	1452	1800	1.9F
	2047		
24 Su		0022	2.9E
	0305	0626	2.5F
	0928	1258	3.2E
	1554	1857	2.0F
	2140		
25 M		0113	2.9E
	0353	0715	2.6F
	1020	1351	3.3E
	1652	1949	1.9F
	2232		
26 Tu ●		0202	2.9E
	0439	0801	2.7F
	1111	1441	3.4E
	1747	2042	1.8F
	2324		
27 W		0250	2.8E
	0524	0849	2.7F
	1201	1531	3.4E
	1841	2139	1.7F
28 Th	0015	0337	2.6E
	0609	0940	2.4F
	1248	1619	3.2E
	1936	2238	1.6F
29 F	0105	0423	2.3E
	0654	1036	2.2F
	1334	1707	3.0E
	2035	2334	1.4F
30 Sa	0155	0509	2.0E
	0741	1131	2.0F
	1420	1757	2.8E
	2136		

December

Day	Slack h m	Max h m	knots
1 Su		0027	1.4F
	0246	0559	1.7E
	0834	1224	1.8F
	1505	1850	2.5E
	2235		
2 M		0119	1.3F
	0339	0700	1.5E
	0936	1316	1.6F
	1552	1948	2.3E
	2325		
3 Tu		0209	1.3F
	0436	0810	1.4E
	1043	1409	1.4F
	1639	2044	2.2E
4 W ◐	0007	0259	1.3F
	0536	0912	1.5E
	1149	1503	1.2F
	1728	2133	2.2E
5 Th	0042	0347	1.4F
	0634	1004	1.7E
	1251	1555	1.2F
	1818	2217	2.2E
6 F	0114	0432	1.6F
	0725	1051	1.9E
	1345	1646	1.1F
	1907	2256	2.2E
7 Sa	0146	0514	1.7F
	0807	1135	2.1E
	1431	1734	1.2F
	1953	2335	2.2E
8 Su	0219	0551	1.8F
	0845	1217	2.3E
	1513	1818	1.3F
	2037		
9 M		0013	2.3E
	0254	0622	1.9F
	0920	1257	2.5E
	1554	1857	1.4F
	2121		
10 Tu		0050	2.3E
	0329	0646	2.1F
	0956	1336	2.7E
	1634	1932	1.4F
	2206		
11 W		0128	2.3E
	0407	0706	2.3F
	1034	1415	2.9E
	1716	2006	1.5F
	2251		
12 Th ○		0206	2.4E
	0446	0732	2.4F
	1115	1454	3.1E
	1759	2042	1.5F
	2337		
13 F		0245	2.4E
	0527	0806	2.6F
	1158	1534	3.2E
	1843	2124	1.5F
14 Sa	0023	0327	2.4E
	0610	0848	2.6F
	1245	1615	3.2E
	1930	2219	1.5F
15 Su	0111	0411	2.4E
	0658	0939	2.5F
	1333	1700	3.1E
	2020	2318	1.5F
16 M	0201	0458	2.3E
	0752	1042	2.4F
	1424	1749	3.0E
	2115		
17 Tu		0016	1.5F
	0255	0553	2.2E
	0855	1153	2.1F
	1518	1850	2.7E
	2211		
18 W ○		0113	1.6F
	0355	0708	2.1E
	1004	1306	1.9F
	1615	2005	2.6E
	2307		
19 Th		0212	1.8F
	0500	0837	2.2E
	1116	1419	1.8F
	1716	2113	2.6E
20 F	0001	0311	1.9F
	0609	0948	2.4E
	1229	1530	1.7F
	1820	2211	2.7E
21 Sa	0055	0411	2.1F
	0717	1049	2.7E
	1339	1639	1.6F
	1924	2306	2.7E
22 Su	0147	0510	2.3F
	0818	1147	2.9E
	1447	1745	1.6F
	2023	2359	2.7E
23 M	0239	0607	2.5F
	0913	1242	3.1E
	1551	1845	1.7F
	2119		
24 Tu		0052	2.7E
	0328	0658	2.6F
	1006	1335	3.3E
	1650	1939	1.7F
	2213		
25 W		0142	2.6E
	0416	0746	2.6F
	1056	1426	3.3E
	1745	2031	1.7F
	2307		
26 Th ●		0231	2.5E
	0502	0833	2.6F
	1144	1514	3.3E
	1836	2126	1.6F
	2359		
27 F		0318	2.4E
	0547	0922	2.4F
	1230	1601	3.2E
	1926	2221	1.5F
28 Sa	0048	0404	2.2E
	0632	1015	2.2F
	1313	1645	3.1E
	2015	2314	1.5F
29 Su	0136	0448	2.0E
	0718	1108	2.0F
	1354	1729	2.8E
	2103		
30 M		0002	1.4F
	0223	0534	1.8E
	0808	1157	1.8F
	1434	1812	2.5E
	2147		
31 Tu		0048	1.4F
	0311	0625	1.6E
	0905	1245	1.5F
	1513	1859	2.3E
	2227		

Time meridian 75° W. 0000 is midnight. 1200 is noon. Times are not adjusted for Daylight Saving Time.

Kingston–Rhinecliff Bridge, Hudson River, 2019

F–Flood, Dir. 011° True   E–Ebb, Dir. 191° True

January

Day	Slack h m	Maximum h m	knots
1 Tu		0243	1.3E
	0526	0823	1.2F
	1128	1529	1.5E
	1814	2100	1.0F
	2343		
2 W		0336	1.3E
	0615	0916	1.3F
	1219	1623	1.6E
	1913	2159	1.1F
3 Th	0039	0425	1.3E
	0703	1002	1.3F
	1306	1714	1.7E
	2008	2250	1.1F
4 F	0131	0512	1.3E
	0749	1043	1.3F
	1351	1805	1.7E
	2058	2338	1.0F
5 Sa ●	0220	0558	1.2E
	0834	1121	1.3F
	1435	1853	1.6E
	2144		
6 Su		0024	1.0F
	0308	0641	1.2E
	0918	1157	1.2F
	1517	1935	1.6E
	2226		
7 M		0108	0.9F
	0353	0718	1.1E
	1001	1232	1.1F
	1556	2007	1.5E
	2305		
8 Tu		0149	0.9F
	0437	0748	1.1E
	1043	1307	1.1F
	1633	2023	1.4E
	2341		
9 W		0225	0.9F
	0519	0817	1.1E
	1126	1345	1.0F
	1709	2036	1.4E
10 Th	0017	0254	0.9F
	0600	0849	1.1E
	1210	1426	0.9F
	1746	2104	1.4E
11 F	0055	0324	0.9F
	0640	0926	1.1E
	1257	1511	0.9F
	1826	2141	1.3E
12 Sa	0135	0401	0.9F
	0720	1008	1.1E
	1348	1602	0.8F
	1911	2227	1.3E
13 Su	0219	0444	0.9F
	0803	1057	1.1E
	1443	1657	0.8F
	2002	2320	1.2E
14 M ☽	0306	0530	1.0F
	0848	1152	1.1E
	1542	1754	0.8F
	2059		
15 Tu		0016	1.2E
	0353	0616	1.1F
	0937	1248	1.2E
	1640	1852	0.8F
	2200		
16 W		0112	1.2E
	0441	0704	1.2F
	1027	1343	1.3E
	1737	1951	0.8F
	2258		
17 Th		0205	1.2E
	0528	0755	1.3F
	1117	1438	1.4E
	1832	2051	0.9F
	2352		
18 F		0258	1.3E
	0615	0846	1.4F
	1205	1532	1.4E
	1925	2146	0.9F
19 Sa	0043	0350	1.3E
	0705	0937	1.4F
	1254	1626	1.5E
	2017	2234	1.0F
20 Su	0133	0443	1.3E
	0756	1026	1.5F
	1343	1722	1.5E
	2107	2321	1.0F
21 M ○	0226	0540	1.3E
	0848	1115	1.5F
	1434	1820	1.5E
	2155		
22 Tu		0009	1.0F
	0320	0638	1.3E
	0940	1204	1.5F
	1525	1914	1.6E
	2242		
23 W		0100	1.1F
	0415	0732	1.4E
	1033	1256	1.4F
	1618	2000	1.6E
	2330		
24 Th		0153	1.1F
	0512	0823	1.4E
	1128	1351	1.3F
	1712	2044	1.6E
25 F	0021	0249	1.1F
	0607	0913	1.3E
	1227	1449	1.2F
	1807	2132	1.5E
26 Sa	0114	0350	1.1F
	0703	1010	1.2E
	1331	1555	1.1F
	1905	2228	1.4E
27 Su ☽	0210	0454	1.1F
	0800	1130	1.2E
	1439	1711	0.9F
	2007	2345	1.2E
28 M	0307	0557	1.1F
	0901	1303	1.2E
	1550	1828	0.9F
	2114		
29 Tu		0112	1.2E
	0403	0656	1.1F
	1003	1413	1.3E
	1659	1940	0.9F
	2222		
30 W		0219	1.2E
	0457	0754	1.1F
	1102	1513	1.5E
	1802	2048	0.9F
	2325		
31 Th		0315	1.2E
	0548	0850	1.2F
	1155	1607	1.6E
	1900	2146	1.0F

February

Day	Slack h m	Maximum h m	knots
1 F	0020	0404	1.2E
	0637	0940	1.2F
	1242	1656	1.6E
	1951	2235	1.0F
2 Sa	0110	0449	1.2E
	0724	1022	1.2F
	1326	1743	1.6E
	2037	2318	1.0F
3 Su	0156	0532	1.2E
	0810	1059	1.2F
	1407	1826	1.5E
	2117	2358	1.0F
4 M ●	0240	0612	1.2E
	0854	1131	1.1F
	1445	1903	1.5E
	2152		
5 Tu		0034	1.0F
	0322	0646	1.2E
	0936	1203	1.1F
	1522	1926	1.4E
	2226		
6 W		0105	1.0F
	0402	0715	1.2E
	1016	1237	1.1F
	1557	1937	1.4E
	2259		
7 Th		0130	1.0F
	0441	0745	1.2E
	1056	1314	1.1F
	1634	2000	1.5E
	2333		
8 F		0157	1.0F
	0519	0817	1.3E
	1137	1355	1.0F
	1713	2033	1.5E
9 Sa	0010	0231	1.1F
	0556	0852	1.3E
	1222	1439	1.0F
	1755	2111	1.4E
10 Su	0049	0311	1.1F
	0633	0932	1.3E
	1311	1528	0.9F
	1841	2154	1.4E
11 M	0133	0356	1.1F
	0714	1017	1.2E
	1408	1623	0.9F
	1932	2245	1.3E
12 Tu ☽	0221	0445	1.1F
	0800	1110	1.2E
	1510	1722	0.8F
	2028	2341	1.2E
13 W	0312	0536	1.1F
	0852	1210	1.2E
	1614	1823	0.8F
	2129		
14 Th		0040	1.1E
	0405	0629	1.2F
	0949	1312	1.2E
	1715	1926	0.7F
	2232		
15 F		0139	1.2E
	0458	0724	1.2F
	1048	1415	1.3E
	1812	2032	0.8F
	2330		
16 Sa		0237	1.2E
	0552	0820	1.3F
	1143	1518	1.4E
	1906	2132	0.9F
17 Su	0025	0334	1.2E
	0646	0916	1.4F
	1236	1618	1.4E
	1958	2222	1.0F
18 M	0118	0431	1.3E
	0741	1010	1.4F
	1328	1716	1.5E
	2046	2309	1.1F
19 Tu ○	0211	0529	1.3E
	0835	1101	1.5F
	1420	1814	1.5E
	2133	2355	1.1F
20 W	0305	0629	1.4E
	0929	1152	1.5F
	1512	1906	1.6E
	2219		
21 Th		0044	1.2F
	0359	0724	1.4E
	1022	1245	1.4F
	1606	1951	1.6E
	2306		
22 F		0135	1.2F
	0453	0814	1.5E
	1116	1340	1.3F
	1700	2033	1.6E
	2355		
23 Sa		0227	1.2F
	0546	0902	1.4E
	1214	1439	1.2F
	1755	2116	1.5E
24 Su	0045	0322	1.2F
	0639	0956	1.3E
	1316	1546	1.0F
	1851	2207	1.3E
25 M	0139	0422	1.1F
	0732	1113	1.3E
	1424	1704	0.9F
	1951	2313	1.2E
26 Tu ◑	0235	0524	1.0F
	0830	1244	1.3E
	1535	1818	0.8F
	2055		
27 W		0043	1.1E
	0332	0625	1.0F
	0931	1354	1.3E
	1644	1927	0.8F
	2202		
28 Th		0155	1.1E
	0429	0725	1.0F
	1032	1454	1.4E
	1746	2031	0.8F
	2305		

March

Day	Slack h m	Maximum h m	knots
1 F		0253	1.1E
	0522	0824	1.0F
	1127	1546	1.5E
	1840	2127	0.9F
	2359		
2 Sa		0342	1.1E
	0613	0916	1.0F
	1215	1632	1.5E
	1925	2213	0.9F
3 Su	0045	0425	1.1E
	0701	0959	1.1F
	1257	1713	1.5E
	2004	2252	1.0F
4 M	0128	0503	1.2E
	0746	1034	1.1F
	1334	1749	1.4E
	2039	2325	1.0F
5 Tu	0208	0536	1.2E
	0829	1104	1.1F
	1410	1815	1.4E
	2112	2352	1.0F
6 W ●	0246	0605	1.2E
	0909	1134	1.1F
	1446	1828	1.4E
	2144		
7 Th		0014	1.1F
	0323	0636	1.3E
	0949	1207	1.1F
	1523	1853	1.4E
	2217		
8 F		0040	1.1F
	0359	0709	1.3E
	1028	1245	1.1F
	1603	1926	1.5E
	2252		
9 Sa		0112	1.2F
	0435	0745	1.4E
	1108	1327	1.1F
	1645	2004	1.5E
	2328		
10 Su		0150	1.2F
	0511	0821	1.4E
	1153	1411	1.1F
	1729	2043	1.5E
11 M	0008	0231	1.2F
	0549	0900	1.4E
	1242	1500	1.0F
	1815	2126	1.4E
12 Tu	0051	0317	1.2F
	0631	0944	1.4E
	1340	1554	0.9F
	1905	2214	1.3E
13 W	0140	0407	1.2F
	0719	1035	1.3E
	1443	1654	0.8F
	2001	2310	1.1E
14 Th ☽	0235	0502	1.2F
	0814	1137	1.2E
	1550	1758	0.7F
	2103		
15 F		0013	1.1E
	0335	0559	1.2F
	0917	1245	1.2E
	1653	1905	0.7F
	2210		
16 Sa		0118	1.1E
	0436	0658	1.2F
	1022	1359	1.2E
	1751	2015	0.8F
	2313		
17 Su		0222	1.2E
	0535	0759	1.2F
	1123	1513	1.3E
	1844	2118	0.9F
18 M	0010	0325	1.2E
	0632	0901	1.3F
	1220	1614	1.4E
	1934	2209	1.0F
19 Tu	0104	0424	1.3E
	0729	0958	1.4F
	1313	1708	1.5E
	2022	2254	1.2F
20 W ○	0156	0523	1.4E
	0824	1051	1.4F
	1406	1801	1.5E
	2108	2339	1.3F
21 Th	0249	0622	1.5E
	0918	1142	1.4F
	1459	1852	1.6E
	2154		
22 F		0025	1.3F
	0340	0717	1.5E
	1011	1236	1.3F
	1553	1937	1.6E
	2240		
23 Sa		0112	1.3F
	0431	0807	1.6E
	1105	1332	1.2F
	1647	2019	1.5E
	2327		
24 Su		0201	1.3F
	0522	0854	1.5E
	1202	1433	1.1F
	1742	2100	1.4E
25 M	0016	0252	1.2F
	0613	0945	1.4E
	1303	1541	1.0F
	1838	2146	1.3E
26 Tu	0107	0348	1.1F
	0704	1057	1.4E
	1408	1656	0.9F
	1935	2243	1.1E
27 W ◑	0202	0450	1.0F
	0758	1222	1.3E
	1517	1805	0.8F
	2035		
28 Th		0010	1.0E
	0301	0554	0.9F
	0857	1330	1.3E
	1623	1908	0.8F
	2139		
29 F		0128	0.9E
	0400	0655	0.9F
	0957	1428	1.3E
	1721	2007	0.8F
	2239		
30 Sa		0227	1.0E
	0457	0754	0.9F
	1053	1518	1.3E
	1808	2059	0.9F
	2331		
31 Su		0316	1.1E
	0549	0847	0.9F
	1140	1600	1.3E
	1847	2142	0.9F

Time meridian 75° W. 0000 is midnight. 1200 is noon. Times are not adjusted for Daylight Saving Time.

Kingston–Rhinecliff Bridge, Hudson River, 2019

F–Flood, Dir. 011° True   E–Ebb, Dir. 191° True

April

Day	Slack (h m)	Maximum (h m)	knots
1 M	0016	0357	1.1E
	0636	0930	0.9F
	1220	1634	1.3E
	1922	2217	1.0F
2 Tu	0055	0428	1.2E
	0720	1004	1.0F
	1257	1656	1.3E
	1955	2244	1.1F
3 W	0132	0452	1.2E
	0801	1034	1.0F
	1333	1706	1.3E
	2028	2305	1.1F
4 Th	0208	0520	1.3E
	0841	1105	1.1F
	1412	1734	1.4E
	2102	2329	1.2F
5 F ●	0242	0555	1.4E
	0921	1140	1.1F
	1452	1813	1.5E
	2137	2359	1.3F
6 Sa	0317	0634	1.4E
	1001	1219	1.2F
	1535	1854	1.5E
	2213		
7 Su		0034	1.3F
	0353	0713	1.5E
	1044	1301	1.2F
	1619	1936	1.5E
	2251		
8 M		0114	1.4F
	0430	0753	1.5E
	1130	1346	1.1F
	1705	2018	1.4E
	2331		
9 Tu		0158	1.4F
	0511	0834	1.5E
	1220	1435	1.0F
	1752	2101	1.3E
10 W	0015	0245	1.3F
	0557	0917	1.4E
	1317	1528	0.9F
	1843	2148	1.2E
11 Th	0107	0336	1.3F
	0648	1007	1.3E
	1420	1629	0.8F
	1939	2244	1.1E
12 F ◐	0206	0433	1.2F
	0745	1108	1.2E
	1526	1737	0.7F
	2042	2350	1.0E
13 Sa	0312	0534	1.1F
	0849	1222	1.2E
	1629	1847	0.7F
	2152		
14 Su		0101	1.1F
	0418	0637	1.1F
	0958	1347	1.2E
	1726	1957	0.8F
	2257		
15 M		0214	1.2F
	0521	0742	1.1F
	1104	1506	1.3E
	1818	2059	1.0F
	2356		
16 Tu		0321	1.3E
	0620	0848	1.2F
	1202	1602	1.4E
	1907	2151	1.2F
17 W	0049	0421	1.4E
	0718	0949	1.3F
	1257	1652	1.5E
	1955	2236	1.3F
18 Th	0140	0518	1.5E
	0813	1043	1.3F
	1351	1742	1.5E
	2042	2319	1.4F
19 F ○	0229	0615	1.6E
	0907	1136	1.3F
	1445	1833	1.5E
	2128		
20 Sa		0003	1.4F
	0319	0710	1.6E
	1000	1229	1.3F
	1539	1921	1.5E
	2214		
21 Su		0048	1.4F
	0408	0800	1.6E
	1054	1327	1.2F
	1634	2004	1.4E
	2300		
22 M		0135	1.3F
	0457	0847	1.6E
	1150	1429	1.1F
	1729	2044	1.3E
	2347		
23 Tu		0223	1.2F
	0547	0936	1.5E
	1249	1535	0.9F
	1823	2126	1.2E
24 W	0037	0315	1.1F
	0636	1037	1.4E
	1350	1643	0.8F
	1917	2215	1.0E
25 Th	0131	0413	0.9F
	0727	1152	1.2E
	1452	1745	0.8F
	2012	2325	0.9E
26 F ◑	0230	0517	0.8F
	0819	1257	1.2E
	1551	1841	0.8F
	2110		
27 Sa		0052	0.9E
	0330	0618	0.8F
	0914	1353	1.2E
	1641	1933	0.8F
	2206		
28 Su		0154	0.9E
	0429	0714	0.7F
	1007	1439	1.2E
	1723	2020	0.8F
	2257		
29 M		0242	1.0E
	0521	0806	0.7F
	1055	1514	1.2E
	1759	2100	0.9F
	2340		
30 Tu		0319	1.1E
	0607	0851	0.8F
	1138	1534	1.2E
	1834	2131	1.0F

May

Day	Slack (h m)	Maximum (h m)	knots
1 W	0019	0343	1.2E
	0650	0928	0.9F
	1218	1545	1.3E
	1909	2155	1.1F
2 Th	0054	0407	1.3E
	0732	1002	1.0F
	1258	1615	1.4E
	1945	2219	1.2F
3 F	0128	0439	1.4E
	0813	1037	1.1F
	1340	1654	1.4E
	2022	2248	1.3F
4 Sa ●	0202	0518	1.4E
	0856	1114	1.1F
	1424	1737	1.4E
	2059	2323	1.4F
5 Su	0238	0600	1.5E
	0939	1155	1.2F
	1509	1823	1.4E
	2138		
6 M		0002	1.5F
	0316	0645	1.6E
	1024	1238	1.1F
	1555	1909	1.4E
	2218		
7 Tu		0044	1.5F
	0358	0729	1.6E
	1111	1324	1.1F
	1642	1954	1.4E
	2300		
8 W		0129	1.5F
	0442	0812	1.6E
	1202	1414	1.0F
	1732	2039	1.3E
	2347		
9 Th		0218	1.4F
	0531	0857	1.5E
	1258	1507	0.9F
	1824	2127	1.2E
10 F	0042	0311	1.3F
	0624	0946	1.4E
	1358	1608	0.8F
	1921	2223	1.1E
11 Sa ○	0144	0409	1.2F
	0722	1046	1.2E
	1500	1718	0.8F
	2025	2330	1.0E
12 Su	0253	0513	1.1F
	0826	1200	1.2E
	1601	1828	0.8F
	2134		
13 M		0048	1.1E
	0402	0620	1.0F
	0935	1329	1.2E
	1657	1934	0.9F
	2240		
14 Tu		0209	1.2E
	0507	0728	1.0F
	1043	1447	1.3E
	1750	2036	1.1F
	2339		
15 W		0318	1.3E
	0608	0839	1.1F
	1144	1542	1.4E
	1839	2129	1.2F
16 Th	0031	0416	1.5E
	0706	0942	1.0F
	1241	1632	1.5E
	1928	2216	1.3F
17 F	0121	0511	1.6E
	0802	1038	1.2F
	1336	1723	1.5E
	2016	2259	1.4F
18 Sa ○	0209	0607	1.6E
	0857	1131	1.2F
	1430	1814	1.5E
	2102	2341	1.4F
19 Su	0257	0702	1.7E
	0951	1225	1.2F
	1525	1904	1.4E
	2148		
20 M		0024	1.4F
	0345	0752	1.7E
	1044	1322	1.1F
	1620	1949	1.3E
	2233		
21 Tu		0109	1.3F
	0434	0839	1.6E
	1137	1422	1.0F
	1713	2029	1.2E
	2320		
22 W		0156	1.2F
	0521	0923	1.5E
	1231	1521	0.9F
	1804	2106	1.1E
23 Th	0009	0243	1.0F
	0608	1009	1.4E
	1325	1620	0.8F
	1854	2146	1.0E
24 F	0101	0335	0.9F
	0653	1102	1.2E
	1416	1715	0.8F
	1943	2235	0.9E
25 Sa	0157	0432	0.8F
	0738	1201	1.1E
	1505	1804	0.8F
	2034	2341	0.8E
26 Su ◑	0256	0530	0.7F
	0825	1251	1.1E
	1550	1847	0.8F
	2125		
27 M		0053	0.9E
	0354	0623	0.7F
	0915	1323	1.1E
	1631	1927	0.8F
	2214		
28 Tu		0144	1.0E
	0446	0712	0.7F
	1005	1341	1.1E
	1709	2001	0.9F
	2258		
29 W		0218	1.1E
	0533	0800	0.7F
	1054	1415	1.2E
	1746	2030	1.0F
	2337		
30 Th		0249	1.2E
	0618	0846	0.8F
	1141	1454	1.3E
	1824	2101	1.1F
31 F	0013	0324	1.3E
	0702	0930	0.9F
	1226	1536	1.3E
	1903	2135	1.3F

June

Day	Slack (h m)	Maximum (h m)	knots
1 Sa	0049	0403	1.4E
	0747	1011	1.0F
	1311	1620	1.4E
	1943	2212	1.4F
2 Su	0125	0445	1.5E
	0833	1052	1.1F
	1358	1706	1.4E
	2025	2252	1.5F
3 M ●	0205	0532	1.6E
	0920	1134	1.1F
	1445	1755	1.4E
	2107	2334	1.5F
4 Tu	0247	0621	1.6E
	1007	1218	1.1F
	1533	1846	1.3E
	2151		
5 W		0018	1.5F
	0333	0709	1.6E
	1055	1305	1.0F
	1622	1934	1.3E
	2237		
6 Th		0106	1.5F
	0421	0756	1.6E
	1145	1355	1.0F
	1713	2021	1.3E
	2327		
7 F		0156	1.4F
	0512	0841	1.5E
	1237	1449	0.9F
	1808	2110	1.2E
8 Sa	0024	0250	1.3F
	0605	0929	1.4E
	1333	1549	0.9F
	1906	2205	1.1E
9 Su	0127	0349	1.1F
	0703	1026	1.3E
	1432	1657	0.9F
	2008	2312	1.1E
10 M ◑	0236	0455	1.0F
	0805	1137	1.2E
	1531	1806	0.9F
	2114		
11 Tu	0346	0605	1.0F
	0913	1304	1.2E
	1628	1909	1.0F
	2219		
12 W		0203	1.2E
	0453	0717	1.0F
	1022	1423	1.3E
	1721	2009	1.2F
	2318		
13 Th		0310	1.4E
	0555	0831	1.0F
	1126	1522	1.4E
	1812	2105	1.3F
14 F	0011	0408	1.5E
	0655	0937	1.1F
	1225	1614	1.4E
	1901	2154	1.4F
15 Sa	0101	0502	1.6E
	0752	1033	1.1F
	1321	1705	1.4E
	1950	2239	1.4F
16 Su	0149	0557	1.7E
	0847	1126	1.1F
	1416	1756	1.3E
	2037	2321	1.4F
17 M ○	0236	0650	1.7E
	0940	1218	1.1F
	1510	1847	1.3E
	2123		
18 Tu		0003	1.3F
	0324	0739	1.7E
	1031	1312	1.0F
	1602	1932	1.2E
	2209		
19 W		0046	1.2F
	0410	0823	1.6E
	1119	1406	1.0F
	1652	2011	1.2E
	2255		
20 Th		0130	1.1F
	0455	0901	1.5E
	1205	1456	0.9F
	1740	2044	1.1E
	2342		
21 F		0213	1.0F
	0537	0929	1.4E
	1249	1545	0.9F
	1825	2117	1.0E
22 Sa	0031	0256	0.9F
	0617	0945	1.3E
	1331	1629	0.8F
	1909	2154	1.0E
23 Su	0123	0343	0.8F
	0656	1012	1.2E
	1412	1710	0.8F
	1953	2238	0.9E
24 M	0217	0434	0.7F
	0738	1053	1.1E
	1454	1744	0.8F
	2038	2330	0.9E
25 Tu ◑	0312	0527	0.7F
	0825	1143	1.1E
	1537	1816	0.9F
	2124		
26 W		0023	1.0E
	0405	0619	0.7F
	0917	1235	1.1E
	1619	1850	1.0F
	2209		
27 Th		0113	1.1E
	0456	0712	0.7F
	1013	1326	1.2E
	1701	1929	1.1F
	2252		
28 F		0200	1.2E
	0545	0805	0.8F
	1107	1415	1.3E
	1743	2011	1.2F
	2332		
29 Sa		0246	1.3E
	0634	0859	0.9F
	1157	1503	1.3E
	1826	2056	1.3F
30 Su	0013	0332	1.4E
	0724	0947	1.0F
	1246	1551	1.3E
	1909	2140	1.4F

Time meridian 75° W. 0000 is midnight. 1200 is noon. Times are not adjusted for Daylight Saving Time.

Kingston–Rhinecliff Bridge, Hudson River, 2019

F–Flood, Dir. 011° True   E–Ebb, Dir. 191° True

July

Day	Slack (h m)	Maximum (h m)	knots
1 M	0055	0419	1.5E
	0813	1032	1.0F
	1334	1640	1.3E
	1955	2225	1.5F
2 Tu ●	0139	0509	1.5E
	0902	1115	1.0F
	1422	1732	1.3E
	2042	2310	1.5F
3 W	0226	0602	1.6E
	0950	1200	1.0F
	1512	1825	1.3E
	2130	2357	1.6F
4 Th	0314	0655	1.6E
	1037	1248	1.0F
	1603	1918	1.3E
	2220		
5 F		0046	1.5F
	0405	0743	1.6E
	1125	1338	1.0F
	1657	2007	1.3E
	2313		
6 Sa		0138	1.4F
	0456	0828	1.5E
	1214	1431	1.0F
	1752	2056	1.3E
7 Su	0010	0233	1.3F
	0550	0915	1.5E
	1307	1529	1.0F
	1848	2149	1.2E
8 M	0112	0332	1.1F
	0646	1007	1.4E
	1403	1633	1.0F
	1947	2253	1.2E
9 Tu ◐	0220	0439	1.0F
	0746	1113	1.3E
	1500	1739	1.0F
	2049		
10 W		0022	1.1E
	0330	0553	0.9F
	0853	1237	1.2E
	1558	1841	1.1F
	2154		
11 Th		0152	1.3E
	0438	0708	0.9F
	1003	1359	1.3E
	1653	1942	1.2F
	2255		
12 F		0259	1.4E
	0543	0824	0.9F
	1110	1503	1.3E
	1746	2041	1.2F
	2350		
13 Sa		0357	1.5E
	0645	0930	1.0F
	1211	1557	1.3E
	1836	2134	1.3F
14 Su	0041	0450	1.6E
	0742	1026	1.1F
	1307	1648	1.3E
	1926	2221	1.3F
15 M	0129	0543	1.7E
	0836	1117	1.1F
	1400	1739	1.3E
	2014	2304	1.3F
16 Tu ○	0216	0633	1.7E
	0925	1205	1.1F
	1451	1828	1.2E
	2101	2345	1.3F
17 W	0302	0720	1.7E
	1010	1253	1.0F
	1539	1912	1.2E
	2146		
18 Th		0024	1.2F
	0345	0759	1.6E
	1051	1338	1.0F
	1625	1949	1.2E
	2231		
19 F		0103	1.1F
	0425	0829	1.5E
	1129	1418	0.9F
	1708	2017	1.2E
	2316		
20 Sa		0141	1.0F
	0503	0842	1.4E
	1206	1453	0.9F
	1749	2044	1.1E
21 Su	0000	0220	0.9F
	0540	0859	1.3E
	1242	1521	0.9F
	1828	2116	1.1E
22 M	0046	0302	0.8F
	0617	0929	1.3E
	1320	1551	0.9F
	1907	2153	1.1E
23 Tu	0135	0348	0.8F
	0658	1009	1.3E
	1401	1628	0.9F
	1947	2238	1.0E
24 W ◑	0228	0440	0.7F
	0744	1058	1.2E
	1445	1710	1.0F
	2029	2329	1.1E
25 Th	0324	0536	0.7F
	0838	1152	1.2E
	1532	1755	1.0F
	2116		
26 F		0024	1.1E
	0421	0632	0.7F
	0937	1248	1.2E
	1619	1842	1.1F
	2205		
27 Sa		0119	1.2E
	0516	0730	0.8F
	1036	1342	1.2E
	1706	1931	1.2F
	2254		
28 Su		0213	1.3E
	0610	0830	0.8F
	1131	1435	1.2E
	1753	2022	1.3F
	2342		
29 M		0306	1.4E
	0703	0926	0.9F
	1223	1527	1.2E
	1842	2113	1.4F
30 Tu	0030	0359	1.4E
	0754	1014	0.9F
	1312	1619	1.3E
	1932	2203	1.5F
31 W ●	0119	0453	1.5E
	0843	1059	1.0F
	1402	1713	1.3E
	2024	2251	1.5F

August

Day	Slack (h m)	Maximum (h m)	knots
1 Th	0209	0548	1.5E
	0930	1144	1.0F
	1453	1809	1.3E
	2115	2340	1.5F
2 F	0259	0642	1.6E
	1016	1230	1.1F
	1546	1904	1.4E
	2207		
3 Sa		0030	1.5F
	0350	0731	1.6E
	1102	1319	1.1F
	1639	1955	1.4E
	2300		
4 Su		0123	1.4F
	0442	0815	1.6E
	1149	1411	1.1F
	1733	2043	1.4E
	2356		
5 M		0218	1.3F
	0536	0900	1.5E
	1240	1506	1.1F
	1828	2133	1.3E
6 Tu	0057	0318	1.1F
	0631	0949	1.4E
	1333	1605	1.1F
	1923	2235	1.2E
7 W ◐	0203	0426	1.0F
	0731	1050	1.3E
	1430	1710	1.1F
	2022		
8 Th		0009	1.2E
	0314	0545	0.9F
	0836	1211	1.2E
	1529	1813	1.1F
	2125		
9 F		0138	1.3E
	0425	0702	0.9F
	0946	1339	1.2E
	1626	1916	1.1F
	2229		
10 Sa		0245	1.4E
	0532	0815	0.9F
	1055	1446	1.2E
	1721	2018	1.1F
	2328		
11 Su		0342	1.5E
	0633	0920	1.0F
	1157	1542	1.2E
	1814	2115	1.2F
12 M	0020	0434	1.6E
	0728	1014	1.0F
	1251	1632	1.2E
	1904	2205	1.2F
13 Tu	0109	0523	1.6E
	0818	1101	1.1F
	1340	1719	1.2E
	1953	2247	1.2F
14 W	0153	0610	1.6E
	0901	1144	1.1F
	1426	1805	1.2E
	2040	2326	1.2F
15 Th ○	0235	0652	1.6E
	0940	1223	1.0F
	1510	1846	1.2E
	2125		
16 F		0001	1.1F
	0314	0725	1.5E
	1014	1258	1.0F
	1551	1918	1.2E
	2207		
17 Sa		0035	1.1F
	0351	0745	1.4E
	1048	1327	1.0F
	1630	1943	1.2E
	2248		
18 Su		0109	1.0F
	0427	0757	1.4E
	1120	1351	1.0F
	1707	2010	1.2E
	2328		
19 M		0146	1.0F
	0504	0822	1.4E
	1155	1419	1.0F
	1743	2040	1.2E
20 Tu	0011	0226	0.9F
	0543	0856	1.4E
	1232	1454	1.1F
	1818	2116	1.2E
21 W	0057	0311	0.9F
	0625	0935	1.3E
	1313	1535	1.1F
	1856	2157	1.2E
22 Th	0149	0403	0.8F
	0713	1022	1.3E
	1358	1622	1.1F
	1938	2245	1.2E
23 F ○	0247	0500	0.8F
	0806	1116	1.2E
	1448	1712	1.1F
	2026	2342	1.2E
24 Sa	0349	0600	0.7F
	0906	1215	1.1E
	1541	1804	1.1F
	2121		
25 Su		0043	1.2F
	0450	0701	0.7F
	1009	1314	1.1E
	1634	1858	1.2F
	2220		
26 M		0145	1.3E
	0548	0805	0.8F
	1108	1411	1.2E
	1728	1953	1.2F
	2316		
27 Tu		0246	1.3E
	0641	0907	0.8F
	1202	1508	1.2E
	1821	2050	1.3F
28 W	0010	0345	1.4E
	0732	0958	0.9F
	1253	1603	1.3E
	1916	2145	1.4F
29 Th	0102	0440	1.5E
	0820	1043	1.0F
	1344	1659	1.3E
	2010	2236	1.4F
30 F ●	0153	0535	1.5E
	0906	1126	1.1F
	1435	1756	1.4E
	2103	2326	1.5F
31 Sa	0244	0629	1.5E
	0951	1212	1.2F
	1527	1852	1.4E
	2156		

September

Day	Slack (h m)	Maximum (h m)	knots
1 Su		0017	1.4F
	0336	0717	1.6E
	1036	1259	1.2F
	1620	1944	1.5E
	2249		
2 M		0110	1.3F
	0429	0802	1.6E
	1123	1349	1.3F
	1712	2031	1.5E
	2344		
3 Tu		0206	1.2F
	0523	0845	1.5E
	1212	1441	1.2F
	1805	2120	1.4E
4 W	0044	0307	1.1F
	0619	0932	1.4E
	1305	1537	1.1F
	1858	2219	1.3E
5 Th ◐	0149	0420	0.9F
	0718	1029	1.2E
	1401	1640	1.1F
	1955	2358	1.2E
6 F	0300	0541	0.8F
	0822	1149	1.1E
	1500	1746	1.0F
	2056		
7 Sa		0122	1.3E
	0411	0654	0.8F
	0931	1321	1.1E
	1600	1851	1.0F
	2201		
8 Su		0227	1.4E
	0518	0803	0.9F
	1040	1428	1.1E
	1658	1956	1.0F
	2303		
9 M		0323	1.5E
	0616	0904	0.9F
	1140	1524	1.1E
	1753	2056	1.1F
	2357		
10 Tu		0412	1.5E
	0706	0955	1.0F
	1230	1612	1.2E
	1844	2147	1.1F
11 W	0043	0457	1.5E
	0749	1037	1.0F
	1315	1656	1.2E
	1933	2228	1.1F
12 Th	0125	0538	1.5E
	0826	1114	1.1F
	1356	1736	1.2E
	2018	2303	1.1F
13 F ○	0203	0612	1.4E
	0900	1145	1.1F
	1435	1810	1.3E
	2101	2334	1.1F
14 Sa	0239	0635	1.4E
	0932	1210	1.1F
	1512	1837	1.3E
	2140		
15 Su		0004	1.1F
	0315	0649	1.4E
	1004	1232	1.1F
	1547	1903	1.3E
	2219		
16 M		0037	1.1F
	0352	0715	1.4E
	1037	1259	1.2F
	1622	1933	1.4E
	2258		
17 Tu		0114	1.0F
	0431	0749	1.5E
	1112	1333	1.2F
	1656	2007	1.4E
	2339		
18 W		0156	1.0F
	0513	0826	1.4E
	1149	1412	1.2F
	1732	2043	1.4E
19 Th	0025	0241	1.0F
	0558	0907	1.4E
	1230	1455	1.2F
	1811	2123	1.4E
20 F	0117	0332	0.9F
	0647	0952	1.3E
	1316	1543	1.2F
	1855	2210	1.3E
21 Sa ○	0217	0429	0.8F
	0740	1045	1.1E
	1409	1636	1.1F
	1946	2307	1.2E
22 Su	0322	0532	0.7F
	0839	1145	1.1E
	1507	1732	1.1F
	2045		
23 M		0012	1.2E
	0425	0636	0.7F
	0944	1249	1.1E
	1608	1830	1.1F
	2150		
24 Tu		0121	1.2E
	0523	0742	0.8F
	1047	1352	1.2E
	1708	1930	1.2F
	2253		
25 W		0230	1.3E
	0616	0846	0.9F
	1144	1454	1.2E
	1806	2031	1.2F
	2351		
26 Th		0332	1.4E
	0705	0939	1.0F
	1236	1552	1.3E
	1902	2130	1.3F
27 F	0045	0426	1.4E
	0753	1024	1.1F
	1327	1649	1.3E
	1958	2224	1.4F
28 Sa ●	0137	0519	1.5E
	0839	1107	1.2F
	1417	1746	1.5E
	2052	2315	1.4F
29 Su	0229	0611	1.5E
	0925	1151	1.3F
	1508	1843	1.5E
	2144		
30 M		0006	1.4F
	0321	0701	1.6E
	1010	1237	1.3F
	1559	1936	1.6E
	2238		

Time meridian 75° W. 0000 is midnight. 1200 is noon. Times are not adjusted for Daylight Saving Time.

Kingston–Rhinecliff Bridge, Hudson River, 2019

F–Flood, Dir. 011° True   E–Ebb, Dir. 191° True

October

Day	Slack h m	Maximum h m	knots
1 Tu		0100	1.3F
	0416	0748	1.5E
	1057	1325	1.3F
	1650	2024	1.5E
	2333		
2 W		0158	1.2F
	0511	0831	1.5E
	1145	1416	1.3F
	1741	2112	1.5E
3 Th	0032	0303	1.0F
	0608	0917	1.3E
	1237	1510	1.2F
	1833	2212	1.4E
4 F	0136	0418	0.9F
	0707	1010	1.2E
	1332	1611	1.1F
	1928	2343	1.3E
5 Sa ◐	0245	0534	0.8F
	0808	1127	1.0E
	1432	1720	1.0F
	2027		
6 Su		0100	1.3E
	0354	0641	0.8F
	0914	1300	1.0E
	1535	1827	0.9F
	2131		
7 M		0203	1.3E
	0456	0742	0.8F
	1019	1407	1.0E
	1636	1932	0.9F
	2232		
8 Tu		0257	1.4E
	0548	0838	0.9F
	1116	1502	1.1E
	1732	2032	0.9F
	2325		
9 W		0343	1.4E
	0631	0926	1.0F
	1203	1548	1.2E
	1823	2123	0.9F
10 Th	0010	0423	1.4E
	0709	1005	1.0F
	1244	1628	1.2E
	1910	2203	1.0F
11 F	0049	0455	1.3E
	0742	1036	1.1F
	1322	1700	1.3E
	1953	2235	1.0F
12 Sa	0125	0514	1.3E
	0815	1101	1.1F
	1357	1724	1.3E
	2033	2304	1.0F
13 Su O	0202	0528	1.3E
	0848	1121	1.2F
	1431	1749	1.3E
	2112	2333	1.1F
14 M	0240	0559	1.4E
	0922	1146	1.2F
	1504	1822	1.4E
	2151		
15 Tu		0008	1.1F
	0320	0637	1.4E
	0957	1218	1.3F
	1538	1858	1.5E
	2231		
16 W		0047	1.1F
	0403	0718	1.4E
	1033	1256	1.3F
	1613	1936	1.5E
	2313		
17 Th		0129	1.1F
	0448	0759	1.4E
	1111	1337	1.4F
	1652	2015	1.5E
18 F	0000	0215	1.0F
	0535	0842	1.3E
	1153	1422	1.3F
	1734	2057	1.5E
19 Sa	0053	0306	0.9F
	0624	0927	1.2E
	1242	1511	1.3F
	1822	2143	1.4E
20 Su	0152	0403	0.8F
	0717	1019	1.1E
	1338	1606	1.2F
	1916	2238	1.3E
21 M O	0256	0507	0.7F
	0816	1120	1.0E
	1441	1705	1.1F
	2016	2345	1.2E
22 Tu	0358	0613	0.7F
	0921	1227	1.0E
	1547	1807	1.1F
	2123		
23 W		0058	1.2E
	0455	0718	0.8F
	1026	1337	1.1E
	1651	1910	1.1F
	2230		
24 Th		0212	1.3E
	0547	0821	0.9F
	1125	1444	1.2E
	1752	2014	1.1F
	2331		
25 F		0316	1.4E
	0636	0916	1.1F
	1218	1545	1.4E
	1850	2117	1.2F
26 Sa	0026	0409	1.4E
	0724	1003	1.2F
	1309	1642	1.5E
	1946	2214	1.3F
27 Su ●	0120	0500	1.5E
	0811	1047	1.4F
	1358	1740	1.5E
	2040	2306	1.3F
28 M	0213	0553	1.5E
	0858	1130	1.4F
	1448	1838	1.6E
	2134	2359	1.3F
29 Tu	0308	0646	1.5E
	0945	1215	1.4F
	1537	1932	1.6E
	2228		
30 W		0055	1.2F
	0404	0735	1.4E
	1032	1303	1.4F
	1628	2021	1.6E
	2323		
31 Th		0156	1.1F
	0501	0820	1.4E
	1120	1352	1.3F
	1719	2110	1.6E

November

Day	Slack h m	Maximum h m	knots
1 F	0021	0302	1.0F
	0558	0905	1.2E
	1211	1445	1.2F
	1810	2206	1.4E
2 Sa	0122	0413	0.9F
	0654	0954	1.1E
	1306	1544	1.0F
	1903	2320	1.3E
3 Su	0225	0519	0.8F
	0751	1102	1.0E
	1405	1652	0.9F
	1957		
4 M ◐		0031	1.3E
	0326	0619	0.8F
	0850	1232	0.9E
	1509	1801	0.8F
	2055		
5 Tu		0131	1.2E
	0421	0713	0.8F
	0949	1338	1.0E
	1611	1902	0.8F
	2152		
6 W		0222	1.2E
	0507	0802	0.9F
	1043	1432	1.0E
	1708	1959	0.8F
	2244		
7 Th		0304	1.2E
	0546	0847	0.9F
	1128	1517	1.1E
	1757	2048	0.8F
	2328		
8 F		0336	1.2E
	0621	0923	1.0F
	1208	1552	1.2E
	1842	2129	0.8F
9 Sa	0008	0352	1.2E
	0655	0950	1.1F
	1243	1615	1.2E
	1924	2202	0.9F
10 Su	0047	0407	1.3E
	0730	1011	1.2F
	1316	1634	1.3E
	2004	2232	1.0F
11 M	0127	0439	1.3E
	0805	1036	1.3F
	1349	1705	1.4E
	2044	2305	1.0F
12 Tu O	0208	0519	1.4E
	0842	1107	1.4F
	1423	1743	1.5E
	2125	2341	1.1F
13 W	0252	0604	1.4E
	0920	1144	1.4F
	1459	1826	1.5E
	2208		
14 Th		0022	1.1F
	0338	0650	1.4E
	0959	1224	1.5F
	1538	1909	1.6E
	2253		
15 F		0106	1.1F
	0425	0735	1.4E
	1040	1308	1.5F
	1621	1952	1.6E
	2341		
16 Sa		0153	1.0F
	0513	0820	1.3E
	1125	1355	1.4F
	1707	2036	1.5E
17 Su	0033	0243	0.9F
	0603	0905	1.2E
	1215	1445	1.3F
	1757	2122	1.4E
18 M	0129	0339	0.8F
	0656	0956	1.1E
	1314	1541	1.2F
	1852	2215	1.3E
19 Tu O	0228	0442	0.8F
	0754	1056	1.1E
	1420	1642	1.1F
	1952	2319	1.2E
20 W	0327	0548	0.8F
	0858	1207	1.1E
	1529	1746	1.0F
	2058		
21 Th		0033	1.2E
	0424	0652	0.9F
	1004	1323	1.1E
	1636	1852	1.0F
	2206		
22 F		0148	1.3E
	0517	0753	1.0F
	1105	1437	1.3E
	1738	2000	1.0F
	2310		
23 Sa		0254	1.3E
	0607	0850	1.2F
	1159	1541	1.4E
	1837	2107	1.1F
24 Su	0008	0350	1.4E
	0656	0941	1.3F
	1250	1638	1.5E
	1934	2207	1.2F
25 M	0104	0442	1.4E
	0745	1027	1.4F
	1339	1735	1.6E
	2030	2301	1.2F
26 Tu ●	0159	0537	1.4E
	0833	1111	1.4F
	1428	1833	1.7E
	2125	2355	1.2F
27 W	0255	0632	1.4E
	0921	1156	1.4F
	1518	1927	1.7E
	2218		
28 Th		0053	1.1F
	0352	0724	1.3E
	1008	1242	1.3F
	1608	2016	1.7E
	2313		
29 F		0153	1.1F
	0449	0810	1.3E
	1057	1331	1.3F
	1658	2103	1.6E
30 Sa	0007	0255	1.0F
	0544	0853	1.2E
	1147	1423	1.1F
	1748	2151	1.5E

December

Day	Slack h m	Maximum h m	knots
1 Su	0102	0356	0.9F
	0636	0937	1.1E
	1240	1518	1.0F
	1837	2245	1.3E
2 M	0156	0454	0.9F
	0727	1029	1.0E
	1338	1620	0.8F
	1925	2346	1.2E
3 Tu	0247	0546	0.8F
	0818	1143	0.9E
	1439	1724	0.7F
	2013		
4 W ◐		0041	1.1E
	0334	0632	0.8F
	0910	1255	0.9E
	1539	1821	0.7F
	2103		
5 Th		0126	1.1E
	0416	0715	0.9F
	1000	1350	1.0E
	1635	1913	0.7F
	2153		
6 F		0157	1.1E
	0455	0752	0.9F
	1045	1433	1.0E
	1724	2001	0.7F
	2242		
7 Sa		0213	1.1E
	0532	0823	1.0F
	1125	1459	1.1E
	1809	2045	0.8F
	2327		
8 Su		0242	1.2E
	0609	0851	1.1F
	1201	1520	1.2E
	1851	2125	0.8F
9 M	0011	0320	1.3E
	0646	0922	1.2F
	1235	1551	1.3E
	1934	2202	0.9F
10 Tu	0055	0402	1.3E
	0726	0956	1.3F
	1310	1628	1.4E
	2018	2240	1.0F
11 W	0141	0446	1.3E
	0806	1034	1.4F
	1347	1712	1.5E
	2103	2319	1.0F
12 Th O	0227	0534	1.3E
	0848	1114	1.5F
	1428	1759	1.6E
	2148		
13 F		0001	1.0F
	0314	0624	1.3E
	0931	1157	1.5F
	1512	1847	1.6E
	2234		
14 Sa		0045	1.0F
	0403	0713	1.3E
	1015	1243	1.5F
	1558	1934	1.6E
	2322		
15 Su		0132	1.0F
	0452	0800	1.3E
	1103	1332	1.5F
	1647	2019	1.6E
16 M	0011	0223	1.0F
	0543	0847	1.3E
	1156	1424	1.3F
	1739	2105	1.5E
17 Tu	0103	0317	0.9F
	0636	0937	1.2E
	1256	1520	1.2F
	1833	2155	1.4E
18 W O	0158	0417	0.9F
	0733	1035	1.1E
	1402	1621	1.1F
	1931	2255	1.3E
19 Th	0255	0521	0.9F
	0835	1146	1.1E
	1511	1727	1.0F
	2034		
20 F		0006	1.2E
	0352	0624	1.0F
	0940	1309	1.2E
	1620	1836	0.9F
	2143		
21 Sa		0122	1.3E
	0447	0724	1.1F
	1042	1431	1.3E
	1724	1949	1.0F
	2250		
22 Su		0234	1.3E
	0539	0824	1.2F
	1139	1536	1.4E
	1825	2101	1.0F
	2352		
23 M		0335	1.4E
	0631	0919	1.3F
	1231	1633	1.6E
	1924	2203	1.1F
24 Tu	0050	0430	1.4E
	0721	1009	1.4F
	1321	1729	1.6E
	2021	2258	1.1F
25 W	0147	0525	1.3E
	0811	1054	1.4F
	1410	1824	1.7E
	2115	2352	1.1F
26 Th ●	0244	0620	1.3E
	0859	1139	1.4F
	1500	1917	1.7E
	2207		
27 F		0047	1.1F
	0339	0713	1.3E
	0948	1225	1.3F
	1549	2004	1.7E
	2257		
28 Sa		0142	1.0F
	0432	0758	1.2E
	1036	1313	1.2F
	1637	2047	1.6E
	2346		
29 Su		0236	1.0F
	0523	0838	1.2E
	1125	1401	1.1F
	1724	2124	1.5E
30 M	0032	0327	0.9F
	0610	0914	1.1E
	1216	1450	1.0F
	1807	2154	1.3E
31 Tu	0115	0414	0.9F
	0655	0950	1.0E
	1309	1540	0.8F
	1848	2214	1.2E

Time meridian 75° W. 0000 is midnight. 1200 is noon. Times are not adjusted for Daylight Saving Time.

Bergen Point Reach (Bayonne Bridge), New York, 2019

F–Flood, Dir. 259° True   E–Ebb, Dir. 076° True

January

Day	Slack	Maximum	knots
1 Tu		0051	1.8F
	0416	0726	1.4E
	1059	1308	1.7F
	1628	1931	1.2E
	2316		
2 W		0134	1.8F
	0513	0816	1.5E
	1151	1353	1.7F
	1732	2020	1.3E
3 Th	0004	0216	1.8F
	0606	0901	1.5E
	1240	1440	1.6F
	1828	2107	1.3E
4 F	0050	0303	1.7F
	0651	0950	1.6E
	1326	1535	1.6F
	1916	2159	1.3E
5 Sa ●	0135	0356	1.7F
	0731	1035	1.6E
	1413	1630	1.7F
	1959	2247	1.3E
6 Su	0220	0443	1.8F
	0808	1115	1.7E
	1457	1710	1.8F
	2040	2329	1.3E
7 M	0302	0521	1.9F
	0842	1153	1.7E
	1536	1744	1.9F
	2118		
8 Tu		0009	1.3E
	0340	0556	1.9F
	0915	1232	1.6E
	1610	1818	1.9F
	2152		
9 W		0053	1.3E
	0410	0632	1.9F
	0946	1318	1.6E
	1638	1855	1.8F
	2224		
10 Th		0142	1.2E
	0436	0711	1.8F
	1018	1406	1.5E
	1704	1937	1.7F
	2255		
11 F		0228	1.3E
	0501	0757	1.6F
	1056	1448	1.6E
	1731	2026	1.6F
	2334		
12 Sa		0307	1.3E
	0533	0850	1.5F
	1143	1525	1.6E
	1806	2118	1.6F
13 Su	0025	0342	1.4E
	0618	0944	1.5F
	1241	1600	1.5E
	1855	2212	1.6F
14 M ◐	0121	0418	1.3E
	0729	1040	1.5F
	1339	1639	1.5E
	2001	2308	1.7F
15 Tu	0213	0504	1.3E
	0859	1141	1.5F
	1432	1736	1.3E
	2109		
16 W		0006	1.9F
	0305	0623	1.3E
	1016	1239	1.6F
	1529	1856	1.3E
	2216		
17 Th		0100	2.0F
	0404	0736	1.4E
	1122	1332	1.7F
	1640	1958	1.4E
	2320		
18 F		0151	2.2F
	0514	0833	1.6E
	1220	1425	1.8F
	1754	2055	1.5E
19 Sa	0019	0244	2.2F
	0617	0934	1.7E
	1315	1524	1.9F
	1855	2159	1.6E
20 Su	0116	0343	2.3F
	0710	1036	1.8E
	1409	1625	2.1F
	1948	2259	1.7E
21 M ○	0213	0441	2.5F
	0800	1128	1.9E
	1502	1717	2.3F
	2040	2351	1.8E
22 Tu	0310	0530	2.6F
	0850	1216	1.9E
	1550	1801	2.4F
	2133		
23 W		0043	1.8E
	0401	0615	2.6F
	0941	1308	1.9E
	1635	1844	2.3F
	2226		
24 Th		0141	1.8E
	0448	0700	2.4F
	1033	1404	1.8E
	1719	1932	2.1F
	2320		
25 F		0234	1.8E
	0535	0751	2.1F
	1127	1449	1.8E
	1805	2026	1.9F
26 Sa	0017	0316	1.8E
	0628	0848	1.9F
	1225	1526	1.7E
	1859	2124	1.8F
27 Su ◐	0114	0353	1.7E
	0730	0945	1.7F
	1323	1602	1.6E
	2000	2221	1.7F
28 M	0206	0434	1.5E
	0835	1044	1.5F
	1415	1642	1.4E
	2059	2323	1.6F
29 Tu	0255	0526	1.4E
	0935	1148	1.5F
	1506	1739	1.2E
	2155		
30 W		0023	1.6F
	0345	0643	1.3E
	1032	1246	1.5F
	1603	1858	1.1E
	2249		
31 Th		0110	1.7F
	0441	0747	1.4E
	1126	1332	1.6F
	1708	1957	1.2E
	2340		

February

Day	Slack	Maximum	knots
1 F		0151	1.7F
	0539	0835	1.5E
	1215	1417	1.6F
	1810	2047	1.2E
2 Sa	0028	0235	1.6F
	0630	0923	1.5E
	1302	1507	1.5F
	1900	2140	1.3E
3 Su	0114	0327	1.6F
	0713	1013	1.6E
	1347	1602	1.6F
	1943	2231	1.3E
4 M ●	0159	0419	1.7F
	0751	1056	1.6E
	1431	1647	1.7F
	2021	2313	1.4E
5 Tu	0242	0500	1.8F
	0826	1133	1.6E
	1511	1722	1.8F
	2055	2350	1.4E
6 W	0320	0536	1.9F
	0858	1210	1.6E
	1546	1756	1.9F
	2124		
7 Th		0028	1.4E
	0352	0611	2.0F
	0927	1251	1.6E
	1615	1830	1.9F
	2147		
8 F		0111	1.3E
	0417	0647	1.9F
	0953	1336	1.5E
	1639	1908	1.9F
	2211		
9 Sa		0157	1.3E
	0441	0729	1.8F
	1024	1420	1.5E
	1702	1953	1.8F
	2244		
10 Su		0239	1.4E
	0510	0818	1.7F
	1103	1459	1.6E
	1732	2044	1.7F
	2330		
11 M		0315	1.4E
	0548	0912	1.6F
	1155	1534	1.6E
	1811	2138	1.7F
12 Tu ◐	0029	0350	1.5E
	0644	1008	1.5F
	1258	1610	1.5E
	1907	2234	1.8F
13 W	0131	0428	1.4E
	0815	1108	1.5F
	1400	1655	1.4E
	2022	2333	1.9F
14 Th	0229	0526	1.3E
	0943	1211	1.6F
	1500	1813	1.3E
	2141		
15 F		0033	2.0F
	0329	0700	1.3E
	1055	1308	1.7F
	1610	1932	1.3E
	2256		
16 Sa		0127	2.1F
	0440	0806	1.5E
	1156	1402	1.8F
	1730	2034	1.5E
17 Su	0001	0221	2.2F
	0553	0907	1.6E
	1251	1459	1.9F
	1836	2137	1.6E
18 M	0100	0319	2.2F
	0652	1012	1.7E
	1344	1602	2.1F
	1930	2241	1.8E
19 Tu ○	0157	0421	2.4F
	0744	1108	1.8E
	1437	1658	2.3F
	2020	2333	1.9E
20 W	0252	0513	2.5F
	0834	1154	1.9E
	1527	1742	2.4F
	2111		
21 Th		0021	1.9E
	0343	0557	2.6F
	0924	1241	1.9E
	1612	1824	2.4F
	2201		
22 F		0113	1.9E
	0429	0640	2.4F
	1013	1333	1.8E
	1655	1907	2.2F
	2251		
23 Sa		0206	1.9E
	0514	0726	2.2F
	1103	1422	1.7E
	1737	1955	2.0F
	2343		
24 Su		0251	1.8E
	0601	0818	1.9F
	1157	1502	1.7E
	1824	2050	1.8F
25 M	0039	0329	1.7E
	0656	0915	1.7F
	1255	1539	1.6E
	1921	2146	1.6F
26 Tu ◐	0133	0407	1.6E
	0801	1012	1.5F
	1351	1617	1.4E
	2024	2243	1.5F
27 W ◐	0223	0449	1.4E
	0903	1115	1.4F
	1444	1704	1.2E
	2124	2346	1.5F
28 Th	0312	0551	1.3E
	1002	1220	1.4F
	1539	1818	1.1E
	2222		

March

Day	Slack	Maximum	knots
1 F		0043	1.5F
	0406	0710	1.3E
	1057	1310	1.5F
	1642	1933	1.1E
	2316		
2 Sa		0127	1.5F
	0507	0806	1.4E
	1147	1353	1.6F
	1747	2027	1.2E
3 Su	0006	0210	1.5F
	0605	0855	1.5E
	1234	1437	1.6F
	1838	2118	1.3E
4 M	0052	0257	1.6F
	0652	0945	1.5E
	1318	1528	1.6F
	1921	2209	1.4E
5 Tu	0136	0350	1.6F
	0732	1032	1.6E
	1402	1618	1.7F
	1957	2253	1.5E
6 W ●	0218	0437	1.8F
	0808	1112	1.6E
	1443	1658	1.8F
	2028	2330	1.5E
7 Th	0257	0515	1.9F
	0839	1148	1.6E
	1519	1732	2.0F
	2054		
8 F		0005	1.5E
	0332	0550	2.0F
	0906	1225	1.6E
	1550	1807	2.0F
	2116		
9 Sa		0043	1.4E
	0401	0626	2.1F
	0931	1305	1.5E
	1615	1844	2.1F
	2139		
10 Su		0126	1.4E
	0427	0705	2.0F
	0959	1351	1.5E
	1638	1925	2.0F
	2212		
11 M		0212	1.4E
	0456	0751	1.8F
	1037	1434	1.5E
	1706	2014	1.9F
	2256		
12 Tu		0253	1.5E
	0532	0845	1.7F
	1126	1513	1.5E
	1743	2108	1.8F
	2351		
13 W		0329	1.5E
	0622	0942	1.6F
	1231	1550	1.5E
	1834	2205	1.8F
14 Th ◐	0058	0406	1.5E
	0727	1042	1.5F
	1342	1633	1.4E
	1953	2305	1.8F
15 F	0203	0453	1.4E
	0919	1146	1.6F
	1445	1741	1.2E
	2125		
16 Sa		0008	1.9F
	0305	0621	1.3E
	1030	1247	1.7F
	1553	1912	1.3E
	2242		
17 Su		0106	2.0F
	0414	0742	1.4E
	1132	1341	1.9F
	1709	2017	1.5E
	2347		
18 M		0200	2.1F
	0530	0842	1.5E
	1227	1435	2.0F
	1816	2117	1.7E
19 Tu	0044	0256	2.2F
	0634	0945	1.6E
	1319	1535	2.1F
	1910	2219	1.8E
20 W ○	0139	0358	2.3F
	0726	1043	1.7E
	1411	1635	2.2F
	1958	2311	1.9E
21 Th	0232	0453	2.4F
	0814	1129	1.8E
	1501	1721	2.4F
	2045	2356	2.0E
22 F	0322	0538	2.5F
	0901	1210	1.8E
	1547	1801	2.4F
	2132		
23 Sa		0041	1.9E
	0408	0619	2.4F
	0948	1256	1.7E
	1628	1841	2.3F
	2218		
24 Su		0132	1.8E
	0451	0701	2.2F
	1035	1347	1.6E
	1707	1923	2.0F
	2306		
25 M		0221	1.8E
	0534	0748	1.9F
	1127	1434	1.5E
	1747	2013	1.8F
	2357		
26 Tu		0302	1.7E
	0622	0842	1.6F
	1225	1515	1.5E
	1835	2107	1.5F
27 W ◐	0053	0340	1.6E
	0721	0939	1.5F
	1326	1554	1.4E
	1941	2203	1.4F
28 Th	0147	0419	1.5E
	0826	1037	1.4F
	1421	1637	1.2E
	2049	2303	1.3F
29 F	0238	0507	1.3E
	0926	1143	1.4F
	1514	1737	1.1E
	2151		
30 Sa		0007	1.3F
	0330	0620	1.2E
	1022	1241	1.5F
	1611	1900	1.1E
	2247		
31 Su		0100	1.4F
	0429	0732	1.3E
	1114	1325	1.6F
	1714	2001	1.2E
	2339		

Time meridian 75° W. 0000 is midnight. 1200 is noon. Times are not adjusted for Daylight Saving Time.

Bergen Point Reach (Bayonne Bridge), New York, 2019

F–Flood, Dir. 259° True   E–Ebb, Dir. 076° True

April

Day	Slack (h m)	Maximum (h m)	knots
1 M		0143	1.5F
	0532	0823	1.4E
	1202	1406	1.6F
	1808	2050	1.4E
2 Tu	0025	0227	1.6F
	0625	0912	1.5E
	1246	1451	1.6F
	1852	2139	1.5E
3 W	0108	0316	1.6F
	0707	1001	1.5E
	1328	1541	1.7F
	1928	2226	1.5E
4 Th	0151	0407	1.8F
	0744	1045	1.6E
	1409	1628	1.8F
	1959	2307	1.6E
5 F ●	0232	0451	1.9F
	0815	1124	1.6E
	1447	1708	2.0F
	2025	2343	1.6E
6 Sa	0311	0529	2.1F
	0844	1200	1.6E
	1521	1744	2.2F
	2049		
7 Su		0019	1.6E
	0347	0606	2.1F
	0911	1238	1.5E
	1551	1821	2.2F
	2116		
8 M		0059	1.5E
	0420	0645	2.0F
	0943	1324	1.5E
	1619	1902	2.2F
	2151		
9 Tu		0148	1.5E
	0452	0729	1.9F
	1022	1414	1.4E
	1650	1949	2.1F
	2234		
10 W		0235	1.6E
	0528	0822	1.7F
	1114	1459	1.4E
	1728	2043	1.9F
	2328		
11 Th		0315	1.6E
	0617	0920	1.6F
	1223	1539	1.4E
	1820	2141	1.8F
12 F ◐	0036	0353	1.5E
	0739	1020	1.5F
	1336	1623	1.4E
	1948	2242	1.8F
13 Sa	0146	0436	1.4E
	0900	1124	1.6F
	1439	1723	1.3E
	2118	2346	1.8F
14 Su	0249	0547	1.3E
	1008	1227	1.7F
	1541	1854	1.3E
	2229		
15 M		0047	1.9F
	0354	0719	1.3E
	1108	1322	1.9F
	1650	2001	1.5E
	2331		
16 Tu		0141	2.0F
	0508	0820	1.4E
	1203	1413	2.0F
	1756	2057	1.7E
17 W	0027	0234	2.1F
	0613	0915	1.6E
	1254	1508	2.1F
	1849	2155	1.8E
18 Th	0119	0332	2.1F
	0705	1012	1.6E
	1343	1607	2.2F
	1935	2247	1.9E
19 F ○	0210	0430	2.2F
	0751	1100	1.7E
	1432	1658	2.3F
	2019	2330	1.9E
20 Sa	0300	0517	2.3F
	0836	1140	1.7E
	1518	1738	2.3F
	2102		
21 Su		0011	1.9E
	0346	0557	2.3F
	0922	1221	1.6E
	1600	1815	2.2F
	2145		
22 M		0055	1.8E
	0428	0636	2.1F
	1009	1309	1.5E
	1638	1854	2.0F
	2228		
23 Tu		0145	1.7E
	0508	0719	1.9F
	1059	1403	1.4E
	1714	1937	1.8F
	2314		
24 W		0233	1.7E
	0549	0808	1.7F
	1155	1450	1.4E
	1753	2029	1.5F
25 Th	0007	0313	1.6E
	0638	0903	1.5F
	1257	1531	1.3E
	1848	2124	1.3F
26 F ◑	0106	0352	1.6E
	0740	1000	1.4F
	1354	1612	1.2E
	2005	2222	1.2F
27 Sa	0201	0434	1.4E
	0844	1058	1.3F
	1444	1701	1.1E
	2113	2323	1.2F
28 Su	0253	0530	1.3E
	0941	1200	1.4F
	1534	1813	1.1E
	2211		
29 M		0023	1.3F
	0347	0646	1.2E
	1035	1250	1.5F
	1629	1925	1.2E
	2304		
30 Tu		0112	1.5F
	0447	0747	1.3E
	1124	1333	1.6F
	1727	2017	1.3E
	2353		

May

Day	Slack (h m)	Maximum (h m)	knots
1 W		0155	1.6F
	0546	0836	1.4E
	1210	1416	1.7F
	1815	2104	1.5E
2 Th	0038	0241	1.6F
	0634	0924	1.5E
	1252	1502	1.8F
	1854	2154	1.5E
3 F	0122	0332	1.7F
	0713	1012	1.6E
	1333	1553	1.9F
	1928	2240	1.6E
4 Sa ●	0206	0424	1.9F
	0748	1056	1.6E
	1413	1640	2.0F
	1958	2320	1.7E
5 Su	0251	0508	2.0F
	0822	1136	1.6E
	1452	1722	2.3F
	2027	2359	1.7E
6 M	0333	0548	2.1F
	0856	1216	1.5E
	1530	1801	2.4F
	2100		
7 Tu		0040	1.7E
	0413	0628	2.1F
	0934	1303	1.4E
	1606	1842	2.3F
	2138		
8 W		0130	1.6E
	0450	0712	2.0F
	1020	1359	1.4E
	1643	1928	2.2F
	2223		
9 Th		0222	1.6E
	0530	0803	1.8F
	1116	1450	1.4E
	1726	2022	2.0F
	2318		
10 F		0306	1.6E
	0620	0901	1.7F
	1226	1533	1.4E
	1825	2122	1.8F
11 Sa	0027	0345	1.6E
	0730	1001	1.6F
	1334	1616	1.4E
	1951	2222	1.7F
12 Su	0137	0426	1.5E
	0843	1103	1.6F
	1432	1710	1.3E
	2108	2326	1.7F
13 M	0238	0523	1.3E
	0946	1208	1.8F
	1528	1832	1.3E
	2214		
14 Tu		0028	1.8F
	0337	0653	1.3E
	1045	1303	1.9F
	1630	1943	1.5E
	2314		
15 W		0122	1.9F
	0443	0756	1.4E
	1139	1352	2.0F
	1733	2037	1.6E
16 Th	0008	0212	2.0F
	0549	0847	1.5E
	1229	1442	2.0F
	1827	2129	1.7E
17 F	0059	0306	1.9F
	0643	0938	1.5E
	1316	1537	2.0F
	1913	2222	1.8E
18 Sa ○	0149	0404	2.0F
	0730	1029	1.5E
	1404	1631	2.1F
	1955	2305	1.8E
19 Su	0238	0455	2.1F
	0814	1113	1.5E
	1450	1714	2.2F
	2035	2344	1.8E
20 M	0325	0536	2.1F
	0859	1153	1.5E
	1533	1751	2.1F
	2114		
21 Tu		0024	1.8E
	0407	0613	2.0F
	0945	1237	1.4E
	1612	1827	2.0F
	2154		
22 W		0110	1.7E
	0444	0652	1.9F
	1033	1330	1.3E
	1646	1907	1.8F
	2235		
23 Th		0201	1.6E
	0520	0736	1.7F
	1124	1423	1.3E
	1720	1953	1.6F
	2322		
24 F		0246	1.6E
	0558	0827	1.5F
	1220	1508	1.4E
	1800	2047	1.4F
25 Sa	0019	0326	1.6E
	0646	0921	1.4F
	1317	1547	1.3E
	1902	2143	1.3F
26 Su ◑	0119	0405	1.5E
	0749	1015	1.4F
	1407	1629	1.2E
	2021	2240	1.2F
27 M	0212	0449	1.4E
	0851	1112	1.4F
	1452	1721	1.1E
	2125	2339	1.3F
28 Tu	0301	0551	1.3E
	0947	1209	1.5F
	1539	1835	1.1E
	2222		
29 W		0035	1.5F
	0354	0703	1.3E
	1039	1257	1.7F
	1632	1938	1.3E
	2315		
30 Th		0122	1.6F
	0453	0757	1.4E
	1128	1342	1.8F
	1728	2028	1.4E
31 F	0005	0208	1.7F
	0551	0845	1.5E
	1213	1427	1.9F
	1816	2117	1.5E

June

Day	Slack (h m)	Maximum (h m)	knots
1 Sa	0053	0258	1.7F
	0639	0935	1.5E
	1256	1518	2.0F
	1856	2210	1.6E
2 Su	0141	0354	1.8F
	0721	1027	1.5E
	1340	1611	2.2F
	1932	2258	1.7E
3 M	0230	0446	2.0F
	0802	1114	1.6E
	1426	1659	2.4F
	2008	2341	1.8E
4 Tu	0318	0530	2.1F
	0844	1159	1.5E
	1513	1743	2.5F
	2047		
5 W		0024	1.8E
	0402	0612	2.1F
	0930	1248	1.5E
	1558	1825	2.4F
	2131		
6 Th		0115	1.7E
	0444	0655	2.1F
	1021	1347	1.5E
	1642	1911	2.3F
	2220		
7 F		0211	1.7E
	0526	0745	1.9F
	1118	1441	1.5E
	1730	2004	2.0F
	2316		
8 Sa		0257	1.7E
	0614	0842	1.8F
	1222	1525	1.6E
	1828	2103	1.8F
9 Su	0022	0337	1.6E
	0716	0942	1.7F
	1326	1607	1.5E
	1942	2203	1.7F
10 M ◐	0128	0416	1.5E
	0822	1042	1.7F
	1421	1654	1.4E
	2052	2304	1.7F
11 Tu	0225	0503	1.4E
	0924	1146	1.8F
	1513	1803	1.4E
	2155		
12 W		0008	1.7F
	0319	0618	1.3E
	1021	1244	1.9F
	1609	1922	1.4E
	2254		
13 Th		0103	1.8F
	0419	0730	1.3E
	1115	1331	2.0F
	1709	2016	1.5E
	2348		
14 F		0151	1.8F
	0524	0821	1.4E
	1205	1417	2.0F
	1805	2104	1.6E
15 Sa	0039	0241	1.8F
	0622	0909	1.4E
	1252	1507	1.9F
	1852	2155	1.7E
16 Su	0128	0337	1.8F
	0711	1001	1.4E
	1338	1602	1.9F
	1933	2241	1.7E
17 M ○	0216	0433	1.8F
	0757	1049	1.4E
	1425	1650	2.0F
	2011	2321	1.7E
18 Tu	0303	0516	1.9F
	0841	1131	1.4E
	1509	1728	2.0F
	2049	2358	1.7E
19 W	0344	0552	2.0F
	0925	1213	1.3E
	1549	1804	2.0F
	2126		
20 Th		0040	1.7E
	0421	0628	1.9F
	1008	1301	1.3E
	1624	1841	1.8F
	2204		
21 F		0128	1.6E
	0454	0707	1.8F
	1050	1354	1.3E
	1654	1922	1.7F
	2245		
22 Sa		0218	1.6E
	0525	0751	1.6F
	1136	1441	1.3E
	1725	2011	1.5F
	2332		
23 Su		0300	1.6E
	0557	0842	1.5F
	1227	1521	1.3E
	1802	2105	1.4F
24 M	0028	0338	1.6E
	0641	0935	1.4F
	1318	1558	1.3E
	1900	2159	1.3F
25 Tu ◑	0124	0416	1.5E
	0743	1028	1.4F
	1404	1638	1.2E
	2021	2256	1.4F
26 W	0214	0501	1.4E
	0847	1124	1.5F
	1447	1734	1.2E
	2130	2354	1.4F
27 Th	0301	0606	1.3E
	0944	1219	1.7F
	1534	1850	1.2E
	2233		
28 F		0048	1.5F
	0354	0715	1.3E
	1039	1309	1.9F
	1629	1950	1.4E
	2331		
29 Sa		0138	1.6F
	0459	0808	1.4E
	1131	1356	2.0F
	1730	2042	1.5E
30 Su	0024	0227	1.7F
	0603	0900	1.4E
	1222	1446	2.1F
	1823	2137	1.6E

Time meridian 75° W. 0000 is midnight. 1200 is noon. Times are not adjusted for Daylight Saving Time.

Bergen Point Reach (Bayonne Bridge), New York, 2019

F–Flood, Dir. 259° True   E–Ebb, Dir. 076° True

July

Day	Slack (h m)	Maximum (h m)	knots
1 M	0116	0324	1.8F
	0655	0958	1.5E
	1312	1542	2.2F
	1908	2234	1.7E
2 Tu ●	0208	0422	1.9F
	0743	1053	1.6E
	1405	1637	2.4F
	1952	2323	1.8E
3 W	0259	0512	2.1F
	0831	1143	1.6E
	1458	1725	2.5F
	2037		
4 Th		0009	1.8E
	0346	0556	2.2F
	0921	1234	1.7E
	1549	1809	2.5F
	2125		
5 F		0100	1.8E
	0430	0639	2.2F
	1013	1332	1.7E
	1637	1855	2.4F
	2216		
6 Sa		0157	1.8E
	0513	0727	2.1F
	1108	1428	1.7E
	1724	1946	2.2F
	2311		
7 Su		0245	1.8E
	0559	0821	1.9F
	1208	1513	1.7E
	1818	2043	1.9F
8 M	0012	0325	1.7F
	0655	0920	1.8F
	1308	1553	1.7E
	1923	2141	1.8F
9 Tu ☽	0113	0402	1.6E
	0758	1019	1.7F
	1403	1635	1.5E
	2030	2241	1.7F
10 W	0209	0443	1.4E
	0859	1121	1.7F
	1454	1730	1.4E
	2133	2344	1.6F
11 Th	0300	0541	1.3E
	0956	1222	1.8F
	1545	1850	1.3E
	2232		
12 F		0043	1.7F
	0356	0700	1.2E
	1050	1311	1.8F
	1643	1954	1.4E
	2327		
13 Sa		0132	1.7F
	0501	0758	1.2E
	1142	1354	1.8F
	1741	2041	1.5E
14 Su	0018	0218	1.7F
	0604	0847	1.3E
	1230	1440	1.8F
	1831	2129	1.6E
15 M	0106	0311	1.6F
	0656	0939	1.3E
	1317	1533	1.7F
	1913	2218	1.6E
16 Tu O	0153	0410	1.7F
	0742	1031	1.3E
	1403	1626	1.8F
	1952	2300	1.7E
17 W	0239	0456	1.8F
	0824	1114	1.3E
	1448	1708	1.9F
	2030	2337	1.7E
18 Th	0321	0531	1.9F
	0904	1154	1.3E
	1529	1743	1.9F
	2106		
19 F		0016	1.6E
	0357	0605	1.9F
	0941	1235	1.3E
	1603	1819	1.9F
	2141		
20 Sa		0059	1.6E
	0429	0640	1.9F
	1015	1323	1.3E
	1632	1856	1.8F
	2215		
21 Su		0147	1.6E
	0456	0719	1.7F
	1048	1411	1.3E
	1657	1939	1.7F
	2250		
22 M		0232	1.6E
	0521	0805	1.6F
	1124	1453	1.4E
	1724	2029	1.6F
	2332		
23 Tu		0311	1.6E
	0551	0856	1.6F
	1210	1529	1.4E
	1802	2122	1.5F
24 W ☽	0025	0346	1.6E
	0632	0948	1.6F
	1303	1604	1.4E
	1900	2217	1.4F
25 Th	0121	0423	1.5E
	0730	1043	1.6F
	1354	1643	1.3E
	2029	2315	1.4F
26 F	0214	0509	1.3E
	0839	1140	1.7F
	1443	1746	1.2E
	2148		
27 Sa		0015	1.5F
	0306	0624	1.2E
	0946	1236	1.9F
	1536	1909	1.3E
	2256		
28 Su		0109	1.6F
	0410	0734	1.3E
	1052	1327	2.0F
	1642	2009	1.5E
	2356		
29 M		0201	1.7F
	0527	0831	1.4E
	1153	1419	2.1F
	1750	2106	1.6E
30 Tu	0050	0256	1.8F
	0631	0931	1.5E
	1250	1515	2.2F
	1846	2208	1.7E
31 W ●	0143	0357	1.9F
	0724	1033	1.6E
	1347	1615	2.4F
	1936	2304	1.8E

August

Day	Slack (h m)	Maximum (h m)	knots
1 Th	0236	0453	2.2F
	0814	1127	1.8E
	1443	1708	2.5F
	2025	2352	1.9E
2 F	0326	0539	2.3F
	0905	1217	1.8E
	1536	1753	2.6F
	2115		
3 Sa		0040	1.9E
	0412	0622	2.4F
	0956	1312	1.9E
	1624	1838	2.5F
	2206		
4 Su		0135	1.8E
	0455	0706	2.3F
	1049	1408	1.9E
	1711	1925	2.3F
	2258		
5 M		0226	1.8E
	0539	0757	2.1F
	1144	1455	1.8E
	1800	2019	2.0F
	2354		
6 Tu		0307	1.8E
	0629	0854	1.9F
	1243	1535	1.8E
	1858	2117	1.8F
7 W ☽	0053	0344	1.6E
	0728	0951	1.7F
	1339	1613	1.6E
	2004	2215	1.6F
8 Th	0149	0422	1.5E
	0830	1050	1.6F
	1429	1658	1.4E
	2107	2318	1.5F
9 F	0242	0509	1.3E
	0929	1154	1.6F
	1519	1805	1.3E
	2207		
10 Sa		0022	1.5F
	0336	0624	1.1E
	1026	1249	1.7F
	1613	1924	1.3E
	2303		
11 Su		0113	1.6F
	0440	0737	1.1E
	1120	1333	1.7F
	1713	2017	1.4E
	2355		
12 M		0158	1.6F
	0546	0829	1.2E
	1210	1417	1.6F
	1809	2103	1.5E
13 Tu	0042	0246	1.6F
	0641	0920	1.3E
	1257	1506	1.6F
	1855	2153	1.5E
14 W	0128	0341	1.6F
	0725	1013	1.3E
	1343	1601	1.7F
	1936	2238	1.6E
15 Th O	0212	0432	1.7F
	0805	1057	1.4E
	1427	1647	1.8F
	2014	2317	1.6E
16 F	0254	0509	1.8F
	0841	1135	1.4E
	1507	1723	1.9F
	2048	2354	1.6E
17 Sa	0332	0542	1.9F
	0913	1212	1.4E
	1542	1757	2.0F
	2120		
18 Su		0032	1.6E
	0403	0616	1.9F
	0940	1252	1.4E
	1610	1832	2.0F
	2148		
19 M		0115	1.5E
	0429	0651	1.9F
	1004	1337	1.4E
	1634	1911	1.9F
	2216		
20 Tu		0201	1.5E
	0451	0732	1.8F
	1031	1422	1.4E
	1658	1956	1.7F
	2249		
21 W		0243	1.5E
	0516	0820	1.7F
	1108	1500	1.4E
	1731	2048	1.6F
	2333		
22 Th		0319	1.5E
	0549	0912	1.7F
	1200	1535	1.5E
	1816	2143	1.5F
23 F O	0031	0354	1.5E
	0635	1007	1.7F
	1301	1610	1.4E
	1929	2241	1.4F
24 Sa	0135	0433	1.4E
	0741	1105	1.7F
	1401	1654	1.3E
	2106	2343	1.5F
25 Su	0234	0533	1.2E
	0903	1205	1.9F
	1458	1817	1.3E
	2223		
26 M		0043	1.6F
	0338	0703	1.2E
	1023	1302	2.0F
	1603	1937	1.4E
	2328		
27 Tu		0136	1.8F
	0455	0808	1.4E
	1132	1355	2.1F
	1719	2037	1.5E
28 W	0024	0230	1.9F
	0607	0908	1.6E
	1233	1451	2.2F
	1825	2140	1.7E
29 Th	0117	0330	2.0F
	0704	1012	1.7E
	1329	1552	2.3F
	1919	2241	1.8E
30 F ●	0210	0431	2.2F
	0754	1108	1.9E
	1425	1649	2.5F
	2009	2331	1.9E
31 Sa	0301	0520	2.4F
	0843	1157	2.0E
	1518	1736	2.6F
	2058		

September

Day	Slack (h m)	Maximum (h m)	knots
1 Su		0016	1.9E
	0349	0602	2.5F
	0933	1247	2.0E
	1607	1819	2.6F
	2148		
2 M		0106	1.8E
	0432	0644	2.4F
	1023	1341	1.9E
	1652	1904	2.4F
	2237		
3 Tu		0159	1.8E
	0515	0730	2.2F
	1115	1432	1.9E
	1738	1954	2.1F
	2330		
4 W		0245	1.7E
	0559	0823	1.9F
	1210	1513	1.8E
	1831	2049	1.8F
5 Th ☽	0029	0323	1.6E
	0653	0919	1.7F
	1307	1550	1.7E
	1933	2147	1.6F
6 F	0128	0401	1.4E
	0757	1017	1.5F
	1400	1630	1.5E
	2038	2248	1.5F
7 Sa	0224	0443	1.2E
	0900	1119	1.5F
	1450	1721	1.3E
	2138	2356	1.4F
8 Su	0318	0546	1.1E
	1000	1223	1.5F
	1542	1840	1.2E
	2235		
9 M		0054	1.5F
	0418	0712	1.1E
	1057	1312	1.5F
	1641	1947	1.3E
	2327		
10 Tu		0137	1.6F
	0523	0811	1.2E
	1148	1354	1.6F
	1743	2036	1.4E
11 W	0015	0220	1.6F
	0619	0900	1.3E
	1235	1439	1.6F
	1834	2124	1.5E
12 Th	0059	0308	1.6F
	0703	0950	1.4E
	1320	1531	1.6F
	1917	2212	1.6E
13 F O	0143	0400	1.7F
	0741	1036	1.5E
	1403	1622	1.7F
	1955	2254	1.6E
14 Sa	0225	0443	1.8F
	0815	1114	1.5E
	1443	1701	1.9F
	2028	2331	1.6E
15 Su	0303	0518	1.9F
	0844	1149	1.5E
	1520	1736	2.0F
	2058		
16 M		0007	1.6E
	0335	0552	2.0F
	0907	1225	1.5E
	1551	1810	2.0F
	2123		
17 Tu		0045	1.5E
	0402	0626	2.0F
	0928	1304	1.4E
	1617	1847	2.0F
	2147		
18 W		0129	1.5E
	0424	0704	2.0F
	0953	1350	1.4E
	1642	1929	1.8F
	2218		
19 Th		0214	1.4E
	0448	0749	1.9F
	1030	1433	1.5E
	1713	2019	1.7F
	2300		
20 F ☽		0255	1.4E
	0520	0841	1.8F
	1118	1511	1.5E
	1753	2115	1.5F
	2357		
21 Sa		0333	1.4E
	0602	0937	1.8F
	1219	1547	1.5E
	1855	2213	1.5F
22 Su	0109	0412	1.4E
	0705	1035	1.7F
	1327	1627	1.4E
	2034	2315	1.5F
23 M	0215	0504	1.2E
	0839	1138	1.8F
	1431	1728	1.3E
	2154		
24 Tu		0018	1.6F
	0319	0634	1.2E
	1005	1239	1.9F
	1536	1907	1.3E
	2300		
25 W		0114	1.8F
	0430	0748	1.4E
	1115	1334	2.1F
	1651	2012	1.5E
	2358		
26 Th		0207	2.0F
	0543	0847	1.6E
	1216	1428	2.2F
	1803	2111	1.6E
27 F	0051	0303	2.1F
	0642	0949	1.8E
	1311	1527	2.2F
	1859	2213	1.7E
28 Sa ●	0143	0404	2.2F
	0732	1046	2.0E
	1405	1627	2.4F
	1949	2305	1.8E
29 Su	0234	0458	2.4F
	0820	1134	2.0E
	1458	1717	2.5F
	2037	2349	1.8E
30 M	0323	0541	2.5F
	0907	1220	2.0E
	1547	1759	2.5F
	2125		

Time meridian 75° W. 0000 is midnight. 1200 is noon. Times are not adjusted for Daylight Saving Time.

Bergen Point Reach (Bayonne Bridge), New York, 2019

F–Flood, Dir. 259° True   E–Ebb, Dir. 076° True

October

Days 1–15

Day	Slack h m	Maximum h m	knots
1 Tu		0034	1.8E
	0407	0621	2.4F
	0955	1309	1.9E
	1632	1841	2.3F
	2213		
2 W		0124	1.7E
	0448	0703	2.2F
	1042	1402	1.8E
	1716	1927	2.1F
	2305		
3 Th		0217	1.6E
	0530	0750	1.9F
	1133	1447	1.8E
	1803	2019	1.8F
4 F	0003	0300	1.5E
	0616	0844	1.6F
	1229	1526	1.7E
	1859	2117	1.6F
5 Sa ◑	0105	0340	1.4E
	0718	0941	1.4F
	1326	1603	1.6E
	2003	2216	1.4F
6 Su	0203	0421	1.2E
	0828	1040	1.3F
	1418	1647	1.4E
	2104	2320	1.4F
7 M	0256	0513	1.1E
	0931	1147	1.3F
	1510	1749	1.2E
	2201		
8 Tu		0025	1.5F
	0350	0633	1.1E
	1029	1245	1.4F
	1606	1908	1.3E
	2254		
9 W		0111	1.6F
	0450	0743	1.2E
	1121	1329	1.5F
	1709	2004	1.4E
	2343		
10 Th		0151	1.6F
	0548	0832	1.4E
	1209	1411	1.6F
	1806	2051	1.5E
11 F	0028	0233	1.7F
	0635	0920	1.5E
	1253	1457	1.6F
	1852	2139	1.5E
12 Sa	0110	0320	1.7F
	0713	1007	1.5E
	1335	1549	1.7F
	1930	2226	1.6E
13 Su ○	0151	0409	1.8F
	0747	1050	1.6E
	1417	1635	1.8F
	2004	2306	1.6E
14 M	0230	0451	1.9F
	0815	1127	1.6E
	1457	1714	1.9F
	2034	2342	1.6E
15 Tu	0305	0527	2.1F
	0838	1202	1.6E
	1533	1750	2.0F
	2100		

Days 16–31

Day	Slack h m	Maximum h m	knots
16 W		0019	1.5E
	0335	0603	2.2F
	0900	1238	1.5E
	1606	1827	2.0F
	2127		
17 Th		0100	1.4E
	0401	0641	2.2F
	0928	1322	1.5E
	1636	1907	1.9F
	2200		
18 F		0150	1.4E
	0429	0724	2.1F
	1006	1411	1.5E
	1707	1955	1.7F
	2244		
19 Sa		0238	1.4E
	0503	0815	1.9F
	1054	1454	1.6E
	1746	2051	1.6F
	2343		
20 Su		0320	1.4E
	0546	0912	1.8F
	1154	1532	1.6E
	1843	2150	1.5F
21 M ○	0059	0400	1.4E
	0652	1011	1.7F
	1306	1611	1.5E
	2014	2251	1.6F
22 Tu	0206	0449	1.3E
	0831	1114	1.8F
	1414	1702	1.4E
	2129	2355	1.7F
23 W	0306	0607	1.3E
	0952	1217	1.9F
	1517	1834	1.3E
	2234		
24 Th		0054	1.9F
	0410	0728	1.4E
	1059	1314	2.0F
	1626	1947	1.4E
	2332		
25 F		0146	2.0F
	0520	0827	1.6E
	1158	1407	2.1F
	1738	2043	1.5E
26 Sa	0025	0238	2.1F
	0620	0924	1.8E
	1252	1502	2.1F
	1837	2140	1.6E
27 Su ●	0116	0336	2.2F
	0710	1022	1.9E
	1345	1602	2.2F
	1927	2236	1.7E
28 M	0206	0433	2.3F
	0756	1111	2.0E
	1437	1655	2.3F
	2014	2321	1.7E
29 Tu	0255	0518	2.4F
	0841	1153	2.0E
	1527	1739	2.3F
	2101		
30 W		0003	1.6E
	0341	0558	2.3F
	0925	1237	1.9E
	1612	1819	2.2F
	2150		
31 Th		0050	1.5E
	0422	0637	2.2F
	1009	1327	1.8E
	1654	1901	2.0F
	2241		

November

Days 1–15

Day	Slack h m	Maximum h m	knots
1 F		0144	1.4E
	0502	0719	1.9F
	1056	1417	1.7E
	1736	1949	1.8F
	2336		
2 Sa		0235	1.4E
	0543	0809	1.6F
	1147	1459	1.7E
	1822	2043	1.6F
3 Su	0038	0318	1.3E
	0635	0905	1.4F
	1246	1538	1.6E
	1920	2140	1.4F
4 M ◑	0137	0358	1.3E
	0746	1002	1.3F
	1344	1618	1.5E
	2023	2238	1.4F
5 Tu	0228	0443	1.2E
	0854	1103	1.2F
	1436	1706	1.3E
	2121	2341	1.4F
6 W	0317	0544	1.1E
	0953	1207	1.3F
	1528	1817	1.2E
	2215		
7 Th		0036	1.5F
	0409	0702	1.2E
	1047	1258	1.4F
	1626	1925	1.3E
	2305		
8 F		0119	1.6F
	0506	0758	1.3E
	1136	1340	1.5F
	1726	2016	1.4E
	2352		
9 Sa		0159	1.7F
	0558	0845	1.4E
	1222	1423	1.6F
	1818	2103	1.5E
10 Su	0035	0243	1.8F
	0641	0933	1.5E
	1306	1512	1.6F
	1900	2151	1.5E
11 M	0115	0331	1.8F
	0716	1021	1.6E
	1350	1604	1.7F
	1937	2237	1.5E
12 Tu ○	0155	0420	2.0F
	0746	1103	1.6E
	1435	1650	1.9F
	2010	2318	1.5E
13 W	0233	0503	2.1F
	0813	1141	1.6E
	1517	1730	2.0F
	2042	2357	1.5E
14 Th	0310	0542	2.3F
	0841	1218	1.6E
	1556	1809	2.0F
	2116		
15 F		0039	1.4E
	0345	0621	2.3F
	0913	1302	1.6E
	1631	1849	2.0F
	2155		

Days 16–30

Day	Slack h m	Maximum h m	knots
16 Sa		0132	1.3E
	0421	0704	2.2F
	0953	1355	1.6E
	1706	1936	1.8F
	2243		
17 Su		0226	1.4E
	0459	0754	2.0F
	1042	1443	1.6E
	1746	2031	1.7F
	2344		
18 M		0311	1.4E
	0546	0851	1.9F
	1143	1523	1.6E
	1841	2129	1.6F
19 Tu ○	0055	0352	1.4E
	0656	0951	1.8F
	1255	1602	1.5E
	1958	2229	1.6F
20 W	0158	0438	1.4E
	0825	1052	1.7F
	1402	1647	1.4E
	2108	2332	1.7F
21 Th	0254	0543	1.3E
	0937	1156	1.8F
	1501	1800	1.3E
	2210		
22 F		0033	1.9F
	0352	0706	1.4E
	1041	1254	1.9F
	1603	1922	1.4E
	2308		
23 Sa		0125	2.0F
	0457	0807	1.6E
	1139	1346	2.0F
	1712	2017	1.5E
24 Su	0000	0214	2.1F
	0558	0900	1.7E
	1233	1438	2.0F
	1814	2109	1.5E
25 M	0050	0307	2.1F
	0649	0956	1.8E
	1325	1535	2.0F
	1906	2204	1.5E
26 Tu ●	0139	0405	2.1F
	0733	1047	1.9E
	1416	1633	2.0F
	1953	2254	1.5E
27 W	0228	0455	2.2F
	0816	1129	1.9E
	1506	1719	2.1F
	2040	2338	1.5E
28 Th	0315	0535	2.2F
	0857	1208	1.8E
	1551	1759	2.1F
	2129		
29 F		0021	1.4E
	0358	0612	2.1F
	0939	1252	1.7E
	1631	1837	2.0F
	2217		
30 Sa		0112	1.3E
	0437	0652	1.9F
	1022	1343	1.7E
	1709	1919	1.8F
	2308		

December

Days 1–15

Day	Slack h m	Maximum h m	knots
1 Su		0207	1.3E
	0514	0736	1.7F
	1109	1431	1.6E
	1748	2008	1.6F
	2342		
2 M	0003	0254	1.3E
	0555	0828	1.4F
	1204	1512	1.6E
	1832	2102	1.5F
3 Tu	0100	0334	1.3E
	0652	0924	1.3F
	1304	1551	1.6E
	1930	2157	1.4F
4 W ◑	0152	0414	1.3E
	0803	1020	1.3F
	1358	1632	1.4E
	2032	2252	1.4F
5 Th	0238	0500	1.2E
	0907	1120	1.3F
	1447	1725	1.3E
	2128	2349	1.5F
6 F	0324	0607	1.2E
	1004	1217	1.4F
	1537	1836	1.3E
	2220		
7 Sa		0040	1.6F
	0414	0717	1.2E
	1058	1306	1.5F
	1634	1937	1.3E
	2309		
8 Su		0125	1.7F
	0510	0809	1.4E
	1149	1351	1.6F
	1733	2025	1.4E
	2355		
9 M		0208	1.8F
	0601	0857	1.5E
	1236	1437	1.6F
	1825	2114	1.4E
10 Tu	0038	0255	1.9F
	0642	0949	1.6E
	1324	1530	1.6F
	1908	2206	1.5E
11 W	0121	0348	2.0F
	0718	1038	1.6E
	1411	1625	1.8F
	1948	2255	1.5E
12 Th ○	0205	0438	2.2F
	0752	1122	1.7E
	1458	1711	1.9F
	2027	2339	1.5E
13 F	0251	0522	2.3F
	0827	1202	1.7E
	1542	1752	2.1F
	2108		
14 Sa		0024	1.5E
	0335	0604	2.4F
	0905	1247	1.7E
	1622	1833	2.1F
	2153		
15 Su		0118	1.4E
	0418	0647	2.3F
	0950	1342	1.7E
	1701	1918	2.0F
	2244		

Days 16–31

Day	Slack h m	Maximum h m	knots
16 M		0215	1.5E
	0502	0736	2.1F
	1041	1433	1.7E
	1743	2011	1.8F
	2342		
17 Tu		0302	1.5E
	0551	0832	2.0F
	1141	1514	1.7E
	1834	2110	1.8F
18 W ○	0047	0343	1.6E
	0656	0931	1.8F
	1248	1552	1.6E
	1941	2208	1.7F
19 Th	0147	0426	1.5E
	0812	1031	1.7F
	1350	1633	1.5E
	2047	2309	1.8F
20 F	0240	0519	1.4E
	0920	1134	1.7F
	1446	1730	1.3E
	2147		
21 Sa		0012	1.9F
	0334	0639	1.4E
	1022	1234	1.8F
	1542	1852	1.3E
	2244		
22 Su		0105	2.0F
	0434	0747	1.5E
	1120	1326	1.8F
	1647	1953	1.3E
	2337		
23 M		0152	2.0F
	0535	0838	1.6E
	1214	1415	1.8F
	1753	2044	1.4E
24 Tu	0027	0241	2.0F
	0628	0931	1.7E
	1305	1510	1.8F
	1848	2137	1.4E
25 W	0116	0336	1.9F
	0713	1023	1.7E
	1355	1610	1.8F
	1937	2231	1.4E
26 Th ●	0205	0430	2.0F
	0754	1106	1.7E
	1443	1700	1.9F
	2023	2317	1.4E
27 F	0253	0514	2.0F
	0834	1144	1.7E
	1528	1738	2.0F
	2109	2359	1.4E
28 Sa	0336	0551	2.0F
	0914	1224	1.7E
	1608	1814	2.0F
	2153		
29 Su		0044	1.3E
	0415	0628	1.9F
	0954	1310	1.6E
	1643	1852	1.9F
	2237		
30 M		0136	1.3E
	0449	0707	1.8F
	1036	1400	1.6E
	1716	1934	1.7F
	2322		
31 Tu		0226	1.3E
	0522	0754	1.6F
	1123	1445	1.6E
	1749	2023	1.6F

Time meridian 75° W. 0000 is midnight. 1200 is noon. Times are not adjusted for Daylight Saving Time.

Delaware Bay Entrance, 2019

F—Flood, Dir. 342° True   E—Ebb, Dir. 152° True

January

Day	Slack	Maximum	knots
1 Tu	0021	0334	2.2F
	0649	0953	1.9E
	1311	1602	1.8F
	1902	2209	1.9E
2 W	0114	0425	2.3F
	0746	1046	2.0E
	1408	1654	1.8F
	1955	2257	2.0E
3 Th	0203	0512	2.4F
	0839	1133	2.0E
	1459	1743	1.7F
	2044	2341	2.0E
4 F	0249	0558	2.4F
	0925	1218	1.9E
	1546	1834	1.7F
	2129		
5 Sa ●		0026	2.0E
	0332	0646	2.3F
	1007	1301	1.8E
	1629	1925	1.6F
	2212		
6 Su		0110	1.9E
	0411	0731	2.3F
	1044	1340	1.8E
	1710	2009	1.6F
	2254		
7 M		0152	1.8E
	0449	0811	2.1F
	1119	1413	1.7E
	1747	2047	1.5F
	2335		
8 Tu		0229	1.6E
	0526	0848	2.0F
	1153	1444	1.7E
	1818	2122	1.4F
9 W	0016	0305	1.5E
	0602	0924	1.8F
	1226	1515	1.6E
	1844	2157	1.3F
10 Th	0055	0343	1.3E
	0640	1004	1.6F
	1302	1551	1.5E
	1912	2237	1.2F
11 F	0135	0427	1.2E
	0719	1050	1.5F
	1341	1636	1.4E
	1946	2322	1.2F
12 Sa	0218	0518	1.1E
	0804	1142	1.3F
	1427	1729	1.4E
	2027		
13 Su		0008	1.2F
	0306	0609	1.1E
	0855	1234	1.3F
	1521	1822	1.4E
	2118		
14 M ☽		0054	1.2F
	0401	0658	1.1E
	0957	1327	1.3F
	1621	1914	1.4E
	2216		
15 Tu		0143	1.3F
	0454	0750	1.2E
	1100	1425	1.3F
	1717	2012	1.4E
	2311		
16 W		0236	1.4F
	0545	0852	1.3E
	1158	1522	1.4F
	1810	2113	1.5E
17 Th	0001	0328	1.7F
	0634	0949	1.5E
	1253	1612	1.4F
	1903	2206	1.7E
18 F	0050	0414	1.9F
	0725	1038	1.7E
	1349	1700	1.6F
	1957	2255	1.8E
19 Sa	0138	0459	2.1F
	0817	1125	1.9E
	1444	1750	1.6F
	2049	2343	1.9E
20 Su	0227	0548	2.2F
	0908	1216	2.1E
	1536	1847	1.7F
	2140		
21 M ○		0034	2.0E
	0317	0643	2.3F
	0958	1308	2.2E
	1628	1942	1.8F
	2231		
22 Tu		0127	2.0E
	0408	0739	2.4F
	1048	1358	2.3E
	1719	2031	1.9F
	2322		
23 W		0218	2.1E
	0503	0831	2.5F
	1140	1446	2.3E
	1810	2118	2.0F
24 Th	0015	0308	2.1E
	0603	0922	2.4F
	1232	1535	2.2E
	1859	2208	2.0F
25 F	0109	0404	2.0E
	0704	1018	2.2F
	1326	1632	2.0E
	1949	2304	2.0F
26 Sa	0206	0507	1.9E
	0808	1121	2.0F
	1423	1734	1.8E
	2042		
27 Su ☽		0002	2.0F
	0308	0611	1.8E
	0919	1224	1.8F
	1525	1833	1.7E
	2143		
28 M		0059	2.0F
	0416	0711	1.7E
	1035	1326	1.6F
	1631	1932	1.7E
	2246		
29 Tu		0159	2.1F
	0522	0817	1.7E
	1147	1433	1.5F
	1732	2036	1.6E
	2346		
30 W		0301	2.1F
	0623	0926	1.6E
	1251	1538	1.5F
	1829	2138	1.7E
31 Th	0041	0356	2.2F
	0720	1023	1.7E
	1350	1632	1.5F
	1926	2230	1.7E

February

Day	Slack	Maximum	knots
1 F	0133	0444	2.2F
	0814	1110	1.7E
	1443	1722	1.4F
	2020	2316	1.7E
2 Sa	0222	0529	2.1F
	0900	1152	1.6E
	1529	1813	1.4F
	2110		
3 Su		0002	1.6E
	0306	0615	2.0F
	0939	1233	1.6E
	1610	1906	1.4F
	2156		
4 M ●		0047	1.6E
	0347	0703	2.0F
	1015	1312	1.6E
	1646	1950	1.5F
	2239		
5 Tu		0131	1.6E
	0426	0746	1.9F
	1049	1346	1.7E
	1716	2026	1.5F
	2318		
6 W		0209	1.5E
	0503	0825	1.9F
	1122	1418	1.7E
	1742	2057	1.6F
	2355		
7 Th		0244	1.5E
	0540	0901	1.8F
	1157	1450	1.8E
	1808	2128	1.6F
8 F	0030	0318	1.5E
	0617	0938	1.7F
	1233	1524	1.7E
	1837	2200	1.5F
9 Sa	0104	0355	1.5E
	0655	1019	1.6F
	1312	1605	1.7E
	1911	2237	1.5F
10 Su	0140	0437	1.4E
	0734	1106	1.5F
	1354	1653	1.6E
	1950	2320	1.5F
11 M	0220	0525	1.4E
	0818	1156	1.4F
	1441	1745	1.6E
	2034		
12 Tu ☾		0006	1.5F
	0307	0613	1.3E
	0910	1247	1.4F
	1536	1836	1.5E
	2126		
13 W		0054	1.5F
	0402	0702	1.3E
	1013	1342	1.3F
	1635	1929	1.5E
	2222		
14 Th		0147	1.6F
	0459	0801	1.4E
	1121	1445	1.3F
	1733	2031	1.5E
	2318		
15 F		0246	1.7F
	0556	0912	1.5E
	1228	1546	1.3F
	1832	2136	1.5E
16 Sa	0013	0343	1.9F
	0654	1015	1.7E
	1334	1641	1.4F
	1934	2233	1.6E
17 Su	0110	0436	2.1F
	0755	1109	1.9E
	1436	1735	1.6F
	2035	2327	1.8E
18 M	0209	0530	2.2F
	0853	1203	2.0E
	1530	1834	1.7F
	2131		
19 Tu ○		0022	1.9E
	0308	0630	2.3F
	0948	1258	2.2E
	1619	1931	1.9F
	2224		
20 W		0119	2.1E
	0406	0731	2.4F
	1040	1349	2.3E
	1707	2020	2.2F
	2315		
21 Th		0211	2.2E
	0505	0825	2.5F
	1131	1436	2.3E
	1754	2104	2.3F
22 F	0006	0301	2.3E
	0605	0915	2.4F
	1221	1523	2.3E
	1839	2150	2.4F
23 Sa	0057	0352	2.2E
	0703	1007	2.2F
	1311	1613	2.1E
	1925	2240	2.4F
24 Su	0149	0448	2.1E
	0800	1103	2.0F
	1401	1708	2.0E
	2013	2334	2.3F
25 M	0245	0547	1.9E
	0901	1201	1.7F
	1454	1804	1.8E
	2106		
26 Tu ☾		0028	2.2F
	0347	0644	1.7E
	1010	1259	1.4F
	1553	1858	1.6E
	2206		
27 W		0124	2.0F
	0452	0742	1.5E
	1123	1402	1.2F
	1656	1957	1.5E
	2309		
28 Th		0224	1.9F
	0553	0852	1.3E
	1230	1512	1.2F
	1759	2104	1.4E

March

Day	Slack	Maximum	knots
1 F	0008	0324	1.9F
	0651	0957	1.3E
	1332	1613	1.2F
	1901	2204	1.4E
2 Sa	0103	0416	1.8F
	0743	1046	1.4E
	1425	1704	1.2F
	2002	2254	1.4E
3 Su	0156	0502	1.8F
	0829	1126	1.4E
	1509	1753	1.3F
	2056	2340	1.4E
4 M	0243	0547	1.8F
	0909	1203	1.5E
	1545	1842	1.4F
	2141		
5 Tu		0025	1.4E
	0326	0635	1.7F
	0945	1240	1.6E
	1614	1924	1.5F
	2220		
6 W ●		0108	1.5E
	0405	0721	1.8F
	1019	1316	1.7E
	1639	1958	1.6F
	2254		
7 Th		0146	1.6E
	0441	0801	1.8F
	1053	1351	1.8E
	1703	2028	1.7F
	2326		
8 F		0220	1.7E
	0516	0838	1.9F
	1129	1424	1.9E
	1731	2056	1.8F
	2357		
9 Sa		0251	1.7E
	0551	0912	1.9F
	1205	1459	2.0E
	1802	2124	1.8F
10 Su	0029	0323	1.7E
	0626	0949	1.8F
	1243	1536	2.0E
	1837	2156	1.8F
11 M	0103	0358	1.7E
	0703	1029	1.7F
	1322	1619	1.9E
	1915	2235	1.8F
12 Tu	0141	0441	1.6E
	0744	1116	1.5F
	1405	1708	1.7E
	1957	2321	1.8F
13 W	0225	0531	1.5E
	0833	1209	1.4F
	1454	1800	1.6E
	2043		
14 Th ☾		0012	1.7F
	0319	0625	1.5E
	0936	1306	1.2F
	1555	1854	1.5E
	2138		
15 F		0107	1.7F
	0422	0724	1.4E
	1055	1413	1.1F
	1702	1956	1.3E
	2241		
16 Sa		0211	1.7F
	0528	0841	1.5E
	1214	1526	1.2F
	1811	2111	1.3E
	2346		
17 Su		0320	1.8F
	0633	0958	1.6E
	1326	1627	1.4F
	1921	2218	1.5E
18 M	0054	0422	2.0F
	0740	1057	1.9E
	1426	1723	1.6F
	2026	2317	1.7E
19 Tu	0203	0521	2.1F
	0843	1152	2.1E
	1517	1819	1.9F
	2123		
20 W ○		0014	2.0E
	0308	0622	2.3F
	0939	1246	2.2E
	1603	1914	2.2F
	2214		
21 Th		0109	2.2E
	0408	0723	2.4F
	1030	1336	2.3E
	1647	2002	2.5F
	2303		
22 F		0201	2.4E
	0505	0816	2.4F
	1118	1421	2.4E
	1731	2046	2.6F
	2352		
23 Sa		0248	2.5E
	0601	0903	2.4F
	1205	1505	2.4E
	1815	2129	2.7F
24 Su	0040	0334	2.4E
	0653	0949	2.2F
	1249	1549	2.3E
	1859	2214	2.6F
25 M	0128	0424	2.1E
	0744	1039	1.9F
	1334	1638	2.0E
	1943	2304	2.4F
26 Tu ☾	0219	0518	1.8E
	0837	1134	1.6F
	1420	1731	1.8E
	2031	2356	2.2F
27 W	0314	0612	1.5E
	0940	1230	1.3F
	1515	1825	1.5E
	2125		
28 Th		0049	1.9F
	0416	0706	1.3E
	1055	1331	1.0F
	1621	1920	1.3E
	2228		
29 F		0145	1.7F
	0517	0808	1.1E
	1208	1445	0.9F
	1733	2028	1.1E
	2333		
30 Sa		0249	1.5F
	0614	0922	1.1E
	1310	1555	1.0F
	1842	2139	1.1E
31 Su	0035	0348	1.5F
	0706	1016	1.2E
	1401	1646	1.1F
	1946	2234	1.1E

Time meridian 75° W. 0000 is midnight. 1200 is noon. Times are not adjusted for Daylight Saving Time.

Delaware Bay Entrance, 2019

F–Flood, Dir. 342° True   E–Ebb, Dir. 152° True

April

Day	Slack h m	Maximum h m	knots
1 M	0132	0436	1.5F
	0753	1055	1.3E
	1439	1728	1.2F
	2037	2318	1.2E
2 Tu	0222	0520	1.6F
	0835	1130	1.4E
	1509	1808	1.4F
	2117	2359	1.4E
3 W	0304	0605	1.6F
	0913	1206	1.6E
	1534	1846	1.5F
	2151		
4 Th		0039	1.5E
	0340	0651	1.7F
	0949	1244	1.8E
	1558	1920	1.7F
	2222		
5 F ●		0116	1.7E
	0414	0733	1.9F
	1024	1321	1.9E
	1625	1952	1.9F
	2252		
6 Sa		0150	1.8E
	0446	0810	2.0F
	1100	1357	2.1E
	1655	2022	2.0F
	2322		
7 Su		0221	1.9E
	0520	0845	2.0F
	1136	1432	2.2E
	1728	2051	2.1F
	2354		
8 M		0252	2.0E
	0555	0919	2.0F
	1213	1508	2.2E
	1804	2122	2.1F
9 Tu	0029	0325	1.9E
	0634	0956	1.8F
	1251	1547	2.0E
	1842	2158	2.1F
10 W	0108	0405	1.8E
	0717	1041	1.6F
	1333	1633	1.8E
	1923	2243	2.0F
11 Th	0153	0456	1.7E
	0808	1137	1.3F
	1421	1728	1.6E
	2009	2339	1.9F
12 F ◐	0247	0557	1.6E
	0912	1240	1.2F
	1524	1827	1.4E
	2105		
13 Sa		0040	1.8F
	0354	0701	1.5E
	1039	1351	1.1F
	1642	1934	1.3E
	2215		
14 Su		0149	1.7F
	0508	0821	1.5E
	1203	1510	1.2F
	1759	2055	1.3E
	2335		
15 M		0306	1.8F
	0620	0945	1.6E
	1312	1614	1.5F
	1911	2208	1.6E
16 Tu	0053	0413	1.9F
	0729	1045	1.9E
	1408	1707	1.8F
	2014	2307	1.9E
17 W	0205	0513	2.1F
	0832	1137	2.1E
	1456	1759	2.1F
	2109		
18 Th		0002	2.2E
	0308	0612	2.2F
	0926	1228	2.3E
	1540	1851	2.4F
	2159		
19 F ○		0056	2.4E
	0405	0707	2.3F
	1014	1317	2.4E
	1623	1940	2.7F
	2246		
20 Sa		0145	2.5E
	0457	0801	2.4F
	1059	1401	2.5E
	1706	2024	2.8F
	2333		
21 Su		0230	2.5E
	0548	0846	2.3F
	1142	1443	2.4E
	1750	2106	2.8F
22 M	0020	0313	2.3E
	0637	0929	2.1F
	1224	1524	2.3E
	1832	2148	2.6F
23 Tu	0105	0357	2.0E
	0723	1015	1.8F
	1306	1608	2.0E
	1914	2233	2.4F
24 W	0151	0445	1.7E
	0811	1106	1.4F
	1350	1658	1.6E
	1957	2323	2.0F
25 Th	0239	0537	1.4E
	0907	1202	1.1F
	1442	1753	1.3E
	2044		
26 F ◑		0015	1.7F
	0333	0628	1.1E
	1021	1302	0.9F
	1550	1849	1.0E
	2144		
27 Sa		0109	1.4F
	0432	0721	1.0E
	1135	1412	0.8F
	1710	1952	0.9E
	2258		
28 Su		0211	1.3F
	0530	0826	0.9E
	1234	1527	0.9F
	1820	2108	0.8E
29 M	0007	0315	1.3F
	0622	0932	1.0E
	1319	1617	1.1F
	1918	2208	1.0E
30 Tu	0105	0408	1.3F
	0711	1017	1.2E
	1354	1653	1.3F
	2004	2250	1.2E

May

Day	Slack h m	Maximum h m	knots
1 W	0154	0452	1.5F
	0756	1054	1.4E
	1422	1725	1.4F
	2041	2328	1.4E
2 Th	0234	0533	1.6F
	0838	1131	1.6E
	1448	1759	1.6F
	2114		
3 F		0004	1.6E
	0309	0616	1.7F
	0916	1209	1.8E
	1516	1834	1.8F
	2145		
4 Sa ●		0040	1.7E
	0342	0700	1.9F
	0953	1249	2.0E
	1547	1911	1.9F
	2216		
5 Su		0116	1.9E
	0415	0740	2.0F
	1030	1328	2.2E
	1620	1946	2.1F
	2248		
6 M		0150	2.0E
	0450	0817	2.0F
	1106	1405	2.2E
	1655	2020	2.3F
	2323		
7 Tu		0224	2.1E
	0529	0853	2.0F
	1144	1442	2.2E
	1732	2054	2.3F
8 W	0001	0259	2.1E
	0611	0931	1.8F
	1224	1521	2.1E
	1812	2131	2.3F
9 Th	0043	0340	2.0E
	0659	1016	1.6F
	1308	1606	1.8E
	1855	2216	2.1F
10 F	0130	0432	1.8E
	0752	1116	1.3F
	1400	1704	1.6E
	1945	2316	2.0F
11 Sa ◑	0226	0538	1.6E
	0858	1224	1.2F
	1508	1811	1.4E
	2046		
12 Su		0024	1.8F
	0336	0648	1.5E
	1024	1334	1.2F
	1631	1922	1.3E
	2207		
13 M		0136	1.7F
	0455	0806	1.5E
	1144	1450	1.4F
	1748	2043	1.4E
	2335		
14 Tu		0255	1.7F
	0609	0927	1.6E
	1247	1554	1.7F
	1856	2156	1.7E
15 W	0055	0404	1.9F
	0716	1028	1.9E
	1341	1646	2.1F
	1956	2254	2.0E
16 Th	0203	0502	2.1F
	0816	1118	2.1E
	1429	1735	2.4F
	2051	2346	2.3E
17 F	0302	0557	2.2F
	0907	1206	2.3E
	1514	1825	2.6F
	2141		
18 Sa ○		0037	2.4E
	0354	0652	2.2F
	0953	1254	2.4E
	1558	1915	2.8F
	2228		
19 Su		0126	2.4E
	0444	0743	2.2F
	1036	1339	2.4E
	1641	2001	2.8F
	2313		
20 M		0210	2.4E
	0532	0828	2.1F
	1118	1420	2.3E
	1724	2042	2.7F
	2358		
21 Tu		0250	2.2E
	0618	0910	1.9F
	1200	1500	2.1E
	1805	2122	2.5F
22 W	0040	0329	1.9E
	0703	0952	1.6F
	1243	1541	1.8E
	1846	2204	2.2F
23 Th	0121	0410	1.6E
	0746	1040	1.3F
	1327	1627	1.5E
	1927	2251	1.9F
24 F	0202	0457	1.3E
	0832	1135	1.1F
	1418	1722	1.2E
	2010	2342	1.5F
25 Sa	0247	0547	1.1E
	0928	1232	0.9F
	1522	1819	0.9E
	2103		
26 Su ◑		0036	1.3F
	0340	0637	1.0E
	1037	1330	0.8F
	1638	1917	0.8E
	2217		
27 M		0133	1.1F
	0440	0730	1.0E
	1134	1435	0.9F
	1742	2023	0.8E
	2331		
28 Tu		0236	1.1F
	0535	0832	1.0E
	1217	1529	1.1F
	1832	2127	0.9E
29 W	0027	0334	1.3F
	0626	0930	1.2E
	1252	1607	1.3F
	1915	2213	1.2E
30 Th	0114	0419	1.4F
	0716	1016	1.4E
	1325	1640	1.5F
	1954	2250	1.4E
31 F	0154	0500	1.6F
	0759	1055	1.7E
	1359	1713	1.7F
	2030	2326	1.6E

June

Day	Slack h m	Maximum h m	knots
1 Sa	0232	0540	1.7F
	0841	1135	1.9E
	1434	1749	1.8F
	2105		
2 Su		0003	1.8E
	0308	0624	1.8F
	0921	1216	2.0E
	1510	1829	2.0F
	2140		
3 M ●		0041	1.9E
	0346	0709	1.9F
	1000	1258	2.1E
	1546	1910	2.2F
	2217		
4 Tu		0121	2.1E
	0426	0752	1.9F
	1040	1339	2.2E
	1624	1951	2.3F
	2256		
5 W		0201	2.2E
	0509	0833	1.9F
	1121	1420	2.1E
	1704	2031	2.4F
	2338		
6 Th		0240	2.2E
	0557	0914	1.8F
	1205	1502	2.0E
	1748	2113	2.4F
7 F	0024	0324	2.1E
	0648	1002	1.6F
	1255	1550	1.8E
	1838	2201	2.2F
8 Sa	0115	0418	1.9E
	0743	1102	1.4F
	1351	1651	1.6E
	1934	2304	2.0F
9 Su	0213	0526	1.7E
	0846	1209	1.4F
	1459	1802	1.5E
	2042		
10 M ◐		0015	1.8F
	0323	0637	1.6E
	1001	1314	1.5F
	1617	1912	1.5E
	2208		
11 Tu		0126	1.7F
	0441	0747	1.6E
	1114	1423	1.7F
	1730	2027	1.6E
	2335		
12 W		0242	1.7F
	0552	0902	1.7E
	1215	1527	2.0F
	1835	2139	1.9E
13 Th	0049	0350	1.9F
	0655	1004	1.9E
	1309	1621	2.3F
	1935	2237	2.1E
14 F	0153	0446	2.0F
	0752	1055	2.1E
	1400	1709	2.5F
	2030	2327	2.2E
15 Sa	0249	0537	2.0F
	0843	1142	2.2E
	1448	1758	2.6F
	2121		
16 Su		0017	2.3E
	0340	0631	2.0F
	0930	1229	2.2E
	1533	1848	2.7F
	2208		
17 M ○		0105	2.2E
	0428	0724	1.9F
	1014	1315	2.2E
	1616	1937	2.6F
	2252		
18 Tu		0149	2.1E
	0515	0811	1.8F
	1058	1358	2.1E
	1659	2020	2.5F
	2334		
19 W		0228	2.0E
	0600	0853	1.7F
	1141	1439	1.9E
	1741	2059	2.3F
20 Th	0013	0304	1.8E
	0642	0933	1.5F
	1226	1519	1.7E
	1821	2138	2.1F
21 F	0050	0339	1.6E
	0720	1016	1.3F
	1310	1601	1.4E
	1901	2221	1.8F
22 Sa	0127	0417	1.4E
	0754	1105	1.2F
	1357	1652	1.1E
	1942	2310	1.5F
23 Su	0206	0504	1.2E
	0829	1155	1.0F
	1449	1747	1.0E
	2029		
24 M		0003	1.3F
	0253	0555	1.2E
	0913	1243	1.0F
	1548	1839	0.9E
	2129		
25 Tu		0056	1.2F
	0349	0644	1.1E
	1007	1332	1.0F
	1646	1930	0.9E
	2238		
26 W		0152	1.2F
	0447	0737	1.2E
	1100	1423	1.1F
	1735	2028	1.0E
	2336		
27 Th		0250	1.2F
	0540	0836	1.3E
	1146	1512	1.3F
	1818	2123	1.2E
28 F	0025	0341	1.4F
	0629	0932	1.5E
	1229	1553	1.5F
	1901	2209	1.4E
29 Sa	0109	0425	1.5F
	0717	1019	1.7E
	1311	1631	1.7F
	1943	2249	1.6E
30 Su	0154	0507	1.6F
	0805	1102	1.8E
	1352	1710	1.9F
	2026	2329	1.8E

Time meridian 75° W. 0000 is midnight. 1200 is noon. Times are not adjusted for Daylight Saving Time.

Delaware Bay Entrance, 2019

F–Flood, Dir. 342° True   E–Ebb, Dir. 152° True

July

Day	Slack	Maximum	knots
1 M	0239	0551	1.7F
	0851	1145	1.9F
	1434	1751	2.1F
	2109		
2 Tu ●		0012	1.9F
	0324	0641	1.7F
	0935	1231	2.0F
	1516	1839	2.2F
	2151		
3 W		0058	2.1E
	0410	0732	1.8F
	1020	1318	2.0E
	1559	1928	2.3F
	2235		
4 Th		0144	2.2E
	0458	0819	1.8F
	1106	1404	2.0E
	1645	2015	2.4F
	2322		
5 F		0229	2.2E
	0548	0904	1.8F
	1155	1450	2.0E
	1736	2102	2.4F
6 Sa	0012	0315	2.1E
	0639	0952	1.8F
	1248	1541	1.9E
	1832	2155	2.2F
7 Su	0105	0409	2.0E
	0732	1048	1.7F
	1344	1643	1.8E
	1934	2257	2.0F
8 M	0203	0515	1.8E
	0827	1150	1.7F
	1447	1752	1.7E
	2044		
9 Tu ☽		0005	1.8F
	0309	0620	1.7E
	0931	1250	1.8F
	1558	1857	1.7E
	2205		
10 W		0112	1.7F
	0421	0724	1.7E
	1039	1352	1.9F
	1707	2004	1.8E
	2326		
11 Th		0222	1.7F
	0528	0831	1.7E
	1141	1456	2.1F
	1811	2116	1.8E
12 F	0036	0330	1.7F
	0628	0936	1.8E
	1238	1554	2.3F
	1912	2216	2.0E
13 Sa	0138	0426	1.8F
	0725	1030	1.9E
	1331	1644	2.4F
	2009	2308	2.0E
14 Su	0235	0518	1.7F
	0819	1118	2.0E
	1422	1732	2.5F
	2101	2356	2.0E
15 M	0326	0611	1.7F
	0909	1205	2.0E
	1510	1822	2.4F
	2148		
16 Tu ○		0043	1.9E
	0414	0706	1.7F
	0957	1253	1.9E
	1554	1912	2.3F
	2229		
17 W		0127	1.9E
	0459	0756	1.6F
	1043	1339	1.8E
	1638	1957	2.2F
	2308		
18 Th		0205	1.8E
	0540	0837	1.6F
	1128	1421	1.7E
	1720	2038	2.1F
	2344		
19 F		0239	1.7E
	0617	0915	1.6F
	1211	1459	1.6E
	1800	2116	1.9F
20 Sa	0019	0310	1.7E
	0647	0951	1.5F
	1251	1538	1.4E
	1839	2155	1.7F
21 Su	0054	0344	1.6E
	0713	1029	1.4F
	1330	1620	1.3E
	1917	2239	1.5F
22 M	0132	0425	1.5E
	0741	1110	1.3F
	1409	1707	1.2E
	1957	2328	1.4F
23 Tu	0214	0514	1.4E
	0816	1154	1.2F
	1453	1754	1.1E
	2042		
24 W ◑		0018	1.3F
	0302	0604	1.4E
	0900	1237	1.2F
	1542	1839	1.1E
	2136		
25 Th		0108	1.2F
	0358	0653	1.4E
	0952	1322	1.3F
	1633	1926	1.1E
	2236		
26 F		0201	1.2F
	0453	0745	1.4E
	1046	1412	1.4F
	1723	2022	1.2E
	2333		
27 Sa		0259	1.3F
	0546	0845	1.4E
	1137	1504	1.5F
	1811	2122	1.3E
28 Su	0028	0351	1.4F
	0638	0942	1.5E
	1225	1552	1.7F
	1900	2214	1.5E
29 M	0123	0439	1.5F
	0731	1032	1.7E
	1313	1637	1.9F
	1951	2302	1.7E
30 Tu	0218	0527	1.5F
	0826	1120	1.8E
	1402	1723	2.1F
	2043	2350	1.9E
31 W ●	0311	0621	1.6F
	0918	1210	1.8E
	1453	1815	2.2F
	2132		

August

Day	Slack	Maximum	knots
1 Th		0041	2.1E
	0401	0717	1.7F
	1008	1303	1.9E
	1544	1912	2.3F
	2222		
2 F		0132	2.2E
	0450	0808	1.9F
	1058	1354	2.0E
	1637	2006	2.4F
	2312		
3 Sa		0220	2.3E
	0538	0853	2.0F
	1148	1443	2.1E
	1734	2056	2.4F
4 Su	0003	0307	2.2E
	0627	0939	2.1F
	1240	1534	2.1E
	1834	2148	2.3F
5 M	0056	0358	2.1E
	0714	1030	2.1F
	1333	1632	2.0E
	1934	2247	2.1F
6 Tu	0150	0457	1.9E
	0804	1126	2.1F
	1430	1735	2.0E
	2039	2350	1.9F
7 W ☾	0248	0558	1.8E
	0900	1223	2.1F
	1534	1836	1.9E
	2152		
8 Th		0051	1.7F
	0352	0656	1.7E
	1002	1321	2.1F
	1642	1938	1.8E
	2308		
9 F		0156	1.5F
	0457	0757	1.7E
	1106	1423	2.1F
	1747	2048	1.7E
10 Sa	0018	0305	1.5F
	0558	0904	1.7E
	1207	1525	2.2F
	1849	2155	1.7E
11 Su	0123	0408	1.5F
	0658	1005	1.7E
	1304	1619	2.2F
	1947	2249	1.7E
12 M	0222	0501	1.5F
	0758	1057	1.7E
	1358	1708	2.2F
	2040	2336	1.7E
13 Tu	0313	0555	1.5F
	0854	1145	1.7E
	1449	1757	2.1F
	2125		
14 W		0021	1.7F
	0358	0650	1.5E
	0945	1235	1.6E
	1536	1848	2.0F
	2204		
15 Th ○		0103	1.7F
	0438	0740	1.6E
	1031	1321	1.6E
	1620	1935	2.0F
	2240		
16 F		0139	1.7E
	0513	0819	1.6F
	1112	1402	1.6E
	1701	2016	1.9F
	2315		
17 Sa		0212	1.8E
	0542	0851	1.7F
	1150	1438	1.6E
	1739	2053	1.9F
	2349		
18 Su		0243	1.8E
	0607	0921	1.7F
	1224	1512	1.5E
	1815	2129	1.8F
19 M	0024	0315	1.8E
	0632	0951	1.6F
	1256	1545	1.5E
	1848	2207	1.7F
20 Tu	0100	0351	1.7E
	0701	1024	1.6F
	1328	1622	1.4E
	1923	2250	1.6F
21 W	0138	0435	1.7E
	0735	1103	1.5F
	1404	1704	1.4E
	2000	2337	1.4F
22 Th	0221	0523	1.6E
	0814	1146	1.5F
	1446	1750	1.3E
	2045		
23 F ○		0025	1.3F
	0310	0613	1.5E
	0900	1231	1.5F
	1536	1837	1.3E
	2141		
24 Sa		0116	1.2F
	0406	0703	1.5E
	0953	1320	1.5F
	1632	1928	1.3E
	2247		
25 Su		0215	1.2F
	0505	0759	1.4E
	1049	1416	1.6F
	1728	2034	1.3E
	2356		
26 M		0320	1.2F
	0604	0906	1.4E
	1145	1516	1.7F
	1825	2145	1.5E
27 Tu	0103	0417	1.3F
	0706	1007	1.5E
	1241	1611	1.9F
	1924	2242	1.7E
28 W	0206	0510	1.4F
	0809	1102	1.6E
	1341	1704	2.0F
	2024	2335	1.9E
29 Th	0301	0605	1.6F
	0907	1156	1.8E
	1441	1801	2.1F
	2120		
30 F ●		0029	2.1E
	0350	0703	1.8F
	0959	1252	2.0E
	1539	1902	2.3F
	2212		
31 Sa		0122	2.2E
	0437	0753	2.1F
	1049	1345	2.2E
	1637	1959	2.4F
	2303		

September

Day	Slack	Maximum	knots
1 Su		0210	2.3E
	0522	0838	2.3F
	1137	1434	2.3E
	1735	2049	2.4F
	2353		
2 M		0255	2.3E
	0607	0922	2.4F
	1227	1523	2.4E
	1832	2138	2.3F
3 Tu	0042	0342	2.2E
	0653	1008	2.5F
	1317	1615	2.3E
	1928	2231	2.1F
4 W	0131	0434	2.1E
	0739	1100	2.4F
	1410	1713	2.1E
	2026	2329	1.8F
5 Th ◔	0222	0531	1.9E
	0829	1155	2.3F
	1509	1811	1.9E
	2131		
6 F		0027	1.6F
	0318	0627	1.7E
	0927	1251	2.2F
	1615	1910	1.6E
	2247		
7 Sa		0129	1.3F
	0423	0725	1.6E
	1032	1350	2.0F
	1721	2017	1.4E
8 Su	0001	0240	1.2F
	0531	0832	1.4E
	1137	1455	1.9F
	1823	2131	1.4E
9 M	0108	0351	1.2F
	0638	0942	1.4E
	1239	1555	1.9F
	1922	2230	1.4E
10 Tu	0207	0448	1.3F
	0745	1039	1.4E
	1339	1646	1.9F
	2014	2315	1.5E
11 W	0255	0539	1.4F
	0844	1129	1.4E
	1433	1733	1.8F
	2058	2354	1.6E
12 Th	0335	0630	1.5F
	0932	1216	1.5E
	1520	1822	1.8F
	2136		
13 F ○		0032	1.6E
	0408	0715	1.6F
	1013	1300	1.5E
	1602	1910	1.8F
	2211		
14 Sa		0109	1.7E
	0436	0750	1.7F
	1048	1338	1.6E
	1639	1952	1.9F
	2245		
15 Su		0142	1.8E
	0500	0820	1.8F
	1119	1412	1.7E
	1712	2028	1.9F
	2319		
16 M		0215	1.9E
	0524	0847	1.8F
	1149	1441	1.7E
	1744	2102	1.9F
	2353		
17 Tu		0247	2.0E
	0552	0914	1.9F
	1218	1510	1.7E
	1815	2135	1.8F
18 W	0028	0321	2.0E
	0623	0943	1.9F
	1249	1541	1.7E
	1847	2212	1.7F
19 Th	0104	0359	1.9E
	0658	1017	1.8F
	1323	1618	1.6E
	1924	2254	1.5F
20 F ◔	0143	0444	1.8E
	0736	1058	1.8F
	1403	1704	1.5E
	2007	2343	1.3F
21 Sa ○	0228	0534	1.6E
	0818	1146	1.7F
	1451	1756	1.4E
	2101		
22 Su		0038	1.2F
	0323	0627	1.4E
	0908	1239	1.6F
	1549	1851	1.4E
	2213		
23 M		0140	1.1F
	0430	0724	1.3E
	1008	1338	1.6F
	1654	1958	1.3E
	2335		
24 Tu		0255	1.1F
	0541	0836	1.2E
	1114	1448	1.7F
	1800	2122	1.5E
25 W	0050	0401	1.3F
	0650	0950	1.3E
	1223	1554	1.8F
	1906	2228	1.7E
26 Th	0154	0456	1.5F
	0757	1050	1.6E
	1332	1653	2.0F
	2011	2323	1.9E
27 F	0247	0549	1.8F
	0855	1146	1.9E
	1438	1752	2.1F
	2110		
28 Sa ●		0016	2.1E
	0333	0643	2.1F
	0946	1241	2.1E
	1539	1853	2.3F
	2202		
29 Su		0107	2.3E
	0417	0734	2.4F
	1034	1333	2.4E
	1635	1949	2.4F
	2251		
30 M		0154	2.4E
	0500	0819	2.6F
	1122	1421	2.5E
	1730	2037	2.4F
	2337		

Time meridian 75° W. 0000 is midnight. 1200 is noon. Times are not adjusted for Daylight Saving Time.

Delaware Bay Entrance, 2019

F–Flood, Dir. 342° True   E–Ebb, Dir. 152° True

October

Day	Slack	Maximum	knots
1 Tu		0238	2.4E
	0544	0901	2.7F
	1210	1507	2.5E
	1823	2123	2.3F
2 W	0022	0322	2.4E
	0629	0945	2.7F
	1259	1554	2.3E
	1915	2211	2.0F
3 Th	0107	0409	2.2E
	0714	1033	2.6F
	1349	1647	2.0E
	2008	2305	1.7F
4 F	0154	0502	1.9E
	0801	1126	2.3F
	1443	1744	1.7E
	2108		
5 Sa ◑		0003	1.4F
	0246	0558	1.6E
	0853	1222	2.1F
	1544	1841	1.4E
	2224		
6 Su		0104	1.1F
	0353	0656	1.4E
	0957	1319	1.8F
	1650	1942	1.2E
	2342		
7 M		0217	1.0F
	0510	0803	1.1E
	1109	1423	1.6F
	1753	2059	1.2E
8 Tu	0049	0336	1.0F
	0624	0920	1.1E
	1218	1529	1.6F
	1849	2204	1.2E
9 W	0144	0432	1.2F
	0732	1022	1.2E
	1321	1623	1.6F
	1940	2247	1.3E
10 Th	0227	0517	1.3F
	0827	1110	1.3E
	1415	1709	1.6F
	2025	2322	1.5E
11 F	0301	0557	1.5F
	0910	1151	1.4E
	1459	1754	1.7F
	2103	2357	1.6E
12 Sa	0329	0635	1.6F
	0944	1230	1.5E
	1536	1839	1.7F
	2139		
13 Su ○		0033	1.7E
	0353	0709	1.7F
	1014	1306	1.6E
	1609	1921	1.8F
	2213		
14 M		0109	1.9E
	0417	0741	1.8F
	1042	1338	1.8E
	1638	1958	1.9F
	2247		
15 Tu		0144	2.0E
	0443	0810	2.0F
	1111	1408	1.8E
	1708	2032	2.0F
	2321		
16 W		0218	2.1E
	0514	0838	2.1F
	1141	1437	1.9E
	1740	2105	1.9F
	2355		
17 Th		0252	2.1E
	0547	0908	2.1F
	1213	1508	1.9E
	1815	2139	1.8F
18 F	0032	0328	2.0E
	0623	0940	2.1F
	1249	1543	1.8E
	1854	2217	1.6F
19 Sa	0111	0409	1.9E
	0701	1018	2.0F
	1330	1627	1.7E
	1940	2308	1.3F
20 Su	0155	0500	1.6E
	0744	1108	1.8F
	1418	1723	1.6E
	2036		
21 M ◐		0010	1.1F
	0252	0558	1.4E
	0834	1209	1.7F
	1518	1826	1.4E
	2151		
22 Tu		0117	1.0F
	0406	0701	1.2E
	0939	1314	1.6F
	1629	1937	1.4E
	2319		
23 W		0233	1.1F
	0526	0816	1.2E
	1058	1429	1.6F
	1743	2104	1.5E
24 Th	0033	0343	1.4F
	0637	0936	1.4E
	1217	1543	1.8F
	1853	2214	1.7E
25 F	0133	0438	1.7F
	0742	1038	1.7E
	1331	1644	2.0F
	1959	2307	2.0E
26 Sa	0223	0527	2.0F
	0838	1133	2.1E
	1437	1741	2.1F
	2056	2358	2.2E
27 Su ●	0309	0618	2.3F
	0929	1226	2.3E
	1534	1839	2.3F
	2146		
28 M		0047	2.3E
	0353	0709	2.6F
	1017	1317	2.5E
	1628	1934	2.3F
	2232		
29 Tu		0135	2.4E
	0436	0756	2.8F
	1104	1404	2.6E
	1719	2022	2.3F
	2317		
30 W		0218	2.5E
	0520	0840	2.9F
	1152	1448	2.5E
	1810	2106	2.2F
31 Th	0000	0300	2.4E
	0604	0923	2.8F
	1239	1532	2.2E
	1900	2151	1.9F

November

Day	Slack	Maximum	knots
1 F	0044	0344	2.1E
	0649	1008	2.6F
	1327	1620	1.9E
	1950	2242	1.6F
2 Sa	0130	0434	1.8E
	0735	1058	2.2F
	1416	1715	1.6E
	2045	2340	1.2F
3 Su	0222	0532	1.5E
	0824	1153	1.9F
	1510	1811	1.3E
	2156		
4 M ◐		0041	1.0F
	0330	0632	1.2E
	0925	1250	1.6F
	1611	1906	1.1E
	2313		
5 Tu		0150	0.9F
	0452	0736	0.9E
	1043	1351	1.4F
	1713	2010	1.0E
6 W	0015	0308	1.0F
	0606	0852	0.9E
	1156	1459	1.3F
	1809	2120	1.1E
7 Th	0105	0404	1.2F
	0707	0958	1.0E
	1258	1556	1.4F
	1859	2208	1.2E
8 F	0143	0443	1.3F
	0755	1042	1.2E
	1348	1641	1.5F
	1944	2245	1.4E
9 Sa	0214	0515	1.5F
	0833	1118	1.4E
	1428	1721	1.6F
	2026	2319	1.6E
10 Su	0241	0547	1.6F
	0905	1153	1.5E
	1502	1802	1.7F
	2103	2355	1.8E
11 M	0307	0620	1.7F
	0934	1227	1.7E
	1533	1844	1.8F
	2139		
12 Tu ○		0033	2.0E
	0335	0656	1.9F
	1004	1301	1.8E
	1603	1925	1.9F
	2214		
13 W		0111	2.1E
	0405	0731	2.0F
	1034	1334	1.9E
	1634	2002	1.9F
	2249		
14 Th		0148	2.2E
	0438	0804	2.2F
	1107	1407	2.0E
	1710	2037	1.9F
	2326		
15 F		0224	2.2E
	0513	0837	2.2F
	1142	1440	2.0E
	1749	2113	1.8F
16 Sa	0004	0301	2.1E
	0551	0912	2.2F
	1221	1517	2.0E
	1834	2153	1.6F
17 Su	0046	0343	1.8E
	0632	0951	2.1F
	1305	1602	1.8E
	1923	2245	1.4F
18 M	0135	0435	1.6E
	0719	1044	1.9F
	1355	1702	1.7E
	2020	2351	1.2F
19 Tu ○	0235	0539	1.4E
	0814	1151	1.7F
	1457	1811	1.5E
	2133		
20 W		0058	1.2F
	0351	0648	1.3E
	0926	1301	1.6F
	1613	1922	1.5E
	2257		
21 Th		0209	1.3F
	0511	0802	1.3E
	1054	1417	1.6F
	1730	2044	1.5E
22 F	0006	0319	1.6F
	0619	0920	1.6E
	1216	1531	1.8F
	1839	2154	1.7E
23 Sa	0103	0414	1.9F
	0721	1023	1.9E
	1328	1632	2.0F
	1942	2248	2.0E
24 Su	0155	0503	2.3F
	0817	1116	2.2E
	1430	1726	2.1F
	2037	2336	2.2E
25 M	0242	0552	2.5F
	0910	1207	2.4E
	1525	1821	2.2F
	2126		
26 Tu ●		0025	2.3E
	0328	0643	2.7F
	0959	1258	2.5E
	1616	1915	2.2F
	2211		
27 W		0112	2.4E
	0412	0733	2.8F
	1046	1346	2.4E
	1706	2005	2.1F
	2255		
28 Th		0157	2.4E
	0457	0819	2.8F
	1133	1430	2.3E
	1756	2050	2.0F
	2339		
29 F		0240	2.2E
	0542	0902	2.7F
	1219	1511	2.1E
	1845	2134	1.7F
30 Sa	0025	0323	2.0E
	0627	0945	2.4F
	1303	1554	1.8E
	1932	2222	1.5F

December

Day	Slack	Maximum	knots
1 Su	0113	0411	1.6E
	0713	1032	2.1F
	1347	1642	1.5E
	2021	2318	1.2F
2 M	0206	0508	1.3E
	0800	1125	1.7F
	1433	1736	1.3E
	2116		
3 Tu		0017	1.1F
	0310	0608	1.0E
	0857	1221	1.4F
	1526	1827	1.1E
	2222		
4 W ◐		0115	1.0F
	0424	0706	0.9E
	1011	1318	1.2F
	1626	1919	1.0E
	2321		
5 Th		0217	1.0F
	0530	0809	0.8E
	1124	1420	1.2F
	1722	2017	1.1E
6 F	0006	0314	1.1F
	0622	0914	0.9E
	1221	1519	1.2F
	1812	2115	1.2E
7 Sa	0043	0355	1.3F
	0704	1002	1.1E
	1307	1606	1.4F
	1859	2202	1.4E
8 Su	0115	0428	1.5F
	0742	1039	1.3E
	1346	1646	1.5F
	1942	2241	1.6E
9 M	0147	0500	1.6F
	0817	1112	1.5E
	1421	1725	1.6F
	2024	2318	1.8E
10 Tu	0220	0533	1.8F
	0851	1147	1.6E
	1455	1806	1.7F
	2104	2357	1.9E
11 W	0254	0611	1.9F
	0926	1224	1.8E
	1530	1851	1.7F
	2143		
12 Th ○		0039	2.0E
	0329	0651	2.1F
	1001	1302	1.9E
	1607	1934	1.8F
	2222		
13 F		0120	2.1E
	0405	0733	2.2F
	1037	1341	2.0E
	1648	2015	1.8F
	2302		
14 Sa		0201	2.1E
	0444	0812	2.3F
	1117	1420	2.1E
	1732	2055	1.7F
	2345		
15 Su		0242	2.0E
	0526	0852	2.3F
	1200	1501	2.1E
	1821	2138	1.6F
16 M	0032	0326	1.8E
	0613	0936	2.2F
	1247	1548	1.9E
	1912	2231	1.5F
17 Tu	0124	0420	1.6E
	0707	1032	2.0F
	1341	1649	1.8E
	2007	2334	1.4F
18 W ○	0224	0528	1.5E
	0808	1141	1.8F
	1444	1759	1.6E
	2113		
19 Th		0038	1.5F
	0336	0636	1.5E
	0924	1250	1.7F
	1559	1906	1.6E
	2226		
20 F		0142	1.6F
	0450	0745	1.6E
	1052	1402	1.7F
	1713	2018	1.6E
	2333		
21 Sa		0248	1.8F
	0556	0859	1.8E
	1210	1514	1.8F
	1818	2128	1.8E
22 Su	0031	0347	2.1F
	0657	1004	2.0E
	1317	1615	1.9F
	1918	2224	2.0E
23 M	0124	0438	2.4F
	0756	1058	2.2E
	1418	1708	2.0F
	2013	2313	2.1E
24 Tu	0215	0527	2.6F
	0851	1148	2.3E
	1513	1801	2.0F
	2104		
25 W		0001	2.2E
	0304	0618	2.7F
	0941	1239	2.3E
	1604	1857	1.9F
	2151		
26 Th ●		0051	2.2E
	0350	0710	2.7F
	1029	1328	2.2E
	1654	1950	1.9F
	2238		
27 F		0139	2.2E
	0437	0759	2.6F
	1114	1412	2.1E
	1743	2036	1.8F
	2325		
28 Sa		0223	2.0E
	0523	0842	2.5F
	1157	1451	1.9E
	1829	2120	1.7F
29 Su	0013	0306	1.8E
	0610	0924	2.2F
	1237	1529	1.7E
	1911	2204	1.5F
30 M	0101	0351	1.5E
	0655	1008	1.9F
	1317	1609	1.5E
	1950	2252	1.3F
31 Tu	0150	0443	1.3E
	0740	1057	1.6F
	1357	1656	1.4E
	2027	2343	1.2F

Time meridian 75° W. 0000 is midnight. 1200 is noon. Times are not adjusted for Daylight Saving Time.

Brandywine Shoal Light, Delaware Bay, 2019

F–Flood, Dir. 330° True   E–Ebb, Dir. 153° True

January

Day	Slack	Maximum	knots
1 Tu		0250	1.5F
	0617	0928	1.4E
	1224	1525	1.3F
	1839	2143	1.3E
2 W	0030	0341	1.6F
	0705	1022	1.5E
	1318	1617	1.4F
	1927	2230	1.3E
3 Th	0114	0426	1.7F
	0750	1108	1.6E
	1406	1700	1.4F
	2013	2313	1.3E
4 F	0157	0506	1.7F
	0832	1149	1.7E
	1450	1740	1.5F
	2058	2353	1.3E
5 Sa ●	0240	0545	1.7F
	0915	1228	1.7E
	1532	1820	1.5F
	2142		
6 Su		0033	1.3E
	0323	0625	1.7F
	0956	1307	1.7E
	1613	1901	1.5F
	2225		
7 M		0113	1.3E
	0405	0708	1.7F
	1038	1344	1.7E
	1652	1944	1.5F
	2307		
8 Tu		0153	1.3E
	0447	0752	1.6F
	1118	1420	1.6E
	1731	2025	1.4F
	2347		
9 W		0232	1.3E
	0529	0836	1.5F
	1159	1456	1.5E
	1810	2104	1.4F
10 Th	0027	0310	1.2E
	0613	0918	1.4F
	1240	1533	1.4E
	1848	2142	1.3F
11 F	0109	0351	1.1E
	0701	1002	1.3F
	1322	1612	1.3E
	1927	2222	1.3F
12 Sa	0153	0437	1.0E
	0754	1049	1.1F
	1408	1657	1.1E
	2008	2305	1.2F
13 Su	0242	0533	1.0E
	0852	1143	1.0F
	1458	1749	1.0E
	2053	2355	1.2F
14 M ◖	0336	0635	1.0E
	0952	1241	1.0F
	1553	1843	1.0E
	2141		
15 Tu		0047	1.3F
	0431	0731	1.1E
	1049	1336	1.0F
	1649	1935	1.1E
	2233		
16 W		0139	1.4F
	0523	0823	1.2E
	1142	1429	1.2F
	1741	2026	1.2E
	2326		
17 Th		0231	1.5F
	0611	0914	1.4E
	1232	1521	1.3F
	1831	2118	1.4E
18 F	0018	0323	1.7F
	0657	1006	1.5E
	1320	1612	1.5F
	1920	2211	1.5E
19 Sa	0111	0416	1.8F
	0746	1058	1.7E
	1411	1701	1.7F
	2012	2305	1.6E
20 Su	0203	0506	1.9F
	0839	1151	1.8E
	1502	1750	1.8F
	2106	2358	1.7E
21 M ○	0256	0557	2.0F
	0933	1244	1.9E
	1555	1842	1.8F
	2200		
22 Tu		0051	1.7E
	0349	0650	2.0F
	1027	1337	1.9E
	1647	1936	1.8F
	2254		
23 W		0145	1.7E
	0442	0746	2.0F
	1121	1428	1.9E
	1739	2031	1.7F
	2348		
24 Th		0238	1.6E
	0535	0842	1.9F
	1214	1519	1.8E
	1832	2125	1.7F
25 F	0044	0330	1.5E
	0633	0938	1.7F
	1309	1610	1.6E
	1925	2219	1.6F
26 Sa	0142	0428	1.4E
	0737	1037	1.5F
	1408	1708	1.4E
	2020	2317	1.4F
27 Su ◐	0245	0540	1.2E
	0846	1144	1.3F
	1511	1817	1.2E
	2116		
28 M		0019	1.4F
	0350	0700	1.2E
	0957	1255	1.2F
	1617	1923	1.1E
29 Tu		0121	1.4F
	0454	0808	1.3E
	1105	1401	1.2F
	1720	2020	1.1E
	2306		
30 W		0217	1.4F
	0549	0905	1.4E
	1204	1501	1.2F
	1815	2113	1.1E
	2356		
31 Th		0309	1.5F
	0636	0955	1.5E
	1254	1552	1.3F
	1903	2201	1.2E

February

Day	Slack	Maximum	knots
1 F	0043	0356	1.6F
	0720	1039	1.6E
	1339	1635	1.4F
	1947	2244	1.2E
2 Sa	0128	0438	1.6F
	0801	1119	1.6E
	1421	1714	1.5F
	2031	2325	1.3E
3 Su	0213	0519	1.7F
	0844	1157	1.6E
	1502	1752	1.5F
	2114		
4 M ●		0006	1.3E
	0257	0559	1.7F
	0926	1234	1.6E
	1542	1831	1.5F
	2157		
5 Tu		0046	1.3E
	0341	0640	1.6F
	1009	1312	1.6E
	1620	1911	1.5F
	2238		
6 W		0126	1.3E
	0423	0724	1.6F
	1049	1348	1.6E
	1657	1950	1.5F
	2317		
7 Th		0206	1.3E
	0506	0807	1.5F
	1129	1423	1.5E
	1731	2027	1.5F
	2355		
8 F		0244	1.3E
	0549	0849	1.4F
	1206	1459	1.4E
	1804	2103	1.4F
9 Sa	0033	0323	1.2E
	0634	0930	1.3F
	1244	1535	1.3E
	1839	2140	1.4F
10 Su	0112	0404	1.2E
	0723	1014	1.2F
	1325	1616	1.2E
	1917	2221	1.4F
11 M	0157	0453	1.1E
	0817	1104	1.1F
	1412	1705	1.1E
	2003	2309	1.3F
12 Tu ◐	0248	0552	1.1E
	0914	1201	1.0F
	1508	1802	1.1E
	2057		
13 W		0005	1.4F
	0346	0654	1.1E
	1013	1301	1.1F
	1611	1901	1.1E
	2156		
14 Th		0104	1.4F
	0445	0752	1.3E
	1111	1359	1.2F
	1712	1958	1.3E
	2257		
15 F		0202	1.6F
	0542	0848	1.4E
	1204	1455	1.4F
	1808	2054	1.4E
	2355		
16 Sa		0300	1.7F
	0636	0945	1.6E
	1259	1551	1.6F
	1902	2151	1.5E
17 Su	0052	0358	1.8F
	0729	1042	1.7E
	1353	1644	1.7F
	1956	2248	1.6E
18 M	0147	0452	2.0F
	0824	1137	1.9E
	1447	1735	1.8F
	2052	2344	1.7E
19 Tu ○	0242	0545	2.0F
	0919	1231	1.9E
	1540	1827	1.8F
	2148		
20 W		0039	1.7E
	0337	0638	2.0F
	1014	1324	1.9E
	1631	1921	1.8F
	2243		
21 Th		0134	1.7E
	0432	0734	1.9F
	1107	1414	1.9E
	1720	2015	1.8F
	2336		
22 F		0228	1.6E
	0527	0831	1.8F
	1159	1502	1.8E
	1808	2106	1.7F
23 Sa	0030	0320	1.5E
	0625	0926	1.6F
	1251	1548	1.6E
	1856	2156	1.6F
24 Su	0124	0415	1.4E
	0726	1021	1.4F
	1345	1638	1.3E
	1946	2248	1.5F
25 M	0220	0519	1.3E
	0831	1122	1.2F
	1443	1737	1.1E
	2037	2344	1.4F
26 Tu ◐	0319	0634	1.2E
	0936	1228	1.1F
	1546	1844	1.0E
	2132		
27 W		0044	1.3F
	0419	0739	1.3E
	1039	1332	1.1F
	1650	1945	1.0E
	2228		
28 Th		0141	1.4F
	0515	0833	1.3E
	1136	1429	1.1F
	1747	2039	1.0E
	2322		

March

Day	Slack	Maximum	knots
1 F		0235	1.4F
	0604	0922	1.4E
	1224	1521	1.2F
	1835	2128	1.1E
2 Sa	0013	0325	1.5F
	0648	1006	1.5E
	1308	1605	1.3F
	1920	2215	1.2E
3 Su	0100	0410	1.5F
	0731	1046	1.6E
	1350	1645	1.4F
	2003	2258	1.2E
4 M	0146	0453	1.6F
	0813	1124	1.6E
	1430	1723	1.5F
	2045	2339	1.3E
5 Tu	0232	0533	1.6F
	0856	1201	1.6E
	1509	1800	1.5F
	2127		
6 W ●		0019	1.3E
	0317	0614	1.6F
	0939	1238	1.5E
	1545	1836	1.5F
	2208		
7 Th		0100	1.3E
	0401	0655	1.5F
	1019	1314	1.5E
	1619	1912	1.5F
	2246		
8 F		0139	1.4E
	0443	0737	1.4F
	1057	1349	1.5E
	1651	1948	1.6F
	2322		
9 Sa		0217	1.4E
	0525	0819	1.4F
	1132	1425	1.4E
	1723	2025	1.6F
	2357		
10 Su		0255	1.4E
	0607	0900	1.3F
	1208	1502	1.4E
	1757	2103	1.6F
11 M	0035	0334	1.3E
	0652	0943	1.2F
	1249	1543	1.3E
	1837	2145	1.6F
12 Tu	0117	0420	1.3E
	0743	1030	1.2F
	1337	1631	1.2E
	1926	2234	1.5F
13 W	0208	0515	1.2E
	0839	1127	1.2F
	1434	1729	1.2E
	2024	2331	1.5F
14 Th ◐	0308	0620	1.2E
	0940	1230	1.2F
	1540	1833	1.2E
	2128		
15 F		0035	1.5F
	0414	0725	1.3E
	1043	1333	1.3F
	1647	1935	1.3E
	2233		
16 Sa		0139	1.6F
	0519	0827	1.5E
	1144	1434	1.5F
	1750	2035	1.4E
	2336		
17 Su		0242	1.7F
	0619	0929	1.7E
	1242	1533	1.6F
	1847	2135	1.5E
18 M	0036	0343	1.8F
	0715	1028	1.8E
	1337	1629	1.7F
	1943	2235	1.6E
19 Tu	0133	0440	1.9F
	0810	1124	1.9E
	1431	1722	1.8F
	2040	2334	1.6E
20 W ○	0231	0534	1.9F
	0905	1217	1.9E
	1522	1812	1.8F
	2136		
21 Th		0030	1.7E
	0328	0627	1.9F
	1000	1308	1.9E
	1611	1904	1.8F
	2230		
22 F		0126	1.7E
	0424	0722	1.8F
	1051	1356	1.8E
	1656	1955	1.8F
	2322		
23 Sa		0219	1.7E
	0519	0818	1.6F
	1141	1441	1.7E
	1741	2044	1.7F
24 Su	0011	0309	1.6E
	0614	0911	1.5F
	1230	1523	1.5E
	1824	2130	1.7F
25 M	0101	0357	1.5E
	0711	1002	1.3F
	1320	1607	1.3E
	1910	2217	1.5F
26 Tu	0151	0451	1.4E
	0808	1055	1.2F
	1414	1656	1.1E
	1959	2307	1.4F
27 W ◐	0243	0554	1.3E
	0906	1154	1.1F
	1512	1759	0.9E
	2052		
28 Th		0004	1.3F
	0339	0659	1.2E
	1004	1255	1.0F
	1615	1905	0.9E
	2150		
29 F		0103	1.3F
	0436	0754	1.2E
	1059	1352	1.1F
	1714	2003	0.9E
	2248		
30 Sa		0159	1.3F
	0529	0843	1.3E
	1149	1444	1.2F
	1805	2055	1.0E
	2343		
31 Su		0252	1.4F
	0616	0928	1.4E
	1234	1532	1.3F
	1851	2144	1.1E

Time meridian 75° W. 0000 is midnight. 1200 is noon. Times are not adjusted for Daylight Saving Time.

Brandywine Shoal Light, Delaware Bay, 2019

F–Flood, Dir. 330° True   E–Ebb, Dir. 153° True

April

Day	Slack h m	Max h m	knots
1 M	0034	0342	1.4F
	0701	1010	1.5E
	1316	1614	1.4F
	1933	2230	1.2E
2 Tu	0121	0427	1.5F
	0744	1049	1.5E
	1354	1651	1.5F
	2015	2312	1.3E
3 W	0208	0508	1.5F
	0826	1125	1.5E
	1431	1726	1.5F
	2056	2352	1.3E
4 Th	0254	0547	1.5F
	0907	1201	1.4E
	1506	1800	1.6F
	2135		
5 F ●		0032	1.4E
	0338	0627	1.4F
	0946	1238	1.4E
	1539	1834	1.6F
	2212		
6 Sa		0110	1.4E
	0419	0707	1.4F
	1024	1315	1.4E
	1612	1911	1.7F
	2248		
7 Su		0149	1.5E
	0459	0748	1.4F
	1100	1353	1.5E
	1647	1950	1.7F
	2324		
8 M		0227	1.5E
	0540	0831	1.4F
	1138	1434	1.5E
	1725	2031	1.7F
9 Tu	0002	0308	1.5E
	0623	0915	1.4F
	1221	1517	1.4E
	1808	2117	1.7F
10 W	0046	0353	1.4E
	0713	1003	1.4F
	1310	1605	1.4E
	1900	2207	1.6F
11 Th	0139	0446	1.4E
	0810	1059	1.3F
	1409	1702	1.3E
	1959	2305	1.6F
12 F ◐	0241	0553	1.4E
	0914	1204	1.3F
	1516	1807	1.2E
	2105		
13 Sa		0012	1.6F
	0350	0704	1.4E
	1021	1310	1.4F
	1627	1915	1.3E
	2213		
14 Su		0121	1.6F
	0500	0811	1.5E
	1126	1415	1.5F
	1734	2019	1.4E
	2320		
15 M		0227	1.7F
	0604	0914	1.7E
	1225	1518	1.6F
	1835	2123	1.4E
16 Tu	0023	0331	1.8F
	0701	1015	1.8E
	1320	1615	1.7F
	1932	2227	1.5E
17 W	0123	0430	1.8F
	0756	1109	1.8E
	1412	1707	1.8F
	2027	2326	1.6E
18 Th	0222	0524	1.8F
	0850	1200	1.8E
	1500	1756	1.8F
	2122		
19 F ○		0023	1.7E
	0320	0616	1.8F
	0943	1249	1.7E
	1546	1843	1.8F
	2214		
20 Sa		0117	1.7E
	0415	0709	1.6F
	1034	1335	1.6E
	1630	1931	1.8F
	2302		
21 Su		0207	1.7E
	0507	0802	1.5F
	1122	1418	1.5E
	1711	2018	1.8F
	2349		
22 M		0252	1.6E
	0558	0851	1.4F
	1208	1458	1.4E
	1753	2103	1.7F
23 Tu	0033	0334	1.6E
	0648	0938	1.3F
	1254	1537	1.2E
	1836	2146	1.6F
24 W	0118	0418	1.4E
	0738	1025	1.2F
	1343	1621	1.1E
	1924	2232	1.4F
25 Th	0206	0508	1.3E
	0830	1117	1.1F
	1437	1714	0.9E
	2016	2325	1.3F
26 F ◑	0258	0609	1.2E
	0923	1214	1.1F
	1536	1820	0.9E
	2114		
27 Sa		0024	1.2F
	0354	0709	1.2E
	1018	1311	1.1F
	1637	1924	0.9E
	2215		
28 Su		0123	1.2F
	0451	0800	1.3E
	1110	1405	1.2F
	1732	2021	1.0E
	2313		
29 M		0219	1.3F
	0544	0847	1.3E
	1156	1454	1.2F
	1820	2112	1.1E
30 Tu	0008	0311	1.3F
	0630	0929	1.3E
	1237	1537	1.3F
	1903	2200	1.2E

May

Day	Slack h m	Max h m	knots
1 W	0058	0359	1.4F
	0713	1009	1.3E
	1314	1616	1.4F
	1943	2243	1.2E
2 Th	0145	0441	1.4F
	0754	1047	1.3E
	1350	1650	1.5F
	2021	2323	1.3E
3 F	0230	0520	1.4F
	0833	1124	1.3E
	1425	1724	1.6F
	2100		
4 Sa ●		0002	1.4E
	0312	0558	1.4F
	0912	1202	1.4E
	1501	1759	1.7F
	2137		
5 Su		0041	1.5E
	0353	0637	1.4F
	0951	1243	1.4E
	1538	1837	1.7F
	2215		
6 M		0120	1.5E
	0433	0719	1.5F
	1031	1325	1.5E
	1618	1919	1.8F
	2254		
7 Tu		0202	1.6E
	0514	0804	1.5F
	1113	1409	1.6E
	1701	2005	1.8F
	2336		
8 W		0245	1.6E
	0558	0851	1.5F
	1159	1455	1.6E
	1747	2055	1.8F
9 Th	0023	0331	1.6E
	0649	0942	1.5F
	1250	1544	1.5E
	1840	2147	1.8F
10 F	0118	0425	1.5E
	0748	1037	1.5F
	1349	1640	1.4E
	1940	2246	1.7F
11 Sa ◐	0221	0531	1.5E
	0853	1142	1.4F
	1456	1746	1.3E
	2046	2353	1.6F
12 Su	0331	0645	1.5E
	1001	1251	1.4F
	1609	1858	1.3E
	2156		
13 M		0105	1.6F
	0443	0755	1.6E
	1106	1358	1.5F
	1720	2007	1.3E
	2307		
14 Tu		0214	1.6F
	0548	0859	1.6E
	1206	1501	1.6F
	1823	2116	1.4E
15 W	0014	0320	1.7F
	0647	0958	1.7E
	1259	1559	1.7F
	1919	2221	1.5E
16 Th	0116	0420	1.7F
	0741	1052	1.7E
	1348	1650	1.8F
	2012	2319	1.6E
17 F	0214	0513	1.7F
	0834	1141	1.7E
	1435	1736	1.8F
	2104		
18 Sa ○		0012	1.7E
	0310	0603	1.6F
	0925	1227	1.6E
	1519	1820	1.8F
	2153		
19 Su		0102	1.7E
	0402	0652	1.5F
	1014	1311	1.5E
	1601	1905	1.8F
	2239		
20 M		0148	1.7E
	0450	0740	1.5F
	1100	1353	1.4E
	1643	1950	1.7F
	2322		
21 Tu		0230	1.7E
	0535	0827	1.4F
	1144	1432	1.3E
	1724	2034	1.7F
22 W	0004	0307	1.6E
	0619	0911	1.4F
	1227	1510	1.2E
	1806	2117	1.6F
23 Th	0046	0345	1.5E
	0704	0954	1.3F
	1313	1550	1.1E
	1852	2201	1.5F
24 F	0130	0427	1.4E
	0752	1040	1.2F
	1402	1637	1.0E
	1944	2250	1.3F
25 Sa	0219	0518	1.3E
	0841	1131	1.1F
	1457	1736	0.9E
	2040	2347	1.2F
26 Su ◑	0314	0617	1.2E
	0933	1227	1.1F
	1556	1844	0.9E
	2142		
27 M		0047	1.2F
	0412	0713	1.2E
	1024	1321	1.1F
	1654	1945	0.9E
	2244		
28 Tu		0145	1.1F
	0508	0801	1.1E
	1111	1410	1.2F
	1745	2038	1.0E
	2342		
29 W		0239	1.2F
	0557	0844	1.2E
	1153	1454	1.3F
	1829	2127	1.1E
30 Th	0033	0328	1.2F
	0640	0925	1.2E
	1230	1534	1.4F
	1908	2211	1.2E
31 F	0119	0411	1.3F
	0720	1006	1.2E
	1307	1612	1.5F
	1945	2251	1.3E

June

Day	Slack h m	Max h m	knots
1 Sa	0202	0450	1.3F
	0759	1048	1.3E
	1345	1649	1.6F
	2023	2330	1.4E
2 Su	0244	0529	1.4F
	0839	1130	1.4E
	1426	1728	1.7F
	2103		
3 M ●		0011	1.5E
	0325	0609	1.5F
	0922	1215	1.5E
	1510	1810	1.8F
	2145		
4 Tu		0054	1.6E
	0407	0653	1.6F
	1007	1301	1.6E
	1555	1855	1.9F
	2230		
5 W		0139	1.7E
	0451	0741	1.6F
	1053	1348	1.7E
	1642	1945	1.9F
	2316		
6 Th		0226	1.8E
	0538	0831	1.7F
	1142	1436	1.7E
	1731	2037	1.9F
7 F	0007	0315	1.7E
	0631	0923	1.6F
	1235	1527	1.6E
	1824	2131	1.8F
8 Sa	0102	0408	1.7E
	0730	1019	1.5F
	1334	1622	1.4E
	1924	2230	1.7F
9 Su	0205	0512	1.6E
	0834	1122	1.4F
	1441	1728	1.3E
	2031	2337	1.6F
10 M ◑	0313	0626	1.5E
	0939	1231	1.4F
	1554	1844	1.2E
	2144		
11 Tu		0050	1.5F
	0425	0737	1.5E
	1043	1339	1.4F
	1705	2000	1.3E
	2258		
12 W		0202	1.5F
	0532	0840	1.5E
	1142	1442	1.5F
	1808	2109	1.4E
13 Th	0006	0309	1.5F
	0631	0939	1.5E
	1234	1540	1.7F
	1903	2212	1.5E
14 F	0108	0409	1.5F
	0724	1032	1.5E
	1321	1630	1.8F
	1953	2307	1.6E
15 Sa	0203	0500	1.5F
	0815	1119	1.5E
	1407	1714	1.8F
	2041	2356	1.7E
16 Su	0255	0546	1.5F
	0904	1203	1.4E
	1451	1756	1.8F
	2127		
17 M ○		0041	1.7E
	0342	0630	1.5F
	0951	1246	1.4E
	1534	1837	1.8F
	2211		
18 Tu		0123	1.7E
	0425	0714	1.5F
	1035	1326	1.4E
	1616	1921	1.7F
	2253		
19 W		0202	1.7E
	0507	0758	1.4F
	1118	1406	1.3E
	1657	2005	1.7F
	2333		
20 Th		0238	1.6E
	0548	0841	1.4F
	1200	1444	1.3E
	1740	2048	1.6F
21 F	0014	0314	1.6E
	0629	0922	1.4F
	1243	1523	1.2E
	1825	2132	1.5F
22 Sa	0057	0352	1.4E
	0713	1004	1.3F
	1328	1606	1.1E
	1914	2219	1.3F
23 Su	0143	0435	1.3E
	0758	1049	1.2F
	1418	1658	1.0E
	2010	2311	1.2F
24 M	0234	0525	1.1E
	0844	1139	1.1F
	1512	1800	0.9E
	2110		
25 Tu ◑		0009	1.1F
	0329	0621	1.0E
	0931	1231	1.1F
	1610	1905	0.9E
	2213		
26 W		0108	1.0F
	0427	0713	1.0E
	1018	1320	1.2F
	1703	2001	1.0E
	2312		
27 Th		0202	1.0F
	0519	0759	1.0E
	1102	1406	1.3F
	1750	2049	1.1E
28 F	0004	0252	1.1F
	0604	0843	1.1E
	1145	1450	1.4F
	1831	2133	1.2E
29 Sa	0049	0337	1.2F
	0646	0928	1.2E
	1228	1534	1.5F
	1909	2216	1.4E
30 Su	0131	0420	1.3F
	0727	1015	1.3E
	1312	1618	1.7F
	1950	2300	1.5E

Time meridian 75° W. 0000 is midnight. 1200 is noon. Times are not adjusted for Daylight Saving Time.

Brandywine Shoal Light, Delaware Bay, 2019

F–Flood, Dir. 330° True   E–Ebb, Dir. 153° True

July

Day	Slack h m	Maximum h m	knots
1 M	0214	0502	1.5F
	0810	1102	1.4E
	1359	1702	1.8F
	2034	2344	1.6E
2 Tu ●	0258	0545	1.6F
	0857	1150	1.6E
	1447	1747	1.9F
	2121		
3 W		0031	1.7E
	0344	0631	1.7F
	0946	1240	1.6E
	1536	1836	2.0F
	2210		
4 Th		0120	1.8E
	0432	0721	1.7F
	1037	1330	1.7E
	1626	1928	2.0F
	2301		
5 F		0210	1.9E
	0522	0814	1.7F
	1128	1421	1.7E
	1717	2022	2.0F
	2353		
6 Sa		0301	1.9E
	0615	0908	1.7F
	1222	1512	1.6E
	1811	2118	1.9F
7 Su	0049	0353	1.7E
	0712	1003	1.6F
	1321	1608	1.5E
	1912	2217	1.7F
8 M	0149	0452	1.6E
	0812	1103	1.5F
	1426	1713	1.3E
	2021	2323	1.5F
9 Tu ☽	0255	0603	1.4E
	0913	1210	1.4F
	1537	1833	1.2E
	2134		
10 W		0036	1.4F
	0405	0715	1.4E
	1014	1316	1.4F
	1647	1951	1.3E
	2249		
11 Th		0149	1.3F
	0514	0818	1.3E
	1112	1419	1.5F
	1749	2058	1.4E
	2357		
12 F		0256	1.3F
	0613	0916	1.3E
	1205	1516	1.6F
	1842	2157	1.5E
13 Sa	0055	0354	1.4F
	0706	1008	1.3E
	1253	1606	1.7F
	1930	2248	1.6E
14 Su	0146	0442	1.4F
	0754	1055	1.3E
	1338	1649	1.7F
	2015	2333	1.7E
15 M	0233	0524	1.5F
	0840	1138	1.3E
	1423	1730	1.7F
	2059		
16 Tu ○		0014	1.7E
	0316	0604	1.5F
	0925	1219	1.3E
	1507	1810	1.7F
	2141		
17 W		0053	1.7E
	0357	0645	1.5F
	1009	1300	1.3E
	1550	1852	1.7F
	2223		
18 Th		0131	1.7E
	0437	0727	1.5F
	1051	1340	1.3E
	1633	1936	1.6F
	2304		
19 F		0207	1.6E
	0515	0809	1.5F
	1132	1419	1.3E
	1716	2021	1.6F
	2344		
20 Sa		0243	1.6E
	0554	0850	1.4F
	1213	1458	1.3E
	1800	2105	1.5F
21 Su	0026	0319	1.5E
	0633	0929	1.4F
	1255	1539	1.2E
	1848	2149	1.3F
22 M	0108	0357	1.3E
	0712	1008	1.3F
	1340	1624	1.1E
	1942	2236	1.2F
23 Tu	0154	0440	1.1E
	0752	1050	1.2F
	1428	1717	1.0E
	2039	2330	1.0F
24 W ☾	0245	0530	1.0E
	0835	1138	1.2F
	1520	1819	1.0E
	2139		
25 Th		0027	1.0F
	0339	0624	0.9E
	0922	1229	1.2F
	1614	1918	1.0E
	2237		
26 F		0122	1.0F
	0435	0716	1.0E
	1012	1319	1.3F
	1706	2008	1.1E
	2329		
27 Sa		0213	1.1F
	0526	0805	1.1E
	1103	1409	1.4F
	1752	2055	1.3E
28 Su	0015	0302	1.2F
	0613	0855	1.2E
	1154	1459	1.5F
	1837	2143	1.4E
29 M	0100	0350	1.4F
	0659	0946	1.4E
	1245	1550	1.7F
	1922	2232	1.5E
30 Tu	0146	0437	1.5F
	0746	1038	1.5E
	1336	1640	1.8F
	2010	2322	1.7E
31 W ●	0235	0524	1.7F
	0837	1130	1.6E
	1428	1730	1.9F
	2102		

August

Day	Slack h m	Maximum h m	knots
1 Th		0013	1.8E
	0325	0612	1.8F
	0930	1222	1.7E
	1520	1820	2.0F
	2155		
2 F		0105	1.9E
	0416	0704	1.8F
	1023	1315	1.7E
	1613	1914	2.0F
	2248		
3 Sa		0156	1.9E
	0507	0758	1.8F
	1117	1408	1.7E
	1706	2010	1.9F
	2341		
4 Su		0247	1.9E
	0558	0853	1.8F
	1212	1501	1.6E
	1802	2107	1.8F
5 M	0035	0337	1.8E
	0651	0946	1.7F
	1309	1556	1.5E
	1904	2205	1.6F
6 Tu	0133	0431	1.5E
	0746	1042	1.6F
	1410	1701	1.3E
	2012	2308	1.4F
7 W ☽	0236	0536	1.3E
	0843	1144	1.5F
	1516	1820	1.3E
	2124		
8 Th		0020	1.2F
	0343	0647	1.2E
	0941	1248	1.4F
	1622	1936	1.3E
	2235		
9 F		0131	1.2F
	0451	0752	1.1E
	1039	1350	1.5F
	1724	2039	1.4E
	2340		
10 Sa		0235	1.2F
	0552	0849	1.1E
	1133	1447	1.5F
	1816	2134	1.5E
11 Su	0034	0332	1.3F
	0643	0941	1.2E
	1224	1538	1.6F
	1903	2222	1.6E
12 M	0121	0418	1.4F
	0729	1029	1.2E
	1311	1623	1.6F
	1946	2305	1.6E
13 Tu	0205	0459	1.4F
	0814	1112	1.3E
	1356	1704	1.7F
	2028	2344	1.6E
14 W	0246	0537	1.5F
	0857	1153	1.3E
	1441	1744	1.7F
	2111		
15 Th ○		0021	1.6E
	0326	0615	1.5F
	0941	1233	1.3E
	1526	1826	1.6F
	2153		
16 F		0058	1.6E
	0405	0655	1.5F
	1023	1314	1.3E
	1610	1909	1.6F
	2235		
17 Sa		0135	1.6E
	0442	0735	1.5F
	1104	1355	1.4E
	1654	1954	1.5F
	2315		
18 Su		0211	1.5E
	0517	0815	1.5F
	1143	1434	1.3E
	1738	2038	1.4F
	2355		
19 M		0246	1.5E
	0551	0852	1.5F
	1222	1512	1.3E
	1824	2120	1.3F
20 Tu	0034	0322	1.3E
	0625	0928	1.4F
	1301	1552	1.2E
	1913	2203	1.2F
21 W	0115	0401	1.2E
	0702	1006	1.4F
	1343	1638	1.1E
	2005	2250	1.0F
22 Th	0200	0446	1.1E
	0743	1050	1.3F
	1430	1732	1.1E
	2059	2344	1.0F
23 F ○	0252	0539	1.0E
	0832	1141	1.3F
	1523	1832	1.1E
	2155		
24 Sa		0041	1.0F
	0349	0637	1.0E
	0928	1238	1.3F
	1620	1929	1.2E
	2250		
25 Su		0136	1.1F
	0448	0733	1.1E
	1028	1335	1.4F
	1716	2022	1.3E
	2342		
26 M		0230	1.3F
	0543	0827	1.3E
	1126	1431	1.6F
	1809	2115	1.5E
27 Tu	0033	0323	1.4F
	0635	0922	1.4E
	1222	1528	1.7F
	1900	2210	1.6E
28 W	0124	0415	1.6F
	0727	1018	1.5E
	1317	1622	1.9F
	1952	2304	1.8E
29 Th	0216	0506	1.7F
	0821	1113	1.6E
	1412	1715	2.0F
	2046	2357	1.9E
30 F ●	0308	0556	1.8F
	0916	1208	1.7E
	1507	1807	2.0F
	2141		
31 Sa		0050	1.9E
	0359	0648	1.8F
	1012	1304	1.7E
	1602	1902	2.0F
	2235		

September

Day	Slack h m	Maximum h m	knots
1 Su		0142	1.9E
	0449	0742	1.8F
	1106	1359	1.7E
	1658	1959	1.9F
	2328		
2 M		0232	1.9E
	0538	0836	1.8F
	1200	1453	1.7E
	1755	2056	1.7F
3 Tu	0021	0320	1.7E
	0627	0927	1.7F
	1254	1546	1.5E
	1856	2153	1.5F
4 W	0116	0409	1.5E
	0717	1019	1.6F
	1351	1646	1.4E
	2001	2252	1.3F
5 Th ☾	0214	0505	1.2E
	0809	1115	1.5F
	1450	1759	1.3E
	2107	2358	1.2F
6 F	0317	0612	1.1E
	0905	1216	1.4F
	1552	1911	1.3E
	2213		
7 Sa		0105	1.1F
	0423	0720	1.0E
	1003	1317	1.4F
	1652	2011	1.4E
	2313		
8 Su		0206	1.1F
	0524	0818	1.0E
	1101	1414	1.4F
	1745	2104	1.4E
9 M	0005	0301	1.2F
	0617	0911	1.1E
	1154	1507	1.5F
	1832	2150	1.5E
10 Tu	0051	0349	1.3F
	0703	1000	1.1E
	1243	1555	1.5F
	1915	2232	1.5E
11 W	0133	0430	1.4F
	0746	1045	1.2E
	1330	1638	1.6F
	1958	2311	1.6E
12 Th	0213	0508	1.5F
	0829	1127	1.3E
	1417	1719	1.6F
	2040	2348	1.6E
13 F ○	0253	0545	1.5F
	0912	1208	1.3E
	1503	1800	1.6F
	2123		
14 Sa		0024	1.6E
	0330	0622	1.5F
	0954	1249	1.4E
	1548	1843	1.5F
	2205		
15 Su		0101	1.5E
	0406	0700	1.6F
	1034	1329	1.4E
	1633	1926	1.5F
	2246		
16 M		0137	1.5E
	0439	0737	1.6F
	1111	1408	1.4E
	1716	2009	1.4F
	2324		
17 Tu		0213	1.4E
	0511	0813	1.6F
	1147	1445	1.4E
	1758	2050	1.3F
18 W	0000	0249	1.3E
	0543	0849	1.6F
	1223	1522	1.3E
	1842	2131	1.2F
19 Th	0038	0327	1.3E
	0619	0928	1.5F
	1302	1603	1.3E
	1928	2214	1.1F
20 F ☾	0121	0410	1.2E
	0702	1011	1.5F
	1346	1651	1.2E
	2019	2304	1.1F
21 Sa	0211	0502	1.1E
	0755	1103	1.4F
	1440	1751	1.2E
	2114		
22 Su		0002	1.1F
	0310	0602	1.1E
	0855	1203	1.4F
	1541	1854	1.2E
	2213		
23 M		0102	1.2F
	0415	0704	1.2E
	0959	1306	1.5F
	1646	1954	1.4E
	2313		
24 Tu		0202	1.3F
	0518	0803	1.3E
	1103	1408	1.6F
	1746	2053	1.5E
25 W	0010	0300	1.5F
	0616	0902	1.4E
	1204	1509	1.7F
	1842	2152	1.7E
26 Th	0105	0357	1.6F
	0712	1002	1.5E
	1302	1608	1.9F
	1936	2249	1.8E
27 F	0158	0451	1.8F
	0808	1101	1.6E
	1400	1703	1.9F
	2032	2343	1.9E
28 Sa ●	0251	0542	1.8F
	0904	1159	1.7E
	1458	1757	1.9F
	2127		
29 Su		0035	1.9E
	0341	0633	1.9F
	1000	1256	1.7E
	1555	1852	1.9F
	2221		
30 M		0126	1.9E
	0428	0725	1.9F
	1053	1351	1.7E
	1651	1949	1.7F
	2314		

Time meridian 75° W. 0000 is midnight. 1200 is noon. Times are not adjusted for Daylight Saving Time.

Brandywine Shoal Light, Delaware Bay, 2019

F–Flood, Dir. 330° True   E–Ebb, Dir. 153° True

October

Day	Slack (h m)	Maximum (h m)	knots
1 Tu		0215	1.7E
	0514	0817	1.8F
	1145	1444	1.7E
	1748	2045	1.6F
2 W	0005	0300	1.6E
	0600	0906	1.8F
	1235	1534	1.6E
	1845	2138	1.4F
3 Th	0056	0345	1.4E
	0646	0954	1.7F
	1327	1626	1.5E
	1943	2231	1.3F
4 F	0150	0433	1.2E
	0736	1044	1.5F
	1420	1727	1.3E
	2042	2329	1.1F
5 Sa	0247	0532	1.0E
	0830	1140	1.4F
	1516	1835	1.3E
	2141		
6 Su		0030	1.1F
	0349	0641	0.9E
	0927	1241	1.3F
	1614	1935	1.3E
	2238		
7 M		0130	1.1F
	0451	0744	0.9E
	1027	1339	1.3F
	1710	2026	1.3E
	2330		
8 Tu		0224	1.2F
	0546	0839	1.0E
	1124	1434	1.4F
	1759	2113	1.4E
9 W	0016	0314	1.3F
	0634	0930	1.1E
	1217	1525	1.4F
	1845	2155	1.4E
10 Th	0058	0358	1.4F
	0718	1017	1.2E
	1306	1612	1.5F
	1928	2235	1.5E
11 F	0138	0438	1.5F
	0800	1101	1.3E
	1354	1655	1.5F
	2010	2312	1.5E
12 Sa	0216	0514	1.5F
	0842	1142	1.3E
	1441	1736	1.5F
	2053	2349	1.5E
13 Su	0252	0549	1.6F
	0922	1222	1.4E
	1527	1816	1.4F
	2135		
14 M		0025	1.4E
	0327	0623	1.6F
	1001	1302	1.4E
	1610	1857	1.4F
	2215		
15 Tu		0102	1.4E
	0400	0658	1.6F
	1038	1339	1.5E
	1651	1938	1.4F
	2252		
16 W		0140	1.4E
	0433	0735	1.7F
	1112	1416	1.5E
	1730	2019	1.3F
	2328		
17 Th		0218	1.4E
	0508	0814	1.7F
	1148	1453	1.5E
	1810	2100	1.3F
18 F	0006	0258	1.4E
	0547	0856	1.7F
	1227	1533	1.4E
	1853	2143	1.3F
19 Sa	0049	0342	1.3E
	0633	0942	1.6F
	1312	1620	1.4E
	1943	2232	1.3F
20 Su	0140	0433	1.3E
	0727	1035	1.6F
	1407	1717	1.3E
	2041	2330	1.3F
21 M	0240	0533	1.2E
	0829	1136	1.5F
	1511	1825	1.3E
	2144		
22 Tu		0034	1.3F
	0348	0639	1.2E
	0936	1243	1.5F
	1621	1932	1.4E
	2249		
23 W		0139	1.4F
	0458	0744	1.3E
	1044	1350	1.6F
	1727	2035	1.6E
	2350		
24 Th		0241	1.5F
	0601	0847	1.4E
	1149	1455	1.7F
	1826	2136	1.7E
25 F	0046	0341	1.7F
	0700	0951	1.5E
	1251	1556	1.8F
	1922	2234	1.8E
26 Sa	0139	0436	1.8F
	0756	1053	1.6E
	1351	1654	1.8F
	2018	2328	1.8E
27 Su	0230	0526	1.9F
	0851	1152	1.7E
	1451	1747	1.8F
	2113		
28 M		0019	1.8E
	0319	0615	1.9F
	0945	1248	1.7E
	1548	1841	1.7F
	2207		
29 Tu		0108	1.7E
	0405	0705	1.9F
	1037	1342	1.8E
	1643	1936	1.6F
	2258		
30 W		0155	1.6E
	0449	0754	1.8F
	1126	1431	1.7E
	1735	2029	1.5F
	2347		
31 Th		0239	1.5E
	0532	0842	1.8F
	1213	1516	1.7E
	1827	2118	1.4F

November

Day	Slack (h m)	Maximum (h m)	knots
1 F	0034	0320	1.3E
	0617	0928	1.7F
	1300	1601	1.5E
	1917	2205	1.3F
2 Sa	0123	0403	1.2E
	0704	1014	1.5F
	1347	1649	1.4E
	2009	2255	1.2F
3 Su	0215	0453	1.0E
	0756	1105	1.4F
	1438	1747	1.3E
	2102	2351	1.1F
4 M	0312	0557	0.9E
	0853	1203	1.3F
	1534	1849	1.2E
	2156		
5 Tu		0049	1.1F
	0413	0705	0.9E
	0953	1303	1.2F
	1631	1943	1.2E
	2249		
6 W		0144	1.1F
	0512	0805	1.0E
	1054	1400	1.3F
	1725	2030	1.3E
	2337		
7 Th		0235	1.2F
	0603	0859	1.1E
	1151	1455	1.3F
	1813	2114	1.3E
8 F	0020	0322	1.3F
	0648	0949	1.2E
	1243	1545	1.4F
	1858	2155	1.3E
9 Sa	0059	0403	1.4F
	0729	1034	1.3E
	1332	1630	1.4F
	1941	2234	1.3E
10 Su	0136	0439	1.5F
	0809	1115	1.4E
	1419	1710	1.4F
	2023	2312	1.3E
11 M	0212	0513	1.6F
	0848	1153	1.4E
	1503	1749	1.4F
	2103	2350	1.3E
12 Tu	0247	0547	1.6F
	0926	1231	1.5E
	1544	1827	1.4F
	2142		
13 W		0028	1.4E
	0323	0623	1.7F
	1002	1308	1.5E
	1622	1906	1.4F
	2220		
14 Th		0109	1.4E
	0401	0702	1.7F
	1039	1346	1.6E
	1700	1947	1.4F
	2258		
15 F		0150	1.5E
	0441	0744	1.8F
	1117	1426	1.6E
	1739	2031	1.5F
	2339		
16 Sa		0233	1.5E
	0523	0830	1.8F
	1159	1508	1.6E
	1824	2116	1.5F
17 Su	0024	0319	1.5E
	0611	0919	1.7F
	1247	1556	1.5E
	1916	2207	1.4F
18 M	0117	0409	1.4E
	0706	1013	1.7F
	1344	1652	1.5E
	2015	2305	1.4F
19 Tu	0218	0509	1.3E
	0809	1115	1.6F
	1449	1801	1.4E
	2120		
20 W		0011	1.4F
	0328	0618	1.2E
	0918	1225	1.6F
	1600	1912	1.5E
	2227		
21 Th		0118	1.4F
	0441	0729	1.3E
	1029	1335	1.6F
	1709	2017	1.6E
	2329		
22 F		0223	1.5F
	0548	0837	1.4E
	1139	1443	1.6F
	1812	2119	1.7E
23 Sa	0026	0324	1.7F
	0647	0944	1.5E
	1244	1547	1.7F
	1909	2218	1.7E
24 Su	0118	0420	1.8F
	0742	1047	1.6E
	1345	1645	1.7F
	2004	2311	1.7E
25 M	0207	0510	1.9F
	0836	1144	1.7E
	1443	1737	1.7F
	2058		
26 Tu		0001	1.6E
	0254	0556	1.9F
	0927	1237	1.8E
	1538	1828	1.6F
	2150		
27 W		0048	1.6E
	0340	0643	1.8F
	1017	1327	1.8E
	1628	1918	1.5F
	2239		
28 Th		0134	1.5E
	0423	0729	1.8F
	1103	1412	1.7E
	1716	2007	1.5F
	2325		
29 F		0216	1.4E
	0506	0816	1.7F
	1147	1453	1.7E
	1801	2053	1.4F
30 Sa	0009	0256	1.3E
	0550	0900	1.6F
	1230	1532	1.6E
	1846	2137	1.3F

December

Day	Slack (h m)	Maximum (h m)	knots
1 Su	0054	0336	1.2E
	0635	0945	1.5F
	1314	1612	1.4E
	1932	2221	1.2F
2 M	0142	0420	1.1E
	0725	1032	1.4F
	1401	1658	1.3E
	2021	2310	1.2F
3 Tu	0235	0515	0.9E
	0821	1126	1.3F
	1453	1755	1.2E
	2111		
4 W		0005	1.1F
	0334	0623	0.9E
	0922	1226	1.2F
	1550	1853	1.2E
	2202		
5 Th		0101	1.1F
	0433	0730	0.9E
	1025	1327	1.2F
	1648	1944	1.1E
	2252		
6 F		0152	1.2F
	0528	0826	1.0E
	1126	1423	1.2F
	1741	2030	1.2E
	2336		
7 Sa		0239	1.3F
	0614	0917	1.2E
	1220	1515	1.2F
	1828	2112	1.2E
8 Su	0016	0322	1.4F
	0655	1003	1.3E
	1308	1601	1.3F
	1910	2154	1.2E
9 M	0054	0400	1.5F
	0734	1043	1.3E
	1352	1642	1.3F
	1950	2234	1.2E
10 Tu	0131	0437	1.6F
	0811	1121	1.4E
	1434	1719	1.3F
	2029	2315	1.3E
11 W	0210	0514	1.6F
	0849	1158	1.5E
	1513	1756	1.4F
	2109	2357	1.4E
12 Th	0252	0552	1.7F
	0929	1237	1.6E
	1551	1836	1.5F
	2150		
13 F		0040	1.5E
	0334	0634	1.8F
	1010	1319	1.6E
	1631	1919	1.6F
	2232		
14 Sa		0126	1.6E
	0419	0720	1.8F
	1052	1402	1.7E
	1714	2005	1.6F
	2317		
15 Su		0212	1.6E
	0505	0809	1.9F
	1138	1448	1.7E
	1801	2055	1.6F
16 M	0005	0300	1.6E
	0554	0901	1.8F
	1229	1537	1.7E
	1855	2147	1.6F
17 Tu	0100	0351	1.5E
	0650	0956	1.8F
	1326	1632	1.6E
	1954	2244	1.5F
18 W	0202	0450	1.4E
	0754	1058	1.6F
	1430	1739	1.5E
	2058	2350	1.4F
19 Th	0312	0602	1.3E
	0905	1209	1.5F
	1541	1852	1.5E
	2203		
20 F		0058	1.5F
	0425	0718	1.3E
	1020	1322	1.5F
	1653	2000	1.5E
	2305		
21 Sa		0204	1.5F
	0533	0831	1.4E
	1132	1432	1.5F
	1758	2102	1.5E
22 Su	0002	0306	1.7F
	0633	0938	1.5E
	1237	1538	1.5F
	1856	2200	1.5E
23 M	0053	0402	1.8F
	0726	1039	1.7E
	1337	1635	1.6F
	1949	2253	1.5E
24 Tu	0142	0451	1.8F
	0817	1132	1.7E
	1431	1724	1.6F
	2041	2341	1.5E
25 W	0229	0535	1.8F
	0906	1220	1.8E
	1521	1810	1.5F
	2130		
26 Th		0027	1.4E
	0314	0619	1.8F
	0953	1305	1.8E
	1607	1855	1.5F
	2216		
27 F		0110	1.4E
	0358	0703	1.8F
	1037	1347	1.7E
	1650	1940	1.5F
	2301		
28 Sa		0152	1.4E
	0441	0748	1.7F
	1119	1425	1.7E
	1731	2024	1.4F
	2343		
29 Su		0231	1.3E
	0524	0833	1.6F
	1200	1501	1.6E
	1812	2106	1.4F
30 M	0026	0310	1.2E
	0609	0917	1.5F
	1241	1537	1.5E
	1855	2148	1.3F
31 Tu	0111	0352	1.2E
	0658	1002	1.4F
	1326	1618	1.4E
	1938	2231	1.3F

Time meridian 75° W. 0000 is midnight. 1200 is noon. Times are not adjusted for Daylight Saving Time.

Reedy Point, Delaware Bay, 2019

F–Flood, Dir. 353° True   E–Ebb, Dir. 162° True

January

Day	Slack	Maximum	knots
1 Tu	0304 / 0916 / 1555 / 2118	0035 / 0615 / 1316 / 1851	2.6E / 2.2F / 2.6E / 1.7F
2 W	0355 / 1008 / 1652 / 2209	0125 / 0705 / 1410 / 1944	2.5E / 2.2F / 2.7E / 1.7F
3 Th	0444 / 1055 / 1745 / 2257	0216 / 0750 / 1503 / 2034	2.5E / 2.2F / 2.6E / 1.7F
4 F	0530 / 1137 / 1833 / 2342	0306 / 0830 / 1554 / 2120	2.4E / 2.2F / 2.6E / 1.6F
5 Sa ●	0614 / 1216 / 1916	0353 / 0903 / 1640 / 2201	2.2E / 2.1F / 2.5E / 1.5F
6 Su	0026 / 0655 / 1253 / 1956	0437 / 0930 / 1722 / 2233	2.1E / 2.1F / 2.4E / 1.4F
7 M	0107 / 0734 / 1329 / 2033	0517 / 0958 / 1801 / 2251	2.0E / 2.0F / 2.3E / 1.4F
8 Tu	0148 / 0813 / 1406 / 2108	0554 / 1030 / 1837 / 2311	1.9E / 2.0F / 2.2E / 1.4F
9 W	0228 / 0852 / 1443 / 2143	0625 / 1107 / 1907 / 2341	1.8E / 2.1F / 2.1E / 1.4F
10 Th	0308 / 0933 / 1522 / 2219	0646 / 1147 / 1925	1.7E / 2.0F / 2.0E
11 F	0350 / 1018 / 1603 / 2259	0020 / 0659 / 1232 / 1921	1.5F / 1.7E / 2.0F / 2.1E
12 Sa	0436 / 1108 / 1648 / 2343	0103 / 0739 / 1321 / 1959	1.6F / 1.7E / 1.9F / 2.1E
13 Su	0526 / 1203 / 1737	0150 / 0828 / 1413 / 2045	1.8F / 1.7E / 1.8F / 2.1E
14 M ☽	0029 / 0620 / 1303 / 1830	0240 / 0929 / 1507 / 2136	1.9F / 1.7E / 1.6F / 2.0E
15 Tu	0118 / 0716 / 1405 / 1926	0331 / 1127 / 1605 / 2235	2.0F / 1.8E / 1.5F / 2.0E
16 W	0209 / 0814 / 1509 / 2024	0425 / 1238 / 1707 / 2347	2.0F / 1.9E / 1.3F / 1.9E
17 Th	0302 / 0911 / 1613 / 2122	0522 / 1341 / 1812	2.1F / 2.0E / 1.3F
18 F	0357 / 1009 / 1714 / 2219	0109 / 0619 / 1443 / 1914	1.9E / 2.2F / 2.2E / 1.3F
19 Sa	0453 / 1105 / 1811 / 2316	0226 / 0715 / 1542 / 2013	1.9E / 2.3F / 2.4E / 1.4F
20 Su	0549 / 1200 / 1903	0333 / 0811 / 1635 / 2108	2.0E / 2.4F / 2.6E / 1.5F
21 M ○	0011 / 0645 / 1255 / 1953	0432 / 0906 / 1726 / 2159	2.1E / 2.4F / 2.7E / 1.6F
22 Tu	0106 / 0740 / 1349 / 2041	0526 / 0959 / 1814 / 2247	2.3E / 2.4F / 2.7E / 1.7F
23 W	0203 / 0835 / 1442 / 2128	0619 / 1051 / 1902 / 2336	2.4E / 2.3F / 2.7E / 1.8F
24 Th	0301 / 0930 / 1533 / 2215	0713 / 1145 / 1950	2.5E / 2.2F / 2.7E
25 F	0358 / 1027 / 1624 / 2305	0030 / 0807 / 1244 / 2038	1.8F / 2.5E / 2.0F / 2.7E
26 Sa	0456 / 1126 / 1715 / 2356	0131 / 0902 / 1350 / 2127	1.9F / 2.5E / 1.8F / 2.6E
27 Su ◐	0555 / 1228 / 1807	0233 / 0959 / 1503 / 2218	2.0F / 2.5E / 1.7F / 2.6E
28 M	0048 / 0654 / 1329 / 1901	0336 / 1058 / 1620 / 2311	2.0F / 2.5E / 1.6F / 2.5E
29 Tu	0140 / 0752 / 1431 / 1955	0442 / 1156 / 1729	2.1F / 2.4E / 1.6F
30 W	0232 / 0847 / 1531 / 2048	0003 / 0544 / 1251 / 1829	2.5E / 2.1F / 2.5E / 1.6F
31 Th	0324 / 0939 / 1628 / 2141	0054 / 0638 / 1344 / 1922	2.4E / 2.1F / 2.5E / 1.6F

February

Day	Slack	Maximum	knots
1 F	0415 / 1027 / 1721 / 2231	0145 / 0726 / 1437 / 2013	2.4E / 2.1F / 2.5E / 1.6F
2 Sa	0503 / 1111 / 1808 / 2318	0236 / 0809 / 1527 / 2100	2.3E / 2.0F / 2.5E / 1.6F
3 Su	0549 / 1151 / 1850	0325 / 0845 / 1613 / 2141	2.2E / 2.0F / 2.4E / 1.5F
4 M ●	0001 / 0631 / 1229 / 1928	0411 / 0912 / 1655 / 2212	2.1E / 1.9F / 2.3E / 1.4F
5 Tu	0042 / 0711 / 1305 / 2003	0453 / 0937 / 1732 / 2223	2.0E / 1.9F / 2.2E / 1.4F
6 W	0122 / 0750 / 1340 / 2035	0531 / 1008 / 1805 / 2239	1.9E / 2.0F / 2.1E / 1.5F
7 Th	0200 / 0829 / 1416 / 2109	0604 / 1043 / 1832 / 2309	1.9E / 2.0F / 2.1E / 1.6F
8 F	0239 / 0910 / 1453 / 2144	0631 / 1122 / 1840 / 2346	1.8E / 2.0F / 2.1E / 1.8F
9 Sa	0318 / 0954 / 1531 / 2222	0639 / 1205 / 1847	1.8E / 2.0F / 2.1E
10 Su	0401 / 1042 / 1614 / 2304	0029 / 0710 / 1253 / 1926	1.9F / 1.8E / 1.9F / 2.2E
11 M	0448 / 1136 / 1701 / 2351	0116 / 0756 / 1344 / 2012	1.9F / 1.8E / 1.8F / 2.1E
12 Tu ◐	0540 / 1236 / 1754	0206 / 0851 / 1438 / 2102	2.1F / 1.8E / 1.6F / 2.1E
13 W	0041 / 0638 / 1339 / 1853	0257 / 1102 / 1536 / 2159	2.2F / 1.8E / 1.4F / 1.9E
14 Th	0135 / 0739 / 1444 / 1954	0352 / 1216 / 1638 / 2320	2.2F / 1.9E / 1.3F / 1.8E
15 F	0233 / 0842 / 1549 / 2056	0451 / 1319 / 1746	2.1F / 2.0E / 1.2F
16 Sa	0333 / 0945 / 1651 / 2158	0059 / 0553 / 1421 / 1854	1.8E / 2.2F / 2.2E / 1.3F
17 Su	0434 / 1046 / 1748 / 2257	0212 / 0655 / 1519 / 1956	1.9E / 2.2F / 2.4E / 1.4F
18 M	0534 / 1144 / 1840 / 2354	0318 / 0755 / 1613 / 2053	2.1E / 2.2F / 2.6E / 1.5F
19 Tu ○	0632 / 1239 / 1928	0416 / 0854 / 1703 / 2144	2.3E / 2.3F / 2.7E / 1.7F
20 W	0049 / 0727 / 1331 / 2015	0510 / 0949 / 1750 / 2230	2.5E / 2.3F / 2.8E / 1.9F
21 Th	0145 / 0822 / 1421 / 2100	0602 / 1041 / 1836 / 2316	2.6E / 2.3F / 2.8E / 2.0F
22 F	0241 / 0915 / 1509 / 2146	0654 / 1133 / 1922	2.6E / 2.1F / 2.7E
23 Sa	0335 / 1009 / 1557 / 2233	0005 / 0746 / 1229 / 2008	2.0F / 2.6E / 2.0F / 2.7E
24 Su	0429 / 1105 / 1645 / 2321	0058 / 0839 / 1333 / 2055	2.1F / 2.5E / 1.8F / 2.6E
25 M	0524 / 1203 / 1736	0154 / 0933 / 1441 / 2144	2.1F / 2.5E / 1.7F / 2.5E
26 Tu ◑	0012 / 0620 / 1303 / 1829	0252 / 1030 / 1552 / 2236	2.0F / 2.4E / 1.5F / 2.4E
27 W	0105 / 0716 / 1403 / 1924	0354 / 1127 / 1701 / 2330	2.0F / 2.4E / 1.5F / 2.3E
28 Th	0158 / 0810 / 1501 / 2018	0503 / 1222 / 1803	1.9F / 2.4E / 1.4F

March

Day	Slack	Maximum	knots
1 F	0252 / 0903 / 1558 / 2112	0023 / 0606 / 1315 / 1857	2.3E / 1.9F / 2.4E / 1.5F
2 Sa	0344 / 0954 / 1650 / 2203	0114 / 0659 / 1406 / 1948	2.2E / 1.9F / 2.3E / 1.5F
3 Su	0435 / 1040 / 1736 / 2251	0206 / 0746 / 1455 / 2034	2.2E / 1.9F / 2.3E / 1.5F
4 M	0523 / 1123 / 1817 / 2336	0256 / 0825 / 1541 / 2115	2.1E / 1.9F / 2.3E / 1.5F
5 Tu	0608 / 1202 / 1854	0344 / 0853 / 1623 / 2142	2.1E / 1.8F / 2.2E / 1.5F
6 W ●	0017 / 0649 / 1238 / 1927	0429 / 0917 / 1700 / 2148	2.1E / 1.8F / 2.2E / 1.5F
7 Th	0056 / 0730 / 1314 / 2000	0509 / 0946 / 1732 / 2208	2.0E / 1.9F / 2.1E / 1.7F
8 F	0134 / 0810 / 1349 / 2034	0546 / 1021 / 1758 / 2239	2.0E / 1.9F / 2.1E / 1.9F
9 Sa	0211 / 0851 / 1425 / 2110	0620 / 1059 / 1808 / 2317	1.9E / 2.0F / 2.1E / 2.0F
10 Su	0249 / 0935 / 1504 / 2148	0651 / 1141 / 1822 / 2359	1.9E / 1.9F / 2.1E / 2.2F
11 M	0330 / 1023 / 1546 / 2231	0708 / 1228 / 1900	1.9E / 1.8F / 2.1E
12 Tu	0415 / 1117 / 1634 / 2319	0046 / 0744 / 1320 / 1946	2.2F / 1.8E / 1.7F / 2.1E
13 W	0507 / 1215 / 1728	0136 / 0917 / 1414 / 2038	2.3F / 1.8E / 1.5F / 2.0E
14 Th ◐	0012 / 0607 / 1318 / 1830	0229 / 1047 / 1512 / 2141	2.2F / 1.8E / 1.4F / 1.8E
15 F	0111 / 0712 / 1422 / 1934	0326 / 1157 / 1615 / 2338	2.1F / 1.9E / 1.3F / 1.8E
16 Sa	0212 / 0819 / 1525 / 2039	0427 / 1259 / 1726	2.0F / 2.1E / 1.3F
17 Su	0316 / 0925 / 1626 / 2143	0053 / 0533 / 1358 / 1839	1.9E / 2.0F / 2.2E / 1.4F
18 M	0420 / 1028 / 1722 / 2243	0159 / 0641 / 1454 / 1943	2.1E / 2.0F / 2.4E / 1.5F
19 Tu	0522 / 1125 / 1813 / 2339	0302 / 0746 / 1548 / 2038	2.3E / 2.1F / 2.5E / 1.7F
20 W ○	0620 / 1218 / 1900	0400 / 0847 / 1637 / 2126	2.5E / 2.1F / 2.7E / 1.9F
21 Th	0033 / 0715 / 1307 / 1946	0453 / 0942 / 1723 / 2210	2.6E / 2.2F / 2.7E / 2.1F
22 F	0126 / 0807 / 1355 / 2030	0544 / 1032 / 1808 / 2252	2.7E / 2.1F / 2.7E / 2.2F
23 Sa	0217 / 0859 / 1441 / 2114	0634 / 1120 / 1853 / 2335	2.7E / 2.0F / 2.6E / 2.2F
24 Su	0308 / 0950 / 1527 / 2159	0724 / 1211 / 1937	2.7E / 1.9F / 2.5E
25 M	0357 / 1042 / 1614 / 2246	0021 / 0814 / 1309 / 2022	2.2F / 2.5E / 1.7F / 2.4E
26 Tu	0447 / 1136 / 1704 / 2335	0111 / 0905 / 1413 / 2109	2.1F / 2.4E / 1.6F / 2.3E
27 W ◑	0540 / 1233 / 1757	0204 / 0959 / 1520 / 2200	2.0F / 2.3E / 1.5F / 2.1E
28 Th	0028 / 0634 / 1330 / 1851	0300 / 1054 / 1628 / 2254	1.9F / 2.2E / 1.4F / 2.1E
29 F	0122 / 0728 / 1425 / 1946	0402 / 1149 / 1732 / 2349	1.8F / 2.2E / 1.4F / 2.1E
30 Sa	0217 / 0822 / 1519 / 2040	0519 / 1240 / 1827	1.7F / 2.2E / 1.4F
31 Su	0312 / 0914 / 1609 / 2133	0042 / 0624 / 1329 / 1917	2.1F / 1.7F / 2.2E / 1.5F

Time meridian 75° W.   0000 is midnight.   1200 is noon.   Times are not adjusted for Daylight Saving Time.

Reedy Point, Delaware Bay, 2019

F–Flood, Dir. 353° True   E–Ebb, Dir. 162° True

April

	Slack	Maximum			Slack	Maximum	
	h m	h m	knots		h m	h m	knots
1 M	0405 1003 1655 2222	0134 0714 1417 2002	2.1E 1.7F 2.2E 1.5F	**16** Tu	0409 1008 1654 2230	0146 0635 1427 1930	2.2E 1.8F 2.4E 1.7F
2 Tu	0456 1048 1736 2308	0225 0755 1502 2039	2.1E 1.7F 2.2E 1.5F	**17** W	0510 1103 1744 2325	0246 0744 1520 2021	2.4E 1.9F 2.5E 1.9F
3 W	0543 1129 1813 2351	0316 0826 1545 2056	2.1E 1.7F 2.1E 1.6F	**18** Th	0608 1153 1831	0342 0844 1609 2107	2.6E 2.0F 2.6E 2.1F
4 Th	0627 1208 1849	0403 0853 1623 2108	2.1E 1.7F 2.1E 1.7F	**19** F ○	0016 0701 1240 1916	0435 0936 1655 2148	2.8E 2.0F 2.6E 2.2F
5 F ●	0030 0710 1245 1924	0447 0924 1657 2136	2.1E 1.8F 2.1E 1.9F	**20** Sa	0105 0752 1326 1959	0525 1022 1740 2226	2.8E 2.0F 2.6E 2.3F
6 Sa	0108 0752 1322 2000	0528 1000 1726 2211	2.1E 1.8F 2.1E 2.1F	**21** Su	0152 0841 1411 2042	0613 1105 1823 2305	2.8E 1.9F 2.5E 2.3F
7 Su	0145 0836 1400 2038	0608 1039 1747 2249	2.1E 1.8F 2.1E 2.3F	**22** M	0238 0929 1457 2126	0701 1151 1906 2346	2.6E 1.8F 2.3E 2.2F
8 M	0224 0921 1441 2119	0650 1121 1807 2332	2.0E 1.8F 2.0E 2.4F	**23** Tu	0324 1018 1544 2211	0748 1241 1950	2.5E 1.6F 2.2E
9 Tu	0305 1009 1525 2204	0734 1207 1844	2.0E 1.7F 2.0E	**24** W	0410 1107 1632 2258	0030 0836 1338 2034	2.1F 2.3E 1.5F 2.1E
10 W	0351 1101 1616 2254	0019 0826 1259 1934	2.4F 1.9E 1.6F 1.9E	**25** Th	0458 1159 1723 2349	0119 0925 1439 2121	1.9F 2.2E 1.4F 1.9E
11 Th	0444 1159 1713 2351	0111 0926 1355 2037	2.3F 1.9E 1.5F 1.8E	**26** F ◔	0550 1252 1817	0211 1016 1543 2214	1.8F 2.1E 1.3F 1.9E
12 F ◑	0546 1159 1817	0207 1033 1454 2217	2.2F 1.9E 1.4F 1.8E	**27** Sa	0044 0643 1343 1912	0306 1108 1649 2311	1.7F 2.0E 1.3F 1.9E
13 Sa	0053 0653 1401 1923	0305 1137 1558 2338	2.0F 2.0E 1.3F 1.9E	**28** Su	0139 0737 1433 2006	0406 1159 1747	1.6F 2.0E 1.3F
14 Su	0158 0801 1501 2029	0409 1237 1713	1.9F 2.1E 1.4F	**29** M	0235 0830 1521 2059	0007 0518 1246 1836	1.9E 1.5F 2.0E 1.4F
15 M	0304 0906 1559 2131	0044 0520 1333 1829	2.0E 1.8F 2.3E 1.5F	**30** Tu	0331 0920 1607 2149	0059 0623 1331 1915	2.0E 1.5F 2.0E 1.5F

May

	Slack	Maximum			Slack	Maximum	
	h m	h m	knots		h m	h m	knots
1 W	0425 1007 1649 2237	0152 0709 1416 1938	2.1E 1.4F 2.0E 1.6F	**16** Th	0458 1037 1715 2311	0228 0743 1450 2003	2.6E 1.8F 2.5E 2.1F
2 Th	0516 1052 1729 2321	0245 0747 1500 1957	2.1E 1.6F 2.0E 1.7F	**17** F	0555 1126 1802 2359	0324 0838 1540 2046	2.7E 1.8F 2.6E 2.2F
3 F	0604 1134 1809	0336 0823 1542 2027	2.2E 1.6F 2.0E 1.9F	**18** Sa ○	0647 1213 1847	0416 0927 1627 2125	2.8E 1.8F 2.5E 2.3F
4 Sa ●	0002 0650 1214 1848	0424 0900 1622 2104	2.2E 1.6F 2.0E 2.1F	**19** Su	0044 0736 1258 1930	0505 1011 1712 2201	2.8E 1.6F 2.4E 2.3F
5 Su	0042 0736 1255 1928	0510 0939 1659 2143	2.2E 1.6F 2.0E 2.3F	**20** M	0127 0823 1343 2012	0552 1052 1755 2237	2.7E 1.7F 2.3E 2.3F
6 M	0122 0821 1337 2010	0554 1020 1734 2225	2.2E 1.7F 2.0E 2.4F	**21** Tu	0209 0908 1428 2054	0638 1131 1837 2314	2.6E 1.6F 2.2E 2.2F
7 Tu	0203 0908 1422 2055	0641 1103 1813 2310	2.2E 1.6F 2.0E 2.5F	**22** W	0251 0952 1514 2137	0722 1211 1918 2355	2.4E 1.5F 2.0E 2.1F
8 W	0247 0956 1511 2143	0729 1150 1901 2358	2.2E 1.6F 1.9E 2.4F	**23** Th	0334 1037 1600 2222	0805 1256 1959	2.2E 1.4F 1.9E
9 Th	0337 1048 1605 2237	0821 1242 2002	2.1E 1.5F 1.9E	**24** F	0419 1122 1648 2311	0039 0848 1343 2041	1.9F 2.1E 1.3F 1.8E
10 F	0432 1143 1705 2337	0051 0916 1340 2109	2.2F 2.1E 1.4F 1.8E	**25** Sa	0507 1210 1739	0128 0932 1430 2129	1.8F 2.0E 1.3F 1.8E
11 Sa ◔	0534 1241 1809	0149 1015 1441 2220	2.1F 2.1E 1.4F 1.9E	**26** Su	0004 0558 1257 1833	0220 1018 1516 2225	1.7F 1.9E 1.3F 1.7E
12 Su	0041 0639 1340 1915	0250 1115 1547 2329	1.9F 2.2E 1.5F 2.0E	**27** M	0059 0650 1344 1927	0313 1106 1605 2326	1.6F 1.9E 1.3F 1.8E
13 M	0147 0744 1437 2019	0357 1212 1705	1.7F 2.3E 1.6F	**28** Tu	0156 0742 1430 2020	0410 1153 1657	1.5F 1.9E 1.4F
14 Tu	0253 0846 1532 2121	0031 0515 1306 1819	2.2E 1.7F 2.4E 1.8F	**29** W	0253 0834 1516 2112	0022 0512 1237 1744	1.9E 1.4F 2.0E 1.6F
15 W	0358 0943 1625 2218	0130 0638 1358 1914	2.4E 1.7F 2.5E 2.0F	**30** Th	0351 0923 1601 2202	0117 0611 1321 1826	2.0E 1.4F 2.0E 1.7F
				31 F	0446 1012 1645 2249	0213 0703 1408 1908	2.1E 1.4F 2.0E 1.9F

June

	Slack	Maximum			Slack	Maximum	
	h m	h m	knots		h m	h m	knots
1 Sa	0539 1058 1730 2334	0308 0750 1458 1950	2.2E 1.4F 2.0E 2.1F	**16** Su	0632 1147 1820	0356 0916 1600 2105	2.8E 1.7F 2.4E 2.3F
2 Su	0630 1144 1814	0401 0835 1549 2034	2.3E 1.5F 2.0E 2.3F	**17** M ○	0023 0719 1233 1903	0444 1000 1646 2140	2.7E 1.7F 2.3E 2.2F
3 M	0017 0719 1229 1900	0451 0919 1637 2118	2.3E 1.5F 2.0E 2.4F	**18** Tu	0103 0804 1317 1945	0530 1039 1729 2212	2.6E 1.6F 2.2E 2.2F
4 Tu	0101 0806 1316 1947	0539 1003 1724 2204	2.4E 1.5F 2.0E 2.5F	**19** W	0142 0846 1401 2026	0613 1112 1810 2247	2.5E 1.5F 2.0E 2.1F
5 W	0147 0854 1406 2036	0627 1048 1814 2251	2.4E 1.5F 2.0E 2.5F	**20** Th	0222 0925 1444 2107	0654 1141 1849 2324	2.3E 1.4F 1.9E 2.1F
6 Th	0236 0942 1459 2128	0717 1135 1909 2341	2.4E 1.5F 2.0E 2.4F	**21** F	0302 1004 1528 2150	0733 1212 1925	2.2E 1.4F 1.8E
7 F	0328 1032 1556 2225	0807 1228 2006	2.3E 1.5F 2.0E	**22** Sa	0343 1044 1612 2235	0005 0809 1250 2000	2.0F 2.1E 1.4F 1.7E
8 Sa	0424 1125 1656 2325	0036 0859 1326 2106	2.2F 2.3E 1.5F 2.0E	**23** Su	0427 1126 1700 2325	0051 0840 1332 2035	1.9F 2.0E 1.4F 1.7E
9 Su	0523 1220 1800	0135 0953 1429 2210	2.0F 2.3E 1.6F 2.1E	**24** M	0514 1209 1751	0140 0904 1416 2122	1.8F 1.9E 1.5F 1.7E
10 M ◑	0030 0624 1316 1905	0239 1050 1536 2313	1.8F 2.4E 1.7F 2.2E	**25** Tu ◔	0020 0603 1254 1844	0231 0925 1503 2233	1.7F 1.9E 1.6F 1.7E
11 Tu	0135 0724 1410 2007	0350 1145 1653	1.6F 2.4E 1.8F	**26** W	0117 0655 1340 1938	0324 1012 1551 2341	1.5F 1.9E 1.7F 1.8E
12 W	0240 0822 1504 2107	0014 0519 1237 1802	2.4E 1.6F 2.5E 2.0F	**27** Th	0216 0747 1427 2031	0420 1114 1643	1.4F 1.9E 1.8F
13 Th	0344 0917 1556 2203	0112 0635 1329 1856	2.5E 1.6F 2.5E 2.1F	**28** F	0316 0839 1515 2124	0042 0521 1212 1735	1.9E 1.3F 1.9E 1.9F
14 F	0444 1010 1646 2254	0208 0734 1420 1944	2.6E 1.7F 2.5E 2.2F	**29** Sa	0416 0932 1605 2215	0141 0621 1309 1827	2.0E 1.3F 1.9E 2.1F
15 Sa	0540 1100 1734 2341	0303 0827 1511 2027	2.7E 1.7F 2.5E 2.3F	**30** Su	0514 1024 1655 2305	0241 0717 1415 1917	2.1E 1.3F 1.9E 2.2F

Reedy Point, Delaware Bay, 2019

F–Flood, Dir. 353° True   E–Ebb, Dir. 162° True

July

Day	Slack (h m)	Maximum (h m)	knots
1 M	0608	0338	2.3E
	1115	0809	1.3F
	1746	1521	1.9E
	2354	2007	2.3F
2 Tu ●	0700	0431	2.4E
	1205	0859	1.4F
	1837	1620	2.0E
		2057	2.4F
3 W	0043	0521	2.5E
	0749	0947	1.5F
	1257	1713	2.0E
	1929	2147	2.5F
4 Th	0134	0610	2.5E
	0837	1033	1.5F
	1350	1806	2.1E
	2022	2236	2.4F
5 F	0227	0659	2.5E
	0924	1121	1.6F
	1447	1901	2.2E
	2116	2328	2.3F
6 Sa	0320	0748	2.5E
	1012	1214	1.6F
	1544	1956	2.2E
	2213		
7 Su	0413	0023	2.1F
	1103	0837	2.5E
	1644	1312	1.7F
	2313	2053	2.3E
8 M	0508	0125	1.9F
	1155	0928	2.5E
	1746	1414	1.8F
		2153	2.3E
9 Tu ◐	0016	0231	1.7F
	0603	0825	2.5E
	1248	1519	1.9F
	1849	2254	2.4E
10 W	0120	0346	1.6F
	0700	1115	2.5E
	1342	1630	2.0F
	1950	2354	2.5E
11 Th	0224	0514	1.6F
	0755	1208	2.5E
	1435	1738	2.1F
	2048		
12 F	0327	0051	2.6E
	0850	0622	1.6F
	1528	1300	2.5E
	2143	1835	2.2F
13 Sa	0427	0146	2.6E
	0944	0718	1.6F
	1619	1352	2.5E
	2234	1924	2.2F
14 Su	0522	0241	2.7E
	1035	0811	1.7F
	1709	1444	2.4E
	2320	2010	2.2F
15 M	0613	0333	2.7E
	1124	0900	1.7F
	1756	1534	2.3E
		2050	2.2F
16 Tu ○	0001	0422	2.6E
	0659	0945	1.6F
	1210	1621	2.2E
	1840	2123	2.1F
17 W	0040	0506	2.6E
	0741	1023	1.5F
	1253	1705	2.1E
	1922	2153	2.1F
18 Th	0118	0547	2.4E
	0820	1052	1.5F
	1335	1745	2.0E
	2002	2223	2.0F
19 F	0155	0625	2.3E
	0856	1109	1.4F
	1415	1822	1.9E
	2041	2257	2.0F
20 Sa	0233	0659	2.2E
	0930	1134	1.4F
	1456	1855	1.8E
	2122	2336	2.0F
21 Su	0311	0726	2.1E
	1006	1207	1.5F
	1537	1919	1.8E
	2204		
22 M	0351	0018	1.9F
	1043	0732	2.0E
	1621	1247	1.6F
	2251	1934	1.7E
23 Tu	0433	0105	1.8F
	1123	0745	2.1E
	1708	1332	1.7F
	2344	2012	1.7E
24 W ◐	0519	0154	1.7F
	1207	0825	2.1E
	1759	1419	1.8F
		2104	1.7E
25 Th	0041	0246	1.6F
	0609	0912	2.1E
	1254	1508	1.9F
	1853	2252	1.7E
26 F	0141	0341	1.4F
	0703	1005	2.0E
	1344	1559	2.0F
	1949		
27 Sa	0243	0009	1.8E
	0759	0441	1.3F
	1435	1107	1.9E
	2045	1655	2.1F
28 Su	0346	0113	1.9E
	0856	0544	1.2F
	1530	1220	1.9E
	2142	1752	2.1F
29 M	0447	0215	2.1E
	0953	0646	1.2F
	1626	1346	1.8E
	2239	1848	2.2F
30 Tu	0544	0315	2.2E
	1050	0745	1.3F
	1723	1501	1.9E
	2334	1944	2.3F
31 W ●	0637	0410	2.4E
	1144	0840	1.4F
	1819	1604	2.0E
		2039	2.3F

August

Day	Slack (h m)	Maximum (h m)	knots
1 Th	0028	0500	2.5E
	0727	0931	1.5F
	1239	1700	2.2E
	1914	2133	2.4F
2 F	0121	0549	2.6E
	0814	1018	1.7F
	1334	1753	2.3E
	2009	2225	2.3F
3 Sa	0214	0636	2.7E
	0901	1106	1.8F
	1431	1847	2.4E
	2104	2317	2.2F
4 Su	0305	0724	2.7E
	0947	1156	1.9F
	1528	1941	2.5E
	2200		
5 M	0355	0012	2.1F
	1036	0811	2.6E
	1626	1251	1.9F
	2258	2036	2.5E
6 Tu	0446	0114	1.9F
	1126	0900	2.6E
	1725	1351	2.0F
	2359	2132	2.5E
7 W ◐	0539	0222	1.7F
	1218	0951	2.5E
	1825	1452	2.0F
		2231	2.5E
8 Th	0101	0338	1.6F
	0633	1044	2.5E
	1312	1558	2.0F
	1925	2330	2.5E
9 F	0204	0457	1.5F
	0729	1139	2.5E
	1406	1709	2.1F
	2022		
10 Sa	0305	0027	2.5E
	0824	0602	1.6F
	1500	1232	2.5E
	2117	1811	2.1F
11 Su	0404	0122	2.6E
	0919	0659	1.6F
	1553	1324	2.4E
	2209	1905	2.1F
12 M	0459	0215	2.6E
	1012	0751	1.6F
	1645	1416	2.4E
	2255	1953	2.1F
13 Tu	0549	0307	2.6E
	1101	0840	1.6F
	1733	1508	2.3E
	2338	2036	2.0F
14 W	0634	0355	2.5E
	1147	0925	1.6F
	1818	1556	2.2E
		2111	2.0F
15 Th ○	0017	0439	2.4E
	0714	1003	1.6F
	1229	1641	2.1E
	1900	2137	1.9F
16 F	0053	0518	2.3E
	0749	1026	1.5F
	1309	1721	1.9E
	1939	2203	1.9F
17 Sa	0129	0553	2.2E
	0822	1036	1.5F
	1348	1757	1.9E
	2018	2234	2.0F
18 Su	0204	0623	2.1E
	0855	1058	1.6F
	1425	1830	1.9E
	2057	2309	2.0F
19 M	0240	0641	2.1E
	0928	1131	1.7F
	1503	1851	1.8E
	2139	2349	1.9F
20 Tu	0317	0634	2.1E
	1003	1210	1.9F
	1543	1854	1.8E
	2224		
21 W	0357	0034	1.9F
	1042	0705	2.2E
	1626	1254	2.0F
	2314	1932	1.8E
22 Th	0441	0123	1.8F
	1126	0748	2.2E
	1715	1342	2.1F
		2020	1.8E
23 F ○	0011	0215	1.6F
	0530	0836	2.1E
	1215	1432	2.2F
	1809	2119	1.7E
24 Sa	0111	0309	1.5F
	0626	0928	2.0E
	1307	1525	2.2F
	1908	2341	1.8E
25 Su	0214	0408	1.3F
	0726	1031	1.9E
	1404	1621	2.1F
	2010		
26 M	0318	0048	1.9E
	0827	0513	1.2F
	1503	1208	1.8E
	2113	1722	2.1F
27 Tu	0420	0150	2.1E
	0929	0620	1.2F
	1605	1335	1.9E
	2215	1824	2.1F
28 W	0518	0250	2.2E
	1029	0723	1.3F
	1706	1446	2.0E
	2315	1925	2.2F
29 Th	0611	0346	2.4E
	1126	0821	1.5F
	1805	1549	2.2E
		2025	2.2F
30 F ●	0010	0437	2.6E
	0701	0913	1.7F
	1222	1645	2.4E
	1902	2122	2.2F
31 Sa	0103	0524	2.7E
	0748	1001	1.9F
	1317	1738	2.6E
	1957	2215	2.2F

September

Day	Slack (h m)	Maximum (h m)	knots
1 Su	0154	0611	2.7E
	0833	1047	2.0F
	1413	1830	2.6E
	2051	2306	2.2F
2 M	0243	0657	2.7E
	0919	1134	2.1F
	1508	1922	2.7E
	2145		
3 Tu	0331	0000	2.0F
	1005	0743	2.6E
	1602	1224	2.1F
	2240	2015	2.6E
4 W	0420	0100	1.8F
	1054	0831	2.6E
	1658	1320	2.1F
	2338	2109	2.5E
5 Th	0511	0208	1.7F
	1146	0920	2.5E
	1754	1418	2.1F
		2206	2.5E
6 F	0038	0321	1.6F
	0605	1012	2.4E
	1240	1520	2.0F
	1852	2303	2.4E
7 Sa	0138	0433	1.5F
	0701	1108	2.3E
	1335	1631	2.0F
	1949		
8 Su	0238	0000	2.4E
	0758	0539	1.5F
	1431	1203	2.3E
	2044	1743	1.9F
9 M	0335	0054	2.4E
	0853	0636	1.6F
	1526	1256	2.3E
	2136	1841	1.9F
10 Tu	0429	0145	2.4E
	0947	0727	1.6F
	1620	1349	2.3E
	2225	1932	1.9F
11 W	0518	0236	2.4E
	1037	0816	1.7F
	1710	1440	2.3E
	2309	2017	1.9F
12 Th	0601	0323	2.4E
	1122	0900	1.6F
	1756	1530	2.2E
	2348	2055	1.9F
13 F	0639	0406	2.3E
	1205	0935	1.6F
	1838	1615	2.2E
		2120	1.8F
14 Sa	0025	0445	2.3E
	0713	0952	1.6F
	1244	1657	2.1E
	1918	2142	1.8F
15 Su	0100	0518	2.2E
	0746	1000	1.7F
	1321	1735	2.0E
	1957	2211	1.9F
16 M	0135	0546	2.1E
	0818	1026	1.8F
	1356	1810	2.0E
	2037	2245	1.9F
17 Tu	0210	0559	2.1E
	0851	1059	2.0F
	1432	1839	1.9E
	2118	2324	1.9F
18 W	0247	0601	2.1E
	0927	1138	2.2F
	1510	1841	1.9E
	2203		
19 Th	0326	0007	1.8F
	1007	0635	2.1E
	1551	1222	2.3F
		1907	1.9E
20 F ◐	0410	0056	1.7F
	1052	0719	2.1E
	1638	1310	2.3F
	2347	1954	1.8E
21 Sa ○	0501	0148	1.6F
	1143	0809	2.0E
	1733	1402	2.3F
		2058	1.8E
22 Su	0047	0243	1.4F
	0559	0904	1.9E
	1240	1456	2.2F
	1836	2319	1.8E
23 M	0149	0342	1.3F
	0703	1016	1.8E
	1340	1555	2.1F
	1942		
24 Tu	0252	0026	1.9E
	0807	0448	1.3F
	1444	1215	1.8E
	2049	1659	2.0F
25 W	0353	0126	2.1E
	0911	0558	1.3F
	1549	1326	1.9E
	2154	1806	2.0F
26 Th	0450	0224	2.2E
	1013	0703	1.5F
	1652	1431	2.1E
	2254	1912	2.0F
27 F	0543	0319	2.4E
	1110	0802	1.7F
	1753	1532	2.4E
		2015	2.1F
28 Sa ●	0632	0410	2.5E
	1205	0854	1.9F
	1849	1628	2.6E
		2114	2.1F
29 Su	0040	0458	2.6E
	0718	0940	2.1F
	1259	1720	2.7E
	1944	2206	2.1F
30 M	0129	0544	2.7E
	0804	1024	2.2F
	1352	1811	2.8E
	2036	2255	2.0F

Time meridian 75° W. 0000 is midnight. 1200 is noon. Times are not adjusted for Daylight Saving Time.

Reedy Point, Delaware Bay, 2019

F–Flood, Dir. 353° True   E–Ebb, Dir. 162° True

October

Day	Slack h m	Maximum h m	knots	Day	Slack h m	Maximum h m	knots
1 Tu	0217	0629	2.6E	**16** W	0142	0528	2.0E
	0849	1108	2.3F		0817	1030	2.2F
	1444	1902	2.7E		1405	1830	2.0E
	2128	2346	1.9F		2101	2302	1.7F
2 W	0304	0715	2.6E	**17** Th	0221	0540	2.0E
	0935	1155	2.3F		0856	1110	2.3F
	1535	1953	2.7E		1442	1908	2.0E
	2221				2146	2345	1.7F
3 Th		0042	1.7F	**18** F	0303	0614	2.0E
	0353	0801	2.5E		0938	1155	2.4F
	1022	1245	2.2F		1524	1950	1.9E
	1626	2044	2.5E		2235		
	2315						
4 F		0147	1.6F	**19** Sa		0033	1.6F
	0443	0849	2.3E		0349	0700	1.9E
	1113	1340	2.1F		1026	1244	2.3F
	1719	2137	2.4E		1612	2045	1.9E
					2329		
5 Sa ◑	0011	0257	1.5F	**20** Su		0126	1.5F
	0537	0941	2.2E		0442	0754	1.8E
	1207	1439	1.9F		1120	1337	2.2F
	1814	2233	2.3E		1709	2152	1.9E
6 Su	0109	0405	1.5F	**21** M ◯	0027	0223	1.4F
	0633	1036	2.2E		0543	0901	1.8E
	1303	1544	1.8F		1220	1434	2.1F
	1909	2328	2.3E		1813	2301	1.9E
7 M	0205	0510	1.5F	**22** Tu	0127	0322	1.4F
	0729	1132	2.2E		0649	1054	1.7E
	1359	1704	1.8F		1324	1534	1.9F
	2004				1922		
8 Tu		0021	2.3E	**23** W		0003	2.0E
	0259	0607	1.5F		0227	0428	1.4F
	0824	1226	2.2E		0754	1210	1.9E
	1456	1811	1.8F		1430	1641	1.8F
	2057				2029		
9 W		0111	2.3E	**24** Th		0101	2.2E
	0351	0659	1.6F		0325	0540	1.5F
	0918	1318	2.2E		0858	1314	2.1E
	1551	1904	1.8F		1536	1753	1.8F
	2147				2132		
10 Th		0158	2.3E	**25** F		0156	2.3E
	0438	0745	1.6F		0421	0646	1.7F
	1008	1410	2.2E		0959	1416	2.3E
	1643	1950	1.8F		1640	1905	1.8F
	2232				2230		
11 F		0244	2.2E	**26** Sa		0250	2.4E
	0520	0827	1.7F		0513	0743	1.9F
	1055	1500	2.2E		1056	1515	2.5E
	1731	2029	1.7F		1741	2010	1.9F
	2314				2324		
12 Sa		0327	2.2E	**27** Su ●		0342	2.5E
	0558	0857	1.7F		0602	0833	2.1F
	1137	1548	2.2E		1150	1611	2.7E
	1815	2056	1.7F		1837	2107	1.9F
	2353						
13 Su ◯		0406	2.2E	**28** M	0013	0430	2.6E
	0633	0905	1.7F		0649	0919	2.3F
	1217	1632	2.2E		1241	1702	2.8E
	1857	2119	1.7F		1930	2157	1.9F
14 M	0029	0441	2.1E	**29** Tu	0101	0516	2.6E
	0707	0924	1.9F		0734	1001	2.3F
	1254	1713	2.1E		1330	1752	2.8E
	1938	2148	1.7F		2021	2244	1.9F
15 Tu	0106	0510	2.1E	**30** W	0149	0601	2.5E
	0741	0954	2.0F		0819	1043	2.4F
	1329	1752	2.1E		1418	1841	2.8E
	2019	2223	1.7F		2110	2330	1.8F
				31 Th	0236	0647	2.4E
					0904	1125	2.3F
					1505	1930	2.6E
					2159		

November

Day	Slack h m	Maximum h m	knots	Day	Slack h m	Maximum h m	knots
1 F		0021	1.7F	**16** Sa	0245	0618	1.9E
	0325	0732	2.3E		0917	1133	2.4F
	0951	1211	2.2F		1507	1951	2.1E
	1553	2018	2.5E		2220		
	2249						
2 Sa		0121	1.5F	**17** Su		0014	1.5F
	0415	0819	2.2E		0336	0713	1.8E
	1040	1302	2.0F		1008	1223	2.3F
	1642	2107	2.3E		1558	2043	2.0E
	2341				2313		
3 Su		0225	1.4F	**18** M		0108	1.5F
	0507	0908	2.1E		0432	0824	1.8E
	1132	1357	1.9F		1104	1318	2.2F
	1733	2158	2.2E		1656	2140	2.0E
4 M ◑	0034	0328	1.4F	**19** Tu ◯	0008	0206	1.5F
	0601	1001	2.0E		0534	0939	1.8E
	1227	1455	1.7F		1207	1417	2.0F
	1827	2250	2.1E		1759	2240	2.1E
5 Tu	0126	0431	1.4F	**20** W	0106	0306	1.5F
	0656	1057	2.0E		0639	1052	1.9E
	1324	1600	1.6F		1312	1519	1.8F
	1921	2341	2.1E		1905	2339	2.2E
6 W	0216	0530	1.5F	**21** Th	0202	0412	1.5F
	0751	1153	2.0E		0744	1159	2.1E
	1421	1721	1.6F		1419	1628	1.7F
	2013				2008		
7 Th		0029	2.1E	**22** F		0034	2.3E
	0304	0621	1.5F		0258	0524	1.7F
	0844	1245	2.1E		0847	1300	2.3E
	1516	1824	1.6F		1525	1747	1.6F
	2103				2108		
8 F		0114	2.1E	**23** Sa		0128	2.4E
	0350	0705	1.6F		0352	0630	1.9F
	0935	1337	2.1E		0947	1359	2.5E
	1611	1912	1.6F		1628	1903	1.7F
	2150				2205		
9 Sa		0158	2.1E	**24** Su		0220	2.4E
	0432	0739	1.7F		0444	0725	2.1F
	1023	1428	2.2E		1043	1457	2.6E
	1702	1951	1.5F		1728	2006	1.7F
	2235				2257		
10 Su		0241	2.1E	**25** M		0313	2.5E
	0512	0756	1.7F		0533	0813	2.2F
	1107	1519	2.2E		1134	1552	2.8E
	1750	2023	1.5F		1823	2100	1.8F
	2317				2347		
11 M		0323	2.0E	**26** Tu ●		0403	2.5E
	0551	0816	1.9F		0621	0858	2.3F
	1148	1607	2.2E		1222	1643	2.8E
	1835	2052	1.5F		1915	2149	1.8F
	2357						
12 Tu ◯		0402	2.0E	**27** W	0035	0450	2.5E
	0629	0848	2.0F		0707	0940	2.4F
	1226	1652	2.2E		1308	1732	2.8E
	1919	2125	1.5F		2004	2233	1.7F
13 W	0036	0438	2.0E	**28** Th	0122	0536	2.4E
	0707	0924	2.2F		0752	1019	2.3F
	1303	1735	2.2E		1352	1819	2.7E
	2003	2202	1.6F		2051	2316	1.7F
14 Th	0117	0510	2.0E	**29** F	0210	0620	2.3E
	0748	1004	2.4F		0837	1059	2.3F
	1341	1818	2.2E		1436	1905	2.6E
	2047	2242	1.6F		2136	2359	1.6F
15 F	0159	0540	1.9E	**30** Sa	0257	0705	2.1E
	0831	1047	2.4F		0922	1141	2.1F
	1422	1903	2.1E		1520	1950	2.4E
	2132	2326	1.6F		2221		

December

Day	Slack h m	Maximum h m	knots	Day	Slack h m	Maximum h m	knots
1 Su		0047	1.5F	**16** M	0325	0734	1.9E
	0345	0749	2.0E		0955	1207	2.2F
	1008	1226	2.0F		1551	2029	2.3E
	1606	2034	2.3E		2255		
	2307						
2 M		0139	1.4F	**17** Tu		0052	1.6F
	0434	0834	1.9E		0423	0833	1.9E
	1057	1317	1.9F		1053	1303	2.1F
	1653	2119	2.1E		1647	2121	2.2E
	2354				2348		
3 Tu		0231	1.4F	**18** W ◯		0150	1.6F
	0525	0923	1.9E		0525	0935	2.0E
	1150	1409	1.7F		1155	1404	1.9F
	1743	2204	2.0E		1746	2216	2.3E
4 W ◑	0042	0320	1.4F	**19** Th		0251	1.7F
	0618	1016	1.8E		0629	1040	2.1E
	1245	1504	1.6F		1301	1508	1.7F
	1835	2251	2.0E		1847	2312	2.3E
5 Th	0128	0411	1.4F	**20** F	0137	0356	1.8F
	0712	1113	1.9E		0732	1144	2.2E
	1341	1602	1.5F		1407	1621	1.6F
	1926	2337	2.0E		1946		
6 F	0213	0501	1.5F	**21** Sa		0007	2.4E
	0805	1208	1.9E		0231	0507	1.9F
	1438	1707	1.4F		0834	1244	2.4E
	2016				1512	1749	1.5F
					2044		
7 Sa		0021	2.0E	**22** Su		0100	2.4E
	0258	0542	1.6F		0324	0614	2.1F
	0856	1301	2.0E		0933	1341	2.6E
	1535	1810	1.4F		1615	1900	1.6F
	2105				2139		
8 Su		0104	2.0E	**23** M		0152	2.5E
	0342	0617	1.7F		0417	0708	2.2F
	0946	1355	2.1E		1027	1438	2.7E
	1630	1859	1.4F		1714	1958	1.6F
	2153				2233		
9 M		0147	2.0E	**24** Tu		0245	2.4E
	0426	0653	1.9F		0508	0757	2.3F
	1033	1449	2.1E		1117	1532	2.7E
	1723	1941	1.3F		1809	2051	1.7F
	2239				2323		
10 Tu		0234	1.9E	**25** W		0337	2.4E
	0510	0732	2.0F		0556	0842	2.3F
	1117	1541	2.2E		1203	1623	2.8E
	1812	2021	1.4F		1859	2139	1.7F
	2324						
11 W		0324	1.9E	**26** Th ●	0012	0426	2.4E
	0553	0814	2.2F		0643	0922	2.3F
	1159	1630	2.3E		1247	1711	2.7E
	1859	2102	1.4F		1946	2222	1.7F
12 Th ◯	0009	0412	1.9E	**27** F	0059	0512	2.3E
	0638	0857	2.3F		0728	1000	2.2F
	1240	1717	2.3E		1328	1756	2.6E
	1945	2143	1.5F		2030	2301	1.6F
13 F	0054	0459	1.9E	**28** Sa	0145	0556	2.2E
	0724	0941	2.4F		0812	1036	2.2F
	1323	1803	2.3E		1409	1839	2.5E
	2031	2225	1.5F		2111	2335	1.5F
14 Sa	0141	0546	1.9E	**29** Su	0230	0638	2.0E
	0811	1027	2.4F		0855	1114	2.1F
	1409	1851	2.3E		1450	1920	2.4E
	2117	2310	1.5F		2151		
15 Su	0231	0638	1.9E	**30** M		0008	1.4F
	0901	1115	2.4F		0314	0719	1.9E
	1458	1939	2.3E		0938	1155	2.0F
	2204	2358	1.6F		1532	1959	2.2E
					2231		
				31 Tu		0044	1.4F
					0359	0800	1.8E
					1023	1240	1.9F
					1615	2035	2.1E
					2312		

Time meridian 75° W.   0000 is midnight.   1200 is noon.   Times are not adjusted for Daylight Saving Time.

Philadelphia (Penns Landing), Delaware River, 2019

F–Flood, Dir. 017° True   E–Ebb, Dir. 201° True

January

Day	Slack	Maximum		Day	Slack	Maximum
	h m	h m / knots			h m	h m / knots
1 Tu	0531	0111 2.3E	16 W	0433	0018 2.2E
	1048	0824 1.8F		0939	0635 1.5F
	1817	1538 2.0E		1740	1251 1.6E
	2256	2058 1.5F		2152	1918 0.9F
2 W	0621	0158 2.3E	17 Th	0532	0109 2.1E
	1142	0921 1.9F		1048	0736 1.5F
	1917	1633 2.2E		1847	1351 1.6E
	2350	2154 1.6F		2300	2031 1.0F
3 Th	0710	0248 2.3E	18 F	0630	0201 2.1E
	1230	1010 2.1F		1148	0842 1.7F
	2012	1724 2.3E		1948	1714 1.8E
		2243 1.6F		2359	2142 1.1F
4 F	0040	0334 2.2E	19 Sa	0727	0253 2.1E
	0756	1050 2.1F		1242	0944 1.9F
	1315	1813 2.3E		2043	1815 2.0E
	2100	2326 1.6F			2237 1.3F
5 Sa ●	0127	0415 2.2E	20 Su	0054	0343 2.1E
	0838	1122 2.0F		0821	1036 2.1F
	1356	1857 2.2E		1332	1909 2.2E
	2141			2132	2324 1.5F
6 Su	0209	0005 1.4F	21 M ○	0146	0429 2.1E
	0915	0453 2.1E		0911	1125 2.2F
	1433	1144 1.9F		1420	1955 2.3E
	2218	1744 2.1E		2218	
7 M	0247	0035 1.2F	22 Tu	0237	0012 1.6F
	0950	0531 2.0E		0959	0516 2.0E
	1505	1205 1.8F		1507	1214 2.3F
	2252	1810 2.1E		2305	2035 2.3E
8 Tu	0320	0047 1.1F	23 W	0327	0100 1.6F
	1023	0610 1.9E		1049	0608 1.9E
	1533	1234 1.7F		1555	1304 2.2F
	2325	1844 2.2E		2353	2110 2.3E
9 W	0348	0108 1.1F	24 Th	0420	0149 1.6F
	1056	0651 1.9E		1141	0708 1.9E
	1558	1309 1.7F		1645	1355 2.1F
	2357	1922 2.3E			2122 2.3E
10 Th	0414	0140 1.1F	25 F	0042	0239 1.6F
	1132	0731 1.8E		0516	0806 1.8E
	1626	1349 1.6F		1237	1448 1.9F
		2001 2.3E		1740	2109 2.3E
11 F	0032	0218 1.2F	26 Sa	0133	0333 1.5F
	0443	0812 1.8E		0616	0902 1.8E
	1215	1432 1.6F		1336	1545 1.7F
	1700	2042 2.3E		1837	2201 2.3E
12 Sa	0110	0301 1.3F	27 Su ◐	0224	0435 1.5F
	0524	0854 1.7E		0718	1011 1.7E
	1306	1520 1.5F		1438	1656 1.5F
	1743	2128 2.3E		1935	2306 2.3E
13 Su	0153	0349 1.3F	28 M	0317	0546 1.5F
	0615	0943 1.7E		0819	1249 1.7E
	1407	1613 1.3F		1543	1815 1.4E
	1834	2223 2.3E		2034	
14 M ◑	0242	0442 1.4F	29 Tu	0410	0000 2.3E
	0715	1045 1.6E		0922	0653 1.6F
	1515	1712 1.2F		1649	1401 1.8E
	1931	2322 2.2E		2134	1928 1.3F
15 Tu	0336	0538 1.4F	30 W	0503	0046 2.3E
	0823	1151 1.6E		1021	0758 1.6F
	1629	1813 1.0F		1753	1509 1.9E
	2038			2231	2035 1.3F
			31 Th	0553	0130 2.2E
				1115	0858 1.7F
				1853	1606 2.0E
				2324	2133 1.4F

February

Day	Slack	Maximum		Day	Slack	Maximum
	h m	h m / knots			h m	h m / knots
1 F	0642	0215 2.2E	16 Sa	0615	0141 2.0E
	1203	0949 1.7F		1128	0822 1.5F
	1947	1656 2.0E		1927	1700 1.8E
		2222 1.4F		2343	2129 1.1F
2 Sa	0011	0300 2.1E	17 Su	0713	0234 2.0E
	0728	1029 1.7F		1224	0930 1.8F
	1246	1741 2.0E		2021	1755 2.0E
	2033	2303 1.3F			2224 1.4F
3 Su	0054	0341 2.1E	18 M	0037	0325 2.0E
	0809	1056 1.7F		0808	1026 2.0F
	1325	1626 1.9E		1316	1847 2.2E
	2111	2334 1.2F		2109	2310 1.6F
4 M ●	0132	0418 2.0E	19 Tu ○	0129	0413 2.0E
	0846	1108 1.6F		0859	1115 2.2F
	1359	1651 1.9E		1405	1932 2.3E
	2143	2343 1.1F		2155	2355 1.7F
5 Tu	0206	0454 2.0E	20 W	0220	0501 2.1E
	0919	1130 1.7F		0947	1203 2.3F
	1429	1723 2.1E		1453	2011 2.4E
	2212	2357 1.1F		2239	
6 W	0235	0530 2.0E	21 Th	0310	0042 1.8F
	0952	1202 1.7F		1036	0553 2.0E
	1458	1801 2.2E		1542	1253 2.2F
	2241			2325	2042 2.4E
7 Th	0301	0027 1.2F	22 F	0401	0129 1.8F
	1026	0609 2.0E		1126	0655 2.0E
	1528	1241 1.8F		1632	1344 2.2F
		1844 2.3E			2038 2.4E
8 F	0329	0105 1.4F	23 Sa	0013	0217 1.7F
	1105	0651 2.0E		0454	0755 2.0E
	1602	1324 1.8F		1220	1437 2.0F
		1930 2.4E		1726	2052 2.4E
9 Sa	0405	0147 1.5F	24 Su	0103	0307 1.7F
	1152	0736 2.0E		0551	0850 1.9E
	1642	1410 1.8F		1317	1533 1.8F
		2015 2.4E		1821	2137 2.3E
10 Su	0034	0233 1.5F	25 M	0153	0403 1.5F
	0450	0821 1.9E		0650	0951 1.9E
	1247	1459 1.6F		1417	1643 1.6F
	1729	2102 2.3E		1917	2233 2.3E
11 M	0122	0322 1.5F	26 Tu ◐	0245	0511 1.4F
	0544	0909 1.8E		0749	1212 1.8E
	1350	1553 1.5F		1519	1800 1.4F
	1821	2156 2.2E		2013	2331 2.2E
12 Tu ◐	0215	0415 1.5F	27 W	0339	0621 1.4F
	0645	1007 1.7E		0848	1315 1.8E
	1458	1652 1.2F		1622	1907 1.3F
	1919	2257 2.1E		2109	
13 W	0313	0513 1.5F	28 Th	0433	0018 2.2E
	0753	1120 1.6E		0946	0726 1.3F
	1610	1754 1.1F		1724	1424 1.8E
	2024	2356 2.1E		2204	2010 1.2F
14 Th	0414	0612 1.4F			
	0910	1230 1.5E			
	1720	1859 1.0F			
	2136				
15 F	0515	0050 2.0E			
	1025	0714 1.5F			
	1826	1559 1.6E			
	2243	2013 1.0F			

March

Day	Slack	Maximum		Day	Slack	Maximum
	h m	h m / knots			h m	h m / knots
1 F	0524	0101 2.1E	16 Sa	0459	0031 1.9E
	1040	0830 1.3F		0957	0653 1.3F
	1820	1357 1.7E		1802	1538 1.7E
	2254	2108 1.1F		2229	1955 1.0F
2 Sa	0613	0143 2.0E	17 Su	0601	0123 1.9E
	1127	0924 1.3F		1104	0804 1.4F
	1911	1423 1.7E		1901	1636 1.8E
	2339	2156 1.1F		2328	2113 1.2F
3 Su	0658	0225 2.0E	18 M	0700	0217 1.9E
	1208	1003 1.3F		1202	0920 1.6F
	1954	1458 1.7E		1954	1728 2.0E
		2233 1.0F			2209 1.5F
4 M	0019	0306 2.0E	19 Tu	0023	0312 1.9E
	0740	1021 1.3F		0756	1019 1.9F
	1245	1533 1.8E		1256	1817 2.2E
	2028	2248 1.0F		2042	2254 1.7F
5 Tu	0054	0344 2.0E	20 W ○	0114	0404 2.0E
	0817	1030 1.4F		0847	1108 2.1F
	1319	1608 2.0E		1347	1903 2.3E
	2058	2250 1.1F		2127	2338 1.9F
6 W ●	0125	0420 2.1E	21 Th	0205	0452 2.1E
	0852	1059 1.6F		0936	1156 2.2F
	1352	1645 2.1E		1437	1942 2.3E
	2127	2317 1.3F		2211	
7 Th	0154	0456 2.1E	22 F	0254	0022 2.0F
	0928	1136 1.7F		1024	0546 2.2E
	1426	1725 2.2E		1526	1245 2.2F
	2158	2353 1.5F		2256	2009 2.4E
8 F	0225	0535 2.2E	23 Sa	0343	0108 2.0F
	1006	1218 1.9F		1113	0653 2.2E
	1503	1810 2.3E		1616	1336 2.2F
	2234			2342	2000 2.4E
9 Sa	0301	0035 1.6F	24 Su	0433	0154 1.9F
	1050	0618 2.2E		1206	0754 2.2E
	1542	1304 1.9F		1709	1427 2.0F
	2315	1900 2.3E			2029 2.4E
10 Su	0341	0120 1.7F	25 M	0030	0240 1.8F
	1140	0706 2.2E		0526	0841 2.2E
	1626	1352 1.8F		1300	1521 1.8F
		1950 2.3E		1802	2111 2.3E
11 M	0002	0208 1.8F	26 Tu	0120	0328 1.6F
	0427	0754 2.1E		0620	0931 2.0E
	1237	1442 1.7F		1356	1626 1.5F
	1715	2038 2.2E		1856	2200 2.1E
12 Tu ○	0054	0258 1.7F	27 W ◐	0211	0422 1.4F
	0520	0843 1.9E		0714	1032 1.9E
	1339	1535 1.5F		1453	1738 1.3F
	1810	2130 2.1E		1949	2254 2.0E
13 W	0151	0351 1.6F	28 Th	0304	0525 1.2F
	0620	0937 1.8E		0807	1134 1.8E
	1444	1634 1.3F		1551	1841 1.1F
	1909	2230 2.0E		2042	2345 1.9E
14 Th ◑	0251	0449 1.5F	29 F	0358	0628 1.0F
	0727	1049 1.6E		0900	1214 1.7E
	1552	1737 1.1F		1647	1940 1.0F
	2013	2335 1.9E		2133	
15 F	0355	0550 1.4F	30 Sa	0450	0029 1.9E
	0841	1212 1.5E		0951	0732 0.9F
	1659	1842 1.0F		1737	1250 1.7E
	2122			2221	2036 0.9F
			31 Su	0539	0109 1.8E
				1038	0839 0.8F
				1820	1326 1.7E
				2304	2123 0.8F

Time meridian 75° W. 0000 is midnight. 1200 is noon. Times are not adjusted for Daylight Saving Time.

Philadelphia (Penns Landing), Delaware River, 2019

F–Flood, Dir. 017° True   E–Ebb, Dir. 201° True

April

Day	Slack (h m)	Maximum (h m)	knots
1 M		0149	1.8E
	0625	0905	0.8F
	1120	1405	1.7E
	1858	2148	0.8F
	2341		
2 Tu		0230	1.9E
	0707	0914	0.9F
	1159	1447	1.9E
	1933	2135	0.9F
3 W	0016	0310	2.0E
	0749	0951	1.2F
	1237	1529	2.0E
	2007	2206	1.2F
4 Th	0049	0350	2.1E
	0829	1031	1.4F
	1316	1611	2.2E
	2043	2243	1.5F
5 F ●	0123	0428	2.2E
	0910	1113	1.7F
	1357	1654	2.3E
	2120	2324	1.8F
6 Sa	0201	0508	2.3E
	0954	1158	1.8F
	1440	1740	2.3E
	2200		
7 Su		0009	1.9F
	0241	0552	2.3E
	1041	1246	1.9F
	1524	1830	2.3E
	2244		
8 M		0056	2.0F
	0324	0641	2.3E
	1133	1335	1.8F
	1611	1923	2.2E
	2334		
9 Tu		0145	2.0F
	0411	0733	2.2E
	1229	1426	1.7F
	1701	2014	2.1E
10 W	0029	0236	1.8F
	0503	0823	2.0E
	1329	1519	1.5F
	1757	2105	2.0E
11 Th	0128	0329	1.7F
	0600	0915	1.8E
	1430	1617	1.3F
	1858	2202	1.8E
12 F ◑	0230	0426	1.5F
	0704	1021	1.7E
	1534	1720	1.2F
	2001	2310	1.7E
13 Sa	0336	0528	1.3F
	0813	1157	1.6E
		1250	1.6E
		1356	1.6E
	1637	1826†	1.1F
14 Su		0014	1.7E
	0442	0633	1.2F
	0928	1508	1.7E
	1736	1938	1.2F
	2215		
15 M		0109	1.7E
	0546	0746	1.3F
	1037	1605	1.9E
	1831	2055	1.4F
	2315		
16 Tu		0205	1.8E
	0646	0911	1.4F
	1138	1654	2.0E
	1924	2152	1.7F
17 W	0009	0309	1.9E
		0402	1.9E
		0505	1.9E
	0743	1011	1.7E
	1233	1740†	2.1E
18 Th	0100	0409	2.1E
		0445	2.0E
		0601	2.1E
	0835	1101	2.0F
	1326	1824†	2.2E
19 F ○	0150	0653	2.3E
	0924	1148	2.1F
	1417	1902	2.3E
	2142		
20 Sa		0003	2.2F
	0238	0738	2.4E
	1012	1237	2.2F
	1508	1830	2.3E
	2225		
21 Su		0047	2.2F
	0325	0814	2.4E
	1100	1326	2.1F
	1557	1919	2.3E
	2310		
22 M		0130	2.1F
	0412	0828	2.4E
	1150	1416	1.9F
	1648	2001	2.3E
	2356		
23 Tu		0212	1.9F
	0500	0834	2.3E
	1242	1505	1.7F
	1739	2041	2.1E
24 W	0044	0252	1.6F
	0548	0907	2.2E
	1333	1559	1.4F
	1830	2124	2.0E
25 Th	0133	0333	1.3F
	0636	0947	2.0E
	1424	1705	1.1F
	1920	2212	1.8E
26 F ◐	0223	0415	1.0F
	0721	1034	1.9E
	1514	1805	0.9F
	2007	2303	1.7E
27 Sa	0315	0459	0.8F
	0803	1120	1.8E
	1601	1849	0.7F
	2054	2350	1.6E
28 Su	0406	0543	0.7F
	0846	1202	1.8E
	1644	1829	0.7F
	2139		
29 M		0032	1.6E
	0456	0628	0.7F
	0931	1242	1.8E
	1722	1903	0.7F
	2221		
30 Tu		0112	1.7E
	0545	0718	0.7F
	1019	1323	1.9E
	1759	1948	0.9F
	2301		

May

Day	Slack (h m)	Maximum (h m)	knots
1 W		0154	1.8E
	0633	0816	0.8F
	1108	1407	2.0E
	1838	2039	1.1F
	2340		
2 Th		0238	1.9E
	0721	0915	1.0F
	1155	1454	2.1E
	1920	2129	1.4F
3 F	0019	0323	2.1E
	0809	1006	1.3F
	1243	1541	2.2E
	2003	2215	1.7F
4 Sa ●	0100	0406	2.2E
	0857	1053	1.6F
	1330	1627	2.3E
	2048	2300	2.0F
5 Su	0143	0448	2.3E
	0944	1140	1.7F
	1418	1713	2.3E
	2133	2347	2.1F
6 M	0227	0533	2.3E
	1033	1229	1.7F
	1505	1802	2.2E
	2219		
7 Tu		0035	2.2F
	0312	0623	2.3E
	1125	1320	1.7F
	1553	1855	2.1E
	2310		
8 W		0125	2.1F
	0359	0717	2.2E
	1220	1411	1.6F
	1645	1948	2.0E
9 Th	0006	0216	1.9F
	0449	0808	2.1E
	1317	1503	1.4F
	1742	2039	1.8E
10 F	0106	0308	1.7F
	0544	0859	1.9E
	1415	1600	1.3F
	1843	2133	1.6E
11 Sa ◐	0209	0405	1.5F
	0645	1001	1.8E
	1513	1703	1.2F
	1947	2241	1.5E
12 Su	0315	0507	1.3F
	0751	1157	1.8E
	1612	1810	1.2F
	2053	2357	1.5E
13 M	0422	0614	1.2F
	0900	1257	1.8E
	1708	1920	1.3F
	2159		
14 Tu		0058	1.6E
	0528	0731	1.2F
	1010	1357	1.9E
	1802	2033	1.5F
	2259		
15 W		0400	1.8E
	0630	0858	1.4F
	1113	1457	2.0E
	1853	2133	1.8F
	2354		
16 Th		0454	2.0E
	0728	1000	1.7F
	1210	1527	2.1E
	1942	2221	2.1F
17 F	0045	0546	2.2E
	0822	1050	1.9F
	1304	1612	2.2E
	2029	2304	2.3F
18 Sa ○	0134	0637	2.4E
	0911	1138	2.0F
	1356	1656	2.3E
	2113	2345	2.3F
19 Su	0221	0723	2.5E
	0959	1225	2.1F
	1446	1745	2.3E
	2156		
20 M		0025	2.3F
	0307	0803	2.6E
	1046	1313	1.9F
	1534	1837	2.2E
	2238		
21 Tu		0105	2.1F
	0351	0831	2.5E
	1133	1359	1.7F
	1622	1926	2.1E
	2322		
22 W		0141	1.9F
	0433	0818	2.4E
	1220	1441	1.5F
	1709	2007	2.0E
23 Th	0007	0215	1.6F
	0514	0837	2.2E
	1306	1516	1.2F
	1755	2047	1.8E
24 F	0052	0250	1.3F
	0553	0908	2.1E
	1350	1543	0.9F
	1840	2127	1.7E
25 Sa	0138	0327	1.1F
	0628	0945	2.0E
	1431	1612	0.8F
	1922	2213	1.5E
26 Su ◐	0224	0408	0.9F
	0658	1029	1.9E
	1510	1649	0.8F
	2002	2302	1.5E
27 M	0313	0454	0.8F
	0727	1116	1.9E
	1548	1730	0.8F
	2043	2351	1.5E
28 Tu	0406	0545	0.8F
	0808	1203	2.0E
	1627	1815	1.0F
	2128		
29 W		0035	1.6E
	0502	0638	0.8F
	0909	1248	2.1E
	1708	1904	1.1F
	2218		
30 Th		0120	1.7E
	0559	0737	0.8F
	1018	1335	2.1E
	1753	1959	1.3F
	2308		
31 F		0208	1.9E
	0656	0842	1.0F
	1119	1424	2.2E
	1842	2057	1.6F
	2356		

June

Day	Slack (h m)	Maximum (h m)	knots
1 Sa		0258	2.0E
	0752	0944	1.2F
	1214	1514	2.2E
	1932	2151	1.9F
2 Su	0043	0347	2.1E
	0844	1036	1.4F
	1306	1602	2.2E
	2023	2240	2.1F
3 M	0130	0433	2.2E
	0934	1125	1.6F
	1356	1648	2.2E
	2112	2328	2.3F
4 Tu	0216	0518	2.2E
	1024	1214	1.6F
	1446	1735	2.1E
	2200		
5 W		0017	2.3F
	0303	0609	2.2E
	1114	1304	1.6F
	1535	1827	2.0E
	2251		
6 Th		0107	2.2F
	0349	0707	2.2E
	1207	1355	1.5F
	1626	1922	1.9E
	2346		
7 F		0158	2.0F
	0438	0800	2.1E
	1301	1446	1.4F
	1723	2014	1.7E
8 Sa	0045	0250	1.8F
	0532	0850	2.0E
	1355	1541	1.3F
	1825	2107	1.6E
9 Su	0147	0345	1.5F
	0630	0948	2.0E
		1119	1.9E
		1158	1.9E
	1450	1643†	1.3F
10 M ◐	0252	0448	1.3F
	0733	1117	2.0E
	1546	1751	1.3F
	2034	2339	1.5E
11 Tu	0400	0558	1.2F
	0838	1221	2.0E
	1640	1900	1.5F
	2140		
12 W		0103	1.6E
	0507	0717	1.2F
	0946	1306	2.1E
	1733	2010	1.6F
	2241		
13 Th		0341	1.8E
	0610	0842	1.4F
	1049	1356	2.2E
	1824	2113	1.9F
	2337		
14 F		0435	2.1E
	0710	0945	1.6F
	1147	1451	2.2E
	1913	2203	2.1F
15 Sa	0028	0526	2.3E
	0806	1036	1.8F
	1241	1543	2.3E
	2001	2247	2.3F
16 Su	0117	0617	2.5E
	0857	1123	1.9F
	1332	1628	2.3E
	2046	2327	2.3F
17 M ○	0203	0704	2.6E
	0943	1209	1.9F
	1421	1712	2.3E
	2128		
18 Tu ●		0005	2.3F
	0246	0745	2.5E
	1028	1254	1.7F
	1507	1758	2.2E
	2209		
19 W		0038	2.1F
	0327	0812	2.4E
	1111	1334	1.5F
	1550	1844	2.0E
	2249		
20 Th		0108	1.9F
	0404	0740	2.3E
	1153	1404	1.2F
	1631	1927	1.9E
	2329		
21 F		0139	1.6F
	0438	0800	2.2E
	1232	1423	1.0F
	1710	2006	1.8E
22 Sa	0009	0212	1.4F
	0509	0830	2.2E
	1309	1448	0.9F
	1746	2043	1.6E
23 Su	0050	0249	1.3F
	0535	0905	2.1E
	1344	1522	0.9F
	1819	2123	1.5E
24 M	0133	0330	1.1F
	0602	0946	2.1E
	1420	1602	1.0F
	1853	2209	1.5E
25 Tu ◑	0222	0418	1.0F
	0637	1035	2.1E
	1458	1649	1.1F
	1935	2303	1.5E
26 W	0319	0511	0.9F
	0724	1128	2.1E
	1541	1739	1.2F
	2029	2358	1.6E
27 Th	0423	0607	0.9F
	0825	1219	2.2E
	1629	1832	1.3F
	2135		
28 F		0049	1.7E
	0529	0707	0.9F
	0939	1308	2.2E
	1721	1928	1.5F
	2238		
29 Sa		0141	1.8E
	0633	0814	0.9F
	1049	1358	2.2E
	1815	2029	1.6F
	2335		
30 Su		0236	1.9E
	0734	0923	1.1F
	1149	1450	2.2E
	1910	2129	1.9F

Time meridian 75° W. 0000 is midnight. 1200 is noon. Times are not adjusted for Daylight Saving Time.
† See page 196 for the remaining currents on this day.

Philadelphia (Penns Landing), Delaware River, 2019

F–Flood, Dir. 017° True   E–Ebb, Dir. 201° True

July

Days 1–15

Day	Slack (h m)	Maximum (h m)	knots
1 M	0027	0333	2.0E
	0830	1020	1.3F
	1244	1539	2.2E
	2005	2223	2.1F
2 Tu ●	0118	0423	2.1E
	0921	1110	1.4F
	1336	1626	2.2E
	2056	2312	2.3F
3 W	0206	0510	2.1E
		0619	2.1E
		0738	2.1E
	1010	1158	1.5F
	1426	1711†	2.1E
4 Th		0001	2.3F
	0253	0603	2.1E
		0644	2.1E
		0822	2.2E
	1059	1248†	1.5F
5 F		0051	2.2F
	0340	0901	2.2E
	1149	1338	1.5F
	1607	1856	1.8E
	2330		
6 Sa		0142	2.1F
	0428	0805	2.1E
	1240	1428	1.5F
	1703	1951	1.7E
7 Su	0027	0234	1.9F
	0521	0845	2.1E
	1332	1521	1.4F
	1804	2045	1.6E
8 M	0127	0329	1.6F
	0618	0938	2.1E
	1425	1621	1.4F
	1907	2147	1.5E
9 Tu ◐	0230	0431	1.4F
	0718	1051	2.1E
	1518	1729	1.4F
	2011	2320	1.5E
10 W		0008	1.5E
	0057	0057	1.5E
	0337	0545	1.3F
	0820	1157	2.2E
	1612	1837†	1.5F
11 Th		0209	1.7E
	0443	0705	1.3F
	0924	1245	2.3E
	1704	1946	1.7F
	2219		
12 F		0315	1.9E
	0548	0823	1.4F
	1027	1332	2.3E
	1756	2051	1.9F
	2316		
13 Sa		0411	2.1E
	0649	0927	1.5F
	1124	1424	2.3E
	1846	2145	2.1F
14 Su	0008	0503	2.3E
	0747	1019	1.7F
	1217	1515	2.3E
	1935	2230	2.2F
15 M	0056	0553	2.4E
	0838	1106	1.7F
	1307	1600	2.3E
	2021	2310	2.2F

Days 16–31

Day	Slack (h m)	Maximum (h m)	knots
16 Tu ○	0141	0640	2.4E
	0923	1149	1.6F
	1353	1642	2.2E
	2103	2343	2.1F
17 W	0222	0720	2.3E
	1004	1228	1.5F
	1436	1721	2.1E
	2142		
18 Th		0008	1.9F
	0259	0623	2.2E
	1042	1257	1.3F
	1514	1802	2.0E
	2218		
19 F		0033	1.8F
	0332	0645	2.2E
	1117	1311	1.1F
	1547	1843	1.9E
	2253		
20 Sa		0103	1.6F
	0402	0717	2.2E
	1150	1333	1.1F
	1615	1922	1.8E
	2329		
21 Su		0139	1.6F
	0428	0752	2.2E
	1223	1405	1.1F
	1640	2000	1.7E
22 M	0008	0218	1.5F
	0456	0830	2.3E
	1257	1443	1.2F
	1709	2039	1.7E
23 Tu	0052	0301	1.4F
	0530	0912	2.3E
	1335	1526	1.2F
	1750	2123	1.7E
24 W ◑	0144	0350	1.3F
	0613	1001	2.2E
	1417	1615	1.3F
	1843	2216	1.6E
25 Th	0245	0444	1.2F
	0704	1057	2.2E
	1506	1709	1.4F
	1944	2320	1.6E
26 F	0354	0543	1.0F
	0803	1153	2.2E
	1601	1804	1.4F
	2055		
27 Sa		0020	1.6E
	0504	0644	1.0F
	0915	1245	2.2E
	1658	1902	1.5F
	2209		
28 Su		0117	1.7E
	0611	0751	0.9F
	1027	1336	2.2E
	1756	2005	1.6F
	2315		
29 M		0217	1.7E
	0715	0903	1.0F
	1129	1427	2.1E
	1855	2110	1.8F
30 Tu	0011	0357	1.8E
	0813	1005	1.2F
	1225	1518	2.1E
	1952	2208	2.0F
31 W ●	0104	0636	2.0E
	0904	1056	1.4F
	1318	1606	2.1E
	2045	2259	2.2F

August

Days 1–15

Day	Slack (h m)	Maximum (h m)	knots
1 Th	0154	0728	2.2E
	0952	1143	1.5F
	1409	1651	2.0E
	2135	2348	2.2F
2 F	0241	0811	2.2E
	1039	1231	1.6F
	1459	1739	2.0E
	2225		
3 Sa		0038	2.2F
	0329	0849	2.3E
	1126	1319	1.6F
	1549	1834	1.9E
	2316		
4 Su		0129	2.1F
	0417	0913	2.2E
	1215	1409	1.6F
	1643	1933	1.8E
5 M	0011	0221	2.0F
	0510	0840	2.2E
	1305	1459	1.5F
	1741	2029	1.7E
6 Tu	0109	0315	1.8F
	0606	0925	2.3E
	1356	1555	1.5F
	1843	2128	1.7E
7 W ◐	0210	0418	1.6F
	0704	1026	2.2E
	1449	1701	1.5F
	1945	2259	1.6E
8 Th	0314	0534	1.4F
	0804	1132	2.3E
	1543	1812	1.5F
	2049		
9 F		0136	1.8E
	0419	0651	1.4F
	0905	1223	2.3E
	1636	1920	1.6F
	2151		
10 Sa		0243	1.9E
	0523	0802	1.4F
	1005	1310	2.3E
	1729	2027	1.7F
	2250		
11 Su		0343	2.0E
	0625	0906	1.4F
	1101	1357	2.2E
	1821	2125	1.8F
	2342		
12 M		0435	2.1E
	0722	0959	1.5F
	1152	1446	2.2E
	1910	2212	1.9F
13 Tu	0030	0523	2.1E
	0813	1045	1.5F
	1239	1531	2.2E
	1957	2251	1.9F
14 W	0113	0607	2.1E
	0856	1124	1.4F
	1322	1611	2.1E
	2038	2319	1.8F
15 Th ○	0152	0453	2.0E
	0933	1153	1.2F
	1400	1647	2.1E
	2116	2336	1.7F

Days 16–31

Day	Slack (h m)	Maximum (h m)	knots
16 F	0227	0520	2.1E
	1004	1202	1.1F
	1433	1722	2.0E
	2150	2359	1.7F
17 Sa	0258	0554	2.1E
	1034	1220	1.1F
	1501	1759	2.0E
	2223		
18 Su		0031	1.7F
	0326	0633	2.2E
	1103	1251	1.2F
	1524	1839	2.0E
	2258		
19 M		0110	1.7F
	0355	0715	2.3E
	1136	1329	1.3F
	1551	1920	2.0E
	2338		
20 Tu		0152	1.7F
	0428	0758	2.3E
	1213	1411	1.4F
	1627	2003	1.9E
21 W	0026	0238	1.6F
	0509	0843	2.3E
	1256	1457	1.5F
	1714	2047	1.9E
22 Th	0121	0327	1.5F
	0556	0931	2.2E
	1344	1547	1.5F
	1809	2138	1.8E
23 F ◑	0224	0422	1.3F
	0651	1028	2.2E
	1438	1641	1.5F
	1911	2242	1.7E
24 Sa	0332	0522	1.2F
	0750	1128	2.1E
	1537	1739	1.5F
	2021	2353	1.6E
25 Su	0442	0624	1.0F
	0859	1224	2.1E
	1640	1839	1.5F
	2140		
26 M		0055	1.6E
	0549	0730	1.0F
	1010	1315	2.0E
	1742	1943	1.5F
	2252		
27 Tu		0158	1.6E
		0310	1.6E
		0418	
	0653	0845	1.0F
	1113	1407†	2.0E
28 W		0520	1.8E
	0750	0951	1.2F
	1209	1500	2.0E
	1941	2156	1.8F
29 Th	0047	0617	2.0E
	0842	1041	1.5F
	1302	1550	2.0E
	2035	2249	2.0F
30 F ●	0138	0707	2.1E
	0929	1127	1.6F
	1353	1636	2.0E
	2125	2338	2.1F
31 Sa	0227	0750	2.2E
	1014	1213	1.7F
	1443	1723	2.0E
	2214		

September

Days 1–15

Day	Slack (h m)	Maximum (h m)	knots
1 Su		0027	2.2F
	0315	0825	2.3E
	1059	1300	1.8F
	1532	1819	2.0E
	2304		
2 M		0118	2.1F
	0404	0841	2.3E
	1146	1348	1.8F
	1624	1922	2.0E
	2357		
3 Tu		0210	2.0F
	0457	0826	2.3E
	1235	1437	1.7F
	1719	2019	2.0E
4 W	0053	0304	1.8F
	0552	0907	2.3E
	1326	1529	1.6F
	1818	2116	1.9E
5 Th ◐	0151	0406	1.6F
	0649	1001	2.3E
	1418	1629	1.5F
	1917	2257	1.8E
6 F	0251	0523	1.5F
	0747	1104	2.2E
	1512	1741	1.5F
	2018		
7 Sa		0058	1.9E
	0354	0634	1.4F
	0844	1159	2.2E
	1607	1851	1.4F
	2118		
8 Su		0159	1.9E
	0456	0740	1.3F
	0942	1246	2.1E
	1702	1959	1.4F
	2217		
9 M		0304	1.9E
	0555	0842	1.3F
	1037	1330	2.1E
	1755	2101	1.4F
	2309		
10 Tu		0357	1.9E
	0650	0936	1.3F
	1126	1415	2.0E
	1846	2151	1.5F
	2356		
11 W		0259	1.8E
	0738	1021	1.2F
	1210	1458	2.0E
	1932	2229	1.4F
12 Th	0037	0329	1.8E
	0818	1054	1.2F
	1249	1538	2.0E
	2014	2250	1.4F
13 F ○	0114	0401	1.9E
	0850	1104	1.1F
	1323	1613	2.0E
	2050	2301	1.4F
14 Sa	0148	0435	2.0E
	0919	1111	1.2F
	1352	1647	2.1E
	2124	2328	1.5F
15 Su	0221	0512	2.1E
	0947	1139	1.4F
	1419	1723	2.1E
	2159		

Days 16–31

Day	Slack (h m)	Maximum (h m)	knots
16 M		0004	1.7F
	0253	0553	2.2E
	1017	1216	1.5F
	1447	1802	2.2E
	2237		
17 Tu		0045	1.7F
	0328	0639	2.3E
	1053	1258	1.7F
	1521	1846	2.2E
	2320		
18 W		0131	1.8F
	0407	0728	2.3E
	1134	1343	1.7F
	1602	1933	2.2E
19 Th	0011	0218	1.7F
	0451	0810	2.3E
	1222	1431	1.7F
	1650	2020	2.1E
20 F	0108	0309	1.6F
	0542	0905	2.2E
	1316	1522	1.7F
	1744	2110	1.9E
21 Sa ◑	0210	0404	1.4F
	0639	0959	2.0E
	1414	1617	1.6F
	1845	2210	1.8E
22 Su	0315	0503	1.2F
	0739	1103	1.9E
	1517	1716	1.4F
	1953	2327	1.7E
23 M	0422	0606	1.1F
	0846	1204	1.9E
	1623	1818	1.4F
	2110		
24 Tu		0036	1.6E
	0526	0711	1.1F
	0955	1258	1.8E
	1729	1923	1.3F
	2226		
25 W		0359	1.7E
	0627	0826	1.1F
	1059	1350	1.8E
	1831	2037	1.4F
	2330		
26 Th		0456	1.3E
	0724	0935	1.3F
	1156	1446	1.9E
	1931	2147	1.6F
27 F	0026	0549	2.0E
	0815	1026	1.6F
	1248	1539	1.9E
	2025	2241	1.9F
28 Sa ●	0118	0638	2.1E
	0902	1111	1.8F
	1339	1627	2.0E
	1801	1846†	2.0E
29 Su	0209	0721	2.2E
	0946	1154	1.9F
	1428	1716	2.1E
	2203		
30 M		0019	2.1F
	0259	0755	2.2E
	1030	1240	2.0F
	1516	1815	2.1E
		1919†	2.1E

Time meridian 75° W. 0000 is midnight. 1200 is noon. Times are not adjusted for Daylight Saving Time.
† See page 196 for the remaining currents on this day.

Philadelphia (Penns Landing), Delaware River, 2019

F–Flood, Dir. 017° True   E–Ebb, Dir. 201° True

October

Day	Slack (h m)	Maximum (h m)	knots
1 Tu		0110	2.1F
	0349	0737	2.3E
	1116	1326	2.0F
	1606	1928	2.2E
	2343		
2 W		0201	2.0F
	0441	0804	2.3E
	1203	1413	1.9F
	1658	2019	2.2E
3 Th	0037	0254	1.9F
	0535	0846	2.3E
	1253	1502	1.8F
	1752	2108	2.1E
4 F	0132	0354	1.7F
	0631	0934	2.2E
	1345	1555	1.6F
	1848	2207	2.0E
5 Sa ☽	0229	0506	1.5F
	0727	1031	2.1E
	1439	1658	1.4F
	1944	2328	1.9E
6 Su	0327	0614	1.3F
	0821	1129	2.0E
	1535	1810	1.2F
	2039		
7 M		0011	1.9E
	0425	0715	1.2F
	0916	1218	1.9E
	1632	1920	1.1F
	2134		
8 Tu		0045	1.8E
	0519	0814	1.1F
	1008	1300	1.9E
	1726	2028	1.0F
	2226		
9 W		0119	1.8E
	0607	0908	1.0F
	1056	1341	1.8E
	1817	2121	0.9F
	2312		
10 Th		0157	1.8E
	0649	0950	1.0F
	1137	1422	1.8E
	1904	2157	1.0F
	2352		
11 F		0236	1.8E
	0725	1010	1.0F
	1213	1502	1.9E
	1946	2205	1.0F
12 Sa	0030	0317	1.9E
	0758	1002	1.1F
	1245	1540	2.0E
	2024	2226	1.2F
13 Su ○	0107	0357	2.0E
	0829	1030	1.4F
	1315	1617	2.1E
	2102	2300	1.4F
14 M	0144	0437	2.2E
	0902	1106	1.6F
	1347	1654	2.2E
	2140	2340	1.6F
15 Tu	0223	0520	2.2E
	0937	1147	1.8F
	1423	1734	2.3E
	2222		
16 W		0024	1.7F
	0303	0607	2.3E
	1017	1232	2.0F
	1502	1819	2.3E
	2309		
17 Th		0111	1.8F
	0347	0658	2.2E
	1102	1319	2.0F
	1545	1909	2.3E
18 F	0001	0201	1.7F
	0434	0749	2.1E
	1154	1408	1.9F
	1633	1959	2.2E
19 Sa	0058	0252	1.6F
	0527	0839	2.0E
	1251	1500	1.8F
	1726	2049	2.0E
20 Su	0157	0346	1.4F
	0625	0931	1.9E
	1352	1554	1.6F
	1825	2146	1.9E
21 M ◑	0259	0445	1.2F
	0727	1034	1.7E
	1458	1654	1.4F
	1930	2301	1.7E
22 Tu	0401	0548	1.2F
	0833	1142	1.6E
	1607	1757	1.2F
	2042		
23 W		0019	1.7E
	0502	0653	1.2F
	0942	1242	1.6E
	1714	1904	1.2F
	2157		
24 Th		0116	1.7E
	0600	0807	1.2F
	1045	1337†	1.7E
25 F		0425	1.9E
	0654	0918	1.5F
	1142	1438	1.8E
	1533	1645†	1.7E
26 Sa	0002	0513	2.0E
	0745	1010	1.8F
	1235	1743	2.0E
	2014	2235	1.8F
27 Su ●	0057	0559	2.1E
	0833	1055	2.0F
	1325	1837	2.2E
	2104	2323	2.0F
28 M	0149	0452	2.2E
	0917	1137	2.2F
	1413	1925	2.3E
	2152		
29 Tu		0011	2.1F
	0240	0542	2.2E
	1001	1221	2.2F
	1501	2005	2.4E
	2240		
30 W		0101	2.1F
	0331	0643	2.3E
	1045	1305	2.2F
	1548	2038	2.4E
	2329		
31 Th		0151	2.0F
	0422	0736	2.3E
	1132	1350	2.1F
	1637	2041	2.4E

November

Day	Slack (h m)	Maximum (h m)	knots
1 F	0020	0242	1.8F
	0514	0821	2.2E
	1220	1434	1.9F
	1727	2058	2.3E
2 Sa	0112	0336	1.6F
	0608	0905	2.1E
	1311	1519	1.6F
	1817	2137	2.2E
3 Su	0205	0440	1.3F
	0701	0954	1.9E
	1403	1607	1.3F
	1907	2224	2.0E
4 M ◑	0257	0546	1.2F
	0753	1049	1.8E
	1458	1658	1.1F
	1955	2313	1.9E
5 Tu	0348	0643	1.0F
	0843	1141	1.7E
	1554	1746	0.8F
	2042	2355	1.8E
6 W	0434	0735	0.9F
	0932	1224	1.6E
	1649	1829	0.6F
	2129		
7 Th		0033	1.8E
	0515	0823	0.8F
	1017	1304	1.6E
	1740	1914	0.6F
	2215		
8 F		0112	1.8E
	0552	0744	0.8F
	1058	1344	1.7E
	1828	2008	0.6F
	2259		
9 Sa		0153	1.9E
	0627	0825	1.0F
	1134	1425	1.8E
	1914	2104	0.8F
	2342		
10 Su		0237	2.0E
	0704	0911	1.2F
	1209	1508	1.9E
	1958	2151	1.1F
11 M	0026	0322	2.1E
	0742	0955	1.6F
	1245	1549	2.1E
	2041	2235	1.3F
12 Tu ○	0110	0407	2.2E
	0823	1038	1.9F
	1324	1630	2.3E
	2125	2319	1.5F
13 W	0155	0451	2.3E
	0906	1123	2.1F
	1405	1712	2.4E
	2210		
14 Th		0005	1.7F
	0240	0537	2.2E
	0950	1209	2.2F
	1448	1759	2.4E
	2259		
15 F		0054	1.7F
	0327	0628	2.2E
	1038	1258	2.2F
	1533	1851	2.3E
	2351		
16 Sa		0144	1.6F
	0415	0721	2.0E
	1131	1348	2.1F
	1620	1944	2.2E
17 Su	0046	0235	1.5F
	0509	0812	1.9E
	1229	1440	1.9F
	1712	2034	2.1E
18 M	0143	0328	1.4F
	0608	0904	1.7E
	1332	1534	1.6F
	1809	2128	2.0E
19 Tu ◑	0241	0426	1.3F
	0712	1003	1.6E
	1439	1633	1.4F
	1911	2239	1.8E
20 W	0340	0530	1.2F
	0818	1118	1.5E
	1548	1738	1.2F
	2018		
21 Th		0001	1.8E
	0437	0635	1.3F
	0925	1228	1.5E
	1657	1847	1.1F
	2130		
22 F		0055	1.9E
	0532	0746	1.4F
	1030	1337	1.6E
	1802	2010	1.2F
	2238		
23 Sa		0146	1.9E
	0625	0859	1.6F
	1127	1425	1.9E
	1903	2130	1.4F
	2339		
24 Su		0244	2.0E
	0716	0954	1.9F
	1220	1525	2.1E
	1959	2225	1.7F
25 M	0034	0339	2.2E
	0804	1039	2.2F
	1310	1619	2.3E
	2050	2313	1.9F
26 Tu ●	0128	0427	2.2E
	0849	1121	2.3F
	1358	1707	2.5E
	2138		
27 W		0001	2.0F
	0220	0515	2.3E
	0933	1203	2.4F
	1445	1758	2.6E
	2225		
28 Th		0049	2.0F
	0310	0608	2.3E
	1017	1245	2.3F
	1531	1845	2.6E
	2313		
29 F		0137	1.9F
	0359	0704	2.2E
	1101	1327	2.1F
	1616	1921	2.5E
	2259		
30 Sa	0001	0224	1.7F
	0448	0751	2.1E
	1148	1406	1.9F
	1700	2038	2.4E
	2351		

December

Day	Slack (h m)	Maximum (h m)	knots
1 Su	0049	0309	1.4F
	0538	0833	1.9E
	1236	1444	1.6F
	1745	2104	2.2E
2 M	0136	0353	1.1F
	0627	0916	1.8E
	1325	1522	1.3F
	1826	2139	2.1E
3 Tu	0221	0427	0.9F
	0714	1001	1.6E
	1415	1602	1.0F
	1905	2221	2.0E
4 W ◑	0303	0451	0.8F
	0759	1052	1.5E
	1506	1646	0.8F
	1941	2307	1.9E
5 Th	0343	0524	0.8F
	0842	1140	1.4E
	1600	1733	0.7F
	2016	2351	1.9E
6 F	0419	0602	0.8F
	0925	1224	1.5E
	1653	1822	0.6F
	2101		
7 Sa		0034	2.0E
	0456	0646	1.0F
	1009	1306	1.6E
	1746	1915	0.6F
	2159		
8 Su		0118	2.1E
	0535	0735	1.1F
	1053	1349	1.7E
	1839	2017	0.8F
	2256		
9 M		0204	2.1E
	0618	0830	1.4F
	1137	1437	1.9E
	1931	2119	1.0F
	2350		
10 Tu		0252	2.2E
	0705	0925	1.7F
	1221	1525	2.1E
	2022	2212	1.2F
11 W	0040	0340	2.3E
	0754	1015	2.0F
	1306	1611	2.2E
	2110	2300	1.4F
12 Th ○	0130	0426	2.3E
	0843	1103	2.2F
	1352	1655	2.3E
	2158	2347	1.6F
13 F	0219	0511	2.2E
	0931	1150	2.3F
	1438	1743	2.3E
	2247		
14 Sa		0036	1.6F
	0307	0600	2.1E
	1020	1240	2.3F
	1523	1837	2.3E
	2338		
15 Su		0127	1.6F
	0356	0653	1.9E
	1114	1331	2.2F
	1611	1933	2.2E
16 M	0031	0217	1.5F
	0449	0746	1.8E
	1212	1422	1.9F
	1701	2023	2.1E
17 Tu	0125	0309	1.4F
	0549	0837	1.6E
	1314	1516	1.7F
	1756	2115	2.0E
18 W ○	0220	0406	1.3F
	0653	0933	1.5E
	1419	1614	1.4F
	1856	2221	2.0E
19 Th ◐	0316	0509	1.3F
	0758	1048	1.4E
	1528	1720	1.2F
	2000	2342	2.0E
20 F	0411	0616	1.3F
	0905	1408	1.4E
	1636	1832	1.1F
	2108		
21 Sa		0036	2.0E
	0505	0725	1.5F
	1010	1518	1.7E
	1742	1957	1.2F
	2215		
22 Su		0124	2.1E
	0557	0837	1.7F
	1109	1615	1.9E
	1844	2114	1.4F
	2316		
23 M		0218	2.2E
	0647	0936	2.0F
	1203	1707	2.2E
	1942	2211	1.7F
24 Tu	0013	0313	2.3E
	0736	1023	2.3F
	1253	1757	2.4E
	2034	2259	1.8F
25 W	0106	0404	2.3E
	0823	1106	2.4F
	1341	1845	2.6E
	2122	2346	1.9F
26 Th ●	0157	0450	2.3E
	0908	1146	2.4F
	1427	1929	2.6E
	2208		
27 F ○		0032	1.9F
	0246	0538	2.2E
	0951	1225	2.3F
	1511	2006	2.6E
	2253		
28 Sa		0117	1.7F
	0332	0628	2.1E
	1034	1302	2.1F
	1553	2024	2.4E
	2337		
29 Su		0158	1.5F
	0417	0716	2.0E
	1117	1336	1.8F
	1632	2004	2.3E
30 M	0020	0228	1.2F
	0500	0757	1.9E
	1200	1408	1.6F
	1709	2028	2.2E
31 Tu	0101	0249	1.0F
	0542	0835	1.7E
	1244	1443	1.3F
	1743	2100	2.2E

Time meridian 75° W. 0000 is midnight. 1200 is noon. Times are not adjusted for Daylight Saving Time.
† See page 196 for the remaining currents on this day.

Chesapeake Bay Entrance, Virginia, 2019

F–Flood, Dir. 297° True   E–Ebb, Dir. 112° True

January

Day	Slack h m	Maximum h m	knots
1 Tu	0151	0514	1.4F
	0850	1124	0.9E
	1512	1732	0.7F
	2013	2323	1.1E
2 W	0247	0602	1.5F
	0947	1226	0.9E
	1602	1818	0.7F
	2106		
3 Th		0016	1.1E
	0334	0651	1.5F
	1034	1321	1.0E
	1642	1909	0.7F
	2155		
4 F		0110	1.1E
	0415	0740	1.5F
	1114	1402	1.0E
	1719	1958	0.7F
	2241		
5 Sa		0155	1.1E
	0452	0822	1.5F
	1152	1436	1.1E
	1759	2039	0.8F
	2325		
6 Su		0233	1.1E
	0529	0859	1.5F
	1229	1511	1.2E
	1844	2117	0.8F
7 M	0007	0307	1.1E
	0607	0936	1.5F
	1307	1550	1.1E
	1930	2157	0.8F
8 Tu	0048	0344	1.0E
	0648	1015	1.4F
	1346	1639	1.1E
	2016	2241	0.7F
9 W	0126	0428	0.9E
	0731	1058	1.4F
	1427	1739	1.0E
	2059	2326	0.7F
10 Th	0205	0530	0.8E
	0814	1142	1.3F
	1509	1828	0.9E
	2137		
11 F		0009	0.7F
	0252	0626	0.8E
	0859	1221	1.1F
	1547	1905	0.9E
	2209		
12 Sa		0049	0.7F
	0355	0711	0.7E
	0946	1258	0.9F
	1616	1934	0.9E
	2235		
13 Su		0132	0.8F
	0508	0754	0.7E
	1036	1336	0.7F
	1637	1959	0.8E
	2303		
14 M		0225	0.9F
	0610	0845	0.6E
	1131	1425	0.5F
	1700	2027	0.9E
	2337		
15 Tu		0333	1.1F
	0708	0945	0.6E
	1235	1532	0.4F
	1733	2109	1.0E
16 W	0021	0427	1.3F
	0805	1041	0.7E
	1352	1628	0.5F
	1818	2202	1.1E
17 Th	0115	0512	1.5F
	0858	1133	0.8E
	1456	1715	0.6F
	1915	2256	1.2E
18 F	0214	0557	1.7F
	0944	1227	1.0E
	1543	1805	0.7F
	2022	2353	1.4E
19 Sa	0309	0648	1.8F
	1029	1321	1.2E
	1626	1902	0.9F
	2127		
20 Su		0054	1.5E
	0400	0744	1.9F
	1114	1408	1.4E
	1713	2001	1.1F
	2227		
21 M		0151	1.6E
	0451	0836	2.0F
	1201	1451	1.5E
	1805	2055	1.2F
	2327		
22 Tu		0241	1.6E
	0547	0926	2.0F
	1250	1537	1.5E
	1901	2147	1.3F
23 W	0028	0330	1.6E
	0647	1017	1.9F
	1339	1631	1.4E
	1955	2242	1.3F
24 Th	0129	0430	1.4E
	0748	1112	1.7F
	1428	1735	1.4E
	2047	2340	1.3F
25 F	0233	0545	1.3E
	0848	1206	1.5F
	1519	1833	1.3E
	2140		
26 Sa		0036	1.3F
	0348	0650	1.1E
	0951	1256	1.2F
	1613	1922	1.3E
	2233		
27 Su		0132	1.3F
	0509	0747	1.0E
	1057	1348	0.9F
	1706	2010	1.2E
	2328		
28 M		0241	1.2F
	0621	0848	0.8E
	1207	1501	0.7F
	1755	2104	1.1E
29 Tu	0025	0403	1.2F
	0728	0956	0.7E
	1326	1618	0.6F
	1845	2203	1.0E
30 W	0128	0459	1.3F
	0834	1058	0.7E
	1441	1708	0.6F
	1940	2258	1.0E
31 Th	0230	0544	1.3F
	0930	1155	0.7E
	1533	1751	0.6F
	2041	2353	1.0E

February

Day	Slack h m	Maximum h m	knots
1 F	0321	0630	1.3F
	1014	1254	0.8E
	1613	1838	0.7F
	2135		
2 Sa		0048	1.1E
	0401	0717	1.3F
	1053	1341	1.0E
	1652	1930	0.7F
	2222		
3 Su		0137	1.1E
	0436	0801	1.4F
	1131	1419	1.1E
	1733	2015	0.8F
	2303		
4 M		0215	1.2E
	0510	0838	1.5F
	1210	1454	1.2E
	1818	2054	0.8F
	2342		
5 Tu		0249	1.2E
	0547	0915	1.5F
	1249	1531	1.1E
	1904	2132	0.8F
6 W	0019	0323	1.1E
	0627	0952	1.5F
	1327	1611	1.1E
	1945	2212	0.8F
7 Th	0058	0401	1.0E
	0711	1032	1.4F
	1402	1659	1.0E
	2021	2255	0.8F
8 F	0139	0452	0.9E
	0755	1113	1.3F
	1431	1748	0.9E
	2050	2339	0.9F
9 Sa	0227	0555	0.8E
	0839	1152	1.1F
	1453	1824	0.9E
	2115		
10 Su		0020	0.9F
	0325	0645	0.8E
	0923	1227	0.9F
	1510	1850	0.9E
	2142		
11 M		0100	1.0F
	0436	0727	0.7E
	1009	1301	0.7F
	1529	1915	0.9E
	2215		
12 Tu		0145	1.1F
	0540	0811	0.6E
	1057	1339	0.5F
	1602	1944	1.0E
	2257		
13 W		0247	1.2F
	0635	0906	0.6E
	1152	1442	0.4F
	1653	2029	1.1E
	2347		
14 Th		0355	1.3F
	0730	1006	0.7E
	1259	1557	0.5F
	1754	2132	1.1E
15 F	0047	0448	1.5F
	0825	1102	0.8E
	1413	1653	0.7F
	1900	2236	1.2E
16 Sa	0155	0537	1.6F
	0918	1157	1.0E
	1512	1745	0.9F
	2010	2337	1.4E
17 Su	0258	0629	1.8F
	1007	1255	1.2E
	1601	1841	1.0F
	2118		
18 M		0041	1.5E
	0354	0726	1.9F
	1055	1348	1.4E
	1648	1941	1.2F
	2219		
19 Tu		0140	1.7E
	0446	0821	1.9F
	1143	1433	1.5E
	1738	2037	1.4F
	2318		
20 W		0231	1.7E
	0541	0910	1.9F
	1230	1517	1.5E
	1830	2128	1.5F
21 Th	0018	0320	1.7E
	0640	0959	1.8F
	1316	1604	1.4E
	1923	2221	1.5F
22 F	0119	0414	1.5E
	0739	1051	1.6F
	1401	1701	1.3E
	2015	2317	1.5F
23 Sa	0220	0524	1.2E
	0836	1142	1.3F
	1445	1802	1.3E
	2106		
24 Su		0013	1.4F
	0330	0631	1.1E
	0933	1230	1.0F
	1533	1855	1.2E
	2200		
25 M		0105	1.3F
	0447	0725	0.9E
	1031	1316	0.8F
	1627	1942	1.1E
	2257		
26 Tu		0204	1.2F
	0557	0819	0.7E
	1130	1411	0.6F
	1724	2033	1.0E
	2357		
27 W		0329	1.1F
	0700	0920	0.6E
	1232	1539	0.5F
	1820	2134	1.0E
28 Th	0102	0437	1.1F
	0800	1022	0.6E
	1346	1642	0.6F
	1919	2235	0.9E

March

Day	Slack h m	Maximum h m	knots
1 F	0208	0522	1.1F
	0856	1118	0.6E
	1452	1725	0.7F
	2021	2329	0.9E
2 Sa	0301	0603	1.1F
	0944	1216	0.7E
	1541	1808	0.7F
	2115		
3 Su		0022	1.0E
	0342	0647	1.2F
	1026	1312	0.9E
	1623	1857	0.8F
	2200		
4 M		0112	1.1E
	0416	0732	1.3F
	1106	1357	1.0E
	1703	1946	0.8F
	2239		
5 Tu		0154	1.2E
	0451	0814	1.4F
	1145	1433	1.1E
	1743	2027	0.9F
	2316		
6 W		0229	1.2E
	0528	0851	1.5F
	1223	1506	1.1E
	1822	2105	0.9F
	2355		
7 Th		0303	1.2E
	0610	0927	1.4F
	1256	1537	1.0E
	1856	2142	1.0F
8 F	0037	0339	1.2E
	0656	1003	1.3F
	1324	1609	0.9E
	1926	2222	1.1F
9 Sa	0121	0423	1.0E
	0742	1042	1.1F
	1344	1643	0.9E
	1953	2305	1.1F
10 Su	0208	0522	0.9E
	0826	1121	0.9F
	1401	1722	0.9E
	2022	2349	1.2F
11 M	0300	0619	0.8E
	0907	1159	0.8F
	1421	1802	0.9E
	2056		
12 Tu		0031	1.2F
	0401	0703	0.8E
	0949	1236	0.7F
	1451	1840	1.0E
	2137		
13 W		0114	1.2F
	0504	0745	0.7E
	1035	1317	0.6F
	1537	1920	1.0E
	2227		
14 Th		0209	1.2F
	0600	0834	0.7E
	1127	1415	0.6F
	1641	2010	1.1E
	2325		
15 F		0324	1.3F
	0654	0935	0.8E
	1229	1535	0.6F
	1750	2116	1.1E
16 Sa	0031	0428	1.4F
	0753	1035	0.9E
	1341	1638	0.8F
	1859	2226	1.2E
17 Su	0145	0520	1.5F
	0851	1132	1.0E
	1446	1731	1.0F
	2009	2328	1.4E
18 M	0254	0613	1.6F
	0945	1231	1.2E
	1538	1825	1.2F
	2116		
19 Tu		0032	1.5E
	0351	0709	1.7F
	1034	1327	1.3E
	1624	1924	1.4F
	2216		
20 W		0132	1.7E
	0444	0805	1.7F
	1121	1413	1.4E
	1710	2019	1.5F
	2314		
21 Th		0223	1.7E
	0538	0854	1.7F
	1206	1455	1.5E
	1758	2110	1.6F
22 F	0012	0310	1.6E
	0635	0940	1.5F
	1248	1536	1.4E
	1848	2200	1.6F
23 Sa	0109	0359	1.4E
	0731	1027	1.3F
	1329	1624	1.3E
	1940	2252	1.5F
24 Su	0206	0500	1.2E
	0823	1116	1.1F
	1410	1725	1.2E
	2031	2346	1.4F
25 M	0307	0607	1.0E
	0913	1204	0.9F
	1455	1825	1.1E
	2125		
26 Tu		0037	1.3F
	0415	0700	0.9E
	1001	1248	0.8F
	1552	1916	1.0E
	2223		
27 W		0127	1.1F
	0521	0748	0.7E
	1050	1334	0.6F
	1700	2006	0.9E
	2324		
28 Th		0232	0.9F
	0618	0839	0.6E
	1144	1443	0.6F
	1802	2104	0.8E
29 F	0026	0359	0.8F
	0712	0941	0.6E
	1249	1611	0.6F
	1900	2206	0.8E
30 Sa	0130	0451	0.9F
	0808	1041	0.7E
	1406	1659	0.7F
	1957	2300	0.9E
31 Su	0228	0530	1.0F
	0903	1137	0.7E
	1506	1740	0.8F
	2050	2351	0.9E

Time meridian 75° W. 0000 is midnight. 1200 is noon. Times are not adjusted for Daylight Saving Time.

Chesapeake Bay Entrance, Virginia, 2019

F–Flood, Dir. 297° True   E–Ebb, Dir. 112° True

April

Day	Slack (h m)	Maximum (h m)	knots
1 M	0314	0611	1.1F
	0951	1234	0.9E
	1551	1823	0.8F
	2135		
2 Tu		0042	1.0E
	0353	0655	1.2F
	1033	1324	1.0E
	1627	1910	0.9F
	2215		
3 W		0129	1.2E
	0431	0741	1.3F
	1110	1402	1.0E
	1658	1955	1.0F
	2255		
4 Th		0209	1.3E
	0512	0821	1.3F
	1142	1433	1.1E
	1726	2034	1.2F
	2336		
5 ● F		0245	1.3E
	0556	0858	1.2F
	1209	1458	1.0E
	1753	2112	1.3F
6 Sa	0020	0320	1.2E
	0643	0933	1.1F
	1231	1522	1.0E
	1823	2151	1.4F
7 Su	0105	0359	1.1E
	0729	1010	0.9F
	1252	1546	1.0E
	1858	2233	1.4F
8 M	0149	0449	1.0E
	0812	1051	0.8F
	1317	1619	1.0E
	1937	2318	1.4F
9 Tu	0236	0549	0.9E
	0852	1134	0.8F
	1350	1712	1.0E
	2020		
10 W		0004	1.4F
	0328	0639	0.9E
	0935	1219	0.7F
	1433	1814	1.0E
	2109		
11 Th		0051	1.4F
	0427	0724	0.9E
	1022	1305	0.7F
	1531	1907	1.0E
	2205		
12 ◐ F		0143	1.3F
	0527	0811	0.9E
	1115	1402	0.7F
	1644	2001	1.1E
	2309		
13 Sa		0255	1.2F
	0624	0910	0.9E
	1213	1520	0.8F
	1756	2108	1.1E
14 Su	0020	0409	1.3F
	0824	1013	1.0E
	1319	1627	1.0F
	1904	2218	1.2E
15 M	0138	0505	1.4F
	0824	1111	1.1E
	1424	1720	1.2F
	2013	2322	1.3E
16 Tu	0252	0557	1.5F
	0920	1207	1.2E
	1516	1812	1.4F
	2118		
17 W		0025	1.5E
	0351	0652	1.5F
	1009	1302	1.3E
	1601	1908	1.6F
	2217		
18 Th		0125	1.6E
	0445	0748	1.4F
	1053	1351	1.4E
	1643	2003	1.7F
	2313		
19 ○ F		0216	1.6E
	0537	0837	1.3F
	1135	1432	1.4E
	1727	2053	1.7F
20 Sa	0007	0300	1.5E
	0631	0921	1.2F
	1216	1510	1.3E
	1815	2139	1.7F
21 Su	0100	0344	1.3E
	0722	1004	1.0F
	1257	1552	1.2E
	1907	2227	1.6F
22 M	0150	0435	1.1E
	0808	1050	0.9F
	1340	1646	1.1E
	1959	2318	1.4F
23 Tu	0240	0538	1.0E
	0850	1137	0.8F
	1426	1754	0.9E
	2051		
24 W		0007	1.2F
	0334	0633	0.9E
	0933	1222	0.8F
	1524	1851	0.9E
	2145		
25 Th		0052	1.0F
	0433	0720	0.8E
	1021	1307	0.7F
	1636	1939	0.8E
	2241		
26 ◑ F		0141	0.9F
	0530	0806	0.8E
	1114	1401	0.6F
	1741	2030	0.8E
	2336		
27 Sa		0249	0.8F
	0623	0902	0.7E
	1214	1526	0.6F
	1835	2128	0.7E
28 Su	0034	0406	0.8F
	0717	1004	0.7E
	1322	1630	0.7F
	1927	2225	0.8E
29 M	0137	0453	0.9F
	0813	1058	0.8E
	1424	1711	0.8F
	2020	2317	0.8E
30 Tu	0238	0533	1.0F
	0904	1148	0.8E
	1509	1750	0.9F
	2109		

May

Day	Slack (h m)	Maximum (h m)	knots
1 W		0009	1.0E
	0329	0614	0.9F
	0945	1236	0.9E
	1541	1832	1.1F
	2155		
2 Th		0103	1.1E
	0413	0658	1.0F
	1017	1317	0.9E
	1606	1917	1.2F
	2238		
3 F		0148	1.2E
	0457	0743	1.0F
	1043	1349	1.0E
	1631	2001	1.4F
	2320		
4 ● Sa		0226	1.3E
	0541	0824	1.0F
	1106	1416	1.1E
	1659	2042	1.5F
5 Su	0003	0301	1.3E
	0626	0902	0.9F
	1132	1441	1.1E
	1732	2122	1.6F
6 M	0046	0336	1.2E
	0710	0941	0.8F
	1205	1510	1.1E
	1814	2204	1.6F
7 Tu	0128	0419	1.1E
	0753	1024	0.8F
	1245	1546	1.1E
	1903	2251	1.6F
8 W	0212	0517	1.1E
	0835	1113	0.8F
	1333	1641	1.0E
	1955	2341	1.6F
9 Th	0300	0616	1.1E
	0921	1204	0.9F
	1426	1756	1.0E
	2050		
10 F		0031	1.5F
	0357	0706	1.1E
	1011	1255	0.9F
	1532	1857	1.1E
	2150		
11 ◐ Sa		0124	1.4F
	0500	0754	1.1E
	1105	1352	0.9F
	1649	1954	1.1E
	2258		
12 Su		0230	1.2F
	0559	0923	1.1E
	1201	1505	1.0F
	1801	2100	1.1E
13 M	0011	0348	1.2F
	0656	0951	1.1E
	1301	1615	1.2F
	1909	2211	1.1E
14 Tu	0133	0449	1.2F
	0753	1048	1.1E
	1401	1710	1.4F
	2017	2315	1.2E
15 W	0251	0541	1.2F
	0849	1142	1.2E
	1454	1800	1.6F
	2122		
16 Th		0018	1.3E
	0353	0634	1.1F
	0938	1236	1.2E
	1540	1854	1.7F
	2219		
17 F		0120	1.4E
	0445	0729	1.1F
	1022	1327	1.3E
	1622	1948	1.8F
	2312		
18 ○ Sa		0209	1.4E
	0535	0819	1.0F
	1104	1410	1.3E
	1704	2037	1.8F
19 Su	0002	0250	1.4E
	0623	0901	0.9F
	1146	1449	1.3E
	1749	2121	1.7F
20 M	0049	0329	1.2E
	0708	0942	0.9F
	1229	1528	1.2E
	1839	2204	1.5F
21 Tu	0132	0411	1.1E
	0749	1024	0.8F
	1315	1614	1.0E
	1929	2250	1.3F
22 W	0213	0506	1.0E
	0830	1112	0.8F
	1403	1718	0.9E
	2018	2337	1.2F
23 Th	0257	0607	0.9E
	0913	1159	0.8F
	1457	1822	0.8E
	2104		
24 F		0021	1.1F
	0348	0656	0.9E
	1002	1243	0.7F
	1602	1910	0.8E
	2152		
25 Sa		0103	1.0F
	0445	0741	0.9E
	1054	1330	0.7F
	1708	1955	0.7E
	2242		
26 ◑ Su		0152	0.9F
	0539	0829	0.8E
	1147	1432	0.6F
	1803	2046	0.7E
	2337		
27 M		0300	0.8F
	0628	0923	0.7E
	1238	1550	0.7F
	1854	2146	0.7E
28 Tu	0041	0407	0.8F
	0713	1014	0.8E
	1327	1639	0.8F
	1950	2243	0.7E
29 W	0157	0453	0.8F
	0756	1058	0.8E
	1409	1718	1.0F
	2046	2337	0.8E
30 Th	0304	0532	0.8F
	0832	1137	0.8E
	1443	1757	1.2F
	2136		
31 F		0032	0.9E
	0355	0613	0.7F
	0902	1215	0.9E
	1514	1840	1.4F
	2221		

June

Day	Slack (h m)	Maximum (h m)	knots
1 Sa		0123	1.1E
	0438	0658	0.7F
	0931	1253	1.0E
	1546	1927	1.6F
	2302		
2 Su		0204	1.2E
	0518	0745	0.7F
	1004	1331	1.1E
	1620	2012	1.7F
	2343		
3 ● M		0239	1.3E
	0559	0830	0.8F
	1044	1408	1.2E
	1700	2056	1.8F
4 Tu	0024	0314	1.3E
	0642	0914	0.8F
	1131	1446	1.3E
	1747	2139	1.8F
5 W	0106	0354	1.3E
	0728	1001	0.9F
	1225	1528	1.3E
	1841	2227	1.8F
6 Th	0150	0448	1.2E
	0815	1053	1.0F
	1321	1623	1.2E
	1938	2320	1.7F
7 F	0238	0553	1.3E
	0904	1149	1.0F
	1421	1740	1.1E
	2036		
8 Sa		0014	1.6F
	0333	0648	1.3E
	0957	1242	1.1F
	1530	1847	1.1E
	2138		
9 Su		0106	1.4F
	0434	0737	1.3E
	1051	1339	1.1F
	1649	1945	1.1E
	2246		
10 ◑ M		0206	1.2F
	0533	0829	1.2E
	1145	1449	1.1F
	1802	2049	1.1E
	2242		
11 Tu	0001	0324	1.1F
	0627	0927	1.2E
	1240	1603	1.3F
	1911	2201	1.1E
12 W	0125	0432	1.0F
	0720	1024	1.2E
	1338	1659	1.5F
	2020	2306	1.1E
13 Th	0249	0524	0.9F
	0813	1117	1.2E
	1434	1749	1.6F
	2124		
14 F		0010	1.1E
	0352	0614	0.8F
	0905	1210	1.2E
	1523	1841	1.7F
	2220		
15 Sa		0113	1.2E
	0441	0708	0.8F
	0952	1304	1.2E
	1607	1935	1.7F
	2309		
16 Su		0201	1.2E
	0525	0800	0.8F
	1037	1352	1.2E
	1649	2023	1.7F
	2354		
17 ○ M		0238	1.2E
	0606	0842	0.8F
	1122	1432	1.2E
	1732	2104	1.6F
18 Tu	0034	0313	1.2E
	0647	0921	0.8F
	1208	1510	1.2E
	1817	2143	1.5F
19 W	0113	0351	1.1E
	0728	1001	0.8F
	1254	1550	1.0E
	1902	2224	1.4F
20 Th	0150	0439	1.0E
	0811	1047	0.8F
	1339	1641	0.9E
	1946	2308	1.3F
21 F	0231	0540	1.0E
	0857	1134	0.8F
	1425	1745	0.8E
	2027	2351	1.2F
22 Sa	0316	0634	1.0E
	0945	1219	0.7F
	1517	1839	0.7E
	2110		
23 Su		0033	1.1F
	0407	0717	1.0E
	1031	1302	0.7F
	1622	1923	0.7E
	2158		
24 M		0114	1.0F
	0456	0757	0.9E
	1112	1350	0.7F
	1726	2009	0.7E
	2252		
25 ◑ Tu		0201	0.8F
	0536	0837	0.8E
	1148	1454	0.7F
	1823	2106	0.6E
	2354		
26 W		0306	0.6F
	0606	0918	0.8E
	1221	1600	0.9F
	1921	2208	0.6E
27 Th	0110	0407	0.6F
	0632	0959	0.8E
	1258	1645	1.1F
	2021	2304	0.7E
28 F	0234	0452	0.5F
	0700	1037	0.9E
	1341	1725	1.3F
	2115	2357	0.8E
29 Sa	0330	0532	0.5F
	0738	1116	1.0E
	1427	1807	1.5F
	2159		
30 Su		0049	0.9E
	0410	0615	0.6F
	0827	1201	1.1E
	1511	1854	1.7F
	2240		

Time meridian 75° W. 0000 is midnight. 1200 is noon. Times are not adjusted for Daylight Saving Time.

Chesapeake Bay Entrance, Virginia, 2019

F–Flood, Dir. 297° True   E–Ebb, Dir. 112° True

July

Day	Slack (h m)	Max (h m)	knots
1 M	0445	0135	1.1E
	0921	0706	0.7F
	1555	1253	1.3E
	2319	1944	1.8F
2 Tu ●	0523	0214	1.2E
	1015	0800	0.8F
	1640	1344	1.4E
		2032	1.9F
3 W	0001	0251	1.3E
	0608	0850	1.0F
	1111	1429	1.5E
	1730	2119	1.9F
4 Th	0044	0332	1.4E
	0659	0940	1.1F
	1210	1515	1.4E
	1826	2208	1.9F
5 F	0130	0422	1.4E
	0751	1033	1.2F
	1310	1609	1.3E
	1925	2301	1.8F
6 Sa	0218	0526	1.4E
	0843	1131	1.2F
	1412	1723	1.2E
	2025	2355	1.6F
7 Su	0310	0627	1.4E
	0936	1227	1.3F
	1521	1834	1.2E
	2127		
8 M	0407	0047	1.4F
	1029	0717	1.4E
	1642	1322	1.3F
	2235	1933	1.1E
9 Tu ☽	0504	0142	1.2F
	1122	0806	1.3E
	1757	1427	1.3F
	2349	2035	1.0E
10 W	0556	0253	0.9F
	1216	0900	1.2E
	1907	1546	1.4F
		2146	0.9E
11 Th	0113	0411	0.8F
	0646	0959	1.2E
	1315	1647	1.5F
	2017	2253	0.9E
12 F	0239	0506	0.7F
	0739	1054	1.1E
	1417	1738	1.5F
	2121	2356	0.9E
13 Sa	0341	0554	0.7F
	0835	1148	1.1E
	1511	1828	1.6F
	2214		
14 Su	0426	0059	0.9E
	0929	0645	0.7F
	1558	1245	1.2E
	2300	1921	1.5F
15 M	0503	0147	1.0E
	1018	0737	0.7F
	1639	1336	1.2E
	2340	2008	1.5F
16 Tu ○	0540	0223	1.1E
	1104	0822	0.8F
	1719	1418	1.2E
		2047	1.5F
17 W	0017	0256	1.1E
	0621	0901	0.8F
	1149	1454	1.2E
	1757	2123	1.5F
18 Th	0053	0332	1.1E
	0706	0939	0.8F
	1231	1529	1.1E
	1837	2200	1.4F
19 F	0131	0415	1.1E
	0751	1021	0.8F
	1312	1610	1.0E
	1918	2241	1.4F
20 Sa	0209	0510	1.0E
	0836	1107	0.8F
	1353	1705	0.9E
	1959	2323	1.3F
21 Su	0249	0606	1.0E
	0917	1152	0.8F
	1438	1806	0.8E
	2042		
22 M	0328	0005	1.2F
	0953	0649	0.9E
	1537	1234	0.8F
	2129	1855	0.8E
23 Tu	0403	0043	1.0F
	1024	0722	0.9E
	1649	1315	0.8F
	2221	1940	0.7E
24 W ◐	0430	0120	0.8F
	1052	0750	0.8E
	1754	1403	0.9F
	2318	2029	0.6E
25 Th	0451	0204	0.5F
	1123	0818	0.8E
	1852	1509	1.0F
		2129	0.6E
26 F	0021	0309	0.4F
	0517	0853	0.9E
	1202	1609	1.2F
	1950	2227	0.6E
27 Sa	0139	0410	0.4F
	0556	0942	0.9E
	1252	1656	1.4F
	2044	2318	0.7E
28 Su	0246	0457	0.5F
	0647	1035	1.1E
	1350	1739	1.5F
	2131		
29 M	0329	0009	0.8E
	0750	0543	0.6F
	1448	1128	1.2E
	2212	1826	1.7F
30 Tu	0407	0101	1.0E
	0857	0635	0.7F
	1539	1227	1.4E
	2254	1919	1.8F
31 W ●	0448	0148	1.2E
	0959	0733	1.0F
	1628	1325	1.5E
	2337	2011	1.9F

August

Day	Slack (h m)	Max (h m)	knots
1 Th	0535	0230	1.4E
	1058	0828	1.2F
	1719	1417	1.6E
		2100	2.0F
2 F	0022	0311	1.5E
	0628	0920	1.3F
	1159	1504	1.6E
	1815	2149	1.9F
3 Sa	0109	0358	1.5E
	0722	1013	1.4F
	1259	1557	1.5E
	1915	2241	1.8F
4 Su	0156	0456	1.4E
	0815	1110	1.4F
	1401	1705	1.3E
	2015	2335	1.6F
5 M	0244	0600	1.4E
	0907	1207	1.4F
	1510	1818	1.2E
	2117		
6 Tu	0336	0027	1.3F
	1000	0653	1.4E
	1629	1302	1.4F
	2223	1918	1.1E
7 W ◐	0431	0118	1.1F
	1055	0742	1.3E
	1745	1402	1.3F
	2333	2017	0.9E
8 Th	0525	0219	0.8F
	1152	0833	1.2E
	1855	1523	1.3F
		2124	0.8E
9 F	0049	0344	0.6F
	0618	0933	1.1E
	1255	1633	1.3F
	2003	2232	0.7E
10 Sa	0212	0447	0.6F
	0713	1033	1.1E
	1403	1725	1.4F
	2107	2332	0.7E
11 Su	0313	0533	0.6F
	0815	1130	1.1E
	1503	1813	1.3F
	2158		
12 M	0356	0031	0.8E
	0913	0619	0.7F
	1550	1227	1.1E
	2241	1902	1.3F
13 Tu	0433	0124	0.9E
	1003	0710	0.8F
	1628	1320	1.2E
	2318	1948	1.4F
14 W	0511	0204	1.0E
	1047	0758	0.8F
	1702	1401	1.2E
	2355	2027	1.4F
15 Th ○	0553	0239	1.1E
	1128	0838	0.9F
	1737	1436	1.2E
		2101	1.5F
16 F	0032	0313	1.1E
	0638	0916	0.9F
	1207	1510	1.2E
	1815	2137	1.5F
17 Sa	0109	0350	1.1E
	0722	0955	0.9F
	1246	1546	1.1E
	1856	2215	1.4F
18 Su	0144	0434	1.0E
	0801	1037	0.9F
	1327	1632	1.0E
	1941	2255	1.3F
19 M	0217	0525	0.9E
	0834	1121	0.9F
	1412	1734	0.9E
	2026	2336	1.1F
20 Tu	0244	0609	0.9E
	0902	1203	0.9F
	1506	1830	0.8E
	2113		
21 W	0304	0014	0.9F
	0928	0641	0.8E
	1613	1243	1.0F
	2200	1915	0.7E
22 Th	0320	0048	0.7F
	0958	0706	0.8E
	1721	1325	1.0F
	2248	1958	0.7E
23 F ○	0344	0124	0.5F
	1035	0732	0.9E
	1817	1418	1.1F
	2338	2047	0.6E
24 Sa	0427	0213	0.4F
	1123	0807	0.9E
	1910	1529	1.1F
		2145	0.6E
25 Su	0034	0329	0.4F
	0525	0902	1.0E
	1219	1627	1.3F
	2004	2240	0.7E
26 M	0142	0430	0.6F
	0629	1009	1.1E
	1325	1715	1.5F
	2055	2331	0.8E
27 Tu	0244	0520	0.8F
	0738	1109	1.3E
	1432	1803	1.6F
	2142		
28 W	0333	0026	1.0E
	0848	0612	1.0F
	1528	1210	1.4E
	2227	1856	1.7F
29 Th	0418	0120	1.2E
	0951	0710	1.2F
	1620	1312	1.6E
	2312	1951	1.8F
30 F ●	0506	0207	1.4E
	1051	0808	1.4F
	1712	1406	1.7E
	2359	2042	1.9F
31 Sa	0556	0250	1.5E
	1150	0901	1.5F
	1808	1455	1.7E
		2131	1.8F

September

Day	Slack (h m)	Max (h m)	knots
1 Su	0045	0334	1.5E
	0650	0953	1.6F
	1250	1545	1.6E
	1908	2221	1.6F
2 M	0130	0424	1.4E
	0742	1048	1.6F
	1351	1647	1.4E
	2008	2314	1.4F
3 Tu	0215	0526	1.3E
	0834	1145	1.6F
	1455	1800	1.2E
	2107		
4 W	0302	0006	1.2F
	0928	0626	1.3E
	1610	1239	1.5F
	2208	1901	1.1E
5 Th ◐	0356	0055	0.9F
	1026	0717	1.2E
	1725	1335	1.3F
	2309	1955	0.9E
6 F	0458	0147	0.7F
	1128	0808	1.1E
	1832	1449	1.2F
		2054	0.7E
7 Sa	0011	0304	0.6F
	0558	0908	1.0E
	1234	1613	1.1F
	1935	2159	0.6E
8 Su	0119	0423	0.6F
	0657	1012	1.0E
	1346	1707	1.1F
	2036	2257	0.6E
9 M	0228	0511	0.7F
	0759	1110	1.0E
	1448	1750	1.1F
	2127	2352	0.7E
10 Tu	0320	0553	0.8F
	0857	1204	1.0E
	1533	1833	1.2F
	2210		
11 W	0402	0050	0.8E
	0946	0639	0.8F
	1609	1256	1.1E
	2249	1918	1.3F
12 Th	0442	0138	1.0E
	1028	0728	0.9F
	1642	1340	1.2E
	2327	1959	1.4F
13 F ○	0521	0216	1.1E
	1106	0812	0.9F
	1717	1417	1.3E
		2036	1.4F
14 Sa	0004	0250	1.1E
	0608	0850	1.0F
	1145	1451	1.3E
	1757	2112	1.4F
15 Su	0040	0322	1.1E
	0637	0927	1.0F
	1225	1527	1.2E
	1842	2148	1.3F
16 M	0111	0354	1.0E
	0709	1006	1.1F
	1308	1608	1.1E
	1930	2227	1.1F
17 Tu	0136	0427	0.9E
	0738	1048	1.1F
	1353	1704	1.0E
	2017	2307	0.9F
18 W	0155	0506	0.8E
	0806	1131	1.2F
	1442	1805	0.9E
	2102	2346	0.8F
19 Th	0212	0547	0.8E
	0837	1213	1.2F
	1539	1852	0.8E
	2144		
20 F	0234	0023	0.6F
	0914	0625	0.8E
	1641	1254	1.2F
	2224	1931	0.7E
21 Sa ○	0311	0100	0.6F
	1000	0701	0.9E
	1738	1341	1.2F
	2307	2013	0.7E
22 Su	0408	0145	0.5F
	1055	0744	1.0E
	1829	1447	1.1F
	2357	2106	0.7E
23 M	0518	0258	0.6F
	1157	0842	1.0E
	1921	1559	1.2F
		2205	0.8E
24 Tu	0059	0410	0.7F
	0627	0953	1.1E
	1307	1653	1.4F
	2017	2301	0.9E
25 W	0207	0504	1.0F
	0737	1057	1.3E
	1420	1743	1.5F
	2110	2356	1.1E
26 Th	0305	0556	1.2F
	0846	1159	1.4E
	1521	1835	1.6F
	2159		
27 F	0353	0052	1.3E
	0949	0652	1.4F
	1615	1301	1.6E
	2246	1932	1.7F
28 Sa ●	0439	0144	1.4E
	1047	0750	1.6F
	1708	1357	1.7E
	2331	2025	1.6F
29 Su	0525	0228	1.5E
	1145	0843	1.7F
	1805	1446	1.7E
		2113	1.5F
30 M	0016	0309	1.5E
	0615	0933	1.8F
	1243	1534	1.6E
	1904	2201	1.4F

Time meridian 75° W. 0000 is midnight. 1200 is noon. Times are not adjusted for Daylight Saving Time.

Chesapeake Bay Entrance, Virginia, 2019

F–Flood, Dir. 297° True   E–Ebb, Dir. 112° True

October

Day	Slack (h m)	Maximum (h m)	knots
1 Tu	0101	0353	1.4E
	0708	1025	1.7F
	1340	1630	1.4E
	2001	2251	1.2F
2 W	0144	0449	1.3E
	0801	1120	1.6F
	1439	1738	1.1E
	2054	2343	1.0F
3 Th	0230	0556	1.1E
	0856	1214	1.4F
	1544	1840	1.0E
	2147		
4 F		0031	0.8F
	0325	0653	1.1E
	0956	1306	1.2F
	1654	1930	0.8E
	2238		
5 Sa (●)		0118	0.7F
	0434	0745	1.0E
	1100	1405	1.0F
	1757	2019	0.7E
	2329		
6 Su		0217	0.6F
	0542	0841	0.9E
	1206	1534	0.9F
	1852	2118	0.6E
7 M	0026	0350	0.6F
	0642	0945	0.9E
	1313	1638	0.9F
	1947	2218	0.6E
8 Tu	0135	0446	0.7F
	0740	1042	0.9E
	1415	1719	1.0F
	2041	2313	0.7E
9 W	0241	0527	0.8F
	0836	1133	0.9E
	1503	1756	1.1F
	2129		
10 Th		0008	0.8E
	0330	0608	0.9F
	0925	1225	1.0E
	1543	1838	1.1F
	2212		
11 F		0102	0.9E
	0409	0654	1.0F
	1006	1314	1.1E
	1620	1923	1.2F
	2251		
12 Sa		0145	1.0E
	0442	0740	1.1F
	1046	1357	1.2E
	1700	2006	1.2F
	2326		
13 Su (○)		0219	1.1E
	0512	0821	1.2F
	1127	1434	1.3E
	1744	2044	1.2F
	2357		
14 M		0248	1.0E
	0540	0858	1.3F
	1209	1510	1.3E
	1833	2121	1.1F
15 Tu	0024	0313	1.0E
	0608	0936	1.4F
	1252	1548	1.2E
	1922	2158	0.9F
16 W	0045	0336	0.9E
	0640	1016	1.7F
	1336	1635	1.0E
	2007	2237	0.8F
17 Th	0107	0403	0.9E
	0716	1059	1.4F
	1420	1734	0.9E
	2048	2319	0.7F
18 F	0134	0444	0.8E
	0757	1144	1.4F
	1508	1825	0.9E
	2125		
19 Sa		0001	0.7F
	0210	0547	0.9E
	0843	1229	1.3F
	1601	1907	0.9E
	2204		
20 Su		0044	0.7F
	0300	0642	0.9E
	0935	1315	1.2F
	1658	1948	0.9E
	2248		
21 M (○)		0132	0.7F
	0407	0732	1.0E
	1034	1413	1.2F
	1752	2037	0.9E
	2339		
22 Tu		0239	0.8F
	0522	0831	1.0E
	1140	1530	1.2F
	1845	2137	0.9E
23 W	0037	0354	0.9F
	0631	0942	1.1E
	1253	1633	1.3F
	1941	2235	1.0E
24 Th	0142	0452	1.2F
	0740	1048	1.2E
	1411	1724	1.4F
	2037	2330	1.2E
25 F	0241	0543	1.4F
	0848	1150	1.4E
	1518	1816	1.4F
	2129		
26 Sa		0025	1.3E
	0330	0636	1.6F
	0949	1253	1.5E
	1614	1912	1.4F
	2217		
27 Su (●)		0118	1.4E
	0414	0733	1.8F
	1046	1350	1.6E
	1708	2007	1.3F
	2302		
28 M		0205	1.5E
	0458	0826	1.9F
	1141	1438	1.6E
	1804	2055	1.2F
	2346		
29 Tu		0246	1.4E
	0545	0915	1.9F
	1236	1523	1.5E
	1859	2141	1.1F
30 W	0030	0328	1.3E
	0637	1004	1.8F
	1328	1611	1.3E
	1950	2228	1.0F
31 Th	0116	0416	1.2E
	0732	1056	1.6F
	1420	1712	1.1E
	2037	2318	0.9F

November

Day	Slack (h m)	Maximum (h m)	knots
1 F	0204	0523	1.0E
	0828	1148	1.3F
	1514	1814	0.9E
	2121		
2 Sa		0007	0.8F
	0300	0629	0.9E
	0925	1237	1.1F
	1613	1903	0.9E
	2206		
3 Su		0052	0.8F
	0410	0721	0.9E
	1024	1324	0.9F
	1712	1949	0.8E
	2256		
4 M (◐)		0142	0.7F
	0522	0811	0.8E
	1121	1423	0.8F
	1803	2039	0.7E
	2351		
5 Tu		0257	0.7F
	0620	0907	0.8E
	1218	1544	0.8F
	1853	2138	0.7E
6 W	0053	0415	0.8F
	0714	1006	0.8E
	1319	1637	0.8F
	1945	2235	0.8E
7 Th	0159	0459	0.8F
	0809	1059	0.8E
	1421	1717	0.9F
	2038	2325	0.8E
8 F	0251	0538	0.9F
	0900	1151	0.9E
	1514	1757	1.0F
	2124		
9 Sa		0014	0.9E
	0328	0618	1.1F
	0946	1246	1.0E
	1601	1841	1.0F
	2202		
10 Su		0100	0.9E
	0356	0703	1.2F
	1029	1336	1.2E
	1646	1928	0.9F
	2233		
11 M		0138	1.0E
	0422	0747	1.4F
	1111	1417	1.3E
	1732	2011	0.9F
	2259		
12 Tu (○)		0208	1.0E
	0447	0828	1.5F
	1153	1453	1.3E
	1820	2050	0.8F
	2323		
13 W		0233	1.0E
	0517	0907	1.6F
	1235	1528	1.2E
	1906	2128	0.8F
	2351		
14 Th		0259	1.0E
	0554	0947	1.6F
	1316	1607	1.1E
	1947	2208	0.7F
15 F	0027	0329	1.0E
	0639	1031	1.6F
	1356	1657	1.0E
	2025	2253	0.7F
16 Sa	0109	0411	1.0E
	0729	1118	1.5F
	1439	1755	1.0E
	2104	2342	0.8F
17 Su	0158	0519	1.0E
	0821	1207	1.4F
	1528	1844	1.0E
	2146		
18 M		0030	0.9F
	0257	0628	1.0E
	0917	1255	1.4F
	1624	1928	1.1E
	2234		
19 Tu (○)		0121	0.9F
	0410	0723	1.0E
	1018	1349	1.2F
	1720	2016	1.1E
	2326		
20 W		0224	1.0F
	0526	0822	1.0E
	1126	1500	1.1F
	1814	2112	1.1E
21 Th	0021	0339	1.1F
	0635	0932	1.1E
	1241	1612	1.1F
	1908	2211	1.2E
22 F	0120	0440	1.3F
	0743	1040	1.1E
	1405	1707	1.1F
	2003	2305	1.2E
23 Sa	0218	0531	1.6F
	0851	1143	1.2E
	1518	1758	1.1F
	2057	2358	1.3E
24 Su	0309	0623	1.7F
	0951	1247	1.3E
	1616	1853	1.0F
	2147		
25 M		0053	1.3E
	0354	0719	1.8F
	1047	1345	1.4E
	1709	1950	1.0F
	2232		
26 Tu (●)		0144	1.4E
	0437	0812	1.9F
	1139	1431	1.4E
	1800	2039	1.0F
	2317		
27 W		0227	1.4E
	0524	0900	1.8F
	1228	1511	1.3E
	1849	2122	0.9F
28 Th	0004	0308	1.3E
	0615	0945	1.7F
	1315	1553	1.2E
	1933	2205	0.9F
29 F	0052	0352	1.1E
	0709	1032	1.5F
	1359	1643	1.0E
	2015	2253	0.7F
30 Sa	0142	0449	1.0E
	0801	1120	1.3F
	1443	1745	0.9E
	2056	2342	0.8F

December

Day	Slack (h m)	Maximum (h m)	knots
1 Su	0235	0558	0.9E
	0850	1206	1.1F
	1531	1838	0.9E
	2142		
2 M		0028	0.8F
	0338	0652	0.8E
	0938	1248	1.0F
	1624	1923	0.9E
	2233		
3 Tu		0113	0.7F
	0449	0738	0.7E
	1026	1332	0.9F
	1716	2007	0.9E
	2325		
4 W (◐)		0208	0.7F
	0549	0827	0.7E
	1117	1429	0.8F
	1804	2058	0.9E
5 Th	0017	0328	0.7F
	0643	0925	0.7E
	1216	1542	0.8F
	1849	2152	0.8E
6 F	0108	0426	0.8F
	0738	1024	0.7E
	1330	1636	0.8F
	1934	2240	0.8E
7 Sa	0155	0507	1.0F
	0834	1119	0.8E
	1445	1718	0.7F
	2017	2322	0.8E
8 Su	0234	0545	1.2F
	0926	1216	0.9E
	1543	1759	0.7F
	2053		
9 M		0003	0.9E
	0306	0626	1.4F
	1011	1312	1.0E
	1631	1844	0.6F
	2124		
10 Tu		0043	0.9E
	0336	0712	1.5F
	1053	1356	1.1E
	1714	1931	0.6F
	2154		
11 W		0122	1.0E
	0408	0758	1.7F
	1134	1431	1.2E
	1754	2016	0.7F
	2229		
12 Th (○)		0157	1.1E
	0444	0840	1.7F
	1213	1504	1.2E
	1834	2058	0.7F
	2310		
13 F		0231	1.2E
	0526	0922	1.7F
	1252	1540	1.2E
	1914	2141	0.8F
14 Sa	0000	0308	1.2E
	0616	1006	1.7F
	1332	1624	1.2E
	1956	2229	0.8F
15 Su	0053	0354	1.2E
	0710	1055	1.6F
	1414	1723	1.2E
	2040	2322	1.0F
16 M	0150	0459	1.1E
	0805	1146	1.6F
	1501	1820	1.2E
	2127		
17 Tu		0015	1.1F
	0253	0614	1.1E
	0902	1236	1.5F
	1554	1909	1.3E
	2218		
18 W (○)		0108	1.1F
	0408	0713	1.1E
	1005	1327	1.3F
	1651	1956	1.3E
	2310		
19 Th		0208	1.2F
	0526	0812	1.1E
	1114	1432	1.1F
	1745	2049	1.3E
20 F	0003	0323	1.3F
	0635	0920	1.0E
	1232	1550	1.0F
	1837	2147	1.2E
21 Sa	0058	0428	1.5F
	0744	1031	1.0E
	1402	1651	0.9F
	1930	2242	1.2E
22 Su	0157	0520	1.6F
	0852	1135	1.1E
	1519	1742	0.9F
	2026	2336	1.2E
23 M	0252	0612	1.7F
	0952	1241	1.1E
	1616	1835	0.8F
	2119		
24 Tu		0032	1.2E
	0341	0707	1.8F
	1046	1338	1.2E
	1704	1932	0.8F
	2209		
25 W		0127	1.3E
	0427	0801	1.8F
	1134	1421	1.2E
	1747	2021	0.8F
	2256		
26 Th (●)		0213	1.3E
	0512	0847	1.7F
	1219	1458	1.2E
	1828	2103	0.8F
	2344		
27 F		0253	1.3E
	0600	0928	1.6F
	1300	1534	1.1E
	1909	2144	0.9F
28 Sa	0032	0332	1.2E
	0648	1009	1.4F
	1338	1617	1.0E
	1951	2227	0.8F
29 Su	0120	0418	1.0E
	0733	1052	1.3F
	1416	1714	1.0E
	2035	2315	0.8F
30 M	0207	0520	0.9E
	0815	1135	1.2F
	1457	1811	1.0E
	2121		
31 Tu		0002	0.8F
	0259	0619	0.8E
	0856	1216	1.1F
	1542	1858	1.0E
	2209		

Time meridian 75° W. 0000 is midnight. 1200 is noon. Times are not adjusted for Daylight Saving Time.

Baltimore Harbor Approach, Maryland, 2019

F–Flood, Dir. 025° True   E–Ebb, Dir. 190° True

January

Day	Slack h m	Max h m	knots
1 Tu		0113	0.5F
	0340	0657	0.7E
	0952	1333	1.2F
	1710	2020	0.9E
	2358		
2 W		0216	0.4F
	0439	0750	0.7E
	1039	1424	1.2F
	1800	2114	1.0E
3 Th	0058	0314	0.4F
	0538	0842	0.7E
	1125	1513	1.2F
	1847	2204	1.0E
4 F	0150	0407	0.4F
	0634	0932	0.6E
	1210	1558	1.2F
	1931	2250	1.1E
5 Sa ●	0237	0457	0.5F
	0728	1020	0.6E
	1255	1642	1.2F
	2012	2332	1.1E
6 Su	0319	0543	0.5F
	0820	1106	0.6E
	1338	1724	1.1F
	2051		
7 M		0013	1.1E
	0359	0627	0.5F
	0910	1152	0.5E
	1422	1805	1.0F
	2129		
8 Tu		0052	1.0E
	0436	0709	0.5F
	0959	1238	0.5E
	1507	1846	1.0F
	2206		
9 W		0131	1.0E
	0512	0751	0.6F
	1049	1325	0.5E
	1555	1928	0.9F
	2243		
10 Th		0209	1.0E
	0546	0834	0.6F
	1140	1415	0.5E
	1647	2013	0.8F
	2322		
11 F		0248	0.9E
	0621	0917	0.6F
	1232	1508	0.4E
	1746	2100	0.6F
12 Sa	0001	0328	0.8E
	0655	1001	0.7F
	1325	1605	0.5E
	1852	2153	0.5F
13 Su	0043	0410	0.8E
	0729	1047	0.8F
	1418	1705	0.5E
	2007	2249	0.4F
14 M ☽	0126	0454	0.7E
	0804	1134	0.8F
	1510	1807	0.6E
	2125	2350	0.3F
15 Tu	0214	0539	0.6E
	0841	1221	0.9F
	1601	1906	0.7E
	2241		
16 W		0052	0.3F
	0305	0627	0.7E
	0920	1309	1.0F
	1650	2002	0.8E
	2349		
17 Th		0152	0.3F
	0359	0716	0.6E
	1003	1357	1.1F
	1738	2053	0.9E
18 F	0045	0248	0.3F
	0456	0807	0.6E
	1049	1444	1.2F
	1824	2141	1.0E
19 Sa	0133	0339	0.4F
	0553	0859	0.6E
	1138	1532	1.3F
	1909	2226	1.1E
20 Su	0215	0428	0.4F
	0650	0951	0.7E
	1230	1620	1.3F
	1953	2310	1.1E
21 M ○	0254	0516	0.5F
	0747	1045	0.7E
	1325	1708	1.3F
	2037	2354	1.2E
22 Tu	0331	0603	0.6F
	0844	1139	0.7E
	1422	1757	1.2F
	2120		
23 W		0037	1.2E
	0408	0650	0.7F
	0942	1235	0.8E
	1521	1848	1.1F
	2204		
24 Th		0121	1.1E
	0447	0739	0.8F
	1041	1333	0.8E
	1624	1940	1.0F
	2249		
25 F		0206	1.1E
	0527	0829	0.9F
	1142	1434	0.8E
	1730	2036	0.8F
	2335		
26 Sa		0254	1.0E
	0609	0922	1.0F
	1244	1538	0.8E
	1842	2135	0.7F
27 Su ◐	0024	0343	0.9E
	0654	1017	1.0F
	1347	1644	0.8E
	1959	2238	0.5F
28 M	0116	0436	0.8E
	0741	1113	1.1F
	1449	1751	0.8E
	2117	2344	0.4F
29 Tu	0213	0532	0.7E
	0830	1211	1.1F
	1549	1857	0.8E
	2233		
30 W		0051	0.4F
	0314	0630	0.7E
	0921	1307	1.1F
	1645	1957	0.9E
	2339		
31 Th		0156	0.4F
	0418	0727	0.6E
	1013	1401	1.1F
	1736	2052	0.9E

February

Day	Slack h m	Max h m	knots
1 F	0036	0254	0.4F
	0520	0823	0.6E
	1104	1451	1.1F
	1824	2141	1.0E
2 Sa	0125	0347	0.5F
	0619	0915	0.6E
	1154	1538	1.1F
	1907	2226	1.0E
3 Su	0208	0434	0.5F
	0712	1004	0.6E
	1241	1622	1.1F
	1948	2307	1.0E
4 M ●	0246	0518	0.6F
	0801	1050	0.6E
	1327	1704	1.0F
	2026	2345	1.0E
5 Tu	0321	0558	0.6F
	0847	1135	0.6E
	1413	1745	1.0F
	2103		
6 W		0022	1.0E
	0355	0637	0.6F
	0932	1218	0.6E
	1459	1825	0.9F
	2139		
7 Th		0058	1.0E
	0426	0715	0.7F
	1016	1303	0.6E
	1546	1906	0.8F
	2215		
8 F		0134	0.9E
	0458	0753	0.7F
	1101	1349	0.6E
	1637	1948	0.7F
	2251		
9 Sa		0210	0.8E
	0528	0833	0.7F
	1149	1439	0.6E
	1734	2034	0.6F
	2328		
10 Su		0247	0.8E
	0600	0915	0.8F
	1239	1532	0.6E
	1837	2123	0.5F
11 M	0007	0326	0.7E
	0633	1000	0.8F
	1332	1630	0.6E
	1948	2218	0.4F
12 Tu ◐	0048	0409	0.6E
	0710	1048	0.9F
	1427	1731	0.6E
	2105	2318	0.3F
13 W	0134	0457	0.6E
	0751	1139	0.9F
	1522	1832	0.7E
	2219		
14 Th		0022	0.3F
	0229	0550	0.5E
	0839	1233	1.0F
	1616	1930	0.8E
	2322		
15 F		0124	0.3F
	0331	0647	0.6E
	0931	1327	1.1F
	1707	2024	0.9E
16 Sa	0013	0221	0.3F
	0436	0745	0.6E
	1028	1420	1.1F
	1757	2113	1.0E
17 Su	0056	0314	0.4F
	0538	0844	0.7E
	1127	1512	1.2F
	1844	2158	1.0E
18 M	0134	0402	0.5F
	0638	0940	0.7E
	1226	1603	1.2F
	1929	2242	1.1E
19 Tu ○	0211	0449	0.7F
	0734	1035	0.8E
	1325	1653	1.2F
	2013	2325	1.1E
20 W	0247	0535	0.8F
	0829	1130	0.9E
	1424	1743	1.1F
	2057		
21 Th		0008	1.1E
	0324	0621	0.9F
	0924	1224	0.9E
	1523	1834	1.0F
	2141		
22 F		0051	1.1E
	0403	0709	1.0F
	1019	1320	0.9E
	1624	1925	0.9F
	2225		
23 Sa		0136	1.0E
	0444	0758	1.0F
	1116	1417	0.9E
	1727	2019	0.8F
	2311		
24 Su		0223	0.9E
	0527	0849	1.1F
	1214	1516	0.9E
	1834	2116	0.6F
25 M	0000	0313	0.8E
	0614	0943	1.1F
	1314	1619	0.8E
	1944	2217	0.5F
26 Tu ◑	0054	0407	0.7E
	0704	1040	1.0F
	1414	1723	0.8E
	2057	2323	0.4F
27 W	0154	0505	0.6E
	0757	1139	1.0F
	1514	1827	0.8E
	2206		
28 Th		0029	0.4F
	0300	0606	0.6E
	0854	1238	1.0F
	1611	1927	0.8E
	2308		

March

Day	Slack h m	Max h m	knots
1 F		0133	0.4F
	0406	0708	0.6E
	0952	1335	1.0F
	1705	2022	0.9E
2 Sa	0000	0230	0.5F
	0509	0806	0.6E
	1048	1428	1.0F
	1753	2110	0.9E
3 Su	0045	0320	0.5F
	0605	0859	0.6E
	1142	1516	1.0F
	1838	2154	0.9E
4 M	0125	0405	0.6F
	0654	0948	0.6E
	1233	1601	1.0F
	1919	2234	0.9E
5 Tu	0200	0445	0.7F
	0739	1033	0.7E
	1321	1644	0.9F
	1958	2311	0.9E
6 W ●	0233	0523	0.7F
	0821	1116	0.7E
	1407	1724	0.9F
	2035	2347	0.9E
7 Th	0304	0600	0.7F
	0902	1159	0.7E
	1454	1805	0.8F
	2112		
8 F		0021	0.9E
	0334	0635	0.8F
	0943	1241	0.7E
	1542	1845	0.7F
	2147		
9 Sa		0056	0.8E
	0403	0712	0.8F
	1025	1325	0.7E
	1633	1927	0.7F
	2223		
10 Su		0130	0.7E
	0432	0750	0.8F
	1109	1412	0.7E
	1728	2012	0.5F
	2259		
11 M		0206	0.7E
	0504	0831	0.9F
	1157	1503	0.7E
	1829	2100	0.4F
	2337		
12 Tu		0246	0.6E
	0539	0916	0.9F
	1249	1558	0.7E
	1935	2154	0.3F
13 W	0020	0331	0.5E
	0620	1006	0.9F
	1344	1657	0.7E
	2043	2254	0.3F
14 Th ☽	0112	0423	0.5E
	0709	1101	0.9F
	1441	1758	0.7E
	2148	2358	0.3F
15 F	0215	0524	0.5E
	0808	1201	0.9F
	1539	1856	0.8E
	2242		
16 Sa		0059	0.3F
	0324	0629	0.5E
	0913	1301	1.0F
	1634	1950	0.9E
	2328		
17 Su		0156	0.4F
	0431	0734	0.6E
	1020	1359	1.0F
	1726	2040	0.9E
18 M	0008	0247	0.6F
	0532	0835	0.7E
	1126	1455	1.0F
	1815	2126	1.0E
19 Tu	0046	0335	0.7F
	0629	0933	0.8E
	1230	1548	1.0F
	1902	2211	1.0E
20 W ○	0123	0422	0.9F
	0722	1027	0.9E
	1330	1640	1.0F
	1948	2254	1.0E
21 Th	0201	0507	1.0F
	0814	1120	1.0E
	1429	1730	1.0F
	2032	2337	1.0E
22 F	0240	0553	1.1F
	0906	1212	1.0E
	1526	1820	0.9F
	2117		
23 Sa		0021	0.9E
	0320	0639	1.1F
	0957	1305	1.0E
	1624	1911	0.8F
	2202		
24 Su		0106	0.9E
	0402	0727	1.1F
	1049	1358	1.0E
	1723	2003	0.7F
	2250		
25 M		0153	0.8E
	0446	0816	1.1F
	1142	1453	1.0E
	1824	2059	0.6F
	2342		
26 Tu		0244	0.7E
	0534	0909	1.0F
	1238	1551	0.9E
	1927	2158	0.5F
27 W ◐	0039	0339	0.6E
	0627	1005	1.0F
	1335	1651	0.9E
	2030	2302	0.5F
28 Th	0143	0441	0.5E
	0724	1104	0.9F
	1433	1752	0.8E
	2131		
29 F		0006	0.5F
	0252	0545	0.5E
	0827	1205	0.8F
	1529	1850	0.8E
	2226		
30 Sa		0106	0.5F
	0357	0649	0.5E
	0931	1304	0.8F
	1623	1943	0.8E
	2314		
31 Su		0200	0.6F
	0456	0748	0.5E
	1033	1359	0.8F
	1714	2031	0.8E
	2356		

Time meridian 75° W.   0000 is midnight.   1200 is noon.   Times are not adjusted for Daylight Saving Time.

Baltimore Harbor Approach, Maryland, 2019

F–Flood, Dir. 025° True   E–Ebb, Dir. 190° True

April

Day	Slack (h m)	Max (h m)	knots
1 M		0247	0.6F
	0547	0842	0.6E
	1131	1450	0.8F
	1800	2115	0.9E
2 Tu	0033	0330	0.7F
	0633	0930	0.7E
	1224	1536	0.8F
	1843	2154	0.9E
3 W	0107	0409	0.8F
	0714	1014	0.7E
	1314	1620	0.8F
	1924	2232	0.8E
4 Th	0139	0445	0.8F
	0754	1057	0.8E
	1403	1703	0.8F
	2003	2307	0.8E
5 F ●	0209	0521	0.9F
	0832	1138	0.9E
	1451	1744	0.7F
	2040	2342	0.8E
6 Sa	0238	0556	0.9F
	0912	1220	0.9E
	1540	1826	0.6F
	2117		
7 Su		0016	0.7E
	0307	0632	1.0F
	0952	1304	0.9E
	1631	1909	0.6F
	2154		
8 M		0051	0.6E
	0338	0710	1.0F
	1035	1349	0.9E
	1725	1954	0.5F
	2232		
9 Tu		0129	0.6E
	0412	0752	1.0F
	1122	1438	0.9E
	1821	2043	0.4F
	2315		
10 W		0212	0.5E
	0452	0838	1.0F
	1211	1530	0.8E
	1919	2137	0.4F
11 Th	0005	0302	0.5F
	0540	0930	0.9F
	1305	1626	0.8E
	2016	2236	0.4F
12 F ◐	0106	0402	0.5F
	0639	1029	0.9F
	1402	1723	0.8E
	2109	2336	0.4F
13 Sa	0215	0510	0.5F
	0749	1133	0.9F
	1500	1820	0.8E
	2156		
14 Su		0035	0.5F
	0324	0620	0.5E
	0905	1237	0.8F
	1557	1914	0.8E
	2239		
15 M		0130	0.6F
	0428	0727	0.6E
	1021	1340	0.8F
	1651	2004	0.9E
	2319		
16 Tu		0221	0.8F
	0526	0829	0.8E
	1131	1438	0.8F
	1743	2052	0.9E
	2358		
17 W		0309	0.9F
	0619	0926	0.9E
	1236	1534	0.8F
	1832	2138	0.9E
18 Th	0038	0355	1.1F
	0710	1019	1.0E
	1336	1626	0.8F
	1920	2222	0.9E
19 F ○	0117	0440	1.2F
	0759	1110	1.1E
	1433	1717	0.8F
	2006	2307	0.9E
20 Sa	0158	0526	1.2F
	0847	1200	1.1E
	1528	1807	0.7F
	2053	2352	0.8E
21 Su	0239	0611	1.2F
	0935	1249	1.1E
	1622	1857	0.7F
	2141		
22 M		0037	0.7E
	0322	0657	1.2F
	1023	1339	1.1E
	1716	1948	0.6F
	2232		
23 Tu		0126	0.7E
	0408	0745	1.1F
	1112	1430	1.0E
	1811	2043	0.5F
	2328		
24 W		0217	0.6E
	0456	0836	1.0F
	1202	1523	1.0E
	1905	2140	0.5F
25 Th	0029	0314	0.5E
	0550	0930	0.9F
	1253	1617	0.9E
	2000	2239	0.5F
26 F ◑	0135	0417	0.4E
	0651	1027	0.8F
	1347	1712	0.8E
	2051	2338	0.5F
27 Sa	0241	0522	0.4E
	0758	1128	0.7F
	1441	1807	0.8E
	2139		
28 Su		0034	0.6F
	0343	0626	0.5E
	0908	1228	0.7F
	1534	1858	0.8E
	2223		
29 M		0124	0.7F
	0437	0726	0.5E
	1015	1325	0.7F
	1626	1945	0.8E
	2302		
30 Tu		0210	0.7F
	0524	0819	0.6E
	1117	1418	0.7F
	1715	2029	0.8E
	2338		

May

Day	Slack (h m)	Max (h m)	knots
1 W		0251	0.8F
	0607	0907	0.7E
	1214	1508	0.6F
	1801	2110	0.8E
2 Th	0011	0330	0.9F
	0647	0952	0.8E
	1307	1554	0.6F
	1844	2148	0.7E
3 F	0043	0407	1.0F
	0726	1036	0.9E
	1358	1639	0.6F
	1926	2225	0.7E
4 Sa ●	0114	0443	1.0F
	0805	1118	1.0E
	1448	1723	0.6F
	2005	2301	0.7E
5 Su	0144	0520	1.1F
	0844	1200	1.0E
	1538	1806	0.5F
	2045	2338	0.6E
6 M	0216	0558	1.1F
	0925	1244	1.0E
	1628	1851	0.5F
	2125		
7 Tu		0016	0.6E
	0251	0638	1.1F
	1008	1328	1.0E
	1717	1937	0.4F
	2209		
8 W		0059	0.5E
	0331	0721	1.1F
	1053	1415	1.0E
	1807	2026	0.4F
	2300		
9 Th		0147	0.5E
	0418	0809	1.0F
	1140	1504	1.0E
	1855	2119	0.4F
	2358		
10 F		0244	0.5E
	0515	0903	0.9F
	1231	1556	0.9E
	1942	2216	0.5F
11 Sa ◐	0105	0349	0.5F
	0623	1003	0.8F
	1325	1649	0.9E
	2027	2313	0.6F
12 Su	0214	0500	0.5F
	0741	1108	0.8F
	1421	1743	0.9E
	2110		
13 M		0010	0.7F
	0320	0612	0.6E
	0904	1215	0.7F
	1517	1837	0.8E
	2152		
14 Tu		0104	0.8F
	0420	0719	0.7E
	1023	1320	0.7F
	1613	1928	0.8E
	2234		
15 W		0155	1.0F
	0516	0820	0.8E
	1135	1421	0.7F
	1708	2018	0.8E
	2315		
16 Th		0243	1.1F
	0608	0916	1.0E
	1240	1518	0.6F
	1800	2106	0.8E
	2357		
17 F		0331	1.2F
	0657	1009	1.1E
	1340	1612	0.6F
	1851	2153	0.8E
18 Sa ○	0039	0416	1.3F
	0744	1059	1.1E
	1435	1704	0.6F
	1941	2239	0.8E
19 Su	0122	0502	1.3F
	0830	1147	1.2E
	1527	1754	0.6F
	2032	2325	0.7E
20 M	0205	0546	1.2F
	0915	1233	1.2E
	1616	1843	0.6F
	2123		
21 Tu		0013	0.6E
	0249	0631	1.2F
	0959	1320	1.1E
	1705	1934	0.5F
	2217		
22 W		0102	0.6E
	0335	0717	1.1F
	1043	1407	1.1E
	1752	2025	0.5F
	2314		
23 Th		0154	0.5E
	0424	0805	1.0F
	1128	1454	1.0E
	1839	2118	0.5F
24 F	0016	0250	0.4E
	0518	0856	0.8F
	1213	1542	0.9E
	1924	2211	0.6F
25 Sa	0119	0350	0.4E
	0619	0950	0.7F
	1301	1631	0.9E
	2008	2304	0.6F
26 Su ◐	0221	0454	0.4E
	0728	1047	0.6F
	1350	1721	0.8E
	2050	2356	0.7F
27 M	0318	0557	0.4E
	0841	1147	0.6F
	1441	1809	0.8E
	2130		
28 Tu		0044	0.7F
	0409	0656	0.5E
	0953	1246	0.5F
	1533	1856	0.8E
	2208		
29 W		0129	0.8F
	0455	0751	0.6E
	1100	1343	0.5F
	1624	1941	0.7E
	2243		
30 Th		0211	0.9F
	0538	0841	0.7E
	1202	1436	0.5F
	1713	2023	0.7E
	2317		
31 F		0251	1.0F
	0619	0929	0.9E
	1259	1526	0.5F
	1759	2104	0.7E
	2350		

June

Day	Slack (h m)	Max (h m)	knots
1 Sa		0330	1.1F
	0659	1013	1.0E
	1352	1614	0.5F
	1844	2144	0.6E
2 Su	0024	0409	1.2F
	0739	1057	1.0E
	1442	1700	0.5F
	1928	2223	0.6E
3 M ●	0059	0448	1.2F
	0820	1140	1.1E
	1530	1746	0.4F
	2013	2305	0.6E
4 Tu	0137	0529	1.2F
	0901	1223	1.1E
	1615	1831	0.4F
	2059	2349	0.6E
5 W	0220	0612	1.2F
	0944	1307	1.1E
	1659	1918	0.5F
	2150		
6 Th		0037	0.5E
	0307	0658	1.1F
	1028	1351	1.1E
	1741	2006	0.5F
	2247		
7 F		0131	0.5E
	0401	0747	1.1F
	1113	1438	1.0E
	1822	2057	0.6F
	2349		
8 Sa		0231	0.5E
	0504	0842	0.9F
	1201	1526	1.0E
	1903	2151	0.6F
9 Su	0055	0338	0.5F
	0617	0941	0.8F
	1251	1616	0.9E
	1944	2246	0.7F
10 M ◑	0202	0448	0.6F
	0738	1046	0.7F
	1344	1708	0.9E
	2027	2342	0.9F
11 Tu	0306	0559	0.7F
	0902	1153	0.6F
	1440	1801	0.8E
	2110		
12 W		0036	1.0F
	0406	0706	0.8E
	1023	1300	0.5F
	1537	1854	0.8E
	2154		
13 Th		0129	1.1F
	0501	0808	0.9E
	1136	1403	0.5F
	1634	1947	0.8E
	2239		
14 F		0220	1.2F
	0553	0904	1.0E
	1241	1503	0.5F
	1731	2038	0.7E
	2324		
15 Sa		0308	1.3F
	0642	0957	1.1E
	1338	1558	0.5F
	1826	2128	0.7E
16 Su	0009	0355	1.3F
	0728	1045	1.1E
	1430	1650	0.5F
	1920	2217	0.7E
17 M ○	0054	0441	1.3F
	0812	1132	1.2E
	1518	1740	0.5F
	2014	2305	0.6E
18 Tu	0139	0526	1.2F
	0855	1216	1.1E
	1603	1828	0.5F
	2107	2353	0.6E
19 W	0225	0609	1.1F
	0936	1259	1.1E
	1645	1915	0.5F
	2201		
20 Th		0042	0.5E
	0311	0653	1.0F
	1016	1341	1.1E
	1726	2002	0.6F
	2257		
21 F		0132	0.5E
	0400	0738	0.9F
	1056	1423	1.0E
	1805	2049	0.6F
	2353		
22 Sa		0225	0.4E
	0453	0825	0.8F
	1137	1506	0.9E
	1844	2137	0.6F
23 Su	0050	0321	0.4E
	0552	0915	0.7F
	1219	1550	0.9E
	1923	2224	0.7F
24 M	0146	0420	0.4E
	0658	1008	0.6F
	1304	1635	0.8E
	2000	2312	0.7F
25 Tu	0241	0521	0.5E
	0812	1106	0.5F
	1351	1720	0.8E
	2037	2359	0.8F
26 W	0332	0622	0.5E
	0927	1206	0.4F
	1440	1806	0.7E
	2114		
27 Th		0045	0.9F
	0420	0719	0.6E
	1040	1306	0.4F
	1531	1852	0.7E
	2150		
28 F		0130	1.0F
	0506	0813	0.8E
	1147	1403	0.4F
	1623	1937	0.6E
	2227		
29 Sa		0213	1.1F
	0550	0903	0.9E
	1247	1457	0.3F
	1714	2022	0.6E
	2305		
30 Su		0256	1.1F
	0633	0950	1.0E
	1340	1548	0.4F
	1804	2107	0.6E
	2345		

Time meridian 75° W. 0000 is midnight. 1200 is noon. Times are not adjusted for Daylight Saving Time.

Baltimore Harbor Approach, Maryland, 2019

F–Flood, Dir. 025° True   E–Ebb, Dir. 190° True

July

	Slack	Maximum			Slack	Maximum
	h m	h m knots			h m	h m knots
1 M	0715 / 1427 / 1854	0339 1.2F / 1034 1.0E / 1636 0.4F / 2153 0.6E	**16** Tu ○	0037 / 0753 / 1457 / 1959	0423 1.2F / 1113 1.1E / 1722 0.5F / 2249 0.6E
2 Tu ●	0028 / 0757 / 1722 / 1945	0422 1.2F / 1117 1.1E / / 2240 0.6E	**17** W	0124 / 0834 / 1537 / 2051	0508 1.1F / 1155 1.1E / 1807 0.6F / 2337 0.6E
3 W	0114 / 0839 / 1549 / 2038	0506 1.3F / 1200 1.1E / 1807 0.5F / 2330 0.6E	**18** Th	0211 / 0913 / 1614 / 2141	0550 1.1F / 1234 1.1E / 1850 0.6F
4 Th	0204 / 0921 / 1627 / 2133	0552 1.2F / 1242 1.1E / 1853 0.6F	**19** F	0257 / 0950 / 1649 / 2230	0023 0.5E / 0632 1.0F / 1313 1.0E / 1932 0.6F
5 F	0258 / 1005 / 1704 / 2231	0022 0.6E / 0640 1.2F / 1325 1.1E / 1941 0.6F	**20** Sa	0345 / 1027 / 1724 / 2320	0111 0.5E / 0714 0.9F / 1351 1.0E / 2014 0.7F
6 Sa	0357 / 1049 / 1742 / 2332	0119 0.6E / 0730 1.0F / 1409 1.1E / 2030 0.7F	**21** Su	0436 / 1105 / 1758	0159 0.5E / 0758 0.8F / 1429 0.9E / 2056 0.7F
7 Su	0503 / 1134 / 1821	0219 0.6E / 0824 0.9F / 1456 1.0E / 2122 0.8F	**22** M	0011 / 0532 / 1144 / 1832	0250 0.5E / 0844 0.7F / 1509 0.8E / 2140 0.7F
8 M	0036 / 0615 / 1222 / 1902	0324 0.6E / 0922 0.8F / 1544 1.0E / 2216 0.9F	**23** Tu	0103 / 0635 / 1224 / 1907	0345 0.5E / 0934 0.5F / 1550 0.8E / 2225 0.8F
9 Tu ◐	0140 / 0733 / 1312 / 1946	0432 0.7E / 1025 0.6F / 1635 0.9E / 2312 1.0F	**24** W ○	0155 / 0746 / 1307 / 1943	0444 0.5E / 1029 0.4F / 1633 0.7E / 2312 0.8F
10 W	0243 / 0855 / 1407 / 2033	0541 0.7E / 1132 0.5F / 1729 0.8E	**25** Th	0248 / 0903 / 1353 / 2020	0544 0.6E / 1128 0.3F / 1719 0.6E
11 Th	0344 / 1016 / 1505 / 2121	0008 1.1F / 0648 0.8E / 1239 0.4F / 1824 0.8E	**26** F	0340 / 1019 / 1444 / 2100	0000 0.9F / 0644 0.6E / 1230 0.3F / 1807 0.6E
12 F	0441 / 1129 / 1607 / 2210	0103 1.1F / 0751 0.9E / 1345 0.4F / 1920 0.7E	**27** Sa	0430 / 1128 / 1540 / 2143	0049 1.0F / 0741 0.7E / 1332 0.3F / 1857 0.6E
13 Sa	0534 / 1232 / 1708 / 2300	0157 1.2F / 0848 1.0E / 1447 0.4F / 2016 0.7E	**28** Su	0519 / 1227 / 1637 / 2230	0137 1.1F / 0834 0.8E / 1429 0.3F / 1948 0.6E
14 Su	0624 / 1327 / 1808 / 2349	0248 1.2F / 0940 1.0E / 1543 0.4F / 2109 0.6E	**29** M	0605 / 1315 / 1734 / 2319	0225 1.1F / 0922 0.9E / 1521 0.3F / 2040 0.6E
15 M	0710 / 1414 / 1905	0337 1.2F / 1028 1.1E / 1635 0.5F / 2200 0.6E	**30** Tu	0649 / 1356 / 1830	0313 1.2F / 1008 1.0E / 1609 0.4F / 2132 0.6E
			31 W ●	0011 / 0733 / 1433 / 1925	0400 1.2F / 1050 1.1E / 1655 0.5F / 2224 0.7E

August

	Slack	Maximum			Slack	Maximum
	h m	h m knots			h m	h m knots
1 Th	0104 / 0816 / 1508 / 2020	0447 1.2F / 1132 1.1E / 1740 0.6F / 2317 0.7E	**16** F	0204 / 0848 / 1532 / 2115	0531 1.0F / 1204 1.0E / 1818 0.7E
2 F	0200 / 0858 / 1544 / 2115	0535 1.2F / 1214 1.1E / 1825 0.7F	**17** Sa	0250 / 0924 / 1604 / 2159	0005 0.6E / 0612 0.9F / 1240 0.9E / 1856 0.7F
3 Sa	0258 / 0941 / 1620 / 2212	0624 1.1F / 1256 1.1E / 1911 0.8F	**18** Su	0337 / 1000 / 1635 / 2243	0049 0.6E / 0652 0.8F / 1315 0.9E / 1934 0.7F
4 Su	0359 / 1024 / 1658 / 2310	0107 0.8E / 0715 1.0F / 1339 1.1E / 1959 0.9F	**19** M	0427 / 1036 / 1706 / 2328	0134 0.6E / 0734 0.7F / 1351 0.8E / 2013 0.8F
5 M	0503 / 1109 / 1738	0205 0.8E / 0808 0.9F / 1425 1.0E / 2050 1.0F	**20** Tu	0521 / 1112 / 1738	0221 0.6E / 0818 0.6F / 1428 0.8E / 2054 0.8F
6 Tu	0010 / 0612 / 1156 / 1822	0306 0.8E / 0905 0.7F / 1513 0.9E / 2144 1.0F	**21** W	0017 / 0620 / 1150 / 1812	0312 0.6E / 0906 0.5F / 1507 0.7E / 2138 0.8F
7 W ◐	0112 / 0726 / 1247 / 1909	0411 0.8E / 1006 0.6F / 1605 0.8E / 2240 1.1F	**22** Th	0108 / 0728 / 1231 / 1848	0408 0.6E / 0959 0.4F / 1549 0.6E / 2225 0.8F
8 Th	0215 / 0843 / 1343 / 1959	0518 0.8E / 1112 0.5F / 1701 0.7E / 2339 1.1F	**23** F ○	0202 / 0841 / 1318 / 1929	0507 0.6E / 1057 0.3F / 1636 0.5E / 2316 0.9F
9 F	0316 / 1000 / 1445 / 2052	0624 0.8E / 1220 0.4F / 1800 0.7E	**24** Sa	0257 / 0954 / 1412 / 2016	0608 0.7E / 1200 0.3F / 1729 0.5E
10 Sa	0415 / 1109 / 1551 / 2148	0037 1.1F / 0728 0.9E / 1327 0.4F / 1900 0.6E	**25** Su	0352 / 1059 / 1513 / 2109	0010 0.9F / 0707 0.7E / 1303 0.3F / 1826 0.5E
11 Su	0510 / 1209 / 1656 / 2243	0135 1.1F / 0826 0.9E / 1429 0.4F / 2000 0.6E	**26** M	0444 / 1151 / 1617 / 2206	0104 1.0F / 0801 0.8E / 1400 0.3F / 1925 0.5E
12 M	0601 / 1259 / 1758 / 2337	0229 1.1F / 0918 1.0E / 1524 0.5F / 2056 0.6E	**27** Tu	0534 / 1233 / 1718 / 2306	0158 1.0F / 0850 0.9E / 1452 0.4F / 2023 0.6E
13 Tu	0647 / 1343 / 1853	0319 1.1F / 1005 1.0E / 1613 0.5F / 2147 0.6E	**28** W	0621 / 1311 / 1816	0250 1.1F / 0936 1.0E / 1540 0.5F / 2119 0.7E
14 W	0028 / 0730 / 1422 / 1944	0406 1.1F / 1047 1.0E / 1658 0.6F / 2236 0.6E	**29** Th	0005 / 0706 / 1346 / 1911	0341 1.1F / 1019 1.0E / 1625 0.7F / 2213 0.8E
15 Th ○	0117 / 0810 / 1458 / 2031	0450 1.0F / 1127 1.0E / 1739 0.6F / 2321 0.6E	**30** F ●	0104 / 0750 / 1420 / 2004	0431 1.1F / 1101 1.0E / 1710 0.8F / 2306 0.9E
			31 Sa	0202 / 0833 / 1456 / 2057	0520 1.1F / 1142 1.1E / 1755 0.9F

September

	Slack	Maximum			Slack	Maximum
	h m	h m knots			h m	h m knots
1 Su	0301 / 0916 / 1534 / 2151	0000 0.9E / 0610 1.0F / 1225 1.0E / 1841 1.0F	**16** M	0333 / 0931 / 1541 / 2207	0028 0.8E / 0632 0.7F / 1238 0.8E / 1853 0.9F
2 M	0400 / 1000 / 1613 / 2245	0053 1.0E / 0700 0.9F / 1308 1.0E / 1928 1.1F	**17** Tu	0422 / 1007 / 1611 / 2250	0110 0.8E / 0713 0.6F / 1312 0.7E / 1930 0.9F
3 Tu	0502 / 1046 / 1656 / 2342	0149 1.0E / 0753 0.8F / 1354 0.9E / 2018 1.1F	**18** W	0515 / 1044 / 1642 / 2335	0155 0.8E / 0757 0.5F / 1348 0.6E / 2010 0.9F
4 W	0607 / 1134 / 1742	0247 0.9E / 0849 0.7F / 1444 0.8E / 2112 1.1F	**19** Th	0612 / 1123 / 1717	0244 0.8E / 0844 0.4F / 1427 0.6E / 2053 0.9F
5 Th ◑	0041 / 0715 / 1228 / 1832	0348 0.9E / 0949 0.5F / 1537 0.7E / 2208 1.1F	**20** F	0024 / 0714 / 1206 / 1756	0336 0.7E / 0936 0.4F / 1510 0.5E / 2141 0.9F
6 F	0141 / 0826 / 1328 / 1928	0452 0.9E / 1054 0.5F / 1636 0.6E / 2308 1.0F	**21** Sa ○	0117 / 0820 / 1256 / 1844	0433 0.7E / 1034 0.3F / 1601 0.5E / 2235 0.9F
7 Sa	0243 / 0935 / 1435 / 2027	0556 0.9E / 1201 0.4F / 1740 0.6E	**22** Su	0213 / 0922 / 1357 / 1941	0532 0.7E / 1135 0.3F / 1701 0.4E / 2334 0.9F
8 Su	0342 / 1038 / 1544 / 2129	0010 1.0F / 0659 0.9E / 1307 0.4F / 1845 0.6E	**23** M	0310 / 1017 / 1504 / 2046	0629 0.8E / 1236 0.3F / 1805 0.5E
9 M	0439 / 1132 / 1649 / 2231	0110 1.0F / 0756 0.9E / 1406 0.5F / 1946 0.6E	**24** Tu	0406 / 1102 / 1610 / 2155	0034 0.9F / 0724 0.8E / 1332 0.4F / 1910 0.6E
10 Tu	0530 / 1219 / 1747 / 2328	0207 0.9F / 0847 0.9E / 1459 0.6F / 2043 0.6E	**25** W	0458 / 1142 / 1710 / 2303	0133 0.9F / 0813 0.9E / 1423 0.6F / 2012 0.7E
11 W	0617 / 1259 / 1838	0258 0.9F / 0933 0.9E / 1545 0.6F / 2134 0.7E	**26** Th	0548 / 1218 / 1806	0230 0.9F / 0900 0.9E / 1510 0.7F / 2109 0.8E
12 Th	0022 / 0701 / 1336 / 1924	0346 0.9F / 1014 0.9E / 1626 0.7F / 2220 0.7E	**27** F	0007 / 0636 / 1254 / 1858	0324 1.0F / 0944 0.9E / 1556 0.9F / 2204 0.9E
13 F ○	0112 / 0741 / 1410 / 2006	0429 0.9F / 1052 0.9E / 1705 0.8F / 2304 0.7E	**28** Sa ●	0108 / 0721 / 1331 / 1949	0415 0.9F / 1027 1.0E / 1640 1.0F / 2256 1.0E
14 Sa	0159 / 0819 / 1441 / 2047	0511 0.9F / 1128 0.9E / 1741 0.8F / 2346 0.8E	**29** Su	0207 / 0806 / 1409 / 2039	0505 0.9F / 1110 1.0E / 1725 1.1F / 2348 1.1E
15 Su	0246 / 0855 / 1511 / 2126	0551 0.8F / 1203 0.8E / 1817 0.8F	**30** M	0304 / 0851 / 1449 / 2130	0555 0.9F / 1153 0.9E / 1811 1.2F

Time meridian 75° W. 0000 is midnight. 1200 is noon. Times are not adjusted for Daylight Saving Time.

Baltimore Harbor Approach, Maryland, 2019

F–Flood, Dir. 025° True E–Ebb, Dir. 190° True

October

Days 1–15

Day	Slack (h m)	Maximum (h m)	knots
1 Tu		0040	1.1E
	0402	0646	0.8F
	0937	1238	0.9E
	1531	1858	1.2F
	2221		
2 W		0132	1.1E
	0500	0739	0.7F
	1025	1326	0.8E
	1616	1948	1.2F
	2314		
3 Th		0227	1.0E
	0559	0834	0.6F
	1117	1417	0.7E
	1705	2040	1.1F
4 F	0009	0324	1.0E
	0701	0933	0.5F
	1215	1513	0.6E
	1758	2137	1.0F
5 Sa	0105	0423	0.9E
	0803	1036	0.5F
	1321	1615	0.5E
	1858	2237	0.9F
6 Su	0203	0524	0.9E
	0903	1140	0.5F
	1430	1722	0.5E
	2003	2339	0.8F
7 M	0301	0623	0.8E
	0958	1242	0.5F
	1538	1828	0.5E
	2111		
8 Tu		0041	0.8F
	0358	0718	0.8E
	1047	1338	0.6F
	1639	1931	0.6E
	2218		
9 W		0139	0.8F
	0450	0808	0.8E
	1130	1427	0.7F
	1732	2026	0.6E
	2319		
10 Th		0232	0.8F
	0538	0853	0.8E
	1208	1511	0.8F
	1818	2116	0.7E
11 F	0014	0321	0.8F
	0623	0934	0.8E
	1244	1550	0.8F
	1900	2201	0.8E
12 Sa	0106	0406	0.7F
	0705	1012	0.8E
	1316	1628	0.9F
	1940	2244	0.8E
13 Su	0154	0449	0.7F
	0745	1049	0.8E
	1347	1704	0.9F
	2018	2325	0.9E
14 M	0242	0530	0.7F
	0824	1124	0.7E
	1417	1739	1.0F
	2056		
15 Tu		0007	0.9E
	0330	0612	0.6F
	0901	1158	0.7E
	1446	1815	1.0F
	2136		

Days 16–31

Day	Slack (h m)	Maximum (h m)	knots
16 W		0049	0.9E
	0420	0655	0.5F
	0939	1234	0.6E
	1517	1852	1.0F
	2217		
17 Th		0133	0.9E
	0511	0739	0.5F
	1018	1311	0.5E
	1550	1932	1.0F
	2301		
18 F		0219	0.9E
	0605	0826	0.4F
	1100	1352	0.5E
	1628	2016	0.9F
	2348		
19 Sa		0308	0.9E
	0700	0918	0.4F
	1149	1440	0.4E
	1714	2105	0.9F
20 Su	0038	0401	0.8E
	0753	1014	0.4F
	1248	1537	0.4E
	1810	2201	0.9F
21 M	0132	0456	0.8E
	0844	1112	0.4F
	1354	1643	0.4E
	1918	2302	0.8F
22 Tu	0228	0551	0.8E
	0929	1209	0.5F
	1501	1753	0.5E
	2034		
23 W		0006	0.8F
	0324	0644	0.8E
	1010	1303	0.6F
	1604	1900	0.6E
	2152		
24 Th		0110	0.8F
	0419	0734	0.8E
	1049	1353	0.8F
	1701	2003	0.7E
	2305		
25 F		0210	0.8F
	0511	0822	0.9E
	1128	1441	0.9F
	1754	2100	0.9E
26 Sa	0011	0306	0.8F
	0602	0908	0.9E
	1207	1528	1.1F
	1845	2154	1.0E
27 Su	0113	0400	0.8F
	0650	0953	0.9E
	1247	1613	1.2F
	1934	2246	1.1E
28 M	0211	0451	0.7F
	0738	1038	0.9E
	1328	1659	1.3F
	2022	2336	1.2E
29 Tu	0306	0542	0.7F
	0826	1124	0.8E
	1410	1745	1.3F
	2110		
30 W		0026	1.2E
	0401	0633	0.7F
	0915	1211	0.8E
	1454	1832	1.3F
	2159		
31 Th		0116	1.2E
	0454	0725	0.6F
	1008	1300	0.7E
	1541	1920	1.2F
	2247		

November

Days 1–15

Day	Slack (h m)	Maximum (h m)	knots
1 F		0207	1.1E
	0548	0820	0.6F
	1104	1353	0.6E
	1631	2011	1.1F
	2337		
2 Sa		0259	1.0E
	0642	0916	0.5F
	1206	1451	0.5E
	1726	2105	0.9F
3 Su	0028	0353	1.0E
	0735	1015	0.5F
	1313	1554	0.5E
	1828	2203	0.8F
4 M	0121	0447	0.9E
	0825	1114	0.5F
	1421	1701	0.4E
	1937	2304	0.7F
5 Tu	0215	0542	0.9E
	0913	1211	0.6F
	1524	1807	0.5E
	2049		
6 W		0006	0.7F
	0309	0634	0.8E
	0957	1303	0.7F
	1620	1908	0.5E
	2200		
7 Th		0105	0.6F
	0401	0722	0.8E
	1038	1350	0.8F
	1709	2003	0.6E
	2304		
8 F		0200	0.6F
	0451	0808	0.8E
	1115	1433	0.9F
	1753	2053	0.7E
9 Sa	0003	0251	0.6F
	0539	0850	0.8E
	1150	1512	0.9F
	1834	2139	0.8E
10 Su	0057	0339	0.6F
	0624	0929	0.7E
	1223	1551	1.0F
	1912	2222	0.9E
11 M	0148	0424	0.6F
	0707	1007	0.7E
	1254	1627	1.1F
	1951	2305	1.0E
12 Tu	0238	0509	0.5F
	0748	1044	0.6E
	1325	1703	1.1F
	2029	2346	1.0E
13 W	0327	0552	0.5F
	0829	1121	0.6E
	1357	1741	1.1F
	2109		
14 Th		0029	1.0E
	0415	0636	0.5F
	0910	1159	0.5E
	1431	1820	1.1F
	2150		
15 F		0112	1.0E
	0503	0722	0.4F
	0954	1240	0.5E
	1510	1901	1.1F
	2232		

Days 16–30

Day	Slack (h m)	Maximum (h m)	knots
16 Sa		0156	1.0E
	0550	0809	0.4F
	1042	1326	0.5E
	1554	1946	1.0F
	2317		
17 Su		0242	1.0E
	0636	0859	0.4F
	1138	1419	0.4E
	1647	2037	0.9F
18 M	0005	0331	0.9E
	0719	0951	0.5F
	1241	1521	0.4E
	1751	2133	0.8F
19 Tu	0055	0421	0.9E
	0801	1046	0.5F
	1347	1630	0.5E
	1907	2235	0.7F
20 W	0148	0512	0.9E
	0841	1141	0.7F
	1452	1741	0.5E
	2029	2341	0.7F
21 Th	0242	0604	0.8E
	0922	1234	0.8F
	1553	1849	0.7E
	2151		
22 F		0047	0.6F
	0338	0655	0.8E
	1002	1325	1.0F
	1649	1952	0.8E
	2307		
23 Sa		0150	0.6F
	0433	0746	0.8E
	1044	1414	1.1F
	1741	2050	0.9E
24 Su	0015	0249	0.6F
	0527	0835	0.8E
	1126	1503	1.2F
	1831	2143	1.1E
25 M	0116	0345	0.6F
	0619	0923	0.8E
	1210	1550	1.3F
	1919	2234	1.1E
26 Tu	0212	0438	0.6F
	0712	1011	0.8E
	1254	1636	1.3F
	2006	2323	1.2E
27 W	0305	0530	0.6F
	0804	1100	0.7E
	1339	1723	1.3F
	2052		
28 Th		0011	1.2E
	0355	0620	0.6F
	0858	1149	0.7E
	1425	1809	1.2F
	2137		
29 F		0058	1.2E
	0443	0711	0.6F
	0953	1240	0.6E
	1513	1856	1.1F
	2222		
30 Sa		0145	1.1E
	0530	0803	0.6F
	1052	1333	0.5E
	1604	1945	1.0F
	2307		

December

Days 1–15

Day	Slack (h m)	Maximum (h m)	knots
1 Su		0233	1.1E
	0616	0855	0.6F
	1153	1430	0.5E
	1700	2036	0.9F
	2353		
2 M		0320	1.0E
	0701	0949	0.6F
	1257	1530	0.4E
	1801	2129	0.8F
3 Tu	0039	0409	0.9E
	0744	1042	0.6F
	1359	1634	0.4E
	1909	2226	0.6F
4 W	0127	0458	0.9E
	0826	1134	0.7F
	1458	1737	0.5E
	2022	2326	0.6F
5 Th	0217	0546	0.8E
	0907	1223	0.8F
	1551	1838	0.5E
	2135		
6 F		0025	0.5F
	0308	0634	0.8E
	0945	1309	0.9F
	1639	1934	0.6E
	2245		
7 Sa		0123	0.5F
	0400	0720	0.7E
	1022	1352	0.9F
	1723	2026	0.7E
	2348		
8 Su		0218	0.4F
	0450	0803	0.7E
	1058	1434	1.0F
	1805	2114	0.8E
9 M	0046	0310	0.4F
	0539	0846	0.6E
	1132	1514	1.1F
	1845	2159	0.9E
10 Tu	0140	0359	0.4F
	0626	0926	0.6E
	1207	1553	1.1F
	1925	2243	1.0E
11 W	0230	0446	0.4F
	0712	1007	0.6E
	1242	1632	1.2F
	2005	2325	1.1E
12 Th	0317	0531	0.4F
	0757	1048	0.6E
	1320	1712	1.2F
	2052		
13 F		0007	1.1E
	0401	0616	0.4F
	0843	1131	0.5E
	1400	1754	1.2F
	2126		
14 Sa		0049	1.1E
	0443	0700	0.4F
	0932	1217	0.5E
	1446	1837	1.1F
	2208		
15 Su		0132	1.1E
	0522	0746	0.5F
	1025	1308	0.5E
	1537	1924	1.0F
	2251		

Days 16–31

Day	Slack (h m)	Maximum (h m)	knots
16 M		0300	1.0E
	0600	0834	0.5F
	1124	1405	0.5E
	1637	2015	0.9F
	2335		
17 Tu		0300	1.0E
	0638	0924	0.6F
	1226	1508	0.5E
	1745	2111	0.8F
18 W	0022	0347	0.9E
	0716	1016	0.7F
	1331	1615	0.5E
	1902	2212	0.7F
19 Th	0112	0436	0.9E
	0756	1110	0.8F
	1434	1725	0.6E
	2025	2318	0.6F
20 F	0204	0528	0.8E
	0838	1204	1.0F
	1535	1833	0.7E
	2149		
21 Sa		0025	0.5F
	0300	0620	0.8E
	0922	1258	1.1F
	1632	1937	0.8E
	2306		
22 Su		0130	0.5F
	0357	0714	0.8E
	1008	1350	1.2F
	1726	2036	1.0E
23 M	0014	0232	0.5F
	0456	0807	0.7E
	1055	1441	1.3F
	1816	2131	1.1E
24 Tu	0114	0330	0.5F
	0555	0859	0.7E
	1142	1530	1.3F
	1904	2221	1.1E
25 W	0207	0425	0.5F
	0652	0951	0.7E
	1230	1618	1.3F
	1950	2309	1.2E
26 Th	0256	0516	0.5F
	0748	1042	0.7E
	1318	1705	1.3F
	2034	2355	1.2E
27 F	0340	0606	0.6F
	0844	1132	0.6E
	1406	1750	1.2F
	2117		
28 Sa		0039	1.1E
	0423	0654	0.6F
	0939	1223	0.6E
	1455	1836	1.1F
	2158		
29 Su		0122	1.1E
	0503	0741	0.6F
	1035	1314	0.5E
	1546	1921	1.0F
	2239		
30 M		0204	1.0E
	0543	0828	0.6F
	1131	1407	0.5E
	1639	2008	0.8F
	2319		
31 Tu		0246	1.0E
	0621	0915	0.7F
	1228	1503	0.5E
	1738	2057	0.7F

Time meridian 75° W. 0000 is midnight. 1200 is noon. Times are not adjusted for Daylight Saving Time.

Chesapeake & Delaware Canal (Chesapeake City), 2019

F–Flood, Dir. 097° True   E–Ebb, Dir. 278° True

January

Date	Slack h m	Max h m	knots
1 Tu		0242	1.9F
	0554	0905	2.5E
	1300	1601	2.1F
	1926	2144	1.2E
2 W	0048	0329	1.8F
	0641	0954	2.5E
	1356	1711	2.1F
	2026	2238	1.1E
3 Th	0135	0417	1.8F
	0727	1041	2.6E
	1449	1810	2.1F
	2121	2330	1.0E
4 F	0221	0504	1.7F
	0810	1125	2.5E
	1537	1855	2.1F
	2211		
5 Sa ●		0017	1.0E
	0307	0550	1.6F
	0850	1207	2.5E
	1619	1929	2.1F
	2257		
6 Su		0059	0.9E
	0353	0633	1.6F
	0927	1246	2.5E
	1656	1954	2.1F
	2338		
7 M		0140	1.0E
	0439	0714	1.5F
	1002	1324	2.4E
	1730	2021	2.1F
8 Tu	0016	0220	1.0E
	0522	0756	1.5F
	1037	1404	2.4E
	1801	2053	2.1F
9 W	0051	0301	1.1E
	0604	0840	1.5F
	1116	1447	2.3E
	1833	2129	2.2F
10 Th	0122	0341	1.2E
	0646	0927	1.5F
	1202	1532	2.2E
	1906	2207	2.2F
11 F	0151	0420	1.4E
	0731	1016	1.5F
	1253	1620	2.0E
	1942	2247	2.2F
12 Sa	0217	0500	1.6E
	0821	1107	1.6F
	1353	1708	1.8E
	2020	2329	2.1F
13 Su	0244	0541	1.8E
	0916	1159	1.6F
	1500	1758	1.6E
	2100		
14 M ☽		0014	2.1F
	0317	0627	2.0E
	1013	1256	1.6F
	1609	1853	1.4E
	2143		
15 Tu		0102	2.1F
	0356	0717	2.2E
	1111	1355	1.7F
	1721	1951	1.2E
	2230		
16 W		0153	2.1F
	0441	0809	2.3E
	1211	1453	1.8F
	1832	2048	1.2E
	2322		
17 Th		0245	2.1F
	0532	0901	2.5E
	1310	1552	1.9F
	1937	2144	1.1E
18 F	0022	0339	2.1F
	0628	0954	2.6E
	1407	1653	2.0F
	2035	2241	1.2E
19 Sa	0126	0437	2.1F
	0725	1048	2.7E
	1501	1753	2.2F
	2130	2340	1.3E
20 Su	0232	0535	2.1F
	0822	1143	2.8E
	1554	1847	2.4F
	2222		
21 M ○		0037	1.4E
	0338	0632	2.2F
	0920	1238	2.8E
	1645	1937	2.6F
	2312		
22 Tu		0131	1.6E
	0440	0727	2.2F
	1019	1332	2.8E
	1735	2026	2.7F
	2359		
23 W		0224	1.7E
	0539	0822	2.3F
	1120	1428	2.7E
	1824	2115	2.7F
24 Th	0044	0317	1.9E
	0636	0918	2.3F
	1222	1526	2.5E
	1914	2204	2.6F
25 F	0128	0409	2.0E
	0733	1016	2.3F
	1328	1624	2.3E
	2004	2251	2.4F
26 Sa	0212	0459	2.2E
	0833	1114	2.2F
	1436	1720	2.0E
	2054	2338	2.2F
27 Su ☽	0257	0548	2.3E
	0934	1215	2.2F
	1544	1817	1.7E
	2144		
28 M		0026	2.1F
	0342	0642	2.3E
	1035	1322	2.1F
	1652	1918	1.4E
	2232		
29 Tu		0116	1.9F
	0430	0738	2.4E
	1136	1433	2.0F
	1800	2020	1.2E
	2321		
30 W		0206	1.8F
	0519	0834	2.4E
	1236	1543	1.9F
	1904	2117	1.1E
31 Th	0012	0256	1.7F
	0610	0925	2.4E
	1333	1651	2.0F
	2003	2211	1.0E

February

Date	Slack h m	Max h m	knots
1 F	0105	0346	1.7F
	0700	1014	2.4E
	1424	1750	2.0F
	2056	2306	1.0E
2 Sa	0158	0436	1.6F
	0747	1101	2.4E
	1510	1835	2.1F
	2145	2358	1.0E
3 Su	0250	0527	1.5F
	0831	1146	2.4E
	1551	1906	2.1F
	2229		
4 M ●		0043	1.1E
	0340	0614	1.5F
	0912	1227	2.4E
	1629	1928	2.1F
	2308		
5 Tu		0121	1.1E
	0426	0657	1.6F
	0952	1307	2.3E
	1705	1953	2.1F
	2342		
6 W		0156	1.2E
	0507	0739	1.6F
	1033	1347	2.3E
	1738	2023	2.1F
7 Th	0011	0230	1.3E
	0545	0822	1.7F
	1116	1429	2.2E
	1809	2057	2.1F
8 F	0033	0305	1.4E
	0622	0906	1.7F
	1201	1512	2.0E
	1839	2133	2.1F
9 Sa	0052	0340	1.6E
	0701	0953	1.8F
	1250	1556	1.8E
	1908	2212	2.1F
10 Su	0113	0418	1.8E
	0746	1042	1.8F
	1343	1641	1.6E
	1939	2253	2.1F
11 M	0143	0459	2.0E
	0837	1132	1.8F
	1441	1728	1.5E
	2015	2337	2.1F
12 Tu ☽	0222	0543	2.2E
	0933	1225	1.7F
	1544	1819	1.3E
	2058		
13 W		0026	2.1F
	0309	0634	2.3E
	1033	1323	1.7F
	1650	1916	1.2E
	2149		
14 Th		0120	2.1F
	0402	0731	2.4E
	1136	1424	1.8F
	1759	2017	1.1E
	2250		
15 F		0217	2.1F
	0501	0830	2.5E
	1239	1524	1.9F
	1905	2117	1.2E
	2359		
16 Sa		0315	2.1F
	0605	0928	2.5E
	1339	1626	2.0F
	2005	2217	1.3E
17 Su	0113	0416	2.1F
	0712	1027	2.6E
	1437	1728	2.2F
	2059	2318	1.5E
18 M	0223	0518	2.2F
	0816	1127	2.7E
	1532	1824	2.4F
	2150		
19 Tu ○		0015	1.7E
	0327	0618	2.3F
	0919	1226	2.7E
	1625	1914	2.6F
	2237		
20 W		0108	1.9E
	0427	0715	2.5F
	1020	1321	2.6E
	1716	2001	2.6F
	2322		
21 Th		0157	2.1E
	0523	0809	2.5F
	1121	1416	2.5E
	1804	2047	2.5F
22 F	0004	0247	2.2E
	0616	0903	2.5F
	1221	1512	2.3E
	1850	2132	2.4F
23 Sa	0045	0336	2.3E
	0710	0959	2.5F
	1322	1606	2.1E
	1936	2218	2.2F
24 Su	0128	0424	2.4E
	0806	1054	2.3F
	1424	1658	1.8E
	2021	2303	2.1F
25 M	0212	0512	2.4E
	0905	1151	2.1F
	1527	1750	1.5E
	2107	2349	1.9F
26 Tu ☽	0259	0602	2.3E
	1005	1252	2.0F
	1629	1846	1.3E
	2155		
27 W		0038	1.8F
	0350	0658	2.3E
	1105	1401	1.8F
	1732	1947	1.1E
	2247		
28 Th		0130	1.7F
	0442	0756	2.2E
	1203	1509	1.8F
	1834	2048	1.1E
	2344		

March

Date	Slack h m	Max h m	knots
1 F		0223	1.6F
	0537	0851	2.2E
	1257	1612	1.8F
	1931	2145	1.1E
2 Sa	0043	0317	1.5F
	0632	0943	2.2E
	1347	1710	1.9F
	2022	2241	1.1E
3 Su	0141	0411	1.5F
	0725	1033	2.2E
	1433	1754	2.0F
	2109	2333	1.2E
4 M	0235	0505	1.5F
	0814	1122	2.2E
	1517	1825	2.1F
	2150		
5 Tu		0018	1.3E
	0323	0556	1.6F
	0902	1208	2.2E
	1558	1851	2.1F
	2226		
6 W ●		0054	1.4E
	0407	0641	1.7F
	0949	1251	2.2E
	1637	1919	2.0F
	2256		
7 Th		0125	1.5E
	0447	0723	1.8F
	1035	1331	2.1E
	1712	1949	2.0F
	2319		
8 F		0155	1.6E
	0523	0805	1.9F
	1120	1411	1.9E
	1743	2023	2.0F
	2335		
9 Sa		0226	1.8E
	0559	0848	2.0F
	1205	1452	1.7E
	1809	2059	2.0F
	2353		
10 Su		0301	2.0E
	0636	0933	2.0F
	1250	1534	1.6E
	1834	2138	2.0F
11 M	0019	0339	2.1E
	0717	1019	1.9F
	1337	1617	1.4E
	1903	2221	2.0F
12 Tu	0055	0422	2.3E
	0806	1108	1.9F
	1429	1702	1.3E
	1940	2307	2.0F
13 W	0141	0509	2.3E
	0901	1200	1.8F
	1526	1753	1.2E
	2030	2358	2.0F
14 Th ☽	0234	0601	2.4E
	1001	1257	1.8F
	1628	1851	1.2E
	2131		
15 F		0055	2.0F
	0334	0700	2.3E
	1105	1358	1.9F
	1733	1955	1.2E
	2241		
16 Sa		0156	2.0F
	0441	0805	2.3E
	1210	1500	2.0F
	1836	2058	1.4E
	2357		
17 Su		0258	2.0F
	0554	0909	2.4E
	1313	1601	2.1F
	1934	2158	1.6E
18 M	0110	0401	2.1F
	0708	1011	2.4E
	1412	1701	2.2F
	2026	2257	1.8E
19 Tu	0216	0506	2.3F
	0816	1114	2.4E
	1509	1758	2.3F
	2114	2352	2.0E
20 W ○	0316	0607	2.5F
	0920	1214	2.4E
	1602	1847	2.4F
	2158		
21 Th		0042	2.2E
	0412	0703	2.6F
	1021	1309	2.3E
	1652	1932	2.4F
	2240		
22 F		0128	2.4E
	0505	0756	2.7F
	1120	1401	2.2E
	1738	2015	2.3F
	2321		
23 Sa		0214	2.5E
	0556	0847	2.7F
	1216	1452	2.0E
	1821	2057	2.1F
24 Su	0000	0300	2.5E
	0647	0939	2.5F
	1312	1542	1.7E
	1902	2141	2.0F
25 M	0041	0347	2.5E
	0739	1031	2.3F
	1408	1631	1.5E
	1943	2225	1.9F
26 Tu	0125	0434	2.4E
	0833	1122	2.1F
	1505	1720	1.3E
	2028	2311	1.7F
27 W ☽	0213	0523	2.3E
	0928	1216	1.9F
	1602	1812	1.2E
	2120		
28 Th		0000	1.6F
	0305	0615	2.1E
	1023	1314	1.8F
	1659	1913	1.1E
	2218		
29 F ☽		0054	1.5F
	0400	0712	2.0E
	1116	1415	1.8F
	1757	2017	1.1E
	2321		
30 Sa		0151	1.4F
	0459	0812	2.0E
	1209	1510	1.8F
	1851	2115	1.2E
31 Su	0023	0248	1.4F
	0600	0908	2.0E
	1300	1600	1.9F
	1941	2208	1.4E

Time meridian 75° W. 0000 is midnight. 1200 is noon. Times are not adjusted for Daylight Saving Time.

Chesapeake & Delaware Canal (Chesapeake City), 2019

F–Flood, Dir. 097° True   E–Ebb, Dir. 278° True

April

Day	Slack	Maximum	knots
1 M	0121	0345	1.4F
	0701	1002	2.0E
	1349	1647	2.0F
	2024	2258	1.5E
2 Tu	0213	0441	1.6F
	0758	1055	2.0E
	1437	1729	2.0F
	2102	2340	1.6E
3 W	0300	0535	1.7F
	0852	1145	2.0E
	1521	1805	2.0F
	2134		
4 Th		0016	1.7E
	0343	0623	1.9F
	0944	1231	1.9E
	1603	1840	1.9F
	2200		
5 F ●		0048	1.9E
	0423	0706	2.1F
	1034	1312	1.8E
	1639	1914	1.9F
	2220		
6 Sa		0118	2.0E
	0501	0748	2.1F
	1121	1352	1.6E
	1710	1949	1.9F
	2239		
7 Su		0150	2.2E
	0539	0830	2.2F
	1205	1431	1.4E
	1736	2027	1.9F
	2304		
8 M		0226	2.3E
	0617	0914	2.1F
	1248	1512	1.3E
	1803	2108	1.9F
	2339		
9 Tu		0307	2.4E
	0658	1000	2.1F
	1333	1556	1.2E
	1836	2154	1.9F
10 W	0022	0353	2.4E
	0744	1049	2.0F
	1422	1644	1.2E
	1922	2244	1.9F
11 Th	0112	0443	2.4E
	0837	1140	2.0F
	1516	1736	1.2E
	2021	2338	1.9F
12 F ◐	0211	0537	2.3E
	0937	1237	2.0F
	1614	1835	1.3E
	2133		
13 Sa		0037	1.9F
	0318	0639	2.2E
	1040	1337	2.0F
	1712	1940	1.4E
	2248		
14 Su		0141	1.9F
	0433	0747	2.2E
	1144	1438	2.1F
	1809	2043	1.6E
15 M	0000	0246	2.0F
	0553	0855	2.2E
	1248	1536	2.2F
	1903	2140	1.9E
16 Tu	0107	0351	2.2F
	0709	0959	2.1E
	1347	1633	2.2F
	1951	2235	2.1E
17 W	0207	0456	2.4F
	0818	1102	2.1E
	1443	1727	2.2F
	2036	2327	2.4E
18 Th	0304	0558	2.6F
	0921	1202	2.0E
	1535	1816	2.2F
	2118		
19 F ○		0015	2.5E
	0357	0654	2.7F
	1020	1254	1.9E
	1623	1900	2.1F
	2159		
20 Sa		0059	2.6E
	0449	0744	2.7F
	1116	1342	1.7E
	1706	1941	2.0F
	2238		
21 Su		0142	2.7E
	0538	0832	2.6F
	1208	1429	1.5E
	1746	2022	1.9F
	2318		
22 M		0226	2.6E
	0625	0919	2.4F
	1259	1515	1.4E
	1824	2104	1.8F
	2357		
23 Tu		0311	2.5E
	0712	1005	2.2F
	1349	1602	1.2E
	1905	2149	1.7F
24 W	0039	0357	2.4E
	0758	1100	2.0F
	1440	1651	1.2E
	1953	2236	1.6F
25 Th	0124	0445	2.2E
	0845	1137	1.9F
	1532	1742	1.1E
	2050	2325	1.4F
26 F ○	0215	0534	2.1E
	0932	1226	1.9F
	1624	1839	1.2E
	2153		
27 Sa		0019	1.3F
	0313	0629	2.0E
	1022	1319	1.9F
	1715	1940	1.2E
	2257		
28 Su		0117	1.3F
	0417	0729	1.9E
	1114	1412	2.0F
	1805	2038	1.4E
	2357		
29 M		0217	1.3F
	0526	0830	1.9E
	1207	1501	2.0F
	1851	2128	1.6E
30 Tu	0053	0316	1.5F
	0635	0927	1.8E
	1300	1547	2.0F
	1931	2213	1.7E

May

Day	Slack	Maximum	knots
1 W	0143	0413	1.7F
	0739	1022	1.8E
	1351	1633	1.9F
	2006	2254	1.9E
2 Th	0230	0510	1.9F
	0838	1116	1.7E
	1437	1716	1.9F
	2035	2333	2.0E
3 F	0315	0601	2.0F
	0934	1204	1.6E
	1520	1758	1.8F
	2100		
4 Sa ●		0008	2.2E
	0358	0647	2.0F
	1025	1248	1.4E
	1558	1838	1.8F
	2125		
5 Su		0043	2.4E
	0440	0730	2.3F
	1114	1328	1.3E
	1631	1917	1.8F
	2154		
6 M		0119	2.5E
	0521	0812	2.3F
	1158	1409	1.2E
	1703	1958	1.9F
	2230		
7 Tu		0158	2.5E
	0601	0856	2.2F
	1242	1452	1.2E
	1739	2043	1.9F
	2312		
8 W		0242	2.6E
	0643	0943	2.2F
	1326	1540	1.2E
	1824	2133	1.9F
9 Th	0000	0332	2.5E
	0729	1033	2.2F
	1414	1632	1.2E
	1921	2227	1.8F
10 F	0055	0425	2.4E
	0822	1124	2.2F
	1505	1725	1.3E
	2029	2324	1.8F
11 Sa ◐	0200	0523	2.3E
	0919	1219	2.2F
	1557	1824	1.5E
	2141		
12 Su		0025	1.8F
	0315	0626	2.2E
	1020	1317	2.2F
	1649	1926	1.7E
	2251		
13 M		0130	1.9F
	0435	0735	2.0E
	1122	1415	2.2F
	1740	2026	2.0E
	2357		
14 Tu		0237	2.1F
	0555	0844	1.9E
	1223	1510	2.2F
	1829	2120	2.2E
15 W	0058	0342	2.2F
	0710	0948	1.9E
	1321	1603	2.1F
	1916	2212	2.4E
16 Th	0156	0448	2.4F
	0817	1049	1.7E
	1415	1655	2.0F
	2000	2301	2.6E
17 F	0252	0552	2.5F
	0919	1146	1.6E
	1504	1744	2.0F
	2042	2349	2.7E
18 Sa ○	0345	0647	2.6F
	1016	1237	1.5E
	1549	1828	1.9F
	2123		
19 Su		0033	2.7E
	0435	0735	2.5F
	1109	1322	1.3E
	1631	1909	1.9F
	2202		
20 M		0115	2.7E
	0522	0818	2.4F
	1157	1404	1.2E
	1711	1950	1.8F
	2241		
21 Tu		0156	2.6E
	0605	0858	2.2F
	1243	1449	1.1E
	1750	2031	1.7F
	2319		
22 W		0238	2.5E
	0644	0938	2.1F
	1328	1535	1.1E
	1834	2116	1.6F
	2358		
23 Th		0323	2.3E
	0721	1018	2.1F
	1413	1623	1.1E
	1924	2203	1.4F
24 F	0040	0410	2.2E
	0759	1100	2.1F
	1459	1712	1.2E
	2023	2253	1.3F
25 Sa	0129	0459	2.1E
	0842	1144	2.1F
	1544	1803	1.3E
	2124	2346	1.3F
26 Su ◐	0228	0551	2.0E
	0929	1231	2.1F
	1628	1857	1.4E
	2224		
27 M		0043	1.3F
	0337	0649	1.9E
	1019	1321	2.1F
	1711	1951	1.6E
	2321		
28 Tu		0143	1.4F
	0451	0751	1.7E
	1112	1410	2.0F
	1751	2040	1.8E
29 W	0016	0243	1.5F
	0606	0850	1.6E
	1205	1457	2.0F
	1828	2124	2.0E
30 Th	0108	0340	1.7F
	0716	0946	1.5E
	1257	1543	1.9F
	1902	2207	2.1E
31 F	0158	0438	1.9F
	0819	1039	1.4E
	1344	1630	1.8F
	1934	2248	2.3E

June

Day	Slack	Maximum	knots
1 Sa	0246	0534	2.0F
	0916	1130	1.3E
	1428	1717	1.8F
	2008	2330	2.5E
2 Su	0334	0624	2.2F
	1009	1218	1.2E
	1509	1803	1.9F
	2043		
3 M ●		0011	2.6E
	0420	0710	2.3F
	1058	1302	1.1E
	1551	1849	1.9F
	2123		
4 Tu		0053	2.7E
	0504	0754	2.3F
	1143	1347	1.1E
	1637	1935	1.9F
	2207		
5 W		0137	2.7E
	0547	0839	2.4F
	1227	1435	1.2E
	1728	2024	1.9F
	2256		
6 Th		0224	2.7E
	0630	0927	2.4F
	1312	1527	1.3E
	1823	2117	1.9F
	2351		
7 F		0317	2.6E
	0717	1017	2.4F
	1358	1620	1.4E
	1925	2214	1.9F
8 Sa	0051	0414	2.5E
	0809	1108	2.4F
	1446	1713	1.6E
	2031	2312	1.9F
9 Su	0202	0513	2.3E
	0904	1200	2.4F
	1534	1808	1.8E
	2138		
10 M ○		0014	1.9F
	0319	0616	2.1E
	1002	1255	2.3F
	1621	1906	2.0E
	2242		
11 Tu		0120	2.0F
	0437	0724	1.9E
	1100	1350	2.2F
	1709	2004	2.2E
	2344		
12 W		0227	2.1F
	0554	0832	1.7E
	1157	1443	2.1F
	1756	2058	2.4E
13 Th	0045	0334	2.3F
	0706	0934	1.6E
	1252	1533	2.0F
	1843	2149	2.6E
14 F	0144	0443	2.3F
	0812	1033	1.4E
	1344	1623	1.9F
	1929	2238	2.7E
15 Sa	0240	0549	2.4F
	0912	1128	1.2E
	1431	1712	1.8F
	2013	2326	2.7E
16 Su	0333	0644	2.4E
	1007	1218	1.1E
	1516	1759	1.8F
	2055		
17 M ○		0011	2.7E
	0422	0729	2.3F
	1057	1302	1.0E
	1600	1842	1.7F
	2135		
18 Tu		0052	2.6E
	0505	0805	2.2F
	1143	1343	1.0E
	1643	1923	1.7F
	2214		
19 W		0131	2.5E
	0543	0837	2.1F
	1224	1426	1.0E
	1727	2004	1.6F
	2250		
20 Th		0211	2.4E
	0616	0909	2.1F
	1303	1510	1.1E
	1813	2048	1.5F
	2328		
21 F		0254	2.3E
	0647	0945	2.1F
	1341	1555	1.2E
	1901	2135	1.4F
22 Sa	0009	0340	2.2E
	0720	1024	2.2F
	1420	1640	1.3E
	1953	2225	1.4F
23 Su	0058	0429	2.1E
	0759	1105	2.2F
	1457	1724	1.4E
	2047	2316	1.4F
24 M	0157	0519	2.0E
	0842	1149	2.2F
	1533	1810	1.6E
	2143		
25 Tu ○		0010	1.4F
	0306	0613	1.8E
	0929	1235	2.1F
	1607	1858	1.7E
	2238		
26 W		0108	1.5F
	0419	0711	1.6E
	1018	1322	2.1F
	1642	1947	1.9E
	2333		
27 Th		0207	1.6F
	0534	0810	1.4E
	1106	1411	2.0F
	1718	2035	2.1E
28 F	0030	0306	1.7F
	0647	0906	1.2E
	1155	1459	1.9F
	1758	2121	2.3E
29 Sa	0125	0404	1.8F
	0752	1000	1.1E
	1244	1548	1.9F
	1841	2207	2.5E
30 Su	0218	0502	1.9F
	0850	1053	1.1E
	1335	1640	1.9F
	1927	2255	2.6E

Time meridian 75° W. 0000 is midnight. 1200 is noon. Times are not adjusted for Daylight Saving Time.

Chesapeake & Delaware Canal (Chesapeake City), 2019

F–Flood, Dir. 097° True   E–Ebb, Dir. 278° True

July

Days 1–15

Day	Slack	Maximum	knots
1 M	0308	0558	2.1F
	0943	1146	1.0E
	1427	1733	1.9F
	2015	2343	2.7E
2 Tu ●	0357	0648	2.2F
	1032	1236	1.1E
	1523	1825	2.0F
	2104		
3 W	0444	0734	2.4F
	1118	1326	1.2E
	1622	1917	2.0F
	2156		
4 Th		0120	2.8E
	0530	0821	2.5F
	1203	1417	1.4E
	1721	2009	2.1F
	2252		
5 F		0212	2.7E
	0615	0909	2.6F
	1247	1510	1.5E
	1819	2104	2.1F
	2351		
6 Sa		0307	2.6E
	0703	0958	2.6F
	1331	1603	1.7E
	1918	2201	2.1F
7 Su	0056	0406	2.5E
	0754	1047	2.5F
	1417	1654	1.9E
	2020	2300	2.1F
8 M	0206	0504	2.2E
	0847	1137	2.4F
	1502	1746	2.1E
	2122		
9 Tu ◐		0001	2.1F
	0320	0604	2.0E
	0942	1228	2.3F
	1548	1840	2.2E
	2224		
10 W		0106	2.2F
	0433	0710	1.7E
	1036	1321	2.1F
	1635	1938	2.4E
	2327		
11 Th		0215	2.2F
	0546	0816	1.5E
	1129	1413	2.0F
	1723	2034	2.5E
12 F	0029	0325	2.2F
	0656	0917	1.3E
	1222	1504	1.9F
	1813	2126	2.6E
13 Sa	0129	0437	2.2F
	0801	1013	1.1E
	1312	1553	1.8F
	1903	2217	2.6E
14 Su	0226	0545	2.2F
	0859	1109	1.0E
	1402	1644	1.7F
	1950	2306	2.6E
15 M	0317	0639	2.2F
	0951	1201	1.0E
	1451	1733	1.7F
	2035	2352	2.5E

Days 16–31

Day	Slack	Maximum	knots
16 Tu ○	0404	0719	2.2F
	1038	1245	1.0E
	1539	1819	1.6F
	2117		
17 W		0032	2.4E
	0443	0747	2.1F
	1119	1325	1.0E
	1627	1902	1.6F
	2156		
18 Th	0518	0811	2.1F
	1156	1404	1.1E
	1713	1943	1.5F
	2234		
19 F		0150	2.3E
	0548	0839	2.1F
	1231	1444	1.2E
	1755	2026	1.5F
	2312		
20 Sa		0231	2.3E
	0618	0912	2.2F
	1302	1524	1.3E
	1837	2111	1.5F
	2354		
21 Su		0316	2.2E
	0649	0949	2.2F
	1331	1603	1.5E
	1919	2159	1.5F
22 M	0043	0403	2.0E
	0724	1028	2.2F
	1359	1642	1.6E
	2006	2248	1.6F
23 Tu	0139	0451	1.9E
	0801	1109	2.2F
	1427	1723	1.8E
	2057	2339	1.6F
24 W ◑	0242	0540	1.7E
	0842	1153	2.1F
	1459	1807	2.0E
	2152		
25 Th		0034	1.6F
	0350	0633	1.4E
	0924	1239	2.0F
	1535	1855	2.1E
	2250		
26 F		0132	1.7F
	0501	0729	1.2E
	1009	1329	2.0F
	1618	1947	2.3E
	2350		
27 Sa		0230	1.7F
	0612	0827	1.1E
	1058	1421	2.0F
	1707	2040	2.4E
28 Su	0050	0329	1.8F
	0718	0923	1.0E
	1154	1514	2.0F
	1802	2132	2.5E
29 M	0147	0429	1.9F
	0816	1018	1.0E
	1257	1610	2.0F
	1859	2225	2.6E
30 Tu	0240	0528	2.0F
	0909	1115	1.1E
	1402	1709	2.0F
	1957	2319	2.7E
31 W ●	0332	0622	2.2F
	0958	1211	1.3E
	1508	1807	2.1F
	2055		

August

Days 1–15

Day	Slack	Maximum	knots
1 Th		0014	2.7E
	0421	0711	2.4F
	1045	1304	1.5E
	1611	1902	2.2F
	2154		
2 F		0107	2.7E
	0510	0758	2.6F
	1129	1354	1.7E
	1710	1956	2.3F
	2253		
3 Sa		0201	2.6E
	0557	0846	2.6F
	1213	1446	1.9E
	1806	2051	2.4F
	2355		
4 Su		0257	2.6E
	0646	0934	2.6F
	1256	1537	2.1E
	1901	2148	2.4F
5 M	0058	0355	2.4E
	0735	1022	2.5F
	1339	1627	2.2E
	1959	2246	2.4F
6 Tu	0205	0452	2.1E
	0826	1110	2.3F
	1424	1717	2.3E
	2100	2345	2.3F
7 W ◐	0314	0549	1.8E
	0917	1158	2.1F
	1511	1809	2.4E
	2202		
8 Th		0049	2.2F
	0422	0649	1.5E
	1008	1249	2.0F
	1600	1906	2.4E
	2305		
9 F		0159	2.1F
	0531	0754	1.3E
	1059	1342	1.9F
	1651	2006	2.4E
10 Sa	0008	0312	2.0F
	0638	0855	1.1E
	1152	1435	1.8F
	1745	2102	2.4E
11 Su	0109	0424	2.0F
	0740	0952	1.0E
	1247	1527	1.7F
	1840	2155	2.4E
12 M	0203	0528	2.0F
	0835	1048	1.0E
	1341	1619	1.6F
	1932	2245	2.4E
13 Tu	0252	0618	2.1F
	0923	1142	1.1E
	1435	1712	1.6F
	2020	2332	2.3E
14 W	0335	0655	2.1F
	1007	1227	1.1E
	1526	1801	1.6F
	2105		
15 Th ○		0014	2.3E
	0414	0718	2.1F
	1045	1305	1.2E
	1614	1845	1.6F
	2147		

Days 16–31

Day	Slack	Maximum	knots
16 F		0053	2.2E
	0449	0739	2.1F
	1120	1340	1.3E
	1657	1926	1.6F
	2228		
17 Sa		0132	2.2E
	0521	0806	2.1F
	1149	1413	1.4E
	1735	2008	1.7F
	2309		
18 Su		0213	2.1E
	0552	0838	2.1F
	1214	1447	1.5E
	1811	2050	1.7F
	2353		
19 M		0255	2.0E
	0622	0914	2.1F
	1235	1522	1.7E
	1847	2135	1.8F
20 Tu	0039	0340	1.8E
	0651	0952	2.1F
	1256	1600	1.9E
	1928	2222	1.8F
21 W	0129	0424	1.6E
	0722	1032	2.0F
	1323	1639	2.0E
	2016	2311	1.8F
22 Th	0225	0510	1.4E
	0756	1115	2.0F
	1358	1722	2.2E
	2110		
23 F ◑		0002	1.7F
	0325	0558	1.3E
	0836	1202	2.0F
	1443	1810	2.3E
	2208		
24 Sa		0058	1.7F
	0428	0652	1.1E
	0924	1254	2.0F
	1534	1904	2.3E
	2310		
25 Su		0157	1.7F
	0535	0752	1.0E
	1020	1350	2.0F
	1631	2003	2.3E
26 M	0012	0257	1.7F
	0639	0852	1.1E
	1127	1448	2.0F
	1734	2102	2.4E
27 Tu	0113	0356	1.9F
	0738	0950	1.2E
	1241	1548	2.0F
	1842	2200	2.5E
28 W	0209	0457	2.1F
	0831	1049	1.4E
	1352	1650	2.1F
	1949	2259	2.5E
29 Th	0303	0554	2.3F
	0920	1146	1.7E
	1458	1751	2.3F
	2052	2358	2.6E
30 F ●	0356	0645	2.4F
	1006	1239	1.9E
	1558	1849	2.5F
	2154		
31 Sa		0054	2.6E
	0447	0732	2.5F
	1050	1328	2.1E
	1654	1943	2.6F
	2255		

September

Days 1–15

Day	Slack	Maximum	knots
1 Su		0149	2.5E
	0536	0818	2.5F
	1133	1416	2.3E
	1748	2037	2.7F
	2355		
2 M		0245	2.4E
	0624	0905	2.4F
	1215	1506	2.4E
	1841	2132	2.6F
3 Tu	0056	0341	2.2E
	0711	0952	2.3F
	1257	1555	2.5E
	1936	2228	2.5F
4 W	0158	0435	1.9E
	0759	1038	2.1F
	1343	1645	2.5E
	2035	2325	2.4F
5 Th ◐	0302	0528	1.6E
	0847	1126	2.0F
	1431	1736	2.4E
	2137		
6 F		0026	2.2F
	0406	0624	1.4E
	0938	1216	1.8F
	1524	1831	2.3E
	2238		
7 Sa		0135	2.0F
	0509	0727	1.2E
	1031	1309	1.7F
	1619	1932	2.2E
	2339		
8 Su		0247	1.9F
	0611	0830	1.1E
	1128	1405	1.6F
	1717	2032	2.2E
9 M	0036	0352	1.9F
	0709	0928	1.1E
	1228	1501	1.5F
	1816	2127	2.1E
10 Tu	0128	0450	1.9F
	0800	1023	1.2E
	1326	1557	1.5F
	1912	2218	2.1E
11 W	0215	0537	2.0F
	0845	1115	1.3E
	1421	1652	1.5F
	2005	2307	2.1E
12 Th	0258	0610	2.0F
	0926	1200	1.4E
	1510	1744	1.6F
	2053	2353	2.1E
13 F ○	0338	0636	2.0F
	1003	1237	1.5E
	1555	1830	1.7F
	2140		
14 Sa		0036	2.1E
	0417	0702	2.0F
	1034	1309	1.6E
	1635	1911	1.8F
	2226		
15 Su		0116	2.0E
	0453	0732	2.0F
	1059	1339	1.7E
	1711	1950	1.9F
	2311		

Days 16–30

Day	Slack	Maximum	knots
16 M		0156	1.9E
	0525	0804	2.0F
	1119	1410	1.9E
	1746	2031	2.0F
	2355		
17 Tu		0236	1.7E
	0553	0839	1.9F
	1136	1443	2.0E
	1821	2115	2.0F
18 W	0039	0317	1.5E
	0618	0952...	
	1159	1520	2.1E
	1900	2200	2.0F
19 Th	0125	0400	1.4E
	0645	0959	1.9F
	1232	1601	2.3E
	1944	2247	1.9F
20 F	0214	0443	1.2E
	0718	1043	1.9F
	1314	1645	2.3E
	2036	2336	1.8F
21 Sa ◑	0307	0531	1.1E
	0801	1132	1.9F
	1404	1735	2.3E
	2132		
22 Su		0030	1.8F
	0403	0624	1.1E
	0858	1227	1.9F
	1502	1831	2.3E
	2233		
23 M		0129	1.8F
	0503	0725	1.1E
	1007	1327	1.9F
	1607	1933	2.2E
	2335		
24 Tu		0228	1.9F
	0603	0828	1.3E
	1122	1429	1.9F
	1719	2038	2.2E
25 W	0038	0327	2.0F
	0700	0928	1.5E
	1238	1532	2.0F
	1835	2140	2.3E
26 Th	0138	0425	2.1F
	0752	1025	1.7E
	1346	1635	2.2F
	1946	2242	2.3E
27 F	0234	0523	2.3F
	0840	1120	2.1E
	1446	1738	2.4F
	2052	2344	2.3E
28 Sa ●	0329	0615	2.4F
	0926	1212	2.3E
	1543	1837	2.7F
	2154		
29 Su		0041	2.3E
	0422	0703	2.4F
	1009	1300	2.5E
	1637	1930	2.8F
	2254		
30 M		0135	2.2E
	0511	0748	2.3F
	1051	1346	2.6E
	1729	2023	2.8F
	2352		

Time meridian 75° W. 0000 is midnight. 1200 is noon. Times are not adjusted for Daylight Saving Time.

Chesapeake & Delaware Canal (Chesapeake City), 2019

F–Flood, Dir. 097° True   E–Ebb, Dir. 278° True

October

Date	Slack (h m)	Maximum (h m)	knots
1 Tu		0228	2.0E
	0558	0833	2.2F
	1133	1433	2.6E
	1821	2116	2.7F
2 W	0049	0321	1.8E
	0642	0918	2.1F
	1215	1522	2.6E
	1914	2210	2.5F
3 Th	0147	0413	1.6E
	0727	1005	1.9F
	1301	1612	2.5E
	2009	2303	2.3F
4 F	0246	0504	1.4E
	0814	1052	1.8F
	1350	1702	2.4E
	2106	2358	2.1F
5 Sa ☽	0344	0556	1.2E
	0907	1142	1.6F
	1445	1754	2.2E
	2203		
6 Su		0058	1.9F
	0441	0656	1.1E
	1005	1236	1.5F
	1543	1852	2.1E
	2257		
7 M		0200	1.9F
	0536	0800	1.2E
	1107	1335	1.4F
	1644	1953	2.0E
	2350		
8 Tu		0255	1.9F
	0628	0859	1.3E
	1209	1434	1.4F
	1747	2051	1.9E
9 W	0040	0343	1.9F
	0717	0951	1.4E
	1307	1532	1.4F
	1849	2145	1.9E
10 Th	0128	0427	2.0F
	0800	1039	1.6E
	1400	1629	1.5F
	1946	2237	1.9E
11 F	0214	0508	2.0F
	0839	1122	1.7E
	1447	1723	1.7F
	2040	2327	1.9E
12 Sa	0259	0546	2.0F
	0913	1159	1.8E
	1530	1811	1.9F
	2132		
13 Su ○		0014	1.8E
	0341	0621	1.9F
	0941	1232	2.0E
	1610	1853	2.0F
	2222		
14 M		0057	1.7E
	0420	0655	1.9F
	1003	1303	2.1E
	1648	1934	2.1F
	2309		
15 Tu		0137	1.6E
	0453	0730	1.8F
	1022	1334	2.2E
	1725	2014	2.1F
	2355		
16 W		0216	1.4E
	0520	0806	1.8F
	1045	1408	2.3E
	1802	2056	2.1F
17 Th	0038	0255	1.2E
	0545	0846	1.8F
	1116	1446	2.4E
	1841	2140	2.0F
18 F	0121	0337	1.1E
	0613	0930	1.8F
	1155	1529	2.4E
	1923	2226	2.0F
19 Sa	0205	0422	1.1E
	0653	1018	1.8F
	1242	1617	2.4E
	2011	2315	1.9F
20 Su	0253	0511	1.1E
	0747	1110	1.8F
	1338	1709	2.3E
	2104		
21 M ○		0007	1.9F
	0344	0605	1.2E
	0855	1207	1.8F
	1442	1807	2.2E
	2202		
22 Tu		0104	2.0F
	0437	0706	1.4E
	1011	1310	1.8F
	1555	1912	2.1E
	2304		
23 W		0202	2.0F
	0532	0809	1.6E
	1125	1415	1.9F
	1714	2020	2.1E
24 Th	0006	0300	2.1F
	0625	0907	1.9E
	1234	1519	2.1F
	1834	2125	2.1E
25 F	0108	0356	2.2F
	0715	1001	2.2E
	1336	1623	2.3F
	1946	2227	2.0E
26 Sa	0206	0451	2.2F
	0802	1054	2.4E
	1434	1727	2.5F
	2051	2329	2.0E
27 Su ●	0302	0545	2.2F
	0847	1145	2.6E
	1529	1826	2.7F
	2153		
28 M		0026	1.9E
	0354	0633	2.2F
	0930	1232	2.7E
	1622	1919	2.8F
	2251		
29 Tu		0118	1.8E
	0442	0718	2.1F
	1012	1318	2.8E
	1714	2010	2.8F
	2346		
30 W		0208	1.6E
	0527	0801	2.0F
	1054	1404	2.8E
	1804	2100	2.6F
31 Th	0040	0258	1.4E
	0609	0845	1.9F
	1137	1450	2.6E
	1853	2150	2.4F

November

Date	Slack (h m)	Maximum (h m)	knots
1 F	0133	0348	1.3E
	0653	0932	1.7F
	1222	1539	2.5E
	1942	2238	2.2F
2 Sa	0225	0437	1.2E
	0742	1020	1.6F
	1309	1628	2.3E
	2030	2324	2.1F
3 Su	0316	0528	1.2E
	0839	1110	1.5F
	1403	1718	2.1E
	2117		
4 M ◑		0012	2.0F
	0405	0622	1.2E
	0941	1204	1.3F
	1502	1811	2.0E
	2205		
5 Tu		0102	2.0F
	0454	0722	1.3E
	1044	1302	1.3F
	1606	1910	1.8E
	2254		
6 W		0153	2.0F
	0542	0820	1.5E
	1143	1402	1.3F
	1713	2011	1.8E
	2344		
7 Th		0241	2.0F
	0627	0910	1.7E
	1239	1501	1.4F
	1820	2108	1.8E
8 F	0036	0326	2.0F
	0709	0955	1.8E
	1329	1558	1.6F
	1924	2203	1.7E
9 Sa	0126	0411	2.0F
	0746	1037	2.0E
	1416	1655	1.8F
	2023	2256	1.6E
10 Su	0214	0455	1.9F
	0817	1116	2.1E
	1501	1748	2.0F
	2119	2347	1.5E
11 M	0259	0538	1.8F
	0845	1153	2.2E
	1544	1834	2.1F
	2213		
12 Tu ○		0033	1.4E
	0339	0618	1.8F
	0909	1228	2.4E
	1627	1916	2.2F
	2303		
13 W		0114	1.2E
	0413	0657	1.8F
	0936	1303	2.5E
	1708	1957	2.2F
	2349		
14 Th		0154	1.1E
	0444	0737	1.8F
	1008	1340	2.5E
	1748	2039	2.2F
15 F	0032	0234	1.0E
	0516	0820	1.8F
	1047	1421	2.5E
	1827	2123	2.1F
16 Sa	0112	0319	1.0E
	0556	0907	1.8F
	1132	1507	2.5E
	1908	2209	2.1F
17 Su	0153	0407	1.1E
	0647	0959	1.8F
	1224	1558	2.4E
	1953	2257	2.1F
18 M	0238	0457	1.3E
	0751	1055	1.8F
	1325	1652	2.3E
	2044	2348	2.2F
19 Tu ◑	0324	0551	1.4E
	0903	1154	1.8F
	1436	1751	2.2E
	2140		
20 W		0042	2.2F
	0413	0649	1.7E
	1014	1257	1.9F
	1554	1857	2.0E
	2239		
21 Th		0138	2.2F
	0502	0749	1.9E
	1121	1402	2.0F
	1715	2006	1.9E
	2341		
22 F		0234	2.2F
	0552	0846	2.2E
	1224	1507	2.2F
	1833	2111	1.8E
23 Sa	0041	0328	2.2F
	0640	0938	2.5E
	1324	1612	2.4F
	1944	2213	1.7E
24 Su	0139	0421	2.1F
	0728	1030	2.6E
	1421	1718	2.5F
	2049	2314	1.6E
25 M	0232	0514	2.0F
	0813	1120	2.8E
	1517	1819	2.6F
	2149		
26 Tu ●		0010	1.5E
	0323	0603	2.0F
	0857	1209	2.8E
	1610	1912	2.6F
	2245		
27 W		0101	1.4E
	0410	0649	1.9F
	0940	1254	2.8E
	1701	2000	2.5F
	2338		
28 Th		0147	1.2E
	0455	0732	1.8F
	1023	1338	2.7E
	1748	2045	2.4F
29 F	0027	0234	1.2E
	0538	0816	1.7F
	1106	1422	2.6E
	1831	2127	2.2F
30 Sa	0113	0322	1.1E
	0620	0901	1.6F
	1148	1508	2.4E
	1910	2207	2.1F

December

Date	Slack (h m)	Maximum (h m)	knots
1 Su	0157	0410	1.2E
	0715	0949	1.5F
	1233	1555	2.2E
	1948	2247	2.1F
2 M	0241	0457	1.2E
	0812	1039	1.4F
	1322	1643	2.1E
	2028	2328	2.1F
3 Tu	0324	0546	1.3E
	0912	1131	1.3F
	1420	1734	2.0E
	2111		
4 W ◑		0013	2.1F
	0407	0638	1.5E
	1011	1227	1.3F
	1526	1829	1.8E
	2158		
5 Th		0100	2.1F
	0449	0731	1.6E
	1107	1326	1.4F
	1636	1930	1.7E
	2249		
6 F		0148	2.1F
	0530	0821	1.8E
	1200	1425	1.5F
	1748	2030	1.6E
	2341		
7 Sa		0236	2.0F
	0609	0907	2.0E
	1252	1523	1.7F
	1858	2126	1.5E
8 Su	0034	0322	1.9F
	0645	0950	2.2E
	1342	1621	1.8F
	2002	2221	1.4E
9 M	0123	0408	1.8F
	0719	1032	2.3E
	1431	1718	2.0F
	2102	2313	1.2E
10 Tu	0209	0455	1.8F
	0751	1114	2.4E
	1519	1811	2.1F
	2157		
11 W		0003	1.1E
	0251	0542	1.8F
	0826	1155	2.5E
	1606	1856	2.2F
	2248		
12 Th ○		0048	1.0E
	0331	0628	1.8F
	0903	1236	2.6E
	1650	1938	2.2F
	2333		
13 F		0130	1.0E
	0414	0713	1.8F
	0945	1318	2.6E
	1732	2020	2.2F
14 Sa	0013	0214	1.0E
	0500	0800	1.9F
	1031	1402	2.6E
	1812	2104	2.3F
15 Su	0052	0301	1.1E
	0553	0851	1.9F
	1123	1452	2.5E
	1853	2151	2.3F
16 M	0132	0351	1.3E
	0651	0946	1.9F
	1220	1545	2.4E
	1938	2239	2.3F
17 Tu	0214	0442	1.5E
	0754	1043	1.9F
	1326	1642	2.3E
	2028	2328	2.3F
18 W ○	0259	0534	1.8E
	0900	1142	1.9F
	1439	1741	2.1E
	2123		
19 Th		0020	2.3F
	0344	0628	2.0E
	1005	1244	2.0F
	1557	1845	1.9E
	2220		
20 F		0114	2.2F
	0431	0726	2.2E
	1108	1350	2.1F
	1714	1953	1.7E
	2318		
21 Sa		0208	2.2F
	0520	0823	2.4E
	1211	1456	2.2F
	1829	2058	1.6E
22 Su	0016	0301	2.1F
	0609	0916	2.6E
	1312	1604	2.3F
	1939	2159	1.4E
23 M	0111	0353	2.0F
	0658	1008	2.7E
	1411	1713	2.4F
	2043	2258	1.3E
24 Tu	0204	0445	1.9F
	0746	1100	2.8E
	1507	1817	2.4F
	2142	2354	1.2E
25 W	0253	0536	1.8F
	0833	1149	2.8E
	1600	1909	2.4F
	2236		
26 Th ●		0044	1.1E
	0341	0624	1.8F
	0918	1235	2.7E
	1648	1951	2.3F
	2324		
27 F		0129	1.1E
	0429	0708	1.7F
	1002	1317	2.6E
	1730	2027	2.2F
28 Sa	0006	0211	1.1E
	0516	0751	1.6F
	1043	1358	2.4E
	1805	2059	2.2F
29 Su	0045	0255	1.1E
	0603	0835	1.5F
	1124	1441	2.3E
	1837	2132	2.1F
30 M	0123	0340	1.2E
	0652	0922	1.4F
	1206	1526	2.2E
	1908	2209	2.2F
31 Tu	0200	0423	1.4E
	0742	1010	1.4F
	1252	1613	2.1E
	1943	2248	2.2F

Time meridian 75° W. 0000 is midnight. 1200 is noon. Times are not adjusted for Daylight Saving Time.

Southport, Cape Fear River, North Carolina 2019

F–Flood, Dir. 048° True   E–Ebb, Dir. 235° True

January

Day	Slack	Maximum	knots
1 Tu		0240	1.8F
	0536	0924	3.5E
	1220	1447	1.7F
	1744	2137	3.1E
2 W	0033	0333	1.8F
	0634	1020	3.6E
	1315	1538	1.6F
	1837	2230	3.1E
3 Th	0122	0425	1.8F
	0727	1110	3.7E
	1405	1627	1.6F
	1927	2319	3.1E
4 F	0210	0515	1.8F
	0815	1157	3.7E
	1452	1715	1.5F
	2015		
5 Sa ●		0003	3.1E
	0256	0556	1.8F
	0900	1239	3.6E
	1536	1757	1.5F
	2101		
6 Su		0042	3.1E
	0341	0626	1.7F
	0941	1317	3.5E
	1618	1833	1.5F
	2145		
7 M		0116	3.0E
	0424	0654	1.7F
	1021	1350	3.4E
	1659	1906	1.5F
	2227		
8 Tu		0147	3.0E
	0505	0724	1.7F
	1058	1417	3.4E
	1737	1939	1.5F
	2307		
9 W		0219	3.0E
	0545	0758	1.6F
	1135	1445	3.3E
	1814	2013	1.5F
	2345		
10 Th		0254	3.0E
	0626	0836	1.6F
	1210	1518	3.3E
	1852	2050	1.5F
11 F	0021	0332	2.9E
	0708	0919	1.5F
	1247	1554	3.3E
	1931	2131	1.5F
12 Sa	0058	0413	2.9E
	0754	1005	1.5F
	1325	1635	3.2E
	2013	2215	1.5F
13 Su	0139	0457	2.8E
	0846	1054	1.4F
	1406	1719	3.1E
	2100	2303	1.5F
14 M ◑	0225	0547	2.7E
	0943	1147	1.3F
	1452	1809	3.0E
	2151	2355	1.6F
15 Tu	0318	0646	2.6E
	1042	1243	1.3F
	1543	1905	2.9E
	2244		
16 W		0050	1.7F
	0417	0753	2.7E
	1140	1339	1.4F
	1640	2006	3.0E
	2338		
17 Th		0145	1.8F
	0521	0902	2.9E
	1236	1433	1.5F
	1742	2107	3.1E
18 F	0032	0239	2.0F
	0625	1007	3.2E
	1329	1525	1.6F
	1846	2209	3.2E
19 Sa	0125	0333	2.2F
	0727	1106	3.5E
	1421	1620	1.7F
	1947	2310	3.5E
20 Su	0217	0428	2.4F
	0825	1200	3.8E
	1512	1715	1.8F
	2046		
21 M O		0007	3.7E
	0311	0524	2.5F
	0922	1251	4.0E
	1602	1808	1.9F
	2144		
22 Tu		0102	3.9E
	0405	0620	2.6F
	1017	1340	4.2E
	1652	1859	2.0F
	2239		
23 W		0155	4.0E
	0458	0715	2.6F
	1110	1429	4.2E
	1741	1951	2.0F
	2332		
24 Th		0247	4.0E
	0552	0811	2.5F
	1201	1516	4.1E
	1831	2045	1.9F
25 F	0024	0340	4.0E
	0648	0911	2.3F
	1251	1603	3.9E
	1922	2145	1.9F
26 Sa	0117	0433	3.8E
	0747	1014	2.1F
	1340	1650	3.5E
	2017	2249	1.7F
27 Su ◐	0211	0531	3.5E
	0850	1119	1.8F
	1431	1742	3.2E
	2114		
28 M		0000	1.6F
	0308	0642	3.3E
	0955	1225	1.6F
	1522	1847	2.9E
	2214		
29 Tu		0115	1.6F
	0407	0758	3.2E
	1059	1329	1.5F
	1616	2009	2.7E
	2314		
30 W		0220	1.6F
	0507	0902	3.2E
	1200	1426	1.4F
	1712	2115	2.7E
31 Th	0010	0316	1.6F
	0605	0958	3.3E
	1254	1517	1.4F
	1808	2211	2.8E

February

Day	Slack	Maximum	knots
1 F	0103	0409	1.6F
	0658	1047	3.4E
	1342	1606	1.4F
	1901	2300	2.9E
2 Sa	0151	0457	1.6F
	0745	1132	3.4E
	1426	1651	1.4F
	1950	2343	3.0E
3 Su	0236	0536	1.6F
	0828	1211	3.4E
	1507	1730	1.5F
	2035		
4 M ●		0020	3.0E
	0318	0603	1.6F
	0908	1244	3.4E
	1546	1801	1.5F
	2117		
5 Tu		0050	3.0E
	0359	0627	1.7F
	0946	1311	3.4E
	1623	1830	1.6F
	2156		
6 W		0118	3.1E
	0437	0654	1.7F
	1023	1337	3.4E
	1658	1900	1.7F
	2233		
7 Th		0149	3.1E
	0515	0726	1.8F
	1059	1407	3.4E
	1733	1933	1.7F
	2309		
8 F		0225	3.2E
	0554	0802	1.8F
	1134	1443	3.5E
	1808	2009	1.8F
	2343		
9 Sa		0303	3.2E
	0634	0842	1.7F
	1209	1521	3.5E
	1845	2049	1.8F
10 Su	0018	0345	3.2E
	0719	0927	1.7F
	1247	1603	3.4E
	1926	2134	1.8F
11 M	0058	0429	3.1E
	0810	1016	1.5F
	1328	1648	3.3E
	2014	2223	1.8F
12 Tu ◐	0145	0519	3.0E
	0909	1110	1.4F
	1417	1738	3.1E
	2109	2318	1.7F
13 W	0242	0617	2.8E
	1013	1210	1.3F
	1514	1835	2.9E
	2210		
14 Th		0017	1.7F
	0347	0726	2.8E
	1116	1313	1.3F
	1619	1941	2.9E
	2312		
15 F		0120	1.8F
	0458	0843	3.0E
	1216	1414	1.4F
	1729	2051	3.0E
16 Sa	0013	0220	1.9F
	0609	0953	3.3E
	1311	1512	1.6F
	1837	2159	3.2E
17 Su	0110	0319	2.1F
	0713	1053	3.7E
	1403	1609	1.7F
	1939	2303	3.5E
18 M	0205	0419	2.3F
	0812	1146	3.9E
	1453	1705	1.9F
	2037		
19 Tu O		0000	3.8E
	0259	0518	2.5F
	0908	1236	4.1E
	1542	1758	2.1F
	2131		
20 W		0053	4.1E
	0353	0614	2.6F
	1001	1323	4.2E
	1629	1846	2.2F
	2224		
21 Th		0144	4.2E
	0446	0706	2.6F
	1051	1409	4.2E
	1717	1933	2.2F
	2315		
22 F		0235	4.3E
	0539	0759	2.4F
	1140	1454	4.0E
	1804	2022	2.1F
23 Sa	0005	0326	4.1E
	0633	0854	2.2F
	1227	1538	3.7E
	1852	2116	2.0F
24 Su	0055	0416	3.9E
	0729	0953	1.9F
	1313	1622	3.4E
	1945	2215	1.8F
25 M	0147	0510	3.6E
	0829	1054	1.7F
	1401	1708	3.0E
	2042	2324	1.6F
26 Tu O	0241	0614	3.2E
	0933	1158	1.4F
	1451	1803	2.6E
	2144		
27 W		0048	1.4F
	0336	0729	3.0E
	1037	1305	1.2F
	1544	1933	2.4E
	2248		
28 Th		0159	1.4F
	0433	0836	3.0E
	1136	1405	1.2F
	1642	2052	2.4E
	2348		

March

Day	Slack	Maximum	knots
1 F		0255	1.4F
	0530	0931	3.0E
	1229	1456	1.2F
	1740	2150	2.6E
2 Sa	0042	0343	1.4F
	0622	1019	3.1E
	1315	1541	1.3F
	1834	2238	2.7E
3 Su	0130	0425	1.4F
	0708	1101	3.2E
	1355	1620	1.4F
	1922	2318	2.8E
4 M	0212	0459	1.5F
	0750	1136	3.2E
	1433	1653	1.5F
	2005	2352	2.9E
5 Tu	0251	0525	1.6F
	0829	1203	3.2E
	1509	1722	1.6F
	2045		
6 W ●		0019	3.0E
	0330	0551	1.7F
	0907	1228	3.3E
	1544	1751	1.7F
	2122		
7 Th		0046	3.2E
	0407	0620	1.8F
	0944	1257	3.4E
	1618	1822	1.9F
	2158		
8 F		0119	3.3E
	0445	0653	1.9F
	1020	1331	3.5E
	1652	1856	2.0F
	2233		
9 Sa		0156	3.4E
	0524	0729	1.9F
	1057	1410	3.6E
	1728	1933	2.1F
	2308		
10 Su		0237	3.5E
	0605	0809	1.9F
	1134	1451	3.6E
	1806	2014	2.2F
	2345		
11 M		0320	3.4E
	0650	0854	1.8F
	1213	1535	3.5E
	1848	2100	2.1F
12 Tu	0027	0406	3.3E
	0743	0945	1.6F
	1258	1622	3.3E
	1938	2151	2.0F
13 W	0118	0457	3.2E
	0843	1041	1.4F
	1352	1713	3.1E
	2037	2249	1.9F
14 Th ◐	0219	0554	3.0E
	0949	1144	1.3F
	1457	1812	2.9E
	2144	2352	1.8F
15 F	0329	0705	3.0E
	1055	1254	1.3F
	1608	1923	2.8E
	2252		
16 Sa		0101	1.8F
	0442	0827	3.1E
	1156	1402	1.4F
	1720	2041	3.0E
	2357		
17 Su		0208	1.9F
	0553	0938	3.4E
	1251	1503	1.6F
	1828	2153	3.3E
18 M	0057	0311	2.1F
	0657	1036	3.8E
	1342	1600	1.9F
	1928	2255	3.7E
19 Tu	0153	0412	2.3F
	0755	1128	4.0E
	1431	1654	2.1F
	2023	2350	4.1E
20 W O	0246	0510	2.4F
	0849	1217	4.1E
	1518	1744	2.2F
	2115		
21 Th		0042	4.3E
	0339	0604	2.5F
	0939	1302	4.1E
	1604	1830	2.3F
	2206		
22 F		0132	4.4E
	0432	0654	2.4F
	1028	1347	4.0E
	1650	1913	2.3F
	2256		
23 Sa		0221	4.3E
	0524	0743	2.3F
	1115	1430	3.8E
	1737	1958	2.2F
	2345		
24 Su		0310	4.2E
	0616	0834	2.0F
	1200	1513	3.5E
	1824	2047	2.0F
25 M	0034	0359	3.9E
	0710	0929	1.7F
	1245	1555	3.2E
	1915	2144	1.7F
26 Tu	0123	0448	3.5E
	0807	1029	1.5F
	1331	1638	2.8E
	2012	2253	1.5F
27 W ◐	0213	0543	3.1E
	0908	1132	1.2F
	1421	1726	2.5E
	2114		
28 Th		0019	1.3F
	0304	0652	2.8E
	1009	1239	1.1F
	1515	1835	2.2E
	2220		
29 F		0130	1.2F
	0356	0801	2.7E
	1106	1340	1.1F
	1611	2023	2.2E
	2322		
30 Sa		0223	1.2F
	0448	0857	2.8E
	1157	1429	1.2F
	1708	2122	2.3E
31 Su	0016	0306	1.2F
	0539	0942	2.8E
	1241	1508	1.3F
	1801	2208	2.5E

Time meridian 75° W. 0000 is midnight. 1200 is noon. Times are not adjusted for Daylight Saving Time.

Southport, Cape Fear River, North Carolina 2019

F–Flood, Dir. 048° True   E–Ebb, Dir. 235° True

April

Day	Slack h m	Maximum h m	knots
1 M	0102	0341	1.3F
	0625	1019	2.9E
	1319	1540	1.4F
	1849	2246	2.7E
2 Tu	0142	0410	1.4F
	0708	1048	3.0E
	1355	1608	1.5F
	1931	2315	2.9E
3 W	0220	0439	1.5F
	0748	1113	3.2E
	1429	1637	1.7F
	2009	2342	3.0E
4 Th	0258	0510	1.7F
	0826	1143	3.3E
	1504	1710	1.9F
	2046		
5 F ●		0014	3.2E
	0336	0544	1.8F
	0904	1219	3.5E
	1538	1745	2.1F
	2123		
6 Sa		0050	3.4E
	0416	0620	1.9F
	0942	1258	3.6E
	1615	1823	2.3F
	2200		
7 Su		0131	3.5E
	0457	0659	1.9F
	1021	1340	3.6E
	1653	1903	2.4F
	2239		
8 M		0214	3.6E
	0541	0741	1.9F
	1102	1425	3.6E
	1734	1946	2.4F
	2322		
9 Tu		0259	3.6E
	0628	0827	1.8F
	1147	1511	3.5E
	1820	2033	2.3F
10 W	0009	0348	3.5E
	0722	0919	1.6F
	1239	1601	3.3E
	1913	2127	2.2F
11 Th	0104	0439	3.4E
	0822	1019	1.4F
	1339	1655	3.1E
	2015	2227	2.0F
12 F ◐	0208	0537	3.2E
	0928	1125	1.3F
	1447	1756	2.9E
	2125	2334	1.8F
13 Sa	0317	0646	3.2E
	1034	1240	1.3F
	1558	1910	2.9E
	2235		
14 Su		0048	1.8F
	0427	0808	3.3E
	1134	1353	1.5F
	1708	2033	3.1E
	2342		
15 M		0200	1.9F
	0535	0918	3.5E
	1229	1454	1.7F
	1812	2144	3.5E
16 Tu	0042	0304	2.1F
	0637	1016	3.8E
	1319	1548	2.0F
	1911	2243	3.9E
17 W	0138	0402	2.3F
	0733	1107	3.9E
	1407	1640	2.2F
	2005	2337	4.2E
18 Th	0232	0458	2.3F
	0825	1155	4.0E
	1453	1728	2.3F
	2057		
19 F ○		0028	4.4E
	0324	0550	2.3F
	0914	1241	4.0E
	1539	1812	2.3F
	2148		
20 Sa		0117	4.4E
	0416	0638	2.2F
	1002	1324	3.8E
	1625	1854	2.3F
	2237		
21 Su		0205	4.3E
	0507	0724	2.0F
	1048	1407	3.6E
	1711	1937	2.1F
	2325		
22 M		0253	4.1E
	0558	0812	1.8F
	1133	1449	3.3E
	1759	2024	1.9F
23 Tu	0012	0339	3.8E
	0649	0904	1.5F
	1218	1530	3.1E
	1849	2118	1.7F
24 W	0057	0424	3.4E
	0743	1002	1.3F
	1304	1611	2.7E
	1944	2224	1.4F
25 Th	0143	0509	3.1E
	0838	1103	1.2F
	1353	1654	2.5E
	2044	2340	1.2F
26 F ◑	0229	0557	2.8E
	0935	1204	1.1F
	1444	1744	2.2E
	2147		
27 Sa		0047	1.1F
	0316	0657	2.6E
	1028	1302	1.1F
	1537	1902	2.1E
	2247		
28 Su		0138	1.1F
	0403	0759	2.6E
	1117	1348	1.1F
	1630	2037	2.2E
	2340		
29 M		0218	1.1F
	0451	0843	2.6E
	1200	1423	1.2F
	1721	2124	2.3E
30 Tu	0026	0251	1.2F
	0538	0915	2.8E
	1239	1451	1.4F
	1808	2159	2.6E

May

Day	Slack h m	Maximum h m	knots
1 W	0107	0322	1.4F
	0622	0946	2.9E
	1314	1521	1.6F
	1851	2229	2.8E
2 Th	0147	0355	1.5F
	0704	1022	3.1E
	1349	1554	1.8F
	1932	2304	3.0E
3 F	0226	0431	1.6F
	0745	1103	3.3E
	1425	1631	2.0F
	2011	2343	3.2E
4 Sa ●	0307	0509	1.7F
	0825	1145	3.4E
	1502	1711	2.2F
	2052		
5 Su		0025	3.4E
	0349	0550	1.8F
	0907	1229	3.5E
	1542	1753	2.4F
	2134		
6 M		0109	3.6E
	0434	0632	1.9F
	0952	1315	3.6E
	1625	1837	2.5F
	2220		
7 Tu		0154	3.7E
	0520	0717	1.9F
	1040	1403	3.6E
	1711	1923	2.5F
	2308		
8 W		0242	3.7E
	0610	0805	1.8F
	1132	1453	3.5E
	1800	2013	2.4F
9 Th	0001	0332	3.7E
	0704	0900	1.6F
	1229	1545	3.4E
	1856	2109	2.3F
10 F	0058	0424	3.6E
	0803	1001	1.5F
	1331	1641	3.2E
	1959	2212	2.1F
11 Sa ◐	0200	0521	3.5E
	0906	1109	1.4F
	1437	1742	3.1E
	2108	2322	1.9F
12 Su	0305	0626	3.4E
	1010	1225	1.5F
	1543	1857	3.0E
	2218		
13 M		0038	1.9F
	0409	0744	3.4E
	1109	1340	1.6F
	1649	2020	3.2E
	2325		
14 Tu		0150	2.0F
	0513	0854	3.5E
	1204	1440	1.8F
	1752	2129	3.6E
15 W	0026	0252	2.1F
	0613	0952	3.7E
	1255	1533	2.0F
	1852	2228	3.9E
16 Th	0122	0348	2.1F
	0708	1045	3.8E
	1342	1623	2.2F
	1946	2322	4.2E
17 F	0216	0442	2.1F
	0759	1134	3.8E
	1429	1712	2.2F
	2039		
18 Sa ○		0013	4.3E
	0308	0533	2.0F
	0848	1220	3.7E
	1515	1758	2.2F
	2129		
19 Su		0101	4.2E
	0400	0621	1.9F
	0935	1304	3.6E
	1602	1840	2.2F
	2217		
20 M		0148	4.1E
	0450	0705	1.8F
	1022	1347	3.4E
	1650	1922	2.0F
	2304		
21 Tu		0234	3.9E
	0538	0750	1.6F
	1107	1429	3.2E
	1737	2006	1.8F
	2348		
22 W		0317	3.6E
	0625	0838	1.4F
	1153	1508	3.0E
	1826	2056	1.6F
23 Th	0030	0355	3.4E
	0713	0930	1.3F
	1238	1546	2.8E
	1917	2152	1.4F
24 F	0111	0429	3.1E
	0802	1022	1.2F
	1323	1624	2.5E
	2011	2249	1.2F
25 Sa	0152	0502	2.9E
	0852	1112	1.1F
	1410	1706	2.4E
	2107	2343	1.1F
26 Su ◑	0234	0540	2.7E
	0942	1159	1.1F
	1457	1753	2.2E
	2203		
27 M		0035	1.1F
	0318	0624	2.6E
	1029	1243	1.1F
	1545	1851	2.2E
	2256		
28 Tu		0120	1.1F
	0403	0715	2.6E
	1113	1323	1.2F
	1633	1956	2.3E
	2345		
29 W		0159	1.2F
	0449	0805	2.7E
	1154	1359	1.4F
	1721	2053	2.5E
30 Th	0030	0236	1.3F
	0535	0853	2.9E
	1232	1436	1.6F
	1809	2142	2.7E
31 F	0113	0314	1.5F
	0621	0940	3.1E
	1311	1515	1.9F
	1855	2229	3.0E

June

Day	Slack h m	Maximum h m	knots
1 Sa	0156	0355	1.6F
	0706	1028	3.2E
	1351	1557	2.1F
	1940	2316	3.2E
2 Su	0240	0438	1.7F
	0752	1117	3.4E
	1433	1642	2.3F
	2027		
3 M ●		0003	3.5E
	0326	0524	1.8F
	0841	1206	3.5E
	1517	1729	2.5F
	2116		
4 Tu		0051	3.7E
	0414	0610	1.8F
	0933	1256	3.6E
	1605	1817	2.6F
	2207		
5 W		0139	3.8E
	0502	0658	1.8F
	1027	1347	3.6E
	1655	1906	2.6F
	2300		
6 Th		0228	3.9E
	0553	0748	1.8F
	1124	1440	3.6E
	1747	1959	2.5F
	2355		
7 F		0319	3.9E
	0645	0843	1.7F
	1221	1533	3.5E
	1843	2057	2.3F
8 Sa	0051	0410	3.8E
	0741	0944	1.6F
	1321	1628	3.4E
	1945	2201	2.2F
9 Su	0148	0503	3.7E
	0841	1051	1.6F
	1421	1728	3.3E
	2052	2311	2.0F
10 M ◐	0248	0603	3.5E
	0942	1204	1.6F
	1524	1841	3.2E
	2200		
11 Tu		0024	1.9F
	0347	0714	3.3E
	1041	1319	1.7F
	1627	2003	3.3E
	2306		
12 W		0135	1.9F
	0447	0827	3.3E
	1137	1422	1.8F
	1730	2112	3.6E
13 Th	0008	0236	1.9F
	0545	0929	3.4E
	1229	1516	2.0F
	1830	2211	3.8E
14 F	0106	0330	1.9F
	0641	1024	3.5E
	1319	1609	2.1F
	1927	2306	4.0E
15 Sa	0200	0424	1.8F
	0733	1115	3.5E
	1407	1703	2.1F
	2019	2356	4.1E
16 Su	0252	0516	1.8F
	0822	1203	3.4E
	1455	1753	2.1F
	2109		
17 M ○		0044	4.0E
	0341	0604	1.7F
	0910	1248	3.4E
	1543	1836	2.0F
	2155		
18 Tu		0128	3.9E
	0428	0648	1.6F
	0957	1330	3.3E
	1630	1914	1.9F
	2239		
19 W		0210	3.7E
	0513	0728	1.5F
	1043	1409	3.1E
	1717	1951	1.8F
	2320		
20 Th		0248	3.5E
	0557	0808	1.5F
	1127	1445	3.0E
	1802	2030	1.6F
	2359		
21 F		0320	3.3E
	0639	0849	1.4F
	1209	1519	2.9E
	1847	2113	1.5F
22 Sa	0036	0348	3.2E
	0721	0929	1.3F
	1249	1553	2.7E
	1934	2157	1.4F
23 Su	0114	0419	3.1E
	0805	1010	1.2F
	1330	1631	2.6E
	2024	2242	1.3F
24 M	0152	0454	3.0E
	0849	1052	1.2F
	1412	1713	2.5E
	2116	2329	1.2F
25 Tu ◑	0233	0536	2.9E
	0935	1135	1.2F
	1455	1801	2.4E
	2209		
26 W		0019	1.2F
	0316	0623	2.8E
	1021	1222	1.3F
	1542	1858	2.4E
	2302		
27 Th		0107	1.2F
	0402	0716	2.8E
	1106	1309	1.4F
	1632	2001	2.5E
	2353		
28 F		0154	1.3F
	0450	0810	2.9E
	1151	1355	1.6F
	1726	2102	2.7E
29 Sa	0042	0239	1.4F
	0542	0905	3.0E
	1236	1442	1.9F
	1821	2159	3.0E
30 Su	0130	0325	1.5F
	0636	0959	3.1E
	1322	1529	2.1F
	1915	2253	3.2E

Time meridian 75° W. 0000 is midnight. 1200 is noon. Times are not adjusted for Daylight Saving Time.

Southport, Cape Fear River, North Carolina 2019

F–Flood, Dir. 048° True   E–Ebb, Dir. 235° True

July

Day	Slack (h m)	Maximum (h m)	knots
1 M	0217	0413	1.6F
	0730	1055	3.3F
	1410	1619	2.3F
	2009	2346	3.5E
2 Tu ●	0306	0502	1.7F
	0826	1149	3.5F
	1459	1710	2.4F
	2103		
3 W		0036	3.8E
	0355	0553	1.8F
	0922	1243	3.6F
	1550	1802	2.5F
	2157		
4 Th		0125	3.9E
	0444	0642	1.9F
	1019	1336	3.7F
	1642	1855	2.6F
	2252		
5 F		0214	4.1E
	0533	0733	1.9F
	1115	1429	3.8F
	1736	1949	2.6F
	2345		
6 Sa		0303	4.1E
	0624	0826	1.9F
	1210	1522	3.8F
	1831	2047	2.4F
7 Su	0038	0352	4.0E
	0717	0925	1.8F
	1305	1616	3.7F
	1931	2150	2.3F
8 M	0132	0443	3.8E
	0812	1028	1.7F
	1402	1714	3.6F
	2035	2257	2.1F
9 Tu ◖	0226	0537	3.5E
	0911	1136	1.7F
	1501	1822	3.4F
	2141		
10 W		0006	1.9F
	0322	0641	3.2E
	1011	1252	1.7F
	1602	1942	3.4E
	2248		
11 Th		0116	1.8F
	0419	0758	3.1E
	1109	1403	1.7F
	1705	2053	3.5E
	2351		
12 F		0218	1.7F
	0517	0907	3.1E
	1206	1503	1.8F
	1807	2154	3.6E
13 Sa	0050	0314	1.6F
	0614	1005	3.2E
	1259	1602	1.9F
	1905	2248	3.8E
14 Su	0143	0408	1.6F
	0708	1058	3.2E
	1349	1700	1.9F
	1957	2337	3.8E
15 M	0232	0500	1.6F
	0759	1147	3.3F
	1438	1750	1.9F
	2045		
16 Tu ○		0023	3.8E
	0318	0547	1.6F
	0847	1231	3.3E
	1525	1829	1.9F
	2129		
17 W		0104	3.7E
	0402	0627	1.6F
	0933	1311	3.2E
	1611	1900	1.8F
	2210		
18 Th		0141	3.6E
	0443	0700	1.6F
	1017	1347	3.2E
	1654	1928	1.7F
	2248		
19 F		0212	3.5E
	0523	0732	1.6F
	1057	1418	3.1E
	1736	1958	1.7F
	2325		
20 Sa		0239	3.4E
	0600	0804	1.5F
	1136	1448	3.0E
	1816	2032	1.6F
21 Su	0000	0307	3.3E
	0637	0839	1.5F
	1212	1521	3.0E
	1857	2111	1.5F
22 M	0035	0340	3.3E
	0715	0916	1.5F
	1247	1558	2.9E
	1942	2153	1.4F
23 Tu	0111	0417	3.2E
	0756	0958	1.4F
	1324	1639	2.8E
	2031	2238	1.3F
24 W ◗	0150	0458	3.1E
	0840	1042	1.4F
	1405	1725	2.7E
	2125	2328	1.2F
25 Th	0232	0544	2.9E
	0928	1132	1.5F
	1453	1818	2.6E
	2222		
26 F		0021	1.2F
	0319	0637	2.8E
	1020	1225	1.5F
	1548	1921	2.6E
	2319		
27 Sa		0116	1.2F
	0413	0736	2.8E
	1114	1320	1.7F
	1648	2029	2.7E
28 Su	0014	0210	1.3F
	0513	0837	2.9E
	1208	1414	1.8F
	1753	2135	3.0E
29 M	0106	0301	1.4F
	0616	0939	3.0E
	1300	1507	2.0F
	1855	2235	3.3E
30 Tu	0156	0353	1.6F
	0718	1040	3.3E
	1353	1601	2.2F
	1954	2330	3.6E
31 W ●	0245	0446	1.8F
	0817	1138	3.5E
	1445	1656	2.4F
	2050		

August

Day	Slack (h m)	Maximum (h m)	knots
1 Th		0021	3.9E
	0334	0538	1.9F
	0914	1233	3.8E
	1538	1752	2.5F
	2145		
2 F		0110	4.1E
	0423	0628	2.0F
	1009	1326	4.0E
	1631	1845	2.6F
	2238		
3 Sa		0158	4.2E
	0511	0717	2.1F
	1102	1418	4.1E
	1724	1939	2.6F
	2330		
4 Su		0245	4.1E
	0600	0808	2.1F
	1154	1510	4.1E
	1818	2035	2.5F
5 M	0020	0332	4.0E
	0650	0902	2.0F
	1247	1603	4.0E
	1915	2135	2.2F
6 Tu	0111	0420	3.7E
	0743	1001	1.9F
	1341	1658	3.7E
	2017	2239	2.0F
7 W ◖	0202	0509	3.4E
	0840	1107	1.7F
	1438	1802	3.5E
	2122	2346	1.7F
8 Th	0255	0607	3.0E
	0941	1226	1.6F
	1538	1920	3.3E
	2229		
9 F		0056	1.5F
	0350	0727	2.8E
	1043	1348	1.6F
	1639	2033	3.3E
	2333		
10 Sa		0202	1.4F
	0449	0847	2.8E
	1144	1453	1.6F
	1741	2133	3.4E
11 Su	0031	0259	1.4F
	0548	0949	2.9E
	1241	1552	1.7F
	1839	2226	3.5E
12 M	0123	0352	1.4F
	0645	1042	3.0E
	1333	1646	1.7F
	1930	2314	3.5E
13 Tu	0208	0442	1.5F
	0736	1130	3.1E
	1421	1731	1.7F
	2015	2357	3.5E
14 W	0251	0524	1.6F
	0823	1212	3.2E
	1505	1806	1.7F
	2056		
15 Th ○		0034	3.5E
	0330	0557	1.6F
	0906	1248	3.2E
	1547	1831	1.7F
	2134		
16 F		0105	3.4E
	0408	0625	1.7F
	0946	1318	3.2E
	1628	1855	1.7F
	2211		
17 Sa		0130	3.4E
	0445	0652	1.7F
	1024	1345	3.2E
	1706	1922	1.8F
	2247		
18 Su		0157	3.4E
	0520	0722	1.7F
	1059	1415	3.2E
	1744	1954	1.7F
	2322		
19 M		0228	3.4E
	0554	0755	1.8F
	1132	1450	3.2E
	1823	2030	1.7F
	2356		
20 Tu		0304	3.4E
	0629	0832	1.8F
	1205	1528	3.2E
	1905	2111	1.6F
21 W	0031	0343	3.3E
	0707	0914	1.8F
	1240	1610	3.1E
	1952	2157	1.5F
22 Th	0109	0426	3.2E
	0751	1000	1.7F
	1322	1656	2.9E
	2047	2247	1.3F
23 F ◗	0153	0513	3.0E
	0842	1052	1.7F
	1412	1748	2.8E
	2148	2344	1.2F
24 Sa	0246	0606	2.8E
	0941	1149	1.6F
	1513	1850	2.7E
	2251		
25 Su		0045	1.2F
	0347	0708	2.7E
	1044	1250	1.7F
	1621	2003	2.8E
	2350		
26 M		0146	1.3F
	0456	0817	2.8E
	1145	1352	1.8F
	1732	2115	3.1E
27 Tu	0045	0243	1.5F
	0605	0926	3.0E
	1243	1451	2.0F
	1838	2218	3.4E
28 W	0135	0338	1.7F
	0709	1030	3.3E
	1338	1548	2.2F
	1939	2313	3.7E
29 Th	0224	0432	1.9F
	0807	1130	3.7E
	1432	1646	2.4F
	2035		
30 F ●		0004	4.0E
	0312	0524	2.1F
	0901	1224	4.0E
	1525	1742	2.5F
	2128		
31 Sa		0052	4.2E
	0400	0613	2.2F
	0954	1316	4.2E
	1618	1835	2.6F
	2220		

September

Day	Slack (h m)	Maximum (h m)	knots
1 Su		0138	4.2E
	0447	0700	2.3F
	1046	1406	4.3E
	1711	1927	2.5F
	2310		
2 M		0224	4.1E
	0534	0748	2.2F
	1137	1457	4.3E
	1804	2020	2.4F
	2359		
3 Tu		0310	3.9E
	0623	0838	2.1F
	1228	1549	4.1E
	1900	2118	2.1F
4 W	0047	0356	3.6E
	0714	0935	1.9F
	1320	1642	3.8E
	2000	2219	1.8F
5 Th ◖	0136	0443	3.2E
	0810	1040	1.7F
	1415	1742	3.4E
	2103	2326	1.5F
6 F	0228	0537	2.8E
	0913	1205	1.5F
	1512	1855	3.2E
	2209		
7 Sa		0038	1.3F
	0323	0655	2.5E
	1019	1334	1.5F
	1611	2008	3.1E
	2312		
8 Su		0146	1.3F
	0422	0826	2.5E
	1124	1437	1.5F
	1710	2108	3.1E
9 M	0008	0243	1.3F
	0522	0930	2.7E
	1223	1530	1.5F
	1805	2200	3.2E
10 Tu	0057	0331	1.4F
	0619	1022	2.8E
	1314	1616	1.5F
	1854	2245	3.3E
11 W	0139	0414	1.5F
	0710	1107	3.0E
	1359	1656	1.6F
	1938	2324	3.3E
12 Th	0218	0449	1.6F
	0754	1146	3.1E
	1440	1726	1.6F
	2017	2356	3.3E
13 F ○	0255	0517	1.7F
	0834	1219	3.1E
	1519	1751	1.7F
	2055		
14 Sa		0021	3.3E
	0330	0543	1.7F
	0912	1245	3.2E
	1557	1816	1.7F
	2131		
15 Su		0046	3.4E
	0405	0611	1.9F
	0947	1312	3.3E
	1635	1845	1.8F
	2207		
16 M		0117	3.4E
	0438	0643	2.0F
	1022	1344	3.3E
	1713	1918	1.8F
	2242		
17 Tu		0152	3.5E
	0513	0717	2.1F
	1055	1421	3.4E
	1752	1954	1.8F
	2318		
18 W		0232	3.5E
	0548	0755	2.1F
	1129	1501	3.4E
	1834	2035	1.7F
	2354		
19 Th		0314	3.4E
	0627	0838	2.1F
	1207	1545	3.3E
	1922	2122	1.5F
20 F ◗	0035	0359	3.2E
	0713	0926	2.0F
	1251	1632	3.2E
	2018	2215	1.4F
21 Sa ○	0124	0447	3.0E
	0807	1021	1.8F
	1346	1725	3.0E
	2120	2314	1.2F
22 Su	0224	0542	2.8E
	0912	1121	1.7F
	1451	1827	2.9E
	2225		
23 M		0020	1.2F
	0333	0647	2.7E
	1020	1227	1.7F
	1603	1941	3.0E
	2326		
24 Tu		0128	1.3F
	0444	0802	2.8E
	1126	1335	1.8F
	1714	2056	3.2E
25 W	0022	0229	1.5F
	0553	0916	3.1E
	1227	1439	2.0F
	1820	2159	3.6E
26 Th	0113	0324	1.8F
	0656	1022	3.5E
	1324	1538	2.2F
	1920	2254	3.8E
27 F	0201	0417	2.0F
	0753	1120	3.9E
	1418	1635	2.4F
	2016	2344	4.0E
28 Sa ●	0249	0508	2.2F
	0846	1213	4.2E
	1511	1731	2.5F
	2108		
29 Su		0032	4.1E
	0336	0556	2.3F
	0938	1304	4.4E
	1604	1823	2.5F
	2158		
30 M		0118	4.1E
	0422	0642	2.4F
	1029	1354	4.4E
	1657	1913	2.4F
	2247		

Time meridian 75° W. 0000 is midnight. 1200 is noon. Times are not adjusted for Daylight Saving Time.

Southport, Cape Fear River, North Carolina 2019

F–Flood, Dir. 048° True   E–Ebb, Dir. 235° True

October

Day	Slack (h m)	Maximum (h m)	knots
1 Tu		0203	3.9E
	0509	0728	2.3F
	1120	1444	4.3E
	1750	2003	2.1F
	2335		
2 W		0249	3.7E
	0557	0816	2.2F
	1210	1535	4.1E
	1844	2059	1.9F
3 Th	0023	0334	3.4E
	0648	0912	1.9F
	1301	1626	3.8E
	1941	2201	1.6F
4 F	0111	0420	3.0E
	0744	1021	1.7F
	1352	1720	3.4E
	2042	2308	1.3F
5 Sa	0203	0510	2.7E
	0847	1152	1.4F
	1445	1824	3.1E
	2145		
6 Su		0019	1.2F
	0257	0619	2.4E
	0954	1311	1.3F
	1539	1935	2.9E
	2244		
7 M		0125	1.2F
	0354	0759	2.3E
	1100	1409	1.3F
	1632	2036	2.9E
	2337		
8 Tu		0218	1.3F
	0452	0904	2.5E
	1158	1455	1.3F
	1724	2125	2.9E
9 W	0024	0300	1.4F
	0547	0955	2.7E
	1248	1534	1.4F
	1811	2207	3.0E
10 Th	0104	0335	1.5F
	0636	1037	2.8E
	1330	1608	1.5F
	1855	2241	3.1E
11 F	0141	0402	1.6F
	0719	1114	2.9E
	1409	1637	1.5F
	1934	2307	3.1E
12 Sa	0216	0429	1.7F
	0758	1143	3.0E
	1447	1705	1.6F
	2012	2333	3.2E
13 Su	0250	0459	1.8F
	0835	1209	3.2E
	1525	1736	1.7F
	2049		
14 M		0004	3.3E
	0324	0532	2.0F
	0911	1239	3.3E
	1604	1809	1.8F
	2126		
15 Tu		0041	3.4E
	0359	0607	2.1F
	0946	1315	3.4E
	1644	1844	1.8F
	2204		
16 W		0121	3.5E
	0436	0645	2.3F
	1023	1355	3.5E
	1725	1923	1.8F
	2243		
17 Th		0203	3.5E
	0515	0725	2.3F
	1102	1438	3.5E
	1809	2006	1.7F
	2325		
18 F		0249	3.4E
	0557	0810	2.3F
	1145	1524	3.5E
	1858	2054	1.6F
19 Sa	0012	0337	3.3E
	0646	0901	2.2F
	1235	1613	3.4E
	1954	2149	1.4F
20 Su	0108	0428	3.1E
	0743	0958	2.0F
	1333	1706	3.3E
	2056	2251	1.3F
21 M	0212	0524	2.9E
	0850	1101	1.8F
	1439	1806	3.2E
	2200	2359	1.3F
22 Tu	0321	0630	2.8E
	1001	1211	1.8F
	1547	1918	3.2E
	2301		
23 W		0110	1.4F
	0431	0748	2.9E
	1108	1322	1.9F
	1655	2033	3.4E
	2357		
24 Th		0214	1.7F
	0537	0905	3.3E
	1211	1427	2.0F
	1800	2137	3.6E
25 F	0049	0309	1.9F
	0639	1010	3.7E
	1308	1526	2.2F
	1859	2232	3.8E
26 Sa	0137	0400	2.1F
	0735	1107	4.0E
	1403	1622	2.3F
	1953	2324	3.9E
27 Su	0225	0451	2.3F
	0829	1200	4.3E
	1456	1717	2.3F
	2045		
28 M		0012	4.0E
	0311	0539	2.4F
	0921	1251	4.4E
	1550	1808	2.2F
	2135		
29 Tu		0058	3.9E
	0359	0626	2.4F
	1013	1341	4.4E
	1642	1857	2.1F
	2224		
30 W		0144	3.7E
	0447	0711	2.3F
	1103	1430	4.2E
	1735	1947	1.9F
	2312		
31 Th		0230	3.5E
	0535	0800	2.1F
	1152	1519	4.0E
	1827	2041	1.6F

November

Day	Slack (h m)	Maximum (h m)	knots
1 F	0000	0315	3.2E
	0626	0857	1.9F
	1240	1607	3.7E
	1920	2142	1.4F
2 Sa	0048	0400	3.0E
	0721	1010	1.6F
	1328	1654	3.3E
	2016	2246	1.3F
3 Su	0138	0447	2.7E
	0822	1130	1.4F
	1415	1744	3.0E
	2112	2350	1.2F
4 M	0229	0540	2.4E
	0926	1234	1.3F
	1502	1842	2.8E
	2207		
5 Tu		0049	1.2F
	0322	0709	2.2E
	1028	1327	1.2F
	1549	1944	2.7E
	2258		
6 W		0138	1.2F
	0415	0825	2.3E
	1124	1410	1.2F
	1637	2034	2.7E
	2344		
7 Th		0216	1.3F
	0506	0917	2.4E
	1213	1446	1.3F
	1723	2111	2.7E
8 F	0024	0246	1.4F
	0554	0958	2.6E
	1256	1517	1.3F
	1807	2139	2.8E
9 Sa	0101	0313	1.5F
	0639	1031	2.7E
	1335	1548	1.4F
	1849	2210	3.0E
10 Su	0136	0343	1.7F
	0719	1100	2.9E
	1415	1621	1.5F
	1929	2246	3.1E
11 M	0211	0417	1.9F
	0758	1132	3.1E
	1454	1657	1.6F
	2009	2326	3.3E
12 Tu	0247	0455	2.1F
	0836	1209	3.3E
	1535	1735	1.7F
	2049		
13 W		0009	3.4E
	0325	0535	2.3F
	0916	1246	3.4E
	1618	1815	1.7F
	2131		
14 Th		0054	3.4E
	0406	0617	2.4F
	0959	1333	3.6E
	1702	1857	1.7F
	2217		
15 F		0140	3.5E
	0450	0702	2.5F
	1045	1419	3.6E
	1748	1942	1.7F
	2306		
16 Sa		0229	3.4E
	0537	0749	2.4F
	1134	1507	3.7E
	1837	2032	1.6F
17 Su	0000	0320	3.4E
	0628	0842	2.3F
	1227	1556	3.6E
	1932	2128	1.5F
18 M	0058	0413	3.3E
	0727	0941	2.1F
	1325	1648	3.5E
	2031	2230	1.5F
19 Tu	0201	0509	3.1E
	0833	1046	2.0F
	1427	1746	3.4E
	2133	2337	1.5F
20 W	0306	0614	3.0E
	0942	1156	1.9F
	1530	1853	3.3E
	2233		
21 Th		0049	1.6F
	0412	0733	3.1E
	1050	1308	1.9F
	1634	2007	3.4E
	2330		
22 F		0156	1.7F
	0517	0851	3.4E
	1153	1413	2.0F
	1736	2113	3.5E
23 Sa	0023	0252	1.9F
	0619	0955	3.7E
	1252	1512	2.1F
	1835	2211	3.7E
24 Su	0113	0344	2.1F
	0717	1053	4.0E
	1348	1607	2.1F
	1930	2304	3.7E
25 M	0202	0436	2.2F
	0812	1147	4.2E
	1442	1702	2.1F
	2022	2354	3.7E
26 Tu	0250	0528	2.3F
	0905	1237	4.3E
	1535	1755	2.0F
	2112		
27 W		0042	3.7E
	0338	0617	2.3F
	0956	1326	4.2E
	1627	1844	1.8F
	2201		
28 Th		0128	3.5E
	0428	0704	2.2F
	1045	1414	4.1E
	1717	1932	1.7F
	2250		
29 F		0214	3.4E
	0517	0753	2.0F
	1132	1500	3.9E
	1806	2022	1.6F
	2337		
30 Sa		0258	3.2E
	0607	0849	1.8F
	1216	1543	3.6E
	1854	2117	1.4F

December

Day	Slack (h m)	Maximum (h m)	knots
1 Su	0024	0341	3.0E
	0659	0954	1.6F
	1259	1621	3.3E
	1943	2212	1.3F
2 M	0110	0421	2.7E
	0753	1051	1.4F
	1341	1656	3.0E
	2033	2302	1.2F
3 Tu	0157	0501	2.5E
	0850	1141	1.3F
	1422	1732	2.8E
	2123	2349	1.2F
4 W	0244	0547	2.3E
	0947	1229	1.2F
	1505	1812	2.7E
	2211		
5 Th		0034	1.1F
	0331	0644	2.2E
	1041	1313	1.2F
	1548	1858	2.6E
	2257		
6 F		0113	1.2F
	0418	0759	2.2E
	1131	1352	1.2F
	1633	1948	2.6E
	2339		
7 Sa		0149	1.3F
	0506	0854	2.4E
	1217	1428	1.3F
	1718	2035	2.7E
8 Su	0018	0224	1.5F
	0553	0935	2.6E
	1301	1504	1.3F
	1803	2120	2.9E
9 M	0056	0300	1.7F
	0638	1016	2.8E
	1343	1541	1.4F
	1848	2207	3.0E
10 Tu	0135	0340	1.9F
	0722	1059	3.0E
	1426	1622	1.5F
	1933	2255	3.2E
11 W	0215	0423	2.1F
	0807	1144	3.3E
	1509	1705	1.6F
	2020	2344	3.3E
12 Th	0258	0508	2.3F
	0853	1229	3.5E
	1554	1750	1.7F
	2109		
13 F		0033	3.4E
	0344	0555	2.4F
	0942	1315	3.7E
	1640	1835	1.8F
	2201		
14 Sa		0123	3.5E
	0432	0643	2.5F
	1033	1402	3.8E
	1727	1922	1.8F
	2255		
15 Su		0214	3.6E
	0522	0734	2.5F
	1125	1451	3.9E
	1816	2013	1.8F
	2351		
16 M		0306	3.6E
	0615	0828	2.4F
	1218	1540	3.9E
	1909	2108	1.7F
17 Tu	0047	0359	3.5E
	0713	0927	2.3F
	1314	1630	3.8E
	2005	2209	1.7F
18 W	0146	0455	3.4E
	0816	1032	2.1F
	1411	1724	3.6E
	2104	2314	1.6F
19 Th	0247	0558	3.3E
	0923	1140	2.0F
	1510	1825	3.4E
	2204		
20 F		0023	1.7F
	0350	0715	3.3E
	1031	1251	1.9F
	1610	1938	3.3E
	2302		
21 Sa		0133	1.8F
	0454	0834	3.4E
	1136	1358	1.9F
	1711	2049	3.3E
	2358		
22 Su		0235	1.9F
	0558	0940	3.7E
	1237	1457	1.9F
	1810	2151	3.4E
23 M	0051	0332	2.0F
	0658	1038	3.9E
	1333	1553	1.8F
	1907	2247	3.5E
24 Tu	0142	0430	2.1F
	0754	1132	4.1E
	1427	1650	1.8F
	2000	2340	3.5E
25 W	0232	0529	2.1F
	0847	1222	4.1E
	1519	1744	1.7F
	2051		
26 Th		0028	3.5E
	0322	0622	2.1F
	0937	1309	4.1E
	1608	1832	1.7F
	2140		
27 F		0115	3.4E
	0411	0707	2.1F
	1024	1353	3.9E
	1655	1916	1.6F
	2228		
28 Sa		0159	3.3E
	0500	0750	1.9F
	1107	1435	3.7E
	1739	1958	1.6F
	2314		
29 Su		0240	3.2E
	0547	0833	1.8F
	1148	1511	3.5E
	1822	2039	1.5F
	2357		
30 M		0317	3.1E
	0634	0916	1.6F
	1226	1542	3.3E
	1904	2120	1.4F
31 Tu	0038	0350	2.9E
	0721	0958	1.5F
	1303	1610	3.1E
	1947	2200	1.3F

Time meridian 75° W. 0000 is midnight. 1200 is noon. Times are not adjusted for Daylight Saving Time.

Wilmington (USS North Carolina), North Carolina 2019

F–Flood, Dir. 000° True   E–Ebb, Dir. 179° True

January

Day	Slack	Maximum	knots
1 Tu	0126	0447	2.1F
	0703	1056	2.2E
	1411	1703	1.4F
	1900	2255	2.0E
2 W	0215	0536	2.2F
	0758	1149	2.2E
	1506	1752	1.4F
	1948	2336	2.1E
3 Th	0302	0624	2.3F
	0850	1240	2.2E
	1556	1840	1.3F
	2036		
4 F		0012	2.2E
	0347	0710	2.3F
	0939	1329	2.2E
	1643	1929	1.3F
	2125		
5 Sa ●		0045	2.2E
	0429	0754	2.3F
	1023	1414	2.2E
	1727	2016	1.3F
	2213		
6 Su		0123	2.1E
	0511	0834	2.2F
	1105	1455	2.2E
	1810	2058	1.2F
	2300		
7 M		0202	2.1E
	0553	0905	2.0F
	1144	1529	2.2E
	1852	2133	1.2F
	2347		
8 Tu		0238	2.0E
	0635	0928	1.8F
	1223	1549	2.1E
	1932	2158	1.1F
9 W	0033	0315	1.8E
	0719	0953	1.6F
	1302	1553	2.0E
	2012	2222	1.0F
10 Th	0118	0354	1.7E
	0804	1025	1.5F
	1341	1622	1.9E
	2053	2255	1.0F
11 F	0202	0436	1.7E
	0850	1105	1.3F
	1422	1702	1.9E
	2135	2337	0.9F
12 Sa	0247	0521	1.6E
	0937	1151	1.2F
	1504	1746	1.8E
	2221		
13 Su		0025	0.9F
	0334	0608	1.6E
	1026	1241	1.1F
	1549	1832	1.9E
	2310		
14 M ◑		0117	1.0F
	0425	0654	1.6E
	1118	1332	1.1F
	1636	1918	2.0E
	2358		
15 Tu		0212	1.1F
	0519	0742	1.7E
	1212	1427	1.1F
	1724	2006	2.1E
16 W	0046	0312	1.3F
	0615	0833	1.7E
	1310	1527	1.1F
	1813	2057	2.2E
17 Th	0134	0413	1.6F
	0712	0930	1.8E
	1412	1629	1.1F
	1905	2151	2.4E
18 F	0222	0509	1.9F
	0810	1031	1.9E
	1515	1729	1.2F
	1959	2246	2.5E
19 Sa	0311	0602	2.2F
	0907	1132	2.0E
	1616	1830	1.2F
	2056	2340	2.5E
20 Su	0400	0656	2.5F
	1001	1233	2.1E
	1713	1934	1.3F
	2153		
21 M ○		0035	2.6E
	0451	0751	2.6F
	1053	1338	2.3E
	1807	2033	1.4F
	2250		
22 Tu		0134	2.6E
	0545	0844	2.7F
	1144	1444	2.3E
	1858	2128	1.5F
	2347		
23 W		0234	2.5E
	0641	0936	2.6F
	1235	1534	2.3E
	1947	2222	1.6F
24 Th	0045	0335	2.5E
	0740	1030	2.3F
	1327	1626	2.2E
	2036	2323	1.6F
25 F	0144	0442	2.4E
	0839	1132	2.0F
	1419	1801	2.1E
	2127		
26 Sa		0030	1.7F
	0244	0612	2.3E
	0940	1241	1.8F
	1511	1855	2.0E
	2220		
27 Su ◐		0133	1.7F
	0345	0720	2.2E
	1043	1346	1.6F
	1603	1939	2.0E
	2315		
28 M		0232	1.8F
	0445	0820	2.1E
	1145	1447	1.4F
	1654	2019	2.0E
29 Tu	0009	0330	1.9F
	0544	0924	2.0E
	1243	1544	1.4F
	1742	2113	2.1E
30 W	0100	0423	2.0F
	0639	1026	1.9E
	1339	1637	1.3F
	1830	2216	2.1E
31 Th	0149	0512	2.1F
	0731	1120	1.9E
	1433	1726	1.3F
	1918	2304	2.1E

February

Day	Slack	Maximum	knots
1 F	0235	0557	2.1F
	0821	1209	2.0E
	1524	1813	1.2F
	2008	2346	2.1E
2 Sa	0320	0642	2.1F
	0908	1257	2.0E
	1610	1901	1.2F
	2059		
3 Su		0026	2.1E
	0404	0724	2.0F
	0951	1342	2.1E
	1654	1948	1.2F
	2148		
4 M ●		0107	2.1E
	0447	0803	1.9F
	1032	1422	2.1E
	1735	2028	1.2F
	2234		
5 Tu		0140	2.0E
	0529	0834	1.8F
	1112	1453	2.0E
	1814	2056	1.2F
	2318		
6 W		0210	2.0E
	0612	0856	1.7F
	1150	1443	1.9E
	1853	2114	1.2F
	2358		
7 Th		0243	1.9E
	0655	0923	1.6F
	1229	1506	1.9E
	1932	2139	1.1F
8 F	0037	0318	1.9E
	0736	0955	1.5F
	1308	1541	1.9E
	2013	2213	1.1F
9 Sa	0116	0357	1.9E
	0818	1034	1.4F
	1348	1623	1.9E
	2056	2256	1.0F
10 Su	0158	0441	1.8E
	0901	1118	1.3F
	1430	1710	1.9E
	2143	2346	1.0F
11 M	0248	0530	1.8E
	0948	1209	1.3F
	1516	1801	2.0E
	2233		
12 Tu ◐		0043	1.1F
	0347	0622	1.8E
	1042	1303	1.2F
	1604	1851	2.1E
	2324		
13 W		0143	1.3F
	0449	0714	1.8E
	1142	1400	1.2F
	1656	1941	2.3E
14 Th	0014	0245	1.5F
	0551	0808	1.8E
	1247	1505	1.1F
	1749	2033	2.4E
15 F	0105	0351	1.8F
	0650	0908	1.8E
	1354	1616	1.2F
	1845	2129	2.4E
16 Sa	0157	0451	2.1F
	0749	1013	1.9E
	1459	1722	1.2F
	1943	2228	2.5E
17 Su	0251	0548	2.3F
	0846	1119	2.0E
	1558	1825	1.4F
	2043	2328	2.5E
18 M	0347	0645	2.5F
	0942	1226	2.1E
	1652	1927	1.5F
	2142		
19 Tu ○		0028	2.6E
	0442	0743	2.5F
	1034	1424	2.2E
	1742	2024	1.7F
	2238		
20 W		0133	2.6E
	0539	0839	2.5F
	1126	1512	2.2E
	1830	2116	1.8F
	2334		
21 Th		0241	2.6E
	0636	0931	2.4F
	1216	1553	2.1E
	1918	2207	1.8F
22 F	0029	0344	2.6E
	0732	1023	2.2F
	1306	1638	2.0E
	2006	2302	1.8F
23 Sa	0125	0451	2.5E
	0827	1120	1.9F
	1356	1737	2.0E
	2056		
24 Su		0004	1.8F
	0222	0600	2.3E
	0922	1222	1.6F
	1445	1830	2.0E
	2149		
25 M		0106	1.8F
	0320	0659	2.2E
	1019	1323	1.5F
	1534	1912	2.0E
	2244		
26 Tu ◐		0205	1.8F
	0419	0752	2.0E
	1116	1420	1.3F
	1624	1948	2.0E
	2338		
27 W		0301	1.8F
	0515	0848	1.9E
	1212	1517	1.3F
	1714	2029	2.1E
28 Th	0029	0354	1.9F
	0608	0948	1.8E
	1306	1611	1.2F
	1804	2133	2.0E

March

Day	Slack	Maximum	knots
1 F	0119	0443	1.9F
	0657	1044	1.9E
	1358	1701	1.2F
	1854	2238	2.0E
2 Sa	0207	0528	1.8F
	0744	1132	1.9E
	1447	1748	1.3F
	1945	2330	2.0E
3 Su	0255	0611	1.8F
	0830	1217	1.9E
	1532	1832	1.3F
	2036		
4 M		0016	2.0E
	0341	0652	1.7F
	0914	1259	1.9E
	1615	1914	1.3F
	2123		
5 Tu		0059	2.0E
	0426	0730	1.6F
	0957	1335	1.8E
	1654	1948	1.3F
	2207		
6 W ●		0113	2.0E
	0509	0800	1.5F
	1037	1318	1.8E
	1733	2008	1.2F
	2246		
7 Th		0135	2.0E
	0550	0825	1.5F
	1116	1348	1.8E
	1812	2032	1.2F
	2323		
8 F		0208	2.0E
	0630	0854	1.5F
	1155	1425	1.8E
	1852	2104	1.3F
	2358		
9 Sa		0244	2.1E
	0709	0928	1.5F
	1234	1506	1.9E
	1933	2141	1.3F
10 Su	0037	0324	2.1E
	0749	1006	1.5F
	1314	1550	1.9E
	2017	2225	1.3F
11 M	0123	0409	2.0E
	0832	1051	1.5F
	1357	1638	2.0E
	2104	2317	1.3F
12 Tu	0219	0500	2.0E
	0922	1142	1.4F
	1445	1731	2.1E
	2154		
13 W		0015	1.4F
	0320	0556	1.9E
	1021	1241	1.3F
	1537	1825	2.2E
	2247		
14 Th ◐		0117	1.5F
	0425	0652	1.9E
	1127	1344	1.2F
	1634	1918	2.3E
	2342		
15 F		0221	1.7F
	0528	0749	2.0E
	1234	1456	1.2F
	1733	2013	2.4E
16 Sa	0039	0329	1.9F
	0627	0848	2.0E
	1339	1614	1.3F
	1833	2112	2.4E
17 Su	0137	0436	2.1F
	0726	0954	2.0E
	1439	1719	1.4F
	1933	2218	2.4E
18 M	0238	0537	2.2F
	0823	1107	2.0E
	1534	1818	1.6F
	2033	2328	2.5E
19 Tu	0339	0636	2.3F
	0920	1308	2.0E
	1625	1915	1.8F
	2131		
20 W ○		0044	2.6E
	0437	0736	2.3F
	1014	1408	2.0E
	1713	2010	2.0F
	2226		
21 Th		0204	2.7E
	0534	0832	2.3F
	1104	1456	2.0E
	1800	2100	2.1F
	2319		
22 F		0302	2.7E
	0628	0923	2.1F
	1153	1537	2.0E
	1847	2149	2.1F
23 Sa	0012	0353	2.7E
	0721	1011	2.0F
	1241	1611	2.0E
	1935	2239	2.0F
24 Su	0106	0445	2.5E
	0811	1101	1.7F
	1328	1645	1.9E
	2024	2336	1.9F
25 M	0200	0541	2.3E
	0901	1158	1.5F
	1415	1742	2.0E
	2115		
26 Tu		0035	1.8F
	0254	0635	2.1E
	0953	1256	1.3F
	1504	1832	2.0E
	2207		
27 W ◐		0132	1.7F
	0348	0723	2.0E
	1047	1354	1.2F
	1555	1915	2.0E
	2301		
28 Th		0227	1.7F
	0441	0809	1.9E
	1141	1451	1.2F
	1649	1959	1.9E
	2354		
29 F		0320	1.6F
	0530	0858	1.9E
	1232	1546	1.2F
	1742	2059	1.9E
30 Sa	0046	0410	1.5F
	0617	0954	1.8E
	1321	1636	1.3F
	1833	2216	1.9E
31 Su	0138	0456	1.5F
	0702	1044	1.8E
	1407	1721	1.3F
	1923	2313	1.9E

Time meridian 75° W. 0000 is midnight. 1200 is noon. Times are not adjusted for Daylight Saving Time.

Wilmington (USS North Carolina), North Carolina 2019

F–Flood, Dir. 000° True   E–Ebb, Dir. 179° True

April

Day	Slack (h m)	Maximum (h m)	knots
1 M	0229	0538	1.4F
	0748	1123	1.8E
	1451	1801	1.3F
	2011		
2 Tu		0000	1.9E
	0319	0617	1.3F
	0833	1123	1.7E
	1533	1833	1.3F
	2056		
3 W		0037	1.9E
	0404	0650	1.3F
	0918	1149	1.7E
	1613	1855	1.3F
	2137		
4 Th		0028	1.9E
	0446	0719	1.3F
	1000	1225	1.7E
	1653	1920	1.3F
	2214		
5 F ●		0056	2.0E
	0525	0749	1.4F
	1040	1305	1.8E
	1732	1955	1.4F
	2251		
6 Sa		0132	2.1E
	0603	0824	1.4F
	1119	1349	1.9E
	1813	2034	1.5F
	2330		
7 Su		0213	2.2E
	0643	0901	1.5F
	1158	1433	2.0E
	1856	2116	1.5F
8 M	0013	0257	2.2E
	0726	0942	1.5F
	1240	1520	2.1E
	1940	2202	1.6F
9 Tu	0104	0345	2.2E
	0814	1025	1.4F
	1326	1609	2.2E
	2027	2253	1.7F
10 W	0200	0438	2.1E
	0909	1123	1.3F
	1418	1703	2.2E
	2117	2351	1.8F
11 Th	0301	0536	2.1E
	1011	1226	1.2F
	1516	1800	2.2E
	2213		
12 F ◐		0053	1.8F
	0403	0635	2.1E
	1117	1337	1.2F
	1619	1858	2.2E
	2314		
13 Sa		0159	1.9F
	0504	0732	2.1E
	1221	1457	1.3F
	1723	1957	2.3E
14 Su	0018	0311	1.9F
	0604	0830	2.1E
	1320	1611	1.5F
	1824	2102	2.3E
15 M	0124	0424	2.0F
	0702	0934	2.0E
	1415	1711	1.7F
	1924	2227	2.4E
16 Tu	0229	0527	2.0F
	0759	1136	2.0E
	1507	1805	1.9F
	2022		
17 W		0001	2.5E
	0332	0627	2.1F
	0855	1246	2.0E
	1556	1859	2.1F
	2119		
18 Th		0109	2.7E
	0431	0725	2.0F
	0949	1343	2.0E
	1644	1952	2.2F
	2213		
19 F ○		0208	2.7E
	0525	0819	2.0F
	1038	1431	2.0E
	1731	2042	2.3F
	2305		
20 Sa		0258	2.7E
	0617	0908	1.9F
	1125	1508	2.0E
	1818	2130	2.3F
	2356		
21 Su		0344	2.6E
	0706	0953	1.7F
	1210	1531	2.0E
	1904	2216	2.2F
22 M	0046	0430	2.5E
	0753	1039	1.5F
	1256	1555	2.0E
	1951	2305	2.0F
23 Tu	0136	0518	2.3E
	0840	1130	1.4F
	1344	1639	2.0E
	2038	2357	1.8F
24 W	0225	0607	2.2E
	0928	1229	1.2F
	1435	1739	1.9E
	2128		
25 Th		0052	1.7F
	0314	0651	2.1E
	1018	1327	1.2F
	1529	1842	1.8E
	2220		
26 F ◑		0144	1.5F
	0401	0728	2.0E
	1109	1424	1.2F
	1625	1934	1.8E
	2316		
27 Sa		0236	1.3F
	0448	0757	1.9E
	1158	1518	1.2F
	1719	2029	1.7E
28 Su	0012	0329	1.2F
	0534	0823	1.9E
	1243	1608	1.3F
	1810	2148	1.7E
29 M	0108	0418	1.1F
	0620	0858	1.8E
	1327	1651	1.3F
	1857	2248	1.7E
30 Tu	0201	0500	1.1F
	0705	0939	1.7E
	1411	1724	1.3F
	1941	2332	1.7E

May

Day	Slack (h m)	Maximum (h m)	knots
1 W	0251	0534	1.0F
	0751	1022	1.7E
	1453	1745	1.3F
	2024	2318	1.8E
2 Th	0336	0601	1.1F
	0836	1104	1.7E
	1536	1808	1.3F
	2105	2343	1.9E
3 F	0417	0633	1.1F
	0920	1146	1.8E
	1617	1844	1.4F
	2146		
4 Sa ●		0019	2.0E
	0457	0711	1.3F
	1001	1230	1.9E
	1657	1926	1.6F
	2227		
5 Su		0101	2.1E
	0538	0753	1.4F
	1041	1316	2.1E
	1738	2011	1.7F
	2311		
6 M		0147	2.2E
	0622	0837	1.4F
	1123	1404	2.2E
	1820	2056	1.9F
	2359		
7 Tu		0236	2.3E
	0711	0923	1.4F
	1208	1452	2.3E
	1905	2142	2.1F
8 W	0050	0326	2.3E
	0804	1012	1.3F
	1259	1543	2.3E
	1954	2233	2.1F
9 Th	0146	0420	2.3E
	0902	1110	1.2F
	1357	1639	2.3E
	2047	2330	2.1F
10 F	0243	0519	2.3E
	1002	1220	1.2F
	1500	1740	2.2E
	2147		
11 Sa ◐		0034	2.0F
	0342	0619	2.2E
	1104	1338	1.3F
	1606	1844	2.2E
	2254		
12 Su		0143	1.9F
	0442	0716	2.2E
	1202	1454	1.5F
	1711	1948	2.2E
13 M	0004	0259	1.9F
	0541	0812	2.1E
	1257	1600	1.7F
	1812	2106	2.3E
14 Tu	0113	0413	1.8F
	0638	0914	2.0E
	1349	1657	1.9F
	1911	2258	2.4E
15 W	0220	0516	1.8F
	0734	1124	1.9E
	1440	1750	2.1F
	2009		
16 Th		0003	2.5E
	0322	0612	1.8F
	0828	1220	2.0E
	1530	1842	2.3F
	2105		
17 F		0101	2.6E
	0419	0707	1.8F
	0919	1311	2.0E
	1618	1934	2.4F
	2158		
18 Sa ○		0156	2.6E
	0511	0759	1.7F
	1007	1356	2.1E
	1704	2023	2.4F
	2249		
19 Su		0245	2.6E
	0600	0847	1.6F
	1053	1429	2.1E
	1749	2109	2.4F
	2338		
20 M		0329	2.5E
	0647	0931	1.5F
	1138	1450	2.1E
	1833	2151	2.3F
21 Tu	0024	0410	2.4E
	0732	1015	1.4F
	1225	1521	2.1E
	1918	2231	2.1F
22 W	0110	0451	2.3E
	0816	1102	1.3F
	1314	1604	2.0E
	2003	2312	1.8F
23 Th	0153	0533	2.2E
	0901	1158	1.2F
	1407	1657	1.8E
	2051	2355	1.6F
24 F	0237	0612	2.1E
	0947	1257	1.1F
	1502	1803	1.7E
	2142		
25 Sa		0043	1.3F
	0321	0641	2.0E
	1034	1352	1.1F
	1557	1902	1.6E
	2238		
26 Su ◑		0131	1.1F
	0407	0704	2.0E
	1121	1444	1.1F
	1650	1945	1.6E
	2336		
27 M		0220	1.0F
	0453	0735	1.9E
	1206	1532	1.1F
	1739	2019	1.5E
28 Tu	0032	0312	0.9F
	0538	0812	1.8E
	1250	1611	1.1F
	1823	2057	1.5E
29 W	0124	0357	0.9F
	0623	0853	1.7E
	1334	1637	1.2F
	1906	2138	1.6E
30 Th	0212	0434	0.9F
	0708	0939	1.8E
	1418	1659	1.2F
	1950	2220	1.6E
31 F	0259	0511	1.0F
	0752	1027	1.8E
	1502	1734	1.4F
	2035	2303	1.8E

June

Day	Slack (h m)	Maximum (h m)	knots
1 Sa	0344	0552	1.1F
	0836	1113	2.0E
	1544	1816	1.6F
	2122	2348	1.9E
2 Su	0429	0638	1.2F
	0921	1200	2.2E
	1625	1902	1.8F
	2209		
3 M ●		0036	2.0E
	0517	0727	1.2F
	1006	1247	2.3E
	1707	1950	2.1F
	2257		
4 Tu		0126	2.2E
	0607	0818	1.3F
	1053	1337	2.4E
	1750	2038	2.3F
	2346		
5 W		0219	2.3E
	0701	0909	1.3F
	1143	1429	2.4E
	1838	2126	2.4F
6 Th	0037	0311	2.4E
	0755	1002	1.3F
	1240	1523	2.4E
	1930	2216	2.4F
7 F	0130	0405	2.4E
	0850	1102	1.3F
	1341	1620	2.3E
	2028	2313	2.2F
8 Sa	0225	0503	2.3E
	0946	1215	1.3F
	1446	1724	2.2E
	2131		
9 Su	0323	0604	2.2F
	1043	1332	1.4F
	1552	1835	2.2E
	2240		
10 M ◐		0132	1.9F
	0421	0703	2.2E
	1139	1441	1.6F
	1656	1949	2.2E
	2351		
11 Tu		0249	1.8F
	0519	0758	2.1E
	1233	1544	1.9F
	1757	2130	2.2E
12 W	0100	0359	1.7F
	0614	0900	2.0E
	1325	1640	2.1F
	1856	2249	2.3E
13 Th	0205	0459	1.6F
	0706	1102	2.0E
	1416	1732	2.3F
	1953	2349	2.4E
14 F	0306	0552	1.6F
	0757	1150	2.0E
	1506	1823	2.4F
	2049		
15 Sa		0044	2.4E
	0401	0644	1.5F
	0846	1233	2.1E
	1553	1913	2.5F
	2142		
16 Su		0137	2.4E
	0451	0735	1.5F
	0934	1312	2.2E
	1638	2001	2.5F
	2231		
17 M ○		0225	2.4E
	0538	0823	1.4F
	1021	1346	2.2E
	1721	2045	2.4F
	2316		
18 Tu ●		0307	2.4E
	0623	0908	1.4F
	1108	1419	2.2E
	1804	2124	2.3F
	2358		
19 W		0345	2.4E
	0706	0950	1.3F
	1157	1456	2.1E
	1847	2158	2.1F
20 Th	0040	0420	2.3E
	0748	1032	1.2F
	1247	1537	1.9E
	1932	2227	1.8F
21 F	0120	0450	2.2E
	0830	1117	1.2F
	1338	1623	1.8E
	2019	2258	1.5F
22 Sa	0201	0512	2.1E
	0913	1209	1.1F
	1430	1715	1.7E
	2108	2337	1.3F
23 Su	0244	0541	2.0E
	0957	1300	1.0F
	1521	1807	1.6E
	2201		
24 M		0023	1.1F
	0328	0617	1.9E
	1043	1340	1.0F
	1610	1848	1.5E
	2255		
25 Tu ◑		0110	1.0F
	0414	0656	1.8E
	1130	1407	1.0F
	1658	1925	1.5E
	2348		
26 W		0157	0.9F
	0459	0735	1.8E
	1216	1445	1.0F
	1744	2004	1.5E
27 Th	0038	0246	0.9F
	0543	0818	1.9E
	1301	1533	1.1F
	1830	2048	1.5E
28 F	0128	0338	0.9F
	0626	0904	1.9E
	1346	1620	1.3F
	1918	2137	1.6E
29 Sa	0219	0430	1.0F
	0710	0954	2.1E
	1430	1706	1.5F
	2008	2229	1.7E
30 Su	0312	0520	1.1F
	0757	1044	2.2E
	1513	1753	1.8F
	2100	2322	1.8E

Time meridian 75° W. 0000 is midnight. 1200 is noon. Times are not adjusted for Daylight Saving Time.

Wilmington (USS North Carolina), North Carolina 2019

F–Flood, Dir. 000° True   E–Ebb, Dir. 179° True

July

Day	Slack h m	Max h m	knots
1 M	0406	0612	1.1F
	0847	1133	2.4E
	1557	1841	2.1F
	2151		
2 Tu ●		0014	2.0E
	0500	0708	1.2F
	0939	1224	2.5E
	1641	1932	2.4F
	2241		
3 W		0109	2.2E
	0554	0805	1.3F
	1032	1316	2.5E
	1729	2023	2.5F
	2331		
4 Th		0204	2.3E
	0647	0900	1.3F
	1127	1412	2.5E
	1820	2113	2.6F
5 F	0022	0258	2.4E
	0739	0954	1.4F
	1226	1508	2.5E
	1917	2204	2.5F
6 Sa	0114	0350	2.4E
	0831	1054	1.4F
	1327	1607	2.4E
	2016	2302	2.3F
7 Su	0209	0447	2.2E
	0924	1205	1.5F
	1430	1714	2.3E
	2120		
8 M		0010	2.0F
	0304	0551	2.1E
	1018	1317	1.6F
	1534	1835	2.2E
	2227		
9 Tu ◗		0124	1.8F
	0401	0656	2.1E
	1114	1423	1.7F
	1637	1957	2.2E
	2335		
10 W		0235	1.6F
	0456	0752	2.0E
	1209	1524	1.9F
	1739	2118	2.1E
11 Th	0041	0340	1.6F
	0547	0917	2.0E
	1302	1621	2.1F
	1837	2229	2.1E
12 F	0143	0437	1.5F
	0637	1031	2.1E
	1353	1713	2.3F
	1934	2328	2.1E
13 Sa	0242	0529	1.4F
	0725	1118	2.1E
	1442	1802	2.4F
	2028		
14 Su		0021	2.2E
	0336	0619	1.3F
	0814	1158	2.2E
	1528	1849	2.4F
	2119		
15 M		0111	2.2E
	0425	0709	1.3F
	0904	1237	2.2E
	1612	1936	2.4F
	2205		
16 Tu O	0510	0758	2.2E
	0954	1320	1.3F
	1655	2018	2.3F
	2248		
17 W		0239	2.3E
	0553	0843	1.3F
	1043	1404	2.1E
	1738	2056	2.1F
	2328		
18 Th		0315	2.2E
	0634	0924	1.3F
	1131	1440	2.1E
	1822	2127	1.9F
19 F	0008	0344	2.2E
	0714	0958	1.3F
	1219	1514	2.0E
	1907	2152	1.7F
20 Sa	0048	0354	2.1E
	0754	1023	1.2F
	1305	1550	1.9E
	1952	2220	1.5F
21 Su	0128	0415	2.0E
	0835	1050	1.1F
	1351	1629	1.7E
	2038	2256	1.3F
22 M	0210	0451	1.9E
	0918	1127	1.0F
	1436	1712	1.6E
	2125	2339	1.2F
23 Tu	0253	0534	1.8E
	1005	1212	0.9F
	1522	1756	1.6E
	2212		
24 W ◑		0025	1.1F
	0337	0618	1.8E
	1053	1301	0.9F
	1611	1840	1.6E
	2302		
25 Th		0113	1.0F
	0420	0702	1.9E
	1141	1352	1.0F
	1702	1924	1.6E
	2353		
26 F		0203	1.0F
	0504	0747	2.0E
	1227	1447	1.1F
	1755	2011	1.6E
27 Sa	0048	0258	1.0F
	0549	0834	2.1E
	1313	1546	1.4F
	1848	2103	1.6E
28 Su	0146	0358	1.0F
	0637	0925	2.3E
	1358	1640	1.7F
	1943	2201	1.7E
29 M	0247	0457	1.0F
	0728	1018	2.4E
	1445	1731	2.0F
	2038	2259	1.9E
30 Tu	0346	0555	1.1F
	0824	1112	2.5E
	1533	1823	2.3F
	2131	2355	2.0E
31 W ●	0442	0656	1.2F
	0922	1206	2.5E
	1624	1917	2.5F
	2223		

August

Day	Slack h m	Max h m	knots
1 Th		0052	2.2E
	0535	0756	1.4F
	1019	1302	2.6E
	1716	2012	2.6F
	2314		
2 F		0149	2.3E
	0626	0852	1.5F
	1116	1401	2.6E
	1812	2104	2.6F
3 Sa	0005	0245	2.3E
	0716	0945	1.6F
	1213	1500	2.6E
	1910	2157	2.4F
4 Su	0058	0337	2.2E
	0806	1042	1.6F
	1311	1601	2.5E
	2009	2255	2.2F
5 M	0151	0433	2.1E
	0857	1148	1.6F
	1412	1712	2.4E
	2109		
6 Tu		0002	1.9F
	0245	0552	2.0E
	0951	1257	1.7F
	1513	1841	2.3E
	2211		
7 W ◗		0112	1.7F
	0338	0709	2.0E
	1047	1401	1.8F
	1616	1949	2.2E
	2315		
8 Th		0216	1.5F
	0429	0754	2.0E
	1143	1501	1.9F
	1717	2055	2.0E
9 F	0017	0317	1.4F
	0519	0844	2.1E
	1236	1558	2.1F
	1815	2202	2.0E
10 Sa	0117	0414	1.3F
	0608	0953	2.1E
	1327	1649	2.2F
	1909	2300	2.0E
11 Su	0213	0505	1.3F
	0657	1048	2.2E
	1416	1737	2.2F
	2000	2351	2.0E
12 M	0305	0554	1.3F
	0748	1135	2.2E
	1503	1822	2.2F
	2048		
13 Tu		0038	2.0E
	0352	0643	1.3F
	0840	1221	2.2E
	1549	1907	2.1F
	2133		
14 W		0122	2.1E
	0435	0731	1.4F
	0931	1310	2.2E
	1633	1950	2.0F
	2215		
15 Th O		0204	2.1E
	0515	0815	1.4F
	1020	1356	2.1E
	1717	2028	1.9F
	2256		
16 F		0240	2.1E
	0555	0852	1.4F
	1105	1430	2.1E
	1801	2059	1.7F
	2336		
17 Sa		0258	2.0E
	0635	0916	1.3F
	1148	1448	2.0E
	1844	2122	1.6F
18 Su	0016	0302	1.9E
	0715	0935	1.2F
	1228	1515	2.0E
	1927	2149	1.5F
19 M	0057	0332	1.8E
	0756	1003	1.1F
	1308	1549	1.9E
	2008	2223	1.4F
20 Tu	0137	0410	1.8E
	0839	1041	1.1F
	1348	1628	1.8E
	2049	2303	1.3F
21 W	0217	0454	1.8E
	0925	1126	1.0F
	1434	1713	1.7E
	2133	2348	1.2F
22 Th	0259	0542	1.9E
	1013	1219	1.0F
	1526	1801	1.7E
	2223		
23 F O		0039	1.1F
	0342	0630	2.0E
	1101	1315	1.1F
	1624	1851	1.7E
	2319		
24 Sa		0132	1.1F
	0430	0718	2.1E
	1150	1413	1.3F
	1723	1942	1.7E
25 Su	0020	0231	1.0F
	0521	0807	2.3E
	1238	1514	1.6F
	1820	2037	1.8E
26 M	0123	0337	1.0F
	0615	0900	2.3E
	1329	1615	1.9F
	1917	2136	1.8E
27 Tu	0226	0445	1.1F
	0712	0957	2.4E
	1422	1712	2.1F
	2013	2237	2.0E
28 W	0325	0547	1.3F
	0812	1056	2.5E
	1517	1809	2.3F
	2109	2336	2.1E
29 Th	0419	0648	1.4F
	0912	1155	2.6E
	1614	1907	2.4F
	2203		
30 F ●		0034	2.1E
	0510	0748	1.6F
	1009	1256	2.6E
	1710	2005	2.4F
	2256		
31 Sa		0135	2.1E
	0559	0842	1.8F
	1104	1400	2.7E
	1807	2100	2.4F
	2348		

September

Day	Slack h m	Max h m	knots
1 Su		0236	2.1E
	0648	0934	1.9F
	1159	1504	2.7E
	1904	2153	2.3F
2 M	0039	0328	2.1E
	0738	1027	1.9F
	1255	1606	2.6E
	2000	2247	2.0F
3 Tu	0130	0421	2.0E
	0829	1128	1.8F
	1353	1722	2.4E
	2056	2349	1.8F
4 W	0220	0554	2.0E
	0921	1234	1.8F
	1453	1833	2.3E
	2153		
5 Th ◗		0053	1.6F
	0310	0649	2.0E
	1017	1336	1.8F
	1553	1931	2.1E
	2252		
6 F		0154	1.4F
	0401	0730	2.0E
	1112	1434	1.9F
	1651	2027	2.0E
	2351		
7 Sa		0253	1.3F
	0452	0812	2.1E
	1206	1529	1.9F
	1745	2126	1.9E
8 Su	0047	0350	1.3F
	0544	0913	2.1E
	1258	1621	1.9F
	1835	2223	1.9E
9 M	0138	0442	1.3F
	0635	1022	2.1E
	1348	1708	1.9F
	1923	2312	1.9E
10 Tu	0227	0530	1.4F
	0728	1118	2.1E
	1438	1753	1.8F
	2009	2356	1.9E
11 W	0312	0616	1.4F
	0820	1208	2.1E
	1527	1837	1.7F
	2054		
12 Th		0038	1.9E
	0354	0700	1.5F
	0909	1256	2.1E
	1614	1921	1.6F
	2139		
13 F O		0118	1.9E
	0435	0741	1.4F
	0955	1342	2.1E
	1658	2000	1.5F
	2222		
14 Sa		0141	1.8E
	0515	0812	1.4F
	1037	1411	2.1E
	1740	2029	1.5F
	2303		
15 Su		0143	1.8E
	0555	0831	1.3F
	1115	1410	2.1E
	1821	2052	1.5F
	2343		
16 M		0216	1.8E
	0635	0856	1.3F
	1151	1438	2.0E
	1900	2119	1.4F
17 Tu	0022	0253	1.8E
	0717	0928	1.3F
	1229	1513	2.0E
	1939	2152	1.4F
18 W	0100	0333	1.9E
	0759	1007	1.3F
	1310	1553	1.9E
	2019	2232	1.3F
19 Th	0139	0418	1.9E
	0843	1053	1.3F
	1358	1639	1.9E
	2105	2318	1.3F
20 F	0221	0507	2.0E
	0929	1146	1.3F
	1454	1731	1.9E
	2157		
21 Sa O		0011	1.2F
	0309	0559	2.1E
	1019	1244	1.4F
	1554	1825	1.9E
	2258		
22 Su		0111	1.1F
	0403	0651	2.2E
	1111	1343	1.6F
	1654	1919	1.9E
23 M	0002	0215	1.1F
	0502	0744	2.2E
	1207	1446	1.7F
	1753	2014	2.0E
24 Tu	0105	0329	1.1F
	0603	0844	2.3E
	1305	1553	1.9F
	1851	2113	2.0E
25 W	0204	0441	1.3F
	0703	0942	2.3E
	1406	1658	2.1F
	1948	2215	2.0E
26 Th	0300	0541	1.5F
	0803	1049	2.4E
	1508	1759	2.2F
	2046	2317	2.0E
27 F	0353	0639	1.7F
	0901	1156	2.6E
	1608	1900	2.2F
	2143		
28 Sa ●		0018	2.0E
	0442	0736	1.9F
	0958	1311	2.7E
	1705	2000	2.2F
	2236		
29 Su		0132	2.0E
	0531	0830	2.0F
	1052	1427	2.7E
	1801	2054	2.2F
	2327		
30 M		0258	2.0E
	0620	0920	2.1F
	1146	1524	2.7E
	1856	2144	2.0F

Time meridian 75° W. 0000 is midnight. 1200 is noon. Times are not adjusted for Daylight Saving Time.

Wilmington (USS North Carolina), North Carolina 2019

F–Flood, Dir. 000° True   E–Ebb, Dir. 179° True

October

Day	Slack	Maximum	knots	Day	Slack	Maximum	knots
1 Tu	0016	0329	2.0E	**16 W**		0216	1.9E
	0709	1011	2.1F		0638	0900	1.5F
	1240	1618	2.6E		1201	1441	2.1E
	1948	2235	1.8F		1913	2124	1.4F
2 W	0104	0403	2.0E	**17 Th**	0019	0259	2.0E
	0759	1106	2.0F		0719	0941	1.6F
	1335	1717	2.4E		1245	1525	2.1E
	2040	2330	1.6F		1958	2206	1.3F
3 Th	0152	0455	2.0E	**18 F**	0100	0345	2.1E
	0849	1206	1.9F		0802	1027	1.7F
	1431	1816	2.2E		1335	1613	2.1E
	2133				2047	2254	1.2F
4 F		0031	1.4F	**19 Sa**	0148	0435	2.1E
	0241	0606	2.0E		0848	1118	1.7F
	0942	1305	1.9F		1430	1707	2.1E
	1525	1907	2.1E		2143	2352	1.1F
	2228						
5 Sa		0131	1.3F	**20 Su**	0243	0530	2.1E
	0333	0658	2.0E		0940	1217	1.8F
	1036	1401	1.8F		1528	1803	2.1E
	1618	1953	2.0E		2245		
	2323						
6 Su		0229	1.3F	**21 M**		0057	1.1F
	0427	0746	2.0E		0345	0628	2.2E
	1131	1455	1.7F		1039	1318	1.8F
	1708	2039	1.9E		1628	1859	2.1E
					2346		
7 M	0014	0325	1.3F	**22 Tu**		0209	1.2F
	0523	0845	1.9E		0450	0726	2.2E
	1226	1548	1.6F		1143	1424	1.8F
	1756	2130	1.9E		1728	1954	2.1E
8 Tu	0101	0417	1.4F	**23 W**	0045	0327	1.3F
	0616	0959	1.9E		0553	0826	2.2E
	1320	1637	1.5F		1249	1537	1.9F
	1842	2221	1.9E		1826	2051	2.1E
9 W	0147	0504	1.5F	**24 Th**	0141	0435	1.6F
	0708	1059	1.9E		0653	0934	2.3E
	1414	1723	1.4F		1355	1648	1.9F
	1928	2305	1.8E		1925	2154	2.0E
10 Th	0231	0547	1.5F	**25 F**	0235	0532	1.8F
	0757	1150	2.0E		0752	1100	2.4E
	1505	1806	1.3F		1500	1751	2.0F
	2014	2334	1.8E		2023	2301	2.0E
11 F	0314	0627	1.5F	**26 Sa**	0327	0627	2.0F
	0843	1236	2.0E		0850	1227	2.6E
	1553	1848	1.3F		1601	1851	2.0F
	2101	2346	1.7E		2119		
12 Sa	0356	0700	1.4F	**27 Su**		0010	2.0E
	0926	1316	2.0E		0417	0722	2.2F
	1636	1924	1.3F		0946	1336	2.7E
	2146				1658	1949	2.0F
					2211		
13 Su		0017	1.7E	**28 M**		0155	2.0E
	0437	0723	1.4F		0505	0815	2.3F
	1006	1308	2.0E		1040	1434	2.7E
	1716	1950	1.3F		1752	2042	1.9F
	2227				2300		
14 M		0054	1.7E	**29 Tu**		0240	2.1E
	0517	0749	1.4F		0553	0905	2.4F
	1044	1327	2.0E		1133	1524	2.7E
	1754	2016	1.3F		1844	2130	1.8F
	2305				2346		
15 Tu		0134	1.8E	**30 W**		0307	2.1E
	0557	0822	1.4F		0641	0953	2.3F
	1121	1402	2.0E		1225	1612	2.5E
	1833	2048	1.4F		1934	2217	1.6F
	2342						
				31 Th	0033	0333	2.1E
					0728	1041	2.2F
					1316	1702	2.4E
					2023	2308	1.4F

November

Day	Slack	Maximum	knots	Day	Slack	Maximum	knots
1 F	0121	0415	2.0E	**16 Sa**	0028	0317	2.3E
	0816	1133	2.0F		0726	1004	2.1F
	1405	1751	2.3E		1317	1552	2.3E
	2112				2035	2237	1.2F
2 Sa		0006	1.3F	**17 Su**	0123	0409	2.2E
	0212	0512	1.9E		0816	1056	2.1F
	0905	1227	1.8F		1410	1646	2.3E
	1453	1837	2.2E		2131	2338	1.1F
	2201						
3 Su		0106	1.2F	**18 M**	0225	0507	2.2E
	0307	0625	1.9E		0912	1154	2.0F
	0958	1322	1.6F		1507	1744	2.3E
	1541	1916	2.1E		2229		
	2250						
4 M		0203	1.3F	**19 Tu**		0050	1.2F
	0404	0724	1.8E		0331	0609	2.1E
	1055	1415	1.4F		1016	1259	1.9F
	1628	1947	2.0E		1606	1841	2.3E
	2338				2328		
5 Tu		0258	1.3F	**20 W**		0206	1.3F
	0501	0822	1.8E		0437	0712	2.2E
	1153	1510	1.3F		1126	1409	1.8F
	1714	2013	1.9E		1706	1936	2.2E
6 W	0024	0350	1.4F	**21 Th**	0024	0320	1.5F
	0554	0931	1.7E		0540	0816	2.2E
	1250	1603	1.2F		1236	1527	1.8F
	1801	2047	1.9E		1805	2033	2.1E
7 Th	0108	0436	1.4F	**22 F**	0118	0424	1.8F
	0643	1034	1.8E		0640	0943	2.3E
	1346	1650	1.1F		1344	1639	1.8F
	1847	2129	1.8E		1902	2136	2.0E
8 F	0152	0517	1.4F	**23 Sa**	0211	0520	2.0F
	0729	1124	1.8E		0739	1126	2.4E
	1437	1732	1.1F		1449	1739	1.8F
	1934	2213	1.7E		1958	2300	2.0E
9 Sa	0237	0551	1.4F	**24 Su**	0303	0613	2.2F
	0813	1207	1.8E		0837	1231	2.5E
	1524	1806	1.1F		1550	1836	1.8F
	2021	2254	1.7E		2051		
10 Su	0320	0614	1.4F	**25 M**		0031	2.0E
	0855	1225	1.8E		0353	0707	2.4F
	1606	1832	1.1F		0934	1331	2.6E
	2105	2334	1.7E		1646	1932	1.7F
					2141		
11 M	0402	0639	1.4F	**26 Tu**		0124	2.1E
	0937	1215	1.8E		0441	0759	2.5F
	1646	1902	1.1F		1027	1425	2.6E
	2145				1739	2023	1.6F
					2229		
12 Tu		0015	1.9E	**27 W**		0206	2.2E
	0442	0714	1.5F		0527	0847	2.5F
	1017	1249	1.9E		1118	1513	2.5E
	1726	1938	1.2F		1829	2111	1.5F
	2223				2315		
13 W		0058	2.0E	**28 Th**		0233	2.2E
	0521	0753	1.7F		0612	0932	2.5F
	1058	1331	2.0E		1206	1556	2.5E
	1808	2018	1.2F		1916	2157	1.4F
	2301						
14 Th		0142	2.1E	**29 F**	0003	0305	2.1E
	0600	0835	1.9F		0658	1014	2.3F
	1141	1415	2.1E		1251	1638	2.4E
	1854	2101	1.3F		2001	2244	1.3F
	2342						
15 F		0229	2.2E	**30 Sa**	0053	0347	2.0E
	0641	0918	2.0F		0744	1056	2.0F
	1227	1503	2.2E		1336	1719	2.3E
	1943	2146	1.2F		2045	2338	1.3F

December

Day	Slack	Maximum	knots	Day	Slack	Maximum	knots
1 Su	0146	0439	1.9E	**16 M**	0106	0349	2.3E
	0832	1141	1.7F		0755	1038	2.3F
	1419	1759	2.2E		1353	1627	2.4E
	2129				2113	2327	1.3F
2 M		0037	1.2F	**17 Tu**	0210	0448	2.2E
	0242	0552	1.8E		0856	1138	2.1F
	0923	1233	1.5F		1449	1725	2.3E
	1503	1833	2.1E		2209		
	2215						
3 Tu		0132	1.3F	**18 W**		0042	1.3F
	0338	0658	1.7E		0315	0554	2.2E
	1019	1326	1.2F		1002	1246	1.9F
	1548	1858	2.0E		1547	1825	2.2E
	2301				2306		
4 W		0225	1.3F	**19 Th**		0157	1.5F
	0432	0750	1.7E		0421	0703	2.2E
	1118	1421	1.1F		1112	1400	1.8F
	1636	1927	1.9E		1647	1922	2.1E
	2348						
5 Th		0316	1.3F	**20 F**	0002	0307	1.7F
	0523	0843	1.6E		0524	0815	2.2E
	1215	1517	1.0F		1222	1518	1.7F
	1723	2002	1.8E		1744	2018	2.1E
6 F	0033	0403	1.3F	**21 Sa**	0056	0409	1.9F
	0610	0949	1.6E		0625	1006	2.2E
	1309	1607	0.9F		1330	1625	1.7F
	1809	2043	1.8E		1838	2124	2.0E
7 Sa	0119	0442	1.3F	**22 Su**	0150	0505	2.2F
	0655	1044	1.6E		0725	1119	2.3E
	1359	1642	0.9F		1434	1723	1.6F
	1854	2127	1.7E		1930	2318	2.1E
8 Su	0204	0510	1.3F	**23 M**	0241	0557	2.4F
	0739	1022	1.6E		0823	1219	2.3E
	1446	1708	0.9F		1534	1817	1.5F
	1937	2213	1.8E		2020		
9 M	0248	0531	1.3F	**24 Tu**		0005	2.2E
	0824	1055	1.6E		0330	0649	2.5F
	1531	1740	0.9F		0919	1316	2.4E
	2019	2257	1.9E		1629	1910	1.5F
					2110		
10 Tu	0329	0604	1.5F	**25 W**		0048	2.2E
	0909	1134	1.7E		0417	0739	2.6F
	1616	1820	1.0F		1011	1407	2.4E
	2101	2341	2.1E		1720	2002	1.4F
					2159		
11 W	0408	0644	1.7F	**26 Th**		0130	2.2E
	0953	1217	1.8E		0502	0825	2.6F
	1701	1904	1.1F		1058	1452	2.4E
	2143				1806	2050	1.4F
					2247		
12 Th		0026	2.2E	**27 F**		0210	2.2E
	0447	0728	2.0F		0546	0908	2.4F
	1038	1304	2.0E		1141	1532	2.4E
	1748	1953	1.1F		1850	2134	1.4F
	2227				2337		
13 F		0113	2.3E	**28 Sa**		0248	2.2E
	0527	0813	2.2F		0630	0946	2.2F
	1122	1353	2.2E		1223	1607	2.3E
	1837	2042	1.2F		1931	2218	1.4F
	2314						
14 Sa		0203	2.4E	**29 Su**	0027	0328	2.0E
	0611	0859	2.3F		0716	1020	2.0F
	1209	1443	2.3E		1304	1639	2.3E
	1928	2132	1.2F		2012	2304	1.3F
15 Su	0007	0255	2.4E	**30 M**	0120	0414	1.9E
	0701	0946	2.4F		0804	1055	1.7F
	1259	1534	2.4E		1345	1707	2.2E
	2020	2225	1.2F		2053	2355	1.2F
				31 Tu	0212	0511	1.8E
					0853	1134	1.4F
					1428	1735	2.0E
					2137		

Time meridian 75° W. 0000 is midnight. 1200 is noon. Times are not adjusted for Daylight Saving Time.

Charleston Harbor (off Ft. Sumter), South Carolina, 2019

F–Flood, Dir. 313° True   E–Ebb, Dir. 127° True

January

Day	Slack	Maximum	knots
1 Tu		0052	1.4F
	0452	0757	2.4E
	1100	1256	1.3F
	1651	2014	2.1E
	2318		
2 W		0157	1.4F
	0547	0850	2.4E
	1152	1347	1.3F
	1743	2105	2.1E
3 Th	0007	0236	1.5F
	0637	0940	2.5E
	1241	1436	1.3F
	1831	2152	2.1E
4 F	0052	0319	1.5F
	0722	1026	2.6E
	1327	1524	1.4F
	1915	2235	2.1E
5 Sa ●	0136	0401	1.6F
	0804	1109	2.6E
	1411	1610	1.5F
	1956	2316	2.1E
6 Su	0216	0442	1.6F
	0843	1150	2.6E
	1452	1656	1.5F
	2035	2354	2.0E
7 M	0255	0524	1.7F
	0920	1230	2.5E
	1533	1741	1.6F
	2113		
8 Tu		0031	2.0E
	0332	0605	1.7F
	0956	1308	2.3E
	1613	1825	1.5F
	2152		
9 W		0107	1.9E
	0409	0648	1.6F
	1032	1346	2.2E
	1653	1910	1.5F
	2232		
10 Th		0144	1.8E
	0448	0731	1.5F
	1108	1424	2.0E
	1733	1956	1.4F
	2314		
11 F		0224	1.7E
	0529	0817	1.4F
	1144	1502	1.9E
	1814	2043	1.4F
	2359		
12 Sa		0308	1.6E
	0616	0904	1.4F
	1223	1543	1.8E
	1857	2131	1.4F
13 Su	0047	0400	1.6E
	0710	0953	1.3F
	1304	1629	1.7E
	1943	2221	1.4F
14 M ☽	0141	0500	1.6E
	0809	1044	1.3F
	1351	1722	1.7E
	2033	2312	1.4F
15 Tu	0241	0605	1.7E
	0913	1137	1.3F
	1446	1822	1.8E
	2127		
16 W		0005	1.5F
	0344	0709	1.3F
	1016	1231	1.3F
	1548	1924	1.9E
	2223		
17 Th		0100	1.7F
	0448	0810	2.2E
	1116	1327	1.4F
	1653	2024	2.1E
	2319		
18 F		0155	1.9F
	0550	0907	2.5E
	1213	1423	1.5F
	1757	2120	2.4E
19 Sa	0014	0251	2.1F
	0648	1001	2.8E
	1307	1519	1.7F
	1856	2214	2.7E
20 Su	0108	0346	2.3F
	0743	1052	3.1E
	1359	1614	1.8F
	1953	2306	2.9E
21 M ○	0201	0440	2.4F
	0835	1142	3.3E
	1449	1708	1.9F
	2047	2358	3.1E
22 Tu	0253	0533	2.5F
	0925	1231	3.3E
	1539	1801	2.0F
	2141		
23 W		0049	3.1E
	0346	0624	2.4F
	1014	1321	3.2E
	1629	1853	1.9F
	2235		
24 Th		0142	3.0E
	0441	0715	2.3F
	1104	1411	3.0E
	1721	1946	1.9F
	2330		
25 F		0236	2.8E
	0537	0806	2.0F
	1153	1503	2.7E
	1814	2039	1.7F
26 Sa	0026	0333	2.6E
	0636	0858	1.8F
	1244	1556	2.4E
	1909	2133	1.6F
27 Su ☾	0125	0432	2.4E
	0737	0949	1.6F
	1335	1652	2.1E
	2005	2227	1.4F
28 M	0225	0532	2.2E
	0837	1040	1.4F
	1427	1751	1.9E
	2102	2321	1.3F
29 Tu	0325	0632	2.1E
	0936	1132	1.2F
	1522	1850	1.8E
	2158		
30 W		0016	1.3F
	0425	0731	2.1E
	1033	1223	1.1F
	1618	1948	1.7E
	2252		
31 Th		0112	1.2F
		0159	1.2F
		0247	1.2F
	0521	0825	2.2E
	1126	1316†	1.1F

February

Day	Slack	Maximum	knots
1 F		0207	1.3F
		0243	1.3F
		0339	1.3F
	0612	0916	2.3E
	1216	1408†	1.2F
2 Sa	0032	0258	1.3F
	0659	1002	2.4E
	1303	1459	1.3F
	1852	2214	2.0E
3 Su	0116	0342	1.5F
	0740	1045	2.4E
	1347	1548	1.4F
	1935	2254	2.0E
4 M ●	0157	0424	1.6F
	0819	1125	2.5E
	1428	1634	1.5F
	2015	2333	2.1E
5 Tu	0236	0504	1.7F
	0855	1204	2.5E
	1507	1719	1.6F
	2055		
6 W		0009	2.1E
	0313	0544	1.7F
	0930	1240	2.4E
	1544	1802	1.6F
	2133		
7 Th		0045	2.1E
	0348	0624	1.7F
	1004	1315	2.3E
	1620	1844	1.6F
	2211		
8 F		0122	2.0E
	0424	0705	1.6F
	1038	1350	2.1E
	1654	1927	1.6F
	2249		
9 Sa		0159	2.0E
	0502	0747	1.6F
	1111	1424	2.0E
	1729	2010	1.5F
	2328		
10 Su		0241	1.9E
	0545	0831	1.5F
	1145	1502	1.9E
	1808	2055	1.5F
11 M	0012	0329	1.8E
	0635	0919	1.4F
	1223	1546	1.8E
	1852	2144	1.5F
12 Tu ☾	0102	0425	1.8E
	0732	1009	1.3F
	1308	1638	1.8E
	1945	2236	1.5F
13 W	0202	0529	1.8E
	0836	1104	1.3F
	1405	1742	1.8E
	2044	2331	1.6F
14 Th	0309	0637	1.9E
	0944	1200	1.3F
	1513	1852	1.9E
	2149		
15 F		0029	1.7F
	0419	0743	2.2E
	1049	1259	1.4F
	1627	1959	2.1E
	2254		
16 Sa		0129	1.8F
	0526	0844	2.5E
	1150	1359	1.5F
	1737	2100	2.4E
	2355		
17 Su		0229	2.0F
	0628	0940	2.8E
	1246	1458	1.7F
	1841	2157	2.8E
18 M	0053	0327	2.2F
	0724	1032	3.1E
	1339	1556	1.9F
	1939	2251	3.1E
19 Tu ○	0148	0423	2.4F
	0816	1123	3.3E
	1429	1651	2.0F
	2034	2343	3.3E
20 W	0241	0516	2.4F
	0906	1211	3.3E
	1517	1743	2.1F
	2126		
21 Th		0033	3.3E
	0333	0606	2.4F
	0954	1259	3.2E
	1605	1834	2.1F
	2218		
22 F		0124	3.2E
	0425	0654	2.2F
	1040	1347	3.0E
	1653	1922	2.0F
	2309		
23 Sa		0216	3.0E
	0518	0741	2.0F
	1126	1435	2.6E
	1743	2011	1.8F
24 Su	0002	0309	2.7E
	0613	0829	1.8F
	1213	1526	2.3E
	1835	2100	1.6F
25 M	0055	0404	2.4E
	0710	0918	1.5F
	1300	1619	1.9E
	1930	2151	1.4F
26 Tu ◐	0151	0502	2.1E
	0807	1008	1.3F
	1350	1717	1.7E
	2028	2243	1.2F
27 W	0250	0602	2.0E
	0905	1059	1.2F
	1443	1816	1.5E
	2127	2338	1.1F
28 Th	0349	0701	1.9E
	1002	1151	1.1F
	1541	1918	1.5E
	2225		

March

Day	Slack	Maximum	knots
1 F		0034	1.1F
	0447	0757	1.9E
	1057	1245	1.1F
	1640	2015	1.5E
	2319		
2 Sa		0157	1.1F
	0541	0848	2.0E
	1148	1340	1.1F
	1736	2105	1.7E
3 Su	0009	0257	1.2F
	0628	0935	2.2E
	1235	1433	1.3F
	1827	2150	1.9E
4 M	0055	0319	1.4F
	0711	1018	2.3E
	1319	1524	1.4F
	1912	2231	2.1E
5 Tu	0137	0402	1.5F
	0751	1058	2.4E
	1400	1611	1.6F
	1954	2310	2.2E
6 W ●	0216	0441	1.6F
	0827	1135	2.4E
	1438	1655	1.7F
	2034	2347	2.3E
7 Th	0253	0520	1.7F
	0902	1211	2.4E
	1513	1737	1.8F
	2111		
8 F		0023	2.3E
	0328	0559	1.7F
	0936	1245	2.3E
	1546	1817	1.8F
	2148		
9 Sa		0100	2.3E
	0403	0638	1.7F
	1009	1318	2.2E
	1617	1857	1.8F
	2225		
10 Su		0137	2.2E
	0440	0719	1.7F
	1041	1353	2.1E
	1651	1939	1.7F
	2303		
11 M		0219	2.1E
	0522	0803	1.6F
	1115	1431	2.0E
	1729	2023	1.7F
	2345		
12 Tu		0306	2.1E
	0611	0850	1.5F
	1154	1516	1.9E
	1815	2112	1.6F
13 W	0035	0400	2.0E
	0707	0941	1.4F
	1241	1610	1.8E
	1911	2205	1.6F
14 Th ◐	0135	0504	2.0E
	0812	1037	1.3F
	1342	1717	1.8E
	2016	2303	1.6F
15 F	0243	0612	2.0E
	0920	1135	1.3F
	1455	1830	1.9E
	2126		
16 Sa		0004	1.7F
	0355	0719	2.2E
	1026	1236	1.4F
	1612	1940	2.1E
	2236		
17 Su		0106	1.8F
	0503	0821	2.5E
	1128	1337	1.5F
	1723	2043	2.5E
	2340		
18 M		0208	1.9F
	0606	0918	2.8E
	1224	1439	1.7F
	1827	2141	2.9E
19 Tu	0040	0308	2.1F
	0703	1011	3.1E
	1316	1538	1.9F
	1925	2235	3.2E
20 W ○	0135	0404	2.2F
	0755	1101	3.2E
	1405	1632	2.1F
	2018	2326	3.4E
21 Th	0227	0455	2.3F
	0843	1149	3.2E
	1452	1723	2.2F
	2109		
22 F		0015	3.4E
	0317	0542	2.2F
	0929	1235	3.1E
	1538	1809	2.1F
	2157		
23 Sa		0104	3.3E
	0407	0628	2.1F
	1014	1321	2.8E
	1623	1855	2.0F
	2245		
24 Su		0153	3.0E
	0457	0713	1.9F
	1057	1407	2.4E
	1710	1940	1.8F
	2334		
25 M		0243	2.7E
	0548	0759	1.7F
	1140	1454	2.1E
	1800	2026	1.6F
26 Tu	0023	0335	2.4E
	0641	0846	1.5F
	1225	1544	1.7E
	1853	2115	1.3F
27 W ☾	0114	0430	2.1E
	0736	0936	1.3F
	1312	1640	1.5E
	1952	2207	1.1F
28 Th	0209	0527	1.8E
	0833	1027	1.1F
	1405	1741	1.3E
	2053	2301	1.0F
29 F	0306	0626	1.8E
	0929	1121	1.1F
	1503	1843	1.3E
	2154	2358	1.0F
30 Sa	0404	0722	1.8E
	1024	1216	1.1F
	1605	1942	1.4E
	2250		
31 Su		0056	1.0F
	0458	0815	1.9E
	1115	1311	1.2F
	1704	2034	1.6E
	2342		

Time meridian 75° W. 0000 is midnight. 1200 is noon. Times are not adjusted for Daylight Saving Time.
† See page 196 for the remaining currents on this day.

Charleston Harbor (off Ft. Sumter), South Carolina, 2019

F–Flood, Dir. 313° True   E–Ebb, Dir. 127° True

April

Day	Slack (h m)	Maximum (h m)	knots
1 M		0153	1.1F
	0549	0902	2.0E
	1203	1406	1.3F
	1757	2121	1.8E
2 Tu	0029	0245	1.3F
	0634	0946	2.2E
	1247	1457	1.5F
	1845	2203	2.1E
3 W	0112	0330	1.5F
	0715	1026	2.3E
	1328	1544	1.7F
	1928	2243	2.3E
4 Th	0152	0412	1.6F
	0754	1103	2.4E
	1405	1628	1.8F
	2009	2322	2.4E
5 F ●	0230	0452	1.7F
	0831	1139	2.4E
	1439	1709	1.9F
	2047		
6 Sa		0000	2.5E
	0306	0532	1.7F
	0906	1214	2.4E
	1511	1748	1.9F
	2125		
7 Su		0038	2.5E
	0343	0612	1.7F
	0941	1250	2.3E
	1544	1829	1.9F
	2203		
8 M		0118	2.5E
	0422	0654	1.7F
	1016	1327	2.2E
	1620	1911	1.9F
	2243		
9 Tu		0201	2.4E
	0506	0738	1.6F
	1054	1409	2.1E
	1702	1956	1.8F
	2328		
10 W		0249	2.3E
	0556	0827	1.5F
	1138	1458	2.0E
	1752	2047	1.7F
11 Th	0019	0344	2.2E
	0653	0920	1.4F
	1232	1556	1.9E
	1851	2143	1.7F
12 F ◑	0119	0446	2.2E
	0756	1016	1.4F
	1337	1704	1.9E
	2000	2242	1.6F
13 Sa	0225	0552	2.2E
	0902	1116	1.4F
	1449	1815	2.0E
	2113	2343	1.7F
14 Su	0333	0657	2.3E
	1006	1217	1.4F
	1602	1924	2.2E
	2222		
15 M		0045	1.7F
	0440	0758	2.5E
	1105	1318	1.6F
	1711	2026	2.6E
	2326		
16 Tu		0146	1.8F
	0541	0855	2.7E
	1200	1419	1.8F
	1813	2124	2.9E
17 W	0025	0245	1.9F
	0638	0948	2.9E
	1251	1517	1.9F
	1909	2217	3.2E
18 Th	0119	0339	2.0F
	0730	1038	3.0E
	1339	1610	2.1F
	2000	2307	3.3E
19 F ○	0211	0429	2.0F
	0817	1125	3.0E
	1425	1657	2.1F
	2049	2355	3.3E
20 Sa	0259	0515	2.0F
	0902	1210	2.8E
	1510	1742	2.1F
	2135		
21 Su		0042	3.2E
	0347	0600	1.9F
	0945	1254	2.5E
	1554	1824	1.9F
	2220		
22 M		0129	3.0E
	0434	0644	1.7F
	1026	1338	2.2E
	1639	1908	1.7F
	2305		
23 Tu		0216	2.6E
	0522	0729	1.6F
	1108	1423	1.9E
	1726	1953	1.5F
	2350		
24 W		0305	2.3E
	0612	0816	1.4F
	1150	1510	1.6E
	1817	2042	1.3F
25 Th	0036	0356	2.0E
	0704	0906	1.3F
	1237	1602	1.4E
	1914	2133	1.1F
26 F ○	0126	0450	1.8E
	0759	0958	1.2F
	1329	1700	1.3E
	2016	2227	1.0F
27 Sa	0218	0546	1.7E
	0854	1052	1.1F
	1427	1802	1.3E
	2117	2323	1.0F
28 Su	0313	0641	1.7E
	0947	1146	1.2F
	1528	1902	1.4E
	2215		
29 M		0019	1.0F
	0407	0734	1.8E
	1038	1241	1.3F
	1627	1957	1.6E
	2308		
30 Tu		0113	1.1F
	0459	0822	1.9E
	1125	1334	1.4F
	1722	2046	1.8E
	2357		

May

Day	Slack (h m)	Maximum (h m)	knots
1 W		0205	1.2F
	0548	0907	2.0E
	1209	1425	1.5F
	1812	2131	2.1E
2 Th	0042	0253	1.4F
	0633	0949	2.2E
	1250	1512	1.7F
	1857	2213	2.3E
3 F	0124	0338	1.5F
	0716	1029	2.3E
	1328	1556	1.8F
	1940	2255	2.5E
4 Sa ●	0204	0421	1.6F
	0756	1107	2.4E
	1403	1639	1.9F
	2022	2335	2.7E
5 Su	0244	0504	1.7F
	0836	1146	2.4E
	1439	1720	2.0F
	2103		
6 M		0017	2.7E
	0324	0546	1.7F
	0915	1225	2.4E
	1516	1803	2.0F
	2144		
7 Tu		0100	2.7E
	0407	0631	1.7F
	0956	1308	2.3E
	1558	1848	2.0F
	2228		
8 W		0146	2.6E
	0454	0718	1.6F
	1041	1354	2.2E
	1645	1936	1.9F
	2317		
9 Th		0236	2.5E
	0545	0809	1.5F
	1133	1447	2.1E
	1739	2029	1.8F
10 F	0010	0331	2.4E
	0643	0903	1.4F
	1231	1548	2.0E
	1842	2126	1.7F
11 Sa ◑	0108	0430	2.4E
	0744	1001	1.4F
	1337	1654	2.0E
	1952	2225	1.7F
12 Su	0209	0532	2.4E
	0845	1100	1.5F
	1445	1802	2.2E
	2102	2325	1.6F
13 M	0312	0635	2.4E
	0945	1200	1.5F
	1552	1907	2.4E
	2209		
14 Tu		0025	1.6F
	0414	0735	2.5E
	1041	1300	1.7F
	1656	2008	2.6E
	2311		
15 W		0123	1.7F
	0514	0831	2.6E
	1135	1358	1.8F
	1756	2105	2.9E
16 Th	0009	0219	1.7F
	0610	0924	2.7E
	1225	1454	1.9F
	1850	2157	3.1E
17 F	0102	0311	1.7F
	0702	1014	2.7E
	1313	1544	2.0F
	1941	2247	3.2E
18 Sa ○	0152	0400	1.7F
	0750	1101	2.6E
	1359	1630	2.0F
	2028	2334	3.2E
19 Su	0239	0446	1.7F
	0834	1145	2.5E
	1443	1713	1.9F
	2112		
20 M		0020	3.0E
	0325	0530	1.7F
	0916	1229	2.3E
	1526	1755	1.8F
	2154		
21 Tu		0105	2.8E
	0410	0615	1.6F
	0956	1311	2.0E
	1610	1838	1.6F
	2236		
22 W		0150	2.5E
	0456	0701	1.5F
	1037	1353	1.8E
	1654	1923	1.5F
	2317		
23 Th		0235	2.3E
	0543	0748	1.4F
	1119	1437	1.6E
	1743	2011	1.3F
24 F	0000	0322	2.0E
	0633	0838	1.3F
	1206	1525	1.4E
	1836	2102	1.2F
25 Sa	0044	0412	1.8E
	0724	0929	1.2F
	1257	1618	1.3E
	1935	2154	1.1F
26 Su	0131	0503	1.7E
	0815	1022	1.2F
	1352	1717	1.3E
	2035	2248	1.1F
27 M	0221	0555	1.7E
	0906	1115	1.3F
	1449	1817	1.4E
	2133	2341	1.1F
28 Tu	0312	0646	1.7E
	0955	1207	1.3F
	1547	1914	1.6E
	2228		
29 W		0033	1.1F
	0404	0736	1.8E
	1041	1258	1.5F
	1642	2006	1.8E
	2319		
30 Th		0124	1.2F
	0456	0823	1.9E
	1126	1348	1.6F
	1734	2055	2.1E
31 F	0007	0214	1.3F
	0546	0909	2.1E
	1208	1436	1.7F
	1823	2142	2.3E

June

Day	Slack (h m)	Maximum (h m)	knots
1 Sa	0053	0302	1.4F
	0635	0953	2.2E
	1249	1523	1.9F
	1911	2227	2.6E
2 Su	0137	0349	1.5F
	0721	1036	2.3E
	1330	1609	2.0F
	1956	2311	2.8E
3 M ●	0221	0436	1.6F
	0807	1120	2.4E
	1411	1654	2.1F
	2042	2356	2.9E
4 Tu	0306	0522	1.7F
	0853	1205	2.5E
	1455	1740	2.1F
	2128		
5 W		0042	2.9E
	0352	0610	1.7F
	0941	1252	2.5E
	1542	1829	2.1F
	2216		
6 Th		0131	2.9E
	0441	0701	1.6F
	1032	1343	2.4E
	1634	1920	2.0F
	2306		
7 F		0222	2.8E
	0534	0754	1.6F
	1128	1439	2.3E
	1732	2014	1.9F
	2359		
8 Sa		0316	2.7E
	0630	0849	1.5F
	1228	1539	2.3E
	1836	2111	1.8F
9 Su	0054	0413	2.6E
	0728	0947	1.5F
	1331	1642	2.3E
	1943	2209	1.7F
10 M ◐	0151	0512	2.5E
	0826	1046	1.6F
	1435	1746	2.3E
	2050	2306	1.6F
11 Tu	0249	0612	2.4E
	0923	1144	1.6F
	1538	1849	2.5E
	2154		
12 W		0003	1.5F
	0348	0710	2.4E
	1017	1241	1.7F
	1639	1949	2.6E
	2254		
13 Th		0057	1.5F
	0445	0807	2.4E
	1110	1336	1.7F
	1737	2045	2.8E
	2350		
14 F		0151	1.5F
	0541	0900	2.4E
	1201	1429	1.7F
	1830	2137	2.9E
15 Sa	0042	0241	1.5F
	0633	0950	2.4E
	1249	1517	1.8F
	1920	2226	2.9E
16 Su	0131	0330	1.5F
	0721	1037	2.3E
	1335	1602	1.8F
	2006	2312	2.9E
17 M ○	0218	0417	1.5F
	0806	1122	2.2E
	1419	1645	1.7F
	2048	2357	2.8E
18 Tu	0303	0502	1.5F
	0847	1204	2.1E
	1502	1728	1.7F
	2129		
19 W		0040	2.7E
	0346	0548	1.5F
	0928	1245	2.0E
	1544	1811	1.6F
	2207		
20 Th		0123	2.5E
	0430	0634	1.4F
	1009	1326	1.8E
	1627	1856	1.5F
	2246		
21 F		0205	2.3E
	0514	0721	1.4F
	1051	1407	1.6E
	1712	1943	1.4F
	2325		
22 Sa		0248	2.1E
	0559	0810	1.3F
	1136	1451	1.5E
	1800	2031	1.3F
23 Su	0005	0331	1.9E
	0646	0900	1.3F
	1225	1539	1.4E
	1854	2121	1.2F
24 M	0047	0416	1.8E
	0733	0950	1.3F
	1316	1632	1.4E
	1951	2212	1.1F
25 Tu ◐	0131	0503	1.7E
	0820	1041	1.3F
	1409	1730	1.5E
	2048	2303	1.1F
26 W	0218	0553	1.7E
	0906	1131	1.4F
	1504	1828	1.6E
	2144	2354	1.2F
27 Th	0308	0644	1.7E
	0953	1221	1.5F
	1559	1925	1.8E
	2239		
28 F		0045	1.2F
	0402	0737	1.8E
	1040	1311	1.6F
	1655	2019	2.1E
	2331		
29 Sa		0137	1.3F
	0458	0829	2.0E
	1127	1401	1.8F
	1749	2110	2.4E
30 Su	0021	0228	1.4F
	0554	0919	2.2E
	1214	1451	1.9F
	1841	2200	2.6E

Time meridian 75° W. 0000 is midnight. 1200 is noon. Times are not adjusted for Daylight Saving Time.

Charleston Harbor (off Ft. Sumter), South Carolina, 2019

F–Flood, Dir. 313° True   E–Ebb, Dir. 127° True

July

Date	Slack h m	Max h m	knots
1 M	0110	0319	1.5F
	0649	1009	2.4E
	1301	1541	2.1F
	1932	2248	2.9E
2 Tu ●	0159	0410	1.6F
	0742	1058	2.5E
	1349	1631	2.2F
	2022	2336	3.0E
3 W	0247	0500	1.7F
	0834	1147	2.6E
	1439	1721	2.2F
	2111		
4 Th		0024	3.1E
	0335	0552	1.7F
	0928	1238	2.7E
	1530	1812	2.2F
	2201		
5 F		0114	3.1E
	0425	0644	1.7F
	1022	1331	2.7E
	1625	1905	2.1F
	2252		
6 Sa		0204	3.0E
	0518	0739	1.7F
	1119	1427	2.6E
	1724	1959	2.0F
	2343		
7 Su		0257	2.8E
	0612	0835	1.7F
	1218	1525	2.5E
	1826	2054	1.8F
8 M	0036	0352	2.7E
	0707	0932	1.7F
	1318	1626	2.5E
	1931	2150	1.7F
9 Tu ◑	0130	0449	2.5E
	0803	1029	1.6F
	1419	1727	2.5E
	2035	2244	1.5F
10 W	0225	0547	2.3E
	0859	1125	1.6F
	1520	1829	2.5E
	2136	2338	1.4F
11 Th	0320	0645	2.2E
	0954	1220	1.6F
	1619	1927	2.5E
	2234		
12 F		0030	1.3F
	0416	0742	2.2E
	1047	1313	1.6F
	1716	2023	2.6E
	2329		
13 Sa		0122	1.3F
	0512	0837	2.1E
	1138	1404	1.5F
	1809	2115	2.6E
14 Su	0021	0212	1.3F
	0605	0928	2.1E
	1228	1452	1.5F
	1858	2204	2.7E
15 M	0109	0302	1.3F
	0654	1015	2.1E
	1314	1537	1.6F
	1943	2250	2.7E
16 Tu ○	0155	0350	1.4F
	0739	1059	2.1E
	1358	1621	1.6F
	2024	2333	2.7E
17 W	0238	0437	1.4F
	0822	1141	2.0E
	1441	1704	1.6F
	2102		
18 Th		0015	2.6E
	0321	0523	1.5F
	0903	1221	2.0E
	1521	1747	1.6F
	2139		
19 F		0055	2.4E
	0402	0608	1.5F
	0943	1300	1.9E
	1602	1830	1.5F
	2215		
20 Sa		0134	2.3E
	0443	0654	1.5F
	1024	1339	1.8E
	1643	1915	1.4F
	2251		
21 Su		0212	2.1E
	0523	0741	1.4F
	1107	1419	1.7E
	1727	2001	1.4F
	2327		
22 M		0250	2.0E
	0604	0828	1.4F
	1152	1503	1.6E
	1815	2048	1.3F
23 Tu	0005	0329	1.8E
	0646	0916	1.4F
	1239	1552	1.6E
	1907	2137	1.2F
24 W ○	0044	0411	1.7E
	0729	1004	1.4F
	1329	1646	1.6E
	2003	2226	1.2F
25 Th	0127	0459	1.7E
	0814	1054	1.4F
	1422	1745	1.7E
	2101	2317	1.2F
26 F	0217	0553	1.7E
	0904	1144	1.5F
	1518	1845	1.8E
	2159		
27 Sa		0009	1.2F
	0313	0653	1.8E
	0956	1236	1.6F
	1617	1944	2.1E
	2256		
28 Su		0103	1.3F
	0416	0753	2.0E
	1050	1329	1.8F
	1717	2041	2.4E
	2352		
29 M		0157	1.4F
	0520	0850	2.2E
	1144	1422	1.9F
	1814	2134	2.7E
30 Tu	0045	0252	1.5F
	0623	0946	2.4E
	1238	1516	2.1F
	1910	2226	3.0E
31 W ●	0136	0346	1.6F
	0722	1039	2.7E
	1332	1610	2.2F
	2002	2315	3.2E

August

Date	Slack h m	Max h m	knots
1 Th	0225	0440	1.8F
	0818	1131	2.9E
	1425	1703	2.3F
	2053		
2 F		0005	3.3E
	0315	0534	1.9F
	0914	1223	3.0E
	1519	1755	2.3F
	2143		
3 Sa		0054	3.3E
	0404	0627	1.9F
	1009	1316	3.0E
	1614	1847	2.2F
	2233		
4 Su		0144	3.1E
	0455	0721	1.9F
	1104	1410	2.9E
	1712	1940	2.0F
	2323		
5 M		0235	2.9E
	0547	0815	1.8F
	1201	1507	2.8E
	1812	2033	1.8F
6 Tu	0013	0328	2.6E
	0641	0911	1.7F
	1259	1605	2.6E
	1913	2126	1.6F
7 W ◑	0105	0423	2.4E
	0737	1006	1.6F
	1358	1705	2.5E
	2015	2219	1.4F
8 Th	0158	0521	2.2E
	0834	1101	1.5F
	1458	1806	2.4E
	2114	2311	1.3F
9 F	0252	0620	2.0E
	0930	1155	1.4F
	1556	1904	2.4E
	2212		
10 Sa		0003	1.2F
	0348	0719	1.9E
	1025	1248	1.4F
	1652	2000	2.4E
	2306		
11 Su		0054	1.1F
	0444	0814	1.9E
	1118	1340	1.3F
	1745	2052	2.4E
	2357		
12 M		0145	1.1F
	0538	0906	1.9E
	1208	1429	1.4F
	1833	2141	2.5E
13 Tu	0045	0236	1.2F
	0629	0953	2.0E
	1254	1515	1.4F
	1917	2225	2.5E
14 W	0130	0325	1.3F
	0715	1037	2.0E
	1338	1558	1.5F
	1957	2307	2.5E
15 Th ○	0212	0413	1.4F
	0758	1117	2.1E
	1420	1641	1.6F
	2034	2347	2.5E
16 F	0252	0458	1.5F
	0839	1156	2.1E
	1459	1722	1.6F
	2110		
17 Sa		0025	2.4E
	0331	0543	1.6F
	0919	1234	2.1E
	1538	1804	1.6F
	2144		
18 Su		0101	2.3E
	0408	0627	1.6F
	0958	1312	2.0E
	1617	1847	1.5F
	2218		
19 M		0136	2.2E
	0444	0710	1.5F
	1038	1350	1.9E
	1657	1930	1.4F
	2251		
20 Tu		0211	2.0E
	0520	0754	1.5F
	1119	1431	1.8E
	1740	2015	1.3F
	2325		
21 W		0246	1.9E
	0557	0840	1.5F
	1202	1517	1.8E
	1829	2102	1.3F
22 Th	0002	0327	1.8E
	0638	0927	1.4F
	1250	1609	1.8E
	1923	2152	1.2F
23 F ◑	0044	0415	1.7E
	0726	1017	1.5F
	1343	1708	1.8E
	2023	2244	1.2F
24 Sa	0135	0512	1.7E
	0820	1109	1.5F
	1442	1811	1.9E
	2125	2338	1.2F
25 Su	0237	0618	1.8E
	0920	1204	1.6F
	1545	1914	2.1E
	2226		
26 M		0034	1.3F
	0347	0725	2.0E
	1021	1300	1.8F
	1649	2014	2.4E
	2325		
27 Tu		0131	1.4F
	0457	0828	2.2E
	1122	1358	2.0F
	1750	2110	2.7E
28 W	0020	0228	1.5F
	0604	0926	2.6E
	1221	1454	2.1F
	1847	2203	3.0E
29 Th	0112	0325	1.7F
	0706	1022	2.9E
	1317	1550	2.3F
	1941	2254	3.2E
30 F ●	0202	0420	1.9F
	0803	1115	3.1E
	1411	1643	2.3F
	2032	2343	3.3E
31 Sa	0250	0514	2.0F
	0858	1206	3.2E
	1505	1735	2.3F
	2121		

September

Date	Slack h m	Max h m	knots
1 Su		0031	3.3E
	0339	0606	2.1F
	0951	1258	3.2E
	1559	1826	2.2F
	2210		
2 M		0120	3.1E
	0428	0658	2.0F
	1045	1351	3.1E
	1655	1916	2.0F
	2258		
3 Tu		0210	2.8E
	0519	0750	1.9F
	1140	1445	2.9E
	1752	2007	1.8F
	2347		
4 W		0301	2.5E
	0612	0843	1.7F
	1235	1542	2.6E
	1851	2058	1.5F
5 Th ◑	0037	0355	2.2E
	0708	0936	1.5F
	1332	1640	2.4E
	1951	2150	1.3F
6 F	0129	0453	1.9E
	0806	1031	1.4F
	1430	1740	2.2E
	2050	2242	1.2F
7 Sa	0223	0554	1.7E
	0905	1125	1.2F
	1528	1838	2.2E
	2146	2334	1.1F
8 Su	0320	0654	1.6E
	1002	1220	1.2F
	1624	1934	2.1E
	2240		
9 M		0027	1.1F
	0418	0751	1.7E
	1056	1313	1.2F
	1716	2026	2.2E
	2330		
10 Tu		0120	1.1F
	0513	0843	1.8E
	1146	1403	1.2F
	1803	2114	2.3E
11 W	0017	0211	1.2F
	0604	0930	1.9E
	1233	1450	1.3F
	1846	2158	2.4E
12 Th	0101	0301	1.4F
	0651	1012	2.0E
	1316	1534	1.5F
	1926	2239	2.4E
13 F ○	0143	0349	1.5F
	0734	1053	2.2E
	1357	1616	1.6F
	2003	2317	2.5E
14 Sa	0221	0434	1.6F
	0815	1131	2.2E
	1436	1657	1.6F
	2038	2353	2.4E
15 Su	0258	0517	1.7F
	0854	1209	2.2E
	1514	1737	1.6F
	2113		
16 M		0028	2.3E
	0332	0558	1.7F
	0932	1246	2.2E
	1551	1818	1.6F
	2146		
17 Tu		0102	2.2E
	0405	0639	1.7F
	1010	1324	2.1E
	1630	1900	1.5F
	2218		
18 W		0135	2.1E
	0437	0721	1.6F
	1049	1404	2.0E
	1711	1944	1.4F
	2251		
19 Th		0211	1.9E
	0514	0805	1.6F
	1131	1449	2.0E
	1759	2030	1.3F
	2328		
20 F ◑		0253	1.8E
	0556	0853	1.5F
	1218	1541	1.9E
	1853	2121	1.2F
21 Sa ○	0012	0344	1.8E
	0648	0944	1.5F
	1313	1639	1.9E
	1954	2215	1.2F
22 Su	0109	0445	1.7E
	0748	1040	1.6F
	1414	1744	2.0E
	2058	2311	1.2F
23 M	0217	0555	1.8E
	0854	1138	1.7F
	1520	1848	2.2E
	2201		
24 Tu		0010	1.3F
	0332	0705	2.0E
	1001	1236	1.8F
	1625	1949	2.4E
	2300		
25 W		0109	1.4F
	0444	0810	2.3E
	1105	1335	1.9F
	1727	2047	2.7E
	2355		
26 Th		0207	1.6F
	0550	0909	2.7E
	1206	1433	2.1F
	1824	2140	3.0E
27 F	0047	0305	1.9F
	0651	1004	3.0E
	1302	1529	2.2F
	1918	2231	3.2E
28 Sa ●	0136	0400	2.1F
	0747	1057	3.3E
	1357	1622	2.3F
	2009	2320	3.3E
29 Su	0224	0453	2.2F
	0841	1148	3.4E
	1450	1712	2.2F
	2057		
30 M		0008	3.2E
	0312	0543	2.2F
	0932	1239	3.3E
	1542	1801	2.1F
	2144		

Time meridian 75° W. 0000 is midnight. 1200 is noon. Times are not adjusted for Daylight Saving Time.

Charleston Harbor (off Ft. Sumter), South Carolina, 2019

F–Flood, Dir. 313° True   E–Ebb, Dir. 127° True

October

Day	Slack	Maximum (h m)	knots	Day	Slack	Maximum (h m)	knots
1 Tu		0055	3.0E	**16** W		0031	2.2E
	0359	0632	2.1F		0328	0610	1.8F
	1023	1330	3.2E		0946	1300	2.3E
	1635	1849	1.9F		1606	1832	1.5F
	2231				2150		
2 W		0143	2.7E	**17** Th		0106	2.1E
	0448	0720	1.9F		0402	0651	1.8F
	1115	1422	2.9E		1026	1342	2.3E
	1729	1938	1.7F		1649	1916	1.4F
	2318				2226		
3 Th		0233	2.3E	**18** F		0145	2.0E
	0540	0810	1.7F		0441	0735	1.7F
	1208	1516	2.6E		1108	1428	2.2E
	1825	2028	1.4F		1736	2003	1.3F
					2307		
4 F	0006	0326	2.0E	**19** Sa		0231	1.9E
	0636	0902	1.4F		0527	0824	1.6F
	1302	1612	2.3E		1157	1519	2.1E
	1923	2119	1.2F		1831	2055	1.2F
					2357		
5 Sa	0057	0422	1.7E	**20** Su		0325	1.8E
	0735	0955	1.2F		0622	0918	1.6F
	1358	1710	2.1E		1253	1618	2.1E
	2020	2212	1.1F		1932	2151	1.2F
6 Su	0152	0523	1.5E	**21** M	0100	0429	1.8E
	0836	1050	1.1F		0726	1016	1.6F
	1453	1808	2.0E		1354	1721	2.1E
	2117	2305	1.0F		2036	2249	1.3F
7 M	0250	0625	1.5E	**22** Tu	0211	0539	1.9E
	0935	1145	1.1F		0836	1115	1.7F
	1548	1904	2.0E		1458	1825	2.3E
	2210	2359	1.1F		2138	2349	1.4F
8 Tu	0348	0723	1.5E	**23** W	0324	0649	2.1E
	1029	1239	1.1F		0946	1215	1.8F
	1639	1956	2.0E		1602	1926	2.5E
	2259				2236		
9 W		0053	1.1F	**24** Th		0049	1.5F
	0445	0815	1.7E		0433	0753	2.4E
	1120	1331	1.2F		1051	1314	1.9F
	1726	2043	2.1E		1703	2023	2.7E
	2346				2330		
10 Th		0145	1.3F	**25** F		0148	1.7F
	0537	0902	1.9E		0538	0852	2.8E
	1207	1419	1.3F		1151	1411	2.0F
	1810	2126	2.2E		1800	2117	2.9E
11 F	0029	0236	1.5F	**26** Sa	0022	0245	1.9F
	0624	0945	2.1E		0637	0947	3.1E
	1251	1505	1.4F		1247	1506	2.1F
	1851	2207	2.3E		1854	2208	3.1E
12 Sa	0110	0323	1.6F	**27** Su	0111	0340	2.1F
	0708	1026	2.2E		0731	1039	3.3E
	1333	1548	1.5F		1341	1558	2.1F
	1929	2245	2.4E		1944	2257	3.1E
13 Su	0148	0407	1.7F	**28** M	0159	0431	2.2F
	0750	1105	2.3E		0823	1130	3.4E
	1412	1629	1.6F		1432	1648	2.1F
	2006	2321	2.4E		2032	2344	3.0E
14 M	0223	0449	1.8F	**29** Tu	0245	0519	2.2F
	0830	1143	2.4E		0913	1219	3.3E
	1450	1710	1.6F		1523	1735	1.9F
	2042	2356	2.3E		2118		
15 Tu	0256	0529	1.8F	**30** W		0031	2.8E
	0908	1221	2.4E		0332	0605	2.0F
	1528	1751	1.6F		1001	1308	3.1E
	2116				1613	1822	1.8F
					2203		
				31 Th		0117	2.5E
					0419	0651	1.8F
					1050	1357	2.8E
					1703	1909	1.6F
					2248		

November

Day	Slack	Maximum (h m)	knots	Day	Slack	Maximum (h m)	knots
1 F		0205	2.1E	**16** Sa		0128	2.1E
	0508	0738	1.6F		0419	0712	1.9F
	1138	1448	2.5E		1054	1410	2.4E
	1756	1957	1.4F		1719	1942	1.4F
	2334				2258		
2 Sa		0254	1.8E	**17** Su		0217	2.1E
	0601	0827	1.4F		0509	0803	1.8F
	1228	1541	2.4E		1143	1502	2.3E
	1851	2048	1.2F		1814	2035	1.3F
					2354		
3 Su	0024	0348	1.5E	**18** M		0314	2.0E
	0659	0919	1.2F		0607	0857	1.7F
	1319	1635	2.0E		1238	1559	2.3E
	1946	2140	1.1F		1913	2131	1.3F
4 M	0117	0446	1.4E	**19** Tu	0058	0417	2.0E
	0800	1013	1.1F		0713	0955	1.7F
	1410	1731	1.8E		1337	1659	2.3E
	2041	2234	1.1F		2014	2230	1.4F
5 Tu	0214	0547	1.3E	**20** W	0206	0525	2.1E
	0859	1107	1.0F		0823	1054	1.7F
	1502	1826	1.8E		1437	1801	2.3E
	2134	2329	1.1F		2114	2330	1.5F
6 W	0313	0646	1.4E	**21** Th	0315	0632	2.2E
	0955	1201	1.1F		0931	1153	1.7F
	1552	1917	1.8E		1538	1902	2.5E
	2223				2211		
7 Th		0023	1.2F	**22** F		0029	1.6F
	0410	0740	1.6E		0421	0735	2.5E
	1047	1253	1.2F		1036	1251	1.8F
	1641	2005	1.9E		1638	2000	2.6E
	2310				2306		
8 F		0115	1.3F	**23** Sa		0128	1.8F
	0504	0829	1.8E		0524	0834	2.8E
	1136	1343	1.3F		1135	1348	1.8F
	1727	2050	2.1E		1736	2054	2.7E
	2354				2358		
9 Sa		0205	1.5F	**24** Su		0225	1.9F
	0554	0914	2.0E		0622	0929	3.0E
	1222	1431	1.4F		1231	1442	1.8F
	1811	2132	2.2E		1830	2146	2.8E
10 Su	0035	0253	1.7F	**25** M	0048	0319	2.0F
	0640	0957	2.2E		0716	1021	3.2E
	1305	1516	1.5F		1324	1534	1.8F
	1854	2211	2.3E		1921	2236	2.8E
11 M	0113	0338	1.8F	**26** Tu	0136	0409	2.1F
	0724	1038	2.4E		0806	1111	3.2E
	1346	1600	1.6F		1414	1622	1.8F
	1934	2250	2.3E		2009	2323	2.7E
12 Tu	0149	0420	1.9F	**27** W	0222	0455	2.0F
	0805	1120	2.5E		0854	1158	3.2E
	1426	1642	1.6F		1502	1709	1.8F
	2013	2327	2.3E		2054		
13 W	0224	0502	1.9F	**28** Th		0008	2.5E
	0846	1158	2.6E		0308	0539	1.9F
	1506	1725	1.6F		0940	1245	3.0E
	2051				1550	1755	1.7F
					2137		
14 Th		0005	2.3E	**29** F		0053	2.3E
	0259	0543	1.9F		0353	0623	1.8F
	0926	1240	2.5E		1024	1332	2.7E
	1546	1808	1.6F		1637	1841	1.5F
	2129				2220		
15 F		0045	2.2E	**30** Sa		0137	2.0E
	0336	0626	1.9F		0439	0708	1.6F
	1008	1323	2.5E		1108	1419	2.4E
	1630	1853	1.5F		1725	1928	1.4F
	2211				2303		

December

Day	Slack	Maximum (h m)	knots	Day	Slack	Maximum (h m)	knots
1 Su		0223	1.8E	**16** M		0207	2.3E
	0527	0755	1.4F		0458	0746	2.0F
	1152	1507	2.1E		1130	1444	2.6E
	1815	2017	1.3F		1755	2017	1.5F
	2349				2350		
2 M		0311	1.5E	**17** Tu		0303	2.3E
	0619	0844	1.3F		0557	0840	1.9F
	1236	1556	1.9E		1223	1539	2.5E
	1907	2109	1.2F		1852	2113	1.5F
3 Tu	0040	0404	1.4E	**18** W	0051	0404	2.2E
	0716	0936	1.2F		0701	0936	1.8F
	1322	1647	1.8E		1318	1636	2.4E
	1959	2201	1.2F		1950	2211	1.5F
4 W	0134	0501	1.3E	**19** Th	0156	0509	2.2E
	0815	1028	1.1F		0809	1033	1.7F
	1409	1739	1.7E		1415	1737	2.4E
	2050	2255	1.2F		2049	2310	1.6F
5 Th	0231	0600	1.4E	**20** F	0302	0614	2.3E
	0912	1121	1.1F		0915	1131	1.6F
	1458	1831	1.7E		1514	1837	2.4E
	2140	2348	1.3F		2146		
6 F	0329	0657	1.5E	**21** Sa		0009	1.6F
	1007	1213	1.1F		0406	0717	2.5E
	1549	1921	1.7E		1019	1227	1.6F
	2228				1613	1936	2.4E
					2242		
7 Sa		0040	1.4F	**22** Su		0107	1.7F
	0425	0750	1.7E		0509	0816	2.7E
	1059	1304	1.2F		1118	1323	1.6F
	1639	2008	1.8E		1712	2033	2.4E
	2313				2336		
8 Su		0131	1.5F	**23** M		0206	1.8F
	0519	0839	1.9E		0607	0911	2.8E
	1149	1354	1.3F		1214	1417	1.6F
	1729	2054	2.0E		1808	2126	2.5E
	2356						
9 M		0220	1.6F	**24** Tu	0027	0301	1.8F
	0609	0926	2.2E		0700	1003	3.0E
	1235	1443	1.4F		1306	1509	1.6F
	1816	2137	2.1E		1900	2216	2.5E
10 Tu	0037	0307	1.8F	**25** W	0116	0351	1.8F
	0656	1011	2.4E		0750	1052	3.0E
	1319	1530	1.5F		1355	1558	1.6F
	1902	2220	2.2E		1948	2303	2.5E
11 W	0117	0352	1.9F	**26** Th	0203	0435	1.8F
	0741	1054	2.6E		0836	1138	2.9E
	1402	1616	1.6F		1442	1644	1.6F
	1946	2301	2.3E		2032	2348	2.4E
12 Th	0156	0436	2.0F	**27** F	0247	0517	1.8F
	0825	1137	2.7E		0918	1223	2.8E
	1445	1701	1.6F		1526	1730	1.6F
	2030	2344	2.4E		2114		
13 F	0236	0521	2.1F	**28** Sa		0030	2.2E
	0909	1221	2.8E		0330	0558	1.7F
	1528	1747	1.6F		0959	1306	2.6E
	2115				1610	1815	1.5F
					2154		
14 Sa		0028	2.4E	**29** Su		0112	2.0E
	0319	0606	2.1F		0412	0641	1.6F
	0954	1306	2.7E		1038	1349	2.4E
	1614	1834	1.6F		1654	1901	1.5F
	2202				2235		
15 Su		0115	2.4E	**30** M		0153	1.8E
	0406	0655	2.1F		0456	0725	1.5F
	1041	1354	2.7E		1116	1431	2.1E
	1703	1924	1.6F		1738	1948	1.4F
	2253				2317		
				31 Tu		0236	1.7E
					0541	0812	1.4F
					1154	1514	1.9E
					1824	2037	1.3F

Time meridian 75° W.   0000 is midnight.   1200 is noon.   Times are not adjusted for Daylight Saving Time.

Savannah River Entrance, Georgia, 2019

F–Flood, Dir. 286° True   E–Ebb, Dir. 110° True

January

Day	Slack	Maximum	knots		Day	Slack	Maximum	knots
1 Tu		0144	2.1F		16 W		0054	2.1F
	0530	0906	2.4E			0431	0715	1.8E
	1142	1414	1.8F			1100	1325	1.6F
	1742	2117	2.0E			1658	1942	1.6E
	2346					2303		
2 W		0238	2.1F		17 Th		0148	2.2F
	0626	1000	2.4E			0529	0825	1.9E
	1236	1507	1.8F			1158	1421	1.7F
	1835	2211	1.9E			1755	2047	1.7E
						2357		
3 Th	0037	0330	2.1F		18 F		0243	2.4F
	0719	1052	2.4E			0628	0936	2.1E
	1327	1557	1.7F			1253	1517	1.8F
	1926	2301	1.9E			1852	2150	1.9E
4 F	0127	0420	2.0F		19 Sa	0051	0339	2.6F
	0808	1141	2.3E			0725	1039	2.3E
	1416	1645	1.7F			1348	1613	1.9F
	2014	2349	1.8E			1947	2250	2.1E
5 Sa ●	0215	0504	2.0F		20 Su	0146	0434	2.8F
	0854	1228	2.2E			0819	1136	2.6E
	1502	1727	1.7F			1440	1707	2.1F
	2059					2041	2348	2.3E
6 Su		0034	1.7E		21 M ○	0240	0528	2.9F
	0300	0544	1.9F			0911	1228	2.7E
	0935	1312	2.2E			1530	1759	2.3F
	1545	1807	1.7F			2134		
	2141							
7 M		0114	1.6E		22 Tu		0044	2.5E
	0342	0620	1.9F			0334	0619	3.0F
	1013	1351	2.0E			1002	1317	2.8E
	1624	1844	1.7F			1617	1848	2.4F
	2221					2226		
8 Tu		0142	1.5E		23 W		0139	2.6E
	0422	0656	1.9F			0427	0710	3.0F
	1049	1424	1.9E			1051	1405	2.8E
	1701	1922	1.8F			1704	1936	2.5F
	2300					2319		
9 W		0148	1.5E		24 Th		0232	2.6E
	0500	0733	1.8F			0520	0800	2.9F
	1124	1444	1.8E			1142	1452	2.8E
	1737	2000	1.8F			1751	2026	2.5F
	2339							
10 Th		0214	1.5E		25 F	0013	0327	2.6E
	0540	0813	1.7F			0615	0852	2.6F
	1200	1456	1.7E			1233	1541	2.6E
	1814	2041	1.8F			1840	2118	2.5F
11 F	0019	0252	1.5E		26 Sa	0109	0424	2.5E
	0622	0856	1.6F			0713	0948	2.3F
	1239	1527	1.7E			1326	1632	2.4E
	1853	2126	1.8F			1932	2214	2.3F
12 Sa	0103	0335	1.5E		27 Su ◑	0206	0527	2.3E
	0709	0944	1.5F			0813	1047	2.1F
	1324	1607	1.6E			1421	1731	2.1E
	1936	2215	1.8F			2027	2315	2.2F
13 Su	0149	0422	1.6E		28 M	0305	0634	2.2E
	0803	1038	1.5F			0916	1148	1.9F
	1413	1653	1.5E			1517	1840	1.9E
	2024	2307	1.8F			2126		
14 M ◐	0240	0514	1.6E		29 Tu		0016	2.1F
	0902	1134	1.5F			0405	0740	2.2E
	1506	1744	1.5E			1017	1248	1.8F
	2116					1614	1949	1.8E
						2223		
15 Tu		0000	1.9F		30 W		0116	2.0F
	0334	0611	1.7E			0504	0841	2.2E
	1002	1230	1.5F			1115	1344	1.7F
	1601	1841	1.5E			1710	2052	1.8E
	2209					2319		
					31 Th		0213	2.0F
						0602	0937	2.2E
						1210	1438	1.6F
						1805	2148	1.8E

February

Day	Slack	Maximum	knots		Day	Slack	Maximum	knots
1 F	0012	0307	1.9F		16 Sa		0222	2.3F
	0655	1028	2.2E			0612	0933	2.1E
	1301	1529	1.6F			1234	1456	1.7F
	1858	2239	1.8E			1833	2144	1.9E
2 Sa	0103	0358	1.9F		17 Su	0033	0320	2.5F
	0744	1117	2.2E			0709	1032	2.3E
	1349	1617	1.6F			1328	1554	1.9F
	1947	2326	1.7E			1931	2246	2.1E
3 Su	0151	0442	1.9F		18 M	0130	0417	2.7F
	0827	1202	2.2E			0803	1124	2.6E
	1434	1701	1.7F			1418	1649	2.1F
	2033					2025	2342	2.4E
4 M ●		0010	1.7E		19 Tu ○	0225	0511	2.8F
	0236	0521	1.9F			0854	1213	2.7E
	0907	1243	2.1E			1506	1740	2.4F
	1515	1741	1.8F			2116		
	2114							
5 Tu		0047	1.6E		20 W		0036	2.6E
	0318	0557	1.9F			0319	0603	2.9F
	0943	1319	2.0E			0942	1259	2.8E
	1553	1818	1.9F			1552	1828	2.6F
	2153					2207		
6 W		0111	1.6E		21 Th		0127	2.8E
	0357	0632	1.9F			0412	0652	2.9F
	1018	1347	1.9E			1030	1345	2.8E
	1628	1854	1.9F			1637	1914	2.7F
	2230					2257		
7 Th		0119	1.6E		22 F		0218	2.8E
	0435	0708	1.9F			0503	0740	2.8F
	1052	1400	1.8E			1118	1429	2.7E
	1703	1930	2.0F			1723	2000	2.7F
	2305					2349		
8 F		0146	1.7E		23 Sa		0309	2.7E
	0513	0745	1.8F			0555	0828	2.6F
	1127	1420	1.8E			1207	1515	2.5E
	1738	2009	2.0F			1810	2049	2.6F
	2343							
9 Sa		0224	1.7E		24 Su	0042	0402	2.5E
	0553	0826	1.8F			0649	0920	2.3F
	1205	1454	1.7E			1257	1602	2.3E
	1815	2051	2.0F			1901	2142	2.4F
10 Su	0024	0306	1.7E		25 M	0138	0500	2.3E
	0637	0911	1.6F			0746	1015	2.0F
	1248	1535	1.7E			1350	1656	2.0E
	1857	2138	1.9F			1956	2240	2.1F
11 M	0111	0353	1.7E		26 Tu ◑	0236	0604	2.1E
	0729	1003	1.5F			0845	1114	1.8F
	1337	1621	1.6E			1445	1802	1.8E
	1945	2231	1.9F			2054	2343	2.0F
12 Tu ◐	0205	0445	1.7E		27 W	0335	0711	2.0E
	0829	1100	1.4F			0946	1214	1.7F
	1432	1712	1.6E			1541	1917	1.7E
	2039	2327	1.9F			2154		
13 W	0305	0543	1.7E		28 Th		0045	1.9F
	0933	1159	1.4F			0434	0813	2.0E
	1531	1810	1.5E			1045	1311	1.6F
	2138					1638	2024	1.7E
						2252		
14 Th		0026	2.0F					
	0408	0651	1.7E					
	1037	1259	1.4F					
	1632	1916	1.5E					
	2238							
15 F		0124	2.2F					
	0511	0815	1.8E					
	1138	1357	1.5F					
	1733	2032	1.7E					
	2336							

March

Day	Slack	Maximum	knots		Day	Slack	Maximum	knots
1 F		0144	1.8F		16 Sa		0105	2.1F
	0531	0909	2.0E			0454	0816	1.8E
	1139	1405	1.6F			1118	1339	1.5F
	1734	2121	1.7E			1718	2035	1.7E
	2346					2321		
2 Sa		0237	1.8F		17 Su		0205	2.3F
	0623	1000	2.0E			0555	0923	2.1E
	1229	1456	1.6F			1213	1438	1.7F
	1827	2212	1.7E			1818	2143	2.0E
3 Su	0036	0326	1.8F		18 M	0020	0303	2.4F
	0710	1046	2.1E			0651	1017	2.3E
	1315	1543	1.7F			1304	1534	2.0F
	1916	2257	1.7E			1915	2240	2.3E
4 M	0124	0410	1.8F		19 Tu	0117	0400	2.5F
	0753	1128	2.0E			0744	1106	2.5E
	1358	1627	1.8F			1353	1628	2.2F
	2001	2338	1.7E			2008	2333	2.5E
5 Tu	0209	0450	1.8F		20 W ○	0212	0454	2.7F
	0833	1207	2.0E			0834	1154	2.6E
	1439	1708	1.9F			1440	1718	2.5F
	2042					2058		
6 W ●		0012	1.7E		21 Th		0024	2.7E
	0251	0528	1.9F			0305	0545	2.7F
	0910	1240	2.0E			0922	1239	2.6E
	1516	1746	2.0F			1526	1805	2.6F
	2120					2147		
7 Th		0029	1.8E		22 F		0113	2.8E
	0331	0605	1.9F			0356	0632	2.7F
	0946	1302	1.9E			1008	1324	2.6E
	1553	1823	2.1F			1611	1850	2.7F
	2156					2236		
8 F		0047	1.8E		23 Sa		0202	2.8E
	0409	0642	2.0F			0446	0718	2.6F
	1022	1319	1.9E			1054	1408	2.5E
	1628	1900	2.2F			1656	1935	2.7F
	2232					2325		
9 Sa		0119	1.9E		24 Su		0251	2.7E
	0448	0720	2.0F			0535	0803	2.4F
	1059	1349	1.9E			1141	1451	2.3E
	1704	1939	2.2F			1743	2022	2.5F
	2310							
10 Su		0159	1.9E		25 M	0016	0341	2.5E
	0528	0800	1.9F			0625	0852	2.2F
	1138	1426	1.8E			1229	1535	2.1E
	1742	2021	2.1F			1832	2112	2.3F
	2352							
11 M		0242	1.9E		26 Tu	0110	0435	2.2E
	0613	0844	1.7F			0718	0944	1.9F
	1221	1509	1.7E			1320	1623	1.9E
	1825	2108	2.0F			1925	2207	2.0F
12 Tu ◐	0042	0331	1.8E		27 W ◑	0206	0535	2.0E
	0705	0935	1.6F			0815	1040	1.7F
	1311	1556	1.6E			1414	1721	1.7E
	1914	2201	2.0F			2023	2308	1.8F
13 W	0141	0424	1.7E		28 Th	0303	0639	1.8E
	0805	1032	1.4F			0913	1139	1.6F
	1408	1649	1.5E			1509	1839	1.5E
	2012	2301	1.9F			2123		
14 Th ◐	0245	0525	1.7E		29 F		0010	1.7F
	0912	1135	1.4F			0359	0740	1.8E
	1511	1750	1.5E			1010	1237	1.6F
	2115					1605	1951	1.5E
						2221		
15 F		0003	2.0F		30 Sa		0108	1.7F
	0351	0639	1.7E			0453	0835	1.8E
	1018	1238	1.4F			1103	1330	1.6F
	1615	1904	1.5E			1700	2049	1.5E
	2219					2315		
					31 Su		0159	1.7F
						0543	0924	1.9E
						1151	1418	1.7F
						1752	2138	1.6E

Time meridian 75° W. 0000 is midnight. 1200 is noon. Times are not adjusted for Daylight Saving Time.

Savannah River Entrance, Georgia, 2019

F–Flood, Dir. 286° True   E–Ebb, Dir. 110° True

April

Day	Slack h m	Max h m	knots
1 M	0006	0246	1.7F
	0629	1008	1.9E
	1235	1504	1.8F
	1840	2221	1.7E
2 Tu	0053	0331	1.8F
	0713	1048	1.9E
	1317	1548	1.9F
	1924	2257	1.8E
3 W	0138	0414	1.8F
	0754	1123	1.9E
	1358	1630	2.1F
	2005	2324	1.8E
4 Th	0221	0456	1.9F
	0835	1151	1.9E
	1437	1711	2.2F
	2045	2345	2.0E
5 F ●	0303	0536	2.0F
	0914	1215	1.9E
	1516	1752	2.3F
	2123		
6 Sa		0016	2.1E
	0343	0616	2.0F
	0953	1244	1.9E
	1554	1832	2.3F
	2202		
7 Su		0055	2.1E
	0425	0656	2.0F
	1033	1321	1.9E
	1634	1913	2.4F
	2244		
8 M		0138	2.1E
	0508	0737	2.0F
	1115	1403	1.9E
	1715	1956	2.3F
	2331		
9 Tu		0225	2.1E
	0555	0822	1.8F
	1201	1448	1.8E
	1800	2044	2.2F
10 W	0025	0315	2.0E
	0648	0913	1.6F
	1254	1538	1.7E
	1852	2139	2.1F
11 Th	0126	0411	1.9E
	0748	1012	1.5F
	1354	1634	1.6E
	1953	2240	2.0F
12 F ◐	0230	0515	1.8E
	0853	1116	1.4F
	1459	1740	1.5E
	2058	2345	2.0F
13 Sa	0334	0636	1.8E
	0957	1221	1.5F
	1603	1911	1.6E
	2205		
14 Su		0048	2.1F
	0435	0802	1.9E
	1055	1322	1.7F
	1704	2033	1.8E
	2308		
15 M		0149	2.2F
	0534	0904	2.1E
	1147	1419	1.9F
	1803	2134	2.1E
16 Tu	0007	0247	2.3F
	0630	0957	2.2E
	1237	1514	2.1F
	1858	2228	2.4E
17 W	0104	0343	2.3F
	0723	1046	2.3E
	1325	1606	2.3F
	1950	2320	2.6E
18 Th	0158	0436	2.4F
	0813	1133	2.4E
	1413	1655	2.4F
	2040		
19 F ○		0010	2.7E
	0250	0526	2.4F
	0900	1220	2.4E
	1500	1742	2.5F
	2128		
20 Sa		0059	2.8E
	0340	0612	2.4F
	0946	1305	2.4E
	1546	1827	2.6F
	2216		
21 Su		0147	2.7E
	0428	0656	2.3F
	1031	1349	2.2E
	1632	1911	2.5F
	2304		
22 M		0235	2.5E
	0515	0740	2.2F
	1116	1431	2.1E
	1718	1956	2.3F
	2353		
23 Tu		0322	2.3E
	0602	0825	2.0F
	1203	1512	1.9E
	1805	2043	2.1F
24 W	0044	0412	2.1E
	0652	0914	1.8F
	1252	1553	1.7E
	1856	2134	1.9F
25 Th	0135	0504	1.9E
	0744	1007	1.6F
	1344	1639	1.5E
	1951	2231	1.7F
26 F ○	0228	0601	1.7E
	0838	1104	1.6F
	1438	1739	1.4E
	2049	2330	1.6F
27 Sa	0319	0659	1.7E
	0932	1159	1.6F
	1532	1904	1.4E
	2147		
28 Su		0027	1.6F
	0409	0752	1.7E
	1021	1251	1.7F
	1624	2006	1.4E
	2241		
29 M		0118	1.6F
	0457	0839	1.7E
	1108	1338	1.8F
	1713	2054	1.5E
	2331		
30 Tu		0205	1.6F
	0544	0921	1.7E
	1151	1423	1.9F
	1800	2132	1.7E

May

Day	Slack h m	Max h m	knots
1 W	0019	0251	1.7F
	0630	0956	1.8E
	1234	1508	2.1F
	1844	2201	1.8E
2 Th	0104	0337	1.8F
	0715	1027	1.8E
	1316	1552	2.2F
	1928	2231	2.0E
3 F	0149	0422	1.9F
	0759	1058	1.9E
	1358	1637	2.3F
	2010	2308	2.1E
4 Sa ●	0234	0506	2.0F
	0842	1134	1.9E
	1441	1721	2.4F
	2054	2350	2.2E
5 Su	0319	0550	2.1F
	0925	1214	2.0E
	1524	1805	2.5F
	2138		
6 M		0035	2.3E
	0404	0633	2.1F
	1009	1258	2.0E
	1607	1850	2.5F
	2225		
7 Tu		0123	2.3E
	0451	0717	2.0F
	1055	1344	1.9E
	1653	1936	2.5F
	2316		
8 W		0213	2.3E
	0540	0805	1.9F
	1145	1434	1.9E
	1741	2026	2.4F
9 Th	0012	0306	2.2E
	0633	0857	1.8F
	1241	1527	1.8E
	1836	2121	2.3F
10 F	0111	0403	2.1E
	0731	0955	1.6F
	1342	1627	1.6E
	1937	2222	2.1F
11 Sa ◐	0212	0507	2.0E
	0831	1059	1.6F
	1445	1741	1.7E
	2044	2327	2.1F
12 Su	0313	0622	2.0E
	0931	1203	1.7F
	1548	1908	1.8E
	2151		
13 M		0032	2.1F
	0413	0737	2.0E
	1026	1303	1.9F
	1647	2019	2.1E
	2254		
14 Tu		0132	2.1F
	0510	0839	2.1E
	1119	1359	2.1F
	1744	2118	2.3E
	2353		
15 W		0229	2.1F
	0606	0933	2.2E
	1209	1451	2.2F
	1839	2212	2.5E
16 Th	0049	0324	2.1F
	0659	1025	2.2E
	1258	1543	2.3F
	1932	2304	2.6E
17 F	0142	0416	2.1F
	0750	1114	2.2E
	1347	1633	2.4F
	2022	2355	2.6E
18 Sa ○	0234	0506	2.1F
	0838	1203	2.2E
	1436	1721	2.4F
	2111		
19 Su		0044	2.6E
	0323	0552	2.1F
	0925	1250	2.1E
	1523	1806	2.4F
	2159		
20 M		0133	2.5E
	0410	0635	2.0F
	1009	1334	2.0E
	1609	1850	2.3F
	2245		
21 Tu		0219	2.4E
	0455	0717	2.0F
	1054	1416	1.9E
	1655	1932	2.2F
	2331		
22 W		0304	2.2E
	0540	0800	1.8F
	1139	1453	1.7E
	1740	2016	2.0F
23 Th	0016	0348	2.0E
	0625	0846	1.7F
	1226	1525	1.6E
	1827	2102	1.8F
24 F	0102	0431	1.8E
	0712	0934	1.6F
	1315	1558	1.4E
	1918	2153	1.6F
25 Sa	0149	0514	1.7E
	0800	1026	1.6F
	1406	1640	1.4E
	2012	2248	1.5F
26 Su ◐	0236	0557	1.6E
	0849	1119	1.7F
	1456	1728	1.3E
	2108	2343	1.5F
27 M	0323	0640	1.5E
	0936	1210	1.8F
	1544	1821	1.4E
	2203		
28 Tu		0035	1.5F
	0410	0722	1.5E
	1022	1257	1.9F
	1632	1918	1.5E
	2254		
29 W		0124	1.6F
	0458	0803	1.6E
	1107	1343	2.0F
	1718	2011	1.7E
	2343		
30 Th		0212	1.7F
	0547	0845	1.6E
	1151	1429	2.1F
	1805	2101	1.9E
31 F	0030	0259	1.8F
	0635	0928	1.7E
	1236	1516	2.3F
	1852	2149	2.0E

June

Day	Slack h m	Max h m	knots
1 Sa	0118	0348	1.9F
	0724	1013	1.8E
	1322	1605	2.4F
	1941	2239	2.2E
2 Su	0207	0436	2.0F
	0811	1100	1.9E
	1409	1653	2.5F
	2029	2329	2.3E
3 M ●	0256	0525	2.0F
	0859	1149	2.0E
	1456	1742	2.7F
	2119		
4 Tu		0021	2.4E
	0345	0612	2.1F
	0946	1238	2.1E
	1544	1830	2.7F
	2210		
5 W		0113	2.5E
	0434	0700	2.1F
	1036	1330	2.1E
	1633	1918	2.7F
	2302		
6 Th		0205	2.5E
	0524	0748	2.1F
	1129	1424	2.1E
	1725	2009	2.6F
	2356		
7 F		0258	2.4E
	0615	0840	2.0F
	1226	1520	2.0E
	1821	2104	2.5F
8 Sa	0052	0353	2.3E
	0708	0937	1.9F
	1326	1623	2.0E
	1922	2204	2.3F
9 Su	0150	0451	2.2E
	0804	1039	1.9F
	1427	1735	2.0E
	2027	2308	2.1F
10 M ○	0249	0556	2.1E
	0900	1141	2.0F
	1527	1851	2.1E
	2133		
11 Tu		0012	2.1F
	0347	0706	2.1E
	0956	1241	2.1F
	1626	1958	2.2E
	2236		
12 W		0112	2.0F
	0444	0811	2.1E
	1050	1336	2.2F
	1724	2059	2.4E
	2335		
13 Th		0208	2.0F
	0540	0910	2.1E
	1143	1430	2.2F
	1820	2154	2.5E
14 F	0031	0303	1.9F
	0635	1004	2.1E
	1234	1522	2.2F
	1914	2247	2.5E
15 Sa	0124	0355	1.9F
	0727	1056	2.0E
	1325	1614	2.2F
	2006	2338	2.5E
16 Su	0216	0445	1.9F
	0816	1146	2.0E
	1415	1704	2.2F
	2055		
17 M ○		0028	2.5E
	0305	0532	1.8F
	0903	1235	1.9E
	1503	1749	2.2F
	2142		
18 Tu		0116	2.4E
	0351	0615	1.8F
	0948	1320	1.8E
	1549	1830	2.1F
	2225		
19 W		0201	2.3E
	0435	0655	1.8F
	1032	1401	1.7E
	1633	1910	2.0F
	2306		
20 Th		0243	2.1E
	0516	0736	1.8F
	1115	1435	1.6E
	1715	1949	1.9F
	2346		
21 F		0320	1.9E
	0557	0817	1.7F
	1159	1454	1.5E
	1759	2031	1.7F
22 Sa	0026	0351	1.8E
	0637	0901	1.7F
	1243	1520	1.4E
	1844	2116	1.6F
23 Su	0108	0410	1.6E
	0719	0947	1.7F
	1329	1558	1.4E
	1934	2206	1.5F
24 M	0151	0437	1.6E
	0803	1037	1.7F
	1415	1642	1.4E
	2027	2259	1.4F
25 Tu ○	0237	0516	1.5E
	0849	1127	1.8F
	1502	1730	1.5E
	2121	2353	1.5F
26 W	0326	0603	1.5E
	0937	1217	1.9F
	1550	1823	1.6E
	2215		
27 Th		0044	1.5F
	0415	0655	1.5E
	1024	1305	2.0F
	1639	1920	1.7E
	2307		
28 F		0135	1.6F
	0507	0750	1.6E
	1112	1354	2.2F
	1730	2020	1.8E
	2359		
29 Sa		0225	1.7F
	0559	0845	1.7E
	1201	1445	2.3F
	1823	2119	2.0E
30 Su	0051	0317	1.8F
	0651	0940	1.8E
	1251	1536	2.5F
	1917	2218	2.2E

Time meridian 75° W. 0000 is midnight. 1200 is noon. Times are not adjusted for Daylight Saving Time.

118

Savannah River Entrance, Georgia, 2019

F–Flood, Dir. 286° True   E–Ebb, Dir. 110° True

July

Day	Slack (h m)	Maximum (h m)	knots
1 M	0143	0409	1.9E
	0743	1034	1.9E
	1341	1629	2.6F
	2010	2315	2.4E
2 Tu ●	0235	0501	2.0F
	0835	1129	2.1E
	1433	1721	2.8F
	2102		
3 W		0010	2.5E
	0325	0552	2.1F
	0926	1224	2.2E
	1524	1811	2.9F
	2153		
4 Th		0103	2.6E
	0415	0642	2.2F
	1018	1319	2.3E
	1617	1902	2.9F
	2245		
5 F		0154	2.7E
	0503	0731	2.3F
	1112	1415	2.3E
	1710	1952	2.8F
	2337		
6 Sa		0244	2.7E
	0551	0821	2.3F
	1207	1512	2.3E
	1806	2046	2.6F
7 Su	0030	0334	2.6E
	0641	0915	2.3F
	1305	1612	2.3E
	1905	2143	2.4F
8 M	0125	0428	2.4E
	0734	1013	2.2F
	1404	1717	2.3E
	2008	2245	2.2F
9 Tu ◑	0222	0527	2.2E
	0829	1114	2.2F
	1503	1827	2.3E
	2112	2347	2.0F
10 W	0319	0635	2.1E
	0926	1215	2.2F
	1603	1935	2.3E
	2215		
11 Th		0048	1.9F
	0416	0744	2.0E
	1023	1313	2.2F
	1702	2037	2.3E
	2314		
12 F		0145	1.8F
	0513	0847	2.0E
	1118	1410	2.2F
	1800	2134	2.4E
13 Sa	0010	0240	1.8F
	0609	0944	2.0E
	1212	1505	2.1F
	1856	2228	2.4E
14 Su	0104	0333	1.7F
	0702	1038	1.9E
	1304	1559	2.1F
	1948	2319	2.4E
15 M	0155	0425	1.7F
	0753	1129	1.9E
	1354	1649	2.0F
	2037		
16 Tu ○		0008	2.3E
	0243	0511	1.9E
	0841	1217	1.8E
	1442	1732	2.0F
	2121		
17 W		0054	2.3E
	0328	0553	1.7F
	0926	1302	1.7E
	1528	1810	2.0F
	2201		
18 Th		0137	2.2E
	0409	0632	1.8F
	1008	1341	1.7E
	1610	1846	1.9F
	2238		
19 F		0215	2.0E
	0447	0709	1.8F
	1048	1409	1.6E
	1650	1923	1.8F
	2314		
20 Sa		0246	1.9E
	0524	0747	1.8F
	1127	1417	1.5E
	1730	2001	1.7F
	2350		
21 Su		0301	1.7E
	0600	0826	1.8F
	1207	1443	1.5E
	1811	2042	1.6F
22 M	0027	0318	1.6E
	0638	0909	1.8F
	1248	1520	1.5E
	1856	2127	1.5F
23 Tu	0109	0351	1.6E
	0718	0955	1.8F
	1332	1604	1.5E
	1945	2218	1.5F
24 W ○	0155	0433	1.5E
	0804	1045	1.8F
	1419	1652	1.6E
	2040	2312	1.4F
25 Th	0244	0521	1.5E
	0853	1138	1.9F
	1511	1745	1.6E
	2137		
26 F		0007	1.5F
	0337	0614	1.5E
	0946	1231	2.0F
	1605	1845	1.7E
	2235		
27 Sa		0101	1.5F
	0431	0712	1.6E
	1039	1324	2.1F
	1702	1950	1.8E
	2332		
28 Su		0155	1.6F
	0527	0814	1.6E
	1132	1418	2.3F
	1800	2100	2.0E
29 M	0027	0250	1.7F
	0624	0916	1.8E
	1225	1512	2.5F
	1857	2205	2.2E
30 Tu	0121	0345	1.8F
	0720	1018	2.0E
	1319	1607	2.7F
	1952	2303	2.4E
31 W ●	0213	0440	2.0F
	0814	1117	2.2E
	1414	1701	2.8F
	2044	2357	2.6E

August

Day	Slack (h m)	Maximum (h m)	knots
1 Th	0303	0532	2.2F
	0907	1214	2.3E
	1508	1754	2.9F
	2135		
2 F		0047	2.7E
	0351	0622	2.4F
	0959	1309	2.5E
	1601	1844	3.0F
	2224		
3 Sa		0135	2.8E
	0437	0710	2.5F
	1051	1403	2.6E
	1654	1934	2.9F
	2314		
4 Su		0223	2.8E
	0524	0759	2.6F
	1145	1457	2.6E
	1749	2025	2.7F
5 M	0006	0311	2.6E
	0612	0850	2.5F
	1240	1554	2.5E
	1845	2120	2.4F
6 Tu	0059	0402	2.4E
	0703	0944	2.4F
	1338	1655	2.4E
	1945	2218	2.2F
7 W ◑	0154	0458	2.2E
	0759	1044	2.3F
	1437	1802	2.3E
	2047	2319	2.0F
8 Th	0250	0604	2.0E
	0857	1147	2.2F
	1538	1910	2.2E
	2150		
9 F		0021	1.8F
	0348	0717	1.9E
	0957	1251	2.1F
	1639	2014	2.2E
	2250		
10 Sa		0120	1.7F
	0446	0824	1.9E
	1055	1351	2.1F
	1738	2112	2.3E
	2347		
11 Su		0216	1.7F
	0542	0923	1.9E
	1150	1449	2.0F
	1834	2206	2.3E
12 M	0040	0310	1.6F
	0637	1017	1.9E
	1243	1543	2.0F
	1925	2256	2.3E
13 Tu	0129	0400	1.7F
	0729	1107	1.9E
	1333	1630	1.9F
	2011	2342	2.3E
14 W	0215	0446	1.7F
	0816	1154	1.8E
	1420	1710	1.9F
	2053		
15 Th ○		0026	2.2E
	0258	0526	1.8F
	0900	1236	1.8E
	1504	1746	1.9F
	2131		
16 F		0106	2.1E
	0337	0603	1.9F
	0939	1312	1.7E
	1545	1820	1.9F
	2206		
17 Sa		0140	2.0E
	0413	0639	1.9F
	1016	1331	1.6E
	1624	1855	1.8F
	2240		
18 Su		0202	1.8E
	0448	0715	2.0F
	1052	1339	1.6E
	1701	1931	1.8F
	2315		
19 M		0212	1.7E
	0522	0752	2.0F
	1127	1409	1.7E
	1740	2010	1.7F
	2351		
20 Tu		0238	1.7E
	0558	0832	1.9F
	1206	1448	1.7E
	1821	2052	1.6F
21 W	0031	0315	1.6E
	0638	0917	1.9F
	1250	1532	1.7E
	1909	2141	1.5F
22 Th	0117	0359	1.5E
	0723	1007	1.8F
	1341	1621	1.6E
	2004	2235	1.4F
23 F ○	0209	0448	1.5E
	0815	1103	1.8F
	1439	1716	1.6E
	2106	2334	1.4F
24 Sa	0305	0542	1.4E
	0912	1200	1.9F
	1540	1818	1.6E
	2210		
25 Su		0033	1.4F
	0404	0644	1.5E
	1011	1258	2.1F
	1641	1931	1.7E
	2310		
26 M		0131	1.5F
	0505	0753	1.6E
	1109	1355	2.2F
	1742	2051	1.9E
27 Tu	0006	0228	1.6F
	0604	0906	1.8E
	1206	1452	2.4F
	1839	2156	2.2E
28 W	0059	0324	1.8F
	0701	1011	2.0E
	1302	1548	2.6F
	1933	2249	2.4E
29 Th	0149	0419	2.1F
	0756	1109	2.3E
	1358	1643	2.8F
	2025	2339	2.6E
30 F ●	0237	0511	2.4F
	0848	1204	2.5E
	1452	1735	2.9F
	2114		
31 Sa		0027	2.7E
	0324	0600	2.6F
	0938	1256	2.7E
	1545	1825	2.9F
	2203		

September

Day	Slack (h m)	Maximum (h m)	knots
1 Su		0113	2.8E
	0410	0647	2.7F
	1029	1348	2.8E
	1638	1914	2.8F
	2251		
2 M		0200	2.7E
	0456	0734	2.8F
	1121	1440	2.8E
	1730	2003	2.7F
	2340		
3 Tu		0247	2.6E
	0544	0823	2.7F
	1215	1534	2.6E
	1823	2054	2.4F
4 W	0032	0336	2.4E
	0634	0916	2.5F
	1312	1632	2.4E
	1920	2149	2.1F
5 Th ◑	0126	0430	2.1E
	0729	1014	2.3F
	1411	1736	2.2E
	2020	2249	1.9F
6 F	0222	0534	1.9E
	0829	1118	2.1F
	1512	1844	2.1E
	2122	2352	1.7F
7 Sa	0320	0650	1.8E
	0931	1225	2.0F
	1613	1948	2.1E
	2222		
8 Su		0053	1.7F
	0418	0800	1.8E
	1031	1329	1.9F
	1711	2046	2.1E
	2318		
9 M		0149	1.6F
	0515	0900	1.8E
	1127	1426	1.9F
	1805	2138	2.2E
10 Tu	0010	0241	1.7F
	0609	0953	1.8E
	1219	1516	1.9F
	1853	2226	2.2E
11 W	0057	0328	1.7F
	0700	1041	1.8E
	1308	1559	1.9F
	1938	2310	2.1E
12 Th	0140	0411	1.8F
	0745	1125	1.8E
	1354	1639	1.8F
	2018	2351	2.1E
13 F ○	0221	0452	1.9F
	0827	1203	1.8E
	1437	1716	1.8F
	2056		
14 Sa		0028	2.0E
	0259	0529	2.0F
	0905	1233	1.8E
	1518	1751	1.9F
	2132		
15 Su		0057	1.9E
	0336	0606	2.1F
	0941	1243	1.8E
	1556	1827	1.9F
	2208		
16 M		0111	1.8E
	0411	0643	2.1F
	1015	1304	1.8E
	1633	1903	1.9F
	2243		
17 Tu		0132	1.7E
	0446	0720	2.1F
	1051	1339	1.9E
	1712	1941	1.8F
	2319		
18 W		0206	1.7E
	0523	0800	2.1F
	1130	1420	1.8E
	1753	2023	1.7F
19 Th	0000	0246	1.6E
	0603	0845	2.0F
	1217	1506	1.8E
	1841	2110	1.5F
20 F ◑	0047	0331	1.5E
	0650	0935	1.9F
	1313	1558	1.7E
	1938	2205	1.4F
21 Sa ○	0142	0422	1.4E
	0744	1033	1.8F
	1416	1655	1.6E
	2043	2306	1.3F
22 Su	0244	0519	1.4E
	0846	1135	1.9F
	1520	1800	1.6E
	2148		
23 M		0010	1.4F
	0347	0626	1.4E
	0950	1237	2.0F
	1623	1922	1.7E
	2248		
24 Tu		0110	1.5F
	0449	0749	1.6E
	1052	1336	2.2F
	1723	2043	2.0E
	2343		
25 W		0208	1.7F
	0548	0907	1.9E
	1151	1434	2.3F
	1819	2141	2.2E
26 Th	0034	0303	2.0F
	0644	1006	2.2E
	1248	1530	2.5F
	1913	2231	2.4E
27 F	0122	0357	2.2F
	0738	1100	2.5E
	1344	1625	2.6F
	2004	2319	2.5E
28 Sa ●	0210	0448	2.5F
	0829	1152	2.7E
	1438	1717	2.7F
	2053		
29 Su		0006	2.6E
	0257	0536	2.7F
	0918	1243	2.8E
	1530	1806	2.7F
	2141		
30 M		0052	2.6E
	0343	0623	2.8F
	1008	1333	2.9E
	1620	1853	2.7F
	2228		

Time meridian 75° W. 0000 is midnight. 1200 is noon. Times are not adjusted for Daylight Saving Time.

Savannah River Entrance, Georgia, 2019

F–Flood, Dir. 286° True   E–Ebb, Dir. 110° True

October

Day	Slack	Maximum	knots
1 Tu		0138	2.6E
	0430	0710	2.8F
	1059	1424	2.8E
	1710	1940	2.5F
	2316		
2 W		0224	2.4E
	0518	0757	2.6F
	1151	1516	2.6E
	1801	2028	2.3F
3 Th	0005	0312	2.2E
	0608	0848	2.4F
	1247	1611	2.4E
	1855	2121	2.0F
4 F	0058	0404	2.0E
	0702	0944	2.2F
	1345	1711	2.2E
	1952	2218	1.8F
5 Sa ◐	0154	0505	1.8E
	0800	1047	2.0F
	1443	1815	2.0E
	2052	2320	1.7F
6 Su	0251	0620	1.7E
	0902	1154	1.8F
	1541	1917	2.0E
	2150		
7 M		0021	1.6F
	0349	0731	1.6E
	1003	1257	1.8F
	1636	2014	2.0E
	2244		
8 Tu		0116	1.7F
	0445	0832	1.7E
	1100	1351	1.8F
	1727	2105	2.0E
	2333		
9 W		0205	1.8F
	0537	0923	1.8E
	1151	1438	1.8F
	1814	2151	2.0E
10 Th	0018	0250	1.9F
	0625	1009	1.8E
	1239	1520	1.8F
	1858	2233	2.0E
11 F	0100	0332	2.0F
	0709	1049	1.9E
	1324	1601	1.8F
	1939	2310	1.9E
12 Sa	0140	0414	2.0F
	0750	1123	1.9E
	1407	1641	1.8F
	2019	2343	1.9E
13 Su ○	0220	0454	2.1F
	0829	1144	1.9E
	1448	1720	1.9F
	2058		
14 M		0006	1.8E
	0258	0533	2.2F
	0906	1203	2.0E
	1528	1758	1.9F
	2136		
15 Tu		0028	1.8E
	0336	0612	2.3F
	0943	1235	2.0E
	1607	1837	1.9F
	2214		
16 W		0100	1.8E
	0414	0652	2.3F
	1023	1315	2.0E
	1648	1917	1.9F
	2253		
17 Th		0139	1.7E
	0454	0734	2.2F
	1106	1400	2.0E
	1733	1959	1.8F
	2336		
18 F		0223	1.7E
	0536	0819	2.1F
	1156	1448	1.9E
	1822	2047	1.6F
19 Sa	0026	0311	1.6E
	0625	0911	2.0F
	1254	1542	1.8E
	1919	2142	1.5F
20 Su	0125	0404	1.5E
	0722	1009	1.9F
	1357	1640	1.8E
	2022	2245	1.4F
21 M ○	0229	0505	1.4E
	0827	1113	1.9F
	1501	1747	1.7E
	2125	2350	1.4F
22 Tu	0333	0620	1.5E
	0934	1218	2.0F
	1603	1910	1.8E
	2224		
23 W		0052	1.6F
	0434	0754	1.7E
	1038	1319	2.1F
	1702	2024	2.0E
	2317		
24 Th		0148	1.8F
	0532	0901	2.0E
	1138	1416	2.2F
	1758	2121	2.1E
25 F	0007	0242	2.1F
	0627	0957	2.3E
	1235	1512	2.3F
	1852	2211	2.3E
26 Sa	0055	0334	2.3F
	0720	1049	2.6E
	1330	1606	2.4F
	1943	2300	2.4E
27 Su ●	0143	0425	2.5F
	0811	1140	2.7E
	1423	1657	2.4F
	2032	2347	2.4E
28 M	0231	0514	2.6F
	0901	1230	2.8E
	1514	1746	2.5F
	2119		
29 Tu		0034	2.4E
	0319	0602	2.7F
	0950	1320	2.8E
	1603	1832	2.4F
	2206		
30 W		0121	2.3E
	0406	0648	2.6F
	1040	1410	2.7E
	1652	1918	2.3F
	2253		
31 Th		0207	2.2E
	0454	0734	2.5F
	1131	1500	2.5E
	1741	2004	2.1F
	2341		

November

Day	Slack	Maximum	knots
1 F		0253	2.1E
	0543	0823	2.3F
	1223	1551	2.3E
	1831	2053	1.9F
2 Sa	0032	0341	1.9E
	0635	0915	2.1F
	1316	1644	2.1E
	1924	2147	1.7F
3 Su	0126	0436	1.7E
	0731	1012	1.8F
	1410	1741	1.9E
	2018	2245	1.6F
4 M ◐	0222	0543	1.5E
	0830	1114	1.7F
	1503	1839	1.8E
	2113	2343	1.6F
5 Tu	0317	0654	1.5E
	0930	1214	1.6F
	1554	1934	1.8E
	2204		
6 W		0037	1.7F
	0410	0755	1.6E
	1027	1307	1.6F
	1643	2024	1.8E
	2251		
7 Th		0124	1.8F
	0500	0846	1.6E
	1119	1354	1.6F
	1730	2109	1.8E
	2335		
8 F		0209	2.0F
	0546	0929	1.7E
	1206	1439	1.7F
	1815	2148	1.8E
9 Sa	0017	0252	2.1F
	0630	1005	1.8E
	1251	1522	1.7F
	1859	2222	1.8E
10 Su	0059	0335	2.1F
	0712	1032	1.9E
	1335	1605	1.8F
	1942	2250	1.8E
11 M	0141	0419	2.2F
	0754	1057	2.0E
	1418	1648	1.9F
	2025	2318	1.8E
12 Tu ○	0222	0502	2.3F
	0836	1132	2.1E
	1501	1731	1.9F
	2106	2354	1.8E
13 W	0304	0545	2.4F
	0918	1213	2.2E
	1544	1813	2.0F
	2148		
14 Th		0034	1.8E
	0346	0628	2.4F
	1002	1258	2.2E
	1629	1856	1.9F
	2231		
15 F		0118	1.8E
	0429	0713	2.4F
	1050	1346	2.2E
	1716	1940	1.9F
	2318		
16 Sa		0206	1.8E
	0516	0800	2.4F
	1142	1437	2.1E
	1806	2029	1.7F
17 Su	0012	0257	1.7E
	0607	0852	2.2F
	1238	1530	2.1E
	1900	2124	1.6F
18 M	0112	0353	1.7E
	0705	0950	2.1F
	1338	1628	2.0E
	1958	2225	1.6F
19 Tu ◐	0214	0458	1.6E
	0811	1053	2.0F
	1439	1732	1.9E
	2058	2329	1.7F
20 W	0316	0620	1.7E
	0918	1158	2.0F
	1540	1847	1.9E
	2154		
21 Th		0030	1.8F
	0416	0743	1.9E
	1023	1300	2.0F
	1638	1959	2.0E
	2248		
22 F		0127	2.0F
	0514	0847	2.2E
	1124	1358	2.1F
	1735	2059	2.1E
	2339		
23 Sa		0220	2.2F
	0609	0943	2.4E
	1221	1454	2.1F
	1829	2152	2.1E
24 Su	0029	0313	2.3F
	0703	1036	2.6E
	1315	1547	2.1F
	1922	2243	2.2E
25 M	0119	0405	2.4F
	0755	1127	2.7E
	1408	1639	2.2F
	2011	2333	2.2E
26 Tu ●	0209	0455	2.5F
	0846	1218	2.7E
	1458	1728	2.2F
	2059		
27 W		0022	2.2E
	0258	0544	2.5F
	0936	1308	2.6E
	1547	1814	2.1F
	2146		
28 Th		0109	2.1E
	0346	0630	2.4F
	1024	1356	2.5E
	1634	1858	2.1F
	2232		
29 F		0155	2.0E
	0434	0714	2.3F
	1111	1443	2.4E
	1720	1942	2.0F
	2319		
30 Sa		0239	1.9E
	0521	0759	2.2F
	1158	1529	2.2E
	1806	2027	1.9F

December

Day	Slack	Maximum	knots
1 Su	0008	0321	1.7E
	0609	0845	2.0F
	1245	1614	2.0E
	1853	2116	1.8F
2 M	0058	0402	1.6E
	0700	0936	1.7F
	1332	1700	1.8E
	1941	2208	1.7F
3 Tu	0149	0445	1.5E
	0755	1031	1.6F
	1420	1747	1.7E
	2030	2301	1.7F
4 W ◐	0240	0537	1.4E
	0852	1127	1.5F
	1508	1836	1.6E
	2118	2352	1.8F
5 Th	0330	0644	1.4E
	0948	1220	1.5F
	1555	1924	1.5E
	2205		
6 F		0041	1.9F
	0417	0744	1.5E
	1040	1310	1.5F
	1643	2008	1.5E
	2251		
7 Sa		0127	2.0F
	0504	0826	1.6E
	1129	1356	1.6F
	1731	2045	1.6E
	2335		
8 Su		0213	2.1F
	0550	0901	1.8E
	1216	1443	1.7F
	1819	2120	1.6E
9 M	0019	0259	2.2F
	0636	0940	1.9E
	1302	1530	1.8F
	1906	2159	1.7E
10 Tu	0104	0346	2.3F
	0723	1023	2.0E
	1349	1617	1.8F
	1952	2242	1.8E
11 W	0150	0433	2.4F
	0810	1109	2.2E
	1436	1705	1.9F
	2038	2327	1.9E
12 Th ○	0236	0521	2.5F
	0858	1158	2.3E
	1524	1751	2.0F
	2125		
13 F		0014	1.9E
	0322	0608	2.6F
	0946	1247	2.4E
	1611	1837	2.0F
	2212		
14 Sa		0103	2.0E
	0410	0655	2.7F
	1035	1336	2.4E
	1659	1924	2.0F
	2302		
15 Su		0154	2.0E
	0459	0743	2.6F
	1126	1426	2.4E
	1747	2013	2.0F
	2356		
16 M		0248	2.0E
	0552	0835	2.5F
	1220	1518	2.3E
	1838	2105	2.0F
17 Tu	0054	0345	1.9E
	0650	0931	2.3F
	1317	1611	2.2E
	1931	2203	1.9F
18 W	0154	0450	1.9E
	0754	1033	2.1F
	1415	1710	2.1E
	2026	2304	2.0F
19 Th ◐	0255	0607	2.0E
	0900	1137	2.0F
	1514	1817	2.0E
	2123		
20 F		0005	2.0F
	0355	0723	2.1E
	1005	1239	2.0F
	1612	1931	2.0E
	2219		
21 Sa		0104	2.1F
	0454	0829	2.3E
	1107	1338	1.9F
	1710	2037	2.0E
	2314		
22 Su		0200	2.2F
	0552	0927	2.4E
	1204	1434	1.9F
	1806	2135	2.0E
23 M	0007	0255	2.3F
	0648	1022	2.5E
	1259	1529	1.9F
	1900	2229	2.0E
24 Tu	0059	0349	2.3F
	0742	1114	2.6E
	1352	1622	1.9F
	1952	2321	2.1E
25 W	0151	0442	2.3F
	0834	1205	2.6E
	1443	1711	1.9F
	2041		
26 Th ●		0011	2.0E
	0241	0531	2.3F
	0922	1254	2.5E
	1531	1757	1.9F
	2128		
27 F		0059	2.0E
	0329	0615	2.3F
	1007	1340	2.5E
	1616	1839	1.9F
	2214		
28 Sa		0144	1.9E
	0415	0655	2.2F
	1050	1424	2.3E
	1658	1920	1.9F
	2258		
29 Su		0224	1.8E
	0459	0735	2.0F
	1131	1504	2.1E
	1739	2001	1.9F
	2342		
30 M		0258	1.7E
	0543	0816	1.9F
	1211	1540	1.9E
	1820	2043	1.8F
31 Tu	0027	0321	1.5E
	0629	0900	1.7F
	1252	1608	1.7E
	1901	2129	1.8F

Time meridian 75° W. 0000 is midnight. 1200 is noon. Times are not adjusted for Daylight Saving Time.

St. Marys River Entrance, Georgia, 2019

F–Flood, Dir. 272° True   E–Ebb, Dir. 093° True

January

Day	Slack h m	Maximum h m	knots
1 Tu		0320	2.7F
	0549	0854	2.5E
	1223	1552	2.2F
	1805	2050	2.4E
2 W	0020	0410	2.8F
	0642	0943	2.5E
	1320	1642	2.2F
	1857	2134	2.3E
3 Th	0112	0456	2.8F
	0730	1025	2.5E
	1408	1729	2.2F
	1945	2212	2.3E
4 F	0156	0540	2.7F
	0815	1103	2.5E
	1449	1813	2.1F
	2029	2252	2.3E
5 Sa ●	0235	0617	2.6F
	0856	1139	2.6E
	1525	1847	2.0F
	2110	2334	2.4E
6 Su	0310	0643	2.5F
	0937	1212	2.6E
	1559	1909	1.9F
	2151		
7 M		0015	2.4E
	0344	0702	2.4F
	1016	1245	2.7E
	1631	1925	1.8F
	2231		
8 Tu		0054	2.5E
	0418	0726	2.3F
	1056	1320	2.7E
	1703	1948	1.8F
	2312		
9 W		0132	2.5E
	0453	0755	2.2F
	1134	1357	2.7E
	1736	2019	1.8F
	2352		
10 Th		0213	2.5E
	0531	0830	2.0F
	1211	1438	2.7E
	1810	2058	1.7F
11 F	0032	0257	2.4E
	0612	0913	1.9F
	1249	1522	2.6E
	1846	2144	1.7F
12 Sa	0116	0346	2.3E
	0658	1001	1.7F
	1330	1611	2.4E
	1927	2231	1.8F
13 Su	0206	0438	2.3E
	0754	1050	1.6F
	1419	1701	2.4E
	2015	2318	1.8F
14 M ☽	0304	0531	2.3E
	0858	1140	1.5F
	1517	1753	2.3E
	2109		
15 Tu		0008	1.9F
	0404	0627	2.3E
	1003	1237	1.4F
	1618	1848	2.4E
	2206		
16 W		0112	2.0F
	0503	0727	2.5E
	1108	1354	1.5F
	1716	1946	2.5E
	2304		
17 Th		0226	2.3F
	0559	0826	2.7E
	1212	1506	1.7F
	1814	2043	2.7E
18 F	0004	0327	2.7F
	0654	0922	3.1E
	1312	1601	2.1F
	1909	2137	3.0E
19 Sa	0104	0420	3.1F
	0747	1016	3.4E
	1405	1655	2.4F
	2002	2231	3.3E
20 Su	0201	0514	3.4F
	0837	1112	3.6E
	1454	1749	2.7F
	2054	2328	3.5E
21 M ○	0254	0608	3.6F
	0927	1207	3.8E
	1542	1840	3.0F
	2146		
22 Tu		0024	3.7E
	0346	0659	3.6F
	1018	1258	4.0E
	1631	1929	3.1F
	2240		
23 W		0115	3.8E
	0440	0748	3.6F
	1109	1344	4.0E
	1720	2019	3.2F
	2334		
24 Th		0204	3.7E
	0535	0841	3.3F
	1200	1431	3.8E
	1810	2116	3.1F
25 F	0028	0255	3.5E
	0632	0942	2.9F
	1250	1521	3.5E
	1902	2218	2.9F
26 Sa	0123	0351	3.1E
	0733	1045	2.6F
	1344	1615	3.1E
	1957	2317	2.8F
27 Su ◐	0221	0450	2.8E
	0838	1144	2.2F
	1441	1710	2.7E
	2056		
28 M		0018	2.5F
	0323	0550	2.5E
	0946	1303	1.9F
	1541	1805	2.4E
	2156		
29 Tu		0146	2.3F
	0423	0700	2.2E
	1053	1433	1.8F
	1641	1907	2.1E
	2255		
30 W		0259	2.4F
	0522	0830	2.1E
	1159	1534	1.9F
	1739	2019	2.0E
	2354		
31 Th		0353	2.4F
	0617	0926	2.2E
	1301	1625	1.9F
	1833	2112	2.0E

February

Day	Slack h m	Maximum h m	knots
1 F	0050	0441	2.5F
	0708	1009	2.2E
	1351	1713	2.0F
	1923	2151	2.0E
2 Sa	0139	0527	2.5F
	0754	1046	2.2E
	1431	1757	2.0F
	2007	2229	2.1E
3 Su	0219	0606	2.5F
	0835	1117	2.3E
	1505	1833	2.0F
	2049	2311	2.2E
4 M ●	0255	0634	2.4F
	0915	1149	2.5E
	1536	1856	1.9F
	2128	2353	2.4E
5 Tu	0328	0650	2.3F
	0953	1222	2.6E
	1605	1906	1.9F
	2207		
6 W		0032	2.6E
	0400	0708	2.3F
	1030	1257	2.8E
	1634	1925	2.0F
	2246		
7 Th		0110	2.7E
	0433	0733	2.3F
	1106	1332	2.9E
	1702	1951	2.0F
	2323		
8 F		0149	2.8E
	0508	0803	2.2F
	1141	1410	2.9E
	1732	2024	2.1F
9 Sa	0000	0230	2.8E
	0546	0840	2.1F
	1214	1451	2.8E
	1805	2103	2.1F
10 Su	0039	0315	2.7E
	0627	0923	1.9F
	1250	1537	2.7E
	1842	2150	2.1F
11 M	0123	0406	2.6E
	0716	1013	1.8F
	1331	1627	2.5E
	1927	2240	2.1F
12 Tu ◐	0218	0459	2.5E
	0816	1105	1.6F
	1427	1719	2.5E
	2022	2331	2.1F
13 W	0323	0554	2.5E
	0925	1200	1.5F
	1536	1815	2.4E
	2126		
14 Th		0031	2.1F
	0429	0654	2.5E
	1035	1312	1.5F
	1644	1915	2.5E
	2233		
15 F		0151	2.3F
	0532	0759	2.7E
	1143	1440	1.7F
	1749	2018	2.7E
	2342		
16 Sa		0308	2.6F
	0631	0900	3.0E
	1249	1547	2.1F
	1849	2117	3.0E
17 Su	0049	0408	3.0F
	0727	0956	3.3E
	1346	1643	2.6F
	1945	2214	3.3E
18 M	0150	0505	3.4F
	0819	1053	3.6E
	1436	1738	3.0F
	2038	2313	3.6E
19 Tu ○	0245	0559	3.6F
	0910	1150	3.8E
	1523	1829	3.3F
	2130		
20 W		0011	3.8E
	0337	0650	3.7F
	0959	1241	4.0E
	1610	1916	3.5F
	2222		
21 Th		0102	4.0E
	0429	0737	3.6F
	1049	1326	4.0E
	1657	2002	3.5F
	2314		
22 F		0148	3.9E
	0521	0825	3.3F
	1137	1409	3.8E
	1744	2052	3.3F
23 Sa	0005	0235	3.6E
	0614	0919	2.9F
	1226	1454	3.4E
	1832	2148	3.0F
24 Su	0057	0324	3.2E
	0709	1019	2.5F
	1316	1543	3.0E
	1923	2245	2.7F
25 M	0151	0418	2.8E
	0809	1116	2.1F
	1410	1635	2.6E
	2019	2341	2.4F
26 Tu ◑	0249	0513	2.4E
	0914	1221	1.7F
	1509	1728	2.2E
	2120		
27 W		0057	2.1F
	0350	0611	2.0E
	1021	1404	1.5F
	1610	1824	1.9E
	2223		
28 Th		0233	2.0F
	0450	0733	1.8E
	1128	1512	1.6F
	1710	1932	1.7E
	2325		

March

Day	Slack h m	Maximum h m	knots
1 F		0332	2.1F
	0548	0901	1.9E
	1232	1604	1.7F
	1806	2044	1.7E
2 Sa	0025	0421	2.2F
	0641	0944	1.9E
	1325	1650	1.8F
	1857	2128	1.9E
3 Su	0118	0506	2.3F
	0728	1014	2.1E
	1405	1733	1.9F
	1943	2206	2.0E
4 M	0200	0546	2.3F
	0810	1042	2.2E
	1438	1809	2.0F
	2025	2246	2.2E
5 Tu	0237	0615	2.3F
	0849	1117	2.4E
	1507	1831	2.1F
	2104	2328	2.4E
6 W ●	0309	0630	2.3F
	0926	1153	2.6E
	1534	1840	2.1F
	2141		
7 Th		0008	2.7E
	0341	0646	2.3F
	1002	1229	2.8E
	1600	1858	2.2F
	2218		
8 F		0047	2.9E
	0413	0710	2.3F
	1037	1306	2.9E
	1627	1923	2.3F
	2254		
9 Sa		0125	3.0E
	0447	0739	2.3F
	1111	1343	3.0E
	1656	1954	2.4F
	2331		
10 Su		0205	3.0E
	0523	0813	2.2F
	1144	1423	2.9E
	1729	2031	2.4F
11 M	0009	0248	3.0E
	0604	0854	2.0F
	1220	1507	2.8E
	1807	2116	2.4F
12 Tu	0052	0337	2.9E
	0651	0944	1.9F
	1301	1557	2.7E
	1853	2209	2.3F
13 W	0145	0431	2.7E
	0749	1040	1.7F
	1356	1651	2.5E
	1950	2306	2.3F
14 Th ◐	0251	0528	2.6E
	0858	1137	1.6F
	1509	1749	2.5E
	2101		
15 F		0007	2.2F
	0402	0628	2.6E
	1011	1246	1.6F
	1623	1851	2.5E
	2215		
16 Sa		0127	2.2F
	0508	0734	2.7E
	1121	1424	1.8F
	1730	1958	2.7E
	2328		
17 Su		0257	2.5F
	0610	0840	2.9E
	1226	1538	2.3F
	1833	2102	3.0E
18 M	0038	0400	2.9F
	0707	0938	3.3E
	1324	1633	2.8F
	1929	2200	3.3E
19 Tu	0140	0456	3.3F
	0800	1034	3.5E
	1415	1725	3.2F
	2022	2259	3.6E
20 W ○	0235	0549	3.5F
	0849	1129	3.7E
	1501	1814	3.5F
	2112	2356	3.8E
21 Th	0326	0638	3.5F
	0937	1220	3.8E
	1545	1858	3.6F
	2202		
22 F		0046	3.9E
	0415	0722	3.4F
	1025	1304	3.8E
	1630	1940	3.6F
	2252		
23 Sa		0129	3.9E
	0504	0805	3.1F
	1113	1344	3.6E
	1715	2024	3.3F
	2341		
24 Su		0211	3.6E
	0553	0853	2.7F
	1200	1426	3.3E
	1800	2113	3.0F
25 M	0029	0255	3.2E
	0643	0948	2.3F
	1248	1510	2.9E
	1848	2209	2.6F
26 Tu	0119	0343	2.8E
	0737	1046	1.9F
	1338	1559	2.4E
	1940	2304	2.2F
27 W	0214	0435	2.3E
	0838	1142	1.6F
	1435	1651	2.1E
	2040		
28 Th		0001	1.8F
	0314	0529	2.0E
	0944	1321	1.3F
	1537	1745	1.8E
	2146		
29 F		0155	1.7F
	0414	0627	1.7E
	1048	1443	1.4F
	1638	1845	1.6E
	2250		
30 Sa		0305	1.8F
	0512	0747	1.7E
	1149	1536	1.6F
	1735	1958	1.6E
	2352		
31 Su		0354	1.9F
	0606	0855	1.8E
	1242	1621	1.8F
	1827	2056	1.8E

Time meridian 75° W. 0000 is midnight. 1200 is noon. Times are not adjusted for Daylight Saving Time.

St. Marys River Entrance, Georgia, 2019

F–Flood, Dir. 272° True   E–Ebb, Dir. 093° True

April

Day	Slack h m	Maximum h m	knots
1 M	0048	0437	2.0F
	0655	0928	2.0E
	1325	1700	1.9F
	1914	2137	2.1E
2 Tu	0134	0515	2.1F
	0738	1001	2.2E
	1400	1733	2.0F
	1957	2217	2.3E
3 W	0213	0544	2.2F
	0818	1038	2.4E
	1429	1751	2.2F
	2036	2258	2.5E
4 Th	0247	0600	2.2F
	0855	1118	2.6E
	1457	1804	2.3F
	2113	2341	2.8E
5 F ●	0319	0619	2.2F
	0931	1158	2.8E
	1524	1827	2.5F
	2149		
6 Sa		0022	3.0E
	0352	0645	2.3F
	1006	1238	2.9E
	1553	1856	2.6F
	2226		
7 Su		0102	3.2E
	0427	0716	2.3F
	1042	1317	3.0E
	1624	1929	2.7F
	2305		
8 M		0142	3.3E
	0505	0751	2.2F
	1119	1358	3.0E
	1700	2006	2.7F
	2346		
9 Tu		0225	3.2E
	0547	0832	2.1F
	1159	1442	2.9E
	1743	2052	2.6F
10 W	0032	0314	3.1E
	0636	0924	1.9F
	1245	1533	2.8E
	1833	2149	2.5F
11 Th	0125	0408	2.9E
	0734	1025	1.8F
	1344	1629	2.6E
	1934	2250	2.4F
12 F ◐	0231	0506	2.7E
	0843	1126	1.8F
	1456	1729	2.5E
	2049	2354	2.3F
13 Sa	0341	0607	2.7E
	0954	1236	1.8F
	1609	1832	2.5E
	2206		
14 Su		0114	2.2F
	0447	0713	2.7E
	1101	1416	2.0F
	1715	1942	2.7E
	2319		
15 M		0250	2.5F
	0548	0821	2.9E
	1203	1529	2.5F
	1816	2049	3.0E

Day	Slack h m	Maximum h m	knots
16 Tu	0028	0353	2.8F
	0645	0920	3.2E
	1300	1621	3.0F
	1913	2148	3.3E
17 W	0130	0446	3.1F
	0738	1012	3.4E
	1351	1709	3.3F
	2004	2243	3.6E
18 Th	0223	0537	3.2F
	0827	1104	3.5E
	1437	1756	3.5F
	2053	2338	3.7E
19 F ○	0312	0624	3.2F
	0914	1154	3.5E
	1520	1839	3.6F
	2141		
20 Sa		0027	3.7E
	0359	0706	3.1F
	1001	1239	3.5E
	1603	1919	3.4F
	2228		
21 Su		0108	3.7E
	0445	0746	2.8F
	1048	1318	3.3E
	1645	1957	3.2F
	2315		
22 M		0146	3.4E
	0531	0827	2.5F
	1134	1357	3.0E
	1729	2039	2.8F
23 Tu	0001	0226	3.1E
	0617	0914	2.1F
	1220	1438	2.7E
	1813	2128	2.4F
24 W	0048	0309	2.7E
	0705	1011	1.7F
	1308	1525	2.3E
	1902	2223	2.0F
25 Th	0139	0359	2.3E
	0800	1105	1.5F
	1401	1616	2.0E
	1957	2316	1.7F
26 F ◑	0234	0451	2.0E
	0900	1200	1.3F
	1501	1710	1.8E
	2103		
27 Sa		0013	1.5F
	0334	0545	1.8E
	1001	1358	1.3F
	1602	1806	1.7E
	2208		
28 Su		0223	1.5F
	0431	0642	1.8E
	1055	1500	1.4F
	1659	1908	1.7E
	2309		
29 M		0319	1.6F
	0525	0744	1.8E
	1146	1544	1.7F
	1752	2011	1.8E
30 Tu	0007	0401	1.8F
	0615	0837	2.0E
	1231	1618	1.9F
	1840	2101	2.1E

May

Day	Slack h m	Maximum h m	knots
1 W	0058	0434	1.9F
	0701	0919	2.2E
	1311	1641	2.1F
	1924	2143	2.4E
2 Th	0142	0457	2.0F
	0743	0959	2.4E
	1346	1658	2.3F
	2004	2225	2.7E
3 F	0220	0519	2.0F
	0822	1041	2.6E
	1418	1724	2.5F
	2043	2310	2.9E
4 Sa ●	0255	0547	2.1F
	0859	1125	2.8E
	1449	1755	2.7F
	2121	2355	3.1E
5 Su	0331	0620	2.2F
	0937	1209	3.0E
	1522	1831	2.8F
	2201		
6 M		0039	3.3E
	0409	0656	2.3F
	1017	1253	3.1E
	1559	1908	2.9F
	2244		
7 Tu		0122	3.4E
	0450	0734	2.3F
	1059	1336	3.1E
	1641	1949	2.9F
	2330		
8 W		0206	3.4E
	0536	0819	2.2F
	1146	1423	3.0E
	1729	2038	2.8F
9 Th	0019	0255	3.2E
	0627	0914	2.1F
	1238	1514	2.9E
	1824	2138	2.6F
10 F	0113	0350	3.1E
	0725	1018	2.0F
	1338	1612	2.7E
	1929	2243	2.4F
11 Sa ◐	0215	0449	2.9E
	0831	1122	2.0F
	1447	1714	2.6E
	2044	2347	2.3F
12 Su	0321	0549	2.8E
	0937	1230	2.1F
	1556	1818	2.6E
	2159		
13 M		0104	2.2F
	0425	0653	2.8E
	1040	1405	2.3F
	1700	1928	2.7E
	2310		
14 Tu		0242	2.4F
	0526	0800	2.9E
	1139	1516	2.7F
	1759	2038	3.0E
15 W	0017	0344	2.6F
	0622	0859	3.0E
	1235	1607	3.1F
	1854	2135	3.2E

Day	Slack h m	Maximum h m	knots
16 Th	0118	0436	2.8F
	0715	0949	3.1E
	1326	1654	3.3F
	1945	2227	3.3E
17 F	0211	0526	2.9F
	0805	1037	3.2E
	1413	1740	3.4F
	2033	2318	3.4E
18 Sa ○	0258	0612	2.8F
	0851	1126	3.1E
	1456	1822	3.3F
	2119		
19 Su		0006	3.4E
	0343	0653	2.7F
	0937	1212	3.0E
	1537	1900	3.2F
	2205		
20 M		0046	3.3E
	0426	0729	2.5F
	1023	1252	2.9E
	1618	1934	2.9F
	2250		
21 Tu		0122	3.2E
	0508	0804	2.2F
	1108	1330	2.8E
	1659	2009	2.6F
	2335		
22 W		0159	2.9E
	0551	0842	1.9F
	1154	1410	2.6E
	1741	2050	2.3F
23 Th	0019	0239	2.7E
	0634	0930	1.7F
	1239	1453	2.3E
	1826	2139	2.0F
24 F	0105	0324	2.4E
	0721	1023	1.5F
	1328	1543	2.1E
	1916	2232	1.7F
25 Sa	0155	0415	2.2E
	0812	1110	1.4F
	1423	1636	1.9E
	2015	2320	1.5F
26 Su ◑	0249	0506	2.0E
	0907	1156	1.3F
	1522	1730	1.8E
	2120		
27 M		0010	1.4F
	0345	0558	2.0E
	0958	1258	1.4F
	1619	1825	1.8E
	2221		
28 Tu		0133	1.3F
	0439	0652	2.0E
	1046	1447	1.5F
	1712	1924	1.9E
	2318		
29 W		0307	1.4F
	0530	0747	2.1E
	1131	1518	1.8F
	1801	2020	2.2E
30 Th	0013	0338	1.6F
	0618	0837	2.3E
	1235	1542	2.1F
	1848	2108	2.5E
31 F	0104	0405	1.8F
	0704	0922	2.5E
	1258	1611	2.3F
	1932	2153	2.7E

June

Day	Slack h m	Maximum h m	knots
1 Sa	0149	0437	1.9F
	0747	1006	2.7E
	1338	1646	2.6F
	2014	2240	3.0E
2 Su	0230	0515	2.1F
	0828	1053	2.8E
	1417	1726	2.8F
	2056	2329	3.2E
3 M ●	0310	0556	2.2F
	0910	1143	3.0E
	1458	1809	3.0F
	2140		
4 Tu		0017	3.4E
	0352	0639	2.3F
	0955	1231	3.2E
	1541	1853	3.1F
	2227		
5 W		0104	3.5E
	0437	0723	2.4F
	1044	1319	3.3E
	1629	1939	3.1F
	2316		
6 Th		0150	3.6E
	0526	0811	2.4F
	1136	1407	3.2E
	1722	2030	3.0F
7 F	0007	0239	3.5E
	0618	0908	2.3F
	1230	1459	3.1E
	1820	2131	2.8F
8 Sa	0100	0333	3.3E
	0714	1014	2.3F
	1329	1558	2.9E
	1925	2237	2.6F
9 Su	0158	0432	3.1E
	0814	1116	2.4F
	1434	1700	2.8E
	2037	2340	2.4F
10 M ◐	0300	0530	2.9E
	0917	1220	2.4F
	1539	1803	2.7E
	2149		
11 Tu		0053	2.2F
	0402	0631	2.8E
	1016	1346	2.6F
	1641	1913	2.7E
	2257		
12 W		0229	2.3F
	0502	0736	2.8E
	1114	1500	2.8F
	1740	2025	2.8E
13 Th	0003	0333	2.4F
	0559	0837	2.8E
	1210	1553	3.0F
	1835	2123	2.9E
14 F	0104	0425	2.5F
	0653	0927	2.8E
	1304	1641	3.1F
	1926	2211	3.0E
15 Sa	0158	0515	2.5F
	0743	1013	2.8E
	1352	1727	3.1F
	2014	2300	3.0E

Day	Slack h m	Maximum h m	knots
16 Su	0244	0603	2.4F
	0830	1059	2.7E
	1436	1810	3.0F
	2059	2346	3.0E
17 M ○	0327	0644	2.3F
	0915	1145	2.7E
	1516	1846	2.9F
	2143		
18 Tu		0025	2.9E
	0407	0718	2.2F
	0959	1227	2.6E
	1555	1916	2.7F
	2226		
19 W		0059	2.9E
	0446	0745	2.0F
	1043	1305	2.6E
	1633	1945	2.4F
	2309		
20 Th		0134	2.8E
	0524	0814	1.8F
	1127	1344	2.5E
	1713	2018	2.2F
	2351		
21 F		0211	2.7E
	0602	0849	1.7F
	1210	1425	2.4E
	1754	2058	2.0F
22 Sa	0033	0253	2.5E
	0641	0934	1.6F
	1255	1511	2.2E
	1839	2146	1.8F
23 Su	0116	0339	2.4E
	0723	1022	1.6F
	1343	1602	2.1E
	1929	2234	1.6F
24 M	0203	0429	2.3E
	0809	1105	1.6F
	1437	1654	2.0E
	2028	2320	1.5F
25 Tu ◑	0255	0519	2.2E
	0858	1148	1.6F
	1533	1747	2.0E
	2129		
26 W		0007	1.4F
	0349	0609	2.1E
	0946	1239	1.6F
	1628	1841	2.1E
	2228		
27 Th		0108	1.3F
	0442	0702	2.2E
	1034	1344	1.8F
	1720	1938	2.2E
	2326		
28 F		0224	1.4F
	0534	0756	2.3E
	1122	1446	2.1F
	1810	2033	2.5E
29 Sa	0023	0318	1.6F
	0624	0848	2.5E
	1212	1532	2.4F
	1859	2123	2.8E
30 Su	0116	0402	1.8F
	0713	0936	2.7E
	1303	1616	2.7F
	1947	2212	3.0E

Time meridian 75° W. 0000 is midnight. 1200 is noon. Times are not adjusted for Daylight Saving Time.

St. Marys River Entrance, Georgia, 2019

F–Flood, Dir. 272° True   E–Ebb, Dir. 093° True

July

Day	Slack	Maximum	knots
1 M	0204	0448	2.1F
	0800	1026	2.9E
	1352	1703	3.0F
	2033	2304	3.3E
2 Tu ●	0249	0536	2.3F
	0847	1119	3.1E
	1440	1752	3.2F
	2121	2357	3.5E
3 W	0335	0625	2.5F
	0937	1213	3.3E
	1529	1842	3.3F
	2210		
4 Th		0048	3.7E
	0422	0713	2.6F
	1029	1304	3.5E
	1621	1930	3.3F
	2301		
5 F		0135	3.8E
	0511	0802	2.7F
	1123	1353	3.5E
	1716	2022	3.2F
	2352		
6 Sa		0223	3.7E
	0602	0858	2.7F
	1218	1445	3.4E
	1815	2122	2.9F
7 Su	0044	0315	3.5E
	0655	1002	2.7F
	1314	1542	3.2E
	1917	2227	2.7F
8 M	0138	0411	3.2E
	0752	1104	2.7F
	1415	1643	2.9E
	2024	2328	2.5F
9 Tu ◑	0237	0508	3.0E
	0852	1204	2.7F
	1518	1745	2.8E
	2134		
10 W		0036	2.2F
	0338	0606	2.8E
	0952	1321	2.6F
	1619	1852	2.6E
	2241		
11 Th		0212	2.1F
	0438	0708	2.6E
	1050	1443	2.7F
	1718	2010	2.6E
	2347		
12 F		0320	2.1F
	0535	0814	2.5E
	1147	1540	2.8F
	1814	2112	2.6E
13 Sa	0050	0414	2.2F
	0631	0908	2.4E
	1244	1630	2.8F
	1907	2200	2.6E
14 Su	0145	0505	2.2F
	0722	0953	2.4E
	1335	1718	2.8F
	1955	2245	2.6E
15 M	0231	0553	2.2F
	0809	1036	2.4E
	1419	1802	2.7F
	2039	2329	2.6E
16 Tu ○	0311	0635	2.1F
	0853	1120	2.4E
	1459	1838	2.6F
	2121		
17 W		0004	2.6E
	0347	0707	2.0F
	0936	1203	2.4E
	1535	1903	2.5F
	2202		
18 Th		0036	2.7E
	0421	0727	1.9F
	1018	1242	2.5E
	1611	1924	2.3F
	2243		
19 F		0109	2.7E
	0455	0746	1.9F
	1100	1320	2.5E
	1647	1951	2.2F
	2322		
20 Sa		0144	2.7E
	0527	0814	1.8F
	1140	1359	2.5E
	1725	2023	2.1F
21 Su	0000	0222	2.7E
	0601	0849	1.8F
	1221	1441	2.5E
	1805	2102	1.9F
22 M	0038	0305	2.6E
	0635	0931	1.8F
	1303	1528	2.4E
	1848	2148	1.7F
23 Tu	0118	0352	2.5E
	0714	1017	1.8F
	1350	1618	2.3E
	1939	2236	1.6F
24 W ◐	0202	0441	2.3E
	0757	1102	1.8F
	1444	1710	2.2E
	2037	2322	1.5F
25 Th	0256	0531	2.3E
	0848	1148	1.9F
	1542	1803	2.2E
	2140		
26 F		0013	1.4F
	0354	0623	2.3E
	0942	1243	1.9F
	1639	1900	2.3E
	2242		
27 Sa		0119	1.3F
	0452	0719	2.3E
	1037	1354	2.1F
	1735	2000	2.5E
	2344		
28 Su		0236	1.5F
	0549	0817	2.5E
	1136	1500	2.4F
	1830	2056	2.6E
29 M	0045	0335	1.8F
	0644	0911	2.8E
	1236	1554	2.7F
	1922	2148	3.1E
30 Tu	0140	0427	2.1F
	0737	1004	3.1E
	1334	1646	3.1F
	2013	2242	3.4E
31 W ●	0229	0519	2.5F
	0828	1059	3.3E
	1427	1739	3.3F
	2102	2338	3.6E

August

Day	Slack	Maximum	knots
1 Th	0316	0612	2.8F
	0919	1156	3.5E
	1519	1831	3.5F
	2152		
2 F		0031	3.8E
	0403	0701	3.0F
	1012	1249	3.7E
	1612	1920	3.5F
	2242		
3 Sa		0119	3.9E
	0451	0749	3.2F
	1106	1339	3.8E
	1707	2011	3.3F
	2333		
4 Su		0205	3.9E
	0540	0842	3.2F
	1200	1429	3.6E
	1803	2107	3.1F
5 M	0023	0254	3.6E
	0631	0942	3.1F
	1254	1523	3.4E
	1902	2210	2.7F
6 Tu	0115	0347	3.3E
	0725	1043	2.9F
	1351	1621	3.0E
	2006	2312	2.4F
7 W ◑	0211	0442	2.9E
	0823	1142	2.7F
	1452	1721	2.7E
	2114		
8 Th		0016	2.1F
	0312	0538	2.6E
	0925	1253	2.5F
	1554	1825	2.5E
	2221		
9 F		0152	1.9F
	0413	0638	2.3E
	1026	1424	2.5F
	1654	1950	2.3E
	2327		
10 Sa		0305	1.9F
	0513	0749	2.1E
	1126	1527	2.5F
	1752	2102	2.3E
11 Su	0032	0400	2.0F
	0609	0855	2.1E
	1226	1618	2.6F
	1846	2151	2.3E
12 M	0128	0450	2.1F
	0702	0939	2.1E
	1320	1706	2.6F
	1934	2233	2.3E
13 Tu	0213	0537	2.1F
	0749	1018	2.2E
	1405	1749	2.6F
	2018	2308	2.4E
14 W	0250	0617	2.1F
	0832	1058	2.2E
	1443	1825	2.5F
	2058	2338	2.4E
15 Th ○	0322	0649	2.1F
	0913	1139	2.4E
	1517	1848	2.4F
	2137		
16 F		0009	2.6E
	0352	0704	2.0F
	0952	1218	2.5E
	1550	1903	2.3F
	2215		
17 Sa		0042	2.7E
	0421	0718	2.0F
	1031	1255	2.6E
	1624	1924	2.2F
	2252		
18 Su		0117	2.8E
	0450	0741	2.0F
	1109	1333	2.7E
	1658	1952	2.1F
	2327		
19 M		0153	2.8E
	0519	0810	2.1F
	1147	1413	2.7E
	1734	2025	2.0F
20 Tu	0002	0232	2.7E
	0550	0846	2.0F
	1225	1456	2.6E
	1814	2106	1.8F
21 W	0037	0316	2.6E
	0625	0930	2.0F
	1306	1544	2.5E
	1858	2154	1.7F
22 Th	0115	0405	2.5E
	0706	1019	2.0F
	1356	1636	2.4E
	1953	2244	1.6F
23 F ○	0204	0456	2.4E
	0757	1109	2.0F
	1457	1730	2.4E
	2058	2336	1.5F
24 Sa	0309	0550	2.3E
	0858	1203	2.0F
	1602	1827	2.4E
	2206		
25 Su		0038	1.4F
	0417	0648	2.3E
	1004	1313	2.1F
	1705	1929	2.5E
	2312		
26 M		0202	1.5F
	0521	0750	2.5E
	1111	1435	2.3F
	1804	2031	2.8E
27 Tu	0017	0316	1.9F
	0621	0850	2.8E
	1218	1538	2.8F
	1900	2128	3.1E
28 W	0115	0411	2.3F
	0718	0946	3.2E
	1320	1633	3.1F
	1952	2222	3.4E
29 Th	0207	0504	2.8F
	0811	1042	3.5E
	1416	1727	3.4F
	2042	2317	3.7E
30 F ●	0254	0556	3.2F
	0902	1140	3.8E
	1509	1819	3.6F
	2131		
31 Sa		0011	3.9E
	0340	0645	3.4F
	0954	1234	4.0E
	1601	1907	3.6F
	2220		

September

Day	Slack	Maximum	knots
1 Su		0059	4.0E
	0426	0731	3.5F
	1046	1323	4.0E
	1653	1955	3.4F
	2310		
2 M		0144	3.9E
	0514	0820	3.5F
	1138	1410	3.8E
	1747	2047	3.1F
3 Tu	0000	0229	3.6E
	0603	0914	3.2F
	1231	1459	3.5E
	1843	2148	2.7F
4 W	0051	0318	3.2E
	0655	1016	2.9F
	1325	1554	3.0E
	1942	2251	2.3F
5 Th ◐	0145	0412	2.8E
	0752	1116	2.6F
	1423	1652	2.6E
	2048	2355	1.9F
6 F	0244	0508	2.4E
	0855	1224	2.3F
	1525	1752	2.3E
	2157		
7 Sa		0128	1.7F
	0347	0606	2.0E
	1001	1402	2.1F
	1627	1911	2.0E
	2303		
8 Su		0246	1.7F
	0449	0717	1.9E
	1105	1509	2.2F
	1726	2045	2.0E
9 M	0007	0342	1.9F
	0546	0843	1.9E
	1206	1600	2.3F
	1820	2134	2.1E
10 Tu	0103	0429	2.0F
	0639	0928	2.0E
	1301	1646	2.4F
	1909	2209	2.2E
11 W	0147	0513	2.1F
	0726	1001	2.1E
	1347	1728	2.4F
	1952	2234	2.2E
12 Th	0222	0552	2.1F
	0808	1034	2.2E
	1424	1803	2.4F
	2032	2302	2.4E
13 F ○	0251	0620	2.2F
	0847	1112	2.4E
	1458	1825	2.3F
	2109	2336	2.5E
14 Sa	0319	0633	2.2F
	0925	1152	2.6E
	1529	1838	2.3F
	2145		
15 Su		0011	2.7E
	0345	0646	2.2F
	1001	1230	2.8E
	1601	1858	2.2F
	2220		
16 M		0048	2.8E
	0411	0709	2.3F
	1038	1308	2.9E
	1633	1924	2.2F
	2254		
17 Tu		0124	2.9E
	0439	0737	2.3F
	1114	1346	3.0E
	1707	1955	2.1F
	2328		
18 W		0203	2.8E
	0509	0810	2.3F
	1151	1427	2.9E
	1745	2032	1.9F
19 Th	0002	0245	2.7E
	0545	0851	2.3F
	1231	1514	2.8E
	1829	2118	1.8F
20 F ◐	0040	0333	2.5E
	0627	0942	2.2F
	1319	1606	2.6E
	1921	2213	1.6F
21 Sa	0128	0426	2.4E
	0720	1039	2.1F
	1420	1702	2.5E
	2027	2311	1.5F
22 Su	0237	0523	2.3E
	0827	1137	2.1F
	1531	1800	2.5E
	2139		
23 M		0013	1.5F
	0353	0622	2.4E
	0943	1247	2.1F
	1638	1903	2.5E
	2248		
24 Tu		0138	1.6F
	0501	0727	2.5E
	1055	1416	2.3F
	1740	2009	2.8E
	2352		
25 W		0302	2.1F
	0603	0832	2.9E
	1205	1527	2.7F
	1837	2108	3.2E
26 Th	0051	0358	2.6F
	0700	0931	3.3E
	1309	1622	3.1F
	1931	2201	3.5E
27 F	0143	0449	3.1F
	0753	1026	3.6E
	1405	1714	3.4F
	2020	2255	3.7E
28 Sa ●	0230	0539	3.5F
	0844	1123	3.9E
	1457	1805	3.5F
	2109	2348	3.9E
29 Su	0315	0626	3.7F
	0934	1217	4.0E
	1547	1852	3.5F
	2157		
30 M		0036	3.9E
	0400	0711	3.7F
	1024	1305	4.0E
	1637	1938	3.3F
	2246		

Time meridian 75° W. 0000 is midnight. 1200 is noon. Times are not adjusted for Daylight Saving Time.

St. Marys River Entrance, Georgia, 2019

F–Flood, Dir. 272° True   E–Ebb, Dir. 093° True

October

Day	Slack h m	Max h m	knots
1 Tu		0121	3.8F
	0447	0756	3.5F
	1115	1349	3.8E
	1728	2025	2.9F
	2336		
2 W		0204	3.5E
	0534	0845	3.2F
	1205	1434	3.5E
	1820	2121	2.5F
3 Th	0025	0249	3.1E
	0624	0943	2.8F
	1257	1523	3.0E
	1916	2227	2.1F
4 F	0118	0339	2.6E
	0719	1047	2.4F
	1352	1617	2.5E
	2018	2332	1.8F
5 Sa ◐	0215	0434	2.2E
	0822	1151	2.1F
	1453	1715	2.1E
	2126		
6 Su	0318	0055	1.5F
	0930	0531	1.9E
	1555	1327	1.8F
	2231	1817	1.9E
7 M	0421	0219	1.6F
	1037	0635	1.7E
	1654	1443	1.9F
	2331	2001	1.8E
8 Tu	0518	0316	1.7F
	1138	0807	1.7E
	1748	1536	2.0F
		2059	1.9E
9 W	0024	0402	1.9E
	0611	0903	1.9F
	1235	1620	2.2E
	1837	2128	2.0F
10 Th	0108	0443	2.1E
	0658	0934	2.1F
	1322	1700	2.2E
	1921	2151	2.2F
11 F	0144	0518	2.2E
	0741	1006	2.3F
	1401	1733	2.2E
	2001	2222	2.4F
12 Sa	0214	0542	2.2F
	0819	1042	2.5E
	1435	1754	2.2F
	2038	2259	2.5E
13 Su ○	0242	0554	2.3F
	0856	1122	2.7E
	1507	1808	2.2F
	2114	2338	2.7E
14 M	0308	0613	2.4F
	0932	1203	2.9E
	1538	1831	2.2F
	2149		
15 Tu		0018	2.8E
	0335	0639	2.5F
	1008	1242	3.1E
	1610	1859	2.1F
	2223		
16 W		0057	2.9E
	0404	0709	2.6F
	1045	1322	3.1E
	1645	1930	2.1F
	2259		
17 Th		0136	2.9E
	0437	0743	2.5F
	1124	1403	3.1E
	1724	2007	2.0F
	2336		
18 F		0219	2.8E
	0516	0824	2.5F
	1207	1449	3.0E
	1809	2054	1.8F
19 Sa	0019	0307	2.6E
	0602	0916	2.3F
	1256	1541	2.8E
	1902	2152	1.7F
20 Su	0112	0401	2.5E
	0659	1018	2.2F
	1356	1638	2.6E
	2007	2255	1.7F
21 M ○	0221	0500	2.4E
	0810	1121	2.1F
	1507	1737	2.6E
	2119		
22 Tu		0000	1.7F
	0337	0602	2.4E
	0930	1230	2.1F
	1615	1840	2.6E
	2226		
23 W		0121	1.9F
	0445	0708	2.6E
	1044	1401	2.3F
	1717	1946	2.8E
	2327		
24 Th		0249	2.3F
	0546	0817	2.9E
	1154	1517	2.6F
	1814	2047	3.1E
25 F	0025	0345	2.9F
	0643	0917	3.3E
	1258	1611	3.0F
	1908	2140	3.4E
26 Sa	0118	0434	3.3F
	0736	1011	3.6E
	1354	1702	3.2F
	1958	2231	3.6E
27 Su ●	0206	0521	3.6F
	0826	1105	3.8E
	1445	1752	3.3F
	2047	2323	3.7E
28 M	0251	0608	3.7F
	0914	1158	3.9E
	1533	1838	3.2F
	2134		
29 Tu		0012	3.6E
	0336	0652	3.7F
	1003	1245	3.9E
	1620	1921	3.0F
	2223		
30 W		0057	3.5E
	0421	0734	3.4F
	1051	1327	3.7E
	1708	2004	2.7F
	2311		
31 Th		0138	3.3E
	0507	0818	3.1F
	1140	1408	3.3E
	1757	2053	2.3F

November

Day	Slack h m	Max h m	knots
1 F	0000	0221	2.9E
	0554	0909	2.6F
	1229	1452	2.9E
	1848	2156	1.9F
2 Sa	0050	0307	2.5E
	0645	1011	2.2F
	1320	1542	2.5E
	1944	2302	1.7F
3 Su	0144	0359	2.1E
	0743	1112	1.9F
	1416	1636	2.1E
	2046		
4 M ◐		0007	1.5F
	0244	0455	1.8E
	0850	1220	1.6F
	1516	1731	1.9E
	2148		
5 Tu		0136	1.4F
	0346	0553	1.7E
	0958	1403	1.6F
	1614	1829	1.8E
	2243		
6 W		0242	1.6F
	0444	0656	1.7E
	1059	1503	1.7F
	1708	1934	1.8E
	2332		
7 Th		0329	1.8F
	0537	0806	1.8E
	1156	1548	1.8F
	1758	2028	2.0E
8 F	0017	0407	2.0F
	0625	0854	2.1E
	1247	1626	1.9F
	1844	2107	2.2E
9 Sa	0057	0437	2.1F
	0709	0932	2.3E
	1331	1656	2.0F
	1926	2144	2.3E
10 Su	0132	0455	2.3F
	0749	1010	2.6E
	1408	1715	2.0F
	2006	2222	2.5E
11 M	0204	0514	2.4F
	0828	1051	2.8E
	1443	1736	2.0F
	2043	2304	2.7E
12 Tu ○	0234	0540	2.5F
	0905	1135	3.0E
	1516	1804	2.1F
	2119	2348	2.8E
13 W	0305	0612	2.7F
	0943	1218	3.1E
	1551	1837	2.1F
	2156		
14 Th		0031	2.9E
	0338	0647	2.7F
	1022	1300	3.3E
	1628	1912	2.1F
	2236		
15 F		0114	3.0E
	0415	0725	2.8F
	1105	1343	3.3E
	1710	1952	2.1F
	2320		
16 Sa		0158	2.9E
	0459	0808	2.7F
	1151	1429	3.2E
	1757	2040	2.0F
17 Su	0008	0246	2.8E
	0550	0901	2.5F
	1242	1520	3.0E
	1850	2141	1.9F
18 M	0104	0342	2.7E
	0650	1005	2.4F
	1339	1617	2.9E
	1952	2246	1.9F
19 Tu ◐	0210	0442	2.6E
	0802	1110	2.2F
	1445	1717	2.8E
	2059	2349	2.0F
20 W	0321	0544	2.6E
	0920	1217	2.2F
	1551	1817	2.8E
	2203		
21 Th		0104	2.2F
	0427	0651	2.7E
	1033	1345	2.2F
	1653	1922	2.9E
	2302		
22 F		0233	2.6F
	0528	0801	2.9E
	1142	1507	2.5F
	1751	2025	3.0E
23 Sa	0000	0332	3.0F
	0625	0903	3.2E
	1245	1602	2.7F
	1846	2119	3.2E
24 Su	0054	0421	3.3F
	0718	0957	3.4E
	1342	1653	2.9F
	1937	2209	3.3E
25 M	0144	0508	3.5F
	0808	1049	3.5E
	1433	1742	2.9F
	2026	2259	3.3E
26 Tu ●	0231	0554	3.5F
	0855	1141	3.6E
	1519	1828	2.8F
	2113	2348	3.2E
27 W	0315	0638	3.4F
	0942	1227	3.5E
	1604	1909	2.7F
	2201		
28 Th		0034	3.1E
	0358	0717	3.2F
	1029	1307	3.4E
	1649	1948	2.4F
	2248		
29 F		0115	3.0E
	0442	0755	2.9F
	1116	1345	3.1E
	1734	2029	2.1F
	2335		
30 Sa		0155	2.7E
	0527	0837	2.7F
	1202	1424	2.9E
	1819	2118	1.8F

December

Day	Slack h m	Max h m	knots
1 Su	0023	0237	2.4E
	0613	0928	2.1F
	1248	1508	2.5E
	1906	2218	1.6F
2 M	0112	0325	2.2E
	0703	1024	1.8F
	1337	1557	2.3E
	1957	2308	1.5F
3 Tu	0206	0418	1.9E
	0802	1114	1.6F
	1431	1649	2.1E
	2052	2355	1.4F
4 W ◐	0304	0513	1.8E
	0907	1205	1.4F
	1527	1740	1.9E
	2145		
5 Th		0120	1.4F
	0402	0608	1.8E
	1009	1404	1.3F
	1622	1833	1.9E
	2233		
6 F		0241	1.6F
	0456	0707	1.8E
	1107	1506	1.4F
	1713	1928	2.0E
	2319		
7 Sa		0322	1.8F
	0546	0805	2.0E
	1203	1544	1.5F
	1802	2020	2.1E
8 Su	0003	0347	2.0F
	0633	0854	2.3E
	1254	1611	1.7F
	1849	2106	2.3E
9 M	0045	0408	2.2F
	0717	0938	2.5E
	1338	1634	1.8F
	1932	2149	2.5E
10 Tu	0125	0437	2.4F
	0759	1021	2.8E
	1417	1704	1.9F
	2013	2233	2.7E
11 W	0203	0511	2.6F
	0840	1108	3.0E
	1455	1740	2.0F
	2053	2320	2.8E
12 Th ○	0240	0550	2.8F
	0921	1155	3.2E
	1533	1819	2.2F
	2134		
13 F		0009	3.0E
	0320	0631	2.9F
	1004	1242	3.4E
	1614	1859	2.3F
	2219		
14 Sa		0055	3.1E
	0403	0713	3.0F
	1050	1326	3.5E
	1658	1943	2.3F
	2308		
15 Su		0142	3.2E
	0451	0759	2.9F
	1138	1412	3.4E
	1746	2032	2.3F
	2359		
16 M		0231	3.1E
	0546	0853	2.7F
	1229	1502	3.3E
	1838	2132	2.3F
17 Tu	0055	0325	3.0E
	0646	0956	2.6F
	1323	1558	3.1E
	1934	2236	2.3F
18 W ○	0156	0425	2.8E
	0754	1100	2.4F
	1423	1656	3.0E
	2036	2337	2.4F
19 Th ◐	0302	0527	2.7E
	0908	1203	2.2F
	1526	1754	2.9E
	2138		
20 F		0044	2.5F
	0407	0632	2.7E
	1020	1326	2.1F
	1628	1856	2.8E
	2237		
21 Sa		0214	2.7F
	0508	0743	2.8E
	1128	1457	2.2F
	1728	2001	2.8E
	2336		
22 Su		0320	2.9F
	0606	0851	3.0E
	1233	1555	2.4F
	1824	2059	2.9E
23 M	0033	0412	3.1F
	0700	0945	3.1E
	1331	1647	2.5F
	1918	2149	2.9E
24 Tu	0127	0501	3.2F
	0751	1036	3.1E
	1422	1738	2.6F
	2007	2238	2.9E
25 W	0215	0548	3.2F
	0838	1127	3.1E
	1507	1824	2.5F
	2055	2327	2.8E
26 Th ●	0259	0631	3.1F
	0924	1212	3.1E
	1550	1903	2.4F
	2140		
27 F		0013	2.8E
	0340	0706	2.9F
	1009	1249	3.1E
	1630	1936	2.3F
	2226		
28 Sa		0053	2.7E
	0421	0738	2.7F
	1052	1323	3.0E
	1710	2007	2.1F
	2311		
29 Su		0131	2.7E
	0502	0810	2.4F
	1135	1358	2.8E
	1748	2041	1.9F
	2355		
30 M		0210	2.5E
	0543	0848	2.2F
	1217	1437	2.7E
	1827	2122	1.7F
31 Tu	0039	0253	2.4E
	0626	0932	1.9F
	1259	1520	2.5E
	1907	2208	1.7F

Time meridian 75° W. 0000 is midnight. 1200 is noon. Times are not adjusted for Daylight Saving Time.

St. Johns River Entrance, Florida, 2019

F–Flood, Dir. 262° True   E–Ebb, Dir. 082° True

January

Day	Slack (h m)	Maximum (h m)	knots
1 Tu	0027	0322	2.3F
	0641	1020	2.2E
	1323	1609	1.7F
	1851	2208	2.1E
2 W	0118	0423	2.3F
	0734	1111	2.2E
	1419	1711	1.7F
	1942	2254	2.1E
3 Th	0209	0517	2.4F
	0823	1200	2.2E
	1511	1759	1.7F
	2030	2336	2.1E
4 F	0257	0600	2.4F
	0909	1246	2.2E
	1557	1836	1.7F
	2115		
5 Sa ●		0013	2.0E
	0342	0637	2.4F
	0953	1326	2.1E
	1640	1909	1.7F
	2157		
6 Su		0047	2.0E
	0424	0713	2.4F
	1035	1357	2.1E
	1721	1942	1.6F
	2239		
7 M		0120	2.0E
	0505	0751	2.3F
	1116	1415	2.0E
	1801	2019	1.6F
	2322		
8 Tu		0156	1.9E
	0545	0831	2.2F
	1156	1439	2.0E
	1842	2059	1.6F
9 W	0005	0235	1.8E
	0628	0913	2.1F
	1235	1512	2.0E
	1924	2143	1.6F
10 Th	0048	0316	1.8E
	0713	0958	2.0F
	1315	1550	1.9E
	2005	2227	1.7F
11 F	0132	0400	1.8E
	0802	1044	1.9F
	1354	1631	1.9E
	2045	2312	1.8F
12 Sa	0217	0447	1.8E
	0854	1129	1.8F
	1433	1715	1.9E
	2124	2356	1.9F
13 Su	0304	0537	1.8E
	0946	1215	1.7F
	1514	1803	1.9E
	2204		
14 M ◐		0042	2.1F
	0354	0631	1.8E
	1038	1303	1.6F
	1558	1854	1.9E
	2246		
15 Tu		0130	2.2F
	0448	0726	1.9E
	1132	1353	1.5F
	1649	1946	1.9E
	2332		
16 W		0222	2.3F
	0546	0821	2.2E
	1228	1448	1.5F
	1745	2038	2.0E
17 Th	0023	0318	2.4F
	0643	0915	2.1E
	1326	1546	1.5F
	1843	2131	2.1E
18 F	0118	0416	2.5F
	0738	1008	2.2E
	1423	1645	1.6F
	1939	2224	2.3E
19 Sa	0214	0512	2.7F
	0832	1102	2.3E
	1517	1741	1.8F
	2035	2317	2.4E
20 Su	0309	0606	2.9F
	0923	1156	2.4E
	1609	1834	1.9F
	2130		
21 M ○		0011	2.4E
	0404	0659	2.9F
	1015	1251	2.5E
	1701	1927	2.1F
	2226		
22 Tu		0107	2.4E
	0459	0751	2.9F
	1106	1346	2.5E
	1752	2021	2.1F
	2324		
23 W		0203	2.3E
	0556	0845	2.8F
	1159	1439	2.5E
	1845	2117	2.2F
24 Th	0023	0301	2.2E
	0656	0942	2.6F
	1252	1533	2.5E
	1938	2214	2.3F
25 F	0122	0401	2.1E
	0759	1039	2.4F
	1345	1629	2.3E
	2032	2309	2.3F
26 Sa	0221	0516	2.0E
	0902	1135	2.2F
	1439	1731	2.2E
	2124		
27 Su ◑		0002	2.3F
	0319	0657	2.0E
	1003	1230	2.0F
	1534	1847	2.1E
	2215		
28 M		0055	2.3F
	0418	0807	2.0E
	1102	1326	1.8F
	1631	1958	2.0E
	2307		
29 Tu		0149	2.2F
	0517	0905	2.0E
	1200	1427	1.6F
	1728	2056	2.0E
30 W	0000	0248	2.1F
	0615	0958	2.0E
	1257	1540	1.5F
	1823	2148	2.0E
31 Th	0053	0355	2.1F
	0710	1050	2.0E
	1353	1650	1.5F
	1917	2237	1.9E

February

Day	Slack (h m)	Maximum (h m)	knots
1 F	0146	0457	2.1F
	0801	1140	2.0E
	1445	1741	1.5F
	2006	2323	1.9E
2 Sa	0236	0544	2.2F
	0847	1227	2.0E
	1532	1819	1.6F
	2052		
3 Su		0003	1.9E
	0323	0620	2.2F
	0930	1308	2.0E
	1615	1849	1.6F
	2136		
4 M ●		0036	1.9E
	0405	0653	2.2F
	1011	1340	2.0E
	1655	1919	1.7F
	2218		
5 Tu		0105	1.9E
	0445	0728	2.2F
	1050	1359	2.0E
	1733	1953	1.7F
	2259		
6 W		0137	1.9E
	0525	0806	2.2F
	1129	1416	2.0E
	1810	2032	1.8F
	2340		
7 Th		0213	1.9E
	0606	0847	2.1F
	1207	1445	2.0E
	1847	2112	1.8F
8 F	0020	0251	1.9E
	0650	0930	2.0F
	1244	1520	2.0E
	1923	2155	1.9F
9 Sa	0100	0333	2.0E
	0737	1015	1.9F
	1321	1558	2.0E
	2001	2239	2.0F
10 Su	0142	0417	2.0E
	0826	1101	1.8F
	1358	1640	2.0E
	2040	2324	2.2F
11 M	0227	0503	2.0E
	0916	1146	1.7F
	1436	1726	2.0E
	2121		
12 Tu ◐		0010	2.3F
	0315	0554	2.0E
	1006	1233	1.6F
	1518	1816	2.0E
	2207		
13 W		0059	2.3F
	0410	0649	2.0E
	1059	1323	1.5F
	1608	1910	2.0E
	2258		
14 Th		0152	2.4F
	0510	0747	2.0E
	1156	1417	1.5F
	1709	2007	2.0E
	2354		
15 F		0249	2.4F
	0613	0846	2.0E
	1255	1517	1.5F
	1815	2105	2.1E
16 Sa	0054	0350	2.5F
	0714	0944	2.1E
	1356	1620	1.6F
	1919	2203	2.2E
17 Su	0156	0451	2.6F
	0810	1042	2.3E
	1454	1721	1.9F
	2019	2300	2.4E
18 M	0255	0549	2.8F
	0904	1140	2.4E
	1547	1817	2.1F
	2117	2359	2.4E
19 Tu ○	0353	0643	2.9F
	0956	1236	2.5E
	1637	1910	2.3F
	2213		
20 W		0057	2.5E
	0449	0735	2.9F
	1047	1330	2.6E
	1726	2002	2.5F
	2309		
21 Th		0155	2.5E
	0545	0828	2.7F
	1138	1421	2.6E
	1814	2054	2.5F
22 F	0005	0251	2.4E
	0643	0923	2.5F
	1229	1511	2.5E
	1905	2148	2.5F
23 Sa	0100	0348	2.3E
	0742	1018	2.3F
	1321	1601	2.3E
	1957	2240	2.5F
24 Su	0155	0451	2.2E
	0842	1112	2.1F
	1413	1655	2.1E
	2050	2332	2.4F
25 M	0250	0619	2.0E
	0940	1205	1.8F
	1505	1758	2.0E
	2143		
26 Tu ◐		0023	2.3F
	0347	0736	1.9E
	1036	1257	1.6F
	1600	1918	1.8E
	2237		
27 W		0115	2.1F
	0445	0837	1.8E
	1131	1351	1.4F
	1656	2028	1.8E
	2331		
28 Th		0211	1.9F
	0544	0932	1.8E
	1226	1454	1.3F
	1753	2125	1.8E

March

Day	Slack (h m)	Maximum (h m)	knots
1 F	0026	0315	1.8F
	0640	1023	1.8E
	1321	1616	1.3F
	1849	2216	1.8E
2 Sa	0121	0426	1.8F
	0732	1112	1.8E
	1414	1716	1.4F
	1942	2305	1.8E
3 Su	0213	0519	1.9F
	0819	1158	1.9E
	1501	1754	1.5F
	2030	2349	1.8E
4 M	0301	0556	2.0F
	0902	1238	2.0E
	1544	1822	1.7F
	2114		
5 Tu		0024	1.9E
	0344	0629	2.1F
	0943	1309	2.0E
	1623	1852	1.8F
	2156		
6 W ●		0049	1.9E
	0426	0704	2.1F
	1021	1327	2.0E
	1659	1925	1.9F
	2235		
7 Th		0116	2.0E
	0506	0741	2.1F
	1059	1344	2.0E
	1733	2002	2.0F
	2313		
8 F		0149	2.1E
	0547	0821	2.0F
	1136	1413	2.0E
	1807	2041	2.1F
	2351		
9 Sa		0226	2.1E
	0629	0903	1.9F
	1213	1448	2.0E
	1842	2124	2.2F
10 Su	0030	0306	2.2E
	0714	0948	1.8F
	1249	1526	2.0E
	1919	2208	2.2F
11 M	0111	0348	2.2E
	0801	1033	1.8F
	1326	1608	2.0E
	2000	2255	2.3F
12 Tu ○	0156	0434	2.2E
	0850	1120	1.7F
	1405	1654	2.0E
	2046	2343	2.4F
13 W	0245	0524	2.1E
	0941	1208	1.6F
	1450	1745	2.0E
	2137		
14 Th ◐		0033	2.4F
	0341	0620	2.0E
	1035	1258	1.6F
	1544	1842	2.0E
	2233		
15 F		0127	2.4F
	0443	0720	2.0E
	1133	1354	1.5F
	1649	1943	2.0E
	2334		
16 Sa		0225	2.4F
	0548	0823	2.0E
	1233	1455	1.6F
	1800	2046	2.1E
17 Su	0038	0328	2.4F
	0651	0926	2.2E
	1333	1601	1.8F
	1907	2149	2.2E
18 M	0143	0433	2.5F
	0749	1026	2.3E
	1430	1704	2.0F
	2008	2252	2.3E
19 Tu	0245	0533	2.6F
	0843	1124	2.5E
	1522	1800	2.4F
	2105	2353	2.5E
20 W ○	0343	0628	2.7F
	0935	1219	2.6E
	1610	1851	2.6F
	2159		
21 Th		0053	2.6E
	0439	0720	2.7F
	1025	1310	2.6E
	1656	1940	2.7F
	2251		
22 F		0148	2.6E
	0533	0810	2.6F
	1115	1358	2.5E
	1742	2029	2.8F
	2343		
23 Sa		0239	2.6E
	0628	0902	2.3F
	1204	1444	2.4E
	1830	2119	2.7F
24 Su	0035	0328	2.4E
	0723	0954	2.1F
	1254	1531	2.2E
	1921	2209	2.5F
25 M	0127	0419	2.2E
	0818	1045	1.9F
	1344	1619	2.0E
	2015	2300	2.3F
26 Tu	0220	0519	1.9E
	0913	1135	1.7F
	1434	1712	1.8E
	2110	2350	2.1F
27 W ◑	0314	0654	1.7E
	1007	1223	1.5F
	1527	1817	1.7E
	2205		
28 Th		0040	2.0F
	0410	0803	1.7E
	1059	1313	1.4F
	1623	1949	1.6E
	2300		
29 F		0132	1.8F
	0507	0859	1.6E
	1151	1407	1.3F
	1722	2055	1.6E
	2355		
30 Sa		0228	1.6F
	0603	0948	1.7E
	1243	1510	1.3F
	1820	2149	1.6E
31 Su	0050	0330	1.6F
	0655	1034	1.7E
	1335	1621	1.4F
	1915	2238	1.7E

Time meridian 75° W. 0000 is midnight. 1200 is noon. Times are not adjusted for Daylight Saving Time.

St. Johns River Entrance, Florida, 2019

F–Flood, Dir. 262° True   E–Ebb, Dir. 082° True

April

Day	Slack	Maximum	knots	Day	Slack	Maximum	knots
1 M	0144	0432	1.7F	16 Tu	0132	0416	2.3F
	0743	1116	1.8E		0728	1013	2.3E
	1422	1709	1.6F		1404	1647	2.3F
	2004	2321	1.8E		1957	2252	2.4E
2 Tu	0234	0519	1.8F	17 W	0235	0518	2.4F
	0827	1152	1.9E		0822	1108	2.5E
	1505	1744	1.8F		1455	1742	2.6F
	2048	2355	1.9E		2051	2354	2.5E
3 W	0320	0558	1.9F	18 Th	0333	0613	2.5F
	0909	1219	2.0E		0913	1159	2.5E
	1544	1817	2.0F		1542	1831	2.8F
	2128				2142		
4 Th		0020	2.0E	19 F		0050	2.7E
	0404	0636	2.0F	O	0427	0704	2.5F
	0948	1239	2.0E		1002	1247	2.5E
	1619	1853	2.1F		1627	1917	2.9F
	2206				2231		
5 F		0048	2.1E	20 Sa		0139	2.7E
●	0445	0714	2.0F		0519	0751	2.3F
	1026	1306	2.0E		1050	1332	2.4E
	1653	1930	2.3F		1712	2003	2.8F
	2243				2320		
6 Sa		0122	2.2E	21 Su		0224	2.6E
	0526	0754	1.9F		0610	0839	2.1F
	1104	1339	2.0E		1137	1416	2.3E
	1727	2010	2.3F		1759	2050	2.7F
	2321						
7 Su		0159	2.3E	22 M	0010	0305	2.4E
	0608	0836	1.8F		0700	0927	1.9F
	1140	1416	2.0E		1225	1500	2.1E
	1803	2054	2.4F		1848	2139	2.5F
8 M	0002	0239	2.3E	23 Tu	0100	0346	2.1E
	0652	0921	1.8F		0752	1015	1.7F
	1218	1456	2.0E		1313	1545	2.0E
	1842	2140	2.4F		1941	2228	2.3F
9 Tu	0045	0323	2.3E	24 W	0150	0431	1.9E
	0740	1008	1.7F		0844	1103	1.5F
	1258	1540	2.0E		1402	1633	1.8E
	1928	2229	2.4F		2036	2317	2.1F
10 W	0133	0409	2.2E	25 Th	0240	0526	1.7E
	0831	1057	1.6F		0935	1150	1.4F
	1343	1628	2.0E		1454	1728	1.6E
	2020	2320	2.4F		2132		
11 Th	0224	0501	2.1E	26 F		0006	1.9F
	0924	1148	1.6F		0332	0711	1.6E
	1434	1721	1.9E		1025	1237	1.4F
	2117			O	1550	1835	1.5E
					2226		
12 F		0012	2.4F	27 Sa		0054	1.7F
◐	0321	0558	2.1E		0425	0813	1.6E
	1020	1241	1.6F		1113	1326	1.3F
	1534	1821	1.9E		1648	2009	1.5E
	2218				2320		
13 Sa		0107	2.4F	28 Su		0144	1.6F
	0423	0701	2.0E		0518	0900	1.6E
	1117	1337	1.7F		1202	1419	1.4F
	1643	1927	1.9E		1747	2109	1.5E
	2322						
14 Su		0206	2.3F	29 M	0014	0238	1.5F
	0527	0808	2.1E		0610	0941	1.7E
	1214	1439	1.8F		1250	1516	1.5F
	1753	2037	2.0E		1842	2156	1.6E
15 M	0027	0310	2.3F	30 Tu	0109	0336	1.5F
	0629	0913	2.2E		0700	1016	1.8E
	1311	1544	2.0F		1336	1610	1.7F
	1858	2146	2.2E		1931	2235	1.7E

May

Day	Slack	Maximum	knots	Day	Slack	Maximum	knots
1 W	0202	0432	1.6F	16 Th	0224	0504	2.2F
	0747	1046	1.9E		0800	1051	2.4E
	1419	1657	1.9F		1428	1723	2.7F
	2015	2308	1.9E		2034	2353	2.5E
2 Th	0252	0520	1.7F	17 F	0321	0559	2.2F
	0830	1117	1.9E		0851	1139	2.4E
	1459	1739	2.1F		1515	1811	2.8F
	2056	2339	2.0E		2124		
3 F	0338	0603	1.8F	18 Sa		0044	2.6E
	0911	1150	2.0E		0413	0648	2.2F
	1537	1819	2.3F	O	0939	1225	2.4E
	2135				1601	1856	2.9F
					2212		
4 Sa		0014	2.2E	19 Su		0130	2.6E
●	0421	0644	1.8F		0502	0732	2.1F
	0950	1226	2.0E		1025	1308	2.3E
	1614	1859	2.5F		1646	1940	2.8F
	2214				2259		
5 Su		0052	2.3E	20 M		0210	2.4E
	0503	0726	1.8F		0550	0815	1.9F
	1028	1305	2.0E		1110	1349	2.2E
	1651	1942	2.5F		1732	2024	2.6F
	2255				2346		
6 M		0132	2.3E	21 Tu		0245	2.2E
	0546	0809	1.8F		0637	0859	1.7F
	1107	1346	2.1E		1156	1431	2.1E
	1730	2027	2.5F		1820	2110	2.4F
	2338						
7 Tu		0215	2.3E	22 W	0034	0319	2.0E
	0632	0856	1.7F		0725	0944	1.6F
	1150	1430	2.1E		1243	1514	1.9E
	1815	2116	2.5F		1910	2158	2.2F
8 W	0025	0300	2.3E	23 Th	0121	0358	1.9E
	0722	0946	1.6F		0814	1031	1.5F
	1236	1516	2.0E		1332	1600	1.7E
	1905	2208	2.5F		2003	2245	2.0F
9 Th	0115	0349	2.3E	24 F	0207	0443	1.7E
	0816	1038	1.6F		0902	1118	1.4F
	1329	1607	1.9E		1423	1650	1.6E
	2003	2301	2.4F		2056	2332	1.8F
10 F	0209	0443	2.2E	25 Sa	0254	0534	1.7E
	0911	1132	1.7F		0949	1203	1.5F
	1427	1703	1.9E		1516	1745	1.5E
	2105	2355	2.4F		2149		
11 Sa	0305	0542	2.1E	26 Su		0018	1.7F
	1007	1227	1.8F		0341	0633	1.7E
	1531	1807	1.8E		1034	1250	1.5F
☽	2209			●	1612	1848	1.4E
					2242		
12 Su		0051	2.3F	27 M		0105	1.6F
	0405	0648	2.1E		0430	0732	1.7E
	1101	1324	1.9F		1118	1337	1.6F
	1639	1921	1.8E		1707	1955	1.5E
	2313				2335		
13 M		0149	2.2F	28 Tu		0155	1.5F
	0507	0757	2.2E		0520	0821	1.7E
	1154	1424	2.0F		1202	1427	1.7F
	1745	2043	2.0E		1801	2049	1.6E
14 Tu	0018	0253	2.2F	29 W	0030	0249	1.4F
	0608	0902	2.3E		0611	0904	1.8E
	1246	1527	2.2F		1246	1519	1.9F
	1846	2156	2.2E		1851	2134	1.7E
15 W	0122	0400	2.1F	30 Th	0124	0344	1.4F
	0706	0959	2.3E		0701	0945	1.9E
	1338	1628	2.5F		1330	1611	2.1F
	1942	2257	2.4E		1937	2215	1.9E
				31 F	0217	0438	1.5F
					0747	1025	1.9E
					1413	1659	2.3F
					2021	2256	2.0E

June

Day	Slack	Maximum	knots	Day	Slack	Maximum	knots
1 Sa	0307	0527	1.6F	16 Su	0357	0633	1.9F
	0830	1107	2.0E		0916	1206	2.2E
	1456	1745	2.5F		1540	1837	2.7F
	2104	2338	2.2E		2153		
2 Su	0353	0613	1.7F	17 M		0122	2.4E
	0912	1149	2.1E		0444	0713	1.8F
	1538	1830	2.6F		1001	1247	2.2E
	2147			O	1626	1919	2.6F
					2239		
3 M		0021	2.3E	18 Tu		0201	2.2E
	0438	0657	1.7F		0529	0752	1.7F
	0953	1233	2.1E		1045	1327	2.1E
●	1620	1916	2.7F		1710	2001	2.5F
	2231				2324		
4 Tu		0106	2.3E	19 W		0232	2.1E
	0523	0743	1.7F		0612	0832	1.6F
	1038	1319	2.1E		1130	1407	2.0E
	1705	2004	2.7F		1755	2044	2.3F
	2318						
5 W		0153	2.3E	20 Th	0009	0258	2.0E
	0611	0833	1.7F		0657	0915	1.5F
	1126	1407	2.1E		1216	1448	1.9E
	1755	2055	2.6F		1842	2128	2.1F
6 Th	0008	0242	2.3E	21 F	0052	0331	1.9E
	0704	0926	1.7F		0742	1000	1.5F
	1221	1457	2.0E		1304	1531	1.7E
	1850	2149	2.5F		1931	2214	2.0F
7 F	0100	0334	2.3E	22 Sa	0134	0410	1.8E
	0759	1022	1.7F		0827	1045	1.5F
	1320	1551	1.9E		1352	1617	1.6E
	1951	2244	2.5F		2021	2259	1.9F
8 Sa	0154	0429	2.3E	23 Su	0216	0453	1.8E
	0855	1118	1.9F		0910	1130	1.6F
	1421	1651	1.9E		1441	1706	1.6E
	2056	2340	2.4F		2113	2344	1.8F
9 Su	0249	0529	2.2E	24 M	0259	0540	1.8E
	0948	1214	2.0F		0952	1214	1.7F
	1525	1800	1.8E		1531	1800	1.6E
	2200				2204		
10 M		0036	2.3F	25 Tu		0030	1.7F
	0347	0637	2.2E		0343	0630	1.8E
	1040	1309	2.1F		1033	1259	1.8F
◐	1628	1935	1.9E	O	1622	1855	1.6E
	2303				2256		
11 Tu		0134	2.1F	26 W		0117	1.6F
	0446	0749	2.2E		0430	0720	1.8E
	1131	1406	2.2F		1114	1346	1.9F
	1731	2057	2.1E		1714	1950	1.7E
					2350		
12 W	0006	0236	2.0F	27 Th		0207	1.5F
	0546	0852	2.3E		0520	0809	1.8E
	1221	1506	2.4F		1157	1436	2.1F
	1830	2157	2.2E		1806	2041	1.8E
13 Th	0109	0343	1.9F	28 F	0044	0301	1.4F
	0644	0946	2.3E		0611	0857	1.9E
	1312	1607	2.5F		1242	1529	2.2F
	1925	2252	2.4E		1857	2130	1.9E
14 F	0209	0450	1.9F	29 Sa	0139	0356	1.4F
	0738	1035	2.3E		0701	0943	2.0E
	1403	1704	2.6F		1330	1622	2.3F
	2017	2346	2.4E		1946	2217	2.0E
15 Sa	0305	0546	1.9F	30 Su	0232	0450	1.5F
	0828	1122	2.2E		0749	1030	2.1E
	1452	1753	2.7F		1419	1714	2.5F
	2106				2034	2305	2.2E

St. Johns River Entrance, Florida, 2019

F–Flood, Dir. 262° True   E–Ebb, Dir. 082° True

July

Day	Slack (h m)	Maximum (h m)	knots
1 M	0322	0542	1.6F
	0836	1117	2.2F
	1508	1804	2.7F
	2122	2353	2.3E
2 Tu ●	0411	0631	1.7F
	0924	1206	2.2F
	1557	1854	2.8F
	2210		
3 W		0043	2.3E
	0459	0721	1.8F
	1015	1256	2.2F
	1647	1944	2.8F
	2259		
4 Th		0134	2.4E
	0549	0812	1.8F
	1110	1348	2.2F
	1740	2036	2.7F
	2350		
5 F		0226	2.4E
	0642	0907	1.9F
	1208	1442	2.1F
	1838	2131	2.6F
6 Sa	0043	0319	2.4E
	0736	1004	2.0F
	1309	1539	2.0E
	1941	2227	2.5F
7 Su	0136	0414	2.4E
	0831	1101	2.1F
	1409	1641	1.9E
	2045	2324	2.4F
8 M	0231	0514	2.3E
	0923	1156	2.2F
	1510	1759	1.9E
	2149		
9 Tu ◐		0020	2.2F
	0327	0622	2.2E
	1015	1250	2.3F
	1610	1944	2.0E
	2251		
10 W		0117	2.0F
	0425	0736	2.2E
	1105	1344	2.4F
	1711	2050	2.1E
	2351		
11 Th		0218	1.9F
	0524	0839	2.2E
	1156	1443	2.4F
	1809	2147	2.2E
12 F	0052	0325	1.7F
	0621	0934	2.1E
	1249	1545	2.4F
	1905	2241	2.2E
13 Sa	0151	0436	1.7F
	0716	1024	2.1E
	1342	1647	2.4F
	1958	2334	2.2E
14 Su	0246	0534	1.7F
	0806	1112	2.1E
	1434	1739	2.5F
	2048		
15 M		0025	2.2E
	0337	0619	1.7F
	0854	1156	2.1E
	1522	1823	2.5F
	2135		
16 Tu ○		0111	2.2E
	0423	0657	1.7F
	0939	1235	2.1E
	1608	1902	2.5F
	2219		
17 W		0150	2.1E
	0505	0731	1.7F
	1023	1311	2.0E
	1651	1939	2.4F
	2301		
18 Th		0219	2.0E
	0546	0807	1.6F
	1107	1346	1.9E
	1734	2018	2.2F
	2342		
19 F		0237	2.0E
	0626	0846	1.6F
	1151	1424	1.9E
	1817	2100	2.1F
20 Sa	0022	0303	2.0E
	0707	0928	1.6F
	1236	1504	1.8E
	1902	2143	2.0F
21 Su	0102	0338	2.0E
	0747	1011	1.7F
	1320	1547	1.8E
	1950	2228	1.9F
22 M	0141	0417	1.9E
	0828	1055	1.8F
	1404	1632	1.8E
	2040	2313	1.8F
23 Tu	0220	0459	1.9E
	0907	1139	1.9F
	1449	1720	1.8E
	2130	2358	1.7F
24 W ○	0300	0545	1.9E
	0947	1223	2.1F
	1536	1810	1.8E
	2220		
25 Th		0043	1.6F
	0342	0634	1.9E
	1028	1309	2.1F
	1627	1904	1.8E
	2311		
26 F		0131	1.5F
	0428	0725	1.9E
	1113	1359	2.2F
	1722	1958	1.9E
27 Sa	0005	0223	1.4F
	0521	0816	1.9E
	1202	1453	2.3F
	1819	2051	1.9E
28 Su	0100	0319	1.4F
	0617	0908	2.0E
	1254	1550	2.4F
	1914	2144	2.0E
29 M	0157	0417	1.5F
	0713	0959	2.1E
	1350	1647	2.5F
	2008	2236	2.1E
30 Tu	0252	0514	1.6F
	0808	1051	2.1E
	1445	1741	2.7F
	2059	2329	2.3E
31 W ●	0344	0608	1.8F
	0903	1145	2.3E
	1539	1833	2.8F
	2149		

August

Day	Slack (h m)	Maximum (h m)	knots
1 Th		0023	2.4E
	0434	0700	2.0F
	0959	1239	2.3E
	1633	1925	2.8F
	2239		
2 F		0116	2.5E
	0524	0753	2.1F
	1055	1334	2.3E
	1729	2018	2.7F
	2330		
3 Sa		0209	2.5E
	0614	0847	2.2F
	1154	1431	2.3E
	1827	2113	2.6F
4 Su	0022	0301	2.5E
	0707	0943	2.3F
	1252	1528	2.2E
	1929	2209	2.4F
5 M	0116	0355	2.4E
	0800	1039	2.4F
	1350	1631	2.1E
	2032	2306	2.3F
6 Tu	0210	0452	2.3E
	0853	1133	2.4F
	1448	1753	2.1E
	2134		
7 W ◐		0002	2.1F
	0305	0557	2.1E
	0946	1226	2.4F
	1547	1929	2.1E
	2234		
8 Th		0058	1.9F
	0402	0715	2.1E
	1039	1320	2.3F
	1646	2034	2.1E
	2332		
9 F		0156	1.7F
	0500	0825	2.0E
	1133	1417	2.2F
	1746	2131	2.1E
10 Sa	0030	0303	1.6F
	0558	0922	2.0E
	1227	1522	2.2F
	1844	2225	2.1E
11 Su	0128	0419	1.5F
	0653	1015	2.0E
	1322	1631	2.2F
	1938	2318	2.0E
12 M	0223	0520	1.6F
	0745	1104	2.0E
	1416	1727	2.2F
	2028		
13 Tu		0007	2.1E
	0313	0605	1.6F
	0833	1151	2.0E
	1505	1809	2.3F
	2113		
14 W		0052	2.1E
	0357	0640	1.7F
	0919	1230	2.0E
	1550	1844	2.3F
	2155		
15 Th ○		0129	2.1E
	0437	0709	1.7F
	1003	1301	2.0E
	1632	1917	2.2F
	2235		
16 F		0155	2.1E
	0515	0741	1.8F
	1045	1329	1.9E
	1713	1953	2.2F
	2313		
17 Sa		0210	2.0E
	0552	0816	1.8F
	1126	1402	1.9E
	1754	2032	2.1F
	2352		
18 Su		0233	2.0E
	0629	0855	1.9F
	1206	1438	2.0E
	1837	2114	2.0F
19 M	0030	0305	2.0E
	0705	0937	1.9F
	1246	1517	2.0E
	1922	2158	1.8F
20 Tu	0107	0342	2.0E
	0743	1020	2.0F
	1327	1559	2.0E
	2010	2242	1.8F
21 W	0144	0422	1.9E
	0822	1105	2.1F
	1409	1644	2.0E
	2058	2327	1.7F
22 Th	0221	0506	1.9E
	0903	1150	2.2F
	1455	1733	1.9E
	2148		
23 F ○		0013	1.6F
	0300	0554	1.9E
	0948	1237	2.2F
	1546	1825	1.9E
	2238		
24 Sa		0100	1.5F
	0346	0647	1.9E
	1036	1328	2.3F
	1644	1921	1.9E
	2331		
25 Su		0152	1.5F
	0441	0742	1.9E
	1130	1422	2.3F
	1745	2019	1.9E
26 M	0028	0248	1.4F
	0545	0839	2.0E
	1227	1522	2.3F
	1846	2117	2.0E
27 Tu	0126	0350	1.5F
	0650	0936	2.1E
	1328	1622	2.5F
	1942	2213	2.2E
28 W	0223	0451	1.8F
	0751	1032	2.3E
	1428	1720	2.6F
	2036	2309	2.3E
29 Th	0317	0548	2.0F
	0849	1129	2.4E
	1526	1815	2.7F
	2127		
30 F ●		0003	2.5E
	0407	0641	2.3F
	0945	1226	2.5E
	1622	1907	2.8F
	2217		
31 Sa		0057	2.6E
	0455	0733	2.5F
	1040	1323	2.5E
	1718	2000	2.7F
	2308		

September

Day	Slack (h m)	Maximum (h m)	knots
1 Su		0148	2.6E
	0543	0824	2.6F
	1135	1419	2.5E
	1815	2054	2.5F
2 M	0000	0239	2.5E
	0634	0917	2.6F
	1231	1514	2.4E
	1914	2149	2.3F
3 Tu	0052	0330	2.4E
	0726	1012	2.6F
	1326	1613	2.3E
	2014	2245	2.1F
4 W	0146	0424	2.2E
	0821	1106	2.5F
	1422	1726	2.1E
	2114	2341	1.9F
5 Th ◐	0240	0524	2.0E
	0917	1159	2.4F
	1520	1904	2.0E
	2212		
6 F		0035	1.7F
	0336	0644	1.9E
	1013	1253	2.2F
	1619	2013	1.9E
	2309		
7 Sa		0130	1.6F
	0434	0807	1.8E
	1109	1349	2.1F
	1719	2111	1.9E
8 Su	0005	0234	1.4F
	0532	0908	1.8E
	1205	1454	1.9F
	1818	2204	1.9E
9 M	0100	0354	1.4F
	0630	1002	1.9E
	1301	1609	1.9F
	1913	2253	1.9E
10 Tu	0153	0459	1.5F
	0724	1052	1.9E
	1355	1709	2.0F
	2001	2339	2.0E
11 W	0242	0544	1.6F
	0813	1138	1.9E
	1445	1750	2.0F
	2045		
12 Th		0021	2.0E
	0325	0615	1.7F
	0859	1218	1.9E
	1530	1821	2.1F
	2126		
13 F ○		0055	2.1E
	0404	0641	1.9F
	0941	1247	2.0E
	1612	1853	2.1F
	2205		
14 Sa		0118	2.1E
	0440	0711	2.0F
	1020	1309	2.0E
	1653	1927	2.1F
	2243		
15 Su		0133	2.1E
	0515	0745	2.1F
	1058	1337	2.1E
	1733	2005	2.0F
	2320		
16 M		0159	2.0E
	0549	0823	2.1F
	1135	1411	2.1E
	1814	2045	1.9F
	2357		
17 Tu		0231	2.0E
	0623	0904	2.1F
	1213	1448	2.2E
	1857	2128	1.8F
18 W	0033	0308	1.9E
	0659	0947	2.2F
	1253	1529	2.1E
	1943	2213	1.7F
19 Th	0109	0348	1.9E
	0739	1033	2.2F
	1336	1613	2.1E
	2031	2259	1.6F
20 F ◐	0146	0432	1.9E
	0824	1121	2.3F
	1423	1701	2.0E
	2121	2346	1.6F
21 Sa ○	0228	0521	1.9E
	0914	1210	2.3F
	1515	1754	2.0E
	2212		
22 Su		0035	1.5F
	0317	0615	1.9E
	1008	1302	2.3F
	1614	1852	1.9E
	2306		
23 M		0127	1.5F
	0418	0715	1.9E
	1107	1357	2.3F
	1717	1954	2.0E
24 Tu	0003	0225	1.6F
	0528	0817	2.0E
	1209	1458	2.3F
	1820	2055	2.1E
25 W	0101	0328	1.7F
	0636	0919	2.1E
	1312	1600	2.4F
	1918	2153	2.3E
26 Th	0157	0431	2.0F
	0739	1020	2.3E
	1415	1701	2.5F
	2013	2249	2.4E
27 F	0249	0529	2.3F
	0836	1119	2.5E
	1515	1758	2.6F
	2104	2343	2.6E
28 Sa ●	0338	0621	2.6F
	0930	1217	2.6E
	1611	1850	2.7F
	2155		
29 Su		0035	2.6E
	0425	0711	2.8F
	1023	1313	2.7E
	1705	1942	2.6F
	2245		
30 M		0125	2.6E
	0512	0800	2.9F
	1115	1406	2.7E
	1800	2033	2.4F
	2336		

Time meridian 75° W. 0000 is midnight. 1200 is noon. Times are not adjusted for Daylight Saving Time.

St. Johns River Entrance, Florida, 2019

F–Flood, Dir. 262° True   E–Ebb, Dir. 082° True

October

Days 1–15

Day	Slack h m	Max h m	knots
1 Tu		0214	2.5E
	0601	0851	2.8F
	1207	1457	2.5E
	1856	2127	2.2F
2 W	0027	0303	2.3E
	0653	0943	2.7F
	1301	1549	2.3E
	1953	2221	1.9F
3 Th	0119	0353	2.1E
	0748	1037	2.5F
	1355	1650	2.1E
	2051	2315	1.7F
4 F	0212	0448	1.9E
	0846	1130	2.3F
	1451	1831	1.9E
	2147		
5 Sa ☽		0007	1.6F
	0307	0557	1.7E
	0945	1223	2.1F
	1549	1947	1.8E
	2242		
6 Su		0100	1.4F
	0405	0741	1.7E
	1042	1317	1.9F
	1647	2044	1.8E
	2335		
7 M		0157	1.4F
	0505	0847	1.7E
	1139	1415	1.7F
	1744	2134	1.8E
8 Tu	0026	0306	1.4F
	0604	0941	1.7E
	1234	1521	1.7F
	1838	2219	1.8E
9 W	0116	0419	1.5F
	0659	1030	1.8E
	1328	1628	1.7F
	1926	2301	1.9E
10 Th	0203	0505	1.7F
	0749	1114	1.8E
	1419	1714	1.8F
	2010	2338	2.0E
11 F	0246	0536	1.8F
	0833	1152	1.9E
	1506	1749	1.8F
	2052		
12 Sa		0009	2.0E
	0325	0605	2.0F
	0914	1219	2.0E
	1549	1823	1.9F
	2132		
13 Su ○		0030	2.0E
	0401	0638	2.2F
	0952	1240	2.1E
	1630	1859	1.9F
	2210		
14 M		0053	2.0E
	0436	0713	2.3F
	1028	1308	2.2E
	1711	1937	1.9F
	2247		
15 Tu		0123	2.0E
	0509	0751	2.3F
	1105	1342	2.2E
	1751	2017	1.8F
	2324		

Days 16–31

Day	Slack h m	Max h m	knots
16 W		0158	2.0E
	0544	0833	2.3F
	1143	1421	2.3E
	1834	2100	1.7F
17 Th	0000	0236	1.9E
	0621	0918	2.3F
	1225	1502	2.2E
	1920	2145	1.6F
18 F	0037	0318	1.9E
	0704	1006	2.3F
	1310	1547	2.2E
	2009	2234	1.5F
19 Sa	0118	0403	1.9E
	0753	1056	2.3F
	1359	1635	2.1E
	2101	2323	1.5F
20 Su	0206	0454	1.8E
	0849	1147	2.3F
	1453	1730	2.0E
	2154		
21 M ○		0015	1.6F
	0302	0551	1.8E
	0949	1240	2.3F
	1551	1829	2.0E
	2248		
22 Tu		0109	1.6F
	0409	0654	1.8E
	1051	1336	2.2F
	1653	1933	2.1E
	2343		
23 W		0207	1.8F
	0520	0802	1.9E
	1156	1437	2.2F
	1755	2037	2.2E
24 Th	0037	0309	2.0F
	0626	0910	2.1E
	1301	1541	2.2F
	1854	2136	2.3E
25 F	0130	0412	2.3F
	0727	1014	2.3E
	1404	1644	2.3F
	1950	2231	2.5E
26 Sa	0221	0509	2.6F
	0822	1114	2.5E
	1504	1742	2.4F
	2042	2323	2.6E
27 Su ●	0310	0601	2.9F
	0914	1211	2.7E
	1559	1834	2.5F
	2132		
28 M		0013	2.6E
	0357	0649	3.0F
	1004	1303	2.7E
	1652	1924	2.4F
	2222		
29 Tu		0102	2.5E
	0444	0737	3.0F
	1054	1352	2.7E
	1744	2012	2.2F
	2311		
30 W		0149	2.4E
	0532	0825	2.9F
	1145	1439	2.5E
	1836	2102	2.0F
31 Th	0000	0236	2.2E
	0623	0916	2.6F
	1236	1526	2.3E
	1930	2154	1.8F

November

Days 1–15

Day	Slack h m	Max h m	knots
1 F	0051	0323	2.0E
	0718	1008	2.4F
	1329	1616	2.0E
	2025	2246	1.6F
2 Sa	0143	0414	1.8E
	0816	1100	2.2F
	1422	1729	1.8E
	2118	2337	1.5F
3 Su	0237	0512	1.6E
	0914	1151	1.9F
	1515	1907	1.7E
	2210		
4 M ☽		0027	1.4F
	0334	0644	1.5E
	1011	1241	1.8F
	1608	2005	1.7E
	2259		
5 Tu		0117	1.4F
	0434	0814	1.5E
	1106	1332	1.6F
	1702	2053	1.7E
	2347		
6 W		0210	1.4F
	0533	0909	1.6E
	1201	1426	1.5F
	1754	2134	1.8E
7 Th	0033	0305	1.6F
	0628	0956	1.6E
	1255	1524	1.5F
	1843	2211	1.9E
8 F	0119	0359	1.7F
	0717	1037	1.8E
	1347	1620	1.5F
	1930	2243	1.9E
9 Sa	0202	0444	1.9F
	0801	1110	1.9E
	1437	1708	1.6F
	2014	2311	2.0E
10 Su	0243	0524	2.1F
	0842	1136	2.0E
	1522	1749	1.7F
	2056	2339	2.0E
11 M	0321	0603	2.3F
	0920	1203	2.1E
	1605	1828	1.8F
	2135		
12 Tu ○		0012	2.0E
	0358	0642	2.4F
	0958	1237	2.2E
	1647	1908	1.8F
	2212		
13 W		0048	2.0E
	0434	0722	2.5F
	1037	1314	2.3E
	1728	1949	1.7F
	2249		
14 Th		0127	2.0E
	0511	0806	2.5F
	1118	1355	2.5E
	1812	2033	1.6F
	2328		
15 F		0208	2.0E
	0552	0852	2.5F
	1203	1438	2.5E
	1859	2121	1.6F

Days 16–30

Day	Slack h m	Max h m	knots
16 Sa	0011	0252	1.9E
	0638	0942	2.4F
	1250	1525	2.2E
	1950	2212	1.5F
17 Su	0059	0340	1.9E
	0732	1034	2.4F
	1341	1615	2.2E
	2044	2305	1.6F
18 M	0155	0433	1.8E
	0833	1128	2.3F
	1434	1710	2.1E
	2137	2359	1.7F
19 Tu ○	0257	0533	1.8E
	0936	1222	2.3F
	1531	1811	2.1E
	2230		
20 W		0053	1.8F
	0403	0640	1.8E
	1041	1318	2.2F
	1631	1916	2.0E
	2321		
21 Th		0150	2.0F
	0510	0756	1.9E
	1145	1418	2.1F
	1732	2020	2.2E
22 F	0013	0250	2.2F
	0614	0910	2.1E
	1249	1522	2.1F
	1832	2120	2.3E
23 Sa	0104	0351	2.5F
	0712	1015	2.3E
	1352	1627	2.1F
	1928	2214	2.4E
24 Su	0155	0449	2.7F
	0806	1113	2.5E
	1451	1727	2.2F
	2021	2305	2.4E
25 M	0245	0542	2.9F
	0857	1207	2.6E
	1546	1819	2.2F
	2111	2354	2.4E
26 Tu ●	0334	0630	3.0F
	0946	1258	2.6E
	1637	1907	2.1F
	2159		
27 W		0041	2.4E
	0421	0717	3.0F
	1036	1344	2.5E
	1726	1952	2.0F
	2246		
28 Th		0127	2.3E
	0509	0803	2.8F
	1125	1427	2.4E
	1815	2038	1.8F
	2334		
29 F		0211	2.2E
	0558	0851	2.6F
	1214	1507	2.1E
	1905	2126	1.6F
30 Sa	0023	0257	2.0E
	0650	0940	2.3F
	1303	1549	1.9E
	1955	2215	1.5F

December

Days 1–15

Day	Slack h m	Max h m	knots
1 Su	0114	0344	1.8E
	0745	1029	2.1F
	1351	1634	1.8E
	2045	2304	1.5F
2 M	0207	0434	1.6E
	0840	1118	1.9F
	1438	1728	1.7E
	2133	2351	1.5F
3 Tu	0301	0532	1.5E
	0935	1205	1.7F
	1526	1842	1.7E
	2219		
4 W ☽		0037	1.6F
	0357	0646	1.4E
	1029	1251	1.6F
	1614	1941	1.7E
	2303		
5 Th		0123	1.6F
	0453	0809	1.5E
	1122	1340	1.5F
	1704	2023	1.8E
	2346		
6 F		0212	1.7F
	0547	0858	1.6E
	1215	1432	1.4F
	1755	2100	1.8E
7 Sa	0030	0303	1.8F
	0637	0935	1.7E
	1309	1527	1.4F
	1845	2138	1.8E
8 Su	0115	0353	2.0F
	0723	1010	1.8E
	1401	1621	1.4F
	1932	2215	1.9E
9 M	0158	0442	2.2F
	0807	1046	2.0E
	1451	1710	1.5F
	2016	2254	1.9E
10 Tu	0241	0528	2.4F
	0849	1125	2.1E
	1537	1755	1.6F
	2057	2334	2.0E
11 W	0323	0612	2.5F
	0931	1205	2.2E
	1621	1839	1.6F
	2137		
12 Th ○		0015	2.0E
	0404	0656	2.6F
	1013	1247	2.2E
	1705	1923	1.7F
	2218		
13 F		0058	2.1E
	0446	0742	2.6F
	1057	1332	2.3E
	1750	2009	1.6F
	2302		
14 Sa		0144	2.0E
	0531	0830	2.6F
	1144	1418	2.3E
	1838	2059	1.6F
	2352		
15 Su		0232	2.0E
	0622	0922	2.5F
	1233	1507	2.3E
	1930	2153	1.7F

Days 16–31

Day	Slack h m	Max h m	knots
16 M	0048	0323	1.9E
	0719	1016	2.4F
	1324	1558	2.3E
	2023	2248	1.8F
17 Tu	0148	0418	1.9E
	0822	1110	2.3F
	1417	1654	2.2E
	2116	2343	2.0F
18 W ○	0249	0519	1.8E
	0926	1205	2.3F
	1512	1754	2.2E
	2207		
19 Th		0037	2.1F
	0352	0631	1.8E
	1030	1301	2.1F
	1610	1859	2.2E
	2257		
20 F		0132	2.3F
	0455	0759	2.0E
	1133	1400	2.0F
	1710	2005	2.2E
	2348		
21 Sa		0229	2.4F
	0556	0915	2.2E
	1236	1504	1.9F
	1810	2105	2.3E
22 Su	0040	0330	2.5F
	0654	1015	2.3E
	1338	1611	1.9F
	1908	2200	2.3E
23 M	0133	0430	2.6F
	0749	1112	2.4E
	1437	1714	1.9F
	2001	2251	2.3E
24 Tu	0225	0526	2.8F
	0841	1206	2.5E
	1531	1807	1.9F
	2051	2340	2.3E
25 W	0316	0615	2.8F
	0931	1258	2.4E
	1621	1853	1.9F
	2138		
26 Th ●		0026	2.3E
	0404	0701	2.8F
	1019	1344	2.3E
	1708	1935	1.8F
	2225		
27 F		0110	2.2E
	0451	0744	2.7F
	1106	1423	2.2E
	1753	2016	1.7F
	2311		
28 Sa		0152	2.1E
	0538	0828	2.5F
	1151	1454	2.1E
	1838	2059	1.6F
	2358		
29 Su		0234	2.0E
	0626	0913	2.2F
	1236	1523	2.0E
	1923	2144	1.6F
30 M	0047	0317	1.8E
	0715	0958	2.0F
	1319	1558	1.9E
	2008	2230	1.6F
31 Tu	0136	0402	1.7E
	0806	1044	1.9F
	1401	1638	1.8E
	2052	2314	1.7F

Time meridian 75° W. 0000 is midnight. 1200 is noon. Times are not adjusted for Daylight Saving Time.

Fort Pierce Inlet Entrance, Florida, 2019

F–Flood, Dir. 258° True   E–Ebb, Dir. 080° True

January

Day	Slack h m	Maximum h m	knots
1 Tu	0034	0424	3.4F
	0700	1036	2.9E
	1322	1642	2.5F
	1855	2214	2.9E
2 W	0126	0516	3.6F
	0755	1130	3.1E
	1422	1731	2.5F
	1945	2256	2.8E
3 Th	0216	0602	3.6F
	0847	1222	3.1E
	1516	1817	2.4F
	2034	2327	2.7E
4 F	0302	0649	3.4F
	0935	1315	3.0E
	1603	1904	2.2F
	2121	2359	2.6E
5 Sa ●	0345	0735	3.2F
	1018	1403	2.9E
	1646	1951	2.1F
	2205		
6 Su		0036	2.5E
	0425	0815	3.0F
	1058	1442	2.8E
	1728	2029	2.0F
	2247		
7 M		0119	2.5E
	0505	0832	2.9F
	1137	1509	2.6E
	1810	2051	2.0F
	2331		
8 Tu		0202	2.5E
	0546	0840	2.8F
	1215	1516	2.5E
	1851	2111	2.0F
9 W	0015	0242	2.5E
	0627	0909	2.8F
	1252	1529	2.5E
	1930	2141	2.1F
10 Th	0100	0322	2.5E
	0710	0944	2.8F
	1327	1557	2.6E
	2008	2218	2.2F
11 F	0145	0406	2.4E
	0753	1025	2.7F
	1402	1635	2.6E
	2044	2301	2.2F
12 Sa	0232	0457	2.2E
	0838	1111	2.5F
	1438	1720	2.6E
	2122	2348	2.3F
13 Su	0325	0555	2.1E
	0930	1200	2.3F
	1518	1808	2.6E
	2203		
14 M ☽		0035	2.4F
	0424	0650	2.1E
	1031	1251	2.1F
	1605	1854	2.7E
	2246		
15 Tu		0124	2.5F
	0524	0743	2.1E
	1136	1343	1.9F
	1658	1940	2.7E
	2333		
16 W		0217	2.6F
	0620	0842	2.2E
	1238	1442	1.8F
	1752	2030	2.8E
17 Th	0021	0320	2.8F
	0714	0949	2.4E
	1338	1547	1.9F
	1846	2126	2.9E
18 F	0114	0422	3.2F
	0807	1047	2.6E
	1435	1645	2.1F
	1941	2222	3.1E
19 Sa	0210	0514	3.5F
	0900	1137	2.8E
	1528	1737	2.3F
	2039	2315	3.3E
20 Su	0308	0605	3.6F
	0950	1229	3.0E
	1617	1832	2.5F
	2136		
21 M ○		0010	3.4E
	0404	0703	3.8F
	1040	1329	3.2E
	1706	1933	2.8F
	2232		
22 Tu		0109	3.5E
	0500	0804	3.8F
	1129	1424	3.3E
	1757	2031	3.0F
	2330		
23 W		0211	3.5E
	0558	0857	3.9F
	1219	1510	3.5E
	1849	2124	3.2F
24 Th	0030	0308	3.5E
	0656	0945	3.8F
	1309	1556	3.5E
	1940	2216	3.3F
25 F	0129	0406	3.3E
	0754	1037	3.5F
	1358	1650	3.4E
	2030	2316	3.3F
26 Sa	0229	0521	3.0E
	0851	1135	3.1F
	1448	1752	3.3E
	2121		
27 Su ◐		0024	3.2F
	0331	0645	2.9E
	0951	1237	2.7F
	1540	1846	3.1E
	2214		
28 M		0131	3.1F
	0436	0752	2.8E
	1055	1341	2.4F
	1636	1933	2.9E
	2309		
29 Tu		0252	3.0F
	0539	0908	2.7E
	1159	1514	2.1F
	1732	2022	2.7E
30 W	0002	0403	3.1F
	0637	1018	2.7E
	1301	1622	2.1F
	1826	2126	2.5E
31 Th	0055	0457	3.2F
	0731	1113	2.8E
	1359	1712	2.1F
	1917	2224	2.4E

February

Day	Slack h m	Maximum h m	knots
1 F	0145	0543	3.2F
	0822	1201	2.8E
	1452	1756	2.1F
	2007	2259	2.4E
2 Sa	0234	0625	3.0F
	0908	1248	2.7E
	1537	1839	2.0F
	2054	2330	2.4E
3 Su	0318	0706	2.9F
	0948	1334	2.6E
	1617	1921	2.0F
	2139		
4 M ●		0006	2.4E
	0358	0738	2.7F
	1026	1409	2.6E
	1655	1955	2.0F
	2221		
5 Tu		0048	2.5E
	0437	0735	2.7F
	1101	1424	2.5E
	1733	2014	2.1F
	2304		
6 W		0134	2.5E
	0517	0804	2.8F
	1137	1426	2.6E
	1812	2039	2.2F
	2348		
7 Th		0218	2.6E
	0559	0839	2.9F
	1212	1449	2.7E
	1849	2111	2.4F
8 F	0032	0259	2.6E
	0643	0917	2.9F
	1246	1520	2.8E
	1925	2147	2.6F
9 Sa	0117	0341	2.6E
	0728	0957	2.8F
	1321	1556	2.9E
	1959	2227	2.7F
10 Su	0203	0428	2.5E
	0815	1042	2.6F
	1355	1638	2.9E
	2033	2312	2.7F
11 M	0252	0523	2.3E
	0907	1131	2.4F
	1433	1726	2.8E
	2110		
12 Tu ◐		0001	2.8F
	0349	0622	2.3E
	1007	1223	2.1F
	1519	1818	2.8E
	2156		
13 W		0051	2.8F
	0451	0717	2.3E
	1111	1316	1.9F
	1618	1909	2.8E
	2251		
14 Th		0145	2.8F
	0552	0814	2.3E
	1215	1414	1.8F
	1723	2002	2.8E
	2352		
15 F		0249	2.9F
	0649	0924	2.4E
	1315	1523	1.8F
	1825	2102	2.9E
16 Sa	0054	0402	3.1F
	0745	1034	2.6E
	1412	1630	2.1F
	1927	2206	3.1E
17 Su	0158	0504	3.4F
	0839	1126	2.9E
	1506	1727	2.5F
	2028	2305	3.3E
18 M	0259	0558	3.6F
	0931	1218	3.1E
	1556	1823	2.8F
	2127		
19 Tu ○		0002	3.5E
	0357	0656	3.7F
	1020	1316	3.3E
	1645	1925	3.1F
	2225		
20 W		0105	3.5E
	0452	0757	3.8F
	1108	1410	3.5E
	1734	2026	3.4F
	2322		
21 Th		0211	3.5E
	0548	0849	3.8F
	1156	1454	3.6E
	1825	2117	3.6F
22 F	0020	0308	3.5E
	0645	0935	3.6F
	1244	1535	3.6E
	1915	2205	3.6F
23 Sa	0117	0405	3.3E
	0741	1022	3.3F
	1332	1619	3.4E
	2003	2300	3.5F
24 Su	0213	0522	3.1E
	0836	1116	2.9F
	1420	1711	3.2E
	2051		
25 M		0004	3.3F
	0311	0640	2.9E
	0933	1217	2.5F
	1510	1808	2.9E
	2141		
26 Tu ◑		0107	3.1F
	0411	0740	2.7E
	1034	1317	2.1F
	1605	1856	2.6E
	2234		
27 W		0220	2.8F
	0512	0845	2.5E
	1136	1441	1.8F
	1702	1941	2.3E
	2329		
28 Th		0337	2.7F
	0609	0954	2.5E
	1235	1558	1.7F
	1758	2031	2.1E

March

Day	Slack h m	Maximum h m	knots
1 F	0022	0435	2.7F
	0702	1050	2.5E
	1330	1651	1.8F
	1850	2138	2.1E
2 Sa	0114	0520	2.7F
	0750	1135	2.5E
	1420	1734	1.9F
	1939	2230	2.2E
3 Su	0203	0558	2.6F
	0833	1214	2.5E
	1504	1811	2.0F
	2027	2305	2.3E
4 M	0249	0626	2.6F
	0912	1248	2.4E
	1542	1842	2.0F
	2113	2341	2.4E
5 Tu	0330	0618	2.5F
	0948	1258	2.4E
	1619	1900	2.1F
	2156		
6 W ●		0021	2.5E
	0410	0646	2.6F
	1023	1305	2.6E
	1654	1928	2.3F
	2239		
7 Th		0107	2.6E
	0450	0727	2.7F
	1057	1334	2.7E
	1729	2003	2.5F
	2321		
8 F		0153	2.7E
	0533	0809	2.8F
	1131	1408	2.9E
	1804	2040	2.8F
9 Sa	0005	0236	2.8E
	0619	0850	2.8F
	1206	1444	3.1E
	1838	2117	3.0F
10 Su	0050	0318	2.8E
	0708	0932	2.8F
	1242	1522	3.1E
	1913	2156	3.1F
11 M	0135	0402	2.7E
	0757	1016	2.6F
	1319	1603	3.1E
	1948	2240	3.1F
12 Tu	0224	0454	2.6E
	0848	1105	2.3F
	1359	1651	3.0E
	2029	2330	3.1F
13 W	0318	0555	2.4E
	0945	1159	2.1F
	1448	1747	2.9E
	2119		
14 Th ☽		0024	3.0F
	0421	0654	2.4E
	1048	1254	1.9F
	1551	1844	2.8E
	2223		
15 F		0120	2.9F
	0525	0752	2.3E
	1151	1352	1.9F
	1705	1942	2.8E
	2334		
16 Sa		0225	2.9F
	0625	0902	2.4E
	1251	1503	2.0F
	1813	2045	2.9E
17 Su	0043	0350	3.0F
	0722	1021	2.7E
	1348	1622	2.4F
	1917	2156	3.0E
18 M	0149	0501	3.3F
	0816	1115	3.0E
	1443	1723	2.8F
	2020	2301	3.3E
19 Tu ○	0251	0554	3.5F
	0907	1203	3.3E
	1533	1819	3.2F
	2119		
20 W		0001	3.4E
	0348	0649	3.6F
	0956	1254	3.5E
	1622	1920	3.5F
	2216		
21 Th		0109	3.5E
	0442	0748	3.6F
	1043	1347	3.6E
	1710	2019	3.8F
	2311		
22 F		0217	3.6E
	0537	0839	3.6F
	1130	1431	3.7E
	1758	2108	3.9F
23 Sa	0006	0312	3.5E
	0632	0923	3.4F
	1218	1510	3.5E
	1847	2152	3.8F
24 Su	0101	0406	3.3E
	0727	1007	3.0F
	1305	1547	3.3E
	1934	2239	3.6F
25 M	0154	0517	3.1E
	0820	1056	2.6F
	1353	1630	2.9E
	2020	2336	3.2F
26 Tu ◑	0247	0627	2.8E
	0914	1154	2.2F
	1441	1722	2.6E
	2108		
27 W ◑		0036	2.9F
	0342	0722	2.6E
	1010	1252	1.8F
	1533	1817	2.3E
	2158		
28 Th		0138	2.5F
	0439	0816	2.4E
	1107	1359	1.6F
	1631	1905	2.1E
	2253		
29 F		0301	2.2F
	0535	0920	2.2E
	1202	1527	1.5F
	1728	1952	1.9E
	2347		
30 Sa		0406	2.2F
	0625	1018	2.2E
	1254	1625	1.6F
	1822	2047	1.9E
31 Su	0040	0451	2.2F
	0710	1101	2.2E
	1341	1708	1.8F
	1912	2152	2.0E

Time meridian 75° W. 0000 is midnight. 1200 is noon. Times are not adjusted for Daylight Saving Time.

Fort Pierce Inlet Entrance, Florida, 2019

F–Flood, Dir. 258° True   E–Ebb, Dir. 080° True

April

Day	Slack h m	Maximum h m	knots
1 M	0129	0524	2.2F
	0751	1131	2.3E
	1424	1742	2.0F
	2001	2239	2.2E
2 Tu	0216	0524	2.3F
	0830	1135	2.4E
	1503	1758	2.1F
	2047	2317	2.3E
3 W	0301	0534	2.4F
	0906	1143	2.5E
	1539	1811	2.4F
	2131	2356	2.5E
4 Th	0344	0609	2.5F
	0941	1211	2.7E
	1612	1844	2.6F
	2213		
5 F ●		0040	2.6E
	0427	0652	2.6F
	1016	1248	2.9E
	1645	1925	2.8F
	2256		
6 Sa		0128	2.8E
	0512	0739	2.6F
	1051	1328	3.0E
	1717	2007	3.1F
	2339		
7 Su		0214	2.9E
	0600	0825	2.7F
	1128	1410	3.2E
	1752	2048	3.3F
8 M	0024	0257	2.9E
	0650	0909	2.6F
	1206	1451	3.3E
	1829	2129	3.4F
9 Tu	0111	0340	2.9E
	0740	0953	2.5F
	1249	1535	3.2E
	1913	2214	3.4F
10 W	0200	0430	2.7E
	0831	1042	2.3F
	1336	1623	3.1E
	2001	2305	3.3F
11 Th	0253	0530	2.6E
	0925	1137	2.2F
	1430	1722	2.9E
	2059		
12 F ◐		0002	3.1F
	0355	0634	2.5E
	1025	1235	2.1F
	1538	1825	2.9E
	2208		
13 Sa		0101	3.0F
	0500	0734	2.5E
	1127	1335	2.1F
	1654	1927	2.8E
	2322		
14 Su		0207	2.9F
	0600	0841	2.6E
	1227	1449	2.3F
	1805	2035	2.8E
15 M	0032	0342	2.9F
	0656	1002	2.9E
	1324	1623	2.7F
	1909	2155	3.0E
16 Tu	0138	0457	3.2F
	0750	1058	3.2E
	1418	1722	3.2F
	2011	2306	3.3E
17 W	0239	0547	3.4F
	0841	1142	3.5E
	1509	1815	3.6F
	2110		
18 Th		0009	3.4F
	0336	0638	3.4F
	0930	1228	3.6E
	1557	1912	3.9F
	2205		
19 F ○		0118	3.5E
	0430	0734	3.4F
	1017	1317	3.6E
	1644	2008	4.0F
	2258		
20 Sa		0221	3.6E
	0524	0826	3.2F
	1104	1404	3.5E
	1730	2056	4.0F
	2350		
21 Su		0312	3.5E
	0618	0911	3.0F
	1151	1442	3.3E
	1817	2137	3.8F
22 M	0042	0401	3.3E
	0711	0953	2.7F
	1239	1518	3.0E
	1904	2217	3.4F
23 Tu	0132	0502	3.0E
	0802	1035	2.3F
	1326	1556	2.7E
	1950	2256	3.0F
24 W	0220	0607	2.7E
	0851	1125	2.0F
	1413	1640	2.4E
	2035	2336	2.6F
25 Th	0309	0658	2.5E
	0941	1218	1.7F
	1503	1735	2.1E
	2122		
26 F ◐		0013	2.3F
	0400	0743	2.3E
	1033	1301	1.5F
	1558	1830	1.9E
	2214		
27 Sa		0051	2.0F
	0452	0829	2.1E
	1124	1349	1.4F
	1657	1918	1.8E
	2308		
28 Su		0133	1.9F
	0540	0924	2.0E
	1212	1550	1.5F
	1752	2008	1.8E
29 M	0001	0257	1.8F
	0623	1006	2.0E
	1257	1638	1.8F
	1844	2108	1.9E
30 Tu	0052	0332	1.9F
	0703	1010	2.2E
	1340	1708	2.0F
	1933	2207	2.1E

May

Day	Slack h m	Maximum h m	knots
1 W	0143	0420	2.1F
	0742	1027	2.4E
	1419	1712	2.3F
	2020	2252	2.3E
2 Th	0232	0458	2.3F
	0821	1056	2.6E
	1455	1733	2.4F
	2105	2332	2.5E
3 F	0320	0537	2.4F
	0859	1130	2.9E
	1529	1807	2.9F
	2148		
4 Sa ●		0015	2.7E
	0406	0621	2.4F
	0937	1209	3.0E
	1602	1849	3.1F
	2231		
5 Su		0102	2.8E
	0453	0709	2.4F
	1015	1252	3.1E
	1636	1935	3.4F
	2315		
6 M		0151	2.9E
	0542	0759	2.5F
	1055	1338	3.2E
	1714	2022	3.6F
7 Tu	0001	0237	3.0E
	0632	0847	2.5F
	1139	1425	3.3E
	1758	2107	3.7F
8 W	0050	0321	3.0E
	0723	0934	2.5F
	1228	1512	3.3E
	1850	2153	3.6F
9 Th	0140	0410	2.9E
	0813	1023	2.4F
	1322	1603	3.2E
	1947	2245	3.5F
10 F	0233	0509	2.7E
	0905	1119	2.4F
	1422	1703	3.0E
	2049	2344	3.2F
11 Sa ◐	0331	0616	2.7E
	1002	1219	2.4F
	1530	1811	2.9E
	2157		
12 Su		0045	3.0F
	0433	0717	2.8E
	1103	1322	2.4F
	1645	1918	2.8E
	2310		
13 M		0151	2.9F
	0533	0818	2.9E
	1201	1440	2.6F
	1755	2030	2.8E
14 Tu	0019	0328	2.8E
	0628	0932	3.1E
	1258	1620	3.1F
	1900	2204	3.0E
15 W	0124	0444	3.1F
	0721	1033	3.3E
	1352	1716	3.6F
	2000	2315	3.2E
16 Th	0226	0534	3.2F
	0813	1119	3.5E
	1444	1806	3.9F
	2058		
17 F		0015	3.4E
	0324	0624	3.1F
	0903	1200	3.5E
	1532	1859	4.0F
	2151		
18 Sa ○		0118	3.5E
	0417	0719	3.0F
	0951	1245	3.4E
	1618	1953	4.0F
	2242		
19 Su		0216	3.5E
	0509	0812	2.9F
	1038	1332	3.2E
	1703	2041	3.9F
	2331		
20 M		0305	3.4E
	0601	0858	2.7F
	1125	1414	3.0E
	1749	2122	3.6F
21 Tu	0020	0349	3.2E
	0652	0938	2.4F
	1212	1451	2.8E
	1835	2154	3.3F
22 W	0107	0438	2.9E
	0740	1013	2.2F
	1300	1527	2.6E
	1920	2215	2.9F
23 Th	0151	0536	2.6E
	0825	1047	1.9F
	1346	1606	2.3E
	2004	2243	2.6F
24 F	0234	0625	2.4E
	0908	1127	1.7F
	1433	1655	2.1E
	2047	2322	2.3F
25 Sa	0317	0659	2.2E
	0954	1209	1.6F
	1525	1752	1.9E
	2134		
26 Su ◐		0005	2.1F
	0401	0711	2.1E
	1040	1251	1.6F
	1622	1846	1.8E
	2226		
27 M		0050	2.0F
	0447	0729	2.1E
	1127	1336	1.6F
	1720	1935	1.8E
	2321		
28 Tu		0137	1.9F
	0532	0802	2.2E
	1210	1429	1.8F
	1813	2028	1.9E
29 W	0016	0230	1.9F
	0614	0844	2.3E
	1251	1537	2.0F
	1903	2130	2.0E
30 Th	0110	0330	1.9F
	0655	0929	2.5E
	1330	1622	2.4F
	1951	2225	2.2E
31 F	0205	0423	2.0F
	0736	1013	2.7E
	1408	1658	2.8F
	2038	2309	2.5E

June

Day	Slack h m	Maximum h m	knots
1 Sa	0257	0509	2.2F
	0818	1054	2.9E
	1446	1736	3.1F
	2123	2351	2.7E
2 Su	0347	0554	2.2F
	0901	1136	3.1E
	1524	1819	3.4F
	2208		
3 M ●		0038	2.8E
	0434	0643	2.3F
	0945	1222	3.2E
	1605	1907	3.5F
	2253		
4 Tu		0130	2.9E
	0523	0736	2.3F
	1031	1312	3.3E
	1650	1959	3.7F
	2341		
5 W		0219	3.0E
	0613	0828	2.5F
	1120	1404	3.4E
	1742	2049	3.8F
6 Th	0031	0306	3.1E
	0704	0917	2.6F
	1215	1456	3.4E
	1840	2138	3.7F
7 F	0121	0353	3.0E
	0754	1008	2.7F
	1314	1549	3.3E
	1940	2230	3.6F
8 Sa	0213	0450	3.0E
	0845	1104	2.7F
	1416	1650	3.1E
	2041	2328	3.3F
9 Su	0306	0557	3.0E
	0939	1206	2.7F
	1523	1803	2.9E
	2146		
10 M ◐		0030	3.1F
	0404	0658	3.1E
	1037	1311	2.8F
	1635	1914	2.8E
	2256		
11 Tu		0134	2.8F
	0503	0753	3.1E
	1135	1431	2.9F
	1744	2032	2.8E
12 W	0003	0304	2.7F
	0559	0856	3.2E
	1231	1608	3.3F
	1847	2210	3.0E
13 Th	0108	0428	2.8F
	0653	1004	3.2E
	1325	1704	3.7F
	1946	2314	3.2E
14 F	0211	0521	2.8F
	0746	1054	3.3E
	1417	1754	3.9F
	2043		
15 Sa		0010	3.3E
	0309	0610	2.8F
	0837	1136	3.2E
	1507	1844	3.9F
	2135		
16 Su		0109	3.4E
	0402	0702	2.7F
	0927	1216	3.1E
	1553	1937	3.8F
	2223		
17 M ○		0204	3.3E
	0452	0756	2.6F
	1014	1301	2.9E
	1637	2025	3.6F
	2309		
18 Tu		0251	3.2E
	0540	0842	2.4F
	1100	1346	2.7E
	1722	2104	3.3F
	2354		
19 W		0331	3.0E
	0627	0920	2.3F
	1146	1425	2.6E
	1806	2128	3.1F
20 Th	0037	0407	2.8E
	0712	0948	2.1F
	1232	1501	2.5E
	1850	2139	2.8F
21 F	0118	0436	2.5E
	0753	1011	2.0F
	1318	1539	2.3E
	1932	2206	2.6F
22 Sa	0155	0447	2.3E
	0832	1043	1.9F
	1404	1622	2.2E
	2014	2243	2.5F
23 Su	0232	0516	2.3E
	0912	1124	1.9F
	1452	1715	2.0E
	2057	2326	2.3F
24 M	0310	0555	2.3E
	0953	1209	1.9F
	1545	1812	1.9E
	2147		
25 Tu ◐		0013	2.2F
	0351	0635	2.3E
	1036	1253	2.0F
	1643	1904	1.9E
	2243		
26 W		0101	2.0F
	0436	0714	2.4E
	1119	1340	2.1F
	1739	1954	1.9E
	2342		
27 Th		0151	1.9F
	0523	0756	2.5E
	1200	1432	2.2F
	1831	2051	2.0E
28 F	0041	0248	1.8F
	0609	0843	2.6E
	1241	1531	2.5F
	1921	2154	2.2E
29 Sa	0139	0349	1.8F
	0654	0933	2.7E
	1323	1624	2.9F
	2010	2246	2.4E
30 Su	0235	0443	2.0F
	0742	1023	2.9E
	1408	1709	3.2F
	2059	2331	2.7E

Time meridian 75° W. 0000 is midnight. 1200 is noon. Times are not adjusted for Daylight Saving Time.

Fort Pierce Inlet Entrance, Florida, 2019

F–Flood, Dir. 258° True   E–Ebb, Dir. 080° True

July

Day	Slack	Maximum	knots
1 M	0327	0531	2.1F
	0831	1110	3.1E
	1456	1755	3.4F
	2146		
2 Tu ●		0017	2.8E
	0415	0621	2.2F
	0922	1159	3.3E
	1546	1846	3.6F
	2234		
3 W		0110	2.9E
	0502	0716	2.4F
	1014	1252	3.4E
	1638	1942	3.7F
	2322		
4 Th		0204	3.1E
	0551	0812	2.6F
	1109	1349	3.4E
	1734	2036	3.8F
5 F	0011	0252	3.2E
	0642	0904	2.8F
	1207	1445	3.5E
	1833	2126	3.8F
6 Sa	0101	0338	3.3E
	0733	0955	3.0F
	1307	1539	3.4E
	1933	2217	3.6F
7 Su	0151	0430	3.3E
	0823	1050	3.1F
	1408	1641	3.1E
	2032	2313	3.4F
8 M	0241	0532	3.3E
	0915	1153	3.1F
	1512	1758	2.9E
	2134		
9 Tu ◑		0014	3.1F
	0335	0634	3.3E
	1010	1259	3.1F
	1621	1915	2.9E
	2240		
10 W		0116	2.7F
	0433	0726	3.2E
	1107	1417	3.1F
	1728	2034	2.8E
	2347		
11 Th		0238	2.5F
	0531	0821	3.1E
	1203	1550	3.3F
	1830	2203	2.9E
12 F	0052	0410	2.4F
	0626	0929	3.0E
	1257	1649	3.6F
	1929	2305	3.1E
13 Sa	0154	0506	2.5F
	0720	1031	2.9E
	1351	1739	3.7F
	2024	2358	3.2E
14 Su	0253	0555	2.5F
	0813	1115	2.9E
	1442	1827	3.6F
	2115		
15 M		0052	3.2E
	0344	0645	2.4F
	0903	1153	2.8E
	1530	1917	3.5F
	2201		
16 Tu ○		0145	3.1E
	0430	0736	2.3F
	0950	1232	2.7E
	1614	2004	3.3F
	2244		
17 W		0230	3.0E
	0513	0821	2.3F
	1035	1316	2.6E
	1656	2041	3.1F
	2325		
18 Th		0305	2.8E
	0556	0857	2.2F
	1120	1358	2.5E
	1737	2054	2.9F
19 F	0003	0327	2.7E
	0637	0918	2.2F
	1205	1436	2.5E
	1820	2105	2.8F
20 Sa	0040	0329	2.6E
	0716	0937	2.2F
	1250	1513	2.4E
	1901	2134	2.7F
21 Su	0114	0347	2.6E
	0753	1007	2.2F
	1334	1554	2.3E
	1943	2210	2.6F
22 M	0148	0419	2.6E
	0828	1045	2.2F
	1420	1641	2.2E
	2026	2252	2.5F
23 Tu	0222	0500	2.6E
	0904	1129	2.3F
	1509	1736	2.1E
	2114	2340	2.3F
24 W ○	0258	0546	2.6E
	0942	1215	2.3F
	1604	1832	2.0E
	2211		
25 Th		0029	2.1F
	0341	0632	2.6E
	1023	1301	2.4F
	1702	1923	2.1E
	2313		
26 F		0119	1.9F
	0432	0718	2.6E
	1108	1350	2.5F
	1758	2017	2.1E
27 Sa	0015	0214	1.7F
	0527	0806	2.6E
	1156	1448	2.6F
	1851	2121	2.2E
28 Su	0114	0317	1.7F
	0621	0859	2.7E
	1247	1552	2.9F
	1943	2223	2.4E
29 M	0211	0419	1.9F
	0715	0956	2.9E
	1342	1648	3.2F
	2035	2312	2.6E
30 Tu	0304	0512	2.1F
	0811	1050	3.1E
	1440	1738	3.4F
	2125	2359	2.8E
31 W ●	0353	0603	2.4F
	0908	1142	3.3E
	1536	1831	3.6F
	2214		

August

Day	Slack	Maximum	knots
1 Th		0052	3.0E
	0440	0700	2.6F
	1004	1239	3.4E
	1631	1929	3.7F
	2301		
2 F		0148	3.2E
	0528	0759	2.9F
	1101	1340	3.5E
	1727	2025	3.8F
	2350		
3 Sa		0236	3.4E
	0618	0853	3.2F
	1159	1438	3.5E
	1825	2115	3.8F
4 Su	0038	0321	3.5E
	0709	0943	3.4F
	1259	1534	3.4E
	1924	2204	3.6F
5 M	0127	0408	3.5E
	0759	1037	3.4F
	1358	1636	3.2E
	2021	2257	3.3F
6 Tu	0216	0503	3.4E
	0849	1138	3.4F
	1459	1800	3.0E
	2120	2358	2.9F
7 W ◑	0307	0604	3.3E
	0941	1244	3.3F
	1603	1915	2.9E
	2223		
8 Th		0100	2.5F
	0404	0659	3.1E
	1037	1359	3.2F
	1708	2027	2.8E
	2329		
9 F		0217	2.2F
	0503	0750	2.8E
	1134	1529	3.1F
	1810	2147	2.8E
10 Sa	0033	0351	2.1F
	0601	0852	2.6E
	1230	1632	3.3F
	1907	2249	2.9E
11 Su	0134	0450	2.2F
	0656	1009	2.5E
	1325	1723	3.3F
	2001	2341	2.9E
12 M	0231	0538	2.3F
	0749	1059	2.5E
	1418	1808	3.3F
	2050		
13 Tu		0030	2.9E
	0320	0624	2.3F
	0840	1134	2.5E
	1506	1853	3.1F
	2134		
14 W		0118	2.8E
	0402	0710	2.3F
	0927	1207	2.5E
	1549	1935	2.9F
	2213		
15 Th ○		0200	2.7E
	0441	0754	2.2F
	1011	1246	2.5E
	1629	2004	2.8F
	2249		
16 F		0228	2.6E
	0519	0826	2.2F
	1054	1329	2.5E
	1709	2005	2.7F
	2324		
17 Sa		0231	2.6E
	0557	0841	2.3F
	1137	1411	2.5E
	1750	2030	2.7F
	2358		
18 Su		0240	2.7E
	0634	0903	2.4F
	1221	1449	2.6E
	1832	2104	2.7F
19 M	0032	0306	2.8E
	0709	0934	2.6F
	1305	1528	2.5E
	1916	2141	2.7F
20 Tu	0105	0339	2.9E
	0742	1010	2.7F
	1349	1611	2.4E
	2001	2223	2.5F
21 W	0139	0417	2.8E
	0815	1051	2.7F
	1434	1702	2.3E
	2050	2310	2.3F
22 Th	0214	0503	2.8E
	0849	1138	2.7F
	1526	1800	2.2E
	2144		
23 F ○		0000	2.1F
	0254	0553	2.7E
	0930	1227	2.7F
	1624	1855	2.2E
	2246		
24 Sa		0052	1.8F
	0347	0645	2.7E
	1020	1318	2.7F
	1725	1948	2.2E
	2349		
25 Su		0147	1.7F
	0453	0736	2.7E
	1121	1415	2.7F
	1823	2049	2.2E
26 M	0049	0249	1.7F
	0557	0832	2.7E
	1223	1524	2.8F
	1918	2200	2.4E
27 Tu	0146	0359	1.9F
	0658	0935	2.9E
	1327	1632	3.1F
	2011	2256	2.6E
28 W	0239	0458	2.3F
	0759	1036	3.1E
	1429	1726	3.4F
	2103	2343	2.9E
29 Th	0329	0551	2.7F
	0858	1133	3.3E
	1528	1819	3.6F
	2151		
30 F ●		0033	3.2E
	0416	0648	3.0F
	0956	1231	3.5E
	1623	1918	3.6F
	2238		
31 Sa		0127	3.4E
	0504	0749	3.3F
	1053	1336	3.5E
	1719	2015	3.7F
	2325		

September

Day	Slack	Maximum	knots
1 Su		0217	3.6E
	0553	0844	3.6F
	1150	1437	3.6E
	1815	2104	3.6F
2 M	0013	0301	3.7E
	0643	0933	3.8F
	1248	1532	3.5E
	1913	2151	3.4F
3 Tu	0102	0344	3.6E
	0733	1023	3.7F
	1344	1635	3.2E
	2009	2242	3.1F
4 W	0151	0432	3.4E
	0822	1121	3.5F
	1441	1802	3.0E
	2106	2341	2.7F
5 Th ◑	0242	0530	3.1E
	0912	1227	3.3F
	1541	1910	2.9E
	2206		
6 F		0046	2.3F
	0337	0630	2.8E
	1007	1338	3.0F
	1644	2013	2.7E
	2309		
7 Sa		0159	2.0F
	0437	0722	2.5E
	1105	1503	2.8F
	1745	2125	2.6E
8 Su	0010	0329	1.9F
	0537	0817	2.3E
	1202	1611	2.8F
	1840	2228	2.6E
9 M	0108	0431	2.0F
	0633	0942	2.2E
	1258	1702	2.9F
	1931	2317	2.7E
10 Tu	0202	0519	2.1F
	0725	1042	2.2E
	1350	1745	2.8F
	2018		
11 W		0000	2.6E
	0248	0601	2.2F
	0815	1114	2.3E
	1438	1822	2.7F
	2059		
12 Th		0039	2.6E
	0329	0640	2.2F
	0902	1143	2.4E
	1522	1850	2.6F
	2135		
13 F ○		0108	2.5E
	0405	0716	2.3F
	0946	1218	2.5E
	1602	1846	2.5F
	2209		
14 Sa		0104	2.5E
	0439	0737	2.4F
	1028	1259	2.5E
	1641	1915	2.6F
	2242		
15 Su		0121	2.7E
	0513	0756	2.5F
	1110	1343	2.6E
	1722	1954	2.6F
	2315		
16 M		0153	2.8E
	0547	0827	2.7F
	1152	1425	2.7E
	1806	2034	2.7F
	2349		
17 Tu		0227	3.0E
	0621	0901	2.9F
	1235	1504	2.7E
	1853	2115	2.6F
18 W	0024	0303	3.1E
	0654	0938	3.1F
	1319	1545	2.7E
	1941	2157	2.5F
19 Th	0100	0342	3.0E
	0728	1019	3.1F
	1404	1632	2.5E
	2029	2243	2.3F
20 F	0139	0427	2.9E
	0805	1105	3.0F
	1453	1728	2.4E
	2122	2334	2.1F
21 Sa ○	0222	0519	2.8E
	0850	1157	3.0F
	1551	1827	2.3E
	2221		
22 Su		0028	1.9F
	0318	0617	2.7E
	0948	1251	2.9F
	1654	1923	2.3E
	2323		
23 M		0123	1.8F
	0430	0714	2.7E
	1058	1350	2.8F
	1755	2022	2.3E
24 Tu	0022	0226	1.8F
	0542	0813	2.7E
	1209	1500	2.8F
	1852	2134	2.5E
25 W	0119	0342	2.1F
	0647	0920	2.9E
	1315	1620	3.0F
	1945	2237	2.8E
26 Th	0213	0449	2.6F
	0749	1029	3.1E
	1419	1717	3.3F
	2037	2324	3.1E
27 F	0304	0543	3.1F
	0850	1129	3.3E
	1518	1809	3.5F
	2126		
28 Sa		0011	3.4E
	0352	0639	3.4F
	0948	1230	3.5E
	1614	1906	3.5F
	2213		
29 Su		0101	3.6E
	0439	0740	3.6F
	1043	1339	3.6E
	1708	2003	3.5F
	2300		
30 M		0153	3.7E
	0527	0835	3.9F
	1138	1441	3.6E
	1804	2053	3.4F
	2348		

Time meridian 75° W. 0000 is midnight. 1200 is noon. Times are not adjusted for Daylight Saving Time.

Fort Pierce Inlet Entrance, Florida, 2019

F–Flood, Dir. 258° True   E–Ebb, Dir. 080° True

October

Day	Slack (h m)	Maximum (h m)	knots
1 Tu		0238	3.7E
	0616	0922	4.0F
	1233	1535	3.5E
	1901	2139	3.2F
2 W	0038	0320	3.5E
	0706	1008	3.8F
	1328	1636	3.3E
	1956	2228	2.8F
3 Th	0128	0404	3.2E
	0755	1101	3.5F
	1421	1756	3.0E
	2050	2326	2.5F
4 F	0218	0456	2.8E
	0845	1207	3.1F
	1516	1858	2.9E
	2146		
5 Sa ◑		0033	2.1F
	0312	0559	2.5E
	0937	1313	2.8F
	1615	1954	2.6E
	2244		
6 Su		0139	1.9F
	0410	0656	2.2E
	1034	1429	2.5F
	1713	2055	2.5E
	2342		
7 M		0300	1.7F
	0511	0746	2.1E
	1131	1542	2.4F
	1807	2157	2.4E
8 Tu	0036	0406	1.8F
	0607	0848	2.0E
	1226	1635	2.4F
	1854	2246	2.4E
9 W	0125	0455	2.0F
	0700	1011	2.0E
	1318	1715	2.3F
	1936	2323	2.4E
10 Th	0209	0534	2.2F
	0749	1049	2.1E
	1406	1743	2.3F
	2015	2342	2.4E
11 F	0248	0607	2.3E
	0836	1118	2.3F
	1451	1738	2.3E
	2051	2339	2.5F
12 Sa	0324	0621	2.4E
	0920	1151	2.4F
	1533	1758	2.4E
	2126	2358	2.6F
13 Su ○	0357	0635	2.6E
	1002	1230	2.5F
	1615	1835	2.4E
	2200		
14 M		0030	2.8E
	0429	0709	2.8F
	1043	1315	2.7E
	1658	1920	2.5F
	2235		
15 Tu		0109	2.9E
	0500	0749	3.0F
	1124	1359	2.8E
	1744	2006	2.5F
	2310		
16 W		0150	3.1E
	0533	0829	3.2F
	1207	1441	2.8E
	1833	2050	2.5F
	2348		
17 Th		0232	3.1E
	0608	0909	3.4F
	1251	1522	2.8E
	1922	2133	2.4F
18 F	0028	0314	3.1E
	0649	0952	3.4F
	1337	1606	2.7E
	2011	2219	2.3F
19 Sa	0112	0359	3.0E
	0735	1039	3.3F
	1427	1700	2.6E
	2101	2311	2.1F
20 Su	0202	0452	2.9E
	0827	1132	3.1F
	1523	1802	2.5E
	2157		
21 M ○		0007	2.0F
	0303	0554	2.8E
	0930	1230	3.0F
	1625	1901	2.5E
	2256		
22 Tu		0104	2.0F
	0417	0657	2.7E
	1044	1330	2.8F
	1727	1958	2.5E
	2355		
23 W		0207	2.1F
	0531	0759	2.8E
	1156	1440	2.8F
	1824	2105	2.7E
24 Th	0051	0328	2.5E
	0638	0911	2.8F
	1303	1608	2.9E
	1917	2213	3.0E
25 F	0145	0445	3.0F
	0740	1029	3.1E
	1407	1709	3.2F
	2008	2303	3.3E
26 Sa	0237	0539	3.5F
	0841	1132	3.3E
	1507	1759	3.3F
	2058	2347	3.5E
27 Su ●	0327	0632	3.8F
	0937	1236	3.5E
	1603	1854	3.3F
	2147		
28 M		0035	3.6E
	0414	0731	4.0F
	1031	1347	3.6E
	1657	1952	3.2F
	2235		
29 Tu		0126	3.6E
	0502	0826	4.1F
	1124	1445	3.6E
	1752	2044	3.1F
	2324		
30 W		0215	3.5E
	0550	0912	4.0F
	1217	1536	3.5E
	1847	2130	2.9F
31 Th	0014	0258	3.3E
	0640	0955	3.7F
	1309	1632	3.2E
	1940	2217	2.6F

November

Day	Slack (h m)	Maximum (h m)	knots
1 F	0105	0339	3.0E
	0730	1041	3.4F
	1359	1741	3.0E
	2031	2311	2.3F
2 Sa	0155	0425	2.6E
	0818	1137	2.9F
	1449	1839	2.8E
	2122		
3 Su		0015	2.0F
	0247	0523	2.3E
	0907	1236	2.6F
	1541	1928	2.5E
	2214		
4 M ◐		0112	1.8F
	0342	0625	2.1E
	1000	1313	2.2F
	1634	2015	2.3E
	2306		
5 Tu		0218	1.7F
	0441	0715	1.9E
	1055	1357	1.9F
	1723	2107	2.2E
	2356		
6 W		0332	1.7F
	0539	0804	1.8E
	1149	1553	1.9F
	1808	2156	2.1E
7 Th	0041	0425	1.9F
	0631	0906	1.8E
	1240	1633	1.9F
	1848	2221	2.2E
8 F	0123	0504	2.1F
	0720	1010	2.0E
	1330	1629	1.9F
	1926	2219	2.3E
9 Sa	0202	0529	2.3F
	0807	1049	2.2E
	1419	1647	2.1F
	2004	2242	2.5E
10 Su	0239	0529	2.5F
	0852	1125	2.4E
	1506	1722	2.2F
	2042	2314	2.8E
11 M	0313	0553	2.8F
	0934	1203	2.6E
	1552	1803	2.3F
	2119	2350	2.9E
12 Tu ○	0345	0630	3.0F
	1016	1246	2.7E
	1637	1848	2.3F
	2157		
13 W		0031	3.0E
	0418	0714	3.2F
	1058	1333	2.8E
	1724	1938	2.3F
	2236		
14 Th		0116	3.1E
	0454	0800	3.4F
	1141	1419	2.9E
	1813	2026	2.3F
	2318		
15 F		0203	3.2E
	0535	0845	3.5F
	1227	1501	2.9E
	1902	2112	2.4F
16 Sa	0004	0250	3.2E
	0623	0930	3.6F
	1315	1545	2.9E
	1951	2159	2.4F
17 Su	0055	0338	3.2E
	0718	1018	3.5F
	1405	1636	2.7E
	2040	2250	2.3F
18 M	0151	0432	3.0E
	0816	1113	3.3F
	1458	1738	2.7E
	2132	2348	2.3F
19 Tu ○	0255	0537	2.8E
	0920	1212	3.1F
	1556	1840	2.7E
	2229		
20 W		0048	2.4F
	0408	0644	2.8E
	1032	1312	2.9F
	1657	1936	2.8E
	2327		
21 Th		0151	2.5F
	0521	0750	2.8E
	1143	1419	2.7F
	1754	2035	3.0E
22 F	0023	0318	2.8F
	0628	0909	2.8E
	1250	1552	2.8F
	1847	2142	3.2E
23 Sa	0118	0441	3.4F
	0730	1036	3.1E
	1354	1658	3.0F
	1940	2238	3.4E
24 Su	0211	0533	3.8F
	0829	1140	3.3E
	1455	1749	3.1F
	2032	2325	3.5E
25 M	0302	0625	4.0F
	0925	1243	3.5E
	1551	1843	3.0F
	2123		
26 Tu ●		0010	3.5E
	0351	0721	4.1F
	1017	1348	3.5E
	1644	1942	2.9F
	2213		
27 W		0101	3.4E
	0439	0816	4.0F
	1108	1442	3.5E
	1737	2035	2.8F
	2302		
28 Th		0153	3.2E
	0527	0903	3.9F
	1158	1530	3.4E
	1830	2121	2.7F
	2352		
29 F		0238	3.0E
	0616	0943	3.6F
	1247	1618	3.2E
	1920	2204	2.4F
30 Sa	0042	0317	2.7E
	0705	1019	3.5F
	1334	1716	2.9E
	2008	2249	2.2F

December

Day	Slack (h m)	Maximum (h m)	knots
1 Su	0132	0358	2.5E
	0751	1048	2.8F
	1419	1811	2.6E
	2053	2341	2.0F
2 M	0220	0446	2.2E
	0837	1120	2.5F
	1502	1853	2.4E
	2138		
3 Tu		0027	1.8F
	0312	0546	2.0E
	0924	1158	2.2F
	1546	1920	2.2E
	2224		
4 W ◐		0058	1.7F
	0408	0640	1.9E
	1014	1239	2.0F
	1631	1928	2.1E
	2309		
5 Th		0132	1.7F
	0506	0727	1.8E
	1108	1322	1.8F
	1715	1950	2.2E
	2353		
6 F		0219	1.8F
	0559	0817	1.8E
	1202	1410	1.7F
	1756	2026	2.2E
7 Sa	0034	0424	2.0F
	0649	0919	1.9E
	1255	1508	1.7F
	1837	2109	2.4E
8 Su	0112	0423	2.3F
	0736	1016	2.1E
	1348	1604	1.8F
	1917	2153	2.6E
9 M	0150	0445	2.6F
	0822	1058	2.3E
	1441	1651	2.0F
	1959	2235	2.8E
10 Tu	0228	0519	2.9F
	0907	1137	2.5E
	1530	1735	2.1F
	2042	2317	2.9E
11 W	0306	0558	3.2F
	0950	1220	2.7E
	1617	1821	2.1F
	2125		
12 Th ○		0000	3.1E
	0345	0644	3.4F
	1034	1308	2.8E
	1703	1912	2.2F
	2210		
13 F		0048	3.1E
	0427	0734	3.5F
	1119	1357	2.9E
	1751	2005	2.3F
	2257		
14 Sa		0140	3.2E
	0515	0825	3.6F
	1206	1443	3.0E
	1840	2054	2.5F
	2348		
15 Su		0232	3.3E
	0610	0913	3.7F
	1255	1527	3.0E
	1929	2142	2.6F
16 M	0044	0323	3.3E
	0709	1002	3.6F
	1344	1615	3.0E
	2017	2233	2.7F
17 Tu	0144	0418	3.1E
	0809	1055	3.4F
	1434	1713	3.0E
	2107	2331	2.7F
18 W ○	0248	0524	2.9E
	0911	1154	3.1F
	1527	1816	3.0E
	2201		
19 Th		0032	2.8F
	0357	0636	2.8E
	1018	1254	2.9F
	1625	1912	3.1E
	2259		
20 F		0136	2.9F
	0509	0745	2.8E
	1128	1359	2.7F
	1724	2006	3.2E
	2356		
21 Sa		0307	3.1F
	0615	0913	2.8E
	1235	1534	2.6F
	1819	2109	3.2E
22 Su	0051	0431	3.5F
	0716	1040	3.1E
	1339	1648	2.7F
	1914	2214	3.3E
23 M	0146	0525	3.9F
	0814	1140	3.3E
	1441	1740	2.8F
	2008	2305	3.3E
24 Tu	0239	0615	4.0F
	0909	1238	3.4E
	1537	1833	2.8F
	2102	2351	3.2E
25 W	0330	0709	3.9F
	1000	1338	3.4E
	1629	1930	2.7F
	2152		
26 Th ●		0040	3.1E
	0418	0803	3.8F
	1049	1431	3.4E
	1719	2023	2.6F
	2241		
27 F		0134	2.9E
	0505	0849	3.6F
	1136	1515	3.3E
	1808	2108	2.5F
	2330		
28 Sa		0220	2.8E
	0552	0927	3.3F
	1221	1556	3.0E
	1855	2147	2.4F
29 Su	0018	0257	2.6E
	0638	0950	3.0F
	1304	1636	2.7E
	1938	2219	2.2F
30 M	0106	0333	2.5E
	0723	1005	2.7F
	1343	1712	2.5E
	2018	2246	2.1F
31 Tu	0153	0414	2.3E
	0806	1035	2.5F
	1420	1720	2.3E
	2057	2319	2.0F

Time meridian 75° W. 0000 is midnight. 1200 is noon. Times are not adjusted for Daylight Saving Time.

Lake Worth Inlet Entrance, Florida, 2019

F–Flood, Dir. 267° True   E–Ebb, Dir. 086° True

January

Day	Slack h m	Maximum h m	knots
1 Tu		0227	1.7F
	0529	0828	1.3E
	1132	1451	1.4F
	1736	2040	1.3E
	2348		
2 W		0331	1.8F
	0623	0928	1.3E
	1229	1553	1.4F
	1827	2136	1.3E
3 Th	0038	0421	1.9F
	0713	1018	1.4E
	1323	1640	1.4F
	1915	2222	1.3E
4 F	0126	0503	1.9F
	0801	1101	1.4E
	1413	1720	1.5F
	2002	2301	1.3E
5 Sa ●	0211	0541	2.0F
	0845	1141	1.4E
	1456	1756	1.4F
	2045	2338	1.3E
6 Su	0252	0618	1.9F
	0925	1222	1.4E
	1535	1832	1.4F
	2126		
7 M		0017	1.3E
	0330	0654	1.9F
	1004	1303	1.4E
	1611	1908	1.4F
	2207		
8 Tu		0059	1.3E
	0408	0729	1.8F
	1043	1340	1.3E
	1647	1945	1.4F
	2249		
9 W		0139	1.2E
	0447	0803	1.6F
	1122	1412	1.3E
	1725	2021	1.3F
	2333		
10 Th		0215	1.1E
	0529	0838	1.5F
	1201	1441	1.2E
	1805	2058	1.3F
11 F	0021	0251	1.0E
	0615	0915	1.3F
	1241	1511	1.1E
	1846	2139	1.3F
12 Sa	0109	0329	0.9E
	0703	0956	1.2F
	1320	1546	1.0E
	1927	2225	1.3F
13 Su	0156	0418	0.9E
	0751	1044	1.1F
	1400	1633	1.0E
	2008	2316	1.3F
14 M ☽	0246	0522	0.9E
	0840	1134	1.1F
	1445	1728	1.0E
	2051		
15 Tu		0006	1.4F
	0339	0618	0.9E
	0934	1224	1.1F
	1536	1820	1.1E
	2140		
16 W		0055	1.5F
	0435	0707	1.3E
	1032	1315	1.2F
	1633	1909	1.2E
	2234		
17 Th		0151	1.6F
	0529	0800	1.2E
	1130	1417	1.2F
	1730	2004	1.3E
	2331		
18 F		0258	1.8F
	0622	0902	1.3E
	1228	1526	1.4F
	1825	2106	1.4E
19 Sa	0029	0400	2.0F
	0715	1000	1.5E
	1326	1624	1.6F
	1920	2206	1.6E
20 Su	0129	0452	2.2F
	0807	1050	1.7E
	1420	1714	1.8F
	2015	2259	1.7E
21 M ○	0227	0541	2.3F
	0858	1140	1.8E
	1511	1805	1.9F
	2109	2353	1.8E
22 Tu	0321	0633	2.4F
	0947	1233	1.8E
	1600	1901	2.0F
	2204		
23 W		0053	1.8E
	0414	0728	2.3F
	1037	1329	1.8E
	1650	1958	2.0F
	2300		
24 Th		0152	1.7E
	0509	0822	2.1F
	1129	1420	1.7E
	1744	2052	2.0F
	2359		
25 F		0247	1.6E
	0609	0915	1.9F
	1223	1509	1.6E
	1842	2150	1.9F
26 Sa	0100	0345	1.4E
	0710	1012	1.7F
	1318	1607	1.4E
	1939	2256	1.8F
27 Su ☽	0201	0502	1.3E
	0810	1117	1.5F
	1414	1723	1.3E
	2034		
28 M		0001	1.7F
	0303	0614	1.2E
	0910	1218	1.4F
	1511	1826	1.2E
	2129		
29 Tu		0058	1.7F
	0406	0708	1.2E
	1010	1315	1.3F
	1610	1915	1.2E
	2223		
30 W		0156	1.7F
	0504	0801	1.2E
	1108	1419	1.2F
	1706	2005	1.1E
	2314		
31 Th		0259	1.7F
	0556	0858	1.2E
	1202	1525	1.2F
	1758	2101	1.1E

February

Day	Slack h m	Maximum h m	knots
1 F	0002	0354	1.7F
	0645	0950	1.3E
	1254	1616	1.3F
	1847	2152	1.2E
2 Sa	0050	0437	1.8F
	0732	1034	1.3E
	1343	1656	1.3F
	1934	2234	1.2E
3 Su	0138	0514	1.8F
	0816	1113	1.4E
	1427	1731	1.4F
	2019	2312	1.3E
4 M ●	0223	0548	1.8F
	0856	1150	1.4E
	1506	1803	1.4F
	2102	2351	1.3E
5 Tu	0304	0620	1.8F
	0933	1227	1.4E
	1541	1836	1.4F
	2143		
6 W		0031	1.2E
	0343	0652	1.7F
	1009	1302	1.3E
	1614	1912	1.5F
	2223		
7 Th		0111	1.2E
	0420	0727	1.5F
	1043	1333	1.3E
	1647	1949	1.5F
	2305		
8 F		0147	1.1E
	0458	0803	1.4F
	1118	1401	1.2E
	1721	2027	1.4F
	2349		
9 Sa		0221	1.1E
	0540	0840	1.3F
	1155	1431	1.2E
	1759	2106	1.4F
10 Su	0034	0257	1.0E
	0626	0921	1.3F
	1235	1505	1.1E
	1840	2150	1.5F
11 M	0121	0340	1.0E
	0717	1007	1.2F
	1317	1548	1.1E
	1924	2241	1.5F
12 Tu ◐	0209	0436	1.0E
	0809	1101	1.2F
	1404	1643	1.1E
	2012	2335	1.6F
13 W	0303	0543	1.1E
	0905	1156	1.2F
	1459	1746	1.2E
	2105		
14 Th		0029	1.7F
	0403	0641	1.2E
	1005	1251	1.2F
	1602	1844	1.3E
	2206		
15 F		0125	1.8F
	0502	0736	1.3E
	1107	1352	1.3F
	1705	1942	1.4E
	2309		
16 Sa		0232	1.9F
	0559	0839	1.4E
	1207	1505	1.4F
	1806	2049	1.5E
17 Su	0012	0342	2.0F
	0654	0943	1.6E
	1306	1611	1.7F
	1905	2156	1.6E
18 M	0116	0439	2.2F
	0748	1037	1.7E
	1403	1705	1.9F
	2004	2253	1.7E
19 Tu ○	0217	0529	2.3F
	0840	1128	1.8E
	1456	1756	2.0F
	2100	2349	1.8E
20 W	0313	0621	2.3F
	0930	1220	1.8E
	1545	1852	2.1F
	2155		
21 Th		0049	1.8E
	0405	0715	2.2F
	1018	1315	1.8E
	1634	1948	2.1F
	2249		
22 F		0147	1.7E
	0458	0808	2.0F
	1108	1405	1.7E
	1725	2040	2.0F
	2346		
23 Sa		0238	1.6E
	0553	0858	1.8F
	1200	1451	1.6E
	1818	2133	1.9F
24 Su	0044	0330	1.4E
	0651	0950	1.6F
	1253	1540	1.4E
	1912	2233	1.8F
25 M	0141	0436	1.2E
	0749	1051	1.4F
	1346	1644	1.2E
	2004	2335	1.7F
26 Tu ◑	0238	0548	1.2E
	0845	1152	1.3F
	1440	1754	1.1E
	2055		
27 W		0030	1.7F
	0336	0643	1.2E
	0942	1246	1.2F
	1537	1845	1.1E
	2146		
28 Th		0121	1.6F
	0433	0731	1.2E
	1038	1341	1.1F
	1634	1931	1.1E
	2236		

March

Day	Slack h m	Maximum h m	knots
1 F		0218	1.6F
	0526	0822	1.2E
	1131	1449	1.1F
	1728	2022	1.0E
	2326		
2 Sa		0319	1.6F
	0614	0916	1.2E
	1221	1548	1.1F
	1818	2118	1.1E
3 Su	0016	0408	1.6F
	0700	1004	1.2E
	1309	1631	1.2F
	1907	2208	1.1E
4 M	0106	0446	1.7F
	0743	1043	1.3E
	1353	1705	1.4F
	1954	2249	1.2E
5 Tu	0155	0518	1.6F
	0824	1118	1.3E
	1433	1735	1.4F
	2038	2326	1.2E
6 W ●	0239	0546	1.6F
	0900	1149	1.3E
	1508	1805	1.5F
	2119		
7 Th		0001	1.2E
	0318	0616	1.5F
	0933	1218	1.3E
	1540	1838	1.5F
	2157		
8 F		0037	1.2E
	0354	0650	1.5F
	1005	1247	1.3E
	1610	1916	1.6F
	2236		
9 Sa		0114	1.2E
	0429	0729	1.4F
	1038	1320	1.3E
	1641	1955	1.6F
	2316		
10 Su		0151	1.2E
	0508	0809	1.4F
	1114	1355	1.3E
	1716	2036	1.6F
11 M	0000	0229	1.2E
	0554	0852	1.3F
	1156	1434	1.3E
	1759	2120	1.7F
12 Tu ◐	0048	0312	1.2E
	0647	0938	1.3F
	1243	1517	1.3E
	1849	2211	1.7F
13 W	0139	0405	1.2E
	0743	1033	1.3F
	1335	1611	1.3E
	1943	2309	1.8F
14 Th ◐	0235	0512	1.2E
	0841	1133	1.3F
	1433	1719	1.3E
	2042		
15 F		0007	1.8F
	0335	0619	1.3E
	0943	1231	1.4F
	1539	1826	1.4E
	2147		
16 Sa		0105	1.9F
	0438	0717	1.4E
	1046	1333	1.4F
	1648	1928	1.4E
	2254		
17 Su		0211	1.9F
	0537	0820	1.5E
	1147	1449	1.5F
	1752	2038	1.5E
18 M	0000	0326	2.0F
	0634	0927	1.6E
	1247	1601	1.8F
	1854	2150	1.6E
19 Tu	0105	0427	2.1F
	0729	1025	1.7E
	1346	1657	2.0F
	1954	2249	1.7E
20 W ○	0207	0518	2.2F
	0821	1115	1.8E
	1440	1748	2.1F
	2051	2344	1.7E
21 Th	0303	0608	2.1F
	0911	1206	1.8E
	1529	1841	2.2F
	2144		
22 F		0042	1.7E
	0354	0701	2.0F
	0959	1259	1.7E
	1616	1935	2.2F
	2236		
23 Sa		0137	1.6E
	0443	0752	1.9F
	1046	1348	1.6E
	1703	2025	2.1F
	2329		
24 Su		0225	1.5E
	0535	0839	1.7F
	1135	1431	1.5E
	1751	2113	1.9F
25 M	0022	0311	1.4E
	0629	0926	1.5F
	1225	1512	1.3E
	1841	2204	1.8F
26 Tu	0116	0404	1.2E
	0723	1018	1.3F
	1316	1601	1.2E
	1930	2301	1.7F
27 W ◑	0209	0513	1.1E
	0817	1119	1.2F
	1407	1709	1.1E
	2018	2356	1.6F
28 Th	0303	0613	1.1F
	0910	1214	1.1F
	1501	1811	1.0E
	2107		
29 F		0044	1.6F
	0358	0700	1.1E
	1004	1302	1.1F
	1559	1859	1.0E
	2159		
30 Sa		0131	1.5F
	0451	0746	1.1E
	1055	1352	1.0F
	1657	1947	1.0E
	2251		
31 Su		0231	1.4F
	0540	0836	1.1E
	1143	1509	1.1F
	1750	2043	1.0E
	2343		

Time meridian 75° W. 0000 is midnight. 1200 is noon. Times are not adjusted for Daylight Saving Time.

Lake Worth Inlet Entrance, Florida, 2019

F–Flood, Dir. 267° True   E–Ebb, Dir. 086° True

April

Day	Slack (h m)	Maximum (h m)	knots
1 M		0332	1.4F
	0625	0927	1.1E
	1229	1601	1.2F
	1840	2139	1.0E
2 Tu	0035	0415	1.4F
	0707	1009	1.2E
	1314	1637	1.3F
	1928	2224	1.1E
3 W	0125	0447	1.4F
	0747	1043	1.2E
	1355	1706	1.4F
	2012	2259	1.1E
4 Th	0211	0513	1.4F
	0823	1110	1.2E
	1432	1733	1.5F
	2052	2331	1.2E
5 F ●	0251	0542	1.4F
	0857	1135	1.3E
	1504	1805	1.6F
	2129		
6 Sa		0003	1.2E
	0327	0616	1.4F
	0929	1205	1.3E
	1535	1843	1.7F
	2206		
7 Su		0040	1.3E
	0403	0657	1.4F
	1003	1241	1.4E
	1606	1925	1.8F
	2246		
8 M		0121	1.3E
	0442	0741	1.4F
	1041	1324	1.4E
	1643	2009	1.9F
	2330		
9 Tu		0204	1.4E
	0528	0827	1.4F
	1125	1408	1.5E
	1728	2056	1.9F
10 W	0021	0250	1.4E
	0622	0916	1.4F
	1217	1455	1.5E
	1823	2147	1.9F
11 Th	0114	0341	1.4E
	0721	1011	1.4F
	1314	1550	1.4E
	1924	2246	1.9F
12 F ◐	0211	0447	1.4E
	0820	1113	1.4F
	1416	1659	1.4E
	2027	2348	1.9F
13 Sa	0311	0559	1.4E
	0922	1216	1.5F
	1523	1814	1.4E
	2134		
14 Su		0049	1.9F
	0415	0701	1.5E
	1026	1319	1.6F
	1634	1920	1.4E
	2243		
15 M		0154	1.9F
	0516	0802	1.5E
	1128	1435	1.7F
	1741	2032	1.5E
	2349		
16 Tu		0310	1.9F
	0613	0910	1.6E
	1228	1551	1.8F
	1843	2144	1.6E
17 W	0054	0415	2.0F
	0709	1011	1.7E
	1327	1648	2.0F
	1943	2244	1.6E
18 Th	0155	0507	2.0F
	0802	1102	1.7E
	1422	1738	2.2F
	2039	2337	1.7E
19 F ○	0251	0555	2.0F
	0852	1151	1.7E
	1511	1828	2.2F
	2131		
20 Sa		0030	1.6E
	0340	0644	1.9F
	0938	1240	1.7E
	1556	1918	2.2F
	2219		
21 Su		0122	1.6E
	0427	0733	1.8F
	1023	1327	1.6E
	1638	2005	2.1F
	2307		
22 M		0208	1.5E
	0513	0818	1.6F
	1109	1408	1.4E
	1721	2049	1.9F
	2357		
23 Tu		0249	1.4E
	0603	0900	1.4F
	1156	1445	1.3E
	1806	2132	1.8F
24 W	0047	0333	1.3E
	0654	0944	1.2F
	1245	1525	1.2E
	1853	2219	1.7F
25 Th	0136	0428	1.1E
	0745	1036	1.1F
	1336	1618	1.0E
	1941	2313	1.6F
26 F ○	0227	0534	1.1E
	0835	1134	1.1F
	1428	1731	1.0E
	2031		
27 Sa		0003	1.5F
	0318	0626	1.1E
	0925	1223	1.0F
	1525	1829	0.9E
	2123		
28 Su		0046	1.4F
	0411	0710	1.1E
	1014	1309	1.0F
	1625	1917	0.9E
	2217		
29 M		0131	1.3F
	0501	0753	1.0E
	1102	1404	1.1F
	1721	2007	0.9E
	2311		
30 Tu		0229	1.2F
	0546	0840	1.0E
	1147	1516	1.1F
	1811	2104	0.9E

May

Day	Slack (h m)	Maximum (h m)	knots
1 W	0003	0331	1.2F
	0627	0926	1.0E
	1230	1601	1.3F
	1858	2153	1.0E
2 Th	0052	0409	1.2F
	0707	1002	1.1E
	1312	1633	1.4F
	1941	2229	1.1E
3 F ○	0140	0440	1.3F
	0744	1030	1.2E
	1351	1702	1.6F
	2021	2300	1.2E
4 Sa ●	0222	0511	1.4F
	0820	1058	1.3E
	1427	1735	1.7F
	2100	2332	1.3E
5 Su	0301	0547	1.5F
	0856	1131	1.4E
	1502	1813	1.9F
	2138		
6 M		0010	1.4E
	0339	0629	1.5F
	0934	1211	1.5E
	1538	1858	2.0F
	2219		
7 Tu		0055	1.5E
	0420	0716	1.6F
	1016	1258	1.6E
	1619	1946	2.1F
	2305		
8 W		0143	1.5E
	0507	0806	1.6F
	1104	1348	1.6E
	1708	2036	2.1F
	2357		
9 Th		0231	1.6E
	0602	0857	1.6F
	1159	1439	1.6E
	1806	2128	2.1F
10 F	0052	0322	1.5E
	0701	0953	1.6F
	1300	1535	1.5E
	1910	2227	2.0F
11 Sa ◐	0149	0424	1.5E
	0801	1057	1.6F
	1403	1646	1.4E
	2016	2332	1.9F
12 Su	0249	0541	1.4E
	0903	1204	1.6F
	1512	1807	1.4E
	2123		
13 M		0034	1.9F
	0352	0646	1.5E
	1006	1308	1.7F
	1623	1915	1.4E
	2232		
14 Tu		0138	1.8F
	0454	0746	1.5E
	1109	1423	1.7F
	1730	2025	1.5E
	2337		
15 W		0254	1.8F
	0553	0853	1.5E
	1209	1539	1.9F
	1832	2136	1.5E
16 Th	0041	0402	1.8F
	0648	0956	1.6E
	1307	1636	2.1F
	1930	2234	1.6E
17 F	0141	0454	1.8F
	0741	1047	1.6E
	1401	1724	2.2F
	2024	2324	1.6E
18 Sa ●	0236	0540	1.8F
	0831	1132	1.6E
	1450	1811	2.2F
	2113		
19 Su		0013	1.6E
	0324	0626	1.7F
	0917	1217	1.5E
	1532	1857	2.1F
	2159		
20 M		0101	1.6E
	0407	0712	1.6F
	1000	1301	1.5E
	1611	1941	2.0F
	2243		
21 Tu		0145	1.5E
	0450	0755	1.5F
	1042	1342	1.4E
	1650	2021	1.9F
	2328		
22 W		0224	1.4E
	0535	0834	1.4F
	1127	1419	1.3E
	1732	2059	1.8F
23 Th	0015	0302	1.3E
	0622	0912	1.3F
	1215	1456	1.2E
	1818	2138	1.6F
24 F	0102	0345	1.2E
	0710	0955	1.2F
	1305	1540	1.0E
	1907	2224	1.5F
25 Sa	0149	0441	1.1E
	0757	1047	1.1F
	1357	1642	0.9E
	1958	2315	1.4F
26 Su ◐	0237	0543	1.0E
	0843	1141	1.1F
	1452	1755	0.9E
	2049		
27 M		0001	1.3F
	0325	0630	1.0E
	0930	1227	1.1F
	1551	1847	0.9E
	2143		
28 Tu		0043	1.2F
	0415	0709	1.0E
	1016	1310	1.1F
	1648	1931	0.9E
	2237		
29 W		0125	1.1F
	0501	0745	0.9E
	1101	1401	1.2F
	1739	2019	0.9E
	2328		
30 Th		0218	1.0F
	0544	0825	1.0E
	1144	1504	1.3F
	1824	2110	0.9E
31 F	0017	0319	1.1F
	0624	0908	1.0E
	1226	1553	1.4F
	1907	2153	1.0E

June

Day	Slack (h m)	Maximum (h m)	knots
1 Sa	0105	0405	1.2F
	0705	0948	1.1E
	1308	1631	1.6F
	1949	2229	1.2E
2 Su	0152	0444	1.3F
	0746	1025	1.3E
	1350	1708	1.9F
	2030	2305	1.4E
3 M ●	0236	0523	1.5F
	0828	1104	1.5E
	1433	1749	2.0F
	2112	2345	1.5E
4 Tu	0319	0607	1.6F
	0911	1148	1.6E
	1517	1835	2.1F
	2156		
5 W		0033	1.6E
	0402	0656	1.7F
	0958	1239	1.7E
	1603	1926	2.2F
	2244		
6 Th		0124	1.7E
	0449	0749	1.7F
	1049	1333	1.7E
	1655	2019	2.2F
	2336		
7 F		0215	1.7E
	0543	0842	1.7F
	1146	1428	1.7E
	1755	2112	2.1F
8 Sa	0032	0306	1.6E
	0643	0939	1.7F
	1249	1525	1.6E
	1900	2210	2.0F
9 Su	0129	0405	1.5E
	0743	1043	1.7F
	1353	1637	1.4E
	2006	2316	1.9F
10 M ◐	0227	0522	1.5E
	0844	1153	1.7F
	1501	1802	1.4E
	2112		
11 Tu		0020	1.8F
	0329	0631	1.5E
	0946	1258	1.8F
	1611	1909	1.4E
	2219		
12 W		0122	1.7F
	0432	0730	1.4E
	1048	1408	1.8F
	1717	2014	1.4E
	2323		
13 Th		0235	1.6F
	0531	0833	1.4E
	1147	1522	1.9F
	1817	2122	1.4E
14 F	0024	0345	1.6F
	0626	0936	1.4E
	1243	1619	2.0F
	1913	2219	1.5E
15 Sa	0123	0438	1.6F
	0718	1027	1.5E
	1336	1706	2.1F
	2005	2306	1.5E
16 Su	0217	0523	1.7F
	0808	1110	1.5E
	1424	1749	2.1F
	2052	2351	1.5E
17 M ○	0304	0606	1.6F
	0853	1151	1.4E
	1506	1832	2.1F
	2135		
18 Tu		0035	1.5E
	0346	0648	1.5F
	0936	1232	1.4E
	1544	1913	2.0F
	2216		
19 W		0119	1.5E
	0425	0728	1.4F
	1017	1314	1.4E
	1621	1951	1.9F
	2258		
20 Th		0157	1.4E
	0504	0806	1.4F
	1100	1354	1.3E
	1701	2027	1.8F
	2341		
21 F		0233	1.3E
	0547	0842	1.3F
	1146	1431	1.2E
	1745	2102	1.6F
22 Sa	0025	0308	1.2E
	0631	0920	1.2F
	1236	1511	1.1E
	1835	2141	1.4F
23 Su	0110	0347	1.1E
	0716	1004	1.2F
	1328	1559	0.9E
	1925	2225	1.3F
24 M	0153	0437	1.0E
	0800	1054	1.2F
	1420	1707	0.8E
	2016	2313	1.2F
25 Tu ◐	0237	0535	0.9E
	0843	1144	1.2F
	1514	1810	0.8E
	2106	2359	1.1F
26 W	0322	0618	0.9E
	0927	1229	1.2F
	1609	1853	0.8E
	2158		
27 Th		0042	1.0F
	0410	0653	0.9E
	1011	1313	1.3F
	1700	1933	0.9E
	2251		
28 F		0128	1.0F
	0457	0730	1.0E
	1056	1405	1.3F
	1747	2019	0.9E
	2341		
29 Sa		0225	1.0F
	0543	0815	1.0E
	1142	1507	1.5F
	1832	2111	1.1E
30 Su	0032	0328	1.2F
	0629	0907	1.2E
	1229	1600	1.7F
	1917	2159	1.3E

Time meridian 75° W. 0000 is midnight. 1200 is noon. Times are not adjusted for Daylight Saving Time.

Lake Worth Inlet Entrance, Florida, 2019

F–Flood, Dir. 267° True   E–Ebb, Dir. 086° True

July

Day	Slack (h m)	Maximum (h m)	knots
1 M	0123	0418	1.4F
	0716	0957	1.4E
	1319	1644	2.0F
	2003	2242	1.5E
2 Tu ●	0213	0503	1.6F
	0804	1044	1.5E
	1411	1729	2.2F
	2050	2326	1.6E
3 W	0300	0549	1.7F
	0854	1132	1.7E
	1501	1817	2.3F
	2136		
4 Th		0014	1.7E
	0346	0640	1.8F
	0944	1225	1.8E
	1552	1909	2.3F
	2225		
5 F		0107	1.8E
	0433	0735	1.9F
	1038	1324	1.8E
	1645	2004	2.2F
	2316		
6 Sa		0200	1.8E
	0526	0830	1.9F
	1136	1420	1.7E
	1745	2057	2.1F
7 Su	0011	0251	1.7E
	0624	0927	1.9F
	1239	1518	1.6E
	1850	2154	1.9F
8 M	0108	0347	1.6E
	0725	1031	1.8F
	1343	1629	1.4E
	1954	2259	1.8F
9 Tu ◑	0205	0500	1.4E
	0824	1141	1.8F
	1448	1755	1.4E
	2058		
10 W		0005	1.6F
	0305	0614	1.4E
	0925	1245	1.8F
	1556	1859	1.4E
	2203		
11 Th		0106	1.5F
	0407	0712	1.4E
	1025	1350	1.8F
	1700	1958	1.3E
	2305		
12 F		0213	1.4F
	0507	0809	1.3E
	1121	1459	1.8F
	1758	2101	1.3E
13 Sa	0004	0325	1.4F
	0602	0910	1.3E
	1215	1558	1.9F
	1851	2158	1.4E
14 Su	0101	0420	1.5F
	0654	1003	1.3E
	1306	1645	2.0F
	1940	2244	1.4E
15 M	0154	0504	1.5F
	0743	1046	1.3E
	1353	1726	2.0F
	2026	2325	1.5E
16 Tu ○	0240	0543	1.5F
	0829	1125	1.3E
	1437	1804	2.0F
	2109		
17 W		0006	1.5E
	0321	0622	1.5F
	0912	1204	1.3E
	1517	1842	1.9F
	2148		
18 Th		0047	1.5E
	0357	0659	1.5F
	0953	1246	1.3E
	1555	1919	1.8F
	2227		
19 F		0127	1.4E
	0433	0736	1.4F
	1035	1329	1.3E
	1634	1954	1.7F
	2306		
20 Sa		0201	1.3E
	0511	0812	1.4F
	1120	1408	1.2E
	1716	2028	1.5F
	2347		
21 Su		0233	1.2E
	0550	0848	1.4F
	1208	1444	1.1E
	1803	2103	1.4F
22 M	0028	0303	1.1E
	0632	0927	1.3F
	1257	1523	1.0E
	1852	2143	1.2F
23 Tu	0108	0337	1.0E
	0715	1012	1.3F
	1345	1610	0.9E
	1941	2228	1.1F
24 W ◐	0148	0419	0.9E
	0756	1101	1.3F
	1434	1713	0.8E
	2029	2317	1.0F
25 Th	0230	0512	0.9E
	0837	1150	1.3F
	1525	1809	0.9E
	2119		
26 F		0005	1.0F
	0317	0603	0.9E
	0921	1236	1.4F
	1618	1853	0.9E
	2213		
27 Sa		0053	1.0F
	0410	0649	1.0E
	1011	1326	1.5F
	1709	1939	1.1E
	2307		
28 Su		0147	1.1F
	0505	0737	1.1E
	1104	1426	1.6F
	1759	2033	1.2E
29 M	0002	0253	1.2F
	0559	0835	1.2E
	1159	1530	1.8F
	1849	2131	1.4E
30 Tu	0056	0356	1.4F
	0652	0935	1.2E
	1256	1624	2.0F
	1939	2222	1.6E
31 W ●	0151	0447	1.7F
	0746	1030	1.6E
	1355	1712	2.2F
	2029	2309	1.7E

August

Day	Slack (h m)	Maximum (h m)	knots
1 Th	0242	0535	1.9F
	0841	1121	1.7E
	1450	1801	2.3F
	2118	2358	1.8E
2 F	0330	0628	2.0F
	0934	1217	1.8E
	1544	1855	2.3F
	2206		
3 Sa		0052	1.8E
	0418	0724	2.0F
	1029	1318	1.8E
	1638	1950	2.2F
	2257		
4 Su		0146	1.8E
	0510	0820	2.1F
	1127	1416	1.7E
	1736	2043	2.0F
	2350		
5 M		0237	1.7E
	0606	0916	2.0F
	1228	1511	1.6E
	1838	2138	1.8F
6 Tu	0046	0329	1.6E
	0705	1017	1.9F
	1330	1618	1.4E
	1940	2240	1.6F
7 W ◐	0142	0436	1.4E
	0803	1126	1.8F
	1432	1740	1.3E
	2041	2347	1.5F
8 Th	0240	0553	1.3E
	0900	1228	1.8F
	1535	1843	1.3E
	2143		
9 F		0046	1.4F
	0340	0651	1.3E
	0957	1326	1.8F
	1637	1937	1.3E
	2243		
10 Sa		0147	1.3F
	0441	0742	1.2E
	1051	1429	1.7F
	1733	2033	1.3E
	2340		
11 Su		0258	1.3F
	0536	0838	1.2E
	1143	1531	1.8F
	1824	2130	1.3E
12 M	0034	0357	1.3F
	0627	0934	1.2E
	1232	1620	1.8F
	1912	2217	1.3E
13 Tu	0125	0442	1.4F
	0716	1020	1.2E
	1321	1700	1.9F
	1957	2258	1.4E
14 W	0211	0520	1.4F
	0804	1100	1.3E
	1408	1736	1.9F
	2039	2336	1.4E
15 Th ○	0252	0555	1.5F
	0848	1139	1.3E
	1451	1810	1.8F
	2118		
16 F		0014	1.4E
	0328	0629	1.5F
	0930	1220	1.3E
	1531	1844	1.7F
	2155		
17 Sa		0051	1.4E
	0402	0704	1.5F
	1011	1303	1.2E
	1610	1918	1.6F
	2231		
18 Su		0125	1.3E
	0435	0741	1.5F
	1054	1342	1.2E
	1649	1953	1.5F
	2307		
19 M		0155	1.2E
	0510	0817	1.5F
	1138	1417	1.1E
	1731	2029	1.3F
	2344		
20 Tu		0223	1.2E
	0547	0854	1.5F
	1223	1450	1.0E
	1816	2107	1.2F
21 W	0022	0254	1.1E
	0627	0935	1.4F
	1309	1528	1.0E
	1904	2149	1.1F
22 Th	0102	0331	1.1E
	0709	1021	1.4F
	1355	1617	0.9E
	1952	2238	1.1F
23 F ◐	0145	0418	1.0E
	0752	1113	1.5F
	1444	1720	1.0E
	2043	2332	1.1F
24 Sa	0234	0518	1.0E
	0840	1205	1.6F
	1538	1817	1.1E
	2139		
25 Su		0024	1.1F
	0331	0617	1.1E
	0935	1256	1.7F
	1634	1908	1.2E
	2237		
26 M		0119	1.2F
	0435	0712	1.2E
	1036	1355	1.7F
	1730	2003	1.3E
	2335		
27 Tu		0225	1.3F
	0536	0812	1.3E
	1138	1504	1.9F
	1823	2106	1.4E
28 W	0033	0336	1.5F
	0634	0919	1.5E
	1240	1607	2.0F
	1917	2204	1.6E
29 Th	0130	0434	1.8F
	0733	1021	1.6E
	1343	1659	2.2F
	2009	2255	1.7E
30 F ●	0224	0525	2.0F
	0830	1116	1.8E
	1442	1749	2.2F
	2100	2345	1.8E
31 Sa	0315	0618	2.1F
	0925	1213	1.8E
	1536	1842	2.2F
	2149		

September

Day	Slack (h m)	Maximum (h m)	knots
1 Su		0038	1.8E
	0403	0714	2.2F
	1020	1314	1.8E
	1629	1937	2.1F
	2238		
2 M		0133	1.8E
	0453	0810	2.2F
	1116	1410	1.7E
	1724	2029	1.9F
	2330		
3 Tu		0223	1.7E
	0547	0903	2.1F
	1214	1502	1.5E
	1823	2121	1.7F
4 W	0024	0311	1.5E
	0643	1000	1.9F
	1313	1601	1.4E
	1922	2219	1.5F
5 Th ◐	0118	0407	1.3E
	0738	1104	1.8F
	1411	1716	1.3E
	2020	2324	1.4F
6 F	0214	0523	1.2E
	0831	1205	1.8F
	1510	1821	1.2E
	2119		
7 Sa		0024	1.3F
	0311	0624	1.1E
	0924	1258	1.7F
	1609	1911	1.2E
	2216		
8 Su		0119	1.2F
	0411	0713	1.1E
	1017	1353	1.6F
	1704	2001	1.2E
	2311		
9 M		0222	1.1F
	0508	0803	1.1E
	1108	1455	1.6F
	1754	2055	1.2E
10 Tu	0002	0328	1.2F
	0600	0859	1.1E
	1158	1550	1.6F
	1840	2146	1.3E
11 W	0050	0417	1.3F
	0650	0952	1.1E
	1249	1633	1.7F
	1925	2228	1.3E
12 Th	0136	0455	1.4F
	0738	1036	1.2E
	1339	1709	1.7F
	2007	2305	1.3E
13 F ○	0218	0528	1.5F
	0824	1116	1.2E
	1426	1740	1.6F
	2046	2339	1.3E
14 Sa	0255	0559	1.5F
	0916	1155	1.2E
	1508	1809	1.6F
	2122		
15 Su		0011	1.3E
	0329	0631	1.6F
	0947	1234	1.2E
	1546	1842	1.5F
	2155		
16 M		0042	1.3E
	0401	0707	1.6F
	1026	1311	1.2E
	1622	1918	1.4F
	2228		
17 Tu		0113	1.3E
	0432	0744	1.6F
	1106	1345	1.2E
	1659	1956	1.3F
	2302		
18 W		0144	1.2E
	0505	0822	1.6F
	1148	1419	1.1E
	1741	2035	1.3F
	2340		
19 Th		0219	1.2E
	0542	0903	1.6F
	1233	1456	1.1E
	1829	2118	1.2F
20 F ◐	0023	0258	1.2E
	0627	0948	1.6F
	1319	1541	1.1E
	1920	2207	1.2F
21 Sa ○	0111	0344	1.2E
	0717	1041	1.7F
	1409	1639	1.1E
	2013	2303	1.2F
22 Su	0204	0444	1.2E
	0811	1137	1.7F
	1504	1745	1.2E
	2110		
23 M		0001	1.3F
	0304	0552	1.2E
	0910	1233	1.8F
	1604	1844	1.3E
	2211		
24 Tu		0058	1.4F
	0412	0654	1.3E
	1016	1332	1.8F
	1704	1940	1.4E
	2311		
25 W		0204	1.4F
	0519	0757	1.4E
	1123	1442	1.9F
	1801	2044	1.5E
26 Th	0011	0321	1.6F
	0621	0909	1.5E
	1229	1551	2.0F
	1856	2148	1.6E
27 F	0110	0424	1.9F
	0722	1015	1.6E
	1333	1647	2.1F
	1950	2242	1.7E
28 Sa ●	0207	0517	2.1F
	0820	1112	1.7E
	1433	1738	2.1F
	2041	2332	1.8E
29 Su	0259	0609	2.2F
	0916	1208	1.8E
	1527	1829	2.1F
	2131		
30 M		0025	1.8E
	0348	0704	2.3F
	1009	1307	1.7E
	1618	1923	2.0F
	2219		

Time meridian 75° W. 0000 is midnight. 1200 is noon. Times are not adjusted for Daylight Saving Time.

Lake Worth Inlet Entrance, Florida, 2019

F–Flood, Dir. 267° True   E–Ebb, Dir. 086° True

October

Day	Slack	Maximum	knots
1 Tu		0119	1.7E
	0436	0758	2.2F
	1102	1401	1.6E
	1710	2014	1.8F
	2308		
2 W		0207	1.6E
	0525	0848	2.1F
	1156	1449	1.5E
	1804	2103	1.6F
3 Th	0000	0251	1.5E
	0617	0938	1.9F
	1251	1539	1.4E
	1900	2154	1.4F
4 F	0053	0338	1.3E
	0708	1035	1.8F
	1345	1643	1.2E
	1955	2254	1.3F
5 Sa ◖	0146	0440	1.1E
	0759	1134	1.7F
	1439	1750	1.2E
	2050	2355	1.2F
6 Su	0240	0551	1.0E
	0848	1226	1.6F
	1534	1842	1.2E
	2144		
7 M		0047	1.1F
	0338	0643	1.0E
	0940	1314	1.5F
	1629	1928	1.2E
	2236		
8 Tu		0140	1.1F
	0437	0731	1.0E
	1033	1409	1.5F
	1720	2016	1.1E
	2325		
9 W		0247	1.1F
	0532	0824	1.0E
	1126	1512	1.4F
	1806	2107	1.2E
10 Th	0012	0346	1.2F
	0623	0922	1.0E
	1218	1603	1.4F
	1850	2154	1.2E
11 F	0057	0428	1.3F
	0712	1012	1.1E
	1310	1640	1.4F
	1932	2232	1.2E
12 Sa	0140	0501	1.5F
	0759	1052	1.1E
	1359	1709	1.4F
	2011	2304	1.2E
13 Su ○	0219	0529	1.6F
	0842	1128	1.2E
	1442	1736	1.4F
	2047	2331	1.3E
14 M	0254	0558	1.6F
	0921	1201	1.2E
	1520	1807	1.4F
	2120	2358	1.3E
15 Tu	0326	0632	1.7F
	0957	1235	1.2E
	1555	1843	1.4F
	2152		
16 W		0030	1.3E
	0356	0710	1.7F
	1034	1311	1.2E
	1630	1924	1.4F
	2226		
17 Th		0107	1.3E
	0428	0752	1.8F
	1114	1349	1.3E
	1710	2007	1.4F
	2306		
18 F		0149	1.4E
	0506	0835	1.8F
	1159	1429	1.3E
	1758	2052	1.4F
	2352		
19 Sa		0232	1.4E
	0554	0921	1.8F
	1248	1514	1.3E
	1852	2142	1.4F
20 Su	0045	0320	1.4E
	0651	1014	1.8F
	1341	1608	1.3E
	1948	2239	1.4F
21 M ○	0143	0420	1.3E
	0751	1114	1.8F
	1437	1717	1.3E
	2046	2341	1.4F
22 Tu	0247	0534	1.3E
	0855	1214	1.9F
	1537	1823	1.4E
	2147		
23 W		0042	1.5F
	0356	0643	1.4E
	1003	1313	1.8F
	1640	1922	1.5E
	2250		
24 Th		0148	1.6F
	0506	0749	1.4E
	1112	1423	1.8F
	1739	2025	1.5E
	2351		
25 F		0307	1.8F
	0610	0903	1.5E
	1218	1538	1.9F
	1835	2132	1.6E
26 Sa	0051	0415	2.0F
	0711	1011	1.6E
	1323	1636	2.0F
	1930	2230	1.7E
27 Su ●	0149	0508	2.2F
	0810	1107	1.7E
	1423	1727	2.0F
	2023	2320	1.7E
28 M	0243	0559	2.3F
	0904	1201	1.7E
	1516	1816	2.0F
	2112		
29 Tu		0010	1.7E
	0331	0651	2.3F
	0955	1256	1.7E
	1605	1908	1.8F
	2200		
30 W		0102	1.7E
	0416	0742	2.2F
	1044	1347	1.6E
	1652	1957	1.7F
	2246		
31 Th		0149	1.6E
	0501	0828	2.1F
	1134	1431	1.5E
	1742	2043	1.5F
	2335		

November

Day	Slack	Maximum	knots
1 F		0230	1.4E
	0547	0913	1.9F
	1225	1514	1.4E
	1834	2128	1.4F
2 Sa	0025	0310	1.3E
	0635	1000	1.8F
	1315	1604	1.2E
	1926	2219	1.2F
3 Su	0117	0358	1.1E
	0724	1054	1.6F
	1405	1708	1.1E
	2016	2318	1.1F
4 M ◐	0209	0507	1.0E
	0813	1147	1.5F
	1456	1807	1.1E
	2106		
5 Tu		0012	1.1F
	0305	0612	1.0E
	0905	1234	1.4F
	1549	1853	1.1E
	2156		
6 W		0059	1.1F
	0405	0702	1.0E
	0959	1319	1.3F
	1641	1936	1.1E
	2244		
7 Th		0151	1.1F
	0503	0752	1.0E
	1055	1414	1.2F
	1729	2023	1.1E
	2330		
8 F		0301	1.2F
	0556	0849	1.0E
	1148	1521	1.2F
	1812	2112	1.1E
9 Sa	0015	0354	1.3F
	0645	0943	1.0E
	1240	1606	1.2F
	1854	2154	1.1E
10 Su	0058	0429	1.4F
	0730	1025	1.1E
	1329	1636	1.2F
	1933	2226	1.1E
11 M	0139	0457	1.6F
	0812	1058	1.1E
	1413	1704	1.3F
	2010	2252	1.2E
12 Tu ○	0216	0526	1.7F
	0850	1127	1.2E
	1452	1735	1.4F
	2045	2320	1.3E
13 W	0250	0559	1.8F
	0926	1159	1.3E
	1528	1812	1.4F
	2120	2355	1.4E
14 Th	0324	0639	1.9F
	1003	1237	1.4E
	1604	1855	1.4F
	2158		
15 F		0036	1.4E
	0359	0724	1.9F
	1044	1321	1.4E
	1644	1942	1.5F
	2240		
16 Sa		0124	1.5E
	0441	0811	2.0F
	1130	1406	1.5E
	1732	2031	1.5F
	2330		
17 Su		0212	1.5E
	0533	0859	2.0F
	1222	1453	1.5E
	1827	2122	1.5F
18 M	0028	0304	1.5E
	0634	0953	2.0F
	1316	1545	1.5E
	1925	2220	1.6F
19 Tu ○	0129	0404	1.4E
	0738	1054	1.9F
	1413	1652	1.4E
	2025	2325	1.6F
20 W	0234	0522	1.4E
	0844	1157	1.9F
	1513	1804	1.4E
	2126		
21 Th		0030	1.7F
	0344	0636	1.4E
	0953	1258	1.8F
	1616	1906	1.5E
	2230		
22 F		0136	1.7F
	0454	0743	1.5E
	1102	1406	1.7F
	1718	2008	1.5E
	2332		
23 Sa		0255	1.9F
	0559	0856	1.5E
	1207	1524	1.7F
	1815	2117	1.5E
24 Su	0032	0404	2.0F
	0659	1003	1.6E
	1310	1625	1.8F
	1911	2216	1.6E
25 M	0130	0457	2.2F
	0756	1057	1.6E
	1409	1715	1.8F
	2004	2306	1.6E
26 Tu ●	0224	0545	2.3F
	0849	1148	1.6E
	1502	1802	1.8F
	2053	2353	1.6E
27 W	0311	0633	2.2F
	0937	1239	1.6E
	1548	1850	1.7F
	2140		
28 Th		0041	1.6E
	0354	0721	2.2F
	1023	1327	1.6E
	1632	1937	1.6F
	2224		
29 F		0126	1.5E
	0434	0805	2.0F
	1108	1409	1.5E
	1717	2020	1.5F
	2309		
30 Sa		0206	1.4E
	0516	0845	1.9F
	1155	1447	1.4E
	1804	2100	1.4F
	2357		

December

Day	Slack	Maximum	knots
1 Su		0244	1.2E
	0601	0925	1.7F
	1242	1527	1.3E
	1852	2143	1.2F
2 M	0048	0325	1.1E
	0650	1009	1.6F
	1329	1617	1.1E
	1939	2233	1.2F
3 Tu	0140	0421	1.0E
	0741	1100	1.4F
	1417	1721	1.1E
	2025	2329	1.1F
4 W ◐	0234	0537	0.9E
	0833	1150	1.3F
	1506	1814	1.0E
	2112		
5 Th		0018	1.2F
	0332	0634	0.9E
	0927	1233	1.2F
	1556	1857	1.0E
	2159		
6 F		0102	1.2F
	0432	0721	0.9E
	1022	1315	1.1F
	1646	1936	1.0E
	2246		
7 Sa		0151	1.2F
	0525	0811	0.9E
	1116	1406	1.0F
	1731	2017	1.0E
	2330		
8 Su		0257	1.3F
	0613	0904	0.9E
	1206	1510	1.0F
	1813	2101	1.0E
9 M	0013	0347	1.4F
	0657	0950	1.0E
	1254	1556	1.1F
	1853	2141	1.0E
10 Tu	0055	0422	1.5F
	0738	1024	1.1E
	1340	1632	1.2F
	1933	2215	1.2E
11 W	0136	0455	1.7F
	0817	1055	1.2E
	1422	1708	1.4F
	2012	2249	1.3E
12 Th ○	0216	0531	1.9F
	0856	1129	1.4E
	1502	1746	1.5F
	2053	2327	1.5E
13 F	0256	0612	2.0F
	0936	1209	1.5E
	1541	1831	1.6F
	2135		
14 Sa		0013	1.6E
	0338	0659	2.1F
	1019	1256	1.6E
	1623	1921	1.7F
	2222		
15 Su		0104	1.6E
	0425	0750	2.1F
	1106	1345	1.6E
	1711	2013	1.7F
	2315		
16 M		0158	1.6E
	0519	0841	2.1F
	1158	1434	1.6E
	1806	2106	1.7F
17 Tu	0015	0252	1.6E
	0622	0935	2.0F
	1254	1526	1.6E
	1905	2205	1.7F
18 W ○	0118	0353	1.5E
	0729	1036	1.9F
	1351	1630	1.5E
	2005	2312	1.8F
19 Th ◐	0224	0514	1.4E
	0835	1141	1.8F
	1451	1747	1.5E
	2107		
20 F		0019	1.8F
	0333	0632	1.4E
	0942	1244	1.7F
	1554	1851	1.5E
	2210		
21 Sa		0124	1.8F
	0442	0736	1.4E
	1050	1350	1.6F
	1656	1952	1.5E
	2312		
22 Su		0240	1.9F
	0545	0845	1.4E
	1153	1508	1.6F
	1755	2059	1.5E
23 M	0011	0349	2.0F
	0644	0950	1.5E
	1254	1611	1.6F
	1850	2200	1.5E
24 Tu	0108	0442	2.1F
	0739	1043	1.6E
	1352	1701	1.7F
	1944	2249	1.5E
25 W	0201	0528	2.2F
	0830	1130	1.6E
	1444	1746	1.7F
	2033	2333	1.5E
26 Th ●	0248	0612	2.2F
	0916	1216	1.6E
	1529	1830	1.6F
	2118		
27 F ○		0016	1.5E
	0329	0656	2.1F
	0958	1302	1.5E
	1610	1914	1.6F
	2201		
28 Sa		0100	1.4E
	0408	0737	2.0F
	1040	1343	1.5E
	1649	1955	1.5F
	2244		
29 Su		0141	1.3E
	0447	0815	1.8F
	1123	1419	1.4E
	1730	2032	1.4F
	2330		
30 M		0220	1.2E
	0530	0851	1.7F
	1207	1454	1.3E
	1814	2110	1.3F
31 Tu	0020	0259	1.1E
	0618	0928	1.5F
	1252	1532	1.2E
	1859	2152	1.3F

Time meridian 75° W. 0000 is midnight. 1200 is noon. Times are not adjusted for Daylight Saving Time.

Port Everglades Entrance, Florida, 2019

F–Flood, Dir. 257° True   E–Ebb, Dir. 075° True

January

Day	Slack (h m)	Maximum (h m)	knots
1 Tu		0302	0.7F
	0538	0915	0.7E
	1200	1524	0.5F
	1743	2134	0.7E
2 W	0019	0355	0.7F
	0632	1008	0.7E
	1255	1616	0.5F
	1834	2224	0.7E
3 Th	0109	0443	0.7F
	0722	1055	0.6E
	1345	1702	0.5F
	1921	2306	0.6E
4 F	0155	0528	0.7F
	0808	1137	0.6E
	1428	1746	0.4F
	2005	2334	0.6E
5 Sa ●	0236	0609	0.6F
	0849	1207	0.6E
	1508	1822	0.4F
	2045	2336	0.6E
6 Su	0314	0642	0.6F
	0927	1208	0.6E
	1546	1836	0.4F
	2123		
7 M		0003	0.6E
	0350	0659	0.6F
	1003	1232	0.6E
	1624	1847	0.4F
	2200		
8 Tu		0038	0.6E
	0428	0715	0.6F
	1038	1306	0.6E
	1704	1921	0.4F
	2239		
9 W		0116	0.6E
	0507	0745	0.6F
	1114	1342	0.6E
	1745	2001	0.4F
	2320		
10 Th		0157	0.6E
	0550	0822	0.6F
	1150	1421	0.6E
	1827	2044	0.5F
11 F	0005	0241	0.6E
	0635	0903	0.5F
	1227	1503	0.6E
	1909	2130	0.5F
12 Sa	0052	0329	0.6E
	0723	0949	0.5F
	1306	1550	0.6E
	1954	2220	0.5F
13 Su	0144	0422	0.6E
	0815	1037	0.5F
	1350	1641	0.6E
	2043	2312	0.5F
14 M ☽	0241	0517	0.5E
	0911	1127	0.4F
	1440	1733	0.6E
	2136		
15 Tu		0006	0.5F
	0341	0611	0.5E
	1010	1219	0.4F
	1537	1825	0.6E
	2232		
16 W		0103	0.5F
	0442	0706	0.6E
	1108	1316	0.4F
	1636	1921	0.6E
	2327		
17 Th		0209	0.5F
	0539	0805	0.6E
	1205	1418	0.4F
	1735	2020	0.6E
18 F	0023	0314	0.6F
	0636	0904	0.6E
	1300	1519	0.5F
	1833	2119	0.7E
19 Sa	0117	0409	0.7F
	0730	0959	0.7E
	1353	1615	0.5F
	1930	2215	0.7E
20 Su	0209	0503	0.7F
	0823	1053	0.7E
	1445	1712	0.5F
	2026	2309	0.8E
21 M ○	0300	0559	0.8F
	0914	1146	0.7E
	1536	1816	0.6F
	2121		
22 Tu		0005	0.8E
	0352	0656	0.8F
	1005	1239	0.8E
	1629	1920	0.6F
	2217		
23 W		0100	0.8E
	0446	0750	0.8F
	1055	1331	0.8E
	1723	2018	0.7F
	2314		
24 Th		0153	0.8E
	0542	0842	0.8F
	1146	1421	0.8E
	1817	2117	0.7F
25 F	0012	0248	0.8E
	0639	0936	0.7F
	1237	1514	0.8E
	1912	2220	0.7F
26 Sa	0110	0350	0.7E
	0737	1036	0.6F
	1330	1616	0.7E
	2007	2324	0.7F
27 Su	0210	0508	0.7E
	0836	1138	0.6F
	1425	1729	0.7E
	2104		
28 M		0026	0.7F
	0313	0633	0.6E
	0937	1243	0.5F
	1522	1856	0.6E
	2202		
29 Tu		0132	0.7F
	0414	0749	0.6E
	1038	1358	0.4F
	1620	2015	0.6E
	2259		
30 W		0237	0.7F
	0513	0854	0.6E
	1137	1504	0.4F
	1716	2117	0.6E
	2354		
31 Th		0333	0.7F
	0607	0949	0.6E
	1233	1558	0.4F
	1809	2207	0.6E

February

Day	Slack (h m)	Maximum (h m)	knots
1 F	0045	0422	0.7F
	0658	1037	0.6E
	1323	1645	0.4F
	1858	2251	0.6E
2 Sa	0131	0505	0.6F
	0743	1120	0.6E
	1407	1727	0.4F
	1943	2326	0.6E
3 Su	0213	0543	0.6F
	0824	1155	0.6E
	1446	1804	0.4F
	2025	2330	0.6E
4 M ●	0251	0615	0.6F
	0901	1157	0.6E
	1523	1828	0.4F
	2104	2347	0.6E
5 Tu	0328	0632	0.6F
	0937	1211	0.6E
	1600	1838	0.4F
	2143		
6 W		0020	0.6E
	0406	0650	0.6F
	1011	1242	0.6E
	1637	1907	0.5F
	2222		
7 Th		0058	0.6E
	0446	0721	0.6F
	1045	1317	0.6E
	1715	1943	0.5F
	2303		
8 F		0137	0.7E
	0527	0757	0.6F
	1119	1354	0.7E
	1754	2022	0.5F
	2345		
9 Sa		0218	0.6E
	0611	0836	0.6F
	1153	1434	0.7E
	1834	2105	0.6F
10 Su	0028	0303	0.6E
	0656	0919	0.5F
	1230	1517	0.6E
	1916	2152	0.6F
11 M	0115	0351	0.6E
	0743	1005	0.5F
	1310	1606	0.6E
	2003	2242	0.5F
12 Tu ◐	0207	0444	0.6E
	0836	1055	0.5F
	1358	1659	0.6E
	2057	2335	0.5F
13 W	0306	0539	0.6E
	0934	1147	0.4F
	1456	1754	0.6E
	2157		
14 Th		0032	0.5F
	0409	0635	0.6E
	1035	1244	0.4F
	1603	1852	0.6E
	2258		
15 F		0137	0.6F
	0510	0734	0.6E
	1135	1349	0.4F
	1709	1954	0.6E
	2357		
16 Sa		0249	0.6F
	0609	0837	0.6E
	1235	1459	0.5F
	1813	2058	0.7E
17 Su	0054	0351	0.7F
	0706	0938	0.7E
	1331	1604	0.5F
	1914	2158	0.7E
18 M	0149	0446	0.7F
	0800	1034	0.7E
	1424	1705	0.6F
	2012	2254	0.8E
19 Tu ○	0241	0541	0.8F
	0851	1127	0.8E
	1515	1809	0.6F
	2108	2350	0.8E
20 W	0333	0638	0.8F
	0941	1220	0.8E
	1606	1910	0.7F
	2202		
21 Th		0045	0.8E
	0426	0731	0.8F
	1030	1310	0.8E
	1657	2005	0.7F
	2257		
22 F		0137	0.8E
	0521	0820	0.7F
	1119	1357	0.8E
	1750	2058	0.7F
	2352		
23 Sa		0228	0.8E
	0617	0910	0.7F
	1209	1445	0.8E
	1843	2155	0.7F
24 Su	0047	0322	0.7E
	0713	1005	0.6F
	1259	1538	0.7E
	1936	2255	0.7F
25 M	0144	0429	0.6E
	0810	1106	0.5F
	1351	1641	0.6E
	2032	2356	0.6F
26 Tu ◑	0242	0559	0.6E
	0909	1211	0.4F
	1448	1810	0.6E
	2130		
27 W		0100	0.6F
	0343	0720	0.5E
	1009	1326	0.4F
	1547	1947	0.5E
	2227		
28 Th		0206	0.6F
	0442	0829	0.5E
	1109	1439	0.4F
	1646	2052	0.5E
	2323		

March

Day	Slack (h m)	Maximum (h m)	knots
1 F		0306	0.6F
	0536	0926	0.5E
	1205	1536	0.4F
	1740	2144	0.6E
2 Sa	0014	0355	0.6F
	0627	1014	0.6E
	1255	1621	0.4F
	1831	2227	0.6E
3 Su	0102	0436	0.6F
	0712	1056	0.6E
	1340	1701	0.4F
	1919	2303	0.6E
4 M	0146	0512	0.6F
	0754	1130	0.6E
	1420	1736	0.4F
	2003	2321	0.6E
5 Tu	0227	0541	0.6F
	0832	1134	0.6E
	1456	1803	0.5F
	2044	2331	0.6E
6 W ●	0306	0600	0.6F
	0907	1146	0.6E
	1532	1822	0.5F
	2124		
7 Th		0002	0.6E
	0346	0624	0.6F
	0942	1216	0.6E
	1608	1849	0.5F
	2204		
8 F		0039	0.7E
	0426	0656	0.6F
	1015	1251	0.7E
	1645	1924	0.6F
	2243		
9 Sa		0117	0.7E
	0507	0732	0.5F
	1049	1328	0.7E
	1722	2001	0.6F
	2324		
10 Su		0156	0.7E
	0549	0811	0.5F
	1123	1407	0.7E
	1803	2042	0.6F
11 M	0007	0238	0.7E
	0632	0853	0.5F
	1200	1449	0.7E
	1846	2127	0.6F
12 Tu ◐	0052	0324	0.6E
	0718	0938	0.5F
	1242	1537	0.6E
	1934	2217	0.6F
13 W	0142	0416	0.6E
	0809	1029	0.5F
	1332	1632	0.6E
	2030	2312	0.6F
14 Th ◑	0240	0513	0.6E
	0908	1124	0.4F
	1434	1731	0.6E
	2132		
15 F		0010	0.6F
	0344	0610	0.6E
	1011	1223	0.4F
	1545	1831	0.6E
	2235		
16 Sa		0115	0.6F
	0447	0711	0.6E
	1114	1332	0.4F
	1655	1935	0.6E
	2336		
17 Su		0230	0.6F
	0546	0816	0.6E
	1214	1454	0.5F
	1800	2043	0.7E
18 M	0035	0337	0.7F
	0643	0920	0.7E
	1311	1604	0.6F
	1901	2147	0.7E
19 Tu	0131	0432	0.7F
	0736	1017	0.8E
	1404	1702	0.7F
	1959	2243	0.8E
20 W ○	0224	0524	0.7F
	0827	1109	0.8E
	1453	1800	0.7F
	2054	2338	0.8E
21 Th	0316	0618	0.7F
	0916	1158	0.8E
	1542	1856	0.8F
	2146		
22 F		0030	0.8E
	0407	0709	0.7F
	1003	1246	0.8E
	1630	1947	0.8F
	2238		
23 Sa		0118	0.8E
	0459	0757	0.6F
	1050	1330	0.8E
	1720	2035	0.7F
	2329		
24 Su		0204	0.7E
	0552	0841	0.6F
	1138	1414	0.7E
	1811	2125	0.7F
25 M	0021	0250	0.7E
	0645	0925	0.5F
	1226	1459	0.6E
	1903	2219	0.6F
26 Tu ◑	0113	0341	0.6E
	0739	1016	0.4F
	1315	1551	0.6E
	1957	2317	0.6F
27 W	0207	0443	0.5E
	0835	1116	0.3F
	1408	1652	0.5E
	2052		
28 Th		0016	0.5F
	0304	0631	0.5E
	0934	1234	0.3F
	1508	1801	0.5E
	2149		
29 F		0120	0.5F
	0402	0753	0.5E
	1033	1401	0.3F
	1609	2014	0.5E
	2244		
30 Sa		0225	0.5F
	0457	0854	0.5E
	1129	1504	0.3F
	1707	2111	0.5E
	2337		
31 Su		0318	0.5E
	0548	0943	0.5E
	1220	1551	0.4F
	1801	2156	0.5E

Time meridian 75° W. 0000 is midnight. 1200 is noon. Times are not adjusted for Daylight Saving Time.

Port Everglades Entrance, Florida, 2019

F–Flood, Dir. 257° True   E–Ebb, Dir. 075° True

April

Day	Slack (h m)	Maximum (h m)	knots
1 M	0028	0400	0.5F
	0634	1023	0.6E
	1305	1629	0.4F
	1851	2232	0.6E
2 Tu	0116	0434	0.5F
	0717	1053	0.6E
	1346	1702	0.5F
	1937	2251	0.6E
3 W	0200	0501	0.5F
	0758	1051	0.6E
	1425	1729	0.5F
	2021	2308	0.6E
4 Th	0243	0524	0.5F
	0835	1113	0.6E
	1501	1754	0.6F
	2102	2340	0.7E
5 F ●	0324	0553	0.5F
	0911	1146	0.7E
	1538	1826	0.6F
	2142		
6 Sa		0016	0.7E
	0404	0629	0.5F
	0945	1223	0.7E
	1615	1902	0.6F
	2222		
7 Su		0054	0.7E
	0445	0708	0.5F
	1021	1302	0.7E
	1654	1941	0.6F
	2304		
8 M		0134	0.7E
	0527	0748	0.5F
	1058	1343	0.7E
	1737	2022	0.6F
	2347		
9 Tu		0216	0.7E
	0611	0831	0.5F
	1139	1427	0.7E
	1824	2108	0.6F
10 W	0033	0302	0.7E
	0659	0918	0.5F
	1225	1516	0.7E
	1915	2159	0.6F
11 Th	0125	0354	0.6E
	0752	1011	0.5F
	1320	1612	0.6E
	2012	2255	0.6F
12 F ◑	0222	0452	0.6E
	0852	1109	0.5F
	1425	1714	0.6E
	2114	2355	0.6F
13 Sa	0324	0553	0.6E
	0955	1213	0.5F
	1537	1817	0.6E
	2218		
14 Su		0100	0.6F
	0426	0654	0.6E
	1057	1330	0.5F
	1646	1923	0.6E
	2319		
15 M		0217	0.6F
	0524	0800	0.7E
	1156	1501	0.6F
	1750	2035	0.7E
16 Tu	0018	0326	0.7F
	0620	0907	0.7E
	1251	1604	0.7F
	1850	2142	0.7E
17 W	0115	0420	0.7F
	0713	1003	0.8E
	1343	1657	0.7F
	1946	2237	0.8E
18 Th	0208	0509	0.7F
	0803	1051	0.8E
	1432	1749	0.8F
	2039	2327	0.8E
19 F ○	0259	0600	0.7F
	0851	1137	0.8E
	1518	1840	0.8F
	2129		
20 Sa		0014	0.8E
	0348	0649	0.6F
	0936	1221	0.8E
	1605	1928	0.7F
	2217		
21 Su		0057	0.7E
	0436	0733	0.5F
	1021	1303	0.7E
	1652	2012	0.7F
	2305		
22 M		0137	0.7E
	0526	0809	0.5F
	1106	1343	0.7E
	1740	2052	0.6F
	2352		
23 Tu		0217	0.6E
	0616	0841	0.4F
	1151	1424	0.6E
	1829	2132	0.6F
24 W	0040	0259	0.6E
	0707	0919	0.3F
	1237	1508	0.5E
	1918	2214	0.5F
25 Th	0128	0348	0.5E
	0759	1005	0.3F
	1327	1600	0.5E
	2009	2301	0.5F
26 F ◐	0220	0446	0.4E
	0855	1100	0.3F
	1423	1700	0.4E
	2104	2350	0.4F
27 Sa	0315	0546	0.4E
	0958	1204	0.3F
	1526	1801	0.4E
	2200		
28 Su		0046	0.4F
	0409	0647	0.4E
	1046	1407	0.3F
	1628	1907	0.4E
	2256		
29 M		0207	0.4F
	0501	0855	0.5E
	1137	1506	0.4F
	1725	2106	0.5E
	2350		
30 Tu		0307	0.5F
	0550	0934	0.5E
	1224	1547	0.5F
	1817	2143	0.5E

May

Day	Slack (h m)	Maximum (h m)	knots
1 W	0042	0345	0.5F
	0635	0938	0.6E
	1308	1621	0.5F
	1906	2206	0.6E
2 Th	0131	0415	0.5F
	0719	1004	0.6E
	1349	1650	0.6F
	1952	2236	0.6E
3 F	0216	0445	0.5F
	0759	1037	0.6E
	1429	1721	0.6F
	2036	2311	0.7E
4 Sa ●	0259	0520	0.5F
	0838	1115	0.6E
	1508	1758	0.6F
	2118	2350	0.7E
5 Su	0340	0600	0.5F
	0916	1155	0.7E
	1548	1839	0.7F
	2200		
6 M		0030	0.7E
	0422	0643	0.5F
	0955	1238	0.7E
	1630	1922	0.7F
	2244		
7 Tu		0112	0.7E
	0506	0727	0.5F
	1037	1322	0.7E
	1716	2006	0.7F
	2329		
8 W		0156	0.7E
	0553	0814	0.5F
	1124	1409	0.7E
	1807	2053	0.7F
9 Th	0018	0244	0.7E
	0644	0904	0.5F
	1216	1459	0.7E
	1901	2146	0.7F
10 F	0109	0337	0.7E
	0739	1001	0.5F
	1314	1557	0.7E
	1958	2243	0.6F
11 Sa ◑	0205	0436	0.7E
	0838	1105	0.5F
	1420	1702	0.7E
	2059	2344	0.6F
12 Su	0305	0538	0.7E
	0940	1214	0.5F
	1530	1808	0.7E
	2202		
13 M		0049	0.6F
	0405	0641	0.7E
	1040	1339	0.6F
	1637	1917	0.7E
	2303		
14 Tu		0205	0.6F
	0502	0748	0.7E
	1137	1458	0.6F
	1739	2036	0.7E
15 W	0003	0315	0.6F
	0557	0858	0.7E
	1231	1556	0.7F
	1837	2145	0.7E
16 Th	0100	0409	0.6F
	0650	0955	0.8E
	1323	1646	0.8F
	1932	2237	0.8E
17 F	0153	0459	0.6F
	0740	1040	0.8E
	1411	1736	0.8F
	2023	2322	0.7E
18 Sa ○	0242	0547	0.6F
	0828	1120	0.7E
	1457	1825	0.8F
	2111		
19 Su		0001	0.7E
	0329	0634	0.5F
	0912	1159	0.7E
	1542	1911	0.7F
	2156		
20 M		0037	0.7E
	0414	0713	0.5F
	0955	1236	0.6E
	1625	1950	0.6F
	2240		
21 Tu		0111	0.6E
	0500	0738	0.4F
	1036	1314	0.6E
	1709	2019	0.6F
	2323		
22 W		0146	0.6E
	0546	0804	0.4F
	1118	1352	0.5E
	1754	2043	0.5F
23 Th	0006	0225	0.5E
	0634	0839	0.3F
	1201	1434	0.5E
	1839	2116	0.5F
24 F	0049	0308	0.5E
	0722	0923	0.3F
	1247	1520	0.5E
	1926	2157	0.5F
25 Sa	0134	0357	0.5E
	0813	1015	0.3F
	1340	1615	0.5E
	2018	2245	0.5F
26 Su ◐	0222	0452	0.5E
	0905	1111	0.3F
	1441	1715	0.5E
	2114	2336	0.4F
27 M	0315	0546	0.5E
	0958	1210	0.3F
	1544	1814	0.5E
	2212		
28 Tu		0029	0.4F
	0408	0639	0.5E
	1050	1316	0.4F
	1645	1913	0.5E
	2310		
29 W		0128	0.4F
	0500	0733	0.5E
	1139	1437	0.5F
	1740	2016	0.5E
30 Th	0005	0232	0.4F
	0549	0828	0.5E
	1227	1529	0.5F
	1831	2112	0.6E
31 F	0058	0324	0.4F
	0636	0917	0.6E
	1312	1609	0.6F
	1921	2157	0.6E

June

Day	Slack (h m)	Maximum (h m)	knots
1 Sa	0146	0406	0.5F
	0721	1001	0.6E
	1357	1647	0.6F
	2007	2239	0.6E
2 Su	0231	0447	0.5F
	0805	1044	0.7E
	1440	1729	0.7F
	2053	2321	0.7E
3 M ●	0314	0531	0.5F
	0848	1129	0.7E
	1523	1816	0.7F
	2137		
4 Tu		0006	0.7E
	0358	0619	0.5F
	0932	1216	0.7E
	1609	1904	0.7F
	2224		
5 W		0052	0.7E
	0445	0710	0.5F
	1020	1304	0.7E
	1658	1952	0.7F
	2311		
6 Th		0139	0.7E
	0536	0802	0.5F
	1112	1354	0.8E
	1750	2041	0.7F
7 F	0001	0227	0.7E
	0629	0856	0.5F
	1208	1446	0.7E
	1845	2134	0.7F
8 Sa	0053	0321	0.7E
	0725	0958	0.6F
	1308	1545	0.7E
	1943	2232	0.7F
9 Su	0146	0421	0.7E
	0822	1106	0.6F
	1412	1652	0.7E
	2043	2333	0.7F
10 M ◑	0243	0524	0.7E
	0921	1217	0.6F
	1518	1801	0.7E
	2145		
11 Tu		0037	0.6F
	0342	0628	0.7E
	1019	1334	0.6F
	1624	1915	0.7E
	2247		
12 W		0152	0.6F
	0440	0738	0.7E
	1116	1445	0.7F
	1725	2044	0.7E
	2347		
13 Th		0303	0.6F
	0535	0900	0.7E
	1211	1543	0.8F
	1822	2147	0.7E
14 F	0045	0400	0.6F
	0629	0959	0.7E
	1304	1634	0.8F
	1916	2238	0.7E
15 Sa	0138	0451	0.5F
	0719	1044	0.7E
	1353	1723	0.8F
	2007	2324	0.7E
16 Su	0227	0539	0.5F
	0807	1118	0.7E
	1439	1810	0.7F
	2053		
17 M ○		0001	0.6E
	0311	0625	0.5F
	0851	1144	0.6E
	1521	1854	0.7F
	2135		
18 Tu ●		0023	0.6E
	0354	0702	0.4F
	0932	1214	0.6E
	1601	1928	0.6F
	2215		
19 W		0047	0.6E
	0435	0716	0.4F
	1011	1249	0.6E
	1640	1946	0.6F
	2254		
20 Th		0119	0.6E
	0518	0736	0.4F
	1050	1326	0.6E
	1721	2005	0.5F
	2332		
21 F		0155	0.6E
	0601	0811	0.4F
	1131	1406	0.6E
	1803	2036	0.5F
22 Sa	0010	0234	0.6E
	0645	0852	0.4F
	1216	1449	0.5E
	1848	2116	0.5F
23 Su	0050	0318	0.6E
	0731	0940	0.4F
	1304	1539	0.5E
	1937	2202	0.5F
24 M	0132	0407	0.5E
	0818	1032	0.4F
	1359	1635	0.5E
	2031	2252	0.5F
25 Tu ◐	0218	0459	0.5E
	0909	1126	0.4F
	1459	1732	0.5E
	2129	2343	0.4F
26 W	0311	0551	0.5E
	1001	1222	0.4F
	1601	1827	0.5E
	2228		
27 Th		0035	0.4F
	0406	0643	0.5E
	1053	1322	0.5F
	1659	1924	0.5E
	2326		
28 F		0133	0.4F
	0500	0737	0.5E
	1145	1429	0.5F
	1754	2022	0.5E
29 Sa	0021	0233	0.4F
	0552	0833	0.6E
	1236	1528	0.6F
	1847	2117	0.6E
30 Su	0113	0328	0.4F
	0642	0926	0.6E
	1325	1616	0.6F
	1938	2206	0.6E

Time meridian 75° W. 0000 is midnight. 1200 is noon. Times are not adjusted for Daylight Saving Time.

138

Port Everglades Entrance, Florida, 2019

F–Flood, Dir. 257° True   E–Ebb, Dir. 075° True

July

Day	Slack (h m)	Maximum (h m)	knots
1 M	0202	0417	0.5F
	0733	1016	0.7E
	1413	1703	0.7F
	2026	2254	0.7E
2 Tu ●	0248	0506	0.5F
	0823	1105	0.7E
	1500	1753	0.7F
	2114	2342	0.7E
3 W	0335	0600	0.5F
	0913	1156	0.8E
	1548	1846	0.7F
	2202		
4 Th		0032	0.7E
	0424	0658	0.6F
	1005	1248	0.8E
	1638	1937	0.8F
	2251		
5 F		0121	0.8E
	0516	0755	0.6F
	1100	1340	0.8E
	1732	2027	0.8F
	2341		
6 Sa		0211	0.8E
	0610	0851	0.6F
	1157	1433	0.8E
	1828	2120	0.7F
7 Su	0032	0303	0.8E
	0705	0954	0.6F
	1257	1532	0.8E
	1926	2217	0.7F
8 M	0124	0402	0.8E
	0800	1101	0.7F
	1358	1639	0.7E
	2025	2318	0.6F
9 Tu ◗	0219	0507	0.7E
	0858	1208	0.7F
	1502	1753	0.7E
	2127		
10 W		0022	0.6F
	0318	0614	0.7E
	0956	1317	0.7F
	1606	1915	0.7E
	2229		
11 Th		0137	0.5F
	0417	0735	0.7E
	1054	1427	0.7F
	1707	2038	0.7E
	2330		
12 F		0250	0.5F
	0514	0900	0.7E
	1151	1527	0.7F
	1805	2140	0.7E
13 Sa	0028	0350	0.5F
	0608	0958	0.7E
	1245	1620	0.7F
	1859	2232	0.7E
14 Su	0123	0441	0.5F
	0700	1046	0.7E
	1335	1708	0.7F
	1948	2319	0.6E
15 M	0211	0529	0.5F
	0748	1127	0.6E
	1420	1753	0.7F
	2033		
16 Tu ○		0001	0.6E
	0254	0614	0.4F
	0831	1149	0.6E
	1500	1834	0.6F
	2113		
17 W		0024	0.6E
	0333	0651	0.4F
	0912	1158	0.6E
	1538	1903	0.6F
	2150		
18 Th		0027	0.6E
	0411	0707	0.4F
	0950	1228	0.6E
	1614	1914	0.6F
	2225		
19 F		0054	0.6E
	0450	0716	0.4F
	1028	1303	0.6E
	1652	1933	0.6F
	2259		
20 Sa		0128	0.6E
	0529	0748	0.4F
	1108	1342	0.6E
	1733	2005	0.6F
	2334		
21 Su		0204	0.6E
	0609	0827	0.5F
	1150	1424	0.6E
	1816	2044	0.5F
22 M	0010	0245	0.6E
	0650	0911	0.5F
	1235	1509	0.6E
	1903	2127	0.5F
23 Tu	0047	0329	0.6E
	0734	0959	0.5F
	1324	1600	0.6E
	1953	2214	0.5F
24 W ○	0128	0418	0.6E
	0821	1050	0.5F
	1418	1654	0.5E
	2048	2304	0.4F
25 Th	0215	0509	0.6E
	0913	1142	0.5F
	1517	1748	0.5E
	2147	2355	0.4F
26 F	0310	0602	0.6E
	1009	1238	0.5F
	1618	1843	0.5E
	2246		
27 Sa		0050	0.4F
	0411	0657	0.5E
	1106	1341	0.5F
	1717	1940	0.5E
	2343		
28 Su		0150	0.4F
	0511	0755	0.6E
	1202	1449	0.6F
	1813	2039	0.6E
29 M	0039	0254	0.4F
	0609	0855	0.6E
	1256	1547	0.6F
	1908	2136	0.6E
30 Tu	0132	0352	0.5F
	0706	0951	0.7E
	1348	1639	0.7F
	2000	2228	0.7E
31 W ●	0223	0446	0.5F
	0802	1045	0.7E
	1437	1731	0.7F
	2050	2320	0.7E

August

Day	Slack (h m)	Maximum (h m)	knots
1 Th	0312	0545	0.6F
	0856	1138	0.8E
	1527	1825	0.8F
	2139		
2 F		0012	0.8E
	0402	0647	0.6F
	0951	1233	0.8E
	1619	1919	0.8F
	2227		
3 Sa		0102	0.8E
	0453	0746	0.7F
	1046	1326	0.8E
	1713	2010	0.8F
	2317		
4 Su		0152	0.8E
	0546	0842	0.7F
	1143	1419	0.8E
	1809	2101	0.7F
5 M	0007	0242	0.8E
	0640	0941	0.7F
	1240	1515	0.8E
	1907	2157	0.7F
6 Tu	0059	0338	0.8E
	0735	1045	0.7F
	1339	1621	0.7E
	2006	2259	0.6F
7 W ◗	0153	0442	0.7E
	0832	1149	0.7F
	1441	1740	0.7E
	2107		
8 Th		0004	0.5F
	0251	0556	0.7E
	0931	1256	0.7F
	1544	1906	0.6E
	2209		
9 F		0119	0.5F
	0352	0732	0.6E
	1031	1405	0.7F
	1646	2023	0.6E
	2310		
10 Sa		0235	0.5F
	0451	0848	0.6E
	1129	1508	0.7F
	1744	2125	0.6E
11 Su	0010	0336	0.5F
	0547	0946	0.6E
	1224	1601	0.7F
	1837	2218	0.6E
12 M	0104	0427	0.5F
	0640	1034	0.6E
	1314	1648	0.7F
	1926	2304	0.6E
13 Tu	0152	0513	0.5F
	0728	1116	0.6E
	1358	1730	0.6F
	2009	2345	0.6E
14 W	0233	0555	0.4F
	0812	1147	0.6E
	1438	1807	0.6F
	2047		
15 Th ○		0013	0.6E
	0310	0630	0.4F
	0853	1147	0.6E
	1515	1832	0.6F
	2122		
16 F		0006	0.6E
	0345	0651	0.4F
	0931	1210	0.6E
	1551	1842	0.6F
	2155		
17 Sa		0028	0.6E
	0421	0700	0.5F
	1009	1243	0.6E
	1629	1905	0.6F
	2228		
18 Su		0101	0.6E
	0457	0728	0.5F
	1047	1321	0.6E
	1709	1938	0.6F
	2301		
19 M		0136	0.7E
	0535	0804	0.5F
	1127	1400	0.6E
	1751	2016	0.5F
	2334		
20 Tu		0215	0.7E
	0614	0845	0.6F
	1209	1443	0.6E
	1835	2057	0.5F
21 W	0010	0256	0.6E
	0655	0929	0.6F
	1254	1529	0.6E
	1922	2142	0.5F
22 Th ◗	0048	0342	0.6E
	0740	1018	0.5F
	1343	1620	0.6E
	2012	2231	0.4F
23 F ◗	0132	0434	0.6E
	0832	1110	0.5F
	1439	1714	0.6E
	2108	2322	0.4F
24 Sa	0226	0528	0.6E
	0931	1205	0.5F
	1541	1809	0.5E
	2209		
25 Su		0017	0.4F
	0332	0625	0.6E
	1032	1305	0.5F
	1643	1906	0.5E
	2310		
26 M		0117	0.4F
	0440	0725	0.6E
	1132	1414	0.6F
	1743	2007	0.6E
27 Tu	0009	0227	0.4F
	0545	0829	0.6E
	1229	1521	0.6F
	1839	2109	0.6E
28 W	0106	0335	0.5F
	0646	0930	0.7E
	1324	1617	0.7F
	1933	2205	0.7E
29 Th	0158	0434	0.6F
	0745	1027	0.8E
	1416	1709	0.7F
	2024	2258	0.8E
30 F ●	0248	0533	0.6F
	0841	1122	0.8E
	1507	1803	0.8F
	2113	2350	0.8E
31 Sa	0337	0635	0.7F
	0935	1217	0.9E
	1559	1858	0.8F
	2202		

September

Day	Slack (h m)	Maximum (h m)	knots
1 Su		0041	0.8E
	0428	0732	0.7F
	1029	1310	0.9E
	1653	1949	0.7F
	2251		
2 M		0130	0.8E
	0519	0826	0.8F
	1124	1401	0.8E
	1749	2040	0.7F
	2341		
3 Tu		0218	0.8E
	0613	0921	0.8F
	1220	1454	0.8E
	1846	2133	0.6F
4 W	0032	0309	0.7E
	0708	1022	0.7F
	1316	1554	0.7E
	1943	2235	0.5F
5 Th ◐	0125	0409	0.7E
	0804	1126	0.7F
	1415	1714	0.6E
	2043	2342	0.5F
6 F	0222	0527	0.6E
	0903	1230	0.6F
	1517	1848	0.6E
	2145		
7 Sa		0056	0.4F
	0323	0715	0.6E
	1004	1338	0.6F
	1618	2002	0.6E
	2247		
8 Su		0213	0.4F
	0425	0827	0.6E
	1102	1443	0.6F
	1716	2104	0.6E
	2346		
9 M		0316	0.4F
	0523	0924	0.6E
	1156	1537	0.6F
	1808	2156	0.6E
10 Tu	0039	0406	0.4F
	0616	1012	0.6E
	1246	1622	0.6F
	1856	2241	0.6E
11 W	0125	0449	0.5F
	0705	1053	0.6E
	1331	1701	0.6F
	1938	2319	0.6E
12 Th	0205	0528	0.5F
	0750	1125	0.6E
	1412	1734	0.6F
	2016	2345	0.6E
13 F ○	0242	0600	0.5F
	0831	1133	0.6E
	1451	1755	0.6F
	2051	2337	0.6E
14 Sa	0316	0622	0.5F
	0919	1151	0.6E
	1529	1810	0.5F
	2125		
15 Su		0001	0.6E
	0351	0638	0.5F
	0948	1223	0.7E
	1608	1837	0.5F
	2157		
16 M		0033	0.7E
	0426	0707	0.6F
	1027	1300	0.7E
	1648	1912	0.5F
	2230		
17 Tu		0109	0.7E
	0503	0742	0.6F
	1106	1338	0.7E
	1729	1950	0.5F
	2304		
18 W		0147	0.7E
	0542	0822	0.6F
	1147	1418	0.7E
	1811	2031	0.5F
	2339		
19 Th		0228	0.7E
	0624	0904	0.6F
	1230	1502	0.6E
	1856	2115	0.5F
20 F	0018	0313	0.6E
	0710	0952	0.6F
	1317	1551	0.6E
	1944	2203	0.4F
21 Sa ○	0104	0405	0.6E
	0803	1044	0.6F
	1411	1645	0.6E
	2040	2256	0.4F
22 Su	0159	0502	0.6E
	0902	1140	0.5F
	1512	1742	0.6E
	2141	2353	0.4F
23 M	0309	0601	0.6E
	1005	1239	0.5F
	1615	1840	0.6E
	2244		
24 Tu		0056	0.4F
	0422	0703	0.6E
	1107	1347	0.6F
	1715	1942	0.6E
	2345		
25 W		0210	0.5F
	0529	0809	0.6E
	1206	1458	0.6F
	1812	2045	0.7E
26 Th		0326	0.5F
	0631	0914	0.7E
	1302	1557	0.7F
	1906	2144	0.7E
27 F	0135	0427	0.6F
	0730	1012	0.8E
	1357	1649	0.7F
	1957	2237	0.8E
28 Sa ●	0225	0523	0.7F
	0826	1107	0.8E
	1449	1741	0.7F
	2047	2327	0.8E
29 Su	0313	0620	0.8F
	0919	1200	0.8E
	1540	1836	0.7F
	2136		
30 M		0017	0.8E
	0402	0716	0.8F
	1011	1252	0.8E
	1633	1928	0.7F
	2224		

Port Everglades Entrance, Florida, 2019

F–Flood, Dir. 257° True   E–Ebb, Dir. 075° True

October

Day	Slack	Maximum	knots
1 Tu		0106	0.8E
	0453	0807	0.8F
	1104	1341	0.8E
	1727	2017	0.6F
	2313		
2 W		0152	0.8E
	0545	0859	0.7F
	1157	1429	0.7E
	1822	2106	0.5F
3 Th	0004	0239	0.7E
	0639	0955	0.7F
	1251	1521	0.6E
	1918	2203	0.5F
4 F	0055	0332	0.6E
	0735	1057	0.6F
	1346	1626	0.6E
	2015	2313	0.4F
5 Sa ◐	0150	0436	0.5E
	0831	1158	0.6F
	1444	1819	0.5E
	2115		
6 Su		0026	0.3F
	0250	0639	0.5E
	0929	1301	0.5F
	1543	1932	0.5E
	2216		
7 M		0141	0.3F
	0353	0755	0.5E
	1027	1406	0.5F
	1639	2034	0.5E
	2313		
8 Tu		0246	0.4F
	0452	0854	0.5E
	1121	1502	0.5F
	1730	2126	0.5E
9 W	0004	0337	0.4F
	0547	0942	0.5E
	1212	1548	0.5F
	1817	2209	0.6E
10 Th	0050	0418	0.5F
	0637	1023	0.6E
	1259	1625	0.5F
	1900	2245	0.6E
11 F	0131	0454	0.5F
	0723	1054	0.6E
	1344	1655	0.5F
	1940	2259	0.6E
12 Sa	0208	0524	0.5F
	0806	1106	0.6E
	1426	1714	0.5F
	2018	2302	0.6E
13 Su ○	0245	0547	0.6F
	0847	1128	0.6E
	1507	1737	0.5F
	2053	2330	0.6E
14 M	0321	0612	0.6F
	0926	1200	0.7E
	1546	1809	0.5F
	2128		
15 Tu		0006	0.7E
	0357	0645	0.6F
	1005	1237	0.7E
	1627	1847	0.5F
	2202		
16 W	0436	0044	0.7E
	1045	0722	0.6F
	1708	1315	0.7E
	2238	1927	0.5F
17 Th	0517	0123	0.7E
	1127	0802	0.6F
	1750	1356	0.7E
	2316	2009	0.5F
18 F	0601	0205	0.7E
	1211	0844	0.6F
	1836	1439	0.7E
		2053	0.5F
19 Sa	0000	0251	0.7E
	0650	0932	0.6F
	1258	1527	0.6E
	1925	2143	0.5F
20 Su	0050	0343	0.6E
	0743	1025	0.6F
	1351	1622	0.6E
	2021	2239	0.4F
21 M ○	0149	0442	0.6E
	0842	1121	0.6F
	1449	1720	0.6E
	2122	2339	0.4F
22 Tu	0259	0544	0.6E
	0944	1220	0.6F
	1550	1819	0.6E
	2224		
23 W	0411	0045	0.5F
	1046	0647	0.6E
	1650	1326	0.6F
	2323	1921	0.7E
24 Th	0517	0205	0.5F
	1146	0753	0.7E
	1746	1439	0.6F
		2024	0.7E
25 F	0019	0323	0.6F
	0618	0901	0.7E
	1244	1541	0.7F
	1840	2125	0.8E
26 Sa	0112	0420	0.7F
	0716	1001	0.8E
	1339	1633	0.7F
	1932	2218	0.8E
27 Su ●	0202	0513	0.8F
	0810	1054	0.8E
	1432	1724	0.7F
	2023	2307	0.8E
28 M	0251	0606	0.8F
	0902	1145	0.8E
	1522	1817	0.6F
	2111	2355	0.8E
29 Tu	0339	0700	0.8F
	0953	1234	0.8E
	1613	1909	0.6F
	2159		
30 W	0428	0042	0.8E
	1043	0749	0.8F
	1704	1319	0.8E
	2246	1956	0.5F
31 Th	0518	0126	0.7E
	1133	0836	0.7F
	1757	1402	0.7E
	2334	2038	0.5F

November

Day	Slack	Maximum	knots
1 F	0610	0210	0.6E
	1223	0924	0.6F
	1850	1447	0.6E
		2123	0.4F
2 Sa	0024	0255	0.6E
	0702	1015	0.6F
	1313	1537	0.5E
	1944	2218	0.3F
3 Su	0115	0347	0.5E
	0754	1108	0.5F
	1404	1637	0.5E
	2040	2331	0.3F
4 M ◐	0211	0449	0.5E
	0848	1159	0.5F
	1458	1752	0.5E
	2136		
5 Tu		0045	0.3F
	0312	0556	0.4E
	0943	1254	0.4F
	1552	1945	0.5E
	2230		
6 W		0158	0.3F
	0414	0800	0.4E
	1038	1401	0.4F
	1643	2042	0.5E
	2320		
7 Th		0254	0.4F
	0510	0859	0.5E
	1132	1458	0.4F
	1731	2126	0.5E
8 F	0007	0338	0.5F
	0602	0942	0.5E
	1224	1538	0.5F
	1817	2155	0.5E
9 Sa	0050	0413	0.5F
	0650	1011	0.6E
	1313	1608	0.5F
	1900	2156	0.6E
10 Su	0132	0443	0.6F
	0736	1029	0.6E
	1359	1633	0.5F
	1942	2224	0.6E
11 M	0212	0511	0.6F
	0820	1059	0.6E
	1442	1704	0.5F
	2021	2259	0.6E
12 Tu ○	0252	0544	0.6F
	0902	1134	0.7E
	1524	1741	0.5F
	2059	2338	0.7E
13 W	0331	0622	0.6F
	0943	1213	0.7E
	1604	1822	0.5F
	2137		
14 Th		0019	0.7E
	0412	0703	0.7F
	1025	1253	0.7E
	1647	1906	0.5F
	2216		
15 F	0456	0102	0.7E
	1108	0745	0.7F
	1731	1335	0.7E
	2300	1951	0.5F
16 Sa	0543	0146	0.7E
	1154	0829	0.7F
	1819	1420	0.7E
	2349	2038	0.5F
17 Su	0634	0234	0.7E
	1242	0916	0.6F
	1911	1508	0.7E
		2130	0.5F
18 M	0043	0327	0.7E
	0727	1009	0.6F
	1333	1603	0.6E
	2006	2229	0.5F
19 Tu ○	0145	0427	0.6E
	0825	1106	0.6F
	1428	1702	0.7E
	2105	2333	0.5F
20 W	0252	0531	0.6E
	0926	1204	0.6F
	1527	1802	0.7E
	2204		
21 Th	0400	0042	0.5F
	1028	0635	0.7E
	1626	1308	0.6F
	2302	1902	0.7E
22 F	0505	0205	0.6F
	1129	0742	0.7E
	1722	1423	0.7F
	2358	2006	0.7E
23 Sa	0605	0317	0.7F
	1227	0854	0.7E
	1817	1530	0.6F
		2110	0.8E
24 Su	0051	0412	0.8F
	0701	0956	0.7E
	1323	1623	0.6F
	1910	2204	0.8E
25 M	0143	0504	0.8F
	0755	1047	0.8E
	1416	1714	0.6F
	2001	2252	0.8E
26 Tu ●	0232	0555	0.8F
	0846	1135	0.7E
	1506	1806	0.6F
	2049	2337	0.7E
27 W	0319	0647	0.8F
	0935	1219	0.7E
	1554	1857	0.5F
	2136		
28 Th		0021	0.7E
	0406	0734	0.7F
	1022	1259	0.7E
	1642	1940	0.4F
	2221		
29 F	0452	0102	0.7E
	1108	0814	0.7F
	1731	1336	0.6E
	2306	2013	0.4F
30 Sa	0539	0142	0.6E
	1152	0848	0.6F
	1821	1415	0.6E
	2352	2043	0.4F

December

Day	Slack	Maximum	knots
1 Su	0626	0223	0.6E
	1236	0917	0.5F
	1910	1456	0.5E
		2121	0.3F
2 M	0039	0308	0.5E
	0713	0952	0.5F
	1320	1543	0.5E
	1959	2210	0.3F
3 Tu	0131	0400	0.5E
	0803	1034	0.5F
	1407	1636	0.5E
	2049	2304	0.3F
4 W ◐	0227	0459	0.4E
	0856	1121	0.4F
	1456	1730	0.5E
	2140		
5 Th		0000	0.3F
	0328	0557	0.4E
	0953	1211	0.4F
	1548	1822	0.5E
	2231		
6 F		0104	0.4F
	0427	0656	0.5E
	1050	1306	0.4F
	1640	1914	0.5E
	2320		
7 Sa		0229	0.4F
	0522	0759	0.5E
	1146	1410	0.4F
	1730	2009	0.5E
8 Su	0008	0321	0.5F
	0614	0900	0.5E
	1239	1508	0.4F
	1817	2101	0.5E
9 M	0055	0400	0.6F
	0703	0945	0.6E
	1329	1552	0.4F
	1904	2146	0.6E
10 Tu	0140	0437	0.6F
	0751	1025	0.6E
	1415	1631	0.4F
	1948	2228	0.6E
11 W	0224	0515	0.6F
	0836	1105	0.6E
	1458	1712	0.5F
	2031	2311	0.7E
12 Th ○	0307	0558	0.7F
	0920	1148	0.7E
	1541	1758	0.5F
	2113	2356	0.7E
13 F	0350	0644	0.7F
	1004	1231	0.7E
	1625	1847	0.5F
	2158		
14 Sa		0043	0.7E
	0436	0729	0.7F
	1049	1316	0.7E
	1712	1937	0.5F
	2247		
15 Su	0525	0130	0.7E
	1135	0815	0.7F
	1802	1402	0.7E
	2340	2028	0.5F
16 M	0617	0220	0.7E
	1223	0903	0.6F
	1855	1451	0.7E
		2123	0.5F
17 Tu	0037	0313	0.7E
	0712	0955	0.7F
	1313	1545	0.7E
	1949	2224	0.6F
18 W ○	0137	0414	0.7E
	0809	1051	0.6F
	1407	1644	0.7E
	2045	2330	0.6F
19 Th	0242	0519	0.7E
	0910	1150	0.6F
	1504	1745	0.7E
	2143		
20 F	0347	0039	0.6F
	1012	0625	0.7E
	1603	1254	0.6F
	2241	1846	0.7E
21 Sa	0450	0157	0.7F
	1113	0736	0.7E
	1701	1413	0.6F
	2338	1953	0.7E
22 Su	0550	0307	0.7F
	1212	0859	0.7E
	1757	1524	0.6F
		2108	0.7E
23 M	0033	0403	0.8F
	0647	1002	0.7E
	1309	1620	0.6F
	1851	2207	0.7E
24 Tu	0126	0455	0.8F
	0741	1053	0.7E
	1402	1712	0.5F
	1943	2253	0.7E
25 W	0216	0545	0.8F
	0831	1140	0.7E
	1451	1803	0.5F
	2031	2332	0.7E
26 Th ●	0302	0634	0.7F
	0917	1217	0.6E
	1537	1852	0.5F
	2116		
27 F		0006	0.7E
	0345	0717	0.7F
	1000	1243	0.6E
	1621	1931	0.4F
	2159		
28 Sa	0427	0040	0.6E
	1041	0750	0.6F
	1705	1311	0.6E
	2241	1952	0.4F
29 Su	0508	0116	0.6E
	1120	0808	0.6F
	1749	1344	0.6E
	2323	2011	0.4F
30 M	0550	0154	0.6E
	1158	0829	0.5F
	1832	1421	0.6E
		2044	0.4F
31 Tu	0007	0235	0.5E
	0634	0903	0.5F
	1236	1502	0.6E
	1916	2127	0.4F

Time meridian 75° W. 0000 is midnight. 1200 is noon. Times are not adjusted for Daylight Saving Time.

Miami Harbor Entrance, Florida, 2019

F–Flood, Dir. 293° True   E–Ebb, Dir. 113° True

January

Day	Slack h m	Maximum h m	knots
1 Tu		0324	2.3F
	0615	0940	2.2E
	1223	1542	1.9F
	1813	2159	2.6E
2 W	0049	0421	2.4E
	0707	1036	2.3E
	1319	1638	1.9F
	1904	2251	2.6E
3 Th	0140	0508	2.5F
	0754	1125	2.3E
	1410	1721	2.0F
	1951	2337	2.6E
4 F	0227	0547	2.6F
	0839	1210	2.4E
	1457	1757	2.0F
	2036		
5 Sa ●		0019	2.5E
	0310	0622	2.5F
	0921	1252	2.4E
	1539	1827	1.9F
	2118		
6 Su		0056	2.5E
	0349	0653	2.5F
	1001	1328	2.3E
	1618	1855	1.9F
	2159		
7 M		0127	2.4E
	0427	0722	2.4F
	1039	1358	2.3E
	1655	1928	1.9F
	2239		
8 Tu		0151	2.4E
	0505	0754	2.3F
	1117	1420	2.2E
	1732	2005	1.9F
	2319		
9 W		0216	2.3E
	0543	0830	2.3F
	1154	1441	2.2E
	1812	2045	1.9F
10 Th	0000	0246	2.3E
	0624	0907	2.2F
	1231	1510	2.1E
	1854	2126	1.9F
11 F	0043	0322	2.2E
	0707	0945	2.1F
	1309	1545	2.1E
	1938	2208	1.9F
12 Sa	0129	0404	2.0E
	0754	1027	2.0F
	1350	1628	2.1E
	2025	2254	1.9F
13 Su	0219	0454	1.8E
	0843	1112	1.8F
	1433	1721	2.0E
	2113	2344	1.8F
14 M ☽	0316	0558	1.7E
	0935	1202	1.7F
	1523	1822	2.0E
	2205		
15 Tu		0037	1.9F
	0418	0704	1.8E
	1033	1256	1.7F
	1620	1920	2.1E
	2300		
16 W		0134	2.0F
	0522	0805	1.8E
	1132	1353	1.7F
	1720	2017	2.3E
	2357		
17 Th		0237	2.1F
	0621	0910	2.0E
	1231	1456	1.8F
	1817	2118	2.5E
18 F	0053	0345	2.4F
	0716	1019	2.2E
	1329	1601	2.0F
	1912	2224	2.7E
19 Sa	0149	0445	2.7F
	0809	1118	2.5E
	1423	1658	2.3F
	2007	2324	3.0E
20 Su	0243	0534	3.0F
	0902	1212	2.8E
	1515	1749	2.6F
	2103		
21 M ○		0020	3.2E
	0335	0623	3.1F
	0952	1304	3.0E
	1605	1841	2.8F
	2158		
22 Tu		0115	3.3E
	0425	0714	3.2F
	1041	1354	3.2E
	1655	1937	2.9F
	2253		
23 W		0208	3.3E
	0516	0807	3.1F
	1128	1441	3.2E
	1747	2035	2.9F
	2348		
24 Th		0259	3.2E
	0608	0900	3.0F
	1216	1528	3.2E
	1841	2131	2.9F
25 F	0044	0350	2.9E
	0703	0950	2.7F
	1305	1620	3.0E
	1937	2226	2.7F
26 Sa	0141	0453	2.5E
	0800	1041	2.4F
	1355	1727	2.7E
	2034	2326	2.5F
27 Su ◐	0240	0610	2.3E
	0857	1137	2.1F
	1448	1839	2.6E
	2131		
28 M		0034	2.3F
	0342	0719	2.1E
	0957	1241	1.8F
	1546	1941	2.5E
	2230		
29 Tu		0144	2.2F
	0447	0819	2.0E
	1058	1356	1.6F
	1648	2038	2.4E
	2328		
30 W		0257	2.1F
	0549	0917	2.0E
	1159	1519	1.6F
	1747	2136	2.3E
31 Th	0024	0400	2.2F
	0643	1015	2.1E
	1257	1620	1.7F
	1840	2230	2.3E

February

Day	Slack h m	Maximum h m	knots
1 F	0117	0450	2.3F
	0732	1106	2.1E
	1349	1707	1.8F
	1929	2318	2.4E
2 Sa	0205	0532	2.4F
	0817	1151	2.2E
	1436	1745	1.9F
	2014		
3 Su		0000	2.4E
	0249	0607	2.4F
	0859	1231	2.3E
	1518	1816	1.9F
	2057		
4 M ●		0037	2.4E
	0329	0638	2.4F
	0938	1307	2.3E
	1555	1842	2.0F
	2139		
5 Tu		0109	2.4E
	0407	0703	2.4F
	1014	1336	2.3E
	1631	1909	2.0F
	2219		
6 W		0135	2.5E
	0443	0729	2.3F
	1050	1357	2.4E
	1706	1942	2.1F
	2259		
7 Th		0158	2.4E
	0518	0801	2.3F
	1124	1417	2.4E
	1742	2019	2.1F
	2338		
8 F		0226	2.4E
	0555	0837	2.3F
	1159	1443	2.4E
	1820	2057	2.1F
9 Sa	0018	0258	2.3E
	0634	0914	2.2F
	1233	1515	2.4E
	1900	2137	2.1F
10 Su	0100	0335	2.2E
	0717	0953	2.1F
	1310	1554	2.3E
	1944	2220	2.1F
11 M	0145	0419	2.0E
	0804	1037	2.0F
	1350	1639	2.2E
	2031	2307	2.1F
12 Tu ◐	0236	0514	1.9E
	0856	1125	1.8F
	1436	1736	2.2E
	2124		
13 W		0000	2.0F
	0337	0621	1.8E
	0954	1220	1.7F
	1534	1840	2.2E
	2222		
14 Th		0058	2.0F
	0446	0730	1.8E
	1057	1318	1.7F
	1642	1944	2.3E
	2325		
15 F		0202	2.1F
	0551	0839	1.9E
	1202	1424	1.8F
	1749	2052	2.4E
16 Sa	0027	0315	2.3F
	0651	0956	2.2E
	1303	1537	2.0F
	1851	2206	2.7E
17 Su	0127	0426	2.6F
	0746	1101	2.5E
	1401	1644	2.4F
	1951	2313	3.0E
18 M	0225	0520	3.0F
	0839	1156	2.9E
	1456	1738	2.7F
	2049		
19 Tu ○		0011	3.2E
	0318	0609	3.1F
	0929	1247	3.2E
	1547	1830	3.0F
	2146		
20 W		0105	3.4E
	0409	0657	3.2F
	1017	1337	3.4E
	1636	1924	3.1F
	2240		
21 Th		0157	3.4E
	0458	0748	3.1F
	1104	1423	3.4E
	1725	2020	3.1F
	2332		
22 F		0246	3.2E
	0548	0839	3.0F
	1150	1508	3.3E
	1817	2113	3.0F
23 Sa	0025	0333	2.9E
	0640	0927	2.7F
	1237	1554	3.1E
	1910	2204	2.8F
24 Su	0118	0426	2.5E
	0734	1014	2.4F
	1326	1649	2.7E
	2005	2257	2.5F
25 M	0212	0536	2.2E
	0830	1106	2.0F
	1417	1803	2.4E
	2101	2358	2.2F
26 Tu ◐	0309	0650	2.0E
	0928	1205	1.7F
	1512	1912	2.2E
	2158		
27 W		0108	2.0F
	0412	0753	1.8E
	1029	1319	1.4F
	1614	2012	2.1E
	2257		
28 Th		0223	1.9F
	0517	0851	1.8E
	1132	1449	1.4F
	1717	2110	2.0E
	2355		

March

Day	Slack h m	Maximum h m	knots
1 F		0333	1.9F
	0615	0949	1.9E
	1230	1558	1.5F
	1814	2205	2.1E
2 Sa	0050	0428	2.0F
	0705	1041	2.0E
	1323	1647	1.7F
	1905	2255	2.2E
3 Su	0140	0511	2.2F
	0749	1126	2.1E
	1410	1727	1.9F
	1952	2337	2.3E
4 M	0226	0547	2.3F
	0831	1205	2.2E
	1451	1759	2.0F
	2036		
5 Tu		0015	2.4E
	0307	0617	2.3F
	0909	1239	2.4E
	1529	1825	2.1F
	2119		
6 W ●		0047	2.5E
	0344	0639	2.4F
	0946	1307	2.4E
	1604	1848	2.2F
	2159		
7 Th		0115	2.5E
	0420	0701	2.4F
	1020	1328	2.5E
	1638	1917	2.3F
	2238		
8 F		0138	2.5E
	0454	0731	2.3F
	1054	1349	2.6E
	1712	1951	2.3F
	2315		
9 Sa		0205	2.5E
	0528	0806	2.3F
	1127	1416	2.6E
	1747	2029	2.3F
	2353		
10 Su		0235	2.4E
	0605	0844	2.2F
	1200	1448	2.6E
	1825	2109	2.3F
11 M ◐	0033	0311	2.3E
	0646	0924	2.2F
	1236	1525	2.5E
	1908	2151	2.3F
12 Tu	0117	0352	2.2E
	0733	1007	2.0F
	1315	1608	2.4E
	1957	2238	2.2F
13 W	0207	0442	2.0E
	0826	1056	1.9F
	1403	1702	2.2E
	2052	2331	2.1F
14 Th ☽	0307	0548	1.8E
	0926	1152	1.8F
	1503	1810	2.2E
	2154		
15 F		0031	2.1F
	0416	0707	1.8E
	1032	1254	1.7F
	1617	1924	2.2E
	2301		
16 Sa		0136	2.1F
	0525	0823	2.0E
	1139	1402	1.8F
	1731	2039	2.4E
17 Su	0007	0251	2.3F
	0627	0939	2.3E
	1242	1522	2.1F
	1838	2158	2.7E
18 M	0109	0411	2.5F
	0722	1044	2.6E
	1341	1636	2.5F
	1938	2304	3.0E
19 Tu	0207	0507	2.9F
	0814	1138	3.0E
	1436	1730	2.9F
	2036		
20 W ○		0000	3.2E
	0300	0553	3.0F
	0904	1228	3.3E
	1526	1819	3.2F
	2131		
21 Th		0052	3.3E
	0350	0638	3.1F
	0952	1316	3.5E
	1615	1908	3.3F
	2223		
22 F		0142	3.3E
	0438	0726	3.0F
	1038	1401	3.5E
	1702	2000	3.2F
	2313		
23 Sa		0228	3.2E
	0526	0814	2.8F
	1123	1444	3.3E
	1750	2049	3.1F
24 Su	0001	0312	2.9E
	0615	0901	2.6F
	1208	1525	3.0E
	1840	2136	2.8F
25 M	0050	0357	2.5E
	0707	0946	2.2F
	1255	1608	2.6E
	1932	2223	2.5F
26 Tu	0140	0453	2.1E
	0801	1032	1.9F
	1344	1708	2.2E
	2026	2315	2.1F
27 W ◐	0233	0613	1.8E
	0858	1125	1.6F
	1437	1835	1.9E
	2123		
28 Th		0020	1.8F
	0332	0722	1.7E
	0958	1232	1.3F
	1536	1941	1.8E
	2222		
29 F		0138	1.7F
	0436	0821	1.7E
	1059	1405	1.2F
	1642	2038	1.8E
	2321		
30 Sa		0255	1.7F
	0538	0916	1.7E
	1157	1524	1.4F
	1744	2133	1.9E
31 Su	0018	0357	1.8F
	0630	1008	1.9E
	1250	1619	1.6F
	1838	2224	2.1E

Time meridian 75° W. 0000 is midnight. 1200 is noon. Times are not adjusted for Daylight Saving Time.

Miami Harbor Entrance, Florida, 2019

F–Flood, Dir. 293° True   E–Ebb, Dir. 113° True

April

Day	Slack	Maximum	knots
1 M	0110	0443	2.0F
	0714	1053	2.1E
	1337	1701	1.9F
	1926	2308	2.2E
2 Tu	0157	0520	2.1F
	0756	1131	2.2E
	1419	1735	2.1F
	2012	2346	2.4E
3 W	0239	0548	2.2F
	0835	1204	2.4E
	1458	1801	2.3F
	2055		
4 Th		0020	2.5E
	0318	0608	2.3F
	0912	1232	2.5E
	1535	1823	2.4F
	2136		
5 F ●		0049	2.5E
	0354	0631	2.3F
	0948	1255	2.6E
	1609	1850	2.5F
	2215		
6 Sa		0115	2.6E
	0429	0700	2.3F
	1023	1320	2.7E
	1644	1923	2.5F
	2253		
7 Su		0143	2.6E
	0504	0736	2.3F
	1057	1350	2.7E
	1719	2002	2.5F
	2331		
8 M		0215	2.5E
	0541	0816	2.3F
	1132	1424	2.7E
	1757	2043	2.5F
9 Tu	0012	0251	2.4E
	0623	0859	2.2F
	1209	1502	2.6E
	1841	2127	2.5F
10 W	0057	0333	2.3E
	0712	0945	2.1F
	1253	1546	2.5E
	1933	2216	2.4F
11 Th	0147	0422	2.1E
	0808	1035	1.9F
	1345	1640	2.3E
	2032	2310	2.2F
12 F ◑	0246	0528	1.9E
	0909	1133	1.8F
	1449	1752	2.2E
	2135		
13 Sa		0011	2.1F
	0353	0657	1.9E
	1015	1238	1.8F
	1605	1918	2.2E
	2243		
14 Su		0117	2.1F
	0501	0814	1.9E
	1121	1349	1.9F
	1721	2037	2.4E
	2349		
15 M		0232	2.2F
	0602	0923	2.4E
	1223	1515	2.2F
	1827	2151	2.6E
16 Tu	0051	0354	2.4F
	0657	1025	2.8E
	1321	1630	2.6F
	1927	2253	2.9E
17 W	0148	0452	2.7F
	0748	1119	3.1E
	1415	1721	3.0F
	2023	2347	3.1E
18 Th	0242	0537	2.9F
	0838	1207	3.3E
	1505	1806	3.2F
	2115		
19 F ○		0036	3.2E
	0331	0619	2.9F
	0925	1254	3.4E
	1553	1850	3.3F
	2204		
20 Sa		0124	3.1E
	0418	0702	2.8F
	1011	1339	3.3E
	1638	1936	3.2F
	2251		
21 Su		0209	3.0E
	0503	0747	2.6F
	1056	1420	3.1E
	1723	2022	2.9F
	2336		
22 M		0250	2.7E
	0550	0833	2.3F
	1140	1457	2.8E
	1809	2106	2.7F
23 Tu	0022	0329	2.4E
	0639	0916	2.1F
	1224	1531	2.4E
	1858	2149	2.4F
24 W	0108	0409	2.0E
	0732	1000	1.8F
	1311	1608	2.1E
	1950	2234	2.1F
25 Th	0158	0514	1.7E
	0826	1047	1.5F
	1401	1710	1.7E
	2045	2326	1.8F
26 F ◐	0251	0642	1.6E
	0922	1144	1.3F
	1458	1858	1.6E
	2142		
27 Sa		0031	1.6F
	0350	0742	1.6E
	1019	1254	1.2F
	1602	1958	1.7E
	2241		
28 Su		0150	1.5F
	0451	0833	1.7E
	1116	1428	1.3F
	1708	2052	1.8E
	2339		
29 M		0307	1.6F
	0545	0922	1.8E
	1209	1539	1.6F
	1806	2144	1.9E
30 Tu	0032	0403	1.7F
	0632	1008	2.0E
	1257	1627	1.9F
	1856	2231	2.1E

May

Day	Slack	Maximum	knots
1 W	0121	0443	1.9F
	0715	1048	2.2E
	1342	1703	2.1F
	1943	2312	2.3E
2 Th	0206	0512	2.1F
	0756	1123	2.4E
	1423	1730	2.3F
	2027	2348	2.4E
3 F	0247	0533	2.2F
	0836	1153	2.5E
	1503	1753	2.5F
	2110		
4 Sa ●		0020	2.5E
	0326	0559	2.2F
	0914	1221	2.7E
	1540	1822	2.6F
	2151		
5 Su		0051	2.5E
	0404	0631	2.3F
	0952	1252	2.8E
	1616	1857	2.7F
	2231		
6 M		0124	2.5E
	0441	0710	2.3F
	1030	1327	2.8E
	1654	1938	2.7F
	2312		
7 Tu		0200	2.6E
	0521	0753	2.3F
	1109	1405	2.8E
	1736	2023	2.7F
	2355		
8 W		0238	2.5E
	0606	0840	2.2F
	1152	1447	2.7E
	1823	2110	2.6F
9 Th	0042	0321	2.4E
	0658	0929	2.1F
	1241	1533	2.6E
	1918	2200	2.5F
10 F	0133	0411	2.2E
	0755	1022	2.0F
	1338	1628	2.3E
	2018	2254	2.3F
11 Sa ◐	0229	0520	2.1E
	0856	1121	2.0F
	1444	1748	2.2E
	2121	2355	2.2F
12 Su	0331	0654	2.1E
	1000	1229	2.0F
	1558	1922	2.2E
	2226		
13 M		0101	2.1F
	0435	0804	2.4E
	1103	1343	2.1F
	1711	2033	2.3E
	2331		
14 Tu		0214	2.1F
	0536	0906	2.6E
	1204	1511	2.4F
	1816	2140	2.5E
15 W		0032	2.2F
	0632	1005	2.9E
	1301	1621	2.7F
	1914	2239	2.7E
16 Th	0129	0436	2.4F
	0723	1059	3.1E
	1355	1710	3.0F
	2007	2332	2.9E
17 F	0222	0522	2.6F
	0812	1148	3.2E
	1445	1753	3.1F
	2057		
18 Sa ○		0021	2.9E
	0312	0602	2.6F
	0900	1234	3.2E
	1531	1833	3.1F
	2144		
19 Su		0107	2.9E
	0358	0642	2.5F
	0946	1318	3.0E
	1615	1914	3.0F
	2229		
20 M		0151	2.8E
	0443	0723	2.3F
	1030	1357	2.8E
	1657	1956	2.8F
	2311		
21 Tu		0230	2.6E
	0527	0806	2.1F
	1112	1431	2.6E
	1740	2037	2.5F
	2354		
22 W		0304	2.3E
	0613	0848	1.9F
	1155	1500	2.3E
	1825	2117	2.3F
23 Th	0038	0335	2.1E
	0701	0930	1.7F
	1239	1530	2.1E
	1914	2158	2.1F
24 F	0123	0408	1.8E
	0751	1013	1.6F
	1327	1609	1.8E
	2006	2243	1.9F
25 Sa	0211	0502	1.6E
	0843	1102	1.4F
	1421	1711	1.6E
	2100	2333	1.7F
26 Su ◐	0302	0641	1.6E
	0936	1159	1.4F
	1520	1859	1.6E
	2156		
27 M		0029	1.6F
	0357	0736	1.6E
	1029	1301	1.4F
	1625	1957	1.7E
	2253		
28 Tu		0126	1.5F
	0453	0821	1.8E
	1122	1409	1.6F
	1727	2049	1.8E
	2348		
29 W		0229	1.5F
	0544	0906	1.9E
	1213	1530	1.8F
	1821	2141	1.9E
30 Th	0039	0336	1.6F
	0631	0951	2.1E
	1300	1619	2.0F
	1910	2229	2.1E
31 F	0128	0420	1.8F
	0715	1033	2.3E
	1346	1653	2.3F
	1957	2311	2.2E

June

Day	Slack	Maximum	knots
1 Sa	0214	0455	2.0F
	0758	1112	2.5E
	1429	1723	2.5F
	2042	2350	2.4E
2 Su	0257	0529	2.2F
	0841	1149	2.7E
	1511	1756	2.7F
	2126		
3 M ●		0028	2.5E
	0339	0606	2.3F
	0923	1227	2.8E
	1552	1834	2.8F
	2210		
4 Tu		0107	2.6E
	0421	0647	2.3F
	1007	1309	2.9E
	1634	1918	2.8F
	2255		
5 W		0149	2.6E
	0504	0734	2.3F
	1052	1353	2.9E
	1720	2006	2.8F
	2340		
6 Th		0231	2.6E
	0552	0825	2.3F
	1141	1439	2.9E
	1810	2057	2.7F
7 F	0028	0316	2.6E
	0645	0918	2.3F
	1235	1528	2.7E
	1905	2148	2.6F
8 Sa	0118	0407	2.4E
	0743	1013	2.3F
	1334	1625	2.4E
	2005	2241	2.4F
9 Su	0211	0517	2.4E
	0842	1114	2.2F
	1438	1752	2.2E
	2106	2340	2.2F
10 M ◐	0308	0643	2.4E
	0943	1222	2.2F
	1548	1917	2.2E
	2208		
11 Tu		0044	2.1F
	0409	0748	2.6E
	1044	1337	2.3F
	1658	2023	2.3E
	2311		
12 W		0154	2.0F
	0510	0847	2.7E
	1144	1500	2.4F
	1802	2125	2.4E
13 Th	0012	0316	2.0F
	0607	0946	2.8E
	1241	1608	2.6F
	1858	2224	2.5E
14 F	0110	0422	2.2F
	0700	1041	2.9E
	1335	1659	2.8F
	1950	2317	2.6E
15 Sa	0204	0510	2.3F
	0750	1131	2.9E
	1425	1741	2.9F
	2039		
16 Su		0006	2.7E
	0254	0551	2.3F
	0838	1217	2.9E
	1511	1820	2.8F
	2124		
17 M ○		0052	2.6E
	0340	0628	2.2F
	0923	1300	2.8E
	1554	1857	2.7F
	2207		
18 Tu		0134	2.6E
	0423	0704	2.1F
	1007	1338	2.6E
	1634	1934	2.6F
	2248		
19 W		0212	2.4E
	0505	0742	2.0F
	1048	1409	2.5E
	1714	2011	2.4F
	2328		
20 Th		0242	2.3E
	0546	0822	1.9F
	1129	1435	2.3E
	1756	2048	2.3F
21 F		0306	2.1E
	0630	0902	1.8F
	1212	1502	2.2E
	1841	2126	2.1F
22 Sa	0050	0331	2.0E
	0715	0943	1.7F
	1257	1537	2.0E
	1928	2206	2.0F
23 Su	0132	0406	1.9E
	0802	1026	1.7F
	1346	1621	1.8E
	2018	2249	1.8F
24 M	0216	0454	1.8E
	0851	1115	1.6F
	1440	1721	1.7E
	2109	2337	1.7F
25 Tu ◐	0303	0558	1.8E
	0941	1208	1.6F
	1539	1839	1.6E
	2203		
26 W		0027	1.6F
	0356	0702	1.8E
	1033	1303	1.7F
	1642	1942	1.7E
	2259		
27 Th		0120	1.5F
	0451	0753	2.0E
	1126	1401	1.8F
	1741	2037	1.8E
	2354		
28 F		0216	1.5F
	0544	0843	2.1E
	1217	1505	1.9F
	1835	2135	1.9E
29 Sa	0047	0317	1.7F
	0634	0937	2.3E
	1307	1606	2.2F
	1925	2232	2.1E
30 Su	0139	0414	1.9F
	0722	1031	2.5E
	1356	1652	2.5F
	2014	2321	2.3E

Time meridian 75° W. 0000 is midnight. 1200 is noon. Times are not adjusted for Daylight Saving Time.

Miami Harbor Entrance, Florida, 2019

F–Flood, Dir. 293° True   E–Ebb, Dir. 113° True

July

Day	Slack (h m)	Maximum (h m)	knots
1 M	0228	0500	2.1F
	0810	1121	2.7E
	1444	1733	2.7F
	2102		
2 Tu ●		0007	2.5E
	0316	0544	2.3F
	0859	1208	2.9E
	1531	1816	2.9F
	2150		
3 W		0053	2.7E
	0401	0629	2.4F
	0949	1257	3.0E
	1617	1902	3.0F
	2237		
4 Th		0140	2.8E
	0448	0720	2.5F
	1039	1346	3.1E
	1705	1953	3.0F
	2323		
5 F		0225	2.9E
	0537	0815	2.6F
	1132	1436	3.0E
	1756	2044	2.9F
6 Sa	0010	0311	2.9E
	0630	0910	2.6F
	1227	1526	2.9E
	1851	2135	2.8F
7 Su	0059	0400	2.8E
	0726	1005	2.6F
	1326	1623	2.6E
	1948	2227	2.5F
8 M	0149	0503	2.7E
	0824	1104	2.5F
	1427	1744	2.3E
	2047	2323	2.3F
9 Tu ◑	0243	0622	2.6E
	0923	1208	2.4F
	1532	1903	2.2E
	2148		
10 W		0025	2.1F
	0341	0728	2.6E
	1023	1324	2.3F
	1640	2007	2.2E
	2250		
11 Th		0133	1.9F
	0443	0828	2.6E
	1123	1442	2.3F
	1744	2108	2.2E
	2351		
12 F		0257	1.8F
	0543	0927	2.6E
	1220	1552	2.4F
	1841	2208	2.3E
13 Sa	0051	0410	1.9F
	0639	1025	2.6E
	1315	1646	2.5F
	1932	2302	2.4E
14 Su	0147	0502	2.0F
	0730	1116	2.6E
	1406	1730	2.6F
	2020	2351	2.4E
15 M	0238	0543	2.0F
	0818	1203	2.6E
	1452	1809	2.6F
	2105		
16 Tu ○		0036	2.5E
	0323	0620	2.0F
	0903	1244	2.6E
	1534	1844	2.6F
	2146		
17 W		0117	2.4E
	0404	0652	2.0F
	0946	1321	2.5E
	1614	1916	2.5F
	2225		
18 Th		0152	2.4E
	0442	0723	2.0F
	1026	1351	2.4E
	1652	1946	2.4F
	2303		
19 F		0219	2.3E
	0520	0757	1.9F
	1106	1414	2.4E
	1730	2019	2.3F
	2339		
20 Sa		0239	2.3E
	0558	0834	1.9F
	1147	1439	2.3E
	1810	2054	2.2F
21 Su	0016	0301	2.2E
	0638	0913	1.9F
	1229	1510	2.2E
	1852	2131	2.1F
22 M	0053	0331	2.2E
	0721	0953	1.9F
	1314	1548	2.1E
	1937	2210	2.0F
23 Tu	0132	0409	2.1E
	0806	1036	1.9F
	1401	1633	1.9E
	2024	2254	1.8F
24 W ◐	0214	0457	2.0E
	0854	1124	1.8F
	1454	1731	1.7E
	2115	2341	1.7F
25 Th	0301	0555	2.0E
	0944	1216	1.8F
	1554	1838	1.7E
	2210		
26 F		0033	1.6F
	0356	0656	2.0E
	1039	1311	1.8F
	1658	1941	1.7E
	2309		
27 Sa		0128	1.6F
	0456	0753	2.1E
	1135	1411	1.9F
	1758	2043	1.8E
28 Su	0008	0228	1.6F
	0554	0852	2.3E
	1231	1519	2.1F
	1854	2152	2.0E
29 M	0106	0335	1.8F
	0650	0957	2.5E
	1327	1623	2.4F
	1947	2255	2.2E
30 Tu	0201	0436	2.1F
	0744	1059	2.7E
	1420	1713	2.7F
	2038	2348	2.5E
31 W ●	0252	0526	2.4F
	0839	1154	3.0E
	1511	1759	3.0F
	2128		

August

Day	Slack (h m)	Maximum (h m)	knots
1 Th		0038	2.8E
	0341	0615	2.6F
	0933	1248	3.2E
	1601	1846	3.1F
	2215		
2 F		0126	3.1E
	0429	0707	2.8F
	1027	1340	3.3E
	1650	1937	3.1F
	2302		
3 Sa		0213	3.2E
	0518	0803	2.9F
	1121	1430	3.2E
	1740	2029	3.0F
	2348		
4 Su		0258	3.2E
	0610	0859	3.0F
	1215	1519	3.0E
	1833	2119	2.9F
5 M	0036	0345	3.1E
	0705	0953	2.9F
	1311	1613	2.7E
	1929	2209	2.6F
6 Tu	0125	0440	2.9E
	0801	1049	2.7F
	1409	1723	2.4E
	2026	2301	2.3F
7 W ◑	0217	0554	2.7E
	0859	1152	2.5F
	1509	1842	2.2E
	2125		
8 Th		0001	2.0F
	0314	0706	2.5E
	0958	1303	2.3F
	1615	1948	2.1E
	2227		
9 F		0111	1.7F
	0416	0808	2.4E
	1059	1419	2.2F
	1720	2049	2.1E
	2330		
10 Sa		0240	1.6F
	0520	0909	2.4E
	1158	1532	2.2F
	1820	2149	2.1E
11 Su	0032	0356	1.7F
	0619	1007	2.4E
	1254	1630	2.3F
	1912	2245	2.2E
12 M	0128	0450	1.8F
	0711	1100	2.4E
	1346	1715	2.4F
	1959	2334	2.3E
13 Tu	0219	0532	1.9F
	0759	1146	2.4E
	1433	1754	2.4F
	2042		
14 W		0017	2.4E
	0303	0608	2.0F
	0844	1226	2.5E
	1515	1828	2.5F
	2122		
15 Th ○		0055	2.4E
	0342	0638	2.0F
	0926	1301	2.5E
	1553	1856	2.4F
	2159		
16 F		0127	2.4E
	0418	0704	2.1F
	1006	1331	2.5E
	1629	1920	2.4F
	2235		
17 Sa		0152	2.4E
	0452	0732	2.1F
	1045	1354	2.5E
	1705	1949	2.3F
	2309		
18 Su		0210	2.4E
	0527	0806	2.2F
	1123	1416	2.4E
	1741	2022	2.3F
	2343		
19 M		0231	2.4E
	0603	0843	2.2F
	1203	1445	2.4E
	1819	2058	2.2F
20 Tu	0017	0300	2.4E
	0642	0921	2.2F
	1243	1519	2.2E
	1859	2136	2.1F
21 W	0053	0335	2.4E
	0724	1002	2.1F
	1326	1559	2.1E
	1944	2217	2.0F
22 Th	0130	0417	2.2E
	0810	1046	2.0F
	1414	1647	1.9E
	2033	2303	1.8F
23 F ◐	0214	0508	2.1E
	0901	1136	2.0F
	1510	1749	1.7E
	2128	2355	1.7F
24 Sa	0306	0610	2.0E
	0957	1232	1.9F
	1616	1859	1.7E
	2230		
25 Su		0051	1.6F
	0412	0716	2.1E
	1058	1332	1.9F
	1723	2007	1.8E
	2334		
26 M		0153	1.6F
	0522	0820	2.2E
	1201	1441	2.1F
	1825	2121	2.0E
27 Tu	0036	0304	1.8F
	0625	0932	2.5E
	1301	1555	2.4F
	1920	2231	2.3E
28 W	0135	0415	2.2F
	0725	1043	2.8E
	1358	1655	2.7F
	2013	2328	2.7E
29 Th	0229	0512	2.6F
	0823	1142	3.1E
	1452	1743	3.0F
	2103		
30 F ●		0019	3.0E
	0320	0603	2.9F
	0919	1236	3.3E
	1543	1829	3.1F
	2151		
31 Sa		0107	3.3E
	0409	0654	3.1F
	1013	1329	3.4E
	1632	1918	3.1F
	2237		

September

Day	Slack (h m)	Maximum (h m)	knots
1 Su		0154	3.5E
	0457	0748	3.2F
	1106	1418	3.3E
	1721	2009	3.0F
	2323		
2 M		0240	3.4E
	0547	0843	3.2F
	1158	1506	3.1E
	1812	2058	2.8F
3 Tu	0010	0325	3.3E
	0640	0935	3.0F
	1251	1555	2.8E
	1906	2147	2.6F
4 W	0059	0414	2.9E
	0735	1027	2.8F
	1345	1657	2.4E
	2002	2238	2.2F
5 Th	0150	0521	2.6E
	0832	1125	2.4F
	1442	1816	2.1E
	2101	2335	1.9F
6 F	0246	0641	2.3E
	0931	1235	2.1F
	1544	1926	2.0E
	2203		
7 Sa		0047	1.6F
	0348	0747	2.2E
	1032	1351	1.9F
	1651	2027	1.9E
	2307		
8 Su		0218	1.4F
	0455	0847	2.1E
	1133	1506	1.9F
	1753	2126	2.0E
9 M	0009	0335	1.5F
	0557	0946	2.1E
	1230	1607	2.0F
	1846	2222	2.1E
10 Tu	0105	0431	1.7F
	0650	1038	2.2E
	1322	1655	2.2F
	1932	2309	2.2E
11 W	0154	0514	1.9F
	0738	1124	2.3E
	1409	1734	2.3F
	2014	2350	2.3E
12 Th	0237	0549	2.1F
	0822	1203	2.4E
	1452	1806	2.4F
	2053		
13 F ○		0026	2.4E
	0315	0619	2.2F
	0904	1238	2.5E
	1530	1831	2.4F
	2129		
14 Sa		0057	2.5E
	0350	0642	2.3F
	0944	1307	2.5E
	1606	1851	2.3F
	2204		
15 Su		0120	2.5E
	0424	0706	2.3F
	1023	1331	2.5E
	1640	1917	2.3F
	2238		
16 M		0139	2.5E
	0457	0737	2.4F
	1100	1354	2.5E
	1714	1950	2.3F
	2311		
17 Tu		0202	2.6E
	0531	0813	2.3F
	1138	1421	2.4E
	1749	2026	2.2F
	2344		
18 W		0232	2.6E
	0608	0851	2.3F
	1216	1454	2.3E
	1828	2105	2.1F
19 Th	0018	0306	2.5E
	0648	0931	2.3F
	1257	1532	2.2E
	1911	2147	2.0F
20 F ◐	0055	0346	2.4E
	0733	1015	2.2F
	1343	1616	2.0E
	2001	2233	1.9F
21 Sa	0139	0434	2.2E
	0826	1105	2.1F
	1437	1714	1.8E
	2058	2325	1.7F
22 Su	0233	0535	2.1E
	0924	1201	2.0F
	1542	1828	1.7E
	2201		
23 M		0024	1.7F
	0342	0649	2.1E
	1029	1303	2.0F
	1652	1944	1.8E
	2307		
24 Tu		0129	1.7F
	0458	0803	2.2E
	1135	1412	2.1F
	1756	2058	2.1E
25 W	0011	0241	1.9F
	0608	0917	2.5E
	1239	1529	2.3F
	1853	2208	2.4E
26 Th	0111	0400	2.3F
	0710	1030	2.8E
	1338	1635	2.7F
	1945	2306	2.8E
27 F	0206	0500	2.8F
	0808	1129	3.1E
	1433	1725	2.9F
	2035	2357	3.2E
28 Sa ●	0258	0550	3.2F
	0904	1223	3.3E
	1524	1810	3.1F
	2124		
29 Su		0045	3.5E
	0347	0639	3.4F
	0957	1314	3.4E
	1613	1856	3.1F
	2211		
30 M		0133	3.5E
	0435	0730	3.4F
	1048	1403	3.3E
	1701	1945	2.9F
	2257		

Time meridian 75° W.   0000 is midnight.   1200 is noon.   Times are not adjusted for Daylight Saving Time.

Miami Harbor Entrance, Florida, 2019

F–Flood, Dir. 293° True   E–Ebb, Dir. 113° True

October

Day	Slack (h m)	Maximum (h m)	knots
1 Tu		0218	3.5E
	0524	0822	3.3F
	1138	1449	3.1E
	1750	2035	2.7F
	2344		
2 W		0302	3.2E
	0614	0912	3.0F
	1228	1535	2.7E
	1842	2124	2.4F
3 Th	0032	0347	2.8E
	0707	1001	2.7F
	1319	1628	2.3E
	1938	2213	2.1F
4 F	0123	0442	2.4E
	0803	1054	2.3F
	1412	1743	2.0E
	2036	2307	1.7F
5 Sa ◐	0217	0608	2.1E
	0900	1158	2.0F
	1510	1859	1.8E
	2136		
6 Su		0017	1.5F
	0317	0720	1.9E
	1000	1315	1.8F
	1613	2000	1.8E
	2238		
7 M		0145	1.3F
	0423	0820	1.9E
	1101	1430	1.7F
	1717	2056	1.8E
	2338		
8 Tu		0303	1.4F
	0528	0916	2.0E
	1159	1535	1.8F
	1811	2149	2.0E
9 W	0033	0402	1.6F
	0623	1008	2.1E
	1252	1626	2.0F
	1857	2236	2.1E
10 Th	0120	0447	1.9F
	0712	1054	2.2E
	1340	1706	2.1F
	1938	2317	2.3E
11 F	0203	0524	2.1F
	0757	1134	2.4E
	1423	1738	2.2F
	2017	2351	2.4E
12 Sa	0243	0553	2.3F
	0840	1209	2.4E
	1503	1801	2.2F
	2055		
13 Su O		0021	2.5E
	0320	0616	2.4F
	0921	1240	2.5E
	1540	1820	2.3F
	2131		
14 M		0045	2.6E
	0355	0639	2.5F
	1000	1306	2.5E
	1615	1846	2.3F
	2206		
15 Tu		0107	2.6E
	0429	0709	2.5F
	1037	1331	2.5E
	1649	1919	2.2F
	2241		
16 W		0134	2.7E
	0503	0744	2.5F
	1115	1400	2.4E
	1724	1957	2.2F
	2315		
17 Th		0206	2.6E
	0539	0824	2.4F
	1153	1433	2.4E
	1803	2039	2.1F
	2351		
18 F		0243	2.6E
	0619	0906	2.4F
	1235	1511	2.3E
	1848	2122	2.0F
19 Sa	0030	0323	2.5E
	0707	0951	2.3F
	1321	1555	2.1E
	1940	2210	1.9F
20 Su	0118	0411	2.3E
	0801	1041	2.2F
	1415	1651	1.9E
	2038	2304	1.8F
21 M O	0216	0512	2.1E
	0902	1138	2.1F
	1516	1807	1.8E
	2141		
22 Tu		0005	1.8F
	0327	0632	2.1E
	1007	1241	1.7F
	1623	1929	2.0E
	2246		
23 W		0111	1.9F
	0444	0752	2.2E
	1114	1348	2.1F
	1728	2039	2.3E
	2349		
24 Th		0225	2.1F
	0554	0908	2.4E
	1218	1503	2.2F
	1825	2145	2.6E
25 F	0048	0347	2.5F
	0656	1017	2.7E
	1317	1614	2.5F
	1917	2244	3.0E
26 Sa	0144	0449	2.9F
	0753	1115	3.0E
	1413	1706	2.8F
	2008	2336	3.3E
27 Su ●	0236	0537	3.2F
	0848	1207	3.2E
	1505	1751	2.9F
	2057		
28 M		0024	3.4E
	0326	0623	3.4F
	0939	1258	3.2E
	1553	1835	2.9F
	2145		
29 Tu		0112	3.4E
	0413	0710	3.4F
	1028	1346	3.1E
	1641	1922	2.7F
	2232		
30 W		0158	3.3E
	0500	0759	3.2F
	1116	1431	2.9E
	1729	2012	2.5F
	2319		
31 Th		0241	3.0E
	0548	0848	2.9F
	1203	1515	2.6E
	1819	2100	2.2F

November

Day	Slack (h m)	Maximum (h m)	knots
1 F	0006	0321	2.7E
	0638	0934	2.6F
	1251	1600	2.3E
	1913	2147	1.9F
2 Sa	0055	0404	2.3E
	0731	1021	2.3F
	1341	1701	1.9E
	2008	2237	1.7F
3 Su	0146	0511	1.9E
	0826	1114	1.9F
	1433	1822	1.7E
	2105	2336	1.4F
4 M ◐	0242	0642	1.7E
	0923	1220	1.7F
	1530	1925	1.7E
	2202		
5 Tu		0052	1.3F
	0345	0744	1.7E
	1022	1332	1.6F
	1629	2017	1.8E
	2259		
6 W		0212	1.4F
	0450	0837	1.8E
	1119	1444	1.6F
	1725	2106	1.9E
	2351		
7 Th		0320	1.6F
	0549	0928	1.9E
	1214	1544	1.7F
	1813	2152	2.0E
8 F	0040	0412	1.8F
	0641	1017	2.1E
	1304	1629	1.9F
	1857	2234	2.2E
9 Sa	0125	0452	2.1F
	0727	1100	2.2E
	1350	1703	2.0F
	1938	2311	2.3E
10 Su	0207	0523	2.3F
	0812	1137	2.3E
	1432	1726	2.1F
	2018	2342	2.5E
11 M	0247	0547	2.4F
	0854	1210	2.4E
	1512	1749	2.1F
	2057		
12 Tu O		0010	2.6E
	0325	0612	2.5F
	0935	1240	2.4E
	1549	1817	2.2F
	2135		
13 W		0038	2.6E
	0402	0642	2.6F
	1015	1310	2.4E
	1626	1852	2.2F
	2213		
14 Th		0110	2.7E
	0438	0719	2.6F
	1054	1343	2.4E
	1704	1932	2.2F
	2251		
15 F		0146	2.7E
	0516	0801	2.6F
	1135	1419	2.4E
	1745	2017	2.1F
	2331		
16 Sa		0226	2.7E
	0559	0846	2.5F
	1218	1458	2.3E
	1832	2105	2.1F
17 Su	0016	0308	2.6E
	0649	0934	2.4F
	1305	1543	2.2E
	1926	2155	2.0F
18 M	0109	0357	2.4E
	0745	1024	2.3F
	1357	1637	2.1E
	2024	2250	2.0F
19 Tu O	0209	0459	2.2E
	0846	1120	2.2F
	1454	1755	2.1E
	2125	2352	2.0F
20 W	0318	0627	2.1E
	0949	1222	2.1F
	1556	1917	2.2E
	2227		
21 Th		0059	2.1F
	0432	0748	2.2E
	1054	1326	2.1F
	1659	2022	2.5E
	2328		
22 F		0212	2.3F
	0541	0857	2.4E
	1157	1437	2.1F
	1757	2124	2.7E
23 Sa	0027	0335	2.6F
	0642	1003	2.6E
	1257	1553	2.3F
	1851	2223	3.0E
24 Su	0123	0438	2.9F
	0738	1101	2.8E
	1353	1650	2.5F
	1943	2317	3.2E
25 M	0216	0526	3.1F
	0831	1153	2.9E
	1446	1736	2.6F
	2033		
26 Tu ●		0006	3.2E
	0306	0609	3.2F
	0921	1243	3.0E
	1535	1819	2.6F
	2122		
27 W		0054	3.2E
	0353	0653	3.1F
	1008	1330	2.9E
	1622	1903	2.5F
	2210		
28 Th		0140	3.0E
	0438	0738	3.0F
	1054	1415	2.8E
	1709	1950	2.3F
	2256		
29 F		0221	2.8E
	0523	0824	2.7F
	1138	1456	2.5E
	1756	2037	2.1F
	2341		
30 Sa		0258	2.5E
	0609	0908	2.5F
	1223	1534	2.3E
	1845	2122	1.9F

December

Day	Slack (h m)	Maximum (h m)	knots
1 Su	0027	0331	2.2E
	0658	0949	2.2F
	1308	1613	2.0E
	1937	2206	1.7F
2 M	0115	0408	1.9E
	0750	1032	2.0F
	1355	1710	1.8E
	2028	2253	1.5F
3 Tu	0207	0511	1.7E
	0843	1120	1.8F
	1444	1830	1.7E
	2120	2348	1.5F
4 W ◐	0303	0650	1.6E
	0938	1214	1.6F
	1536	1924	1.7E
	2212		
5 Th		0050	1.5F
	0406	0747	1.7E
	1033	1310	1.5F
	1631	2009	1.8E
	2304		
6 F		0157	1.6F
	0508	0837	1.7E
	1129	1410	1.5F
	1723	2053	1.9E
	2355		
7 Sa		0315	1.7F
	0604	0928	1.8E
	1221	1522	1.6F
	1812	2138	2.1E
8 Su	0043	0411	2.0F
	0654	1017	2.0E
	1311	1612	1.7F
	1857	2221	2.2E
9 M	0129	0448	2.2F
	0741	1100	2.1E
	1357	1646	1.9F
	1940	2300	2.4E
10 Tu	0214	0517	2.4F
	0826	1139	2.2E
	1442	1717	2.0F
	2023	2336	2.5E
11 W	0256	0545	2.5F
	0910	1216	2.3E
	1523	1751	2.1F
	2106		
12 Th O		0012	2.7E
	0337	0619	2.6F
	0953	1252	2.4E
	1604	1829	2.2F
	2149		
13 F		0051	2.8E
	0417	0658	2.7F
	1035	1330	2.5E
	1645	1912	2.2F
	2232		
14 Sa		0132	2.8E
	0459	0743	2.7F
	1118	1410	2.5E
	1729	2001	2.2F
	2318		
15 Su		0216	2.8E
	0544	0831	2.7F
	1203	1451	2.5E
	1818	2052	2.3F
16 M		0301	2.7E
	0635	0920	2.6F
	1250	1535	2.5E
	1911	2144	2.3F
17 Tu	0103	0351	2.5E
	0731	1010	2.5F
	1339	1629	2.4E
	2008	2239	2.3F
18 W O	0203	0454	2.3E
	0830	1104	2.3F
	1432	1742	2.4E
	2107	2340	2.3F
19 Th ◐	0309	0624	2.2E
	0931	1203	2.2F
	1529	1902	2.5E
	2207		
20 F		0047	2.3F
	0418	0740	2.2E
	1034	1306	2.1F
	1631	2005	2.6E
	2308		
21 Sa		0200	2.4F
	0526	0845	2.3E
	1137	1415	2.0F
	1731	2106	2.7E
22 Su	0007	0323	2.5F
	0627	0949	2.4E
	1237	1537	2.1F
	1828	2207	2.9E
23 M	0104	0428	2.8F
	0722	1048	2.6E
	1335	1641	2.2F
	1922	2302	2.9E
24 Tu	0158	0517	2.9F
	0814	1141	2.7E
	1429	1728	2.3F
	2013	2353	3.0E
25 W	0248	0600	2.9F
	0903	1230	2.7E
	1519	1810	2.3F
	2103		
26 Th ●		0041	2.9E
	0334	0640	2.9F
	0949	1316	2.7E
	1605	1851	2.2F
	2150		
27 F		0125	2.8E
	0418	0721	2.7F
	1032	1359	2.6E
	1649	1933	2.1F
	2234		
28 Sa		0203	2.6E
	0500	0802	2.6F
	1114	1436	2.5E
	1732	2015	2.0F
	2317		
29 Su		0235	2.4E
	0542	0840	2.4F
	1155	1507	2.3E
	1816	2055	1.9F
30 M	0000	0302	2.3E
	0626	0916	2.3F
	1235	1532	2.1E
	1901	2134	1.8F
31 Tu	0044	0331	2.1E
	0713	0954	2.1F
	1316	1600	2.0E
	1947	2215	1.7F

Time meridian 75° W. 0000 is midnight. 1200 is noon. Times are not adjusted for Daylight Saving Time.

Key West, Florida, 2019

F–Flood, Dir. 020° True   E–Ebb, Dir. 195° True

January

Day	Slack	Maximum	knots
1 Tu	0054	0445	1.3F
	0728	1038	1.4E
	1319	1624	0.9F
	1858	2233	1.7E
2 W	0144	0534	1.4F
	0822	1127	1.5E
	1408	1704	1.0F
	1945	2312	1.9E
3 Th	0227	0613	1.5F
	0906	1207	1.6E
	1452	1737	1.1F
	2028	2345	2.0E
4 F	0305	0643	1.6F
	0945	1245	1.7E
	1534	1811	1.3F
	2111		
5 Sa ●		0020	2.1E
	0342	0706	1.6F
	1021	1320	1.8E
	1616	1851	1.3F
	2154		
6 Su		0057	2.1E
	0420	0729	1.6F
	1058	1356	1.9E
	1659	1936	1.4F
	2238		
7 M		0137	2.1E
	0500	0802	1.6F
	1135	1432	1.9E
	1743	2024	1.4F
	2323		
8 Tu		0219	2.1E
	0544	0842	1.6F
	1214	1508	1.8E
	1830	2110	1.4F
9 W	0009	0302	2.0E
	0630	0922	1.5F
	1254	1545	1.7E
	1916	2154	1.4F
10 Th	0055	0345	1.8E
	0718	1003	1.4F
	1333	1623	1.6E
	2004	2239	1.2F
11 F	0142	0430	1.6E
	0807	1046	1.3F
	1412	1705	1.5E
	2054	2325	1.1F
12 Sa	0232	0519	1.4E
	0857	1131	1.1F
	1452	1752	1.4E
	2147		
13 Su		0016	0.9F
	0330	0615	1.1E
	0953	1220	0.9F
	1537	1844	1.3E
	2244		
14 M ☽		0113	0.8F
	0440	0719	1.0E
	1056	1314	0.8F
	1630	1940	1.3E
	2341		
15 Tu		0223	0.8F
	0555	0836	0.9E
	1201	1416	0.8F
	1729	2040	1.4E
16 W	0033	0352	1.0F
	0700	1001	1.1E
	1301	1524	0.8F
	1826	2138	1.6E
17 Th	0119	0446	1.2F
	0755	1056	1.3E
	1355	1625	1.0F
	1918	2231	1.8E
18 F	0202	0523	1.5F
	0844	1139	1.6E
	1443	1715	1.2F
	2009	2318	2.1E
19 Sa	0244	0558	1.8F
	0929	1220	1.8E
	1529	1801	1.3F
	2059		
20 Su		0005	2.3E
	0329	0639	1.9F
	1014	1302	2.0E
	1613	1849	1.5F
	2150		
21 M ○		0053	2.5E
	0416	0726	2.0F
	1059	1346	2.1E
	1658	1940	1.5F
	2241		
22 Tu		0143	2.6E
	0505	0816	2.0F
	1144	1429	2.1E
	1744	2033	1.6F
	2333		
23 W		0232	2.5E
	0557	0904	1.9F
	1228	1513	2.0E
	1832	2123	1.6F
24 Th	0027	0322	2.3E
	0650	0948	1.7F
	1312	1556	1.9E
	1923	2213	1.5F
25 F	0122	0412	2.1E
	0744	1031	1.5F
	1354	1642	1.8E
	2015	2305	1.4F
26 Sa	0219	0507	1.7E
	0838	1114	1.2F
	1435	1732	1.6E
	2112		
27 Su ◐		0004	1.2F
	0324	0611	1.3E
	0935	1201	1.0F
	1519	1829	1.5E
	2214		
28 M		0120	1.0F
	0439	0732	1.0E
	1038	1255	0.8F
	1611	1932	1.4E
	2319		
29 Tu		0306	0.9F
	0559	0909	1.0E
	1145	1400	0.7F
	1713	2044	1.4E
30 W	0022	0426	1.1F
	0707	1019	1.1E
	1249	1530	0.7F
	1816	2156	1.5E
31 Th	0115	0516	1.2F
	0801	1109	1.3E
	1344	1636	0.9F
	1914	2246	1.7E

February

Day	Slack	Maximum	knots
1 F	0200	0553	1.4F
	0843	1151	1.6E
	1432	1721	1.1F
	2006	2325	1.8E
2 Sa	0241	0622	1.5F
	0921	1228	1.8E
	1516	1800	1.3F
	2053		
3 Su		0003	2.0E
	0321	0647	1.6F
	0957	1303	1.9E
	1557	1841	1.4F
	2139		
4 M ●		0041	2.1E
	0401	0714	1.7F
	1033	1336	2.0E
	1638	1923	1.5F
	2223		
5 Tu		0121	2.2E
	0442	0747	1.7F
	1110	1409	2.0E
	1720	2007	1.5F
	2306		
6 W		0202	2.1E
	0525	0823	1.7F
	1147	1442	1.9E
	1802	2049	1.5F
	2350		
7 Th		0242	2.1E
	0607	0900	1.6F
	1223	1514	1.9E
	1845	2128	1.4F
8 F	0033	0321	1.9E
	0650	0935	1.5F
	1258	1548	1.8E
	1928	2206	1.3F
9 Sa	0116	0402	1.7E
	0732	1011	1.4F
	1330	1625	1.7E
	2011	2245	1.2F
10 Su	0200	0445	1.4E
	0815	1051	1.2F
	1403	1706	1.6E
	2057	2327	1.0F
11 M	0251	0535	1.2E
	0904	1136	1.0F
	1440	1753	1.5E
	2148		
12 Tu ◐		0017	0.9F
	0355	0636	0.9E
	1008	1229	0.8F
	1527	1849	1.4E
	2247		
13 W		0117	0.9F
	0516	0750	0.9E
	1124	1332	0.7F
	1633	1952	1.4E
	2348		
14 Th		0240	1.0F
	0631	0929	1.0E
	1235	1448	0.7F
	1747	2100	1.5E
15 F	0045	0422	1.2F
	0733	1041	1.3E
	1336	1609	0.9F
	1854	2207	1.8E
16 Sa	0138	0514	1.5F
	0825	1127	1.6E
	1427	1708	1.2F
	1954	2304	2.1E
17 Su	0229	0556	1.8F
	0913	1208	1.9E
	1512	1757	1.4F
	2049	2355	2.4E
18 M	0318	0639	1.9F
	0957	1249	2.1E
	1555	1844	1.6F
	2142		
19 Tu ○		0044	2.6E
	0406	0723	2.0F
	1040	1330	2.2E
	1638	1933	1.7F
	2233		
20 W		0133	2.6E
	0455	0807	1.9F
	1122	1410	2.2E
	1722	2023	1.7F
	2324		
21 Th		0221	2.5E
	0543	0848	1.8F
	1202	1450	2.2E
	1808	2110	1.7F
22 F	0016	0307	2.3E
	0631	0925	1.6F
	1240	1530	2.1E
	1857	2154	1.6F
23 Sa	0108	0354	1.9E
	0718	0959	1.4F
	1316	1610	1.9E
	1947	2238	1.4F
24 Su	0201	0442	1.5E
	0806	1036	1.2F
	1352	1653	1.8E
	2039	2323	1.1F
25 M	0259	0538	1.2E
	0857	1118	1.0F
	1429	1741	1.6E
	2135		
26 Tu ◑		0018	0.9F
	0407	0651	0.9E
	0958	1209	0.8F
	1516	1838	1.4E
	2238		
27 W		0155	0.8F
	0524	0836	0.8E
	1109	1313	0.6F
	1623	1946	1.3E
	2342		
28 Th		0353	0.8F
	0634	0953	1.0E
	1220	1441	0.6F
	1741	2111	1.3E

March

Day	Slack	Maximum	knots
1 F	0042	0449	1.0F
	0729	1047	1.3E
	1321	1613	0.8F
	1850	2223	1.5E
2 Sa	0134	0527	1.2F
	0814	1130	1.6E
	1411	1706	1.1F
	1948	2310	1.7E
3 Su	0220	0558	1.4F
	0853	1207	1.8E
	1455	1748	1.4F
	2037	2349	2.0E
4 M	0302	0626	1.6F
	0931	1241	1.9E
	1535	1826	1.5F
	2123		
5 Tu		0026	2.1E
	0343	0654	1.7F
	1007	1312	2.0E
	1614	1905	1.6F
	2205		
6 W ●		0104	2.2E
	0423	0724	1.7F
	1042	1341	2.0E
	1653	1944	1.6F
	2247		
7 Th		0142	2.2E
	0502	0756	1.7F
	1115	1410	2.0E
	1732	2022	1.6F
	2328		
8 F		0219	2.1E
	0541	0829	1.6F
	1148	1441	2.0E
	1810	2057	1.5F
9 Sa	0009	0256	1.9E
	0619	0902	1.5F
	1219	1514	2.0E
	1849	2131	1.4F
10 Su	0049	0334	1.7E
	0657	0937	1.4F
	1249	1549	1.9E
	1927	2206	1.3F
11 M	0131	0415	1.5E
	0739	1016	1.2F
	1321	1628	1.8E
	2008	2246	1.2F
12 Tu	0219	0503	1.2E
	0829	1101	1.0F
	1357	1714	1.7E
	2056	2334	1.1F
13 W	0320	0603	1.0E
	0935	1156	0.8F
	1445	1811	1.5E
	2157		
14 Th ◐		0035	1.0F
	0441	0719	0.9E
	1056	1303	0.7F
	1556	1918	1.5E
	2308		
15 F		0155	1.0F
	0602	0859	1.0E
	1212	1425	0.7F
	1723	2034	1.6E
16 Sa	0019	0400	1.2F
	0709	1021	1.3E
	1315	1600	0.9F
	1840	2151	1.8E
17 Su	0121	0503	1.5F
	0804	1111	1.7E
	1406	1703	1.3F
	1944	2255	2.1E
18 M	0217	0549	1.8F
	0852	1152	1.9E
	1452	1752	1.6F
	2041	2347	2.4E
19 Tu	0308	0630	1.9F
	0935	1231	2.1E
	1534	1838	1.8F
	2134		
20 W ○		0036	2.5E
	0355	0710	1.9F
	1015	1309	2.2E
	1617	1924	1.9F
	2224		
21 Th		0122	2.5E
	0440	0747	1.8F
	1054	1347	2.3E
	1700	2010	1.8F
	2314		
22 F		0207	2.4E
	0523	0822	1.7F
	1130	1424	2.3E
	1744	2053	1.7F
23 Sa	0003	0251	2.1E
	0606	0853	1.5F
	1205	1501	2.2E
	1829	2132	1.6F
24 Su	0052	0333	1.8E
	0650	0926	1.4F
	1238	1538	2.0E
	1916	2206	1.4F
25 M	0140	0417	1.4E
	0735	1002	1.2F
	1313	1617	1.8E
	2003	2241	1.1F
26 Tu	0230	0506	1.1E
	0826	1045	1.0F
	1351	1702	1.6E
	2054	2323	1.0F
27 W ◑	0326	0611	0.9E
	0927	1139	0.8F
	1440	1756	1.4E
	2153		
28 Th		0020	0.8F
	0434	0751	0.9E
	1038	1245	0.7F
	1548	1903	1.2E
	2300		
29 F		0205	0.7F
	0546	0919	1.0E
	1151	1410	0.7F
	1713	2028	1.2E
30 Sa	0008	0407	0.9F
	0648	1018	1.3E
	1253	1547	0.9F
	1828	2159	1.4E
31 Su	0107	0455	1.1F
	0738	1104	1.6E
	1345	1646	1.2F
	1928	2253	1.7E

Time meridian 75° W. 0000 is midnight. 1200 is noon. Times are not adjusted for Daylight Saving Time.

Key West, Florida, 2019

F—Flood, Dir. 020° True   E—Ebb, Dir. 195° True

April

Day	Slack (h m)	Maximum (h m)	knots
1 M	0158	0530	1.4F
	0822	1142	1.8E
	1429	1730	1.4F
	2019	2334	1.9E
2 Tu	0242	0600	1.5F
	0900	1214	1.9E
	1510	1808	1.6F
	2104		
3 W		0010	2.1E
	0322	0627	1.6F
	0935	1242	2.0E
	1548	1844	1.7F
	2147		
4 Th		0044	2.1E
	0400	0654	1.6F
	1008	1308	2.1E
	1624	1918	1.7F
	2227		
5 F ●		0119	2.1E
	0437	0722	1.6F
	1040	1336	2.1E
	1700	1951	1.6F
	2306		
6 Sa		0155	2.0E
	0512	0754	1.6F
	1110	1407	2.1E
	1735	2023	1.5F
	2346		
7 Su		0231	1.8E
	0549	0829	1.5F
	1140	1441	2.1E
	1809	2056	1.5F
8 M	0026	0310	1.7E
	0629	0907	1.4F
	1212	1518	2.1E
	1846	2132	1.5F
9 Tu	0109	0352	1.5E
	0714	0949	1.2F
	1248	1559	2.0E
	1928	2214	1.4F
10 W	0157	0440	1.4E
	0809	1037	1.1F
	1330	1646	1.8E
	2018	2304	1.3F
11 Th	0256	0540	1.2E
	0915	1134	0.9F
	1424	1745	1.7E
	2123		
12 F ◐		0008	1.2F
	0411	0655	1.1E
	1031	1244	0.8F
	1539	1855	1.5E
	2241		
13 Sa		0130	1.1F
	0531	0827	1.1E
	1146	1410	0.8F
	1708	2015	1.6E
	2358		
14 Su		0335	1.2F
	0641	0954	1.4E
	1249	1548	1.1F
	1828	2140	1.8E
15 M	0106	0445	1.5F
	0737	1048	1.7E
	1342	1653	1.4F
	1934	2248	2.1E
16 Tu	0204	0532	1.7F
	0825	1131	2.0E
	1429	1743	1.7F
	2032	2340	2.3E
17 W	0254	0612	1.8F
	0908	1209	2.2E
	1513	1829	1.9F
	2125		
18 Th		0026	2.4E
	0338	0647	1.7F
	0946	1245	2.3E
	1555	1914	1.9F
	2215		
19 F ○		0110	2.3E
	0420	0719	1.6F
	1021	1321	2.3E
	1637	1957	1.8F
	2302		
20 Sa		0153	2.1E
	0501	0749	1.5F
	1056	1356	2.3E
	1719	2035	1.7F
	2348		
21 Su		0233	1.9E
	0541	0821	1.4F
	1130	1432	2.2E
	1801	2106	1.5F
22 M	0033	0313	1.6E
	0624	0857	1.3F
	1205	1508	2.1E
	1843	2133	1.4F
23 Tu	0116	0354	1.4E
	0711	0937	1.2F
	1243	1547	1.9E
	1928	2205	1.2F
24 W	0159	0439	1.2E
	0804	1024	1.0F
	1327	1631	1.6E
	2016	2247	1.1F
25 Th	0246	0536	1.1E
	0903	1119	0.9F
	1419	1724	1.4E
	2113	2341	0.9F
26 F ◐	0344	0657	1.0E
	1009	1225	0.8F
	1526	1830	1.2E
	2221		
27 Sa		0052	0.8F
	0453	0833	1.1E
	1118	1343	0.8F
	1647	1951	1.2E
	2333		
28 Su		0249	0.8F
	0601	0942	1.3E
	1221	1512	0.9F
	1803	2127	1.3E
29 M	0037	0410	1.0F
	0658	1033	1.5E
	1315	1620	1.2F
	1906	2231	1.6E
30 Tu	0132	0455	1.2F
	0744	1112	1.7E
	1402	1709	1.4F
	1958	2315	1.8E

May

Day	Slack (h m)	Maximum (h m)	knots
1 W	0217	0528	1.4F
	0824	1143	2.1E
	1443	1748	1.5F
	2045	2350	1.9E
2 Th	0258	0555	1.5F
	0859	1207	2.0E
	1520	1821	1.6F
	2127		
3 F		0023	1.9E
	0335	0619	1.5F
	0931	1232	2.1E
	1554	1850	1.6F
	2207		
4 Sa ●		0056	1.9E
	0410	0647	1.5F
	1002	1301	2.1E
	1627	1918	1.6F
	2246		
5 Su		0132	1.9E
	0447	0721	1.5F
	1033	1334	2.2E
	1700	1950	1.6F
	2325		
6 M		0210	1.8E
	0526	0800	1.4F
	1107	1412	2.2E
	1735	2026	1.6F
7 Tu	0007	0250	1.7E
	0610	0843	1.3F
	1144	1452	2.2E
	1814	2107	1.6F
8 W	0051	0334	1.7E
	0659	0929	1.2F
	1227	1537	2.1E
	1900	2152	1.6F
9 Th	0141	0423	1.5E
	0755	1020	1.1F
	1316	1627	2.0E
	1956	2246	1.5F
10 F	0238	0521	1.4E
	0857	1119	1.0F
	1416	1727	1.8E
	2103	2350	1.3F
11 Sa ◐	0344	0631	1.3E
	1005	1229	0.9F
	1530	1838	1.6E
	2220		
12 Su		0112	1.2F
	0458	0753	1.3E
	1115	1354	1.0F
	1656	1959	1.6E
	2338		
13 M		0300	1.2F
	0606	0917	1.4E
	1220	1530	1.2F
	1815	2128	1.7E
14 Tu	0047	0418	1.3F
	0704	1020	1.7E
	1316	1641	1.5F
	1924	2238	1.9E
15 W	0146	0508	1.5F
	0753	1106	1.9E
	1407	1734	1.7F
	2023	2331	2.1E
16 Th	0235	0547	1.5F
	0835	1145	2.1E
	1452	1821	1.8F
	2116		
17 F		0017	2.1E
	0319	0620	1.5F
	0912	1220	2.3E
	1534	1904	1.8F
	2205		
18 Sa ○		0059	2.0E
	0359	0648	1.4F
	0948	1254	2.3E
	1614	1943	1.7F
	2249		
19 Su		0139	1.9E
	0438	0718	1.4F
	1024	1329	2.3E
	1653	2015	1.6F
	2331		
20 M		0217	1.8E
	0519	0754	1.3F
	1101	1405	2.2E
	1732	2038	1.5F
21 Tu	0010	0255	1.6E
	0604	0835	1.3F
	1140	1443	2.0E
	1813	2104	1.4F
22 W	0049	0334	1.5E
	0652	0920	1.2F
	1223	1523	1.9E
	1857	2139	1.3F
23 Th	0129	0416	1.4E
	0744	1008	1.1F
	1311	1607	1.7E
	1945	2223	1.2F
24 F	0212	0505	1.3E
	0839	1102	1.0F
	1403	1659	1.5E
	2041	2315	1.1F
25 Sa	0302	0607	1.2E
	0938	1203	1.0F
	1505	1800	1.3E
	2146		
26 Su ◐		0019	1.0F
	0402	0725	1.2E
	1042	1311	0.9F
	1616	1914	1.2E
	2255		
27 M		0133	0.9F
	0509	0848	1.2E
	1145	1430	0.9F
	1732	2041	1.2E
28 Tu	0002	0301	0.9F
	0609	0951	1.4E
	1242	1548	1.1F
	1839	2202	1.3E
29 W	0059	0407	1.0F
	0659	1035	1.5E
	1331	1645	1.3F
	1936	2252	1.5E
30 Th	0148	0448	1.2F
	0741	1105	1.7E
	1413	1727	1.4F
	2025	2330	1.6E
31 F	0230	0518	1.3F
	0818	1129	1.9E
	1450	1759	1.5F
	2108		

June

Day	Slack (h m)	Maximum (h m)	knots
1 Sa		0002	1.7E
	0309	0546	1.3F
	0852	1156	2.0E
	1523	1823	1.6F
	2148		
2 Su		0035	1.7E
	0347	0617	1.3F
	0926	1229	2.1E
	1556	1849	1.7F
	2228		
3 M ●		0112	1.8E
	0427	0654	1.4F
	1002	1307	2.2E
	1630	1922	1.7F
	2308		
4 Tu		0152	1.8E
	0509	0738	1.3F
	1042	1348	2.3E
	1708	2004	1.8F
	2351		
5 W		0235	1.8E
	0555	0826	1.3F
	1126	1433	2.3E
	1753	2050	1.8F
6 Th	0037	0319	1.8E
	0645	0916	1.3F
	1215	1521	2.2E
	1844	2139	1.7F
7 F	0126	0408	1.7E
	0738	1008	1.3F
	1309	1613	2.1E
	1943	2234	1.6F
8 Sa	0218	0502	1.6E
	0835	1106	1.2F
	1410	1712	1.9E
	2048	2336	1.4F
9 Su	0316	0605	1.5E
	0937	1213	1.1F
	1520	1821	1.7E
	2159		
10 M ◐		0048	1.2F
	0420	0716	1.4E
	1043	1333	1.1F
	1641	1941	1.6E
	2314		
11 Tu		0212	1.1F
	0524	0833	1.5E
	1150	1510	1.2F
	1802	2112	1.5E
12 W	0023	0338	1.1F
	0623	0945	1.6E
	1251	1629	1.4F
	1914	2227	1.6E
13 Th	0123	0437	1.2F
	0714	1038	1.9E
	1345	1726	1.6F
	2015	2321	1.7E
14 F	0213	0520	1.2F
	0759	1119	2.0E
	1432	1813	1.7F
	2107		
15 Sa		0006	1.8E
	0258	0553	1.3F
	0840	1155	2.1E
	1513	1854	1.7F
	2152		
16 Su		0047	1.8E
	0339	0622	1.3F
	0919	1229	2.2E
	1551	1928	1.7F
	2232		
17 M ○		0125	1.8E
	0419	0655	1.3F
	0958	1304	2.2E
	1628	1952	1.6F
	2309		
18 Tu		0201	1.8E
	0501	0735	1.3F
	1039	1342	2.1E
	1706	2012	1.5F
	2345		
19 W		0237	1.7E
	0545	0820	1.3F
	1122	1422	2.0E
	1747	2042	1.5F
20 Th	0022	0314	1.7E
	0632	0906	1.3F
	1208	1504	1.9E
	1832	2120	1.5F
21 F	0101	0353	1.6E
	0721	0953	1.3F
	1255	1548	1.8E
	1921	2204	1.4F
22 Sa	0142	0435	1.5E
	0811	1042	1.2F
	1345	1636	1.6E
	2014	2252	1.3F
23 Su	0226	0524	1.4E
	0905	1136	1.1F
	1440	1731	1.4E
	2111	2346	1.1F
24 M	0316	0621	1.3E
	1003	1235	1.0F
	1543	1834	1.2E
	2214		
25 Tu ◐		0044	1.0F
	0411	0723	1.2E
	1104	1342	0.9F
	1656	1947	1.1E
	2320		
26 W		0147	0.9F
	0510	0829	1.3E
	1204	1505	0.9F
	1809	2118	1.1E
27 Th	0021	0255	0.8F
	0605	0930	1.4E
	1256	1618	1.1F
	1912	2227	1.2E
28 F	0116	0358	0.9F
	0652	1013	1.5E
	1340	1705	1.3F
	2004	2310	1.3E
29 Sa	0204	0442	1.0F
	0735	1048	1.8E
	1418	1737	1.4F
	2049	2345	1.5E
30 Su	0247	0519	1.1F
	0816	1124	2.0E
	1453	1801	1.6F
	2130		

Time meridian 75° W. 0000 is midnight. 1200 is noon. Times are not adjusted for Daylight Saving Time.

Key West, Florida, 2019

F–Flood, Dir. 020° True   E–Ebb, Dir. 195° True

July

Day	Slack	Maximum	knots
1 M		0019	1.7E
	0329	0556	1.2F
	0857	1203	2.1E
	1529	1828	1.7F
	2210		
2 Tu ●		0056	1.8E
	0410	0637	1.3F
	0941	1245	2.3E
	1608	1905	1.8F
	2251		
3 W		0137	1.9E
	0453	0724	1.4F
	1026	1331	2.4E
	1651	1951	1.9F
	2335		
4 Th		0220	2.0E
	0538	0814	1.4F
	1115	1419	2.4E
	1740	2041	1.9F
5 F	0021	0304	2.0E
	0626	0905	1.5F
	1207	1508	2.4E
	1833	2131	1.8F
6 Sa	0107	0350	1.9E
	0717	0957	1.4F
	1302	1600	2.2E
	1931	2222	1.7F
7 Su	0155	0440	1.8E
	0810	1051	1.4F
	1401	1656	2.0E
	2031	2316	1.4F
8 M	0244	0535	1.6E
	0908	1153	1.3F
	1507	1802	1.7E
	2134		
9 Tu ◐		0014	1.2F
	0337	0637	1.5E
	1012	1309	1.2F
	1625	1919	1.4E
	2243		
10 W		0118	1.0F
	0435	0745	1.5E
	1120	1449	1.1F
	1748	2054	1.3E
	2352		
11 Th		0237	0.8F
	0535	0900	1.5E
	1225	1617	1.3F
	1903	2213	1.3E
12 F	0056	0358	0.9F
	0632	1006	1.7E
	1322	1717	1.4F
	2004	2309	1.4E
13 Sa	0151	0452	1.0F
	0724	1055	1.8E
	1410	1803	1.5F
	2053	2354	1.6E
14 Su	0237	0531	1.1F
	0811	1133	2.0E
	1451	1839	1.6F
	2134		
15 M		0033	1.7E
	0320	0605	1.2F
	0856	1208	2.0E
	1529	1908	1.6F
	2209		
16 Tu ○		0109	1.8E
	0400	0641	1.3F
	0940	1244	2.1E
	1606	1929	1.6F
	2244		
17 W		0143	1.9E
	0441	0722	1.4F
	1023	1323	2.1E
	1645	1951	1.6F
	2319		
18 Th		0217	1.9E
	0524	0806	1.4F
	1107	1404	2.1E
	1726	2024	1.6F
	2355		
19 F		0251	1.9E
	0608	0850	1.5F
	1151	1445	2.0E
	1811	2103	1.6F
20 Sa	0034	0327	1.8E
	0653	0934	1.4F
	1237	1528	1.9E
	1858	2144	1.5F
21 Su	0112	0404	1.7E
	0741	1018	1.4F
	1324	1612	1.7E
	1946	2226	1.4F
22 M	0151	0445	1.6E
	0829	1104	1.2F
	1413	1659	1.5E
	2036	2311	1.2F
23 Tu	0231	0530	1.5E
	0922	1154	1.1F
	1508	1754	1.2E
	2130	2359	1.0F
24 W ○		0620	1.4E
	0313	1250	0.9F
	1019	1857	1.0E
	1616		
	2233		
25 Th		0052	0.8F
	0403	0715	1.3E
	1118	1357	0.8F
	1733	2014	0.9E
	2340		
26 F		0152	0.7F
	0502	0814	1.3E
	1214	1537	0.9F
	1843	2156	0.9E
27 Sa	0044	0301	0.7F
	0602	0915	1.4E
	1303	1640	1.1F
	1940	2251	1.2E
28 Su	0140	0409	0.8F
	0657	1010	1.6E
	1346	1716	1.3F
	2027	2329	1.4E
29 M	0228	0500	1.0F
	0749	1058	1.9E
	1427	1745	1.6F
	2110		
30 Tu		0004	1.7E
	0311	0543	1.2F
	0838	1144	2.2E
	1509	1818	1.8F
	2152		
31 W ●		0042	1.9E
	0353	0627	1.4F
	0927	1230	2.4E
	1553	1858	1.9F
	2234		

August

Day	Slack	Maximum	knots
1 Th		0122	2.0E
	0435	0714	1.5F
	1016	1318	2.5E
	1640	1944	2.0F
	2317		
2 F		0204	2.1E
	0518	0804	1.6F
	1107	1407	2.5E
	1729	2033	1.9F
3 Sa	0001	0246	2.1E
	0604	0854	1.6F
	1159	1456	2.5E
	1821	2119	1.8F
4 Su	0044	0330	2.1E
	0653	0943	1.6F
	1253	1546	2.2E
	1914	2203	1.7F
5 M	0126	0414	2.0E
	0745	1034	1.5F
	1350	1639	1.9E
	2008	2248	1.4F
6 Tu	0208	0502	1.8E
	0840	1130	1.3F
	1453	1739	1.5E
	2105	2336	1.1F
7 W ◐	0252	0556	1.6E
	0941	1240	1.1F
	1606	1853	1.2E
	2208		
8 Th		0029	0.9F
	0341	0657	1.5E
	1047	1423	1.0F
	1729	2032	1.0E
	2318		
9 F		0133	0.7F
	0443	0807	1.4E
	1155	1602	1.1F
	1845	2156	1.1E
10 Sa	0027	0304	0.6F
	0551	0929	1.5E
	1255	1702	1.2F
	1945	2253	1.3E
11 Su	0127	0426	0.8F
	0654	1031	1.6E
	1346	1745	1.3F
	2030	2337	1.5E
12 M	0217	0514	1.0F
	0750	1114	1.8E
	1428	1818	1.4F
	2108		
13 Tu		0015	1.7E
	0300	0552	1.2F
	0839	1152	1.9E
	1507	1843	1.5F
	2142		
14 W		0049	1.9E
	0340	0628	1.4F
	0924	1228	2.1E
	1546	1904	1.6F
	2217		
15 Th ○		0121	2.0E
	0419	0706	1.5F
	1007	1306	2.1E
	1625	1930	1.7F
	2252		
16 F		0153	2.0E
	0459	0747	1.6F
	1049	1346	2.2E
	1706	2004	1.7F
	2328		
17 Sa		0225	2.0E
	0541	0829	1.6F
	1132	1426	2.1E
	1749	2041	1.7F
18 Su	0004	0258	2.0E
	0623	0910	1.5F
	1216	1506	2.0E
	1832	2118	1.6F
19 M	0039	0332	1.9E
	0707	0949	1.4F
	1300	1546	1.8E
	1915	2156	1.4F
20 Tu	0113	0407	1.8E
	0751	1028	1.3F
	1345	1628	1.5E
	1959	2235	1.3F
21 W	0146	0446	1.7E
	0837	1110	1.1F
	1434	1716	1.2E
	2048	2318	1.0F
22 Th	0221	0531	1.5E
	0927	1157	0.9F
	1534	1813	0.9E
	2148		
23 F ◐		0008	0.8F
	0303	0623	1.4E
	1024	1253	0.8F
	1651	1924	0.8E
	2301		
24 Sa		0107	0.7F
	0401	0723	1.3E
	1125	1404	0.8F
	1808	2105	0.8E
25 Su	0014	0219	0.6F
	0517	0830	1.4E
	1223	1602	1.0F
	1911	2227	1.1E
26 M	0116	0344	0.8F
	0629	0939	1.6E
	1317	1656	1.3F
	2003	2310	1.4E
27 Tu	0207	0448	1.0F
	0730	1039	1.9E
	1406	1734	1.6F
	2048	2347	1.7E
28 W	0251	0535	1.3F
	0825	1131	2.2E
	1454	1811	1.8F
	2132		
29 Th		0025	2.0E
	0332	0619	1.5F
	0917	1219	2.5E
	1541	1852	2.0F
	2214		
30 F ●		0104	2.2E
	0414	0704	1.7F
	1007	1307	2.6E
	1628	1935	2.0F
	2255		
31 Sa		0144	2.2E
	0456	0753	1.8F
	1058	1356	2.6E
	1716	2018	1.9F
	2336		

September

Day	Slack	Maximum	knots
1 Su		0225	2.3E
	0541	0841	1.8F
	1150	1443	2.4E
	1804	2059	1.8F
2 M	0015	0306	2.2E
	0629	0928	1.7F
	1243	1530	2.1E
	1853	2138	1.6F
3 Tu	0053	0347	2.1E
	0719	1014	1.5F
	1338	1619	1.7E
	1943	2217	1.3F
4 W	0131	0430	1.9E
	0811	1102	1.3F
	1436	1714	1.3E
	2035	2259	1.1F
5 Th ◐	0209	0517	1.7E
	0908	1158	1.1F
	1542	1823	1.0E
	2134	2349	0.8F
6 F	0254	0612	1.5E
	1010	1330	0.9F
	1658	2004	0.8E
	2244		
7 Sa		0050	0.6F
	0356	0718	1.3E
	1118	1531	0.8F
	1813	2130	0.9E
	2357		
8 Su		0214	0.6F
	0516	0843	1.3E
	1223	1636	1.0F
	1911	2229	1.2E
9 M	0101	0358	0.7F
	0630	1006	1.4E
	1317	1632	1.2F
	1957	2313	1.5E
10 Tu	0152	0454	1.0F
	0730	1057	1.6E
	1404	1749	1.3F
	2036	2351	1.7E
11 W	0236	0534	1.3F
	0821	1136	1.9E
	1446	1814	1.5F
	2112		
12 Th		0024	1.9E
	0316	0611	1.5F
	0906	1213	2.1E
	1526	1838	1.6F
	2147		
13 F ○		0055	2.0E
	0354	0647	1.6F
	0949	1249	2.2E
	1605	1906	1.7F
	2222		
14 Sa		0124	2.1E
	0433	0725	1.7F
	1031	1327	2.2E
	1645	1938	1.7F
	2257		
15 Su		0155	2.1E
	0512	0804	1.7F
	1112	1405	2.1E
	1724	2013	1.7F
	2330		
16 M		0226	2.1E
	0552	0842	1.6F
	1154	1443	2.0E
	1804	2048	1.6F
17 Tu	0003	0258	2.0E
	0632	0918	1.5F
	1237	1521	1.7E
	1845	2123	1.4F
18 W	0034	0333	1.9E
	0711	0952	1.3F
	1319	1600	1.5E
	1926	2201	1.2F
19 Th	0105	0410	1.8E
	0751	1029	1.2F
	1404	1644	1.2E
	2014	2243	1.0F
20 F ◐	0139	0452	1.7E
	0835	1113	1.1F
	1457	1738	1.0E
	2113	2334	0.8F
21 Sa ○	0221	0544	1.5E
	0929	1207	1.0F
	1607	1846	0.9E
	2228		
22 Su		0035	0.7F
	0322	0647	1.4E
	1037	1314	0.9F
	1728	2014	0.9E
	2345		
23 M		0150	0.6F
	0447	0759	1.4E
	1149	1500	1.0F
	1838	2152	1.1E
24 Tu	0049	0322	0.8F
	0609	0916	1.6E
	1253	1632	1.5F
	1935	2245	1.5E
25 W	0142	0435	1.1F
	0716	1026	1.9E
	1350	1719	1.6F
	2024	2326	1.8E
26 Th	0227	0525	1.5F
	0814	1121	2.3E
	1441	1800	1.8F
	2108		
27 F		0005	2.1E
	0310	0610	1.7F
	0907	1210	2.5E
	1529	1839	1.9F
	2149		
28 Sa ●		0043	2.2E
	0352	0655	1.9F
	0958	1257	2.6E
	1615	1918	1.9F
	2228		
29 Su		0122	2.3E
	0435	0742	1.9F
	1049	1344	2.5E
	1700	1956	1.8F
	2306		
30 M		0201	2.4E
	0519	0829	1.8F
	1140	1430	2.2E
	1745	2034	1.6F
	2343		

Time meridian 75° W. 0000 is midnight. 1200 is noon. Times are not adjusted for Daylight Saving Time.

Key West, Florida, 2019

F–Flood, Dir. 020° True   E–Ebb, Dir. 195° True

October

Day	Slack (h m)	Maximum (h m)	knots
1 Tu		0240	2.3E
	0605	0913	1.7F
	1231	1515	1.9E
	1830	2110	1.4F
2 W	0019	0319	2.2E
	0652	0953	1.5F
	1323	1600	1.6E
	1918	2147	1.2F
3 Th	0056	0359	2.0E
	0741	1030	1.3F
	1414	1649	1.3E
	2008	2229	1.0F
4 F	0135	0442	1.7E
	0832	1110	1.0F
	1509	1750	1.0E
	2106	2319	0.8F
5 Sa ◗	0222	0534	1.5E
	0930	1201	0.8F
	1612	1920	0.9E
	2213		
6 Su		0022	0.7F
	0325	0638	1.2E
	1035	1327	0.7F
	1721	2052	0.9E
	2325		
7 M		0141	0.7F
	0447	0758	1.2E
	1144	1547	0.8F
	1824	2155	1.2E
8 Tu	0029	0321	0.8F
	0605	0935	1.3E
	1245	1638	1.0F
	1915	2244	1.4E
9 W	0122	0427	1.1F
	0708	1036	1.6E
	1337	1713	1.2F
	1959	2323	1.7E
10 Th	0208	0512	1.4F
	0801	1118	1.8E
	1422	1742	1.4F
	2039	2356	1.9E
11 F	0249	0551	1.6F
	0847	1155	2.0E
	1504	1809	1.6F
	2115		
12 Sa		0026	2.0E
	0328	0627	1.7F
	0930	1231	2.1E
	1543	1837	1.6F
	2150		
13 Su ○		0053	2.1E
	0406	0702	1.7F
	1012	1307	2.1E
	1621	1907	1.6F
	2222		
14 M		0121	2.1E
	0443	0738	1.7F
	1053	1343	2.0E
	1659	1940	1.6F
	2254		
15 Tu		0152	2.1E
	0519	0812	1.6F
	1134	1419	1.8E
	1738	2016	1.5F
	2326		
16 W		0225	2.1E
	0555	0844	1.5F
	1214	1457	1.7E
	1818	2053	1.3F
	2357		
17 Th		0301	2.0E
	0631	0918	1.4F
	1255	1536	1.5E
	1901	2133	1.2F
18 F	0031	0339	1.9E
	0709	0956	1.4F
	1339	1620	1.4E
	1950	2217	1.0F
19 Sa	0110	0423	1.8E
	0754	1040	1.3F
	1429	1712	1.2E
	2049	2309	0.9F
20 Su	0158	0516	1.6E
	0851	1135	1.2F
	1532	1817	1.1E
	2159		
21 M ○		0012	0.8F
	0303	0621	1.5E
	1003	1245	1.1F
	1649	1936	1.1E
	2312		
22 Tu		0128	0.8F
	0428	0736	1.5E
	1121	1418	1.1F
	1802	2107	1.2E
23 W	0017	0300	0.9F
	0552	0857	1.6E
	1232	1602	1.3F
	1903	2214	1.5E
24 Th	0113	0419	1.2F
	0702	1013	1.9E
	1333	1659	1.5F
	1954	2301	1.8E
25 F	0202	0514	1.6F
	0803	1111	2.2E
	1426	1741	1.7F
	2039	2342	2.1E
26 Sa	0247	0601	1.8F
	0859	1201	2.4E
	1513	1819	1.8F
	2120		
27 Su ●		0020	2.3E
	0331	0647	1.9F
	0951	1247	2.4E
	1558	1855	1.7F
	2158		
28 M		0058	2.4E
	0414	0734	1.9F
	1041	1333	2.2E
	1641	1930	1.6F
	2235		
29 Tu		0136	2.4E
	0457	0819	1.8F
	1130	1417	2.0E
	1724	2006	1.5F
	2311		
30 W		0214	2.3E
	0541	0858	1.6F
	1218	1459	1.8E
	1808	2044	1.3F
	2349		
31 Th		0252	2.2E
	0625	0929	1.5F
	1303	1541	1.5E
	1855	2124	1.2F

November

Day	Slack (h m)	Maximum (h m)	knots
1 F	0029	0331	2.0E
	0710	0957	1.3F
	1346	1625	1.3E
	1946	2208	1.0F
2 Sa	0112	0414	1.7E
	0758	1032	1.1F
	1431	1716	1.1E
	2041	2259	0.9F
3 Su	0202	0503	1.5E
	0851	1119	0.9F
	1521	1825	1.0E
	2143		
4 M ◐		0000	0.8F
	0303	0605	1.3E
	0954	1221	0.8F
	1622	1955	1.0E
	2249		
5 Tu		0112	0.8F
	0418	0720	1.2E
	1103	1346	0.8F
	1729	2110	1.2E
	2353		
6 W		0236	0.9F
	0536	0852	1.2E
	1210	1534	0.9F
	1828	2207	1.4E
7 Th	0049	0354	1.1F
	0642	1008	1.5E
	1307	1629	1.1F
	1918	2251	1.6E
8 F	0138	0448	1.3F
	0738	1057	1.7E
	1356	1707	1.3F
	2001	2325	1.8E
9 Sa	0222	0530	1.5F
	0827	1137	2.0E
	1440	1738	1.4F
	2039	2353	2.0E
10 Su	0302	0607	1.6F
	0912	1213	1.9E
	1520	1806	1.5F
	2114		
11 M		0019	2.1E
	0339	0640	1.7F
	0955	1247	1.9E
	1558	1836	1.5F
	2146		
12 Tu ○		0047	2.1E
	0413	0710	1.7F
	1035	1322	1.8E
	1636	1909	1.4F
	2219		
13 W		0120	2.1E
	0447	0740	1.6F
	1114	1358	1.8E
	1715	1946	1.3F
	2252		
14 Th		0155	2.1E
	0521	0813	1.6F
	1154	1436	1.7E
	1756	2027	1.3F
	2328		
15 F		0234	2.1E
	0557	0850	1.6F
	1234	1516	1.6E
	1842	2111	1.2F
16 Sa	0008	0316	2.1E
	0638	0931	1.5F
	1318	1600	1.5E
	1932	2158	1.1F
17 Su	0054	0403	1.9E
	0728	1019	1.5F
	1407	1651	1.4E
	2028	2251	1.0F
18 M	0147	0457	1.8E
	0828	1115	1.3F
	1505	1752	1.3E
	2130	2354	1.0F
19 Tu ○	0253	0601	1.6E
	0939	1224	1.2F
	1613	1903	1.3E
	2238		
20 W		0106	1.0F
	0413	0716	1.6E
	1056	1346	1.2F
	1724	2022	1.4E
	2344		
21 Th		0235	1.1F
	0536	0839	1.6E
	1209	1524	1.2F
	1827	2137	1.6E
22 F	0044	0402	1.3F
	0650	1001	1.8E
	1313	1631	1.4F
	1920	2233	1.8E
23 Sa	0138	0505	1.6F
	0755	1103	2.0E
	1408	1718	1.5F
	2006	2317	2.1E
24 Su	0227	0556	1.8F
	0852	1154	2.1E
	1456	1757	1.5F
	2048	2357	2.3E
25 M	0312	0643	1.9F
	0944	1239	2.1E
	1540	1831	1.5F
	2127		
26 Tu ●		0034	2.3E
	0354	0728	1.9F
	1032	1323	2.0E
	1622	1906	1.4F
	2206		
27 W		0111	2.3E
	0436	0809	1.7F
	1117	1404	1.8E
	1705	1943	1.3F
	2245		
28 Th		0149	2.2E
	0516	0841	1.6F
	1158	1444	1.7E
	1748	2023	1.2F
	2326		
29 F		0228	2.1E
	0558	0902	1.4F
	1237	1522	1.6E
	1835	2106	1.2F
30 Sa	0009	0308	1.9E
	0641	0928	1.3F
	1315	1601	1.5E
	1924	2152	1.1F

December

Day	Slack (h m)	Maximum (h m)	knots
1 Su	0056	0351	1.7E
	0727	1005	1.2F
	1354	1645	1.4E
	2016	2241	1.1F
2 M	0145	0439	1.5E
	0819	1051	1.1F
	1438	1738	1.3E
	2111	2337	1.0F
3 Tu	0241	0535	1.4E
	0917	1148	1.0F
	1530	1845	1.2E
	2211		
4 W ◐		0040	1.0F
	0347	0643	1.2E
	1023	1254	0.9F
	1633	2001	1.2E
	2314		
5 Th		0151	1.0F
	0502	0803	1.2E
	1131	1409	0.9F
	1736	2115	1.3E
6 F	0014	0314	1.0F
	0613	0933	1.3E
	1233	1530	1.0F
	1831	2210	1.5E
7 Sa	0107	0422	1.2F
	0715	1035	1.4E
	1327	1626	1.1F
	1918	2248	1.7E
8 Su	0154	0512	1.4F
	0809	1120	1.6E
	1414	1704	1.2F
	1959	2317	1.8E
9 M	0234	0550	1.5F
	0856	1157	1.6E
	1457	1736	1.3F
	2036	2345	2.0E
10 Tu	0310	0620	1.6F
	0938	1229	1.7E
	1536	1808	1.3F
	2112		
11 W		0016	2.1E
	0344	0644	1.6F
	1017	1303	1.7E
	1615	1843	1.3F
	2148		
12 Th ○		0051	2.1E
	0417	0712	1.7F
	1054	1339	1.7E
	1705	1923	1.3F
	2245		
13 F		0130	2.2E
	0452	0747	1.7F
	1133	1417	1.8E
	1738	2008	1.3F
	2308		
14 Sa		0213	2.2E
	0533	0829	1.7F
	1215	1459	1.8E
	1823	2055	1.3F
	2353		
15 Su		0258	2.2E
	0619	0914	1.7F
	1259	1543	1.8E
	1912	2143	1.3F
16 M	0044	0347	2.1E
	0712	1004	1.6F
	1347	1631	1.7E
	2004	2236	1.2F
17 Tu	0139	0441	2.0E
	0812	1059	1.5F
	1439	1727	1.6E
	2101	2335	1.2F
18 W ○	0242	0544	1.8E
	0919	1202	1.3F
	1538	1831	1.5E
	2205		
19 Th ◐		0044	1.1F
	0358	0656	1.6E
	1031	1313	1.2F
	1641	1941	1.5E
	2312		
20 F		0211	1.2F
	0521	0821	1.5E
	1144	1436	1.1F
	1744	2055	1.6E
21 Sa	0017	0349	1.3F
	0640	0950	1.6E
	1250	1557	1.1F
	1841	2202	1.8E
22 Su	0116	0458	1.6F
	0748	1056	1.7E
	1349	1654	1.2F
	1932	2253	2.0E
23 M	0208	0552	1.7F
	0846	1147	1.8E
	1439	1736	1.2F
	2018	2335	2.2E
24 Tu	0254	0639	1.8F
	0936	1232	1.8E
	1523	1813	1.3F
	2101		
25 W		0013	2.2E
	0335	0720	1.7F
	1019	1313	1.8E
	1605	1848	1.3F
	2143		
26 Th ●		0050	2.2E
	0414	0755	1.6F
	1057	1350	1.8E
	1646	1926	1.3F
	2225		
27 F		0128	2.1E
	0453	0818	1.5F
	1133	1426	1.8E
	1728	2008	1.3F
	2309		
28 Sa		0208	2.1E
	0533	0836	1.5F
	1208	1500	1.7E
	1813	2051	1.3F
	2353		
29 Su		0248	2.0E
	0615	0906	1.4F
	1244	1536	1.7E
	1859	2135	1.3F
30 M	0039	0331	1.9E
	0701	0944	1.4F
	1322	1615	1.6E
	1947	2220	1.3F
31 Tu	0126	0416	1.7E
	0750	1029	1.3F
	1403	1659	1.5E
	2038	2310	1.2F

Time meridian 75° W. 0000 is midnight. 1200 is noon. Times are not adjusted for Daylight Saving Time.

Tampa Bay Entrance (Egmont Channel), Florida, 2019

F–Flood, Dir. 120° True   E–Ebb, Dir. 298° True

January

Day	Slack (h m)	Maximum (h m, knots)
1 Tu	0616, 2250	0201 1.6E, 0925 1.3F, 1425 *, 2001 1.1F
2 W	0704, 2325	0244 1.8E, 1013 1.5F, 1519 *, 2044 1.1F
3 Th	0744, 2359	0321 2.0E, 1052 1.7F, 1605 *, 2121 1.1F
4 F	0818	0355 2.1E, 1127 1.7F, 1646 *, 2155 1.2F
5 Sa ●	0033, 0850	0428 2.1E, 1201 1.7F, 1725 *, 2228 1.2F
6 Su	0107, 0920	0502 2.1E, 1233 1.6F, 1803 *, 2303 1.2F
7 M	0144, 0951	0538 2.1E, 1307 1.6F, 1840 *, 2342 1.2F
8 Tu	0225, 1023, 1751, 2050	0616 2.0E, 1341 1.5F, 1919 0.3E
9 W	0308, 1055, 1813, 2148	0025 1.1F, 0655 1.9E, 1416 1.5F, 1957 0.4E
10 Th	0356, 1127, 1835, 2252	0114 1.0F, 0735 1.7E, 1450 1.4F, 2037 0.5E
11 F	0447, 1159, 1858	0209 0.9F, 0817 1.5E, 1523 1.4F, 2119 0.6E
12 Sa	0004, 0544, 1230, 1922	0308 0.8F, 0902 1.2E, 1556 1.3F, 2208 0.8E
13 Su	0123, 0655, 1300, 1950	0414 0.7F, 0957 0.8E, 1631 1.2F, 2303 1.0E
14 M ◐	0244, 0842, 1329, 2023	0535 0.7F, 1109 0.4E, 1710 1.0F
15 Tu	0403, 2103	0001 1.2E, 0717 0.8F, 1229 *, 1757 0.9F
16 W	0512, 2149	0055 1.5E, 0842 1.1F, 1340 *, 1855 0.9F
17 Th	0611, 2237	0145 1.8E, 0939 1.5F, 1440 *, 1956 1.0F
18 F	0701, 2326	0232 2.2E, 1024 1.8F, 1533 *, 2051 1.1F
19 Sa	0748	0320 2.4E, 1105 2.0F, 1622 *, 2140 1.3F
20 Su	0015, 0832	0408 2.6E, 1146 2.0F, 1708 *, 2227 1.4F
21 M ○	0105, 0915	0458 2.7E, 1227 2.0F, 1754 *, 2315 1.5F
22 Tu	0158, 0957, 1706, 2023	0549 2.6E, 1308 1.9F, 1840 0.4E
23 W	0255, 1038, 1730, 2136	0008 1.4F, 0639 2.3E, 1350 1.8F, 1927 0.6E
24 Th	0355, 1115, 1757, 2255	0107 1.3F, 0729 2.0E, 1430 1.7F, 2015 0.8E
25 F	0500, 1148, 1826	0214 1.1F, 0818 1.6E, 1509 1.5F, 2106 1.0E
26 Sa	0022, 0613, 1216, 1858	0327 1.0F, 0910 1.0E, 1546 1.4F, 2204 1.1E
27 Su ◐	0155, 0746, 1316, 1935	0448 0.8F, 1011 0.5E, 1623 1.2F, 2311 1.3E
28 M	0329, 2019	0628 0.8F, 1131 *, 1704 1.0F
29 Tu	0455, 2111	0024 1.4E, 0813 0.9F, 1258 *, 1757 0.9F
30 W	0603, 2207	0130 1.5E, 0923 1.2F, 1415 *, 1910 0.8F
31 Th	0655, 2259	0226 1.7E, 1009 1.4F, 1518 *, 2019 0.8F

February

Day	Slack (h m)	Maximum (h m, knots)
1 F	0735, 2345	0313 1.8E, 1046 1.6F, 1606 *, 2110 0.9F
2 Sa	0808	0351 1.9E, 1116 1.6F, 1644 *, 2149 1.1F
3 Su	0025, 0837	0424 1.9E, 1144 1.6F, 1716 *, 2225 1.2F
4 M ●	0103, 0903, 1608, 1928	0456 2.0E, 1210 1.6F, 1746 0.3E, 2300 1.3F
5 Tu	0142, 0927, 1622, 2013	0528 2.0E, 1235 1.6F, 1816 0.4E, 2338 1.3F
6 W	0222, 0952, 1638, 2059	0602 1.9E, 1301 1.5F, 1846 0.6E
7 Th	0305, 1017, 1656, 2148	0018 1.3F, 0636 1.8E, 1328 1.5F, 1917 0.8E
8 F	0352, 1042, 1715, 2240	0103 1.2F, 0712 1.6E, 1356 1.5F, 1948 0.9E
9 Sa	0442, 1107, 1737, 2338	0152 1.1F, 0750 1.4E, 1426 1.4F, 2022 1.1E
10 Su	0540, 1131, 1801	0247 1.0F, 0830 1.0E, 1457 1.3F, 2102 1.2E
11 M	0043, 0651, 1151, 1830	0348 0.9F, 0917 0.6E, 1530 1.2F, 2150 1.3E
12 Tu ◐	0158, 1907	0504 0.8F, 1022 *, 1606 1.0F, 2253 1.4E
13 W	0321, 1956	0649 0.9F, 1156 *, 1652 0.9F
14 Th	0444, 2101	0008 1.6E, 0828 1.2F, 1326 *, 1801 0.8F
15 F	0553, 2212	0118 1.8E, 0928 1.5F, 1436 *, 1932 0.9F
16 Sa	0649, 2317	0219 2.1E, 1012 1.8F, 1530 *, 2045 1.1F
17 Su	0736	0314 2.4E, 1050 2.0F, 1614 *, 2142 1.3F
18 M	0016, 0817, 1516, 1845	0405 2.5E, 1125 2.0F, 1655 0.4E, 2231 1.5F
19 Tu ○	0111, 0855, 1533, 1948	0454 2.5E, 1159 2.0F, 1734 0.7E, 2320 1.6F
20 W	0207, 0929, 1554, 2049	0541 2.3E, 1233 1.9F, 1815 0.9E
21 Th	0304, 1000, 1618, 2150	0011 1.6F, 0627 2.0E, 1306 1.8F, 1856 1.2E
22 F	0405, 1028, 1645, 2255	0107 1.5F, 0711 1.6E, 1339 1.6F, 1937 1.4E
23 Sa	0509, 1051, 1714	0208 1.3F, 0755 1.2E, 1412 1.5F, 2021 1.5E
24 Su	0005, 0622, 1108, 1747	0315 1.1F, 0841 0.7E, 1445 1.3F, 2108 1.5E
25 M	0124, 1823	0430 0.9F, 0936 *, 1519 1.1F, 2205 1.4E
26 Tu ◐	0251, 1906	0605 0.8F, 1055 *, 1557 0.9F, 2323 1.3E
27 W	0420, 2005	0757 0.9F, 1241 0.3F, 1648 0.7F
28 Th	0535, 2124	0053 1.3E, 0909 1.2F, 1411 *, 1820 0.6F

March

Day	Slack (h m)	Maximum (h m, knots)
1 F	0631, 2239	0206 1.4E, 0953 1.4F, 1514 *, 2005 0.6F
2 Sa	0712, 2337	0300 1.6E, 1026 1.5F, 1557 *, 2105 0.8F
3 Su	0744, 1447, 1819	0341 1.7E, 1052 1.6F, 1629 0.3E, 2147 1.0F
4 M	0022, 0809, 1454, 1903	0413 1.7E, 1115 1.6F, 1655 0.5E, 2222 1.2F
5 Tu	0102, 0831, 1502, 1942	0442 1.8E, 1134 1.6F, 1719 0.7E, 2256 1.3F
6 W ●	0141, 0851, 1512, 2019	0510 1.7E, 1154 1.6F, 1743 0.8E, 2331 1.4F
7 Th	0221, 0911, 1525, 2058	0540 1.6E, 1214 1.5F, 1807 1.0E
8 F	0304, 0931, 1542, 2140	0009 1.4F, 0613 1.5E, 1238 1.5F, 1834 1.2E
9 Sa	0352, 0952, 1604, 2225	0052 1.4F, 0648 1.3E, 1304 1.5F, 1904 1.4E
10 Su	0446, 1013, 1628, 2316	0139 1.3F, 0725 1.0E, 1333 1.4F, 1938 1.6E
11 M	0548, 1032, 1657	0233 1.3F, 0805 0.7E, 1404 1.3F, 2016 1.7E
12 Tu ◐	0015, 0710, 1042, 1730	0334 1.1F, 0852 0.3E, 1438 1.1F, 2103 1.7E
13 W	0127, 1812	0450 1.1F, 0957 *, 1518 1.0F, 2206 1.7E
14 Th ◐	0251, 1908	0630 1.1F, 1144 0.3F, 1610 0.8F, 2333 1.7E
15 F	0417, 2030	0808 1.3F, 1326 0.3F, 1735 0.7F
16 Sa	0529, 2202	0059 1.8E, 0907 1.6F, 1433 *, 1930 0.8F
17 Su	0626, 2319	0209 2.0E, 0949 1.8F, 1519 *, 2049 1.1F
18 M	0711, 1359, 1815	0306 2.1E, 1023 1.9F, 1557 0.6E, 2146 1.4F
19 Tu	0023, 0748, 1412, 1914	0356 2.1E, 1054 2.0F, 1633 0.9E, 2235 1.6F
20 W ○	0120, 0820, 1429, 2007	0441 2.0E, 1123 1.9F, 1708 1.3E, 2322 1.8F
21 Th	0217, 0847, 1449, 2058	0525 1.8E, 1151 1.8F, 1745 1.5E
22 F	0314, 0911, 1514, 2151	0011 1.7F, 0607 1.5E, 1218 1.7F, 1822 1.8E
23 Sa	0415, 0931, 1542, 2246	0102 1.6F, 0649 1.1E, 1247 1.5F, 1901 1.9E
24 Su	0522, 0948, 1613, 2345	0159 1.4F, 0732 0.7E, 1317 1.4F, 1940 1.9E
25 M	0641, 0958, 1646	0302 1.3F, 0817 0.3E, 1349 1.2F, 2023 1.8E
26 Tu ◐	0051, 1724	0412 1.1F, 0911 *, 1425 1.0F, 2112 1.6E
27 W	0206, 1807	0536 0.9F, 1031 0.3F, 1506 0.8F, 2220 1.3E
28 Th	0328, 1905	0718 1.0F, 1227 0.3F, 1604 0.6F
29 F	0445, 2037	0002 1.2E, 0834 1.1F, 1355 *, 1743 0.4F
30 Sa	0544, 2216	0130 1.2E, 0919 1.3F, 1451 *, 1947 0.5F
31 Su	0628, 1339, 1738, 2324	0228 1.3E, 0951 1.4F, 1529 0.4E, 2054 0.8F

Time meridian 75° W. 0000 is midnight. 1200 is noon. Times are not adjusted for Daylight Saving Time.
If three consecutive entries are marked (F) the middle one is not a true maximum but an intermediate value to show the current pattern.
* Current weak and variable.

Tampa Bay Entrance (Egmont Channel), Florida, 2019

F–Flood, Dir. 120° True   E–Ebb, Dir. 298° True

April

Day	Slack (h m)	Maximum (h m)	knots
1 M		0311	1.4E
	0700	1014	1.5F
	1343	1558	0.6E
	1829	2138	1.0F
2 Tu	0015	0344	1.4E
	0725	1033	1.5F
	1349	1622	0.8E
	1908	2214	1.2F
3 W	0058	0414	1.4E
	0744	1050	1.5F
	1356	1642	1.1E
	1942	2248	1.4F
4 Th	0139	0443	1.4E
	0802	1107	1.5F
	1405	1703	1.3E
	2016	2323	1.5F
5 F ●	0222	0513	1.2E
	0819	1126	1.5F
	1419	1726	1.5E
	2051		
6 Sa		0000	1.5F
	0308	0547	1.1E
	0836	1149	1.5F
	1438	1754	1.7E
	2130		
7 Su		0042	1.5F
	0402	0624	0.8E
	0855	1214	1.4F
	1503	1826	1.9E
	2213		
8 M		0131	1.5F
	0503	0704	0.6E
	0913	1244	1.3F
	1533	1904	2.0E
	2303		
9 Tu		0227	1.4F
	0617	0748	0.3E
	0925	1318	1.2F
	1608	1946	2.1E
10 W	0002	0332	1.3E
		0840	*
		1357	1.0F
	1648	2036	2.0E
11 Th	0112	0446	1.3E
		0955	*
		1446	0.9F
	1736	2142	1.8E
12 F ◗	0230	0612	1.3E
		1150	0.3F
		1555	0.7F
	1841	2312	1.7E
13 Sa	0347	0734	1.4F
		1321	*
		1740	0.6F
	2016		
14 Su		0043	1.7E
	0454	0832	1.6F
		1417	*
		1936	0.7F
	2202		
15 M		0154	1.7E
	0549	0914	1.7F
	1247	1458	0.6E
	1736	2053	1.1F
	2325		

Day	Slack (h m)	Maximum (h m)	knots
16 Tu		0250	1.7E
	0631	0947	1.8F
	1258	1534	1.1E
	1838	2149	1.4F
17 W	0032	0338	1.6E
	0705	1016	1.8F
	1314	1607	1.5E
	1928	2237	1.7F
18 Th	0131	0422	1.4E
	0731	1042	1.8F
	1333	1641	1.8E
	2015	2322	1.8F
19 F ○	0229	0504	1.2E
	0753	1107	1.7F
	1355	1715	2.0E
	2100		
20 Sa		0008	1.8F
	0329	0545	0.9E
	0811	1132	1.6F
	1421	1751	2.2E
	2146		
21 Su		0057	1.7F
	0433	0627	0.6E
	0828	1159	1.5F
	1450	1828	2.2E
	2234		
22 M		0150	1.5F
	0545	0711	0.3E
	0841	1229	1.3F
	1523	1907	2.1E
	2326		
23 Tu		0250	1.3F
		0759	*
		1304	1.2F
	1600	1948	1.9E
24 W	0022	0353	1.2F
		0855	*
		1345	1.0F
	1640	2035	1.7E
25 Th	0125	0502	1.1F
		1015	0.3F
		1436	0.7F
	1726	2135	1.4E
26 F ◗	0231	0618	1.1F
		1159	*
		1542	0.5F
	1822	2302	1.2E
27 Sa	0335	0730	1.1F
		1317	*
		1715	0.4F
	1948		
28 Su		0033	1.1E
	0433	0822	1.2F
	1225	1410	0.3E
	1615	1912	0.4F
	2139		
29 M		0137	1.1E
	0519	0856	1.3F
	1229	1447	0.6E
	1732	2031	0.7F
	2302		
30 Tu		0224	1.1E
	0554	0922	1.3F
	1236	1516	0.9E
	1822	2121	1.0F

May

Day	Slack (h m)	Maximum (h m)	knots
1 W	0002	0303	1.1E
	0621	0942	1.4F
	1243	1540	1.2E
	1900	2201	1.2F
2 Th	0052	0337	1.0E
	0641	1000	1.4F
	1252	1600	1.4E
	1934	2237	1.4F
3 F	0139	0410	0.9E
	0659	1019	1.4F
	1305	1622	1.7E
	2008	2314	1.5F
4 Sa ●	0228	0444	0.7E
	0715	1040	1.4F
	1323	1648	2.0E
	2043	2353	1.6F
5 Su	0323	0521	0.6E
	0731	1104	1.4F
	1347	1720	2.2E
	2123		
6 M		0037	1.6F
	0426	0603	0.4E
	0746	1132	1.4F
	1417	1758	2.3E
	2208		
7 Tu		0129	1.6F
		0648	*
		1205	1.3F
	1453	1841	2.3E
	2300		
8 W		0228	1.6F
		0739	*
		1245	1.1F
	1536	1930	2.3E
	2358		
9 Th		0332	1.5F
		0839	*
		1334	1.0F
	1625	2025	2.1E
10 F	0102	0437	1.5F
		1000	*
		1440	0.8F
	1722	2132	1.9E
11 Sa ◗	0208	0543	1.5F
		1141	*
		1605	0.6F
	1835	2256	1.6E
12 Su	0310	0648	1.5F
		1257	*
		1751	0.6F
	2016		
13 M		0022	1.5E
	0407	0743	1.5F
	1128	1349	0.6E
	1638	1938	0.8F
	2207		
14 Tu		0131	1.3E
	0456	0828	1.4F
	1144	1431	1.1E
	1752	2054	1.1F
	2335		
15 W		0227	1.2E
	0535	0903	1.6F
	1203	1508	1.5E
	1848	2150	1.4F

Day	Slack (h m)	Maximum (h m)	knots
16 Th	0046	0316	1.0E
	0606	0934	1.6F
	1224	1542	1.9E
	1935	2238	1.7F
17 F	0148	0400	0.8E
	0629	1001	1.6F
	1247	1615	2.1E
	2018	2322	1.7F
18 Sa ○	0249	0443	0.6E
	0647	1027	1.6F
	1312	1649	2.3E
	2059		
19 Su		0006	1.7F
	0353	0525	0.3E
	0703	1053	1.5F
	1340	1724	2.3E
	2141		
20 M		0052	1.6F
		0609	*
		1122	1.4F
	1412	1802	2.3E
	2224		
21 Tu		0141	1.5F
		0655	*
		1155	1.3F
	1448	1842	2.2E
	2309		
22 W		0235	1.4F
		0744	*
		1234	1.1F
	1528	1925	2.0E
	2357		
23 Th		0329	1.3F
		0840	*
		1322	0.9F
	1612	2012	1.8E
24 F	0047	0422	1.3F
		0948	*
		1419	0.7F
	1701	2105	1.6E
25 Sa	0137	0514	1.2F
		1109	*
		1527	0.6F
	1756	2210	1.3E
26 Su ◗	0225	0605	1.2F
		1221	*
		1646	0.4F
	1909	2327	1.1E
27 M	0311	0654	1.2F
	1100	1314	0.4E
	1547	1823	0.4F
	2051		
28 Tu		0036	0.9E
	0352	0737	1.2F
	1112	1355	0.8E
	1706	1956	0.6F
	2232		
29 W		0131	0.8E
	0429	0812	1.2F
	1125	1427	1.1E
	1801	2100	0.9F
	2349		
30 Th		0218	0.7E
	0459	0841	1.2F
	1138	1454	1.4E
	1844	2146	1.2F
31 F	0051	0259	0.6E
	0523	0907	1.3F
	1154	1519	1.7E
	1921	2227	1.4F

June

Day	Slack (h m)	Maximum (h m)	knots
1 Sa	0148	0338	0.5E
	0543	0932	1.3F
	1215	1546	2.0E
	1958	2306	1.6F
2 Su	0247	0417	0.3E
	0559	0959	1.4F
	1241	1619	2.3E
	2037	2348	1.7F
3 M ●		0500	*
		1029	1.4F
	1312	1657	2.4E
	2119		
4 Tu		0035	1.7F
		0547	*
		1103	1.4F
	1349	1742	2.5E
	2207		
5 W		0127	1.7F
		0639	*
		1143	1.3F
	1433	1831	2.5E
	2258		
6 Th		0224	1.7F
		0734	*
		1232	1.2F
	1523	1924	2.4E
	2352		
7 F		0320	1.7F
		0835	*
		1334	1.0F
	1620	2020	2.2E
8 Sa	0045	0413	1.6F
		0946	*
		1449	0.8F
	1724	2123	1.8E
9 Su	0137	0504	1.6F
		1106	*
		1615	0.7F
	1841	2237	1.5E
10 M	0226	0555	1.5F
	0950	1218	0.6E
	1506	1753	0.6F
	2023	2354	1.1E
11 Tu	0310	0645	1.4F
	1016	1314	1.0E
	1644	1936	0.8F
	2217		
12 W		0103	0.8E
	0350	0733	1.4F
	1044	1402	1.4E
	1756	2054	1.1F
	2353		
13 Th		0203	0.6E
	0424	0816	1.4F
	1113	1443	1.8E
	1852	2152	1.4F
14 F	0111	0255	0.4E
	0452	0853	1.4F
	1142	1521	2.0E
	1938	2239	1.6F
15 Sa	0220	0342	0.3E
	0514	0926	1.4F
	1212	1556	2.2E
	2019	2321	1.7F

Day	Slack (h m)	Maximum (h m)	knots
16 Su		0427	*
		0956	1.4F
	1242	1631	2.3E
	2058		
17 M ○		0511	*
		1027	1.4F
	1315	1708	2.3E
	2135		
18 Tu ●		0044	1.6F
		0555	*
		1059	1.4F
	1350	1746	2.3E
	2212		
19 W		0127	1.5F
		0640	*
		1136	1.3F
	1428	1827	2.2E
	2251		
20 Th		0211	1.4F
		0727	*
		1219	1.1F
	1511	1909	2.0E
	2329		
21 F		0255	1.4F
		0815	*
		1309	1.0F
	1557	1952	1.9E
22 Sa	0008	0335	1.4F
		0907	*
		1406	0.9F
	1646	2038	1.7E
23 Su	0046	0412	1.3F
		1005	*
		1508	0.7F
	1739	2128	1.4E
24 M	0122	0448	1.3F
		1106	*
		1615	0.7F
	1842	2227	1.1E
25 Tu ◐	0157	0526	1.2F
	0919	1203	0.6E
	1500	1735	0.5F
	2011	2334	0.8E
26 W	0231	0606	1.1F
	0943	1252	0.9E
	1623	1913	0.6F
	2204		
27 Th		0039	0.6E
	0304	0649	1.1F
	1008	1332	1.2E
	1730	2035	0.8F
	2344		
28 F		0136	0.4E
	0333	0733	1.1F
	1035	1408	1.5E
	1822	2132	1.1F
29 Sa		0226	*
		0814	1.2F
	1105	1443	1.9E
	1907	2218	1.4F
30 Su		0313	*
		0853	1.2F
	1137	1520	2.2E
	1949	2259	1.6F

Time meridian 75° W. 0000 is midnight. 1200 is noon. Times are not adjusted for Daylight Saving Time.
If three consecutive entries are marked (F) the middle one is not a true maximum but an intermediate value to show the current pattern.
* Current weak and variable.

Tampa Bay Entrance (Egmont Channel), Florida, 2019

F–Flood, Dir. 120° True   E–Ebb, Dir. 298° True

July

Days 1–15

Day	Slack (h m)	Maximum (h m)	knots
1 M		0358	*
		0931	1.3F
	1214	1601	2.4E
	2031	2342	1.7F
2 Tu ●		0445	*
		1010	1.4F
	1254	1646	2.6E
	2115		
3 W		0026	1.8F
		0535	*
		1052	1.4F
	1339	1735	2.6E
	2201		
4 Th		0114	1.8F
		0627	*
		1140	1.4F
	1430	1827	2.5E
	2247		
5 F		0203	1.7F
		0720	*
		1235	1.3F
	1526	1919	2.4E
	2333		
6 Sa		0250	1.7F
		0814	*
		1341	1.1F
	1627	2013	2.1E
7 Su	0016	0335	1.6F
	0723	0913	0.4E
	1122	1455	1.0F
	1733	2108	1.6E
8 M	0056	0417	1.5F
	0752	1018	0.7E
	1314	1615	0.8F
	1851	2211	1.2E
9 Tu ◑	0132	0459	1.4F
	0826	1128	0.9E
	1501	1747	0.7F
	2034	2323	0.7E
10 W	0205	0544	1.3F
	0905	1234	1.2E
	1636	1932	0.8F
	2241		
11 Th		0037	0.4E
	0233	0633	1.2F
	0947	1333	1.5E
	1752	2055	1.1F
12 F		0144	*
		0727	1.2F
	1030	1423	1.8E
	1850	2153	1.3F
13 Sa		0243	*
		0819	1.2F
	1111	1508	2.0E
	1937	2238	1.5F
14 Su		0334	*
		0902	1.2F
	1150	1548	2.1E
	2016	2317	1.6F
15 M		0420	*
		0941	1.3F
	1227	1624	2.1E
	2051	2353	1.6F

Days 16–31

Day	Slack (h m)	Maximum (h m)	knots
16 Tu ○		0502	*
		1016	1.3F
	1303	1700	2.2E
	2123		
17 W		0027	1.5F
		0542	*
		1051	1.3F
	1340	1736	2.1E
	2154		
18 Th		0101	1.5F
		0621	*
		1129	1.3F
	1420	1814	2.1E
	2225		
19 F		0134	1.4F
		0659	*
		1211	1.2F
	1502	1852	2.0E
	2255		
20 Sa		0208	1.4F
	0605	0738	0.3E
	0915	1257	1.1F
	1548	1930	1.8E
	2325		
21 Su		0240	1.4F
	0625	0818	0.4E
	1019	1349	1.0F
	1636	2009	1.6E
	2355		
22 M		0312	1.3F
	0647	0859	0.5E
	1128	1445	1.0F
	1727	2051	1.3E
23 Tu	0025	0343	1.3F
	0710	0944	0.7E
	1244	1545	0.8F
	1827	2139	1.0E
24 W ○	0053	0416	1.2F
	0737	1037	0.8E
	1406	1656	0.7F
	1949	2239	0.6E
25 Th	0120	0452	1.1F
	0810	1136	1.0E
	1531	1830	0.6F
	2153	2353	0.3E
26 F	0145	0535	1.0F
	0850	1235	1.3E
	1651	2012	0.8F
27 Sa		0105	*
		0629	1.0F
	0936	1328	1.6E
	1757	2119	1.2F
28 Su		0206	*
		0731	1.0F
	1025	1417	1.9E
	1851	2207	1.5F
29 M		0259	*
		0829	1.2F
	1114	1505	2.2E
	1937	2248	1.7F
30 Tu		0347	*
		0919	1.3F
	1202	1552	2.4E
	2021	2327	1.8F
31 W ●		0433	*
		1006	1.5F
	1251	1641	2.6E
	2103		

August

Days 1–15

Day	Slack (h m)	Maximum (h m)	knots
1 Th		0006	1.8F
		0519	*
		1053	1.6F
	1342	1731	2.6E
	2143		
2 F		0046	1.8F
	0437	0606	0.3E
	0741	1144	1.6F
	1436	1820	2.4E
	2223		
3 Sa		0126	1.7F
	0502	0653	0.5E
	0854	1240	1.5F
	1534	1909	2.1E
	2300		
4 Su		0206	1.6F
	0529	0741	0.7E
	1010	1343	1.3F
	1637	1957	1.7E
	2334		
5 M		0246	1.5F
	0558	0831	1.0E
	1132	1452	1.1F
	1744	2047	1.3E
6 Tu	0004	0324	1.4F
	0632	0926	1.1E
	1303	1609	0.9F
	1905	2144	0.8E
7 W ◑	0030	0402	1.3F
	0710	1032	1.2E
	1440	1738	0.8F
	2058	2254	0.3E
8 Th	0050	0444	1.1F
	0756	1148	1.3E
	1616	1925	0.8F
9 F		0018	*
		0535	1.0F
	0852	1304	1.5E
	1738	2052	1.1F
10 Sa		0136	*
		0644	0.9F
	0953	1410	1.6E
	1839	2148	1.3F
11 Su		0241	*
		0759	0.9F
	1051	1503	1.8E
	1926	2229	1.5F
12 M		0334	*
		0855	1.1F
	1140	1546	1.9E
	2003	2303	1.5F
13 Tu		0415	*
		0938	1.2F
	1223	1621	1.9E
	2034	2332	1.5F
14 W		0449	*
		1014	1.3F
	1301	1653	2.0E
	2100	2358	1.5F
15 Th ○	0345	0521	0.3E
	0701	1049	1.4F
	1338	1724	2.0E
	2125		

Days 16–31

Day	Slack (h m)	Maximum (h m)	knots
16 F		0022	1.4F
	0400	0552	0.4E
	0746	1124	1.4F
	1417	1756	1.9E
	2148		
17 Sa		0047	1.4F
	0416	0622	0.6E
	0831	1202	1.4F
	1458	1829	1.8E
	2212		
18 Su		0113	1.4F
	0434	0654	0.7E
	0919	1244	1.3F
	1542	1904	1.6E
	2237		
19 M		0141	1.3F
	0455	0726	0.9E
	1009	1331	1.2F
	1630	1940	1.4E
	2302		
20 Tu		0211	1.3F
	0518	0800	1.0E
	1104	1423	1.1F
	1722	2019	1.1E
	2327		
21 W		0243	1.2F
	0544	0838	1.1E
	1205	1520	1.0F
	1824	2102	0.8E
	2351		
22 Th		0317	1.1F
	0614	0923	1.2E
	1318	1628	0.9F
	1951	2159	0.4E
23 F ◑	0011	0354	1.0F
	0652	1023	1.2E
	1443	1800	0.8F
	2321		
24 Sa		0440	0.9F
	0742	1141	1.4E
	1613	1950	0.9F
25 Su		0050	*
		0543	0.8F
	0847	1257	1.6E
	1730	2102	1.2F
26 M		0159	*
		0708	0.9F
	0959	1401	1.9E
	1830	2149	1.5F
27 Tu		0253	*
		0823	1.1F
	1104	1455	2.1E
	1918	2227	1.7F
28 W		0337	*
		0920	1.4F
	1202	1546	2.3E
	2000	2301	1.8F
29 Th	0238	0417	0.4E
	0610	1009	1.6F
	1256	1633	2.4E
	2037	2334	1.8F
30 F ●	0256	0457	0.7E
	0712	1057	1.8F
	1349	1720	2.3E
	2112		
31 Sa		0007	1.7F
	0317	0538	0.9E
	0812	1146	1.8F
	1445	1806	2.0E
	2144		

September

Days 1–15

Day	Slack (h m)	Maximum (h m)	knots
1 Su		0040	1.6F
	0343	0620	1.2E
	0912	1240	1.7F
	1544	1851	1.7E
	2213		
2 M		0114	1.5F
	0411	0704	1.4E
	1015	1339	1.5F
	1648	1937	1.3E
	2239		
3 Tu		0149	1.4F
	0444	0749	1.5E
	1124	1445	1.3F
	1759	2024	0.8E
	2302		
4 W		0226	1.2F
	0520	0837	1.5E
	1242	1558	1.1F
	1926	2118	0.4E
	2318		
5 Th ◐		0304	1.1F
	0601	0935	1.4E
	1411	1725	0.9F
		2231	*
6 F		0348	0.9F
	0650	1054	1.3E
	1545	1911	0.9F
7 Sa		0010	*
		0445	0.8F
	0756	1234	1.3E
	1709	2037	1.1F
8 Su		0137	*
		0614	0.7F
	0921	1355	1.4E
	1813	2130	1.3F
9 M		0240	*
		0752	0.8F
	1039	1452	1.5E
	1859	2206	1.4F
10 Tu		0325	*
		0854	1.0F
	1136	1534	1.6E
	1934	2235	1.5F
11 W	0211	0359	0.4E
	0558	0936	1.2F
	1222	1606	1.7E
	2001	2259	1.5F
12 Th	0221	0427	0.6E
	0642	1012	1.4F
	1301	1635	1.7E
	2024	2318	1.4F
13 F ○	0232	0452	0.7E
	0720	1044	1.5F
	1337	1702	1.7E
	2043	2337	1.4F
14 Sa	0243	0516	0.9E
	0756	1117	1.5F
	1415	1731	1.6E
	2102	2356	1.4F
15 Su	0257	0541	1.1F
	0833	1153	1.5F
	1456	1802	1.5E
	2122		

Days 16–30

Day	Slack (h m)	Maximum (h m)	knots
16 M		0018	1.3F
	0314	0608	1.2E
	0912	1232	1.5F
	1541	1836	1.3E
	2143		
17 Tu		0044	1.3F
	0336	0638	1.4E
	0954	1316	1.4F
	1631	1912	1.0E
	2205		
18 W		0113	1.2F
	0402	0711	1.5E
	1042	1406	1.3F
	1728	1951	0.8E
	2228		
19 Th		0146	1.1F
	0433	0749	1.5E
	1137	1504	1.2F
	1837	2036	0.4E
	2246		
20 F		0223	1.0F
	0509	0834	1.5E
	1245	1614	1.0F
		2135	*
21 Sa ◑		0306	0.9F
	0552	0934	1.5E
	1409	1743	1.0F
		2309	*
22 Su		0401	0.7F
	0650	1059	1.4E
	1539	1924	1.1F
23 M		0049	*
		0520	0.7F
	0812	1234	1.5E
	1658	2034	1.3F
24 Tu		0155	*
		0704	0.8F
	0946	1347	1.8E
	1759	2120	1.6F
25 W	0109	0242	0.3E
	0430	0825	1.1F
	1103	1444	2.0E
	1847	2156	1.7F
26 Th	0119	0320	0.6E
	0543	0923	1.2F
	1207	1533	2.0E
	1926	2227	1.8F
27 F	0133	0356	1.0E
	0640	1012	1.8F
	1304	1619	2.0E
	1959	2256	1.7F
28 Sa ●	0151	0432	1.3E
	0733	1059	1.9F
	1359	1703	1.8E
	2028	2324	1.7F
29 Su	0213	0509	1.6E
	0824	1146	2.0F
	1456	1746	1.5E
	2053	2352	1.6F
30 M	0238	0548	1.8E
	0916	1237	1.8F
	1557	1830	1.1E
	2116		

Time meridian 75° W. 0000 is midnight. 1200 is noon. Times are not adjusted for Daylight Saving Time.
If three consecutive entries are marked (F) the middle one is not a true maximum but an intermediate value to show the current pattern.
* Current weak and variable.

Tampa Bay Entrance (Egmont Channel), Florida, 2019

F–Flood, Dir. 120° True   E–Ebb, Dir. 298° True

October

Day	Slack (h m)	Maximum (h m / knots)
1 Tu	0307, 1011, 1704, 2136	0022 1.4F, 0628 1.9E, 1332 1.6F, 1915 0.7E
2 W	0341, 1110, 1820, 2152	0054 1.3F, 0711 1.9E, 1435 1.4F, 2002 0.4E
3 Th	0419, 1217, 2057	0129 1.1F, 0756 1.8E, 1546 1.2F, *
4 F	0502, 1335, 2216	0211 0.9F, 0847 1.6E, 1706 1.0F, *
5 Sa ◐	0553, 1500	0301 0.8F, 0958 1.3E, 1839 1.0F
6 Su	0702, 1620	0004 *, 0410 0.6F, 1149 1.1E, 2000 1.1F
7 M	0844, 1725	0127 *, 0551 0.5F, 1322 1.2E, 2053 1.2F
8 Tu	1021, 1812	0221 *, 0740 0.6F, 1421 1.3E, 2129 1.3F
9 W	0058, 0523, 1128, 1847	0300 0.5F, 0845 0.9E, 1503 1.3F, 2155 1.4E
10 Th	0108, 0611, 1217, 1913	0331 0.7F, 0929 1.2E, 1537 1.4F, 2215 1.4E
11 F	0118, 0649, 1258, 1933	0356 0.9E, 1004 1.4F, 1606 1.4E, 2233 1.4F
12 Sa	0126, 0722, 1337, 1950	0417 1.2E, 1036 1.5F, 1634 1.3E, 2249 1.4F
13 Su ○	0137, 0754, 1416, 2007	0438 1.4E, 1109 1.6F, 1703 1.2E, 2307 1.3F
14 M	0150, 0827, 1459, 2024	0500 1.5E, 1143 1.7F, 1735 1.0E, 2328 1.3F
15 Tu	0209, 0903, 1548, 2044	0527 1.7E, 1221 1.6F, 1810 0.8E, 2353 1.2F
16 W	0234, 0942, 1643, 2103	0558 1.8E, 1305 1.6F, 1848 0.6E
17 Th	0304, 1028, 1749, 2122	0022 1.2F, 0635 1.9E, 1357 1.5F, 1931 0.4E
18 F	0339, 1122	0057 1.0F, 0717 1.9E, 1458 1.4F, 2020 *
19 Sa	0421, 1228	0138 0.9F, 0805 1.8E, 1608 1.3F, 2127 *
20 Su	0512, 1346, 2309	0231 0.8F, 0906 1.7E, 1726 1.2F, *
21 M ○	0618, 1506	0342 0.6F, 1033 1.5E, 1847 1.3F
22 Tu	0753, 1617, 2355	0042 *, 0518 0.6F, 1213 1.5E, 1953 1.4F
23 W	0339, 0942, 1716	0140 0.3F, 0706 0.8F, 1328 1.5E, 2040 1.5F
24 Th	0004, 0503, 1108, 1803	0222 0.7E, 0827 1.1F, 1426 1.6E, 2117 1.6F
25 F	0019, 0605, 1216, 1840	0258 1.1E, 0925 1.5F, 1516 1.5E, 2147 1.7F
26 Sa	0037, 0656, 1316, 1910	0333 1.6E, 1014 1.8F, 1601 1.4E, 2215 1.6F
27 Su ●	0058, 0743, 1414, 1934	0407 1.9E, 1100 2.0F, 1644 1.1E, 2242 1.6F
28 M	0121, 0829, 1513, 1955	0442 2.2E, 1145 2.0F, 1727 0.9E, 2309 1.5F
29 Tu	0148, 0915, 1616, 2013	0519 2.3E, 1233 1.9F, 1810 0.6E, 2337 1.4F
30 W	0219, 1004, 1727, 2030	0559 2.3E, 1326 1.7F, 1856 0.3E
31 Th	0254, 1056	0008 1.3F, 0640 2.2E, 1425 1.5F, 1945 *

November

Day	Slack (h m)	Maximum (h m / knots)
1 F	0334, 1153	0045 1.1F, 0724 1.9E, 1529 1.3F, 2042 *
2 Sa	0419, 1257	0130 0.9F, 0814 1.7E, 1637 1.2F, 2158 *
3 Su	0511, 1404	0229 0.7F, 0915 1.4E, 1747 1.1F, 2336 *
4 M ◐	0617, 1511	0344 0.5F, 1046 1.1E, 1856 1.1F
5 Tu	0755, 1610, 2339	0052 *, 0521 0.4F, 1223 1.0E, 1952 1.1F
6 W	0410, 0948, 1659, 2352	0144 0.4E, 0709 0.5F, 1329 1.0E, 2032 1.2F
7 Th	0518, 1109, 1738	0223 0.7E, 0825 0.8F, 1418 1.0E, 2101 1.2F
8 F	0004, 0605, 1208, 1807	0254 1.0E, 0914 1.1F, 1458 1.0E, 2123 1.2F
9 Sa	0015, 0643, 1256, 1829	0319 1.3E, 0953 1.3F, 1532 0.9E, 2142 1.3F
10 Su	0026, 0716, 1340, 1848	0340 1.5E, 1027 1.5F, 1604 0.8E, 2201 1.3F
11 M	0040, 0748, 1425, 1904	0401 1.7E, 1101 1.7F, 1636 0.7E, 2222 1.3F
12 Tu ○	0058, 0820, 1513, 1921	0425 1.9E, 1136 1.7F, 1710 0.5E, 2245 1.3F
13 W	0121, 0856, 1608, 1938	0455 2.1E, 1216 1.7F, 1749 0.4E, 2313 1.2F
14 Th	0150, 0936	0531 2.2E, 1301 1.7F, 1831 *, 2345 1.1F
15 F	0225, 1023	0612 2.2E, 1355 1.7F, 1919 *
16 Sa	0307, 1117	0023 1.0F, 0659 2.2E, 1455 1.5F, 2014 *
17 Su	0356, 1218	0113 0.9F, 0752 2.0E, 1557 1.5F, 2122 *
18 M	0455, 1323	0218 0.7F, 0854 1.8E, 1659 1.4F, 2251 *
19 Tu ○	0608, 1427, 2221	0341 0.6F, 1014 1.5E, 1800 1.4F
20 W	0215, 0749, 1527, 2239	0013 0.3E, 0520 0.6F, 1146 1.3E, 1859 1.4F
21 Th	0401, 0945, 1620, 2301	0110 0.7E, 0705 0.8F, 1303 1.2E, 1949 1.4F
22 F	0517, 1119, 1705, 2324	0155 1.1E, 0827 1.2F, 1404 1.1E, 2030 1.4F
23 Sa	0615, 1233, 1741, 2348	0234 1.6E, 0927 1.5F, 1456 0.9E, 2105 1.5F
24 Su	0704, 1337, 1809	0310 2.0E, 1017 1.8F, 1543 0.7E, 2136 1.5F
25 M	0014, 0749, 1438, 1832	0345 2.3E, 1101 2.0F, 1628 0.5E, 2205 1.5F
26 Tu ●	0043, 0832, 1540, 1852	0421 2.4E, 1145 2.0F, 1712 0.4E, 2234 1.4F
27 W	0113, 0914	0458 2.5E, 1230 1.9F, 1756 *, 2305 1.3F
28 Th	0147, 0957	0538 2.4E, 1318 1.7F, 1842 *, 2339 1.2F
29 F	0225, 1042	0620 2.2E, 1410 1.5F, 1931 *
30 Sa	0307, 1128	0020 1.1F, 0704 2.0E, 1503 1.4F, 2025 *

December

Day	Slack (h m)	Maximum (h m / knots)
1 Su	0354, 1217	0109 0.9F, 0751 1.8E, 1555 1.3F, 2127 *
2 M	0447, 1306	0210 0.7F, 0844 1.5E, 1644 1.2F, 2240 *
3 Tu	0548, 1355, 2151	0321 0.5F, 0948 1.2E, 1732 1.1F, 2352 0.3E
4 W ◐	0201, 0708, 1442, 2214	0442 0.5F, 1108 0.9E, 1820 1.1F
5 Th	0338, 0859, 1526, 2235	0049 0.6E, 0618 0.5F, 1224 0.8E, 1906 1.0F
6 F	0452, 1045, 1606, 2253	0133 0.9E, 0751 0.7F, 1325 0.6E, 1946 1.0F
7 Sa	0546, 1201, 1641, 2311	0208 1.1E, 0854 1.0F, 1414 0.5E, 2020 1.0F
8 Su	0628, 1302, 1710, 2330	0237 1.4E, 0940 1.3F, 1457 0.5E, 2049 1.1F
9 M	0705, 1355, 1733, 2352	0303 1.7E, 1018 1.5F, 1536 0.4E, 2116 1.1F
10 Tu	0740, 1447, 1753	0329 2.0E, 1055 1.7F, 1614 0.3E, 2144 1.2F
11 W	0018, 0815	0359 2.2E, 1132 1.7F, 1653 *, 2214 1.2F
12 Th ○	0049, 0853	0434 2.3E, 1212 1.8F, 1735 *, 2248 1.2F
13 F	0125, 0935	0516 2.4E, 1257 1.8F, 1821 *, 2326 1.2F
14 Sa	0208, 1021	0602 2.4E, 1347 1.7F, 1911 *
15 Su	0257, 1110	0013 1.1F, 0653 2.3E, 1440 1.7F, 2004 *
16 M	0353, 1201	0111 1.0F, 0746 2.1E, 1531 1.6F, 2104 *
17 Tu	0457, 1251	0223 0.8F, 0845 1.8E, 1620 1.5F, 2212 0.4E
18 W ○	0029, 0613, 1340, 2049	0344 0.7F, 0953 1.4E, 1708 1.4F, 2325 0.7E
19 Th	0226, 0753, 1426, 2122	0517 0.7F, 1114 1.0E, 1757 1.3F
20 F	0402, 0957, 1509, 2156	0029 1.0E, 0700 0.8F, 1234 0.7E, 1848 1.2F
21 Sa	0519, 1145, 1549, 2231	0123 1.4E, 0828 1.2F, 1342 0.5E, 1938 1.2F
22 Su	0619, 1309, 1625, 2307	0209 1.8E, 0931 1.5F, 1441 0.3E, 2024 1.2F
23 M	0709, 2342	0251 2.1E, 1021 1.8F, 1533 *, 2104 1.3F
24 Tu	0753	0331 2.3E, 1104 1.9F, 1621 *, 2140 1.3F
25 W	0017, 0833	0409 2.4E, 1144 1.9F, 1705 *, 2214 1.3F
26 Th ●	0053, 0911	0447 2.4E, 1224 1.8F, 1748 *, 2250 1.3F
27 F	0131, 0947	0527 2.3E, 1304 1.7F, 1831 *, 2327 1.2F
28 Sa	0211, 1024	0608 2.2E, 1345 1.6F, 1914 *
29 Su	0255, 1100	0010 1.1F, 0650 2.0E, 1426 1.5F, 1958 *
30 M	0343, 1136, 1908, 2230	0059 1.0F, 0732 1.8E, 1504 1.4F, 2044 0.3E
31 Tu	0434, 1212, 1934, 2350	0155 0.8F, 0816 1.6E, 1539 1.3F, 2135 0.4E

Time meridian 75° W. 0000 is midnight. 1200 is noon. Times are not adjusted for Daylight Saving Time.
If three consecutive entries are marked (F) the middle one is not a true maximum but an intermediate value to show the current pattern.
* Current weak and variable.

Tampa Bay (Sunshine Skyway Bridge), Florida, 2019

F–Flood, Dir. 059° True   E–Ebb, Dir. 238° True

January

Date	Slack (h m)	Maximum (h m, knots)
1 Tu	0559, 1250, 1616, 2300	0218 1.4E, 0904 1.0F, 1436 0.3E, 1955 1.0F
2 W	0656, 2337	0309 1.6E, 1004 1.2F, 1533 *, 2036 1.0F
3 Th	0743	0353 1.7E, 1054 1.3F, 1622 *, 2113 1.0F
4 F	0011, 0823	0430 1.8E, 1138 1.4F, 1704 *, 2146 1.0F
5 Sa ●	0042, 0859	0500 1.8E, 1216 1.4F, 1740 *, 2220 1.0F
6 Su	0114, 0932	0526 1.8E, 1249 1.3F, 1811 *, 2255 1.1F
7 M	0147, 1002	0552 1.8E, 1318 1.3F, 1841 *, 2334 1.1F
8 Tu	0224, 1032	0622 1.8E, 1346 1.3F, 1913 *
9 W	0305, 1103	0017 1.1F, 0656 1.8E, 1415 1.3F, 1949 *
10 Th	0351, 1134, 1844, 2229	0103 1.0F, 0736 1.7E, 1446 1.3F, 2031 0.3E
11 F	0443, 1207, 1907, 2343	0155 1.0F, 0820 1.5E, 1520 1.3F, 2118 0.5E
12 Sa	0540, 1240, 1933	0254 0.9F, 0909 1.3E, 1556 1.2F, 2208 0.6E
13 Su	0103, 0649, 1314, 2004	0402 0.8F, 1003 1.0E, 1634 1.1F, 2302 0.8E
14 M ◑	0230, 0819, 1348, 2039	0520 0.7F, 1103 0.6E, 1716 1.0F
15 Tu	0356, 1012, 1423, 2118	0001 1.0E, 0654 0.7F, 1213 0.3E, 1803 1.0F
16 W	0513, 2200	0107 1.2E, 0823 0.9F, 1334 *, 1855 0.9F
17 Th	0617, 2246	0209 1.5E, 0931 1.1F, 1446 *, 1949 1.0F
18 F	0711, 2334	0302 1.7E, 1027 1.3F, 1544 *, 2039 1.1F
19 Sa	0759	0351 2.0E, 1116 1.5F, 1634 *, 2127 1.2F
20 Su	0024, 0845	0438 2.1E, 1159 1.5F, 1718 *, 2216 1.3F
21 M ○	0115, 0928	0523 2.2E, 1238 1.6F, 1800 *, 2308 1.4F
22 Tu	0208, 1010, 1711, 2016	0609 2.2E, 1315 1.5F, 1842 0.3E
23 W	0303, 1050, 1732, 2128	0003 1.4F, 0654 2.1E, 1351 1.5F, 1926 0.5E
24 Th	0402, 1127, 1757, 2244	0059 1.3F, 0741 1.8E, 1428 1.4F, 2015 0.7E
25 F	0506, 1203, 1827	0201 1.2F, 0832 1.5E, 1506 1.3F, 2110 0.8E
26 Sa	0004, 0617, 1237, 1902	0311 1.0F, 0927 1.1E, 1546 1.2F, 2211 1.0E
27 Su ◐	0130, 0744, 1309, 1943	0431 0.9F, 1028 0.7E, 1628 1.1F, 2317 1.1E
28 M	0303, 0939, 1341, 2030	0605 0.8F, 1139 0.3E, 1714 0.9F
29 Tu	0432, 2122	0034 1.2E, 0747 0.9F, 1309 *, 1808 0.8F
30 W	0547, 2215	0153 1.3E, 0905 1.0F, 1432 *, 1912 0.7F
31 Th	0646, 2305	0256 1.4E, 1003 1.2F, 1536 *, 2010 0.8F

February

Date	Slack (h m)	Maximum (h m, knots)
1 F	0733, 2349	0345 1.5E, 1051 1.3F, 1625 *, 2056 0.8F
2 Sa	0810	0423 1.6E, 1128 1.4F, 1703 *, 2136 0.9F
3 Su	0028, 0841	0452 1.7E, 1159 1.4F, 1732 *, 2213 1.0F
4 M ●	0104, 0908	0515 1.7E, 1223 1.4F, 1756 *, 2251 1.0F
5 Tu	0141, 0931, 1637, 2003	0538 1.7E, 1243 1.3F, 1820 0.3E, 2331 1.1F
6 W	0221, 0955, 1646, 2050	0606 1.7E, 1303 1.3F, 1845 0.5E
7 Th	0304, 1020, 1700, 2141	0013 1.2F, 0638 1.7E, 1326 1.4F, 1915 0.6E
8 F	0351, 1047, 1720, 2237	0057 1.2F, 0714 1.6E, 1352 1.3F, 1950 0.8E
9 Sa	0443, 1115, 1743, 2336	0146 1.1F, 0754 1.3E, 1423 1.3F, 2029 0.9E
10 Su	0541, 1144, 1811	0241 1.0F, 0840 1.1E, 1457 1.2F, 2114 1.0E
11 M	0042, 0652, 1211, 1844	0345 0.9F, 0931 0.7E, 1535 1.1F, 2205 1.1E
12 Tu ◑	0200, 0830, 1235, 1923	0501 0.8F, 1031 0.4E, 1616 1.0F, 2304 1.2E
13 W	0326, 2011	0640 0.8F, 1146 *, 1706 0.9F
14 Th	0449, 2110	0017 1.3E, 0817 1.0F, 1323 *, 1808 0.8F
15 F	0558, 2214	0140 1.5E, 0923 1.2F, 1445 *, 1920 0.8F
16 Sa	0654, 2318	0246 1.7E, 1014 1.4F, 1541 *, 2026 1.0F
17 Su	0740	0340 1.9E, 1055 1.5F, 1624 *, 2123 1.2F
18 M	0019, 0822, 1525, 1842	0427 2.1E, 1131 1.6F, 1703 0.3E, 2217 1.4F
19 Tu ○	0117, 0859, 1537, 1942	0512 2.1E, 1203 1.6F, 1739 0.6E, 2310 1.5F
20 W	0213, 0935, 1554, 2041	0555 2.0E, 1233 1.5F, 1817 0.8E
21 Th	0310, 1007, 1616, 2142	0004 1.5F, 0637 1.8E, 1304 1.5F, 1856 1.1E
22 F	0409, 1038, 1642, 2246	0058 1.5F, 0720 1.5E, 1335 1.4F, 1938 1.2E
23 Sa	0513, 1107, 1713, 2354	0156 1.4F, 0805 1.1E, 1408 1.3F, 2025 1.3E
24 Su	0625, 1134, 1748	0301 1.2F, 0856 0.7E, 1445 1.1F, 2118 1.3E
25 M	0109, 0800, 1154, 1827	0418 1.0F, 0956 0.3E, 1525 1.0F, 2220 1.2E
26 Tu ◐	0235, 1914	0551 0.9F, 1112 *, 1610 0.8F, 2339 1.2E
27 W	0404, 2013	0738 0.9F, 1300 *, 1707 0.6F
28 Th	0522, 2123	0120 1.2E, 0856 1.1F, 1435 *, 1825 0.5F

March

Date	Slack (h m)	Maximum (h m, knots)
1 F	0622, 2232	0236 1.3E, 0949 1.2F, 1535 *, 1949 0.5F
2 Sa	0707, 2329	0326 1.4E, 1030 1.3F, 1616 *, 2047 0.6F
3 Su	0741	0403 1.5E, 1100 1.3F, 1647 *, 2131 0.8F
4 M	0017, 0807, 1516, 1902	0430 1.5E, 1123 1.3F, 1710 0.4E, 2209 1.0F
5 Tu	0059, 0829, 1518, 1940	0452 1.5E, 1141 1.3F, 1730 0.5E, 2248 1.1F
6 W ●	0140, 0849, 1522, 2018	0516 1.5E, 1157 1.4F, 1750 0.7E, 2327 1.2F
7 Th	0222, 0909, 1533, 2100	0544 1.5E, 1214 1.4F, 1814 0.9E
8 F	0306, 0932, 1549, 2145	0008 1.3F, 0616 1.4E, 1236 1.4F, 1841 1.1E
9 Sa	0355, 0956, 1611, 2233	0051 1.3F, 0651 1.2E, 1302 1.4F, 1913 1.3E
10 Su	0449, 1021, 1636, 2326	0138 1.2F, 0731 1.0E, 1332 1.3F, 1948 1.4E
11 M	0552, 1046, 1706	0232 1.1F, 0815 0.7E, 1405 1.2F, 2030 1.4E
12 Tu	0027, 0713, 1105, 1740	0336 1.0F, 0907 0.4E, 1442 1.0F, 2120 1.4E
13 W	0140, 1822	0455 0.9F, 1012 *, 1526 0.9F, 2223 1.3E
14 Th ◑	0304, 1918	0636 0.9F, 1139 *, 1622 0.7F, 2343 1.3E
15 F	0425, 2033	0807 1.1F, 1331 *, 1738 0.7F
16 Sa	0533, 2157	0118 1.4E, 0905 1.3F, 1444 *, 1910 0.7F
17 Su	0626, 2315	0231 1.6E, 0947 1.4F, 1529 *, 2026 0.9F
18 M	0710, 1409, 1806	0325 1.8E, 1021 1.5F, 1606 0.5E, 2125 1.2F
19 Tu	0022, 0747, 1417, 1904	0411 1.8E, 1051 1.5F, 1640 0.8E, 2219 1.4F
20 W ○	0122, 0820, 1431, 1957	0454 1.8E, 1119 1.5F, 1714 1.1E, 2311 1.6F
21 Th	0220, 0849, 1450, 2049	0535 1.6E, 1147 1.5F, 1749 1.4E
22 F	0317, 0917, 1513, 2143	0002 1.6F, 0615 1.4E, 1215 1.5F, 1826 1.6E
23 Sa	0416, 0943, 1541, 2240	0054 1.6F, 0656 1.1E, 1245 1.4F, 1904 1.7E
24 Su	0522, 1006, 1612, 2340	0148 1.4F, 0739 0.7E, 1316 1.2F, 1944 1.6E
25 M	0640, 1023, 1646	0250 1.2F, 0827 0.4E, 1350 1.1F, 2030 1.5E
26 Tu	0046, 0928, 1723	0404 1.0F, 1427 *, 2124 1.4E
27 W ◐	0202, 1805	0534 0.9F, 1052 *, 1512 0.7F, 2235 1.2F
28 Th	0325, 1900	0715 0.9F, 1251 0.3F, 1611 0.5F
29 F	0439, 2020	0017 1.1E, 0828 1.1F, 1425 *, 1737 0.3F
30 Sa	0537, 2151	0151 1.1E, 0915 1.2F, 1515 *, 1923 0.4F
31 Su	0621, 1407, 1735, 2305	0246 1.2E, 0949 1.3F, 1548 0.3E, 2032 0.6F

Time meridian 75° W. 0000 is midnight. 1200 is noon. Times are not adjusted for Daylight Saving Time.
If three consecutive entries are marked (F) the middle one is not a true maximum but an intermediate value to show the current pattern.
* Current weak and variable.

Tampa Bay (Sunshine Skyway Bridge), Florida, 2019

F–Flood, Dir. 059° True   E–Ebb, Dir. 238° True

April

Day	Slack h m	Max h m	knots
1 M		0323	1.3E
	0653	1014	1.3F
	1405	1614	0.5E
	1825	2120	0.8F
2 Tu	0004	0353	1.3E
	0718	1032	1.3F
	1404	1636	0.7E
	1905	2201	1.0F
3 W	0053	0420	1.3E
	0738	1048	1.3F
	1407	1656	0.9E
	1942	2241	1.2F
4 Th	0139	0448	1.2E
	0757	1104	1.3F
	1416	1717	1.2E
	2020	2322	1.3F
5 F ●	0225	0519	1.1E
	0817	1124	1.4F
	1430	1741	1.4E
	2059		
6 Sa		0003	1.3F
	0313	0553	1.0E
	0838	1149	1.4F
	1449	1809	1.5E
	2142		
7 Su		0047	1.3F
	0406	0630	0.8E
	0900	1217	1.3F
	1514	1841	1.6E
	2228		
8 M		0135	1.3F
	0507	0711	0.6E
	0921	1248	1.2F
	1542	1917	1.7E
	2320		
9 Tu		0230	1.2F
	0623	0756	0.3E
	0937	1322	1.1F
	1616	2000	1.7E
10 W	0020	0338	1.1F
		0853	*
		1400	1.0F
	1654	2052	1.6E
11 Th	0129	0458	1.0F
		1010	*
		1449	0.8F
	1742	2200	1.5E
12 F ◑	0245	0626	1.1F
		1149	0.3F
		1558	0.6F
	1845	2324	1.4E
13 Sa	0357	0740	1.2F
		1328	*
		1730	0.6F
	2015		
14 Su		0057	1.4E
	0458	0830	1.3F
		1427	*
		1912	0.7F
	2154		
15 M		0210	1.5E
	0548	0907	1.4F
	1255	1507	0.5E
	1721	2029	0.9F
	2318		
16 Tu		0304	1.5E
	0629	0938	1.5F
	1304	1542	0.9E
	1822	2128	1.2F
17 W	0029	0350	1.5E
	0703	1006	1.5F
	1318	1616	1.3E
	1914	2221	1.5F
18 Th	0131	0433	1.3E
	0732	1034	1.5F
	1336	1650	1.6E
	2003	2311	1.6F
19 F ○	0229	0514	1.1E
	0759	1101	1.5F
	1358	1724	1.8E
	2051		
20 Sa		0000	1.6F
	0327	0554	0.9E
	0823	1130	1.4F
	1424	1759	1.9E
	2140		
21 Su		0050	1.6F
	0429	0634	0.6E
	0844	1200	1.3F
	1452	1834	1.9E
	2231		
22 M		0142	1.4F
	0539	0716	0.3E
	0900	1232	1.2F
	1524	1911	1.8E
	2324		
23 Tu		0240	1.3F
		0804	*
		1306	1.0F
	1557	1952	1.7E
24 W	0022	0349	1.1F
		0905	*
		1343	0.9F
	1634	2039	1.5E
25 Th	0126	0506	1.0F
		1030	0.3F
		1427	0.6F
	1715	2139	1.3E
26 F ○	0233	0626	1.0F
		1213	0.3F
		1529	0.5F
	1807	2254	1.1E
27 Sa	0336	0733	1.0F
		1341	*
		1657	0.3F
	1923		
28 Su		0023	1.0E
	0430	0818	1.1F
		1430	*
		1842	0.4F
	2106		
29 M		0137	1.0E
	0513	0849	1.1F
	1249	1503	0.4E
	1720	2005	0.5F
	2235		
30 Tu		0227	1.0E
	0546	0912	1.2F
	1247	1530	0.7E
	1812	2101	0.8F
	2348		

May

Day	Slack h m	Max h m	knots
1 W		0307	1.0E
	0614	0931	1.2F
	1251	1554	1.0E
	1855	2148	1.0F
2 Th	0048	0343	0.9E
	0638	0950	1.3F
	1301	1618	1.3E
	1935	2232	1.2F
3 F ○	0142	0419	0.8E
	0700	1011	1.3F
	1317	1643	1.5E
	2014	2316	1.3F
4 Sa ●	0235	0455	0.7E
	0721	1037	1.3F
	1337	1711	1.7E
	2055		
5 Su		0000	1.4F
	0330	0533	0.6E
	0741	1105	1.3F
	1401	1743	1.8E
	2138		
6 M		0046	1.4F
	0432	0614	0.4E
	0759	1137	1.3F
	1430	1818	1.9E
	2226		
7 Tu		0137	1.3F
		0657	*
		1212	1.2F
	1504	1857	1.9E
	2318		
8 W		0235	1.3F
		0747	*
		1250	1.1F
	1543	1943	1.8E
9 Th	0015	0341	1.2F
		0851	*
		1336	0.9F
	1629	2040	1.7E
10 F	0117	0450	1.2F
		1013	*
		1435	0.8F
	1725	2150	1.5E
11 Sa ◑	0220	0555	1.2F
		1140	*
		1557	0.6F
	1837	2308	1.4E
12 Su	0320	0654	1.2F
		1258	*
		1734	0.6F
	2015		
13 M		0030	1.3E
	0413	0741	1.3F
	1133	1355	0.5E
	1617	1914	0.7F
	2158		
14 Tu		0143	1.2E
	0459	0819	1.3F
	1146	1439	0.9E
	1731	2031	1.0F
	2326		
15 W		0240	1.1E
	0538	0852	1.4F
	1205	1518	1.3E
	1829	2130	1.2F
16 Th	0041	0329	1.0E
	0612	0922	1.4F
	1227	1554	1.6E
	1919	2223	1.4F
17 F	0146	0414	0.8E
	0641	0952	1.4F
	1251	1629	1.8E
	2006	2313	1.5F
18 Sa ○	0246	0457	0.6E
	0707	1021	1.4F
	1318	1704	2.0E
	2051		
19 Su		0001	1.6F
	0347	0538	0.5E
	0729	1052	1.3F
	1346	1738	2.0E
	2136		
20 M		0048	1.5F
	0452	0618	0.3E
	0746	1125	1.3F
	1417	1812	2.0E
	2222		
21 Tu		0137	1.4F
		0700	*
		1159	1.1F
	1449	1847	1.9E
	2309		
22 W		0229	1.3F
		0746	*
		1235	1.0F
	1524	1925	1.8E
	2357		
23 Th		0326	1.2F
		0841	*
		1315	0.9F
	1603	2009	1.6E
24 F	0046	0422	1.1F
		0951	*
		1403	0.7F
	1647	2100	1.4E
25 Sa	0135	0515	1.1F
		1104	*
		1506	0.5F
	1741	2159	1.2E
26 Su ○	0223	0604	1.0F
		1214	*
		1626	0.4F
	1851	2304	1.1E
27 M	0308	0648	1.0F
	1108	1315	0.3E
	1521	1758	0.4F
	2027		
28 Tu		0014	0.9E
	0349	0725	1.0F
	1111	1401	0.6E
	1647	1929	0.6F
	2206		
29 W		0122	0.8E
	0427	0757	1.1F
	1123	1437	0.9E
	1749	2038	0.8F
	2333		
30 Th		0219	0.7E
	0500	0826	1.1F
	1140	1510	1.2E
	1839	2134	1.0F
31 F	0048	0308	0.6E
	0530	0855	1.2F
	1201	1541	1.5E
	1923	2224	1.2F

June

Day	Slack h m	Max h m	knots
1 Sa	0154	0352	0.5E
	0557	0924	1.2F
	1226	1614	1.7E
	2006	2313	1.3F
2 Su	0256	0436	0.3E
	0620	0956	1.3F
	1254	1648	1.9E
	2050		
3 M ●		0000	1.4F
		0519	*
		1030	1.3F
	1326	1725	2.0E
	2135		
4 Tu		0048	1.4F
		0604	*
		1108	1.3F
	1403	1805	2.1E
	2223		
5 W		0138	1.4F
		0650	*
		1150	1.2F
	1444	1849	2.0E
	2313		
6 Th		0231	1.4F
		0742	*
		1236	1.1F
	1530	1938	1.9E
7 F	0004	0326	1.3F
		0844	*
		1331	1.0F
	1624	2034	1.8E
8 Sa	0055	0418	1.3F
		0954	*
		1438	0.8F
	1728	2139	1.5E
9 Su	0145	0507	1.2F
		1104	*
		1602	0.7F
	1846	2248	1.3E
10 M ◐	0233	0555	1.2F
	0949	1212	0.5E
	1443	1735	0.7F
	2024		
11 Tu		0000	1.0E
	0319	0641	1.2F
	1013	1315	0.8E
	1617	1913	0.8F
	2208		
12 W		0113	0.8E
	0402	0725	1.2F
	1041	1409	1.2E
	1731	2032	1.0F
	2344		
13 Th		0218	0.6E
	0441	0805	1.2F
	1112	1456	1.5E
	1831	2134	1.2F
14 F	0106	0314	0.5E
	0518	0843	1.2F
	1144	1538	1.7E
	1922	2229	1.4F
15 Sa	0215	0403	0.4E
	0551	0918	1.2F
	1217	1617	1.9E
	2008	2313	1.5F
16 Su	0318	0449	0.3E
	0557	0924	1.2F
	1249	1653	2.0E
	2050		
17 M ○		0004	1.5F
		0531	*
		1026	1.2F
	1321	1727	2.0E
	2131		
18 Tu		0047	1.4F
		0611	*
		1101	1.1F
	1353	1759	1.9E
	2211		
19 W		0128	1.4F
		0649	*
		1138	1.1F
	1428	1831	1.9E
	2249		
20 Th		0208	1.3F
		0728	*
		1217	1.0F
	1505	1906	1.8E
	2326		
21 F		0247	1.2F
		0811	*
		1300	0.9F
	1547	1945	1.7E
22 Sa	0002	0325	1.2F
		0859	*
		1350	0.8F
	1634	2029	1.5E
23 Su	0038	0401	1.2F
		0952	*
		1450	0.7F
	1729	2119	1.3E
24 M	0114	0436	1.1F
	0846	1045	0.3E
	1256	1600	0.6F
	1835	2214	1.1E
25 Tu ○	0150	0513	1.1F
	0906	1140	0.5E
	1437	1720	0.6F
	2001	2314	0.8E
26 W	0227	0553	1.0F
	0931	1239	0.8E
	1606	1852	0.6F
	2145		
27 Th		0022	0.5E
	0304	0637	1.0F
	1000	1336	1.0E
	1719	2016	0.8F
	2330		
28 F		0135	0.4E
	0340	0722	1.0F
	1032	1425	1.3E
	1819	2122	1.0F
29 Sa		0239	*
		0805	1.1F
	1107	1509	1.6E
	1910	2218	1.2F
30 Su		0334	*
		0846	1.1F
	1144	1551	1.8E
	1957	2310	1.3F

Time meridian 75° W. 0000 is midnight. 1200 is noon. Times are not adjusted for Daylight Saving Time.
If three consecutive entries are marked (F) the middle one is not a true maximum but an intermediate value to show the current pattern.
* Current weak and variable.

Tampa Bay (Sunshine Skyway Bridge), Florida, 2019

F–Flood, Dir. 059° True   E–Ebb, Dir. 238° True

July

Day	Slack h m	Maximum h m	knots
1 M		0425	*
		0926	1.2F
	1224	1632	2.0E
	2042	2357	1.4F
2 Tu ●		0512	*
		1008	1.2F
	1306	1715	2.1E
	2127		
3 W		0041	1.5F
		0557	*
		1053	1.3F
	1350	1759	2.2E
	2212		
4 Th		0124	1.5F
		0641	*
		1143	1.3F
	1439	1844	2.1E
	2256		
5 F		0206	1.4F
		0727	*
		1236	1.2F
	1533	1931	2.0E
	2339		
6 Sa		0248	1.4F
		0818	*
		1335	1.1F
	1632	2023	1.7E
7 Su	0020	0330	1.3F
	0718	0916	0.4E
	1122	1443	1.0F
	1739	2120	1.4E
8 M	0059	0411	1.2F
	0746	1017	0.6E
	1258	1602	0.8F
	1858	2222	1.0E
9 Tu ◑	0138	0452	1.2F
	0820	1121	0.8E
	1436	1731	0.8F
	2037	2329	0.7E
10 W	0217	0537	1.1F
	0858	1230	1.1E
	1607	1910	0.8F
	2231		
11 Th		0046	0.4E
	0257	0627	1.0F
	0941	1340	1.3E
	1725	2035	1.0F
12 F		0204	*
		0720	1.0F
	1026	1440	1.5E
	1829	2140	1.2F
13 Sa		0309	*
		0811	1.0F
	1110	1530	1.7E
	1921	2234	1.3F
14 Su		0404	*
		0855	1.0F
	1153	1614	1.8E
	2006	2321	1.4F
15 M		0452	*
		0935	1.0F
	1231	1651	1.8E
	2045		
16 Tu ○		0001	1.4F
		0532	*
		1013	1.0F
	1307	1722	1.8E
	2119		
17 W		0036	1.4F
		0606	*
		1050	1.1F
	1341	1749	1.8E
	2150		
18 Th		0106	1.4F
		0635	*
		1128	1.1F
	1417	1816	1.8E
	2219		
19 F		0133	1.3F
		0704	*
		1209	1.1F
	1456	1846	1.8E
	2247		
20 Sa		0158	1.3F
	0600	0735	0.3E
	0918	1252	1.0F
	1540	1921	1.7E
	2315		
21 Su		0225	1.3F
	0615	0810	0.4E
	1019	1340	1.0F
	1629	2001	1.5E
	2343		
22 M		0254	1.2F
	0633	0851	0.6E
	1124	1434	0.9F
	1723	2045	1.3E
23 Tu	0013	0326	1.2F
	0657	0936	0.7E
	1236	1537	0.8F
	1828	2136	1.0E
24 W ◐	0042	0402	1.1F
	0726	1027	0.9E
	1357	1650	0.7F
	1951	2232	0.6E
25 Th	0112	0442	1.0F
	0802	1124	1.0E
	1525	1821	0.7F
	2143		
26 F	0141	0528	1.0F
	0843	1231	1.2E
	1647	1959	0.8F
27 Sa		0101	*
		0622	0.9F
	0931	1342	1.4E
	1757	2113	1.0F
28 Su		0224	*
		0722	0.9F
	1021	1443	1.6E
	1854	2211	1.2F
29 M		0328	*
		0818	1.0F
	1114	1535	1.8E
	1943	2300	1.4F
30 Tu		0419	*
		0910	1.1F
	1206	1622	2.0E
	2027	2341	1.5F
31 W ●		0503	*
		1000	1.2F
	1258	1706	2.1E
	2108		

August

Day	Slack h m	Maximum h m	knots
1 Th		0018	1.5F
		0543	*
		1051	1.3F
	1350	1750	2.1E
	2148		
2 F		0052	1.5F
	0443	0621	0.3E
	0801	1143	1.4F
	1444	1833	2.0E
	2225		
3 Sa		0125	1.4F
	0501	0701	0.5E
	0907	1238	1.4F
	1541	1917	1.8E
	2300		
4 Su		0159	1.4F
	0523	0744	0.7E
	1017	1336	1.3F
	1643	2004	1.5E
	2334		
5 M		0233	1.3F
	0549	0833	0.9E
	1131	1441	1.2F
	1751	2056	1.1E
6 Tu	0006	0311	1.2F
	0621	0929	1.1E
	1251	1556	1.0F
	1912	2154	0.7E
7 W ◐	0036	0351	1.1F
	0700	1031	1.2E
	1419	1723	0.9F
	2101	2302	0.3E
8 Th	0104	0437	1.0F
	0747	1144	1.2E
	1551	1907	0.9F
9 F		0029	*
		0530	0.8F
	0842	1312	1.3E
	1713	2036	1.0F
10 Sa		0204	*
		0638	0.7F
	0943	1428	1.4E
	1820	2140	1.2F
11 Su		0315	*
		0749	0.7F
	1043	1525	1.6E
	1912	2230	1.3F
12 M		0409	*
		0846	0.8F
	1137	1610	1.6E
	1953	2311	1.4F
13 Tu		0451	*
		0931	0.9F
	1222	1644	1.7E
	2026	2343	1.4F
14 W		0524	*
		1010	0.9F
	1300	1710	1.7E
	2054		
15 Th ○		0009	1.4F
	0407	0550	0.3E
	0730	1047	1.0F
	1336	1732	1.7E
	2117		
16 F		0029	1.4F
	0416	0612	0.4E
	0807	1124	1.1F
	1414	1756	1.7E
	2139		
17 Sa		0047	1.3F
	0424	0633	0.6E
	0847	1203	1.2F
	1454	1824	1.6E
	2200		
18 Su		0105	1.3F
	0434	0658	0.7E
	0932	1244	1.2F
	1538	1857	1.5E
	2224		
19 M		0128	1.3F
	0450	0727	0.9E
	1021	1329	1.1F
	1628	1934	1.3E
	2249		
20 Tu		0156	1.3F
	0512	0803	1.0E
	1116	1420	1.1F
	1723	2016	1.0E
	2316		
21 W		0228	1.2F
	0539	0844	1.1E
	1216	1520	1.0F
	1830	2104	0.7E
	2341		
22 Th		0304	1.1F
	0610	0932	1.2E
	1327	1631	0.8F
	2000	2201	0.4E
23 F ◐	0002	0345	1.0F
	0649	1028	1.2E
	1452	1803	0.8F
		2311	*
24 Sa		0433	0.9F
	0736	1138	1.3E
	1618	1949	0.9F
25 Su		0047	*
		0534	0.8F
	0837	1305	1.4E
	1732	2102	1.1F
26 M		0223	*
		0650	0.8F
	0946	1423	1.6E
	1831	2154	1.3F
27 Tu		0324	*
		0804	0.9F
	1054	1520	1.8E
	1919	2236	1.5F
28 W		0408	*
		0904	1.1F
	1158	1608	1.9E
	2000	2310	1.5F
29 Th	0304	0445	0.3E
	0627	0959	1.3F
	1257	1651	2.0E
	2037	2341	1.5F
30 F ●	0313	0519	0.6E
	0726	1051	1.5F
	1354	1733	1.9E
	2110		
31 Sa	0327	0554	0.9E
	0822	1144	1.6F
	1450	1815	1.8E
	2142		

September

Day	Slack h m	Maximum h m	knots
1 Su		0037	1.4F
	0345	0630	1.1E
	0920	1237	1.6F
	1549	1856	1.5E
	2211		
2 M		0107	1.4F
	0409	0710	1.3E
	1021	1332	1.5F
	1652	1940	1.1E
	2239		
3 Tu		0139	1.3F
	0439	0754	1.4E
	1126	1435	1.3F
	1803	2030	0.7E
	2305		
4 W		0214	1.2F
	0513	0844	1.5E
	1237	1548	1.1F
	1934	2128	0.3E
	2326		
5 Th ◐		0254	1.0F
	0553	0944	1.4E
	1358	1716	1.0F
		2242	*
6 F		0341	0.8F
	0641	1058	1.3E
	1528	1901	1.0F
7 Sa		0024	*
		0439	0.6F
	0741	1239	1.2E
	1650	2027	1.1F
8 Su		0209	*
		0600	0.5F
	0858	1410	1.3E
	1756	2125	1.2F
9 M		0316	*
		0736	0.5F
	1016	1508	1.4E
	1845	2209	1.3F
10 Tu		0402	*
		0842	0.6F
	1121	1551	1.4E
	1923	2243	1.4F
11 W	0247	0436	0.4E
	0628	0928	0.8F
	1212	1621	1.5E
	1951	2308	1.4F
12 Th	0255	0502	0.5E
	0707	1006	0.9F
	1255	1645	1.5E
	2013	2326	1.4F
13 F ○	0259	0522	0.6E
	0741	1042	1.0F
	1334	1706	1.4E
	2031	2340	1.3F
14 Sa	0303	0540	0.8E
	0815	1118	1.2F
	1413	1731	1.4E
	2049	2355	1.3F
15 Su	0310	0559	1.0E
	0851	1156	1.2F
	1455	1759	1.3E
	2108		
16 M		0014	1.4F
	0323	0622	1.2E
	0931	1236	1.3F
	1541	1832	1.1E
	2130		
17 Tu		0038	1.4F
	0343	0651	1.4E
	1016	1321	1.3F
	1633	1910	0.9E
	2153		
18 W		0107	1.3F
	0408	0725	1.5E
	1106	1411	1.2F
	1734	1951	0.7E
	2217		
19 Th		0139	1.2F
	0438	0804	1.5E
	1202	1511	1.1F
	1849	2041	0.4E
	2237		
20 F		0215	1.1F
	0513	0851	1.5E
	1309	1625	0.9F
		2142	*
21 Sa ◑		0257	0.9F
	0553	0950	1.4E
	1428	1757	0.9F
		2303	*
22 Su		0351	0.8F
	0645	1103	1.3E
	1551	1934	1.0F
23 M		0054	*
		0502	0.6F
	0755	1236	1.4E
	1702	2039	1.2F
24 Tu		0221	*
		0635	0.6F
	0922	1401	1.5E
	1758	2123	1.4F
25 W		0310	*
		0800	0.8F
	1046	1459	1.7E
	1844	2158	1.5F
26 Th		0346	0.4E
	0546	0904	1.1F
	1158	1547	1.7E
	1922	2227	1.5F
27 F	0155	0419	0.8E
	0645	0959	1.4F
	1301	1630	1.7E
	1955	2254	1.5F
28 Sa ●	0206	0451	1.1E
	0737	1051	1.6F
	1400	1712	1.6E
	2024	2321	1.5F
29 Su	0222	0525	1.4E
	0829	1142	1.7F
	1458	1753	1.3E
	2051	2349	1.5F
30 M	0244	0601	1.7E
	0921	1233	1.7F
	1559	1834	1.0E
	2116		

Time meridian 75° W. 0000 is midnight. 1200 is noon. Times are not adjusted for Daylight Saving Time.
If three consecutive entries are marked (F) the middle one is not a true maximum but an intermediate value to show the current pattern.
* Current weak and variable.

Tampa Bay (Sunshine Skyway Bridge), Florida, 2019

F–Flood, Dir. 059° True   E–Ebb, Dir. 238° True

October

Day	Slack	Maximum	knots
1 Tu		0019	1.4F
	0312	0639	1.8F
	1017	1327	1.6F
	1705	1917	0.7F
	2139		
2 W		0051	1.3F
	0344	0720	1.8E
	1116	1428	1.4F
	1822	2006	0.4E
	2158		
3 Th		0126	1.2F
	0420	0806	1.7E
	1221	1540	1.2F
	2107		*
4 F		0206	1.0F
	0500	0902	1.5E
	1335	1705	1.0F
	2229		*
5 Sa ◖		0253	0.7F
	0546	1012	1.3E
	1455	1840	1.0F
6 Su		0019	*
		0355	0.5F
	0642	1148	1.2E
	1610	1959	1.1F
7 M		0159	*
		0523	0.4F
	0802	1327	1.1E
	1712	2051	1.2F
8 Tu		0257	*
		0713	0.4F
	0938	1430	1.2E
	1759	2129	1.3F
9 W	0141	0335	0.4E
	0539	0827	0.5F
	1057	1511	1.2E
	1834	2157	1.3F
10 Th	0145	0404	0.6E
	0628	0916	0.7F
	1157	1543	1.2E
	1859	2216	1.3F
11 F	0147	0427	0.8E
	0705	0956	0.9F
	1247	1609	1.1E
	1919	2231	1.3F
12 Sa	0150	0446	1.0E
	0738	1033	1.1F
	1332	1635	1.1E
	1936	2245	1.3F
13 Su ○	0156	0504	1.2E
	0812	1111	1.2F
	1416	1703	1.0E
	1953	2302	1.3F
14 M	0208	0525	1.4E
	0848	1150	1.3F
	1502	1735	0.9E
	2012	2326	1.4F
15 Tu	0226	0551	1.6E
	0928	1232	1.3F
	1553	1811	0.7E
	2033	2353	1.3F
16 W	0250	0621	1.7E
	1011	1317	1.3F
	1651	1850	0.5E
	2054		
17 Th		0025	1.3F
	0319	0656	1.8E
	1100	1409	1.2F
	1802	1934	0.3E
	2112		
18 F		0059	1.2F
	0353	0737	1.7E
	1156	1512	1.1F
	2027		*
19 Sa		0137	1.0F
	0431	0826	1.6E
	1259	1626	1.1F
	2138		*
20 Su		0223	0.8F
	0516	0927	1.5E
	1409	1747	1.1F
	2309		*
21 M ○		0326	0.7F
	0613	1044	1.4E
	1520	1903	1.2F
22 Tu		0049	*
		0451	0.6F
	0733	1211	1.4E
	1622	1959	1.3F
23 W		0158	*
		0632	0.6F
	0913	1332	1.4E
	1715	2039	1.3F
24 Th	0033	0242	0.5E
	0453	0759	0.8F
	1044	1433	1.4E
	1758	2111	1.4F
25 F	0039	0318	0.8E
	0558	0904	1.1F
	1201	1523	1.4E
	1834	2140	1.4F
26 Sa	0051	0351	1.2E
	0652	0958	1.4F
	1308	1607	1.2E
	1905	2207	1.4F
27 Su ●	0109	0425	1.6E
	0742	1050	1.6F
	1410	1650	1.1E
	1932	2235	1.5F
28 M	0131	0500	1.9E
	0830	1141	1.7F
	1510	1732	0.8E
	1957	2305	1.4F
29 Tu	0158	0536	2.0E
	0920	1231	1.6F
	1614	1815	0.6E
	2019	2337	1.4F
30 W	0229	0615	2.1E
	1012	1324	1.5F
	1725	1859	0.3E
	2038		
31 Th		0012	1.3F
	0303	0655	2.0E
	1107	1423	1.4F
		1948	*

November

Day	Slack	Maximum	knots
1 F		0049	1.1F
	0341	0738	1.8E
	1205	1530	1.2F
		2050	*
2 Sa		0130	0.9F
	0421	0828	1.6E
	1307	1643	1.1F
		2213	*
3 Su		0217	0.7F
	0505	0929	1.4E
	1411	1756	1.1F
		2348	*
4 M ◐		0321	0.5F
	0557	1042	1.2E
	1512	1904	1.1F
5 Tu		0116	*
		0446	0.3F
	0708	1204	1.0E
	1605	1954	1.1F
6 W		0212	*
		0629	0.3F
	0848	1318	0.9E
	1649	2029	1.1F
7 Th	0027	0250	0.5E
	0518	0756	0.5F
	1022	1412	0.9E
	1723	2054	1.1F
8 F	0029	0319	0.7E
	0609	0853	0.7F
	1137	1453	0.8E
	1751	2113	1.2F
9 Sa	0033	0344	1.0E
	0650	0940	0.9F
	1240	1528	0.8E
	1813	2130	1.2F
10 Su	0042	0406	1.3E
	0728	1023	1.1F
	1334	1602	0.7E
	1834	2150	1.2F
11 M	0056	0429	1.5E
	0805	1105	1.2F
	1426	1637	0.6E
	1854	2215	1.3F
12 Tu ○	0116	0455	1.7E
	0843	1147	1.3F
	1520	1715	0.5E
	1914	2243	1.3F
13 W	0142	0526	1.9E
	0924	1232	1.3F
	1619	1755	0.3E
	1934	2316	1.3F
14 Th	0211	0600	1.9E
	1009	1319	1.3F
		1838	*
		2352	1.2F
15 F	0245	0639	1.9E
	1058	1413	1.3F
		1926	*
16 Sa	0324	0031	1.1F
	1151	0723	1.9E
		1514	1.2F
		2024	*
17 Su	0408	0115	1.0F
	1247	0814	1.8E
		1617	1.2F
		2138	*
18 M	0459	0209	0.8F
	1345	0917	1.6E
		1718	1.2F
		2258	*
19 Tu ○	0604	0322	0.6F
	1442	1028	1.4E
		1814	1.2F
20 W		0015	*
	0730	0451	0.6F
	1535	1144	1.3E
	2303	1904	1.2F
21 Th	0336	0118	0.4E
	0914	0630	0.6F
	1623	1300	1.1E
	2316	1945	1.3F
22 F	0458	0207	0.8E
	1050	0758	0.9F
	1704	1405	1.0E
	2334	2021	1.3F
23 Sa	0601	0248	1.2E
	1213	0904	1.1F
	1740	1500	0.9E
	2357	2053	1.3F
24 Su	0655	0327	1.6E
	1325	1000	1.4F
	1812	1548	0.7E
		2124	1.4F
25 M	0023	0404	1.9E
	0744	1053	1.5F
	1429	1634	0.6E
	1840	2157	1.4F
26 Tu ●	0053	0442	2.0E
	0831	1143	1.6F
	1532	1718	0.4E
	1906	2231	1.4F
27 W	0125	0520	2.1E
	0918	1232	1.6F
	1638	1802	0.3E
	1928	2307	1.3F
28 Th	0200	0558	2.1E
	1006	1321	1.5F
		1847	*
		2345	1.2F
29 F	0236	0638	2.0E
	1055	1414	1.4F
		1935	*
30 Sa	0314	0024	1.1F
	1143	0718	1.9E
		1509	1.3F
		2031	*

December

Day	Slack	Maximum	knots
1 Su	0355	0107	0.9F
	1231	0802	1.7E
		1603	1.2F
		2138	*
2 M	0440	0156	0.7F
	1317	0851	1.5E
		1653	1.1F
		2247	*
3 Tu	0531	0257	0.6F
	1402	0946	1.2E
		1739	1.1F
		2353	*
4 W ◐	0635	0412	0.4F
	1443	1045	1.0E
	2240	1821	1.0F
5 Th		0053	0.3F
	0309	0538	0.4F
	0804	1148	0.8E
	1521	1858	1.0F
	2247		
6 F	0434	0143	0.6F
	0946	0711	0.5F
	1556	1256	0.7E
	2259	1931	1.0F
7 Sa	0538	0222	0.9F
	1120	0825	0.7F
	1628	1357	0.5E
	2317	2001	1.0F
8 Su	0629	0255	1.2F
	1240	0923	0.9F
	1657	1448	0.4E
	2339	2032	1.1F
9 M	0713	0327	1.4E
	1348	1013	1.1F
	1725	1534	0.3E
		2103	1.2F
10 Tu	0006	0359	1.7E
	0756	1101	1.2F
		1618	*
		2136	1.2F
11 W	0036	0433	1.9E
	0838	1147	1.3F
		1702	*
		2211	1.3F
12 Th ○	0110	0510	2.0E
	0921	1233	1.4F
		1747	*
		2250	1.2F
13 F	0146	0550	2.1E
	1006	1319	1.4F
		1832	*
		2332	1.2F
14 Sa	0227	0632	2.0E
	1052	1408	1.4F
		1921	*
15 Su	0312	0018	1.1F
	1139	0717	2.0E
		1458	1.3F
		2015	*
16 M	0403	0110	1.0F
	1226	0808	1.8E
		1546	1.3F
		2118	*
17 Tu	0501	0211	0.9F
	1312	0905	1.6E
		1632	1.3F
		2223	*
18 W ○	0611	0326	0.7F
	1357	1009	1.3E
	2111	1715	1.2F
		2326	0.4E
19 Th	0739	0153	*
	1441	0451	0.7F
	2135	1115	1.1E
		1759	1.2F
20 F	0334	0029	0.7F
	0924	0627	0.7F
	1523	1228	0.8E
	2204	1844	1.1F
21 Sa	0455	0129	1.1F
	1108	0757	0.9F
	1604	1341	0.6E
	2237	1929	1.1F
22 Su	0601	0222	1.4E
	1241	0907	1.1F
	1643	1444	0.4E
	2312	2011	1.2F
23 M	0657	0310	1.7E
	1357	1006	1.3F
	1720	1539	0.3E
	2350	2052	1.2F
24 Tu	0746	0353	1.9E
		1058	1.5F
		1629	*
		2131	1.2F
25 W	0028	0435	2.0E
	0832	1147	1.5F
		1715	*
		2210	1.2F
26 Th ●	0105	0514	2.1E
	0915	1231	1.5F
		1758	*
		2249	1.2F
27 F	0143	0550	2.0E
	0957	1313	1.5F
		1839	*
		2329	1.1F
28 Sa	0220	0625	2.0E
	1036	1353	1.4F
		1919	*
29 Su	0259	0011	1.1F
	1113	0700	1.8E
		1431	1.3F
		2001	*
30 M	0341	0054	1.0F
	1147	0737	1.7E
		1507	1.2F
		2046	*
31 Tu	0426	0141	0.8F
	1220	0817	1.5E
		1540	1.2F
		2133	*

Time meridian 75° W. 0000 is midnight. 1200 is noon. Times are not adjusted for Daylight Saving Time.
If three consecutive entries are marked (F) the middle one is not a true maximum but an intermediate value to show the current pattern.
* Current weak and variable.

Old Tampa Bay Entrance (Port Tampa), Florida, 2019

F–Flood, Dir. 025° True   E–Ebb, Dir. 211° True

January

Day	Slack (h m)	Maximum (h m)	knots
1 Tu	0641	0320	1.2E
	1249	0934	0.9F
	1727	1512	0.4E
	2334	2026	0.8F
2 W	0741	0424	1.3E
	1405	1035	1.1F
	1812	1613	0.4E
		2109	0.8F
3 Th	0010	0516	1.4E
	0834	1127	1.2F
	1509	1702	0.4E
	1855	2149	0.8F
4 F	0043	0601	1.4E
	0920	1217	1.3F
	1600	1746	0.3E
	1936	2226	0.8F
5 Sa ●	0113	0641	1.4E
	1002	1303	1.3F
	1645	1827	0.3E
	2014	2302	0.8F
6 Su	0145	0710	1.4E
	1040	1345	1.3F
	1724	1906	0.3E
	2050	2340	0.9F
7 M	0220	0719	1.3E
	1114	1421	1.2F
	1757	1943	0.3E
	2127		
8 Tu	0300	0022	0.9F
	1144	0716	1.3E
	1825	1451	1.2F
	2208	2018	0.4E
9 W	0343	0107	0.9F
	1211	0739	1.4E
	1849	1516	1.1F
	2256	2052	0.5E
10 Th	0432	0155	1.0F
	1236	0816	1.3E
	1911	1538	1.0F
	2352	2128	0.6E
11 F	0526	0246	0.9F
	1302	0900	1.3E
	1934	1603	1.0F
		2208	0.7E
12 Sa	0054	0342	0.9F
	0628	0949	1.1E
	1332	1635	1.0F
	2000	2254	0.8E
13 Su	0203	0449	0.8F
	0738	1045	0.9E
	1405	1712	0.9F
	2029	2345	0.9E
14 M ◐	0322	0610	0.7F
	0901	1148	0.7E
	1443	1755	0.9F
	2103		
15 Tu	0449	0039	0.9E
	1036	0735	0.7F
	1527	1254	0.5E
	2142	1841	0.8F
16 W	0607	0143	1.0E
	1213	0902	0.8F
	1619	1408	0.3E
	2226	1931	0.8F
17 Th	0714	0320	1.1E
	1345	1016	1.0F
	1716	1529	0.3E
	2314	2025	0.8F
18 F	0813	0434	1.3E
	1501	1114	1.2F
	1813	1636	0.3E
		2122	0.8F
19 Sa	0005	0525	1.5E
	0905	1206	1.3F
	1556	1731	0.3E
	1909	2215	0.9F
20 Su	0059	0610	1.6E
	0952	1254	1.4F
	1638	1820	0.3E
	2004	2307	1.0F
21 M ○	0154	0651	1.6E
	1035	1337	1.4F
	1713	1907	0.4E
	2059	2358	1.1F
22 Tu	0250	0731	1.6E
	1116	1415	1.3F
	1743	1952	0.5E
	2155		
23 W	0347	0053	1.1F
	1154	0809	1.6E
	1811	1448	1.3F
	2254	2035	0.7E
24 Th	0445	0150	1.1F
	1229	0847	1.4E
	1838	1519	1.2F
	2358	2119	0.8E
25 F	0549	0248	1.1F
	1302	0928	1.2E
	1908	1551	1.1F
		2207	0.9E
26 Sa	0109	0352	0.9F
	0700	1015	1.0E
	1334	1626	1.0F
	1941	2305	1.0E
27 Su ◐	0226	0512	0.8F
	0818	1113	0.7E
	1408	1706	0.9F
	2017		
28 M	0351	0013	1.0E
	0948	0644	0.8F
	1445	1217	0.5E
	2059	1751	0.8F
29 Tu	0517	0134	1.0E
	1129	0810	0.8F
	1532	1326	0.3E
	2145	1839	0.7F
30 W	0630	0309	1.1E
	2236	0926	0.9F
		1447	*
		1930	0.6F
31 Th	0731	0421	1.2E
	2326	1028	1.1F
		1602	*
		2026	0.5F

February

Day	Slack (h m)	Maximum (h m)	knots
1 F	0823	0513	1.3E
	1515	1119	1.2F
	1839	1656	0.3E
		2122	0.6F
2 Sa	0011	0557	1.4E
	0906	1204	1.3F
	1553	1739	0.3E
	1930	2210	0.6F
3 Su	0054	0632	1.4E
	0944	1244	1.3F
	1624	1816	0.4E
	2013	2251	0.7F
4 M ●	0135	0655	1.3E
	1015	1319	1.3F
	1648	1849	0.5E
	2052	2332	0.8F
5 Tu	0217	0701	1.3E
	1042	1346	1.2F
	1707	1920	0.5E
	2130		
6 W	0301	0015	1.0F
	1103	0703	1.3E
	1723	1405	1.2F
	2210	1949	0.6E
7 Th	0346	0101	1.0F
	1122	0725	1.3E
	1738	1421	1.1F
	2255	2018	0.8E
8 F	0434	0148	1.1F
	1143	0800	1.3E
	1755	1439	1.1F
	2344	2048	0.9E
9 Sa	0527	0237	1.1F
	1207	0841	1.2E
	1815	1504	1.1F
		2120	1.0E
10 Su	0040	0330	1.0F
	0627	0926	1.0E
	1236	1534	1.1F
	1841	2155	1.0E
11 M	0143	0435	0.8F
	0738	1019	0.8E
	1309	1610	1.0F
	1911	2238	1.0E
12 Tu ◐	0259	0559	0.7F
	0904	1122	0.5E
	1345	1655	0.9F
	1948	2332	1.0E
13 W	0430	0731	0.8F
	1049	1234	0.3E
	1426	1748	0.8F
	2032		
14 Th	0554	0041	1.0E
		0901	0.9F
		1355	*
	2128	1848	0.7F
15 F	0702	0320	1.1E
		1011	1.1F
		1526	*
	2237	1954	0.7F
16 Sa	0759	0434	1.3E
		1103	1.3F
		1632	*
	2349	2105	0.7F
17 Su	0847	0520	1.5E
	1532	1148	1.4F
	1913	1721	0.4E
		2209	0.9F
18 M	0057	0559	1.6E
	0929	1227	1.4F
	1558	1804	0.6E
	2012	2305	1.1F
19 Tu ○	0201	0635	1.6E
	1006	1301	1.4F
	1620	1845	0.7E
	2106	2358	1.2F
20 W	0301	0709	1.6E
	1039	1331	1.3F
	1641	1925	0.9E
	2159		
21 Th	0357	0053	1.3F
	1109	0744	1.4E
	1703	1358	1.3F
	2254	2004	1.1E
22 F	0454	0148	1.3F
	1137	0820	1.3E
	1727	1424	1.2F
	2352	2043	1.2E
23 Sa	0554	0244	1.2F
	1205	0859	1.0E
	1755	1452	1.1F
		2124	1.2E
24 Su	0056	0345	1.1F
	0701	0943	0.8E
	1233	1524	1.0F
	1826	2210	1.1E
25 M	0208	0503	0.9F
	0818	1037	0.5E
	1304	1600	0.9F
	1901	2317	1.0E
26 Tu ◐	0330	0634	0.8F
	0952	1144	0.3E
	1338	1643	0.7F
	1940		
27 W	0457	0104	1.0E
		0758	0.9F
		1301	*
	2025	1738	0.5F
28 Th	0610	0256	1.0E
		0912	1.0F
		1429	*
	2124	1842	0.4F

March

Day	Slack (h m)	Maximum (h m)	knots
1 F	0710	0408	1.1E
		1012	1.1F
		1551	*
	2239	1951	0.4F
2 Sa	0759	0457	1.2E
	1453	1059	1.3F
	1837	1643	0.3E
	2348	2103	0.4F
3 Su	0839	0535	1.3E
	1519	1138	1.3F
	1929	1721	0.4E
		2200	0.6F
4 M	0044	0602	1.3E
	0912	1211	1.3F
	1539	1753	0.6E
	2011	2245	0.8F
5 Tu	0134	0618	1.2E
	0937	1237	1.2F
	1554	1822	0.7E
	2050	2327	0.9F
6 W ●	0220	0623	1.2E
	0957	1255	1.2F
	1606	1849	0.8E
	2127		
7 Th	0304	0010	1.1F
	1014	0636	1.2E
	1618	1308	1.1F
	2207	1915	1.0E
8 F	0349	0054	1.1F
	1031	0704	1.2E
	1630	1325	1.1F
	2249	1941	1.1E
9 Sa	0437	0141	1.2F
	1052	0741	1.1E
	1647	1347	1.2F
	2336	2007	1.2E
10 Su	0531	0230	1.1F
	1117	0822	1.0E
	1708	1415	1.1F
		2035	1.2E
11 M	0029	0323	1.0F
	0634	0908	0.8E
	1147	1448	1.1F
	1736	2106	1.2E
12 Tu	0131	0429	0.9F
	0751	1001	0.5E
	1219	1524	1.0F
	1809	2144	1.2E
13 W	0248	0602	0.8F
	0927	1108	0.3E
	1253	1608	0.8F
	1849	2235	1.1E
14 Th ◐	0419	0735	0.8F
		1228	*
		1707	0.6F
	1941		
15 F	0539	0001	1.0E
		0854	1.0F
		1356	*
	2049	1821	0.5F
16 Sa	0642	0316	1.1E
		0955	1.2F
		1523	*
	2221	1941	0.6F
17 Su	0734	0418	1.3E
	1423	1040	1.3F
	1816	1621	0.4E
	2351	2102	0.7F
18 M	0818	0500	1.4E
	1445	1117	1.3F
	1921	1704	0.6E
		2210	0.9F
19 Tu	0105	0535	1.5E
	0855	1148	1.3F
	1504	1742	0.9E
	2016	2306	1.2F
20 W ○	0210	0607	1.5E
	0926	1215	1.3F
	1522	1819	1.1E
	2107	2358	1.3F
21 Th	0307	0640	1.4E
	0954	1240	1.3F
	1541	1855	1.3E
	2157		
22 F	0402	0051	1.4F
	1019	0715	1.2E
	1602	1305	1.2F
	2249	1932	1.4E
23 Sa	0457	0144	1.4F
	1043	0752	1.0E
	1626	1332	1.2F
	2343	2008	1.4E
24 Su	0556	0238	1.3F
	1109	0832	0.8E
	1653	1402	1.1F
		2043	1.4E
25 M	0043	0338	1.1F
	0703	0917	0.6E
	1137	1435	1.0F
	1722	2117	1.2E
26 Tu	0150	0454	1.0F
	0822	1010	0.3E
	1207	1510	0.8F
	1755	2155	1.1E
27 W ◐	0307	0622	0.9F
		1120	*
		1552	0.7F
	1832		
28 Th	0428	0014	0.9E
		0739	0.9F
		1240	*
	1917	1647	0.5F
29 F	0538	0222	0.9E
		0846	1.0F
		1404	*
	2020	1803	0.3F
30 Sa	0633	0335	1.0E
		0941	1.1F
		1522	*
	2155	1924	0.3F
31 Su	0719	0422	1.1E
	1403	1025	1.2F
	1825	1613	0.4E
	2326	2045	0.4F

Time meridian 75° W. 0000 is midnight. 1200 is noon. Times are not adjusted for Daylight Saving Time.
If three consecutive entries are marked (F) the middle one is not a true maximum but an intermediate value to show the current pattern.
* Current weak and variable.

Old Tampa Bay Entrance (Port Tampa), Florida, 2019

F–Flood, Dir. 025° True   E–Ebb, Dir. 211° True

April

Day	Slack (h m)	Maximum (h m)	knots	Day	Slack (h m)	Maximum (h m)	knots
1 M		0454	1.1E	16 Tu		0428	1.2E
	0755	1059	1.2F		0737	1036	1.2F
	1423	1650	0.6E		1347	1642	0.9E
	1917	2148	0.6F		1923	2212	1.0F
2 Tu	0033	0515	1.1E	17 W	0113	0504	1.2E
	0823	1125	1.2F		0810	1102	1.2F
	1438	1721	0.8E		1406	1719	1.2E
	2000	2237	0.8F		2016	2306	1.2F
3 W	0128	0527	1.1E	18 Th	0215	0537	1.2E
	0845	1142	1.1F		0839	1126	1.2F
	1451	1749	1.0E		1426	1754	1.4E
	2040	2320	1.0F		2106	2357	1.4F
4 Th	0218	0543	1.1E	19 F	0312	0611	1.1E
	0903	1155	1.1F		0904	1150	1.2F
	1503	1815	1.1E		1448	1830	1.5E
	2120				2155		
5 F ●		0004	1.1F	20 Sa		0049	1.4F
	0306	0608	1.0E		0406	0648	0.9E
	0921	1211	1.1F		0929	1217	1.2F
	1515	1840	1.2E		1511	1904	1.6E
	2201				2244		
6 Sa		0049	1.2F	21 Su		0141	1.4F
	0354	0642	1.0E		0500	0728	0.7E
	0941	1234	1.2F		0954	1247	1.2F
	1531	1904	1.3E		1536	1937	1.5E
	2244				2336		
7 Su		0137	1.2F	22 M		0235	1.3F
	0445	0722	0.9E		0601	0811	0.6E
	1005	1302	1.2F		1021	1320	1.1F
	1551	1928	1.4E		1604	2007	1.4E
	2331						
8 M		0228	1.1F	23 Tu	0032	0333	1.1F
	0544	0807	0.7E		0709	0858	0.4E
	1032	1335	1.1F		1051	1356	1.0F
	1617	1957	1.4E		1634	2034	1.3E
9 Tu	0025	0324	1.0F	24 W	0133	0443	1.0F
	0655	0856	0.5E			0952	*
	1102	1411	1.0F			1434	0.8F
	1647	2030	1.3E		1707	2104	1.1E
10 W	0129	0437	0.9F	25 Th	0238	0601	1.0F
	0820	0953	0.3E			1058	*
	1132	1451	0.9F			1518	0.6F
	1724	2110	1.2E		1746	2145	1.0E
11 Th	0243	0610	0.9F	26 F ◗	0345	0708	1.0F
		1107	*			1214	*
		1538	0.7F			1614	0.5F
	1810	2206	1.1E		1837	2318	0.8E
12 F ◑	0404	0728	1.0F	27 Sa	0448	0805	1.0F
		1231	*			1324	*
		1643	0.5F			1733	0.3F
	1911				1947		
13 Sa	0514	0023	1.0E	28 Su		0210	0.8E
	0832	1.1F			0539	0854	1.0F
		1352	*		1230	1431	0.3E
		1812	0.5F		1646	1859	0.4F
	2037				2124		
14 Su	0611	0244	1.1E	29 M		0306	0.8E
	0924	1.2F			0619	0934	1.0F
	1306	1506	0.3E		1253	1527	0.5E
	1709	1941	0.5F		1759	2019	0.5F
	2227				2301		
15 M	0658	0346	1.2E	30 Tu	0652	0342	0.8E
	1004	1.2F		1003	1.0F	
	1327	1600	0.6E		1311	1609	0.8E
	1824	2106	0.7F		1854	2129	0.7F
	2359						

May

Day	Slack (h m)	Maximum (h m)	knots	Day	Slack (h m)	Maximum (h m)	knots
1 W	0016	0408	0.9E	16 Th	0118	0431	0.9E
	0718	1024	1.0F		0718	1013	1.1F
	1327	1644	1.0E		1311	1700	1.4E
	1943	2223	0.9F		2015	2307	1.2F
2 Th	0118	0436	0.9E	17 F	0222	0510	0.8E
	0741	1040	1.0F		0748	1040	1.1F
	1343	1715	1.2E		1336	1739	1.5E
	2028	2311	1.1F		2105	2358	1.4F
3 F	0215	0507	0.9E	18 Sa ○	0319	0548	0.7E
	0803	1059	1.1F		0817	1108	1.1F
	1400	1743	1.3E		1402	1816	1.6E
	2112	2358	1.2F		2153		
4 Sa ●	0309	0543	0.8E	19 Su	0414	0050	1.4F
	0828	1123	1.1F		0846	0628	0.6E
	1419	1808	1.4E		1429	1138	1.1F
	2156				2241	1851	1.6E
5 Su		0047	1.2F	20 M	0509	0142	1.4F
	0402	0624	0.7E		0915	0712	0.5E
	0855	1152	1.1F		1458	1211	1.1F
	1442	1833	1.5E		2330	1921	1.5E
	2242						
6 M	0500	0139	1.3F	21 Tu	0608	0233	1.3F
	0710	0.6E			0947	0758	0.4E
	0923	1225	1.1F		1528	1247	1.0F
	1509	1900	1.5E			1944	1.4E
	2332						
7 Tu	0607	0233	1.2F	22 W	0020	0326	1.2F
	0800	0.4E			0711	0845	0.3E
	0954	1303	1.1F		1020	1327	0.9F
	1540	1933	1.4E		1600	2007	1.3E
8 W	0027	0332	1.1F	23 Th	0110	0423	1.1F
		0853	*			0935	*
		1345	1.0F			1410	0.8F
	1616	2013	1.4E		1638	2039	1.2E
9 Th	0128	0443	1.0F	24 F	0200	0524	1.0F
		0953	*			1031	*
		1431	0.8F			1457	0.7F
	1700	2103	1.3E		1723	2122	1.1E
10 F	0232	0559	1.0F	25 Sa	0249	0619	1.0F
		1107	*			1133	*
		1526	0.7F			1554	0.6F
	1754	2215	1.1E		1820	2220	1.0E
11 Sa ◗	0337	0701	1.0F	26 Su ◗	0336	0704	0.9F
		1223	*		1037	1232	0.3E
		1639	0.5F		1433	1708	0.5F
	1908				1933	2337	0.9E
12 Su	0436	0031	1.0E	27 M	0419	0741	0.9F
	0752	1.1F		1105	1327	0.5E
	1136	1331	0.3E		1605	1832	0.5F
	1539	1814	0.5F		2102		
	2049						
13 M	0527	0153	1.0E	28 Tu	0456	0047	0.8E
	0836	1.1F		0812	0.9F	
	1201	1436	0.6E		1128	1422	0.7E
	1714	1945	0.6F		1724	1951	0.6F
	2238				2235		
14 Tu	0610	0258	1.0E	29 W	0529	0150	0.7E
	0914	1.1F		0839	0.9F	
	1224	1532	0.9E		1150	1517	0.9E
	1823	2108	0.8F		1828	2106	0.7F
					2357		
15 W	0006	0350	1.0E	30 Th	0600	0254	0.7E
	0646	0945	1.1F		0907	0.9F	
	1247	1619	1.1E		1213	1603	1.1E
	1922	2213	1.1F		1924	2210	0.9F
				31 F	0109	0350	0.6E
					0632	0936	1.0F
					1237	1643	1.3E
					2015	2304	1.1F

June

Day	Slack (h m)	Maximum (h m)	knots	Day	Slack (h m)	Maximum (h m)	knots
1 Sa	0215	0439	0.6E	16 Su	0332	0000	1.3F
	1303	1009	1.0F		0739	0535	0.5E
	2104	1717	1.4E		1327	1034	1.0F
		2356	1.2F		2152	1821	1.5E
2 Su	0317	0525	0.5E	17 M ○		0051	1.4F
	0740	1043	1.1F		0425	0619	0.4E
	1332	1749	1.5E		0816	1110	1.0F
	2152				1358	1900	1.5E
					2237		
3 M ●		0049	1.3F	18 Tu		0140	1.4F
	0418	0613	0.4E		0516	0704	0.4E
	0816	1119	1.1F		0853	1146	0.9F
	1405	1820	1.5E		1431	1929	1.4E
	2240				2320		
4 Tu	0520	0144	1.3F	19 W	0605	0226	1.3F
	0852	0705	0.4E		0930	0749	0.3E
	1440	1159	1.1F		1505	1226	0.9F
	2330	1856	1.5E			1943	1.4E
5 W	0625	0237	1.3F	20 Th	0001	0309	1.2F
	0931	0758	0.3E		0652	0831	0.3E
	1520	1243	1.0F		1010	1309	0.9F
		1938	1.5E		1543	1956	1.3E
6 Th	0022	0329	1.2F	21 F	0039	0349	1.1F
		0852	*		0732	0912	0.3E
		1332	0.9F		1055	1355	0.8F
	1605	2027	1.4E		1625	2025	1.3E
7 F	0114	0425	1.1F	22 Sa	0114	0427	1.0F
		0947	*		0806	0954	0.3E
		1426	0.8F		1149	1444	0.8F
	1658	2122	1.3E		1715	2105	1.2E
8 Sa	0206	0522	1.1F	23 Su	0145	0502	0.9F
		1050	*		0834	1040	0.4E
		1526	0.7F		1253	1538	0.7F
	1803	2233	1.1E		1814	2153	1.1E
9 Su	0256	0613	1.0F	24 M	0215	0532	0.9F
	0947	1155	0.4E		0859	1129	0.5E
	1403	1643	0.6F		1404	1645	0.6F
	1926	2355	1.0E		1924	2251	0.9E
10 M	0344	0655	1.0F	25 Tu ◗	0245	0602	0.8F
	1018	1257	0.6E		0925	1219	0.7E
	1540	1816	0.6F		1525	1804	0.6F
	2104				2044	2354	0.8E
11 Tu	0429	0102	0.9E	26 W	0320	0635	0.8F
	0733	0.9F		0953	1310	0.8E
	1048	1359	0.8E		1648	1924	0.6F
	1707	1946	0.7F		2215		
	2244						
12 W	0510	0205	0.7E	27 Th	0359	0056	0.6E
	0810	0.9F		0712	0.9F	
	1119	1504	1.0E		1025	1409	0.9E
	1818	2107	0.9F		1802	2046	0.8F
					2344		
13 Th	0011	0309	0.6E	28 F	0443	0203	0.5E
	0548	0846	0.9F		0753	0.9F	
	1150	1603	1.3E		1100	1519	1.1E
	1919	2213	1.1F		1907	2200	0.9F
14 F	0127	0404	0.6E	29 Sa	0530	0316	0.4E
	0625	0923	0.9F		0839	0.9F	
	1222	1652	1.4E		1137	1619	1.3E
	2015	2308	1.2F		2005	2300	1.1F
15 Sa	0234	0451	0.5E	30 Su	0617	0421	0.4E
	0702	0959	1.0F		0927	0.9F	
	1255	1738	1.5E		1216	1708	1.4E
	2105				2057	2355	1.2F

Time meridian 75° W. 0000 is midnight. 1200 is noon. Times are not adjusted for Daylight Saving Time.
If three consecutive entries are marked (F) the middle one is not a true maximum but an intermediate value to show the current pattern.
* Current weak and variable.

Old Tampa Bay Entrance (Port Tampa), Florida, 2019

F–Flood, Dir. 025° True   E–Ebb, Dir. 211° True

July

Day	Slack h m	Maximum h m	knots
1 M	0331	0516	0.3E
	0705	1013	1.0F
	1258	1751	1.5E
	2146		
2 Tu ●		0048	1.3F
	0429	0608	0.3E
	0753	1059	1.0F
	1342	1834	1.6E
	2233		
3 W		0138	1.4F
	0521	0701	0.3E
	0841	1145	1.0F
	1429	1917	1.6E
	2319		
4 Th		0224	1.3F
	0608	0751	0.3E
	0932	1236	1.0F
	1519	1958	1.5E
5 F	0003	0305	1.3F
	0649	0839	0.4E
	1027	1330	1.0F
	1613	2039	1.4E
6 Sa	0045	0345	1.2F
	0723	0925	0.5E
	1130	1426	0.9F
	1713	2123	1.3E
7 Su	0125	0423	1.1F
	0753	1016	0.6E
	1243	1528	0.8F
	1822	2214	1.1E
8 M	0203	0502	1.0F
	0823	1113	0.7E
	1402	1643	0.7F
	1942	2315	0.9E
9 Tu ◐	0240	0541	0.9F
	0854	1215	0.8E
	1528	1814	0.7F
	2112		
10 W		0018	0.7F
	0318	0621	0.8F
	0931	1322	1.0E
	1655	1943	0.8F
	2249		
11 Th		0122	0.5E
	0400	0703	0.8F
	1012	1441	1.1E
	1811	2105	0.9F
12 F	0021	0234	0.4E
	0449	0748	0.8F
	1056	1557	1.3E
	1916	2212	1.1F
13 Sa	0144	0346	0.3E
	0540	0838	0.8F
	1140	1655	1.4E
	2012	2308	1.2F
14 Su	0250	0443	0.3E
	0633	0927	0.8F
	1223	1744	1.5E
	2101	2358	1.3F
15 M	0342	0531	0.4E
	0723	1012	0.8F
	1303	1828	1.5E
	2145		
16 Tu ○		0045	1.4F
	0426	0615	0.4E
	0809	1053	0.8F
	1341	1904	1.5E
	2225		
17 W		0128	1.4F
	0505	0657	0.4E
	0851	1133	0.8F
	1418	1928	1.4E
	2300		
18 Th		0206	1.3F
	0538	0735	0.4E
	0929	1214	0.9F
	1456	1935	1.3E
	2331		
19 F		0237	1.2F
	0606	0809	0.5E
	1008	1258	0.9F
	1537	1942	1.3E
	2357		
20 Sa		0301	1.1F
	0629	0841	0.5E
	1051	1344	0.9F
	1622	2008	1.3E
21 Su	0019	0319	1.0F
	0648	0912	0.6E
	1140	1432	0.9F
	1713	2044	1.2E
22 M	0041	0339	1.0F
	0706	0944	0.7E
	1235	1523	0.9F
	1810	2127	1.1E
23 Tu	0105	0404	1.0F
	0726	1022	0.8E
	1338	1624	0.8F
	1916	2218	0.9E
24 W ○	0133	0437	0.9F
	0752	1107	0.9E
	1450	1741	0.7F
	2033	2318	0.7E
25 Th	0207	0519	0.9F
	0824	1158	0.9E
	1617	1906	0.7F
	2206		
26 F		0023	0.9F
	0247	0606	0.9F
	0904	1256	1.0E
	1741	2035	0.8F
	2345		
27 Sa		0133	0.3E
	0337	0755	0.8F
	0952	1425	1.1E
	1852	2154	1.0F
28 Su		0257	*
		0755	0.8F
	1046	1613	1.2E
	1953	2255	1.2F
29 M		0413	*
		0856	0.8F
	1142	1709	1.4E
	2045	2347	1.3F
30 Tu	0335	0511	0.3E
	0651	0956	0.9F
	1239	1754	1.5E
	2132		
31 W ●		0034	1.4F
	0416	0602	0.4E
	0751	1049	1.0F
	1337	1835	1.6E
	2214		

August

Day	Slack h m	Maximum h m	knots
1 Th		0116	1.4F
	0450	0648	0.5E
	0846	1141	1.1F
	1433	1912	1.6E
	2254		
2 F		0153	1.4F
	0519	0732	0.6E
	0939	1234	1.1F
	1529	1948	1.5E
	2330		
3 Sa		0224	1.3F
	0544	0813	0.7E
	1034	1330	1.2F
	1626	2024	1.4E
4 Su	0003	0252	1.2F
	0608	0853	0.8E
	1133	1426	1.1F
	1727	2102	1.2E
5 M	0034	0320	1.1F
	0633	0935	0.9E
	1238	1526	1.0F
	1834	2146	1.0E
6 Tu	0104	0351	1.0F
	0701	1023	1.0E
	1351	1638	0.9F
	1950	2239	0.7E
7 W ◐	0134	0427	0.9F
	0735	1126	1.0E
	1513	1809	0.8F
	2117	2343	0.5E
8 Th	0208	0510	0.8F
	0814	1248	1.0E
	1642	1938	0.8F
	2259		
9 F		0053	0.3E
	0251	0602	0.7F
	0902	1430	1.1E
	1801	2059	0.9F
10 Sa		0213	*
		0659	0.6E
	1000	1555	1.2E
	1906	2205	1.1F
11 Su		0338	*
		0801	0.5E
	1103	1653	1.4E
	2001	2259	1.3F
12 M	0252	0439	0.3E
	0627	0907	0.5F
	1201	1739	1.4E
	2047	2345	1.4F
13 Tu	0331	0526	0.4E
	0726	1003	0.6F
	1251	1818	1.4E
	2127		
14 W		0026	1.4F
	0404	0606	0.5E
	0813	1047	0.7F
	1335	1847	1.4E
	2200		
15 Th ○		0102	1.4F
	0430	0641	0.6E
	0853	1127	0.8F
	1416	1903	1.3E
	2227		
16 F		0131	1.3F
	0450	0711	0.6E
	0929	1208	0.9F
	1456	1905	1.3E
	2249		
17 Sa		0150	1.2F
	0505	0738	0.7E
	1005	1250	1.0F
	1538	1917	1.3E
	2306		
18 Su		0203	1.1F
	0516	0803	0.8E
	1044	1334	1.1F
	1623	1945	1.2E
	2322		
19 M		0218	1.1F
	0528	0827	0.9E
	1128	1421	1.1F
	1712	2022	1.1E
	2342		
20 Tu		0239	1.1F
	0544	0854	1.0E
	1218	1510	1.0F
	1808	2104	1.0E
21 W	0007	0306	1.1F
	0607	0925	1.1E
	1316	1608	0.9F
	1914	2153	0.8E
22 Th	0038	0340	1.0F
	0637	1002	1.1E
	1426	1726	0.8F
	2034	2252	0.5E
23 F ◑	0113	0422	0.9F
	0715	1050	1.1E
	1554	1859	0.7F
	2215		
24 Sa		0002	0.3E
	0152	0514	0.8F
	0800	1155	1.0E
	1723	2031	0.8F
25 Su		0121	*
		0617	0.7E
	0856	1340	1.0E
	1836	2146	1.0F
26 M		0252	*
		0726	0.6E
	1007	1609	1.2E
	1935	2242	1.2F
27 Tu		0409	*
		0839	0.7E
	1124	1700	1.4E
	2024	2327	1.3F
28 W	0310	0502	0.4E
	0656	0949	0.8F
	1236	1739	1.5E
	2107		
29 Th		0005	1.4F
	0336	0545	0.5E
	0756	1047	1.0F
	1342	1814	1.6E
	2144		
30 F ●		0038	1.4F
	0358	0625	0.7E
	0849	1140	1.2F
	1442	1848	1.5E
	2216		
31 Sa		0107	1.3F
	0417	0703	0.9E
	0940	1233	1.3F
	1539	1922	1.4E
	2245		

September

Day	Slack h m	Maximum h m	knots
1 Su		0132	1.2F
	0435	0740	1.1E
	1032	1327	1.3F
	1635	1958	1.3E
	2312		
2 M		0157	1.2F
	0456	0817	1.2E
	1128	1422	1.3F
	1734	2036	1.0E
	2337		
3 Tu		0225	1.1F
	0520	0854	1.3E
	1229	1521	1.1F
	1840	2119	0.8E
4 W	0004	0255	1.0F
	0550	0935	1.2E
	1338	1633	1.0F
	1955	2210	0.5E
	2350		
5 Th ◑	0034	0331	0.9F
	0626	1029	1.1E
	1457	1804	0.9F
	2125	2316	0.3E
6 F	0110	0414	0.8F
	0707	1216	1.0E
	1624	1930	0.9F
7 Sa		0034	*
		0509	0.6E
	0757	1418	1.0E
	1742	2045	1.0F
8 Su		0201	*
		0619	0.4E
	0901	1542	1.1E
	1845	2148	1.2F
9 M		0328	*
		0736	0.4E
	1026	1637	1.2E
	1936	2238	1.3F
10 Tu	0226	0427	0.4E
	0633	0856	0.4F
	1144	1718	1.3E
	2019	2319	1.4F
11 W	0257	0509	0.5E
	0728	0958	0.6F
	1244	1750	1.3E
	2054	2354	1.3F
12 Th	0321	0544	0.7E
	0811	1042	0.7F
	1332	1811	1.2E
	2122		
13 F ○		0021	1.3F
	0339	0613	0.8E
	0847	1121	0.9F
	1415	1820	1.2E
	2142		
14 Sa		0039	1.2F
	0350	0639	0.9E
	0922	1201	1.0F
	1457	1827	1.1E
	2157		
15 Su		0050	1.1F
	0358	0701	1.0E
	0957	1242	1.1F
	1539	1848	1.1E
	2210		
16 M		0103	1.1F
	0407	0722	1.1E
	1035	1326	1.3F
	1624	1921	1.1E
	2227		
17 Tu		0123	1.1F
	0420	0743	1.2E
	1117	1412	1.1F
	1714	2001	0.9E
	2250		
18 W		0150	1.2F
	0440	0809	1.3E
	1206	1502	1.0F
	1814	2045	0.8E
	2318		
19 Th		0222	1.1F
	0508	0839	1.3E
	1304	1602	0.9F
	1925	2135	0.5E
	2350		
20 F ◑		0259	1.0F
	0542	0916	1.3E
	1415	1727	0.8F
	2054	2237	0.3E
21 Sa ○	0026	0341	0.9F
	0623	1003	1.2E
	1540	1901	0.8F
		2356	*
22 Su		0436	0.7E
	0713	1114	1.0E
	1705	2022	0.9F
23 M		0120	*
		0550	0.6E
	0818	1401	1.0E
	1812	2127	1.1F
24 Tu		0249	*
		0712	0.5E
	0946	1547	1.2E
	1906	2216	1.2F
25 W	0158	0357	0.4E
	0554	0834	0.6F
	1122	1635	1.3E
	1952	2254	1.3F
26 Th	0222	0444	0.6E
	0701	0948	0.9F
	1241	1711	1.4E
	2030	2325	1.3F
27 F	0241	0522	0.8E
	0757	1046	1.1F
	1348	1744	1.4E
	2102	2351	1.3F
28 Sa ●	0258	0557	1.1F
	0848	1139	1.3F
	1448	1817	1.3E
	2130		
29 Su		0014	1.2F
	0315	0632	1.3E
	0937	1231	1.4F
	1544	1852	1.2E
	2155		
30 M		0038	1.2F
	0334	0707	1.4E
	1028	1324	1.4F
	1639	1930	1.0E
	2218		

Time meridian 75° W. 0000 is midnight. 1200 is noon. Times are not adjusted for Daylight Saving Time.
If three consecutive entries are marked (F) the middle one is not a true maximum but an intermediate value to show the current pattern.
* Current weak and variable.

Old Tampa Bay Entrance (Port Tampa), Florida, 2019

F–Flood, Dir. 025° True   E–Ebb, Dir. 211° True

October

Day	Slack (h m)	Maximum (h m)	knots
1 Tu		0106	1.2F
	0357	0742	1.5F
	1121	1419	1.3F
	1739	2011	0.8E
	2243		
2 W		0137	1.2F
	0425	0818	1.5F
	1220	1517	1.2F
	1845	2057	0.6E
	2311		
3 Th		0212	1.1F
	0456	0855	1.4E
	1326	1628	1.0F
	2002	2150	0.4E
	2345		
4 F		0250	0.9F
	0532	0937	1.2E
	1439	1755	1.3F
		2258	*
5 Sa ◐		0333	0.7F
	0614	1129	1.0E
	1558	1912	1.0F
6 Su		0020	*
		0429	0.5F
	0703	1347	1.0E
	1710	2019	1.1F
7 M		0142	*
		0547	0.3F
	0809	1507	1.0E
	1808	2117	1.2F
8 Tu	0106	0302	0.3E
	0510	0715	0.3F
	0946	1601	1.1E
	1856	2204	1.2F
9 W	0139	0400	0.5E
	0623	0840	0.4F
	1121	1639	1.1E
	1935	2241	1.2F
10 Th	0204	0440	0.7E
	0714	0945	0.6F
	1228	1705	1.0E
	2006	2309	1.2F
11 F	0222	0512	0.8E
	0756	1031	0.8F
	1322	1720	1.0E
	2028	2327	1.1F
12 Sa	0235	0539	1.0E
	0834	1112	0.9F
	1410	1732	1.0E
	2044	2338	1.1F
13 Su ○	0244	0603	1.1E
	0911	1152	1.1F
	1455	1752	0.9E
	2059	2350	1.1F
14 M	0253	0623	1.2E
	0949	1235	1.2F
	1541	1822	0.9E
	2116		
15 Tu		0010	1.1F
	0307	0642	1.3E
	1029	1321	1.2F
	1630	1901	0.8E
	2139		
16 W		0038	1.2F
	0327	0704	1.4E
	1113	1410	1.1F
	1725	1945	0.7E
	2206		
17 Th		0111	1.2F
	0354	0733	1.4E
	1204	1503	1.1F
	1832	2033	0.5E
	2237		
18 F		0148	1.1F
	0426	0807	1.4E
	1303	1608	1.0F
	1951	2128	0.3E
	2311		
19 Sa		0229	1.0F
	0503	0848	1.3E
	1410	1734	0.9F
		2235	*
20 Su		0316	0.8F
	0548	0940	1.2E
	1525	1854	1.0F
		2357	*
21 M ○		0415	0.6F
	0645	1105	1.0E
	1637	1959	1.0F
22 Tu		0117	*
		0539	0.5F
	0802	1337	1.0E
	1738	2053	1.1F
23 W	0037	0231	0.3E
	0436	0709	0.5F
	0946	1504	1.1E
	1827	2136	1.2F
24 Th	0101	0333	0.6E
	0558	0835	0.7F
	1127	1557	1.1E
	1908	2210	1.2F
25 F	0121	0418	0.8E
	0700	0948	0.9F
	1246	1637	1.1E
	1943	2236	1.2F
26 Sa	0139	0456	1.1E
	0754	1045	1.2F
	1353	1712	1.1E
	2012	2300	1.2F
27 Su ●	0158	0531	1.4E
	0845	1137	1.3F
	1453	1747	1.0E
	2038	2324	1.2F
28 M	0219	0606	1.5E
	0934	1229	1.4F
	1549	1825	0.9E
	2104	2351	1.2F
29 Tu	0244	0641	1.6E
	1024	1323	1.4F
	1645	1907	0.7E
	2130		
30 W		0023	1.2F
	0312	0717	1.6E
	1117	1418	1.4F
	1745	1953	0.6E
	2159		
31 Th		0059	1.1F
	0344	0752	1.5E
	1213	1515	1.2F
	1852	2042	0.4E
	2233		

November

Day	Slack (h m)	Maximum (h m)	knots
1 F		0138	1.0F
	0418	0828	1.4E
	1313	1621	1.1F
	2005	2136	0.3E
	2312		
2 Sa		0220	0.9F
	0455	0906	1.2E
	1415	1735	1.1F
		2242	*
3 Su		0307	0.7F
	0537	0956	1.0E
	1520	1842	1.0F
		2357	*
4 M ◐		0403	0.5F
	0628	1233	0.9E
	1621	1940	1.1F
5 Tu		0107	*
		0520	0.3F
	0737	1347	1.0E
	1714	2030	1.1F
6 W	0006	0214	0.4E
	0440	0648	0.3F
	0911	1446	0.8E
	1757	2113	1.0F
7 Th	0033	0312	0.6E
	0553	0809	0.4F
	1048	1527	0.8E
	1831	2145	1.0F
8 F	0053	0358	0.8E
	0648	0919	0.6F
	1204	1556	0.8E
	1857	2206	1.0F
9 Sa	0109	0433	1.0E
	0734	1014	0.8F
	1307	1621	0.7E
	1918	2220	1.0F
10 Su	0122	0503	1.1E
	0818	1100	1.0F
	1403	1650	0.7E
	1938	2237	1.0F
11 M	0137	0529	1.3E
	0900	1146	1.1F
	1456	1724	0.7E
	2001	2300	1.1F
12 Tu ○	0155	0551	1.4E
	0942	1233	1.2F
	1549	1803	0.6E
	2028	2329	1.1F
13 W	0219	0613	1.4E
	1026	1323	1.2F
	1644	1848	0.5E
	2058		
14 Th		0003	1.1F
	0248	0639	1.5E
	1114	1415	1.2F
	1745	1938	0.4E
	2132		
15 F		0041	1.1F
	0321	0713	1.5E
	1205	1510	1.1F
	1856	2031	0.3E
	2208		
16 Sa		0125	1.0F
	0358	0755	1.4E
	1301	1612	1.1F
		2128	*
17 Su		0212	0.9F
	0441	0843	1.3E
	1400	1723	1.0F
		2235	*
18 M		0304	0.7F
	0533	0944	1.2E
	1500	1826	1.0F
		2349	*
19 Tu ○		0410	0.6F
	0640	1122	1.1E
	1558	1918	1.0F
	2303		
20 W		0056	0.3E
	0258	0537	0.5F
	0809	1256	1.0E
	1651	2002	1.0F
	2330		
21 Th		0159	0.5E
	0437	0709	0.6F
	0956	1408	0.9E
	1736	2040	1.0F
	2354		
22 F		0259	0.8E
	0553	0834	0.7F
	1131	1511	0.9E
	1814	2112	1.0F
23 Sa	0016	0351	1.0E
	0656	0947	1.0F
	1251	1601	0.8E
	1847	2142	1.0F
24 Su	0039	0436	1.3E
	0751	1045	1.2F
	1400	1644	0.7E
	1918	2211	1.1F
25 M	0105	0516	1.5E
	0844	1138	1.3F
	1502	1725	0.7E
	1949	2242	1.1F
26 Tu ●	0134	0554	1.6E
	0934	1231	1.4F
	1558	1808	0.6E
	2021	2316	1.1F
27 W	0206	0633	1.6E
	1023	1324	1.4F
	1654	1854	0.5E
	2055	2352	1.1F
28 Th	0240	0712	1.6E
	1113	1417	1.4F
	1751	1942	0.4E
	2132		
29 F		0032	1.1F
	0315	0748	1.5E
	1203	1508	1.3F
	1850	2032	0.3E
	2213		
30 Sa		0115	1.0F
	0352	0819	1.4E
	1253	1602	1.2F
	1949	2122	0.3E
	2300		

December

Day	Slack (h m)	Maximum (h m)	knots
1 Su		0200	0.8F
	0432	0850	1.2E
	1342	1700	1.1F
		2217	*
2 M		0249	0.7F
	0517	0928	1.1E
	1429	1755	1.0F
	2132	2318	0.3E
3 Tu	0107	0344	0.6F
	0612	1019	1.0E
	1514	1841	1.0F
	2211		
4 W ◐		0016	0.4E
	0226	0453	0.5F
	0721	1126	0.8E
	1554	1919	0.9F
	2242		
5 Th		0110	0.5E
	0352	0615	0.4F
	0844	1228	0.7E
	1630	1948	0.8F
	2306		
6 F		0203	0.6E
	0511	0734	0.5F
	1016	1325	0.6E
	1701	2012	0.8F
	2326		
7 Sa		0258	0.8E
	0615	0850	0.7F
	1140	1425	0.6E
	1731	2038	0.8F
	2347		
8 Su		0347	1.0E
	0711	0956	0.8F
	1253	1525	0.5E
	1801	2109	0.9F
9 M	0011	0428	1.2E
	0802	1051	1.0F
	1401	1617	0.5E
	1835	2143	1.0F
10 Tu	0038	0504	1.3E
	0851	1142	1.1F
	1504	1705	0.5E
	1911	2220	1.0F
11 W	0110	0535	1.4E
	0938	1234	1.2F
	1602	1753	0.4E
	1951	2259	1.1F
12 Th ○	0145	0607	1.5E
	1024	1326	1.3F
	1700	1844	0.4E
	2032	2340	1.1F
13 F	0223	0642	1.5E
	1111	1417	1.3F
	1759	1938	0.3E
	2116		
14 Sa		0024	1.0F
	0304	0724	1.5E
	1159	1506	1.2F
	1858	2030	0.3E
	2203		
15 Su		0114	1.0F
	0349	0810	1.4E
	1248	1555	1.2F
	1950	2123	0.3E
	2259		
16 M		0206	0.9F
	0440	0859	1.3E
	1335	1646	1.1F
	2034	2218	0.3E
17 Tu	0008	0303	0.8F
	0540	0955	1.2E
	1421	1755	1.0F
	2111	2320	0.4E
18 W ○	0129	0411	0.7F
	0655	1106	1.0E
	1506	1817	0.9F
	2142		
19 Th ◐		0020	0.5E
	0258	0537	0.6F
	0824	1215	0.9E
	1549	1854	0.9F
	2211		
20 F		0119	0.7E
	0428	0708	0.7F
	1004	1319	0.7E
	1631	1929	0.9F
	2240		
21 Sa		0224	0.9E
	0546	0833	0.8F
	1138	1426	0.6E
	1711	2007	0.9F
	2312		
22 Su		0331	1.2E
	0652	0947	1.0F
	1301	1531	0.5E
	1750	2047	0.9F
	2347		
23 M		0427	1.4E
	0751	1047	1.2F
	1414	1626	0.5E
	1831	2129	0.9F
24 Tu	0024	0517	1.5E
	0844	1140	1.3F
	1516	1714	0.4E
	1913	2211	1.0F
25 W	0102	0602	1.6E
	0934	1232	1.4F
	1609	1801	0.4E
	1957	2252	1.0F
26 Th ●	0142	0646	1.6E
	1019	1322	1.4F
	1657	1848	0.4E
	2041	2333	1.0F
27 F ○	0221	0725	1.5E
	1103	1408	1.4F
	1744	1935	0.4E
	2125		
28 Sa		0015	1.0F
	0300	0754	1.5E
	1145	1451	1.3F
	1828	2019	0.4E
	2209		
29 Su		0100	0.9F
	0339	0812	1.4E
	1223	1531	1.2F
	1908	2101	0.4E
	2256		
30 M		0147	0.9F
	0421	0831	1.3E
	1258	1607	1.1F
	1942	2142	0.4E
	2348		
31 Tu		0235	0.8F
	0509	0901	1.2E
	1329	1639	1.0F
	2011	2224	0.5E

Time meridian 75° W. 0000 is midnight. 1200 is noon. Times are not adjusted for Daylight Saving Time.
If three consecutive entries are marked (F) the middle one is not a true maximum but an intermediate value to show the current pattern.
* Current weak and variable.

Johns Pass Entrance, Florida, 2019

F–Flood, Dir. 053° True   E–Ebb, Dir. 222° True

January

Date	Slack (h m)	Maximum (h m)	knots
1 Tu		0026	1.4E
	0352	0635	0.3F
	1004	1248	0.4E
	1626		*
2 W		0109	1.6E
	0437	0742	0.4F
	1114	1338	0.3E
	1713		*
3 Th		0149	1.8E
	0520	0822	0.5F
	1205	1418	0.3E
	1625	1804	0.3F
	2133		
4 F		0228	1.8E
	0602	0851	0.6F
	1244	1454	0.3E
	1708	1859	0.3F
	2213		
5 Sa ●		0307	1.8E
	0643	0913	0.6F
	1313	1527	0.3E
	1755	1951	0.3F
	2252		
6 Su		0347	1.8E
	0724	0933	0.6F
	1334	1604	0.3E
	1844	2038	0.3F
	2333		
7 M		0426	1.6E
	0803	0958	0.5F
	1351	1642	0.4E
	1935	2124	0.3F
8 Tu	0014	0505	1.5E
	0842	1028	0.5F
	1409	1721	0.5E
	2030	2212	0.3F
9 W	0055	0541	1.3E
	0920	1102	0.4F
	1431	1800	0.5E
	2305		*
10 Th		0613	1.1E
	0958	1138	0.3F
	1455	1840	0.6E
11 F		0006	*
		0644	0.9E
	1035	1216	0.3F
	1519	1926	0.7E
12 Sa		0117	*
		0716	0.7E
	1257		*
		2029	0.7F
13 Su		0239	*
		0753	0.6E
	1343		*
		2151	0.9E
14 M ◐		0343	*
		0850	0.4E
	1432		*
		2257	1.1E
15 Tu	0246	0436	0.3F
	0724	1015	0.3E
	1521		*
		2347	1.3E
16 W	0328	0534	0.4F
	0917	1133	0.3E
	1413	1610	0.3F
	1814		
17 Th		0033	1.6E
	0411	0652	0.5F
	1036	1237	0.3E
	1459	1659	0.3F
	1931		
18 F		0117	1.8E
	0456	0754	0.7F
	1132	1330	0.3E
	1547	1754	0.4F
	2054		
19 Sa		0201	2.0E
	0541	0834	0.7F
	1217	1419	0.4E
	1639	1852	0.5F
	2158		
20 Su		0246	2.0E
	0627	0900	0.7F
	1257	1508	0.5E
	1736	1949	0.5F
	2256		
21 M ○		0333	2.0E
	0712	0922	0.7F
	1334	1601	0.6E
	1836	2042	0.5F
	2352		
22 Tu		0421	1.8E
	0756	0951	0.6F
	1409	1655	0.7E
	1937	2135	0.5F
23 W	0049	0508	1.6E
	0838	1025	0.5F
	1442	1748	0.8E
	2042	2231	0.4F
24 Th	0147	0554	1.4E
	0921	1102	0.4F
	1513	1840	0.9E
	2154	2334	0.3F
25 F	0248	0637	1.1E
	1003	1141	0.4F
	1541	1936	0.9E
26 Sa		0050	*
		0720	0.8E
	1046	1224	0.3F
	1603	2044	1.0E
27 Su ◑		0251	*
		0807	0.5E
	1311		*
		2159	1.2E
28 M		0358	*
		0919	*
	1403		*
		2301	1.3E
29 Tu	0238	0453	0.3F
		1153	*
	1458		*
		2353	1.5E
30 W	0326	0558	0.3F
		1300	*
	1552		*
31 Th		0039	1.7E
	0410	0714	0.4F
	1346		*
	1645		*

February

Date	Slack (h m)	Maximum (h m)	knots
1 F		0121	1.7E
	0453	0800	0.5F
	1208	1423	0.3E
	1742		*
2 Sa		0201	1.8E
	0534	0830	0.5F
	1226	1454	0.3E
	1846		*
3 Su		0239	1.7E
	0615	0850	0.6F
	1238	1521	0.4E
	1800	1947	0.3F
	2243		
4 M ●		0316	1.6E
	0653	0902	0.5F
	1248	1551	0.5E
	1849	2036	0.3F
	2328		
5 Tu		0353	1.4E
	0729	0921	0.5F
	1301	1626	0.6E
	1938	2119	0.3F
6 W	0011	0428	1.2E
	0802	0947	0.5F
	1319	1704	0.7E
	2028	2204	0.3F
7 Th	0051	0502	1.1E
	0831	1017	0.4F
	1339	1743	0.8E
	2253		*
8 F		0535	0.9E
	0857	1049	0.4F
	1356	1822	0.9E
	2348		*
9 Sa		0606	0.8E
	0917	1123	0.4F
	1408	1905	1.0E
10 Su		0051	*
		0639	0.6E
	0935	1201	0.3F
	1424	1956	1.0E
11 M		0204	*
		0715	0.5E
	0957	1243	0.3F
	1454	2059	1.2E
12 Tu ◐	0117	0316	0.3F
	0552	0804	*
	1029	1337	0.3F
	1538	2207	1.3E
13 W	0208	0415	0.4F
		0932	*
	1438		*
		2308	1.5E
14 Th	0257	0513	0.5F
		1116	*
		1539	0.3F
	1735		
15 F		0001	1.7E
	0344	0634	0.6F
	1233		*
		1637	0.3F
	1902		
16 Sa		0051	1.9E
	0431	0748	0.6F
	1127	1328	0.3E
	1545	1738	0.4F
	2046		
17 Su		0139	1.9E
	0518	0832	0.7F
	1200	1415	0.5E
	1646	1844	0.4F
	2200		
18 M		0225	1.9E
	0603	0852	0.6F
	1230	1503	0.7E
	1747	1947	0.5F
	2301		
19 Tu ○		0311	1.8E
	0646	0852	0.6F
	1259	1553	0.8E
	1846	2043	0.5F
	2358		
20 W		0358	1.6E
	0726	0916	0.6F
	1327	1645	0.9E
	1945	2135	0.5F
21 Th	0053	0444	1.3E
	0802	0947	0.5F
	1353	1736	1.1E
	2045	2229	0.4F
22 F	0149	0528	1.1E
	0836	1021	0.5F
	1416	1825	1.2E
	2150	2331	0.3F
23 Sa	0248	0609	0.8E
	0908	1058	0.4F
	1432	1915	1.3E
	2300		
24 Su		0045	0.3F
	0352	0646	0.5E
	0935	1138	0.3F
	1432	2010	1.3E
25 M	0009	0232	0.3F
	0503	0722	0.3E
	0953	1223	0.3F
	1441	2114	1.4E
26 Tu ◑	0112	0335	0.3F
		0805	*
		1316	*
		2220	1.4E
27 W	0207	0426	0.3F
		1207	*
		1420	*
		2317	1.5E
28 Th	0256	0517	0.4F
		1259	*
		1526	*

March

Date	Slack (h m)	Maximum (h m)	knots
1 F		0007	1.6E
	0341	0623	0.4F
	1339		*
	1628		*
2 Sa		0053	1.6E
	0424	0727	0.4F
	1138	1413	0.3E
	1552	1732	0.3F
3 Su		0133	1.6E
	0505	0804	0.5F
	1143	1441	0.5E
	1855		*
4 M		0210	1.5E
	0544	0823	0.5F
	1149	1504	0.6E
	1800	2010	0.3F
	2235		
5 Tu		0244	1.3E
	0619	0825	0.5F
	1159	1530	0.7E
	1845	2040	0.3F
	2320		
6 W ●		0317	1.2E
	0650	0842	0.5F
	1214	1602	0.8E
	1929	2114	0.3F
7 Th	0001	0350	1.0E
	0718	0908	0.5F
	1233	1640	0.9E
	2013	2152	0.3F
8 F	0042	0423	0.9E
	0740	0936	0.5F
	1249	1719	1.1E
	2058	2237	0.3F
9 Sa	0128	0458	0.8E
	0758	1006	0.5F
	1300	1759	1.2E
	2148	2328	0.3F
10 Su	0223	0534	0.7E
	0813	1038	0.5F
	1313	1841	1.3E
	2242		
11 M		0026	0.3F
	0329	0611	0.5E
	0832	1112	0.4F
	1339	1927	1.4E
	2340		
12 Tu ◐		0134	0.4F
	0440	0652	0.4E
	0856	1153	0.4F
	1416	2022	1.4E
13 W	0038	0250	0.4F
		0741	*
		1251	0.3F
	1504	2127	1.5E
14 Th ◐	0134	0355	0.5F
		0907	*
		1406	0.3F
	1605	2232	1.6E
15 F	0228	0452	0.5F
		1112	*
	1520		*
		2333	1.7E
16 Sa	0319	0612	0.5F
	1028	1235	0.3E
	1445	1626	0.3F
	1906		
17 Su		0027	1.8E
	0407	0739	0.6F
	1058	1324	0.5E
	1552	1732	0.3F
	2051		
18 M		0118	1.7E
	0453	0827	0.6F
	1127	1408	0.7E
	1653	1846	0.4F
	2205		
19 Tu		0204	1.6E
	0536	0851	0.5F
	1154	1453	0.9E
	1752	1958	0.4F
	2306		
20 W ○		0250	1.5E
	0616	0815	0.5F
	1220	1540	1.1E
	1848	2050	0.5F
21 Th	0002	0334	1.2E
	0651	0840	0.5F
	1244	1629	1.3E
	1943	2137	0.5F
22 F	0055	0418	1.0E
	0723	0911	0.5F
	1304	1718	1.4E
	2038	2226	0.4F
23 Sa	0150	0501	0.7E
	0750	0945	0.5F
	1319	1804	1.5E
	2135	2323	0.4F
24 Su	0250	0541	0.5E
	0812	1020	0.5F
	1323	1849	1.5E
	2235		
25 M		0030	0.3F
	0357	0617	0.3E
	0824	1059	0.4F
	1331	1936	1.5E
	2336		
26 Tu		0155	0.3F
		0648	*
		1142	0.3F
	1355	2030	1.5E
27 W ◑	0035	0303	0.3F
		0715	*
		1238	*
		2133	1.4E
28 Th	0131	0353	0.3F
		1157	*
		1351	*
		2237	1.4E
29 F	0223	0437	0.3F
		1242	*
	1510		*
		2334	1.4E
30 Sa	0310	0523	0.3F
	1042	1318	0.3E
	1520	1622	*
	2333		
31 Su		0023	1.3E
	0354	0626	0.3F
	1040	1350	0.5E
		1739	*

Time meridian 75° W. 0000 is midnight. 1200 is noon. Times are not adjusted for Daylight Saving Time.
If three consecutive entries are marked (F) the middle one is not a true maximum but an intermediate value to show the current pattern.
* Current weak and variable.

Johns Pass Entrance, Florida, 2019

F–Flood, Dir. 053° True   E–Ebb, Dir. 222° True

April

Day	Slack (h m)	Maximum (h m)	knots
1 M		0105	1.3E
	0433	0728	0.3F
	1045	1416	0.6E
		1946	*
2 Tu		0140	1.2E
	0509	0736	0.4F
	1055	1438	0.8E
	1750	2022	0.3F
	2223		
3 W		0211	1.1E
	0541	0736	0.4F
	1111	1503	0.9E
	1831	2042	0.3F
	2307		
4 Th		0241	1.0E
	0608	0801	0.4F
	1130	1535	1.1E
	1910	2104	0.4F
	2350		
5 F ●		0313	0.8E
	0631	0829	0.5F
	1147	1612	1.2E
	1949	2137	0.4F
6 Sa	0035	0348	0.7E
	0649	0858	0.5F
	1200	1652	1.3E
	2031	2219	0.5F
7 Su	0127	0427	0.6E
	0707	0929	0.5F
	1212	1734	1.5E
	2116	2307	0.5F
8 M	0227	0509	0.5E
	0727	1002	0.5F
	1235	1816	1.6E
	2207		
9 Tu		0002	0.5F
	0334	0553	0.4E
	0752	1039	0.5F
	1309	1901	1.7E
	2303		
10 W		0105	0.5F
	0445	0638	0.3E
	0822	1124	0.4F
	1352	1952	1.7E
11 Th	0003	0219	0.5F
		0731	*
		1229	0.3F
	1447	2052	1.6E
12 F ◐	0103	0331	0.5F
		0857	*
		1351	0.3F
	1559	2200	1.6E
13 Sa	0200	0427	0.5F
		1113	*
		1511	*
		2305	1.6E
14 Su	0254	0532	0.4F
	0942	1225	0.4E
	1450	1623	0.3F
	1920		
15 M		0005	1.5E
	0342	0724	0.4F
	1015	1312	0.7E
	1555	1736	0.3F
	2056		
16 Tu		0058	1.4E
	0426	0814	0.4F
	1045	1355	1.0E
	1654	1944	0.4F
	2209		
17 W		0145	1.3E
	0505	0702	0.4F
		0748	0.4F
		0841	0.4F
	1112	1438†	1.2E
18 Th		0229	1.1E
	0541	0731	0.4F
	1137	1523	1.4E
	1843	2110	0.5F
19 F O	0006	0311	0.9E
	0613	0804	0.5F
	1159	1608	1.5E
	1933	2141	0.5F
20 Sa	0100	0354	0.7E
	0641	0838	0.5F
	1216	1654	1.6E
	2022	2220	0.5F
21 Su	0156	0436	0.5E
	0706	0913	0.5F
	1227	1738	1.7E
	2112	2307	0.4F
22 M	0256	0517	0.3E
	0725	0950	0.5F
	1236	1821	1.7E
	2205		
23 Tu		0001	0.4F
		0554	*
		1029	0.4F
	1257	1903	1.6E
	2300		
24 W		0103	0.4F
		0628	*
		1115	0.3F
	1327	1949	1.5E
	2356		
25 Th		0212	0.3F
		0700	*
		1216	*
		2043	1.4E
26 F O	0053	0309	0.3F
		0749	*
		0911	*
		1126	*
		1336†	*
27 Sa	0148	0353	0.3F
		1211	*
		1507	*
		2254	1.1E
28 Su	0237	0428	0.3F
	0858	1247	0.4E
		1632	*
		2349	1.0E
29 M		0500	*
		1318	0.6E
		1811	*
30 Tu		0032	0.9E
		0532	*
		1344	0.8E
		1922	*

May

Day	Slack (h m)	Maximum (h m)	knots
1 W		0107	0.9E
	0430	0607	0.3F
	0958	1407	1.0E
	1730	2003	0.3F
	2209		
2 Th		0137	0.8E
	0457	0642	0.3F
	1021	1433	1.2E
	1807	2028	0.4F
	2257		
3 F		0207	0.7E
	0521	0717	0.4F
	1042	1505	1.3E
	1844	2050	0.5F
	2345		
4 Sa ●		0241	0.7E
	0542	0751	0.5F
	1059	1542	1.5E
	1922	2121	0.5F
5 Su	0035	0320	0.6E
	0602	0825	0.5F
	1114	1623	1.6E
	2003	2200	0.6F
6 M	0131	0404	0.5E
	0626	0900	0.6F
	1137	1707	1.7E
	2047	2246	0.6F
7 Tu	0231	0452	0.4E
	0656	0938	0.6F
	1211	1751	1.8E
	2137	2337	0.6F
8 W	0335	0541	0.3E
	0732	1021	0.5F
	1253	1837	1.8E
	2231		
9 Th		0033	0.5F
	0438	0631	0.3E
	0817	1114	0.4F
	1345	1926	1.7E
	2330		
10 F		0135	0.5F
		0728	*
		1224	0.3F
	1452	2022	1.6E
11 Sa ☾	0031	0245	0.4F
		0852	*
		1346	*
		2128	1.4E
12 Su	0130	0341	0.4F
	0743	1055	0.4E
		1511	*
		2238	1.3E
13 M	0224	0415	0.3F
	0838	1203	0.7E
		1630	*
		2342	1.1E
14 Tu	0312	0448	0.3F
		0605	0.3F
	0921	0653	0.3F
	1554	1252	1.0E
		1828†	0.3F
15 W		0039	1.0E
	0352	0525	0.3F
		0644	0.3F
		0751	0.3F
	0956	1336†	1.3E
16 Th		0128	0.9E
	0429	0606	0.3F
	1026	1419	1.5E
	1742	2038	0.5F
	2320		
17 F		0211	0.7E
	0503	0648	0.4F
	1052	1500	1.7E
	1830	2113	0.5F
18 Sa O	0017	0253	0.6E
	0534	0729	0.4F
	1113	1543	1.8E
	1915	2139	0.5F
19 Su	0110	0334	0.4E
	0604	0809	0.5F
	1131	1626	1.8E
	1959	2207	0.5F
20 M	0204	0416	0.3E
	0633	0848	0.5F
	1148	1709	1.8E
	2044	2243	0.5F
21 Tu		0459	*
		0928	0.4F
	1210	1751	1.7E
	2131	2326	0.5F
22 W		0539	*
		1011	0.4F
	1240	1831	1.6E
	2222		
23 Th		0013	0.4F
		0617	*
		1103	0.3F
	1317	1912	1.4E
	2315		
24 F		0103	0.3F
		0655	*
		1208	*
		1956	1.2E
25 Sa	0011	0156	0.3F
		0749	*
		0925	*
		1032	*
		1330†	*
26 Su		0247	*
		1127	0.4E
		1523	*
		2152	0.8E
27 M		0327	*
		1207	0.6E
		1635	*
		2257	0.7E
28 Tu		0402	*
		1239	0.8E
		1735	*
		2347	0.6E
29 W		0437	*
		1306	1.0E
		1844	*
30 Th		0027	0.6E
		0513	*
		1331	1.2E
	1702	1935	0.3F
	2200		
31 F		0102	0.6E
	0410	0552	0.3F
	0921	1401	1.4E
	1738	2008	0.4F
	2255		

June

Day	Slack (h m)	Maximum (h m)	knots
1 Sa		0139	0.5E
	0433	0633	0.4F
	0947	1434	1.6E
	1815	2034	0.6F
	2348		
2 Su		0218	0.5E
	0457	0715	0.4F
	1011	1513	1.7E
	1854	2105	0.7F
3 M ●		0301	0.5E
	0526	0757	0.5F
	1041	1555	1.9E
	1936	2142	0.7F
4 Tu	0134	0349	0.4E
	0603	0839	0.6F
	1118	1641	1.9E
	2020	2223	0.7F
5 W	0229	0442	0.4E
	0646	0924	0.6F
	1202	1727	1.9E
	2108	2308	0.6F
6 Th	0322	0535	0.4E
	0738	1013	0.5F
	1255	1814	1.8E
	2200	2356	0.5F
7 F	0411	0627	0.4E
	0843	1113	0.4F
	1359	1902	1.7E
	2256		
8 Sa		0046	0.4F
	0456	0725	0.4E
	1018	1223	0.3F
	1518	1953	1.4E
	2354		
9 Su		0138	0.3F
	0539	0844	0.5E
		1346	*
		2054	1.1E
10 M ☾	0052	0230	0.3F
	0624	1026	0.7E
		1524	*
		2206	0.9E
11 Tu		0317	*
		1136	1.0E
	1447	1654	0.3F
	1931	2319	0.7F
12 W		0359	*
		1228	1.2E
	1546	1829	0.3F
	2116		
13 Th		0024	0.6E
	0314	0440	0.3F
	0856	1313	1.5E
	1638	1943	0.4F
	2236		
14 F		0117	0.5E
	0351	0523	0.3F
	0933	1355	1.7E
	1725	2030	0.5F
	2339		
15 Sa		0202	0.4E
	0427	0609	0.3F
	1002	1435	1.8E
	1809	2102	0.6F
16 Su	0032	0243	0.4E
		0658	0.4F
	1029	1516	1.9E
	1851	2126	0.6F
17 M O	0118	0323	0.3E
	0542	0745	0.4F
	1056	1557	1.9E
	1932	2146	0.6F
18 Tu	0158	0404	0.3E
	0624	0830	0.4F
	1126	1639	1.8E
	2014	2213	0.5F
19 W	0229	0447	0.3E
	0710	0915	0.4F
	1202	1720	1.7E
	2057	2248	0.5F
20 Th	0254	0528	0.3E
	0803	1003	0.3F
	1244	1759	1.5E
	2142	2326	0.4F
21 F	0314	0607	*
		1058	*
		1836	1.3E
	2230		
22 Sa		0007	0.3F
	0337	0647	0.4E
		1203	*
		1912	1.0E
23 Su		0050	*
		0737	0.4E
		1324	*
		1948	0.8E
24 M		0135	*
		0917	0.5E
		1516	*
		2031	0.6E
25 Tu		0221	*
		1107	0.7E
		1611	*
		2130	0.5E
26 W		0304	*
		1146	0.9E
		1659	*
		2241	0.4E
27 Th		0346	*
		1219	1.1E
	1552	1754	0.3F
	2044	2342	0.3E
28 F		0426	*
		1252	1.3E
	1628	1859	0.4F
	2203		
29 Sa		0033	0.3E
	0321	0509	0.3F
	0749	1327	1.6E
	1705	1947	0.5F
	2303		
30 Su		0119	0.4E
	0352	0555	0.3F
	0847	1405	1.8E
	1745	2020	0.6F
	2355		

Time meridian 75° W. 0000 is midnight. 1200 is noon. Times are not adjusted for Daylight Saving Time.
If three consecutive entries are marked (F) the middle one is not a true maximum but an intermediate value to show the current pattern.
* Current weak and variable.
† See page 196 for the remaining currents on this day.

Johns Pass Entrance, Florida, 2019

F–Flood, Dir. 053° True   E–Ebb, Dir. 222° True

July

Days 1–15

Day	Slack (h m)	Maximum (h m)	knots
1 M		0204	0.4E
	0428	0646	0.4F
	0937	1446	1.9E
	1827	2049	0.7F
2 Tu ●	0042	0250	0.4E
	0511	0737	0.5F
	1025	1529	2.0E
	1910	2121	0.7F
3 W	0127	0341	0.4E
	0602	0827	0.5F
	1117	1616	2.0E
	1955	2157	0.7F
4 Th	0210	0435	0.5E
	0659	0917	0.6F
	1212	1704	1.9E
	2040	2235	0.6F
5 F	0251	0529	0.6E
	0801	1011	0.5F
	1314	1752	1.7E
	2128	2316	0.5F
6 Sa	0329	0622	0.6E
	0913	1112	0.4F
	1421	1838	1.4E
	2217	2359	0.4F
7 Su	0406	0719	0.7E
	1039	1223	0.3F
	1532	1925	1.1E
	2308		
8 M		0044	0.3F
	0440	0829	0.8E
		1352	*
		2017	0.8E
9 Tu ◑	0000	0132	0.3F
	0513	0954	1.0E
		1547	*
		2126	0.5E
10 W		0222	*
		1104	1.2E
	1436	1654	0.3F
	1946	2258	0.4E
11 Th		0312	*
		1159	1.4E
	1530	1810	0.3F
	2150		
12 F		0024	0.3E
		0400	*
		1245	1.6E
	1617	1930	0.4F
	2306		
13 Sa		0122	0.3E
		0447	*
		1328	1.8E
	1701	2017	0.5F
	2359		
14 Su		0206	0.3E
		0538	*
		1408	1.9E
	1743	2045	0.6F
15 M	0037	0244	0.3E
	0450	0634	0.3F
	0954	1448	1.9E
	1823	2105	0.6F

Days 16–31

Day	Slack (h m)	Maximum (h m)	knots
16 Tu ○	0106	0320	0.3E
	0540	0731	0.3F
	1037	1528	1.8E
	1904	2120	0.6F
17 W	0126	0357	0.4E
	0631	0822	0.3F
	1120	1608	1.7E
	1943	2141	0.5F
18 Th	0141	0436	0.4E
	0722	0910	0.3F
	1205	1648	1.5E
	2022	2209	0.5F
19 F	0156	0516	0.5E
	0817		0.3F
	1252	1726	1.3E
	2101	2242	0.4F
20 Sa	0214	0554	0.6E
		1053	*
		1800	1.1E
	2138	2317	0.3F
21 Su	0235	0633	0.7E
		1155	*
		1830	0.9E
	2214	2354	0.3F
22 M	0256	0717	0.7E
		1307	*
		1859	0.7E
23 Tu		0033	*
		0812	0.8E
		1438	*
		1929	0.5E
24 W ◐		0116	*
		0928	0.9E
		1538	*
		2010	0.3E
25 Th		0203	*
		1037	1.1E
		1626	*
		2126	*
26 F		0254	*
		1127	1.3E
	1513	1715	0.3F
		2301	*
27 Sa		0344	*
		1212	1.5E
	1553	1818	0.5F
28 Su		0014	*
		0434	0.3F
	0634	1255	1.7E
	1634	1926	0.6F
	2312		
29 M		0109	0.3E
	0328	0528	0.3F
	0803	1337	1.9E
	1717	2008	0.7F
	2353		
30 Tu		0157	0.4E
	0420	0627	0.4F
	0924	1421	1.9E
	1801	2034	0.7F
31 W ●	0030	0244	0.5E
	0516	0726	0.5F
	1028	1506	1.9E
	1845	2058	0.7F

August

Days 1–15

Day	Slack (h m)	Maximum (h m)	knots
1 Th	0104	0334	0.6E
	0615	0822	0.5F
	1127	1553	1.8E
	1929	2127	0.7F
2 F	0138	0428	0.7E
	0714	0915	0.5F
	1226	1641	1.7E
	2010	2200	0.6F
3 Sa	0210	0522	0.8E
	0817	1010	0.5F
	1327	1728	1.4E
	2051	2236	0.5F
4 Su	0241	0614	1.0E
	0925	1111	0.4F
	1430	1813	1.1E
	2131	2315	0.4F
5 M	0311	0707	1.1E
	1041	1223	0.3F
	1536	1855	0.8E
	2210	2356	0.4F
6 Tu	0337	0807	1.1E
	1159	1419	0.3F
	1645	1939	0.5E
	2250		
7 W ◑		0041	0.3F
	0354	0919	1.2E
	1312	1540	0.3F
		2036	*
8 Th		0131	*
		1028	1.4E
	1414	1637	0.3F
		2307	*
9 F		0227	*
		1125	1.5E
	1504	1739	0.3F
10 Sa		0039	*
		0324	*
		1215	1.7E
	1550	1900	0.4F
11 Su		0129	*
		0420	*
		1300	1.7E
	1632	1954	0.5F
	2359		
12 M		0209	0.3E
		0518	*
		1341	1.8E
	1714	2022	0.5F
13 Tu	0017	0242	0.3E
		0622	*
		1421	1.7E
	1754	2042	0.5F
14 W	0029	0313	0.4E
	0544	0729	0.3F
	1029	1459	1.6E
	1834	2050	0.5F
15 Th ○	0039	0344	0.5E
	0634	0824	0.3F
	1118	1537	1.4E
	1911	2106	0.5F

Days 16–31

Day	Slack (h m)	Maximum (h m)	knots
16 F	0049	0418	0.7E
	0724	0910	0.3F
	1204	1614	1.2E
	1945	2131	0.5F
17 Sa	0104	0456	0.8E
	0814	0955	0.3F
	1249	1649	1.1E
	2016	2200	0.4F
18 Su	0122	0534	0.9E
	0908	1044	0.3F
	1333	1721	0.9E
	2042	2231	0.4F
19 M	0139	0613	0.9E
		1138	*
		1751	0.7E
	2059	2303	0.4F
20 Tu	0148	0653	1.0E
		1239	*
		1820	0.6E
	2109	2337	0.3F
21 W	0159	0738	1.1E
		1350	*
		1851	0.4E
	2121		
22 Th		0013	0.3F
	0224	0833	1.2E
	1301	1500	0.3F
	1726	1929	0.3E
23 F ○		0100	*
		0937	1.3E
	1349	1554	0.3F
		2032	*
24 Sa		0204	*
		1039	1.4E
	1435	1644	0.4F
		2231	*
25 Su		0310	*
		1134	1.6E
	1521	1740	0.5F
26 M		0006	*
		0412	*
		1225	1.7E
	1606	1904	0.6F
	2302		
27 Tu		0105	0.3E
	0325	0512	0.3F
	0757	1312	1.8E
	1651	2000	0.6F
	2333		
28 W		0152	0.5E
	0425	0618	0.4F
	0928	1359	1.8E
	1736	2020	0.6F
29 Th	0002	0238	0.7E
	0524	0724	0.5F
	1036	1444	1.7E
	1819	2029	0.6F
30 F ●	0031	0326	0.8E
	0623	0823	0.5F
	1136	1531	1.6E
	1900	2054	0.6F
31 Sa	0059	0418	1.0E
	0721	0916	0.5F
	1234	1618	1.3E
	1937	2125	0.6F

September

Days 1–15

Day	Slack (h m)	Maximum (h m)	knots
1 Su	0126	0510	1.2E
	0820	1010	0.5F
	1332	1704	1.1E
	2010	2158	0.5F
2 M	0151	0600	1.3E
	0923	1109	0.4F
	1433	1747	0.8E
	2040	2234	0.5F
3 Tu	0212	0649	1.4E
	1030	1220	0.3F
	1539	1827	0.5E
	2105	2313	0.4F
4 W	0221	0741	1.4E
	1139	1409	0.3F
	1650	1905	0.3E
	2120	2355	0.3F
5 Th ◑	0226	0841	1.4E
	1244	1519	0.3F
		1945	*
6 F		0045	*
		0946	1.5E
	1342	1611	0.3F
		2339	*
7 Sa		0147	*
		1048	1.5E
	1433	1659	0.3F
8 Su		0038	*
		0257	*
		1143	1.6E
	1519	1757	0.4F
9 M		0120	*
		0404	*
		1231	1.6E
	1602	1911	0.4F
	2326		
10 Tu		0155	0.4E
		0509	*
		1315	1.5E
	1644	1952	0.4F
	2332		
11 W		0226	0.5E
		0628	*
		1355	1.5E
	1725	2015	0.4F
	2339		
12 Th		0254	0.6E
	0542	0811	0.3F
	1023	1431	1.3E
	1802	2015	0.4F
	2347		
13 F ○		0322	0.8E
	0630	0842	0.3F
	1112	1505	1.2E
	1835	2029	0.4F
14 Sa	0000	0354	0.9E
	0716	0912	0.4F
	1156	1537	1.0E
	1904	2053	0.5F
15 Su	0018	0431	1.0E
	0801	0947	0.4F
	1238	1609	0.8E
	1927	2120	0.5F

Days 16–30

Day	Slack (h m)	Maximum (h m)	knots
16 M	0035	0509	1.1E
	0847	1028	0.3F
	1322	1642	0.7E
	1943	2149	0.5F
17 Tu	0045	0547	1.2E
	0935	1115	0.3F
	1411	1716	0.6E
	1953	2218	0.4F
18 W	0054	0626	1.3E
	1026	1209	0.3F
	1509	1750	0.5E
	2007	2249	0.4F
19 Th	0114	0707	1.4E
	1119	1309	0.3F
	1615	1827	0.3E
	2028	2321	0.4F
20 F	0146	0754	1.4E
	1214	1418	0.4F
		1909	*
21 Sa ○		0008	0.3F
	0229	0852	1.5E
	1308	1522	0.4F
		2011	*
22 Su		0128	*
		0957	1.5E
	1400	1615	0.5F
		2215	*
23 M		0249	*
		1100	1.6E
	1451	1705	0.5F
24 Tu		0004	*
		0400	*
		1157	1.6E
	1540	1821	0.5F
	2228		
25 W		0058	0.4E
	0328	0506	0.3F
	0810	1250	1.7E
	1626	1953	0.5F
	2257		
26 Th		0143	0.7E
	0429	0618	0.4F
	0936	1338	1.6E
	1710	2022	0.5F
	2325		
27 F		0228	0.9E
	0527	0735	0.5F
	1043	1424	1.4E
	1750	1950	0.5F
	2352		
28 Sa ●		0314	1.2E
	0624	0835	0.5F
	1143	1509	1.2E
	1826	2019	0.5F
29 Su	0018	0403	1.3E
	0720	0912	0.5F
	1240	1554	1.0E
	1858	2050	0.5F
30 M	0043	0452	1.5E
	0815	1011	0.5F
	1337	1639	0.8E
	1926	2124	0.5F

Time meridian 75° W. 0000 is midnight. 1200 is noon. Times are not adjusted for Daylight Saving Time.
If three consecutive entries are marked (F) the middle one is not a true maximum but an intermediate value to show the current pattern.
* Current weak and variable.

Johns Pass Entrance, Florida, 2019

F–Flood, Dir. 053° True   E–Ebb, Dir. 222° True

October

Day	Slack (h m)	Maximum (h m)	knots
1 Tu	0103	0540	1.6E
	0911	1104	0.4F
	1438	1722	0.5E
	1949	2159	0.5F
2 W	0114	0627	1.6E
	1009	1207	0.4F
	1546	1801	0.3E
	2005	2236	0.4F
3 Th	0120	0713	1.6E
	1109	1330	0.3F
		1838	*
		2318	0.4F
4 F	0139	0803	1.6E
	1208	1444	0.3F
	1913		*
5 Sa ☾		0010	*
		0901	1.5E
	1305	1535	0.3F
		2016	*
		2116†	*
6 Su		0120	*
		1006	1.4E
	1358	1617	0.3F
7 M		0018	*
		0242	*
		1108	1.4E
	1447	1657	0.3F
	2224		
8 Tu		0056	0.3E
		0359	*
		1202	1.3E
	1533	1743	0.3F
	2224		
9 W		0130	0.5E
		0515	*
		1249	1.2E
	1614	1904	0.3F
	2231		
10 Th		0200	0.7E
		0725	*
		1328	1.1E
	1652	1939	0.3F
	2241		
11 F		0228	0.9E
	0533	0812	0.3F
	1015	1401	1.0E
	1726	1922	0.3F
	2256		
12 Sa		0255	1.0E
	0617	0844	0.4F
	1103	1431	0.9E
	1755	1946	0.4F
	2315		
13 Su ○		0326	1.1E
	0659	0907	0.4F
	1146	1500	0.8E
	1818	2014	0.4F
	2333		
14 M		0400	1.3E
	0739	0933	0.4F
	1228	1532	0.7E
	1836	2043	0.5F
	2347		
15 Tu		0438	1.4E
	0819	1008	0.4F
	1315	1607	0.6E
	1849	2112	0.5F
	2356		
16 W		0517	1.5E
	0901	1050	0.5F
	1408	1647	0.5E
	1906	2143	0.5F
17 Th	0013	0557	1.6E
	0947	1139	0.5F
	1508	1730	0.4E
	1930	2216	0.5F
18 F	0043	0638	1.6E
	1037	1234	0.5F
	1613	1814	0.3E
	2001	2255	0.4F
19 Sa	0122	0724	1.6E
	1132	1335	0.5F
		1901	*
		2354	0.3F
20 Su	0213	0817	1.6E
	1230	1442	0.5F
		2007	*
21 M ○		0116	0.3F
	0319	0921	1.5E
	1328	1539	0.4F
		2204	*
22 Tu		0241	*
		1028	1.5E
	1423	1625	0.4F
	2057	2348	0.4E
23 W	0222	0356	0.3F
	0635	1131	1.4E
	1513	1706	0.4F
	2138		
24 Th		0043	0.7E
	0329	0508	0.3F
	0820	1228	1.3E
	1558	1746	0.4F
		1845†	0.4F
25 F		0129	1.0E
	0428	0645	0.4F
	0943	1319	1.2E
	1639	1827	0.4F
	2243		
26 Sa		0213	1.3E
	0525	0816	0.5F
	1051	1405	1.1E
	1715	1905	0.4F
	2311		
27 Su ●		0258	1.5E
	0620	0900	0.5F
	1151	1449	0.9E
	1748	1942	0.5F
	2337		
28 M		0344	1.6E
	0711	0935	0.5F
	1248	1532	0.7E
	1818	2017	0.5F
29 Tu	0000	0430	1.7E
	0801	1010	0.5F
	1346	1616	0.5E
	1845	2053	0.5F
30 W	0016	0516	1.8E
	0850	1051	0.5F
	1447	1700	0.3E
	1908	2130	0.5F
31 Th	0027	0600	1.8E
	0940	1138	0.4F
		1742	*
		2209	0.4F

November

Day	Slack (h m)	Maximum (h m)	knots
1 F		0643	1.7E
	0043	1232	0.4F
	1033	1821	*
		2255	0.3F
2 Sa	0112	0727	1.6E
	1128	1333	0.3F
		1859	*
	2353		*
3 Su		0816	1.4E
		1438	0.3F
	1225	1956	*
		2114	*
		2248	*
4 M ◐		0108	*
		0917	1.2E
	1321	1526	0.3F
		2342	*
5 Tu		0239	*
		1026	1.1E
		1603	*
6 W		0023	0.4E
		0412	*
		1129	1.0E
		1637	*
7 Th		0058	0.7E
		0539	*
		1220	0.9E
		1711	*
8 F		0130	0.9E
		0702	*
		1259	0.8E
		1746	*
9 Sa		0157	1.0E
	0517	0754	0.3F
	1004	1329	0.7E
	1645	1823	0.3F
	2203		
10 Su		0224	1.2E
	0556	0829	0.4F
	1053	1357	0.6E
	1709	1859	0.3F
	2226		
11 M		0254	1.4E
	0634	0852	0.4F
	1138	1427	0.6E
	1729	1934	0.4F
	2245		
12 Tu ○		0328	1.5E
	0711	0915	0.5F
	1224	1502	0.5E
	1746	2008	0.5F
	2258		
13 W		0406	1.6E
	0748	0946	0.6F
	1313	1542	0.5E
	1808	2042	0.5F
	2317		
14 Th		0446	1.7E
	0828	1025	0.6F
	1407	1628	0.4E
	1837	2118	0.5F
	2346		
15 F		0529	1.8E
	0912	1110	0.6F
	1504	1717	0.4E
	1914	2159	0.5F
16 Sa	0026	0612	1.8E
	1001	1200	0.6F
	1602	1807	0.3E
	1959	2249	0.4F
17 Su	0115	0658	1.7E
	1056	1253	0.5F
	1656	1859	0.3E
	2101	2355	0.4F
18 M	0218	0748	1.6E
	1154	1351	0.4F
	1747	2006	0.3E
	2259		
19 Tu ○		0114	0.3F
	0344	0848	1.4E
	1254	1448	0.4F
	1842	2150	0.4E
20 W		0239	*
		0957	1.2E
	1351	1536	0.3F
	1941	2324	0.7E
21 Th	0220	0401	0.3F
	0649	1106	1.1E
	1441	1617	0.3F
	2035		
22 F		0022	1.0E
	0326	0526	0.3F
	0829	1208	1.0E
	1524	1656	0.3F
	2120		
23 Sa		0110	1.3E
	0424	0722	0.4F
	0955	1302	0.8E
	1602	1738	0.3F
	2157		
24 Su		0154	1.5E
	0518	0821	0.5F
	1104	1350	0.7E
	1637	1821	0.4F
	2228		
25 M		0237	1.7E
	0608	0903	0.5F
	1205	1433	0.6E
	1710	1905	0.4F
	2255		
26 Tu ●		0320	1.8E
	0655	0936	0.6F
	1301	1516	0.4E
	1743	1947	0.5F
	2318		
27 W		0404	1.9E
	0739	0959	0.6F
	1355	1600	0.3E
	1815	2028	0.5F
	2337		
28 Th		0448	1.9E
	0823	1026	0.5F
		1646	*
		2109	0.5F
	2358		
29 F		0531	1.8E
	0908	1102	0.5F
		1730	*
		2154	0.4F
30 Sa	0027	0612	1.7E
	0956	1145	0.4F
		1811	*
		2244	0.3F

December

Day	Slack (h m)	Maximum (h m)	knots
1 Su		0653	1.5E
	0106	1231	0.4F
	1047	1852	*
		2347	*
2 M		0735	1.3E
		1321	0.3F
	1142	1945	*
3 Tu		0105	*
		0823	1.0E
		1413	*
		2251	0.4E
4 W ◐		0255	*
		0924	0.8E
		1501	*
		2340	0.6E
5 Th		0419	*
		1038	0.7E
		1541	*
6 F		0020	0.8E
		0519	*
		1141	0.6E
		1618	*
7 Sa		0053	1.0E
		0627	*
		1223	0.5E
		1654	*
8 Su		0122	1.2E
	0451	0727	0.3F
	0956	1255	0.4E
		1732	*
9 M		0150	1.4E
	0527	0806	0.4F
	1050	1327	0.4E
	1622	1813	0.3F
	2128		
10 Tu		0221	1.5E
	0603	0832	0.5F
	1137	1403	0.4E
	1644	1855	0.4F
	2152		
11 W		0256	1.7E
	0639	0854	0.6F
	1224	1442	0.4E
	1710	1938	0.4F
	2218		
12 Th ○		0334	1.8E
	0717	0923	0.7F
	1311	1527	0.4E
	1746	2020	0.5F
	2253		
13 F		0417	1.8E
	0757	0959	0.7F
	1400	1617	0.4E
	1830	2104	0.5F
	2336		
14 Sa		0502	1.9E
	0841	1040	0.7F
	1448	1710	0.4E
	1921	2152	0.5F
15 Su	0028	0548	1.8E
	0929	1124	0.6F
	1534	1802	0.5E
	2022	2249	0.5F
16 M		0634	1.7E
	1020	1211	0.5F
	1617	1856	*
	2144	2356	0.4F
17 Tu	0247	0722	1.4E
	1116	1300	0.4F
	1657	2001	0.6E
	2327		
18 W ○		0114	0.3F
	0409	0816	1.2E
	1213	1351	0.3F
	1738	2131	0.7E
19 Th	0059	0247	0.3F
	0528	0923	0.9E
	1309	1442	0.3F
	1822	2256	1.0E
20 F	0215	0422	0.3F
	0657	1039	0.7E
		1529	*
		2356	1.2E
21 Sa	0318	0549	0.3F
	0847	1152	0.6E
	1444	1613	0.3F
		2014	*
22 Su		0046	1.5E
	0413	0718	0.4F
	1018	1253	0.5E
	1524	1657	0.3F
	2102		
23 M		0131	1.7E
	0503	0817	0.5F
	1127	1343	0.4E
	1602	1743	0.4F
	2140		
24 Tu		0213	1.9E
	0549	0856	0.6F
	1222	1427	0.3E
	1641	1833	0.3F
	2213		
25 W		0255	1.9E
	0631	0923	0.6F
	1309	1509	0.3E
	1723	1923	0.4F
	2242		
26 Th ●		0336	1.9E
	0712	0938	0.6F
	1348	1552	0.3E
	1809	2011	0.4F
	2314		
27 F		0418	1.8E
	0753	0956	0.6F
	1419	1637	0.3E
	1858	2058	0.4F
	2350		
28 Sa		0501	1.7E
	0835	1026	0.5F
	1442	1720	0.3E
	1952	2146	0.4F
29 Su	0033	0541	1.5E
	0918	1102	0.4F
	1500	1801	0.4E
	2055	2241	0.3F
30 M	0124	0620	1.3E
	1004	1142	0.4F
	1518	1841	0.5E
		2344	*
31 Tu		0656	1.1E
	1053	1224	0.3F
	1540	1929	0.5E

Time meridian 75° W. 0000 is midnight. 1200 is noon. Times are not adjusted for Daylight Saving Time.
If three consecutive entries are marked (F) the middle one is not a true maximum but an intermediate value to show the current pattern.
* Current weak and variable.
† See page 196 for the remaining currents on this day.

St. Andrew Bay Entrance, Florida, 2019

F–Flood, Dir. 046° True   E–Ebb, Dir. 225° True

January

Day	Slack (h m)	Maximum (h m, knots)
1 Tu	0606, 1903	1448 1.7F
2 W	0633, 1933	0007 2.1E, 1524 2.0F
3 Th	0707, 2011	0053 2.4E, 1605 2.1F
4 F	0745, 2052	0139 2.6E, 1219 1.6F, 1308 1.6F, 1658 2.2F
5 Sa ●	0822, 2132	0228 2.7E, 1233 1.6F, 1424 1.6F, 1759 2.1F
6 Su	0856, 2210	0314 2.6E, 1250 1.6F, 1533 1.4F, 1850 2.1F
7 M	0925, 2244	0348 2.6E, 1312 1.6F, 1620 1.3F, 1931 2.0F
8 Tu	0943, 2314	0405 2.4E, 1336 1.5F, 1653 1.1F, 2005 1.7F
9 W	0948, 2340	0415 2.3E, 1403 1.4F, 1720 0.9F, 2034 1.4F
10 Th	0946	0433 2.2E, 1428 1.3F, 1746 0.7F, 2100 1.1F
11 F	0003, 0942	0457 1.9E, 1449 1.2F, 1819 0.4F, 2128 0.7F
12 Sa	0022, 0938	0524 1.6E, 1458 1.1F, 1912 *, 2223 *
13 Su	0933, 1823	0550 1.1F, 1412 1.1F, 2111 0.4E
14 M ◐	0913, 1821	0029 *, 0546 0.6E, 1409 1.2F, 2154 0.9E
15 Tu	0635, 1830	0253 0.4E, 0346 0.4E, 1429 1.4E, 2232 1.5E
16 W	0546, 1852	1455 1.6F, 2316 2.0E
17 Th	0603, 1927	0904 1.2F, 1125 1.1F, 1527 1.7F
18 F	0636, 2010	0007 2.4E, 0954 1.6F, 1246 1.3F, 1608 1.9F
19 Sa	0717, 2058	0059 2.8E, 1045 1.8F, 1347 1.5F, 1705 2.0F
20 Su	0802, 2147	0152 3.0E, 1132 2.0F, 1445 1.5F, 1809 2.1F
21 M ○	0849, 2235	0247 3.1E, 1216 2.0F, 1537 1.3F, 1901 2.2F
22 Tu	0936, 2322	0337 3.1E, 1259 1.8F, 1620 1.1F, 1946 2.1F
23 W	1018	0418 2.8E, 1339 1.5F, 1656 0.7F, 2029 1.9F
24 Th	0005, 1039	0451 2.4E, 1414 1.2F, 1730 0.3F, 2115 1.5F
25 F	0042, 0938	0518 1.8E, 1443 0.8F, 1808 *, 2210 0.9F
26 Sa	0109, 0901, 1655	0538 1.1E, 1120 0.5F, 1318 0.4F, 1456 0.5F, 1900† 0.4E
27 Su ◐	0108, 0806, 1642	0546 0.4E, 1150 0.9F, 2045 0.9F
28 M	0450, 1646	0107 *, 0218 0.3E, 1233 1.3F, 2203 1.4F
29 Tu	0453, 1716	1324 1.6F, 2302 1.9F
30 W	0528, 1803	1413 1.8F, 2355 2.2F
31 Th	0606, 1857	1015 1.4F, 1124 1.4F, 1500 2.0F

February

Day	Slack (h m)	Maximum (h m, knots)
1 F	0643, 1950	0044 2.3E, 1038 1.4F, 1224 1.4F, 1547 2.0F
2 Sa	0718, 2037	0130 2.4E, 1100 1.4F, 1316 1.3F, 1642 1.9F
3 Su	0749, 2118	0213 2.4E, 1119 1.4F, 1409 1.2F, 1746 1.8F
4 M ●	0811, 2154	0251 2.3E, 1141 1.3F, 1504 1.0F, 1841 1.7F
5 Tu	0819, 2226	0317 2.2E, 1205 1.3F, 1549 0.7F, 1923 1.6F
6 W	0815, 2255	0328 2.0E, 1230 1.2F, 1621 0.5F, 1959 1.4F
7 Th	0808, 2322	0342 1.9E, 1255 1.0F, 1645 *, 2032 1.2F
8 F	0802, 2347	0407 1.7E, 1315 0.9F, 1707 *, 2105 0.9F
9 Sa	0758, 1601, 1925	0436 1.4E, 1109 0.8F, 1735 0.4E, 2146 0.5F
10 Su	0008, 0752, 1602	0506 1.0E, 1123 0.9F, 1810 0.7E, 2246 *
11 M	0728, 1609	0220 0.3E, 0326 0.3E, 0534 0.4E, 1153 1.0F, 1900 1.0E
12 Tu ◑	0358, 1627	1235 1.1F, 2020 1.3F
13 W	0400, 1701	1327 1.3F, 2145 1.8F
14 Th	0437, 1750	0800 1.3F, 1056 1.1F, 1417 1.5F, 2252 2.2E
15 F	0524, 1852	0835 1.6F, 1157 1.2F, 1503 1.7F, 2354 2.5E
16 Sa	0611, 1955	0919 1.8F, 1245 1.2F, 1553 1.8F
17 Su	0656, 2054	0050 2.7E, 1006 1.8F, 1330 1.2F, 1654 1.9F
18 M	0740, 2150	0142 2.8E, 1051 1.7F, 1416 1.0F, 1802 1.9F
19 Tu ○	0822, 2245	0232 2.7E, 1132 1.4F, 1503 0.7F, 1859 1.9F
20 W	0855, 2339	0320 2.4E, 1209 1.1F, 1547 *, 1947 1.8F
21 Th	0822	0400 2.0E, 1046 0.7F, 1625 *, 2031 1.5F
22 F	0034, 0740, 1439	0431 1.4E, 0914 0.4F, 1123 *, 1307 0.3F, 1700† 0.7E
23 Sa	0144, 0714, 1355, 2023	0455 0.8E, 0931 0.8F, 1732 1.1E, 2215 0.5F
24 Su	1337	0107 *, 0229 *, 0509 *, 0959 1.1F, 1806† 1.3F
25 M	1424	0056 *, 0410 0.3F, 0501 0.3F, 1035 1.4F, 1854 1.4F
26 Tu ◑	0255, 1518	1124 1.5F, 2125 1.6F
27 W	0348, 1614	1231 1.6F, 2244 1.8F
28 Th	0437, 1712	0844 1.4F, 1053 1.3F, 1343 1.6F, 2342 2.0F

March

Day	Slack (h m)	Maximum (h m, knots)
1 F	0522, 1815	0852 1.4F, 1143 1.2F, 1442 1.6F
2 Sa	0559, 1918	0029 2.0E, 0909 1.3F, 1227 1.0F, 1534 1.6F
3 Su	0628, 2010	0107 2.0E, 0932 1.3F, 1308 0.8F, 1629 1.4F
4 M	0646, 2052	0138 1.9E, 0958 1.2F, 1349 0.6F, 1732 1.3F
5 Tu	0649, 2130	0159 1.7E, 1023 1.1F, 1430 0.3F, 1831 1.2F
6 W ●	0643, 2207	0210 1.6E, 1046 0.9F, 1508 *, 1916 1.1F
7 Th	0638, 2245	0230 1.4E, 1054 0.8F, 1537 0.3E, 1955 1.0F
8 F	0634, 1339, 1812, 2326	0303 1.2E, 0902 0.8F, 1602 0.7E, 2032 0.9F
9 Sa	0631, 1332, 1908	0343 0.9E, 0911 1.0F, 1629 1.0E, 2110 0.7F
10 Su	0017, 0622, 1323, 2017	0422 0.5E, 0926 1.1F, 1700 1.4E, 2158 0.4F
11 M	1334	0045 *, 0240 *, 0500 *, 0946 1.1F, 1736† 1.6E
12 Tu ◑	1409	0020 *, 0353 0.6F, 0534 0.5F, 1013 1.2F, 1820 1.8E
13 W	0155, 1501	1054 1.2F, 1924 1.8E
14 Th ◐	0248, 1601	0653 1.4F, 1031 1.2F, 1215 1.2F, 2107 2.0E
15 F	0344, 1705	0725 1.7F, 1115 1.1F, 1344 1.3F, 2232 2.2E
16 Sa	0441, 1821	0801 1.8F, 1153 1.0F, 1447 1.5F, 2336 2.4E
17 Su	0534, 1941	0840 1.8F, 1230 0.8F, 1543 1.5F
18 M	0620, 2052	0030 2.3E, 0919 1.5F, 1308 0.5F, 1647 1.5F
19 Tu	0657, 2159	0118 2.1E, 0958 1.2F, 1348 *, 1759 1.4F
20 W ○	0706, 1551, 2313	0204 1.8E, 1032 0.8F, 1304 0.3F, 1431 0.3F, 1901 1.4F
21 Th	0624, 1234	0250 1.3E, 0758 0.3F, 0911 0.3F, 1054 0.4F, 1514† 0.8E
22 F	0039, 0556, 1137, 1834	0334 0.8E, 0755 0.7F, 1555 1.3E, 2038 0.9F
23 Sa	1112, 1945	0410 *, 0814 1.1F, 1631 1.7F, 2130 0.5F, 2323 0.4F
24 Su	1147, 2127	0142 0.6F, 0436 0.3F, 0839 1.1F, 1703 1.9E
25 M	1231	0305 0.8F, 0450 0.7F, 0907 1.7F, 1732 2.0E
26 Tu	0055, 1323	0937 1.7F, 1804 1.9E
27 W ◐	0159, 1421	1015 1.6F, 1847 1.7E
28 Th	0248, 1521	0753 1.5F, 1024 1.4F, 1132 1.4F, 2216 1.7E
29 F	0332, 1619	0746 1.5F, 1106 1.1F, 1311 1.2F, 2312 1.7E
30 Sa	0409, 1715	0749 1.4F, 1144 0.8F, 1423 1.1F, 2351 1.6E
31 Su	0435, 1811	0802 1.3F, 1220 0.5F, 1518 1.0F

Time meridian 75° W. 0000 is midnight. 1200 is noon. Times are not adjusted for Daylight Saving Time.
If three consecutive entries are marked (F) the middle one is not a true maximum but an intermediate value to show the current pattern.
* Current weak and variable.
† See page 196 for the remaining currents on this day.

St. Andrew Bay Entrance, Florida, 2019

F–Flood, Dir. 046° True   E–Ebb, Dir. 225° True

April

Day	Slack (h m)	Maximum (h m)	knots
1 M		0016	1.4E
	0446	0821	1.2F
		1254	*
		1612	0.8F
	1910		
2 Tu		0026	1.3E
	0446	0839	1.1E
		1326	*
		1716	0.7F
	2006		
3 W		0030	1.1E
	0444	0844	0.9F
	1154	1355	0.4E
	1555	1823	0.6F
	2102		
4 Th		0056	0.9E
	0442	0746	0.9F
	1142	1421	0.8E
	1708	1915	0.6F
	2211		
5 F ●		0136	0.6E
	0441	0744	1.1F
	1135	1448	1.2E
	1803	1959	0.6F
6 Sa	0017	0228	0.3E
	0434	0756	1.2F
	1127	1520	1.6E
	1851	2041	0.6F
		2304	0.3F
7 Su		0022	0.4F
		0331	*
		0813	1.3F
	1129	1556	1.9E
	1945	2131†	0.4F
8 M		0146	0.7F
		0425	0.4F
		0832	1.5F
	1149	1633	2.2E
	2105		
9 Tu		0249	1.1F
		0510	0.8F
		0852	1.5F
	1223	1713	2.4E
	2348		
10 W		0346	1.4F
		0555	1.2F
		0910	1.5F
	1309	1758	2.4E
11 Th	0109	0449	1.7F
	1409	1855	2.3E
12 F ◐	0207	0558	1.8F
	1518	2032	2.1E
13 Sa	0259	0647	1.9F
		1106	1.0F
		1316	1.1F
	1628	2204	2.1E
14 Su	0348	0724	1.8F
		1135	0.7F
		1433	1.2F
	1744	2305	2.0E
15 M	0432	0757	1.5F
		1209	*
		1534	1.1F
	1923	2356	1.7E
16 Tu	0455	0826	1.1F
	1130	1245	0.3E
	1359	1641	0.9F
	2059		
17 W		0042	1.2E
	0426	0848	0.7F
	1101	1323	0.8E
	1536	1804	0.8F
	2240		
18 Th		0026	0.7E
	0356	0621	0.6F
	1035	1403	1.3E
	1705	1920	0.7F
19 F ○		0211	*
		0636	1.0F
	0955	1446	1.8E
	1819	2332	0.8F
20 Sa		0302	0.4F
		0703	1.4F
	1004	1529	2.2E
	1927		
21 Su		0058	1.0F
		0352	0.8F
		0733	1.8F
	1037	1608	2.5E
	2050	2304	0.3F
22 M		0215	1.3F
		0430	1.1F
		0803	2.0F
	1117	1641	2.5E
	2300		
23 Tu		0312	1.4F
		0455	1.3F
		0833	2.0F
	1201	1710	2.4E
24 W	0016	0403	1.5F
		0510	1.5F
		0901	1.9F
	1247	1736	2.2E
25 Th	0109	0850	1.6F
	1336	1805	1.9E
26 F ◑	0148	0647	1.5F
	1427	1841	1.6E
27 Sa	0214	0627	1.5F
		1115	0.8F
		1224	0.8F
	1516	1938	1.3E
28 Su	0226	0641	1.4F
		1139	0.4F
		1357	0.6F
	1559	2109	1.2E
29 M	0227	0659	1.3F
		1207	*
		1458	0.4F
	1638	2145	1.0E
30 Tu	0225	0714	1.2F
	1041	1234	0.4E
		1552	*
		2220	0.8E

May

Day	Slack (h m)	Maximum (h m)	knots
1 W	0219	0711	1.1F
	1017	1257	0.7E
		1659	*
		2302	0.6E
2 Th	0209	0608	1.1F
	1009	1317	1.1E
		1834	*
		2354	*
3 F		0621	1.2F
	1006	1340	1.5E
	1807	2233	0.3F
4 Sa ●		0056	*
		0643	1.4F
	1006	1410	1.8E
	1848	2347	0.7F
5 Su		0210	0.6F
		0707	1.6F
	1017	1449	2.3E
	1935		
6 M		0050	1.2F
		0344	0.9F
		0732	1.7F
	1041	1533	2.7E
	2038		
7 Tu		0148	1.5F
		0442	1.1F
		0758	1.8F
	1115	1618	2.9E
	2214		
8 W		0240	1.8F
		0526	1.4F
		0824	1.8F
	1156	1701	2.9E
	2338		
9 Th		0328	2.0F
		0616	1.6F
		0849	1.8F
	1244	1745	2.8E
10 F	0041	0418	2.0F
	1341	1836	2.5E
11 Sa ◐	0131	0511	2.0F
	1444	1949	2.1E
12 Su	0210	0601	1.8F
		1038	0.7F
		1252	0.9F
	1548	2121	1.8E
13 M	0231	0639	1.5F
		1110	*
		1420	0.7F
	1652	2221	1.3E
14 Tu	0221	0708	1.1F
	1000	1146	0.5F
	1335	1527	0.5F
	1907	2310	0.8E
15 W	0158	0419	0.6F
		0525	0.6F
		0723	0.7F
	0933	1223	1.1F
	1516	1641†	0.3F
16 Th		0426	1.0F
	0913	1301	1.7F
	1707	2131	0.6F
17 F		0041	0.4F
		0456	1.3F
	0856	1342	2.2F
	1834	2308	1.0F
18 Sa ○		0128	0.9F
		0537	1.7F
	0908	1425	2.5E
	1938		
19 Su		0026	1.3F
		0230	1.3F
		0622	2.0F
	0940	1512	2.7E
	2045		
20 M		0130	1.6F
		0342	1.5F
		0704	2.2F
	1019	1556	2.8E
	2152		
21 Tu		0215	1.7F
		0431	1.6F
		0741	2.2F
	1100	1630	2.8E
	2250		
22 W		0250	1.7F
		0507	1.5F
		0815	2.1F
	1141	1655	2.6E
	2338		
23 Th		0321	1.7F
		0540	1.5F
		0844	1.9F
	1220	1715	2.3E
24 F	0015	0351	1.6F
		0631	1.4F
		0856	1.5F
	1257	1736	2.0E
25 Sa	0037	0421	1.5F
	1330	1801	1.8E
26 Su ◑	0044	0450	1.4F
	1359	1830	1.5E
27 M	0042	0516	1.3F
		1132	*
		1316	*
		1905	1.1E
28 Tu	0035	0529	1.2F
	0940	1148	0.4E
		1434	*
		2000	0.8E
29 W	0021	0412	1.2F
	0906	1205	0.8F
		1534	*
		1805	0.5E
		1954†	0.4E
30 Th		0416	1.4F
	0855	1220	1.2F
		1659	0.3E
		1740	0.3E
		2054†	*
31 F		0436	1.5F
	0855	1240	1.7F
	1921	2209	0.5F
		2257	0.5F

June

Day	Slack (h m)	Maximum (h m)	knots
1 Sa		0506	1.6F
	0901	1308	2.1E
	1914	2308	0.9F
2 Su		0040	0.9F
		0546	1.7F
	0917	1345	2.5E
	1940	2356	1.4F
3 M ●		0228	1.2F
		0628	1.8F
	0945	1432	2.9E
	2024		
4 Tu		0044	1.8F
		0355	1.4F
		0705	2.0F
	1021	1523	3.1E
	2123		
5 W		0133	2.0F
		0444	1.5F
		0741	2.1F
	1103	1611	3.2E
	2225		
6 Th		0220	2.1F
		0524	1.5F
		0815	2.1F
	1147	1655	3.2E
	2323		
7 F		0303	2.1F
		0605	1.5F
		0851	1.9F
	1234	1735	2.9E
8 Sa	0013	0345	2.0F
		0707	1.4F
		0936	1.5F
	1323	1816	2.4E
9 Su	0050	0425	1.7F
		0900	0.9F
		1053	1.0F
	1413	1903	1.8E
10 M ◐	0059	0504	1.4F
		0958	0.3F
		1234	0.5F
	1501	2009	1.2E
11 Tu	0035	0536	1.0F
	0851	1040	0.4F
		1411	*
		2124	0.5F
12 W	0003	0301	0.9F
	0817	1120	1.1F
		1527	*
		1700	*
		1948†	*
13 Th		0309	1.3F
	0800	1201	1.8F
	1820	2110	0.7F
14 F		0334	1.6F
	0755	1243	2.2E
	1852		
15 Sa		0409	1.9F
	0813	1327	2.6E
	1932		
16 Su		0010	1.5F
		0054	1.5F
		0456	2.1F
	0847	1414	2.8E
	2016		
17 M ○		0042	1.7F
		0212	1.7F
		0553	2.2F
	0927	1505	2.9E
	2101		
18 Tu		0114	1.8F
		0329	1.7F
		0645	2.3F
	1008	1550	2.8E
	2144		
19 W		0144	1.8F
		0421	1.5F
		0728	2.2F
	1048	1622	2.7E
	2221		
20 Th		0211	1.7F
		0500	1.4F
		0805	2.0F
	1124	1641	2.5E
	2248		
21 F		0236	1.6F
		0533	1.2F
		0837	1.7F
	1156	1653	2.3E
	2302		
22 Sa		0301	1.5F
		0610	1.0F
		0902	1.3F
	1221	1709	2.0E
	2302		
23 Su		0324	1.4F
	1240	1730	1.8E
	2255		
24 M		0342	1.3F
	1242	1752	1.4E
	2245		
25 Tu ◑		0342	1.2F
		1115	*
		1209	*
		1804	1.0E
	2229		
26 W		0301	1.3F
	0750	1109	0.6E
		1413	0.4E
		1704	0.7E
	2202		
27 Th		0303	1.4F
	0737	1118	1.1E
		1532	0.5E
		1647	0.5E
	1956		
28 F		0320	1.5F
	0741	1135	1.6E
	1849		
29 Sa		0344	1.7F
	0753	1206	2.0E
	1852	2216	1.0F
		2307	1.0F
30 Su		0416	1.8F
	0817	1246	2.5E
	1915	2254	1.5F

Time meridian 75° W. 0000 is midnight. 1200 is noon. Times are not adjusted for Daylight Saving Time.
If three consecutive entries are marked (F) the middle one is not a true maximum but an intermediate value to show the current pattern.
* Current weak and variable.
† See page 196 for the remaining currents on this day.

St. Andrew Bay Entrance, Florida, 2019

F–Flood, Dir. 046° True   E–Ebb, Dir. 225° True

July

Day	Slack	Maximum	knots
1 M		0114	1.3F
		0503	1.9F
	0851	1333	2.8E
	1950	2337	1.8F
2 Tu ●		0235	1.5F
		0601	2.0F
	0932	1425	3.1E
	2034		
3 W		0021	2.0F
		0341	1.5F
	1016	0651	2.1F
	2123	1520	3.2E
4 Th		0107	2.1F
		0426	1.4F
	1102	0734	2.2F
	2213	1607	3.2E
5 F		0150	2.0F
		0503	1.3F
	1147	0814	2.1F
	2259	1647	3.0E
6 Sa		0231	1.8F
		0539	1.0F
	1230	0856	1.8F
	2332	1722	2.6E
7 Su		0306	1.5F
		0620	0.7F
	1310	0946	1.3F
	2321	1753	2.0E
8 M		0337	1.1F
		0725	0.3F
	1343	1053	0.7F
	2239	1821	1.2E
9 Tu ◑		0357	0.8F
	0703	0901	0.3E
		1224	*
		1839	0.5E
	2157		
10 W		0123	0.8F
	0628	1004	1.0E
		1420	*
		1534	*
11 Th		0148	1.3F
	0617	1054	1.6E
	1736		
12 F		0223	1.7F
	0628	1143	2.1E
	1808		
13 Sa		0301	2.0F
	0703	1231	2.4E
	1846	2308	1.5F
	2355		
14 Su		0343	2.1F
	0748	1319	2.6E
	1925	2333	1.6F
15 M		0101	1.6F
		0434	2.2F
	0834	1408	2.7E
	2004	2358	1.6F
16 Tu ○		0202	1.5F
		0536	2.1F
	0918	1458	2.7E
	2041		
17 W		0023	1.6F
		0307	1.4F
	1000	0635	2.1F
	2110	1540	2.6E
18 Th		0048	1.5F
		0400	1.2F
	1036	0721	2.0F
	2127	1605	2.4E
19 F		0114	1.4F
		0439	0.9F
	1107	0759	1.8F
	2125	1616	2.2E
20 Sa		0140	1.3F
		0509	0.7F
	1131	0832	1.4F
	2115	1624	2.0E
21 Su		0204	1.2F
		0534	0.4F
	1151	0901	1.0F
	2104	1641	1.8E
22 M		0223	1.1F
		0600	*
	1203	0929	0.6F
	2053	1703	1.4E
23 Tu		0223	1.0F
		0636	*
		1007	*
	2039	1725	1.0E
24 W ◐		0116	1.0F
	0538	0739	0.4E
		1139	0.3F
	2016	1602	0.6E
25 Th		0135	1.2F
	0543	0924	0.8E
	1838		
26 F		0203	1.3F
	0557	1007	1.3E
	1739		
27 Sa		0235	1.5F
	0622	1050	1.8E
	1750	2055	1.1F
		2247	1.0F
28 Su		0309	1.7F
	0701	1140	2.2E
	1819	2131	1.5F
29 M		0023	1.2F
		0349	1.8F
	0748	1233	2.6E
	1856	2217	1.7F
30 Tu		0122	1.4F
		0442	1.9F
	0838	1326	2.9E
	1937	2303	1.9F
31 W ●		0217	1.4F
		0548	2.0F
	0929	1419	3.0E
	2020	2346	1.9F

August

Day	Slack	Maximum	knots
1 Th		0310	1.2F
		0645	2.1F
	1019	1512	3.0E
	2104		
2 F		0028	1.7F
		0356	1.0F
	1109	0732	2.1F
	2144	1557	2.8E
3 Sa		0109	1.4F
		0434	0.6F
	1156	0815	1.9F
	2201	1634	2.4E
4 Su		0146	1.1F
		0509	*
	1239	0900	1.5F
	2107	1704	1.8E
5 M		0217	0.7F
		0543	*
	1317	0951	1.0F
	2034	1728	1.1E
		2243	0.5F
6 Tu		0106	0.3F
		0234	0.4F
	0412	0623	0.6F
	0857	1055	0.4F
		1410†	*
7 W ◑	0355	0727	0.9E
		1230	*
		1344	*
		2352	1.2F
8 Th	0358	0920	1.4E
	1605		
9 F		0045	1.5F
	0434	1030	1.8E
	1652	2112	1.3F
		2209	1.3F
10 Sa		0144	1.7F
	0524	1129	2.1E
	1738	2122	1.4F
		2317	1.4F
11 Su		0237	1.9F
	0624	1222	2.3E
	1820	2151	1.5F
12 M		0011	1.3F
		0327	2.0F
	0726	1310	2.4E
	1858	2222	1.4F
13 Tu		0100	1.2F
		0421	1.9F
	0821	1355	2.3E
	1930	2250	1.4F
14 W		0148	1.1F
		0526	1.8F
	0907	1436	2.2E
	1954	2315	1.3F
15 Th ○		0240	0.8F
		0626	1.7F
	0946	1509	2.1E
	2000	2339	1.1F
16 F		0329	0.5F
		0714	1.5F
	1019	1527	1.8E
	1950		
17 Sa		0002	1.0F
		0407	*
	1047	0753	1.3F
	1939	1534	1.6E
18 Su		0022	0.9F
		0433	*
	1110	0827	1.1F
	1930	1550	1.4E
		2216	0.8F
19 M	0320	0454	0.3E
	0627	0900	0.8F
	1131	1615	1.1E
	1921	2221	0.9F
20 Tu	0315	0517	0.6E
	0734	0936	0.4F
	1145	1643	0.8E
	1909	2240	1.0F
21 W	0318	0546	0.9E
		1024	*
		1348	0.3E
		1527	*
		1709†	*
22 Th	0327	0626	1.1E
		1159	0.3E
		1315	0.3E
	1536	2349	1.1F
23 F ◐	0350	0725	1.3E
	1538		
24 Sa		0049	1.2F
	0427	0855	1.6E
	1611	1952	1.2F
		2244	1.1F
25 Su		0151	1.4F
	0517	1015	2.0E
	1655	2013	1.5F
		2342	1.1F
26 M		0244	1.5F
	0618	1121	2.3E
	1742	2051	1.7F
27 Tu		0027	1.1F
		0334	1.7F
	0727	1220	2.5E
	1827	2134	1.7F
28 W		0109	1.0F
		0431	1.7F
	0831	1313	2.6E
	1909	2218	1.6F
29 Th		0152	0.8F
		0541	1.8F
	0930	1403	2.5E
	1948	2300	1.4F
30 F ●		0237	0.5F
		0643	1.8F
	1029	1452	2.3E
	2014	2337	1.0F
31 Sa		0322	*
		0733	1.7F
	1130	1538	1.9E
	1949		

September

Day	Slack	Maximum	knots
1 Su	0223	0010	0.6F
	0526	0402	0.4F
	1238	0818	1.5F
	1916	1615	1.3E
		2050†	0.4F
2 M		0032	*
		0438	0.9E
	0644	0904	1.1F
	1407	1645	0.7E
	1852	2105	0.8F
3 Tu	0021	0511	1.3E
	0803	0958	0.6F
		1233	0.3E
		1412	0.4F
		1707†	*
4 W	0045	0544	1.5E
		1110	*
		1226	*
		1540	0.6E
		1715†	0.5F
5 Th ◑	0135	0622	1.6E
	1408	2244	1.5F
6 F	0234	0738	1.6E
	1507	2348	1.6F
7 Sa	0336	1007	1.8E
	1601	2016	1.5F
		2239	1.3F
8 Su		0109	1.6F
	0438	1113	2.0E
	1651	2025	1.5F
		2327	1.2F
9 M		0219	1.6F
	0542	1205	2.0E
	1733	2042	1.4F
10 Tu		0010	0.9F
		0315	1.5F
	0651	1247	1.9E
	1805	2105	1.3F
11 W		0051	0.7F
		0410	1.4F
	0752	1321	1.8E
	1823	2130	1.1F
12 Th		0132	0.4F
		0514	1.2F
	0841	1348	1.6E
	1822	2153	1.0F
13 F ○		0213	*
		0618	1.1F
	0920	1404	1.3E
	1812	2210	0.8F
14 Sa		0252	*
		0708	1.0F
	0957	1412	1.1E
	1804	2036	0.8F
15 Su	0100	0324	0.5E
	0529	0749	0.9F
	1033	1437	0.9E
	1757	2033	1.0F
16 M	0053	0348	0.9E
	0624	0825	0.7F
	1113	1515	0.6E
	1749	2045	1.1F
17 Tu	0046	0412	1.2E
		0714	*
	1213	0902	0.5F
	1733	1557	0.3E
		2101	1.2F
18 W	0043	0440	1.5E
	0814	0946	0.3F
		1217	*
		1434	0.3E
		1637†	*
19 Th	0100	0513	1.8E
		1055	*
		1200	*
		1539	0.6E
		1713†	0.5F
20 F ◐	0134	0553	1.9E
		1653	1.0F
	1329	1746	1.0F
		2158	1.3F
21 Sa	0224	0644	1.9E
	1418	1834	1.4F
22 Su	0325	0806	2.0E
	1508	1902	1.7F
		2308	1.1F
23 M		0108	1.2F
	0429	0947	2.1E
	1601	1936	1.8F
		2339	1.0F
24 Tu		0224	1.3F
	0541	1058	2.2E
	1654	2011	1.8F
25 W		0013	0.7F
		0323	1.4F
	0704	1156	2.2E
	1741	2048	1.6F
26 Th		0049	0.4F
		0423	1.4F
	0824	1247	2.0E
	1817	2124	1.2F
27 F		0126	*
		0536	1.3F
	0939	1334	1.7E
	1824	2157	0.8F
28 Sa ●	0024	0207	0.4F
	0344	0646	1.2F
	1100	1422	1.2E
	1751	1942	0.4F
		2056†	0.3F
29 Su		0249	1.0E
	0513	0740	1.1F
	1237	1511	0.6E
	1726	1934	0.7F
	2301		
30 M		0332	1.5E
	0624	0828	0.9F
		1045	0.6F
		1140	0.7F
		1555†	*

Time meridian 75° W. 0000 is midnight. 1200 is noon. Times are not adjusted for Daylight Saving Time.
If three consecutive entries are marked (F) the middle one is not a true maximum but an intermediate value to show the current pattern.
* Current weak and variable.
† See page 196 for the remaining currents on this day.

St. Andrew Bay Entrance, Florida, 2019

F–Flood, Dir. 046° True   E–Ebb, Dir. 225° True

October

Day	Slack	Maximum	knots
1 Tu		0410	1.9E
	0733	0921	0.6F
		1042	0.5F
		1322	0.8F
		1630†	0.4F
2 W		0445	2.2E
	0903	1442	1.0F
		1655	0.9F
		2044	1.8F
3 Th	0001	0516	2.2E
	1208	1552	1.2F
		1707	1.2F
		2114	1.8E
4 F	0050	0549	2.1E
	1324	2147	1.7F
5 Sa ◐	0146	0627	1.9E
	1417	1934	1.6F
		2203	1.5F
		2247	1.5F
6 Su	0248	0930	1.7E
	1501	1922	1.5F
		2247	1.1F
7 M		0034	1.2F
	0349	1041	1.7E
	1537	1928	1.5F
		2325	0.8F
8 Tu		0159	1.1F
	0446	1127	1.6E
	1601	1942	1.3F
9 W		0002	0.4F
		0301	0.9F
	0541	1159	1.4E
	1606	1959	1.2F
10 Th		0038	*
		0355	0.7F
	0638	1217	1.1E
	1601	2013	1.0F
	2333		
11 F		0112	0.3E
	0247	0458	0.5F
	0739	1212	0.8E
	1555	2008	0.9F
	2313		
12 Sa		0144	0.7F
	0415	0611	0.4F
	0839	1225	0.6E
	1546	1912	1.0F
	2306		
13 Su ○		0210	1.0E
	0527	0709	0.4F
	1001	1259	0.3E
	1529	1919	1.2F
	2302		
14 M		0235	1.3E
	0618	0755	0.4F
		1345	*
		1935	1.3F
	2300		
15 Tu		0302	1.7E
	0702	0837	0.4F
		1020	0.3F
		1229	0.4F
		1450†	0.3F
16 W		0335	2.0E
	0749	1340	0.7F
		1601	0.6F
	2330	2013	1.6F
17 Th		0412	2.3E
	0900	1436	1.1F
		1651	0.9F
		2033	1.6F
18 F	0001	0451	2.5E
	1115	1527	1.4F
		1736	1.2F
		2051	1.6F
19 Sa	0043	0534	2.5E
	1237	1619	1.7F
		1842	1.5F
		2033	1.5F
20 Su	0137	0623	2.4E
	1333	1720	1.8F
21 M ○	0242	0733	2.2E
	1421	1815	1.9F
		2258	1.0F
22 Tu		0030	1.1F
	0351	0913	2.1E
	1504	1856	1.8F
		2320	0.7F
23 W		0207	1.0F
	0501	1024	1.9E
	1539	1930	1.6F
		2351	*
24 Th		0312	0.9F
	0633	1120	1.6E
	1554	1959	1.2F
	2301		
25 F		0026	0.3E
	0149	0416	0.8F
	0830	1210	1.2E
	1537	2020	0.8F
	2234		
26 Sa		0102	0.9E
	0325	0543	0.6F
	1023	1258	0.6E
	1515	1749	0.6F
	2212		
27 Su ●		0141	1.4E
	0456	0937	0.7F
		1345	*
	2137	1808	1.0F
28 M		0222	1.9E
	0613	1117	0.9F
		1439	0.5F
	2142	1838	1.4F
29 Tu		0235	2.3E
	0721	1237	1.2F
		1537	1.0F
	2214	1911	1.8F
30 W		0349	2.6E
	0840	1351	1.5F
		1624	1.3F
	2254	1944	2.0F
31 Th		0427	2.7E
	1030	1448	1.6F
		1658	1.4F
	2338	2016	2.1F

November

Day	Slack	Maximum	knots
1 F		0500	2.6E
	1147	1534	1.7F
		1727	1.5F
		2048	2.0F
2 Sa	0024	0528	2.4E
	1243	1621	1.6F
		1757	1.6F
		2116	1.7F
3 Su	0112	0556	2.1E
	1324	1711	1.6F
4 M ◐	0202	0628	1.7E
	1350	1751	1.5F
		2249	0.8F
		2349	0.8F
5 Tu	0251	0708	1.4E
	1400	1816	1.4F
		2318	0.3F
6 W		0132	0.5F
	0333	0813	1.1E
	1357	1835	1.3F
		2351	*
7 Th		0241	0.3F
	0405	0909	0.9E
	1350	1848	1.1F
	2208		
8 F		0022	0.5E
		0337	*
	1335	0942	0.6E
	2149	1726	1.1F
9 Sa		0048	0.9E
		0441	*
		0707	0.3E
		0758	*
		1014†	0.4E
10 Su		0110	1.3E
		0927	*
		1051	*
		1748	1.4F
	2143		
11 M		0130	1.6E
	0708	1103	0.4F
		1147	0.4F
	2147	1817	1.5F
12 Tu ○		0154	2.0E
	0717	1157	0.7F
		1311	0.7F
	2201	1846	1.6F
13 W		0228	2.3E
	0749	1245	1.2F
		1507	1.1F
	2226	1915	1.8F
14 Th		0310	2.7E
	0840	1335	1.5F
		1624	1.2F
	2258	1942	1.9F
15 F		0356	2.9E
	0954	1421	1.8F
		1709	1.4F
	2338	2010	1.9F
16 Sa		0440	3.0E
	1107	1506	2.0F
		1753	1.5F
		2036	1.8F
17 Su	0022	0523	2.9E
	1207	1550	2.0F
		1902	1.6F
		2059	1.6F
18 M	0114	0609	2.7E
	1257	1636	2.0F
19 Tu ○	0212	0704	2.3E
	1335	1724	1.8F
		2221	0.8F
20 W		0006	0.9F
	0314	0825	1.8E
	1354	1807	1.5F
		2251	*
21 Th		0151	0.6F
	0415	0941	1.4E
	1349	1840	1.2F
	2141	2325	0.4E
22 F	0118	0305	0.4F
	0527	1036	0.8E
	1329	1602	0.7F
		1710	0.7F
		1858†	0.8F
23 Sa	0002	0416	1.1E
		0544	*
		0752	*
		1126†	0.3F
24 Su		0040	1.7E
	0520	0912	0.7F
		1216	0.4F
	2039	1627	1.4F
25 M		0120	2.2E
	0639	1044	1.1F
		1308	1.0F
	2048	1706	1.7F
26 Tu ●		0204	2.6E
	0736	1200	1.5F
		1409	1.4F
	2120	1754	2.0F
27 W		0251	2.8E
	0834	1301	1.7F
		1523	1.6F
	2159	1842	2.2F
28 Th		0339	2.9E
	0934	1350	1.8F
		1617	1.6F
	2242	1924	2.3F
29 F		0420	2.9E
	1030	1428	1.8F
		1657	1.6F
	2325	2002	2.2F
30 Sa		0451	2.7E
	1117	1501	1.8F
		1733	1.5F
		2037	2.0F

December

Day	Slack	Maximum	knots
1 Su	0005	0512	2.5E
	1154	1531	1.6F
		1816	1.4F
		2109	1.6F
2 M	0043	0530	2.1E
	1216	1559	1.5F
		1902	1.6F
		2059	1.6F
3 Tu	0115	0550	1.8E
	1220	1624	1.4F
4 W ◐	0139	0610	1.4E
	1213	1645	1.3F
		2310	*
5 Th	0048		*
		0628	1.1F
	1159	1636	1.2F
	2112	2335	0.5E
6 F		0216	*
		0557	0.8F
	1133	1541	1.3F
	2041	2358	0.9E
7 Sa		0320	0.4E
		0535	0.6F
	1044	1550	1.5F
		1710	0.7F
	2033	1858†	0.8F
8 Su		0016	1.3E
	0832	1610	1.6F
	2034		
9 M		0032	1.7E
	0738	1639	1.7F
	2043		
10 Tu		0054	2.1E
	0734	1719	1.7F
	2102		
11 W		0126	2.4E
	0749	1153	1.3F
		1337	1.3F
	2130	1806	1.8F
12 Th ○		0209	2.8E
	0820	1229	1.7F
		1529	1.5F
	2206	1848	2.0F
13 F		0259	3.0E
	0905	1312	1.9F
		1625	1.5F
	2247	1926	2.1F
14 Sa		0349	3.2E
	0958	1356	2.1F
		1704	1.5F
	2330	2002	2.1F
15 Su		0434	3.2E
	1051	1438	2.1F
		1742	1.4F
		2038	1.9F
16 M	0015	0515	3.0E
	1138	1518	2.0F
		1828	1.3F
		2120	1.6F
17 Tu	0101	0554	2.6E
	1215	1556	1.7F
		1951	1.0F
		2222	1.1F
18 W ○	0149	0635	2.0E
	1227	1631	1.4F
		2124	0.4F
		2354	0.6F
19 Th	0235	0725	1.3E
	2031	1207	1.0F
		1702	1.0F
		2214	0.3E
20 F		0140	*
		0840	0.6E
	1137	1445	0.8F
	1953	2256	1.0F
21 Sa		0308	*
		0435	*
		0727	*
		0948	*
		1448†	1.2F
22 Su	0600	0844	0.7F
		1040	0.6F
	1932	1512	1.6F
23 M	0634	0021	2.2E
		1015	1.2F
		1141	1.1F
	1951	1545	1.9F
24 Tu	0715	0106	2.6E
		1124	1.5F
		1248	1.5F
	2027	1628	2.1F
25 W	0758	0154	2.8E
		1206	1.7F
		1353	1.7F
	2109	1726	2.2F
26 Th ●	0843	0245	2.9E
		1243	1.8F
		1503	1.7F
	2152	1825	2.3F
27 F	0927	0335	2.9E
		1318	1.8F
		1601	1.5F
	2235	1913	2.3F
28 Sa	1005	0414	2.8E
		1348	1.7F
		1643	1.3F
	2314	1955	2.1F
29 Su	1032	0439	2.6E
		1416	1.6F
		1719	1.1F
	2347	2032	1.8F
30 M	1041	0452	2.3E
		1441	1.4F
		1754	0.9F
		2105	1.3F
31 Tu	0013	0502	2.0E
	1035	1503	1.3F
		1839	0.7F
		2134	0.8F

Time meridian 75° W. 0000 is midnight. 1200 is noon. Times are not adjusted for Daylight Saving Time.
If three consecutive entries are marked (F) the middle one is not a true maximum but an intermediate value to show the current pattern.
* Current weak and variable.
† See page 196 for the remaining currents on this day.

Mobile Bay Entrance, Alabama, 2019

F–Flood, Dir. 025° True   E–Ebb, Dir. 190° True

January

Day	Slack (h m)	Maximum (h m / knots)
1 Tu	0801 / 2003	0100 1.5E / 1239 1.7F
2 W	0826 / 2033	0117 1.9E / 1309 2.0F
3 Th	0856 / 2104	0144 2.1E / 1340 2.2F
4 F	0927 / 2136	0216 2.3E / 1412 2.3F
5 Sa ●	1000 / 2209	0251 2.4E / 1448 2.4F
6 Su	1036 / 2245	0329 2.4E / 1528 2.4F
7 M	1113 / 2322	0409 2.4E / 1611 2.3F
8 Tu	1150 / 2357	0450 2.3E / 1655 2.0F
9 W	1224	0529 2.0E / 1737 1.7F
10 Th	0025 / 1248	0603 1.6E / 1811 1.3F
11 F	0035 / 1246	0622 1.1E / 1812 0.8F
12 Sa	0006 / 1154 / 2248	0553 0.7E / 1607 0.6F
13 Su	0838 / 1905	0306 0.5E / 1522 0.6F
14 M ◑	0708 / 1848	0225 0.8E / 1508 0.9F
15 Tu	0702 / 1906	0206 1.1E / 1152 1.2F / 1410 1.1F / 1508 1.1F
16 W	0724 / 1935	0155 1.4E / 1203 1.6F
17 Th	0757 / 2011	0052 1.8E / 1234 2.1F
18 F	0836 / 2051	0128 2.2E / 1315 2.4F
19 Sa	0919 / 2136	0211 2.6E / 1401 2.6F
20 Su ○	1005 / 2223	0257 2.7E / 1450 2.7F
21 M	1052 / 2310	0342 2.7E / 1537 2.6F
22 Tu	1138 / 2355	0424 2.5E / 1619 2.2F
23 W	1220	0500 2.1E / 1644 1.7F
24 Th	0033 / 1252	0519 1.5E / 1649 1.2F
25 F	0049 / 1256 / 2354	0459 1.0E / 1611 0.7F
26 Sa	1856	0430 0.6E / 0959 * / 1102 * / 1539 0.6F
27 Su ◐	0645 / 1821	0240 0.6E / 1024 0.7F / 1228 0.7F / 1503 0.7F
28 M	0638 / 1835	0019 1.0E / 1057 1.2F
29 Tu	0658 / 1903	0021 1.4E / 1132 1.6F
30 W	0727 / 1935	0023 1.7E / 1205 1.8F
31 Th	0759 / 2009	0045 1.9E / 1239 2.0F

February

Day	Slack (h m)	Maximum (h m / knots)
1 F	0833 / 2044	0118 2.1E / 1313 2.1F
2 Sa	0909 / 2121	0155 2.2E / 1352 2.2F
3 Su	0948 / 2200	0236 2.2E / 1435 2.2F
4 M ●	1028 / 2240	0319 2.2E / 1523 2.0F
5 Tu	1109 / 2319	0403 2.1E / 1614 1.8F
6 W	1147 / 2352	0446 1.8E / 1713 1.5F
7 Th	1218	0527 1.4E / 1827 1.1F
8 F	0006 / 1226 / 2340	0602 0.9E / 1934 0.6F
9 Sa	1128	0604 0.5E / 1458 0.4F / 1922 * / 2032 *
10 Su	0642 / 1718	0142 0.4E / 1414 0.5F / 2021 0.4E / 2128 0.3E
11 M	0519 / 1723	0129 0.6E / 1031 0.6E / 1135 0.6F / 1355 0.7F / 2119† 0.8E
12 Tu ◑	0534 / 1750	0116 0.9E / 1030 1.1F / 1303 1.0F / 1401 1.0F / 2219† 1.2E
13 W	0607 / 1826	0119 1.3E / 1053 1.5F / 2321 1.7E
14 Th	0647 / 1906	1131 1.9F
15 F	0731 / 1951	0021 2.0E / 1216 2.2F
16 Sa	0819 / 2039	0118 2.3E / 1307 2.4F
17 Su	0909 / 2128	0213 2.5E / 1402 2.4F
18 M	1000 / 2219	0305 2.4E / 1517 2.2F
19 Tu ○	1050 / 2308	0353 2.1E / 1739 1.9F
20 W	1136 / 2352	0434 1.7E / 1854 1.4F
21 Th	1215	0458 1.1E / 1533 0.7F / 1725 0.7F / 2000 0.8F
22 F	0016 / 1228	0358 0.5E / 0727 0.4E / 0913 0.4E / 1444 0.4F / 1824† *
23 Sa	1623	0227 * / 0803 * / 1046 * / 1414 0.3F / 1922† 0.5E
24 Su	0423 / 1630	0053 0.4E / 0843 0.8F / 2019 0.9E
25 M	0444 / 1701	0923 1.1F / 2114 1.2E
26 Tu ◐	0521 / 1739	1002 1.4F / 2207 1.5E
27 W	0600 / 1817	1040 1.6F / 2259 1.6E
28 Th	0640 / 1856	1118 1.7F / 2351 1.7E

March

Day	Slack (h m)	Maximum (h m / knots)
1 F	0722 / 1937	1158 1.8F
2 Sa	0805 / 2020	0043 1.8E / 1242 1.8F
3 Su	0851 / 2106	0135 1.8E / 1332 1.8F
4 M	0939 / 2155	0228 1.8E / 1432 1.6F
5 Tu	1030 / 2246	0320 1.6E / 1604 1.4F
6 W ●	1121 / 2342	0411 1.3E / 1734 1.1F
7 Th	1213	0502 1.0E / 1844 0.8F
8 F	0051 / 1313	0555 0.6E / 1943 0.4F
9 Sa		0007 * / 0226 * / 0706 * / 1312 * / 1707† 0.3E
10 Su	1423	0512 0.4F / 1812 0.6E / 2130 0.4E / 2345 0.4E
11 M	0235 / 1513	0647 0.7F / 1908 1.0E / 2226 0.7E / 2336 0.7E
12 Tu	0326 / 1602	0801 1.1F / 2005 1.3E
13 W	0417 / 1650	0900 1.5F / 2106 1.6E
14 Th ◑	0510 / 1740	0956 1.8F / 2215 1.8E
15 F	0604 / 1833	1051 2.0F / 2336 2.0E
16 Sa	0701 / 1927	1148 2.0F
17 Su	0759 / 2022	0128 2.0E / 1250 1.9F
18 M	0858 / 2120	0315 1.9E / 1643 1.7F
19 Tu	0959 / 2221	0432 1.6E / 1800 1.4F
20 W ○	1103 / 2333	0557 1.2E / 1908 1.0F
21 Th		0745 0.7E / 1351 * / 1554 * / 2017 0.5F
22 F		0052 * / 0319 * / 0959 * / 1242 * / 1648† 0.5E
23 Sa	1156	0519 0.6F / 1739 0.9E
24 Su	0112 / 1355	0631 1.0F / 1828 1.2E
25 M	0212 / 1452	0724 1.3F / 1915 1.4E
26 Tu	0305 / 1542	0809 1.4F / 2001 1.5E
27 W ◐	0355 / 1628	0852 1.5F / 2050 1.5E
28 Th	0444 / 1715	0935 1.6F / 2143 1.5E
29 F	0534 / 1803	1020 1.6F / 2243 1.5E
30 Sa	0628 / 1854	1109 1.5F / 2353 1.4E
31 Su	0727 / 1949	1201 1.4F

Time meridian 90° W. 0000 is midnight. 1200 is noon. Times are not adjusted for Daylight Saving Time.
If three consecutive entries are marked (F) or (E) the middle one is not a true maximum but an intermediate value to show the current pattern.
* Current weak and variable.
† See page 196 for the remaining currents on this day.

Mobile Bay Entrance, Alabama, 2019

F–Flood, Dir. 025° True   E–Ebb, Dir. 190° True

April

Day	Slack (h m)	Maximum (h m)	knots
1 M	0831, 2051	0112 / 1301	1.3E / 1.1F
2 Tu	0944, 2210	0236 / 1517	1.0E / 0.8F
3 W	1119	0404 / 1823	0.8E / 0.6F
4 Th	0101, 1512, 2157	0540 / 0752 / 0856 / 1933 / 0.3F	0.5E / 0.4E / 0.4E / 0.4F
5 F ●	0432, 1846	0104 / 1401	0.4F / 0.5E
6 Sa	0925, 2307	0234 / 1550	0.7F / 0.8E
7 Su	1119	0344 / 1645	1.0F / 1.2E
8 M	0022, 1240	0450 / 1737	1.2F / 1.4E
9 Tu	0122, 1349	0556 / 1828	1.5F / 1.7E
10 W	0219, 1452	0701 / 1921	1.7F / 1.9E
11 Th	0317, 1553	0805 / 2017	1.9F / 1.9E
12 F ◐	0417, 1653	0906 / 2117	1.9F / 1.9E
13 Sa	0518, 1753	1004 / 2226	1.8F / 1.7E
14 Su	0623, 1855	1058	1.6F
15 M	0731, 2000	0230 / 1142 / 1358 / 1606	1.4E / 1.1F / 1.1F / 1.1F
16 Tu	0851	0351 / 1205 / 1327 / 1727 / 2313	1.0E / 0.6F / 0.5F / 0.8F / *
17 W		0004 / 0534 / 1200 / 1406 / 1844†	* / 0.6E / * / * / 0.5F
18 Th	0504, 1841	0127 / 0859 / 1003 / 1451	0.4F / 0.3E / 0.3E / 0.7E
19 F ○	0834, 2208	0233 / 1537	0.9F / 1.2E
20 Sa	1022, 2321	0334 / 1621	1.3F / 1.5E
21 Su	1135	0430 / 1704	1.5F / 1.7E
22 M	0016, 1233	0521 / 1745	1.7F / 1.8E
23 Tu	0104, 1325	0608 / 1826	1.7F / 1.8E
24 W	0149, 1413	0655 / 1907	1.7F / 1.8E
25 Th	0234, 1502	0743 / 1951	1.7F / 1.7E
26 F ◐	0320, 1554	0832 / 2037	1.6F / 1.5E
27 Sa	0412, 1649	0922 / 2129	1.4F / 1.3E
28 Su	0509, 1749	1013 / 2233	1.1F / 0.9E
29 M	0617, 1857	1103	0.8F
30 Tu	0809	0025 / 1152 / 1529 / 1654 / 2208†	0.5E / 0.4F / 0.3F / 0.3F / *

May

Day	Slack (h m)	Maximum (h m)	knots
1 W		0327 / 0554 / 0928	* / * / *
2 Th	0652, 1927	0009 / 1329	0.4F / 0.6E
3 F	0818, 2106	0103 / 1413	0.8F / 1.0E
4 Sa ●	0920, 2206	0155 / 1458	1.2F / 1.4E
5 Su	1016, 2259	0246 / 1543	1.5F / 1.7E
6 M	1111, 2351	0338 / 1628	1.8F / 2.0E
7 Tu	1207	0432 / 1715	2.0F / 2.2E
8 W	0044, 1305	0528 / 1802	2.1F / 2.3E
9 Th	0137, 1404	0625 / 1850	2.2F / 2.2E
10 F	0233, 1503	0723 / 1936	2.1F / 2.1E
11 Sa ◐	0329, 1602	0816 / 2016	1.8F / 1.7E
12 Su	0425, 1701	0902 / 2042	1.4F / 1.2E
13 M	0522, 1757	0932 / 2047	0.9F / 0.6E
14 Tu	0620	0024 / 0239 / 0926 / 1317 / 1636†	0.4E / 0.5E / 0.3F / * / *
15 W	0509, 2005	0040 / 1326	0.3F / 0.6E
16 Th	0802, 2047	0113 / 1400	0.9F / 1.2E
17 F	0855, 2135	0154 / 1439	1.4F / 1.7E
18 Sa ○	0944, 2220	0237 / 1519	1.8F / 2.0E
19 Su	1030, 2302	0319 / 1557	2.0F / 2.2E
20 M	1111, 2341	0359 / 1635	2.1F / 2.2E
21 Tu	1150	0440 / 1712	2.1F / 2.2E
22 W	0018, 1227	0522 / 1750	2.1F / 2.1E
23 Th	0055, 1305	0606 / 1828	2.0F / 2.0E
24 F ◐	0132, 1344	0652 / 1906	1.8F / 1.7E
25 Sa	0210, 1424	0739 / 1941	1.5F / 1.4E
26 Su ◐	0244, 1457	0824 / 2004	1.2F / 1.0E
27 M	0304, 1449	0903 / 2001	0.7F / 0.5E
28 Tu	0241	0612 / 1743	0.3F / *
29 W	0748, 1956	0439 / 1442	0.3F / 0.5E
30 Th	0746, 2009	0009 / 1316	0.7F / 0.9E
31 F	0815, 2044	0035 / 1338	1.1F / 1.3E

June

Day	Slack (h m)	Maximum (h m)	knots
1 Sa	0853, 2123	0114 / 1413	1.6F / 1.7E
2 Su	0934, 2205	0156 / 1452	1.9F / 2.1E
3 M ●	1017, 2249	0241 / 1533	2.2F / 2.4E
4 Tu	1103, 2335	0328 / 1616	2.4F / 2.5E
5 W	1151	0418 / 1700	2.5F / 2.6E
6 Th	0023, 1241	0508 / 1743	2.5F / 2.5E
7 F	0111, 1332	0557 / 1822	2.3F / 2.3E
8 Sa	0158, 1420	0642 / 1851	2.0F / 1.8E
9 Su ◐	0242, 1501	0714 / 1905	1.5F / 1.2E
10 M	0312, 1513, 2351	0714 / 1903 / *	0.9F / 0.7E
11 Tu	0951	0108 / 0607 / 1321 / 1521 / 1822†	* / 0.5F / 0.3E / 0.3E / 0.4E
12 W	0759, 2010	0008 / 0302 / 0405 / 1259	0.6F / 0.5F / 0.5F / 1.0E
13 Th	0800, 2023	0037 / 1316	1.3F / 1.5E
14 F	0829, 2056	0112 / 1349	1.8F / 2.0E
15 Sa	0906, 2132	0148 / 1424	2.1F / 2.3E
16 Su	0943, 2209	0224 / 1500	2.3F / 2.4E
17 M ○	1018, 2243	0259 / 1536	2.4F / 2.5E
18 Tu	1051, 2317	0335 / 1612	2.4F / 2.4E
19 W	1123, 2350	0413 / 1649	2.3F / 2.4E
20 Th	1155	0453 / 1726	2.2F / 2.2E
21 F	0023, 1227	0535 / 1802	2.0F / 1.9E
22 Sa	0054, 1255	0616 / 1833	1.7F / 1.6E
23 Su	0117, 1307	0652 / 1847	1.3F / 1.1E
24 M	0119, 1235	0705 / 1833	0.8F / 0.7E
25 Tu ○	0024, 1103, 2050	0447 / 1547	0.5F / 0.5E
26 W	0729, 1936	0348 / 1427	0.6F / 0.7E
27 Th	0720, 1937	0025 / 0148 / 0339 / 1416	0.8F / 0.8F / 0.8F / 1.1E
28 F	0742, 2004	0012 / 1303	1.2F / 1.5E
29 Sa	0814, 2038	0034 / 1327	1.7F / 1.9E
30 Su	0850, 2116	0109 / 1404	2.0F / 2.2E

Time meridian 90° W. 0000 is midnight. 1200 is noon. Times are not adjusted for Daylight Saving Time.
If three consecutive entries are marked (F) or (E) the middle one is not a true maximum but an intermediate value to show the current pattern.
* Current weak and variable.
† See page 196 for the remaining currents on this day.

Mobile Bay Entrance, Alabama, 2019

F–Flood, Dir. 025° True   E–Ebb, Dir. 190° True

July

Day	Slack (h m)	Maximum (h m)	knots
1 M	0929, 2157	0150 / 1444	2.3F / 2.5E
2 Tu ●	1011, 2240	0234 / 1526	2.6F / 2.7E
3 W	1055, 2325	0320 / 1609	2.7F / 2.8E
4 Th	1141	0407 / 1650	2.6F / 2.6E
5 F	0009, 1226	0451 / 1727	2.4F / 2.3E
6 Sa	0052, 1307	0527 / 1751	2.0F / 1.8E
7 Su	0128, 1334	0546 / 1751	1.4F / 1.2E
8 M	0144, 1307, 2257, 2341	0521 / 1737 / —	0.9F / 0.7E / *
9 Tu ◐	0815, 1941	0438 / 1600 / 2311	0.6F / 0.5E / 0.7F
10 W	0705, 1919	0123 / 0337 / 1237 / 2343	0.6F / 0.7F / 1.0F / 1.3F
11 Th	0713, 1936	1239	1.6E
12 F	0743, 2008	0019 / 1302	1.8F / 2.0E
13 Sa	0818, 2044	0055 / 1333	2.1F / 2.2E
14 Su	0854, 2119	0131 / 1406	2.3F / 2.3E
15 M	0929, 2153	0205 / 1441	2.3F / 2.4E
16 Tu ○	1002, 2227	0240 / 1518	2.3F / 2.4E
17 W	1035, 2301	0316 / 1556	2.3F / 2.3E
18 Th	1108, 2335	0356 / 1635	2.2F / 2.2E
19 F	1140	0437 / 1713	2.0F / 1.9E
20 Sa	0008, 1207	0517 / 1749	1.6F / 1.5E
21 Su	0033, 1219	0551 / 1812	1.2F / 1.1E
22 M	0034, 1153, 2339	0550 / 1735	0.7F / 0.6E
23 Tu	1027, 1952	0343 / 1434	0.5F / 0.5E
24 W ○	0625, 1832	0257 / 1403	0.6F / 0.7E
25 Th	0622, 1838	0245 / 1350 / 2331	0.8F / 1.1E / 1.2F
26 F	0647, 1907	0146 / 0252 / 1353 / 2347	1.1F / 1.1F / 1.4F / 1.6F
27 Sa	0720, 1942	1237	1.7E
28 Su	0757, 2021	0018 / 1313	1.9F / 2.1E
29 M	0836, 2103	0058 / 1355	2.2F / 2.4E
30 Tu	0919, 2147	0142 / 1440	2.5F / 2.6E
31 W ●	1003, 2232	0228 / 1524	2.6F / 2.6E

August

Day	Slack (h m)	Maximum (h m)	knots
1 Th	1049, 2318	0315 / 1608	2.5F / 2.4E
2 F	1134	0358 / 1646	2.2F / 2.1E
3 Sa	0002, 1216	0427 / 1712	1.7F / 1.5E
4 Su	0039, 1243	0435 / 1654	1.1F / 0.9E
5 M	0056, 1214	0357 / 1612 / 2119 / 2256	0.6F / 0.5E / * / *
6 Tu	0611, 1800	0319 / 1409 / 2149	0.5F / 0.5E / 0.7F
7 W ◐	0540, 1757	0030 / 0233 / 1131 / 2227	0.6F / 0.6F / 1.0E / 1.3F
8 Th	0602, 1826	1127 / 2307	1.4E / 1.6F
9 F	0638, 1904	1157 / 2347	1.7E / 1.9F
10 Sa	0717, 1943	1232	1.9E
11 Su	0755, 2021	0025 / 1308	2.0F / 2.1E
12 M	0833, 2059	0103 / 1345	2.1F / 2.1E
13 Tu	0910, 2136	0140 / 1424	2.1F / 2.1E
14 W	0947, 2215	0221 / 1505	2.0F / 2.0E
15 Th ○	1026, 2255	0306 / 1548	1.9F / 1.9E
16 F	1105, 2335	0400 / 1632	1.7F / 1.6E
17 Sa	1142	0521 / 1716	1.3F / 1.3E
18 Su	0011, 1205	0643 / 1758	1.0F / 0.8E
19 M	0031, 1139	0747 / 1832	0.5F / 0.3E
20 Tu	1628	0228 / 0627 / 0844 / 1307	* / * / * / 0.3E
21 W	0422, 1622	0128 / 0731 / 0938 / 1257 / 2135†	0.4F / 0.5E / 0.4E / 0.6E / 0.7F
22 Th	0447, 1658	0119 / 0831 / 1029 / 1252 / 2150	0.6F / 0.8E / 0.8E / 0.9E / 1.1F
23 F ○	0523, 1741	0933 / 1123 / 1303 / 2224	1.2E / 1.2E / 1.2E / 1.4F
24 Sa	0604, 1825	1039 / 2305	1.5E / 1.7F
25 Su	0646, 1911	1148 / 2351	1.8E / 2.0F
26 M	0730, 1958	1253	2.1E
27 Tu	0817, 2047	0039 / 1351	2.2F / 2.2E
28 W	0905, 2137	0132 / 1447	2.2F / 2.2E
29 Th	0956, 2229	0233 / 1540	2.0F / 2.0E
30 F ●	1048, 2320	0535 / 1633	1.8F / 1.6E
31 Sa	1140	0656 / 1923	1.3F / 1.0E

September

Day	Slack (h m)	Maximum (h m)	knots
1 Su	0009, 1228	0319 / 0445 / 0810 / 1718 / 1820†	0.6F / 0.6F / 0.8F / 0.4E / 0.3E
2 M		0223 / 0544 / 0928 / 1323 / 1910†	* / * / * / * / 0.3F
3 Tu	1457	0144 / 0641 / 2000	* / 0.6E / 0.8E
4 W	0333, 1546	0738 / 2048	1.1E / 1.3E
5 Th ◐	0419, 1638	0835 / 2133	1.4E / 1.5F
6 F	0506, 1729	0933 / 2217	1.6E / 1.7F
7 Sa	0552, 1817	1030 / 2258	1.6E / 1.7F
8 Su	0636, 1902	1126 / 2339	1.7E / 1.7F
9 M	0719, 1946	1221	1.7E
10 Tu	0801, 2032	0021 / 1314	1.7F / 1.7E
11 W	0846, 2121	0107 / 1408	1.6F / 1.6E
12 Th	0936, 2214	0203 / 1504	1.4F / 1.4E
13 F ○	1033, 2315	0348 / 1601	1.2F / 1.1E
14 Sa	1147	0537 / 1705	0.9F / 0.8E
15 Su	0034, 1424	0656 / 1907	0.6F / 0.4E
16 M	0510, 1915	0800 / 1118 / 1453	0.3F / * / 0.3F
17 Tu		0437 / 0859 / 1107 / 1639	0.5E / * / * / 0.6F
18 W	0101, 1347	0541 / 1802	0.8F / 0.9F
19 Th	0225, 1448	0637 / 1917	1.1E / 1.2F
20 F	0326, 1544	0733 / 2022	1.4E / 1.4F
21 Sa ○	0420, 1639	0830 / 2121	1.6E / 1.7F
22 Su	0512, 1734	0932 / 2216	1.7E / 1.8F
23 M	0604, 1830	1043 / 2310	1.8E / 1.9F
24 Tu	0657, 1928	1211	1.8E
25 W	0752, 2028	0005 / 1454	1.8F / 1.7E
26 Th	0851, 2133	0103 / 0213 / 0423 / 1614	1.5F / 1.5F / 1.5F / 1.4E
27 F	0958, 2249	0546 / 1741	1.3F / 1.1E
28 Sa ●	1137	0657 / 1949	0.9F / 0.6E
29 Su	0811, 1146	0124 / 0326 / 0811 / 1450†	* / * / 0.5F / 0.4F
30 M	0830, 2230	0419 / 1621	0.7F / 0.9F

Time meridian 90° W. 0000 is midnight. 1200 is noon. Times are not adjusted for Daylight Saving Time.
If three consecutive entries are marked (F) or (E) the middle one is not a true maximum but an intermediate value to show the current pattern.
* Current weak and variable.
† See page 196 for the remaining currents on this day.

Mobile Bay Entrance, Alabama, 2019

F–Flood, Dir. 025° True   E–Ebb, Dir. 190° True

October

Day	Slack (h m)	Maximum (h m, knots)
1 Tu	1216	0510 1.2E; 1741 1.2F
2 W	0049, 1328	0600 1.5E; 1846 1.5F
3 Th	0206, 1428	0649 1.6E; 1939 1.6F
4 F	0306, 1523	0737 1.7E; 2027 1.6F
5 Sa ◐	0359, 1615	0824 1.6E; 2111 1.6F
6 Su	0448, 1704	0914 1.6E; 2155 1.5F
7 M	0535, 1755	1007 1.4E; 2239 1.4F
8 Tu	0623, 1851	1110 1.3E; 2326 1.2F
9 W	0716, 1957	1228 1.1E
10 Th	0819, 2122	0019 1.0F; 1407 0.8E
11 F	0953, 2336	0158 0.6F; 0415 0.6E; 0510 0.6F; 1600 0.6E
12 Sa	1412	0632 0.4F; 1752 0.3E; 1843 0.3E; 2218 0.4E
13 Su ○	1840	0759 *; 0848 *; 1317 0.6F
14 M	0759, 2127	0219 0.7E; 1424 0.9F
15 Tu	1040, 2254	0331 1.0E; 1525 1.2F
16 W	1152	0424 1.3E; 1626 1.4F
17 Th	0009, 1253	0514 1.6E; 1727 1.6F
18 F	0116, 1350	0603 1.8E; 1828 1.7F
19 Sa	0218, 1445	0653 1.9E; 1929 1.8F
20 Su	0317, 1541	0744 1.9E; 2028 1.9F
21 M ○	0415, 1639	0835 1.8E; 2123 1.8F
22 Tu	0514, 1740	0928 1.6E; 2215 1.5F
23 W	0614, 1846	1022 1.3E; 1259 1.2E; 1352 1.2E; 2258 1.1F
24 Th	0719, 2007	1047 0.7E; 1135 0.7E; 1523 0.9E; 2326 0.5F
25 F		0125 0.5F; 0506 0.7F; 1022 *; 1220 *; 1708† 0.5E
26 Sa	1724	0149 0.5F; 0631 0.4F; 0941 *; 1316 0.5F
27 Su ●	0650, 2027	0229 0.8E; 1413 1.1F
28 M	0941, 2159	0314 1.4E; 1510 1.5F
29 Tu	1054, 2310	0400 1.8E; 1606 1.8F
30 W	1152	0444 2.0E; 1659 1.9F
31 Th	0010, 1243	0527 2.1E; 1749 2.0F

November

Day	Slack (h m)	Maximum (h m, knots)
1 F	0104, 1329	0609 2.0E; 1835 1.9F
2 Sa	0151, 1412	0649 1.9E; 1920 1.8F
3 Su	0235, 1452	0728 1.7E; 2004 1.6F
4 M ◐	0317, 1532	0808 1.5E; 2049 1.4F
5 Tu	0401, 1614	0847 1.3E; 2135 1.1F
6 W	0450, 1700	0922 0.9E; 2220 0.7F
7 Th	0544, 1753	0927 0.5E; 2301 0.3F
8 F		0320 *; 0446 *; 0853 *; 1130 *; 1505† *
9 Sa	0637, 1925	0122 0.3E; 1209 0.5F
10 Su	0801, 2018	0126 0.7E; 1255 1.0F
11 M	0858, 2111	0201 1.2E; 1342 1.4F
12 Tu ○	0952, 2203	0243 1.5E; 1431 1.7F
13 W	1043, 2255	0327 1.8E; 1520 1.9F
14 Th	1133, 2347	0410 2.1E; 1611 2.1F
15 F	1222	0455 2.2E; 1703 2.2F
16 Sa	0039, 1311	0539 2.3E; 1756 2.2F
17 Su	0132, 1401	0623 2.3E; 1849 2.1F
18 M	0226, 1451	0705 2.1E; 1939 1.9F
19 Tu ○	0320, 1542	0742 1.7E; 2023 1.5F
20 W	0414, 1632	0807 1.3E; 2052 0.9F
21 Th	0505, 1713	0816 0.7E; 1222 0.3E; 1404 0.4E; 2020 0.3F
22 F		0128 *; 0407 *; 0804 *; 1230 0.3F; 1605† *
23 Sa	0809, 1955	0110 0.7E; 1257 1.0F
24 Su	0829, 2039	0140 1.3E; 1336 1.6F
25 M	0915, 2128	0220 1.9E; 1419 2.0F
26 Tu ●	1003, 2216	0301 2.2E; 1504 2.3F
27 W	1048, 2301	0342 2.4E; 1547 2.3F
28 Th	1130, 2342	0421 2.4E; 1628 2.3F
29 F	1208	0459 2.4E; 1708 2.2F
30 Sa	0017, 1242	0536 2.2E; 1748 2.0F

December

Day	Slack (h m)	Maximum (h m, knots)
1 Su	0049, 1313	0611 2.0E; 1828 1.8F
2 M	0117, 1340	0644 1.8E; 1909 1.5F
3 Tu	0142, 1402	0713 1.4E; 1947 1.2F
4 W ◐	0155, 1408	0729 1.0E; 2017 0.7F
5 Th	0122, 1327, 2341	0724 0.6E; 1731 0.4F
6 F	0912, 1943	0436 0.3E; 1618 0.4F
7 Sa	0748, 1938	0234 0.6E; 1211 0.8F
8 Su	0757, 2004	0107 1.0E; 1225 1.2F
9 M	0830, 2041	0124 1.4E; 1301 1.7F
10 Tu	0911, 2123	0158 1.8E; 1342 2.0F
11 W ○	0953, 2205	0237 2.1E; 1425 2.2F
12 Th	1036, 2248	0318 2.4E; 1511 2.4F
13 F	1119, 2332	0400 2.5E; 1557 2.5F
14 Sa	1202	0441 2.6E; 1644 2.5F
15 Su	0017, 1246	0521 2.5E; 1730 2.3F
16 M	0103, 1329	0558 2.3E; 1812 2.0F
17 Tu	0147, 1410	0627 1.9E; 1843 1.5F
18 W ○	0224, 1438	0642 1.3E; 1842 1.0F
19 Th	0234, 1408, 2149	0641 0.8E; 1746 0.5F
20 F	0837, 1943	0600 0.4E; 1149 0.6F; 1422 0.5F; 1622 0.5F
21 Sa	0750, 1939	0045 0.9E; 1216 1.3F
22 Su	0801, 2009	0056 1.6E; 1252 1.8F
23 M	0836, 2049	0130 2.1E; 1332 2.2F
24 Tu	0917, 2130	0209 2.4E; 1412 2.4F
25 W ●	0957, 2210	0247 2.6E; 1451 2.5F
26 Th	1035, 2245	0325 2.6E; 1528 2.5F
27 F	1110, 2317	0401 2.5E; 1603 2.4F
28 Sa	1141, 2345	0436 2.4E; 1639 2.2F
29 Su	1209	0511 2.2E; 1715 2.0F
30 M	0009, 1234	0545 1.9E; 1751 1.7F
31 Tu	0030, 1251	0613 1.5E; 1822 1.3F

Time meridian 90° W. 0000 is midnight. 1200 is noon. Times are not adjusted for Daylight Saving Time.
If three consecutive entries are marked (F) or (E) the middle one is not a true maximum but an intermediate value to show the current pattern.
* Current weak and variable.
† See page 196 for the remaining currents on this day.

Calcasieu Pass, Louisiana 2019

F–Flood, Dir. 356° True   E–Ebb, Dir. 175° True

January

Day	Slack (h m)	Maximum (h m)	knots
1 Tu	0036	0546	2.5E
	1026	1341	2.0F
	1752	2037	0.6E
2 W		0005	*
		0617	2.8E
	1106	1425	2.3F
	1910	2150	0.5E
3 Th		0036	*
		0647	3.0E
	1145	1507	2.4F
	2020	2236	0.4E
4 F		0102	*
		0719	3.1E
	1225	1549	2.4F
	2124	2311	0.3E
5 Sa ●		0123	*
		0756	3.1E
	1305	1632	2.2F
		2340	*
6 Su		0142	*
		0841	3.0E
	1346	1718	2.0F
7 M		0011	*
		0202	*
		0929	2.9E
	1427	1806	1.9F
8 Tu		0053	*
		0240	*
		1016	2.7E
	1505	1849	1.8F
	2319		
9 W		0142	0.4E
		0355	0.4E
		1059	2.4E
	1540	1921	1.7F
	2328		
10 Th		0220	0.7E
		0530	0.5E
		1143	2.1E
	1611	1945	1.6F
	2338		
11 F		0252	1.0E
		0707	0.5E
		1234	1.6E
	1641	2004	1.3F
	2342		
12 Sa		0320	1.3E
		0827	0.3E
		1337	1.1E
	1712	2019	1.0F
	2330		
13 Su		0344	1.5E
		0953	*
		1454	0.7F
	1748	2030	0.6F
	2255		
14 M ◐		0403	1.7E
	0859	1139	0.5F
	1424	1621	0.3F
		2030	*
15 Tu		0418	2.0E
	0911	1231	1.2F
		1754	*
		2019	*
16 W		0438	2.4E
	0935	1308	1.8F
	1801		
17 Th		0508	2.9E
	1009	1343	2.4F
	1906		
18 F		0546	3.3E
	1048	1420	2.8F
		2212	*
		2318	*
19 Sa		0630	3.7E
	1132	1500	3.0F
		2205	*
20 Su ○		0033	*
		0720	3.9E
	1219	1543	3.1F
		2231	*
21 M		0128	*
		0820	3.8E
	1309	1629	2.9F
	2140	2305	0.3E
22 Tu		0227	*
		0927	3.6E
	1402	1718	2.7F
	2156	2345	0.5E
23 W		0339	*
		1032	3.2E
	1455	1808	2.4F
	2210		
24 Th		0030	0.8E
		0502	*
		1135	2.7E
	1549	1854	2.1F
	2224		
25 F		0116	1.2E
	0510	0635	0.3F
	0758	1247	2.0E
	1644	1936	1.6F
	2235		
26 Sa		0201	1.6E
	0614	0807	0.5F
	1010	1411	1.3E
	1741	2012	1.0F
	2240		
27 Su ◐		0243	1.9E
	0713	0941	0.8F
	1248	1543	0.8E
	1851	2046	0.5F
	2233		
28 M		0326	2.2E
	0811	1130	1.3F
	1521	1741	0.4E
		2118	*
29 Tu		0411	2.4E
	0910	1244	1.8F
	1721	2010	0.4E
		2153	0.3E
30 W		0500	2.5E
	1005	1337	2.1F
	1841	2150	0.5E
		2300	0.5E
31 Th		0548	2.7E
	1054	1421	2.3F
	1940	2221	0.5E

February

Day	Slack (h m)	Maximum (h m)	knots
1 F		0001	0.4E
		0632	2.8E
	1138	1500	2.4F
	2025	2240	0.4E
2 Sa		0043	*
		0713	2.9E
	1217	1536	2.3F
	2057	2250	0.3E
3 Su		0119	*
		0756	2.9E
	1252	1609	2.1F
	2112	2257	0.3E
4 M ●		0157	*
		0841	2.9E
	1324	1640	2.0F
	2120	2315	0.4E
5 Tu		0240	*
		0925	2.7E
	1355	1711	1.8F
	2130	2344	0.6E
6 W		0333	*
		1008	2.4E
	1425	1740	1.7F
	2142		
7 Th		0020	0.9E
		0436	*
		1050	2.1E
	1455	1808	1.5F
	2152		
8 F		0058	1.1E
		0549	*
		1133	1.6E
	1527	1832	1.2F
	2153		
9 Sa		0131	1.3E
		0707	*
		1225	1.2E
	1559	1849	0.8F
	2131		
10 Su		0154	1.5E
	0644	0816	0.3F
	1006	1334	0.7E
	1633	1855	0.4F
	2052		
11 M		0205	1.6E
	0700	0925	0.6F
		1459	*
		1839	*
12 Tu ◐		0211	1.9E
	0727	1100	1.0F
		1658	*
		1803	*
13 W		0233	2.2E
	0805	1210	1.6F
	1833		
14 Th		0321	2.6E
	0852	1254	2.1F
	1904		
15 F		0424	2.9E
	0944	1330	2.5F
	1928		
16 Sa		0528	3.3E
	1034	1405	2.8F
		2207	*
		2329	*
17 Su		0627	3.6E
	1122	1441	3.0F
	1941	2127	0.3E
18 M		0053	*
		0726	3.7E
	1208	1519	2.9F
	1948	2147	0.5E
19 Tu ○	0001	0153	0.5F
	0320	0830	3.6E
	1255	1558	2.7F
	2000	2218	0.9E
20 W	0051	0255	0.7F
	0437	0936	3.2E
	1342	1638	2.4F
	2015	2252	1.2E
21 Th	0153	0402	0.8F
	0558	1037	2.7E
	1432	1719	1.9F
	2030	2329	1.6E
22 F	0300	0516	0.9F
	0735	1138	2.1E
	1525	1800	1.4F
	2042		
23 Sa		0008	1.9E
	0407	0640	1.0F
	0925	1249	1.4E
	1621	1839	0.9F
	2048		
24 Su		0047	2.2E
	0513	0804	1.2F
	1125	1415	0.8E
	1730	1912	0.4F
	2040		
25 M		0129	2.3E
	0619	0930	1.4F
	1351	1601	0.4E
		1937	*
26 Tu ◑		0214	2.3E
	0728	1112	1.6F
	1617	1839	*
27 W		0309	2.3E
	0838	1230	1.8F
	1750		
28 Th		0416	2.3E
	0945	1324	2.1F
	1844		

March

Day	Slack (h m)	Maximum (h m)	knots
1 F		0528	2.4E
	1040	1405	2.1F
	1917	2212	0.5E
		2344	0.5E
2 Sa		0624	2.6E
	1122	1438	2.1F
	1928	2205	0.5E
3 Su		0043	*
		0708	2.7E
	1156	1505	2.1F
	1927	2159	0.6E
4 M		0127	*
		0749	2.7E
	1224	1528	2.0F
	1927	2203	0.8E
5 Tu		0210	*
		0830	2.6E
	1249	1548	1.8F
	1933	2222	1.0E
6 W ●	0133	0255	0.3F
	0414	0913	2.3E
	1314	1609	1.6F
	1944	2249	1.2E
7 Th	0220	0346	0.3F
	0510	0957	2.0E
	1343	1632	1.4F
	1952	2316	1.4E
8 F	0308	0442	0.4F
	0621	1043	1.6E
	1417	1654	1.0F
	1947	2340	1.6E
9 Sa	0349	0545	0.5F
	0800	1132	1.1E
	1457	1712	0.6F
	1922	2355	1.7E
10 Su	0423	0654	0.7F
	0950	1234	0.7E
		1717	*
		2357	1.8E
11 M	0455	0757	1.0F
	1158	1359	0.3E
		1659	*
		2355	2.1E
12 Tu ◐	0532	0859	1.3F
	1502		
	1750		
13 W		0009	2.3E
	0619	1020	1.5F
	1712		
14 Th ◑		0054	2.5E
	0718	1144	1.8F
	1800		
15 F		0225	2.6E
	0823	1234	2.2F
	1826		
16 Sa		0405	2.8E
	0925	1310	2.5F
	1825		
17 Su		0529	3.0E
	1020	1343	2.6F
	1814	2033	0.5E
18 M		0010	*
		0635	3.2E
	1108	1414	2.7F
	1811	2035	0.8E
	2334		
19 Tu		0115	0.5F
	0242	0736	3.2E
	1152	1446	2.5F
	1816	2059	1.2E
20 W ○	0001	0212	1.0F
	0411	0838	2.9E
	1235	1519	2.2F
	1825	2129	1.7E
21 Th	0043	0310	1.3F
	0533	0940	2.5E
	1320	1553	1.7F
	1836	2202	2.1E
22 F	0132	0411	1.5F
	0701	1040	2.0E
	1409	1628	1.2F
	1846	2235	2.4E
23 Sa	0227	0519	1.6F
	0840	1142	1.4E
	1506	1701	0.7F
	1849	2309	2.5E
24 Su	0326	0636	1.7F
	1022	1256	0.8E
		1732	*
		2343	2.6E
25 M	0429	0757	1.7F
	1222	1433	0.4E
		1717	*
	1753		
26 Tu ◑		0021	2.6E
	0538	0916	1.7F
	1442		
27 W		0108	2.4E
	0652	1048	1.7F
	1633		
28 Th		0214	2.3E
	0807	1206	1.8F
	1731		
29 F		0338	2.2E
	0916	1258	1.8F
	1757		
30 Sa		0502	2.2E
	1010	1333	1.9F
	1757	2119	0.6E
		2347	0.4E
31 Su		0602	2.2E
	1049	1359	1.9F
	1749	2056	0.7E

Time meridian 90° W. 0000 is midnight. 1200 is noon. Times are not adjusted for Daylight Saving Time.
* Current weak and variable.

Calcasieu Pass, Louisiana 2019

F–Flood, Dir. 356° True   E–Ebb, Dir. 175° True

April

Day	Slack (h m)	Maximum (h m)	knots
1 M		0049	*
		0647	2.3E
	1118	1419	1.8F
	1745	2049	1.0E
2 Tu	0015	0133	0.3F
	0252	0728	2.2E
	1142	1434	1.7F
	1748	2103	1.4E
3 W	0032	0215	0.6F
	0403	0811	2.0E
	1206	1450	1.6F
	1752	2125	1.7E
4 Th	0058	0258	0.8F
	0507	0858	1.8E
	1233	1508	1.3F
	1753	2148	1.9E
5 F ●	0129	0344	1.0F
	0617	0949	1.4E
	1307	1527	0.9F
	1742	2207	2.0E
6 Sa	0200	0434	1.1F
	0742	1043	1.0E
	1351	1542	0.4F
	1720	2219	2.1E
7 Su	0233	0530	1.3F
	0919	1142	0.7E
		1547	*
		2225	2.2E
8 M	0308	0634	1.5F
	1104	1303	0.3E
		1530	*
		2231	2.4E
9 Tu	0349	0739	1.7F
	1322	2249	2.7E
10 W	0439	0840	1.8F
	1520	2321	2.8E
11 Th	0541	0949	1.9F
	1626		
12 F ◑		0015	2.7E
	0650	1105	2.0F
	1700		
13 Sa		0211	2.5E
	0759	1201	2.2F
	1703		
14 Su		0411	2.5E
	0903	1239	2.3F
	1653	1945	0.7E
	2311		0.4E
15 M		0538	2.5E
	0959	1310	2.3F
	1647	1930	1.0E
	2321		
16 Tu		0037	0.3F
	0150	0643	2.5E
	1048	1339	2.1F
	1648	1947	1.5E
	2325		
17 W		0134	1.0F
	0343	0744	2.3E
	1133	1408	1.9F
	1653	2012	2.1E
	2353		
18 Th		0226	1.6F
	0508	0847	2.0E
	1217	1438	1.5F
	1659	2041	2.5E
19 F ○	0030	0319	1.9F
	0630	0949	1.6E
	1302	1507	1.0F
	1704	2112	2.8E
20 Sa	0113	0415	2.1F
	0759	1048	1.2E
	1354	1535	0.5F
	1704	2145	2.9E
21 Su	0202	0517	2.1F
	0934	1151	0.7E
		1600	*
		2219	3.0E
22 M	0257	0632	2.0F
	1115	1315	0.4E
		1612	*
		2255	2.9E
23 Tu	0359	0750	2.0F
	1317	2334	2.7E
24 W	0508	0901	1.8F
	1502		
25 Th		0023	2.5E
	0619	1014	1.7F
	1600		
26 F ◑		0134	2.2E
	0726	1123	1.6F
	1621		
27 Sa		0300	2.0E
	0824	1211	1.6F
	1619		
28 Su		0419	1.9E
	0913	1243	1.6F
	1613	1931	0.8E
	2352		0.4E
29 M		0523	1.8E
	0951	1305	1.5F
	1612	1925	1.2E
30 Tu		0052	*
		0615	1.7E
	1023	1321	1.4F
	1615	1940	1.6E
	2345		

May

Day	Slack (h m)	Maximum (h m)	knots
1 W		0134	0.6F
	0329	0702	1.6E
	1053	1336	1.3F
	1617	2000	2.0E
	2359		
2 Th		0213	1.1F
	0442	0753	1.4E
	1125	1352	1.1F
	1615	2019	2.2E
3 F	0019	0252	1.4F
	0551	0849	1.2E
	1201	1409	0.8F
	1604	2035	2.4E
4 Sa ●	0043	0333	1.7F
	0708	0950	0.9E
	1246	1422	0.4F
	1546	2047	2.6E
5 Su	0110	0419	1.9F
	0837	1050	0.6E
		1428	*
		2059	2.7E
6 M	0143	0511	2.1F
	1012	1200	0.3E
		1417	*
		2118	2.9E
7 Tu	0225	0614	2.2F
	1201	2147	3.0E
8 W	0316	0720	2.2F
	1344	2227	3.0E
9 Th	0415	0820	2.3F
	1445	2315	2.9E
10 F	0520	0916	2.2F
	1517		
11 Sa ◑		0025	2.6E
	0626	1014	2.1F
	1525		
12 Su		0231	2.2E
	0731	1109	2.0F
	1521	1831	0.8E
		2137	0.6E
13 M		0421	2.0E
	0834	1153	1.8F
	1519	1825	1.2E
		2354	*
14 Tu		0545	1.8E
	0934	1229	1.7F
	1521	1841	1.7E
	2248		
15 W		0059	0.9F
	0314	0653	1.7E
	1029	1300	1.4F
	1526	1904	2.3E
	2310		
16 Th		0149	1.6F
	0447	0759	1.5E
	1120	1329	1.1F
	1532	1929	2.7E
	2341		
17 F		0237	2.1F
	0608	0906	1.2E
	1208	1356	0.7F
	1536	1957	3.1E
18 Sa ○	0018	0325	2.4F
	0730	1007	0.9E
	1257	1422	0.4F
	1536	2028	3.2E
19 Su	0059	0417	2.5F
	0858	1105	0.6E
		1443	*
		2103	3.2E
20 M	0146	0517	2.3F
	1028	1210	0.3E
		1452	*
		2142	3.1E
21 Tu	0241	0629	2.2F
	1213	2225	3.0E
22 W	0341	0741	2.0F
	1348	2310	2.7E
23 Th	0443	0838	1.9F
	1427		
24 F		0001	2.5E
	0540	0927	1.7F
	1434		
25 Sa		0105	2.1E
	0628	1012	1.5F
	1432		
26 Su ◑		0219	1.8E
	0710	1052	1.3F
	1431	1755	0.9E
		2138	0.6E
27 M		0331	1.5E
	0749	1125	1.2F
	1434	1801	1.3E
		2351	*
28 Tu		0440	1.3E
	0829	1151	1.1F
	1439	1819	1.7E
	2304		
29 W		0048	0.4F
	0232	0544	1.1E
	0914	1213	0.9F
	1441	1840	2.1E
	2305		
30 Th		0128	1.0F
	0405	0643	0.9E
	1005	1234	0.7F
	1437	1858	2.4E
	2319		
31 F		0204	1.6E
	0520	0744	0.8E
	1058	1253	0.5F
	1428	1912	2.7E
	2339		

June

Day	Slack (h m)	Maximum (h m)	knots
1 Sa		0239	2.0F
	0631	0852	0.6E
		1310	*
		1926	2.9E
2 Su	0004	0318	2.3F
	0751	0959	0.5E
		1321	*
		1943	3.1E
3 M ●	0035	0402	2.5F
	0918	1101	0.3E
		1324	*
		2009	3.3E
4 Tu	0115	0454	2.6F
		1217	*
		1311	*
		2048	3.4E
5 W	0204	0553	2.6F
	1217	2139	3.3E
6 Th	0300	0656	2.5F
	1311	2235	3.1E
7 F	0400	0750	2.5F
	1330	2337	2.8E
8 Sa	0459	0836	2.3F
	1334		
9 Su ◑		0102	2.3E
	0558	0920	2.0F
	1335	1637	0.9E
		2025	0.5E
10 M		0249	1.8E
	0658	1006	1.6F
	1338	1659	1.3E
	2232		
11 Tu		0427	1.4E
	0802	1053	1.2F
	1344	1727	1.8E
	2154		
12 W		0016	0.7F
	0237	0554	1.1E
	0912	1139	0.9F
	1350	1756	2.3E
	2220		
13 Th		0113	1.5F
	0427	0713	0.9E
	1026	1217	0.6F
	1357	1825	2.8E
	2254		
14 F		0200	2.1F
	0553	0834	0.8E
	1132	1250	0.3F
	1402	1853	3.1E
	2331		
15 Sa		0245	2.5F
	0711	0944	0.7E
		1319	*
		1924	3.3E
16 Su	0010	0331	2.6F
	0829	1038	0.5E
		1342	*
		1957	3.3E
17 M ○	0053	0420	2.5F
	0947	1130	0.3E
		1359	*
		2038	3.2E
18 Tu	0141	0515	2.3F
		1238	*
		1352	*
		2124	3.1E
19 W	0232	0618	2.1F
	1234	2212	2.9E
20 Th	0323	0717	2.0F
	1257	2258	2.7E
21 F	0410	0800	1.8F
	1251	2346	2.4E
22 Sa	0449	0829	1.6F
	1246	1555	0.6E
		1819	0.5E
23 Su		0039	2.0E
	0522	0851	1.4F
	1246	1559	0.9E
		2004	0.5E
24 M		0142	1.5E
	0551	0910	1.2F
	1249	1623	1.3E
		2139	0.3E
25 Tu ◑		0252	1.1E
	0624	0932	0.9F
	1249	1650	1.6E
		2338	*
26 W		0407	0.7E
	0705	0959	0.6F
	1242	1716	1.9E
	2203		
27 Th		0036	0.8F
	0315	0526	0.5E
	0806	1032	0.3F
	1226	1737	2.3E
	2216		
28 F		0115	1.4F
	0447	0639	0.4E
		1109	*
		1756	2.6E
	2237		
29 Sa		0150	2.0F
	0601	0755	0.4E
		1141	*
		1815	2.9E
	2303		
30 Su		0225	2.4F
	0712	0919	0.3E
		1206	*
		1839	3.3E
	2336		

Time meridian 90° W. 0000 is midnight. 1200 is noon. Times are not adjusted for Daylight Saving Time.
* Current weak and variable.

Calcasieu Pass, Louisiana 2019

F–Flood, Dir. 356° True   E–Ebb, Dir. 175° True

July

Day	Slack (h m)	Maximum (h m)	knots
1 M	0825	0303	2.7F
		1016	0.3E
		1229	*
		1910	3.5E
2 Tu ●	0015	0346	2.9F
		1059	*
		1252	*
		1953	3.6E
3 W	0100	0433	2.8F
		1141	*
		1323	*
		2048	3.6E
4 Th	0151	0525	2.7F
		1228	*
		1411	*
		2151	3.4E
5 F	0246	0619	2.6F
	1127	1315	0.3E
		1534	*
		2254	3.0E
6 Sa	0340	0708	2.4F
	1132	1356	0.6E
		1725	0.3E
7 Su ◐	0434	0000	2.5E
	1138	0750	2.1F
		1433	1.0E
		1916	*
8 M	0529	0124	1.9E
	1144	0828	1.6F
		1510	1.5E
		2053	*
9 Tu ◑	0627	0257	1.3E
	1149	0906	1.1F
	2020	1548	1.9E
		2248	0.7F
10 W	0135	0435	0.8E
	0738	0947	0.6F
	1151	1629	2.3E
	2107		
11 Th	0354	0019	1.4F
	2154	0618	0.6E
		1037	*
		1711	2.6E
12 F	0534	0117	2.0F
	2240	0809	0.5E
		1130	*
		1751	2.8E
13 Sa	0651	0205	2.4F
	2325	0934	0.6E
		1215	*
		1830	3.0E
14 Su	0757	0249	2.6F
		1023	0.5E
		1250	*
		1908	3.1E
15 M	0008	0333	2.6F
	0859	1100	0.4E
		1319	*
		1948	3.2E
16 Tu ○	0051	0416	2.4F
		1131	*
		1344	*
		2033	3.1E
17 W	0134	0501	2.2F
		1158	*
		1411	*
		2121	3.0E
18 Th	0215	0546	2.0F
		1227	*
		1450	*
		2206	2.8E
19 F	0253	0626	1.8F
	1059	1301	0.4E
		1553	*
		2248	2.5E
20 Sa	0327	0657	1.6F
	1059	1336	0.7E
		1715	0.3E
		2331	2.1E
21 Su	0355	0720	1.4F
	1100	1409	1.0E
		1846	0.3E
22 M	0422	0019	1.6E
	1100	0737	1.2F
		1439	1.3E
		2006	*
23 Tu	0449	0118	1.1E
	1049	0753	0.9F
		1508	1.5E
		2124	*
24 W ◑	0521	0231	0.7E
	1024	0804	0.6F
	2030	1533	1.8E
		2308	0.5F
25 Th	0203	0355	0.3E
	0604	0806	0.3F
	0948	1556	2.0E
	2053		
26 F	2123	0017	1.1F
		0533	*
		0754	*
		1622	2.3E
27 Sa	0548	0100	1.7F
	2157	1653	2.6E
28 Su	0649	0136	2.2F
	2236	1731	3.0E
29 M	0741	0210	2.6F
	2317	1813	3.4E
30 Tu		0246	2.9F
		1015	*
		1210	*
		1900	3.6E
31 W ●	0001	0325	2.9F
		1021	*
		1309	*
		1955	3.7E

August

Day	Slack (h m)	Maximum (h m)	knots
1 Th	0047	0406	2.9F
	0914	1045	0.3E
		1406	*
		2059	3.5E
2 F	0135	0449	2.7F
	0923	1116	0.5E
		1514	0.3F
		2203	3.2E
3 Sa	0225	0533	2.4F
	0932	1152	0.9E
	1500	1631	0.3F
	1751	2306	2.7E
4 Su	0316	0616	2.0F
	0942	1232	1.3E
	1615	1759	0.4F
	1939		
5 M	0408	0012	2.0E
	0951	0658	1.5F
	1722	1315	1.7E
	2146	1930	0.7F
6 Tu	0504	0134	1.4E
	0956	0735	1.0F
	1824	1358	2.1E
		2057	1.0F
7 W ◑	0013	0306	0.8E
	0611	0810	0.5F
	0954	1443	2.3E
	1926	2240	1.3F
8 Th	0247	0500	0.4E
	2030	0842	*
		1532	2.5E
9 F	0451	0012	1.8F
	2133	0731	0.4E
		0913	0.3F
		1628	2.6E
10 Sa	0612	0113	2.2F
	2230	1728	2.7E
11 Su	0711	0202	2.4F
	2320	1004	0.6E
		1148	0.5E
		1822	2.8E
12 M	0758	0245	2.5F
		1026	0.5E
		1238	0.3E
		1909	2.9E
13 Tu	0003	0322	2.4F
	0835	1042	0.4E
		1316	*
		1952	2.9E
14 W	0041	0356	2.2F
	0856	1051	0.4E
		1353	*
		2034	2.9E
15 Th ○	0114	0425	2.0F
	0902	1100	0.4E
		1434	*
		2115	2.7E
16 F	0144	0451	1.8F
	0903	1119	0.6E
		1523	*
		2156	2.4E
17 Sa	0212	0515	1.6F
	0907	1146	0.9E
		1622	*
		2237	2.1E
18 Su	0239	0539	1.3F
	0911	1218	1.2E
		1730	*
		2320	1.6E
19 M	0307	0602	1.1F
	0911	1249	1.4E
		1846	*
20 Tu	0339	0011	1.2E
	0856	0621	0.8F
	1800	1316	1.6E
	2211	1956	0.4F
21 W	0414	0115	0.7E
	0827	0631	0.4F
	1830	1335	1.7E
		2102	0.7F
22 Th	0038	0238	0.3E
	1904	0622	*
		1348	1.9E
		2227	1.0F
23 F ◑	1945	0428	*
		0549	*
		1408	2.1E
		2353	1.5F
24 Sa	0538	1452	2.3E
	2034		
25 Su	0624	0043	1.9F
	2125	1557	2.6E
26 M	0657	0119	2.3F
	2215	1705	2.9E
27 Tu	0715	0152	2.6F
	2301	1805	3.3E
28 W	0718	0223	2.8F
	2345	0918	0.3E
		1232	*
		1902	3.4E
29 Th	0718	0256	2.8F
	1151	0925	0.6E
	1454	1333	0.4E
		2002	3.4E
30 F ●	0029	0330	2.6F
	0723	0949	0.9E
	1228	1433	0.7F
	1618	2106	3.1E
31 Sa	0113	0406	2.3F
	0732	1019	1.3E
	1320	1537	0.9F
	1741	2209	2.7E

September

Day	Slack (h m)	Maximum (h m)	knots
1 Su	0200	0443	1.9F
	0745	1053	1.8E
	1420	1647	1.1F
	1916	2311	2.1E
2 M	0251	0522	1.4F
	0757	1130	2.1E
	1524	1805	1.3F
	2105		
3 Tu	0347	0019	1.4E
	0806	0601	0.9F
	1629	1208	2.4E
	2259	1929	1.5F
4 W	0456	0144	0.8E
	0805	0638	0.4F
	1736	1250	2.5E
		2051	1.6F
5 Th ◐	0115	0327	0.4E
		0710	*
		1339	2.5E
	1846	2225	1.7F
6 F	0331	1437	2.4E
	2000	2358	1.9F
7 Sa	0508	1551	2.4E
	2114		
8 Su	0608	0101	2.2F
	2217	1714	2.4E
9 M	0648	0148	2.3F
	2307	0954	0.6E
		1138	0.6E
		1818	2.5E
10 Tu	0710	0224	2.2F
	2345	0955	0.6E
		1240	0.3E
		1905	2.6E
11 W	0713	0253	2.1F
		0954	0.6E
		1323	*
		1943	2.6E
12 Th	0015	0315	1.9F
	0707	0952	0.8E
	1241	1403	0.3F
	1522	2021	2.5E
13 F ○	0039	0332	1.7F
	0704	1002	1.0E
	1308	1446	0.5F
	1622	2101	2.2E
14 Sa	0102	0348	1.5F
	0706	1022	1.3E
	1347	1534	0.5F
	1722	2143	1.9E
15 Su	0127	0407	1.2F
	0708	1046	1.6E
	1431	1627	0.6F
	1833	2229	1.5E
16 M	0157	0427	0.9F
	0704	1110	1.7E
	1514	1727	0.7F
	2004	2318	1.1E
17 Tu	0235	0445	0.6F
	0648	1129	1.8E
	1554	1834	0.9F
	2143		
18 W		0018	0.7F
		0455	*
	1631	1139	1.9E
	2334	1940	1.1F
19 Th		0140	0.3E
		0444	*
	1710	1140	2.1E
		2041	1.3F
20 F	0200	1145	2.3E
	1756	2153	1.5F
21 Sa ◑	0410	1212	2.4E
	1853	2322	1.7F
22 Su	0515	1326	2.4E
	1956		
23 M	0552	0018	2.0F
	2058	1524	2.5E
24 Tu	0603	0054	2.3F
	2153	1657	2.7E
25 W	0553	0123	2.4F
	2241	0831	0.5E
		1141	0.3E
		1807	2.9E
26 Th	0543	0151	2.5F
	1129	0809	0.8E
	1409	1255	0.3F
	2325	1907	2.9E
27 F	0541	0219	2.4F
	1141	0827	1.3E
	1550	1351	0.9F
		2008	2.7E
28 Sa ●	0007	0249	2.1F
	0546	0854	1.8E
	1217	1447	1.4F
	1715	2112	2.4E
29 Su	0050	0321	1.7F
	0555	0927	2.2E
	1302	1546	1.7F
	1843	2214	1.9E
30 M	0137	0354	1.2F
	0605	1002	2.6E
	1353	1650	1.9F
	2020	2317	1.4E

Time meridian 90° W. 0000 is midnight. 1200 is noon. Times are not adjusted for Daylight Saving Time.
* Current weak and variable.

Calcasieu Pass, Louisiana 2019

F–Flood, Dir. 356° True   E–Ebb, Dir. 175° True

October

Day	Slack	Max	knots
1 Tu	0232	0428	0.7F
	0613	1038	2.9E
	1450	1803	2.0F
	2201		
2 W		0029	0.9E
		0502	*
		1115	2.9E
	1552	1924	2.0F
	2352		
3 Th		0205	0.5E
		0530	*
		1156	2.8E
	1701	2043	2.0F
4 F	0157	1244	2.6E
	1817	2207	1.9F
5 Sa ◖	0342	1351	2.4E
	1934	2334	1.9F
6 Su	0450	1519	2.2E
	2047		
7 M		0035	1.9F
	0528	1649	2.1E
	2149		
8 Tu		0117	1.9F
	0540	0902	0.7E
		1140	0.5E
		1753	2.2E
	2235		
9 W		0146	1.8F
	0535	0850	0.8E
		1244	*
		1838	2.1E
	2308		
10 Th		0206	1.7F
	0526	0837	1.1E
	1205	1328	0.3F
	1452	1918	2.0E
	2333		
11 F		0219	1.6F
	0521	0842	1.4E
	1216	1408	0.7F
	1605	1958	1.9E
	2354		
12 Sa		0232	1.4F
	0521	0900	1.8E
	1240	1449	1.0F
	1710	2044	1.6E
13 Su O	0018	0247	1.2F
	0519	0922	2.0E
	1309	1533	1.2F
	1818	2135	1.3E
14 M	0048	0304	0.8F
	0513	0943	2.2E
	1341	1620	1.3F
	1938	2228	1.0E
15 Tu	0129	0320	0.4F
	0457	1000	2.2E
	1414	1714	1.4F
	2109	2327	0.7E
16 W		0328	*
		1011	2.3E
	1450	1816	1.6F
	2245		
17 Th		0044	0.4E
		0315	*
		1018	2.4E
	1531	1922	1.7F
18 F	0040	1030	2.5E
	1618	2024	1.8F
19 Sa	0228	1054	2.7E
	1715	2126	1.9F
20 Su	0341	1134	2.6E
	1819	2236	2.0F
21 M O	0426	1253	2.4E
	1924	2334	2.0F
22 Tu	0440	1519	2.3E
	2027		
23 W		0013	2.1F
	0430	0801	0.7E
		1003	0.6E
		1659	2.3E
	2125		
24 Th		0043	2.0F
	0418	0703	1.0E
		1212	*
		1811	2.2E
	2216		
25 F		0111	1.9F
	0413	0715	1.6E
	1105	1312	0.9F
	1519	1913	2.1E
	2302		
26 Sa		0138	1.7F
	0416	0737	2.2E
	1128	1404	1.6F
	1650	2017	1.9E
	2346		
27 Su ●		0207	1.4F
	0423	0806	2.7E
	1203	1456	2.1F
	1813	2122	1.5E
28 M	0031	0237	1.0F
	0431	0839	3.1E
	1245	1550	2.4F
	1940	2225	1.2E
29 Tu	0122	0307	0.6F
	0437	0916	3.3E
	1333	1650	2.4F
	2113	2328	0.8E
30 W		0335	*
		0955	3.3E
	1428	1800	2.4F
	2250		
31 Th		0047	0.4E
		0358	*
		1036	3.1E
	1530	1920	2.2F

November

Day	Slack	Max	knots
1 F	0038	1119	2.9E
	1639	2034	2.1F
2 Sa	0216	1209	2.6E
	1752	2143	1.9F
3 Su	0320	1317	2.3E
	1900	2253	1.8F
4 M ◑	0354	1441	2.0E
	2002	2349	1.6F
5 Tu	0402	0746	0.7E
		0900	0.7E
		1600	1.8E
	2054		
6 W		0025	1.5F
	0356	0721	0.9E
		1140	0.4E
		1706	1.7E
	2137		
7 Th		0049	1.4F
	0350	0710	1.2E
		1244	*
		1800	1.5E
	2210		
8 F		0104	1.2F
	0347	0719	1.6E
	1131	1327	0.7F
	1528	1848	1.4E
	2238		
9 Sa		0117	1.1F
	0347	0736	2.0E
	1145	1405	1.1F
	1642	1938	1.2E
	2308		
10 Su		0133	1.0F
	0346	0757	2.4E
	1206	1443	1.5F
	1750	2034	1.0E
	2343		
11 M		0150	0.7F
	0341	0816	2.6E
	1231	1523	1.8F
	1902	2135	0.8E
12 Tu O	0028	0205	0.4F
	0329	0833	2.9E
	1259	1607	2.0F
	2025	2237	0.6E
13 W		0214	*
		0847	2.7E
	1331	1657	2.1F
	2154	2345	0.4E
14 Th		0206	*
		0904	2.8E
	1411	1757	2.1F
	2329		
15 F		0928	2.9E
	1458	1904	2.2F
16 Sa	0104	1002	2.9E
	1552	2003	2.2F
17 Su	0210	1045	2.8E
	1651	2053	2.2F
18 M	0248	1138	2.6E
	1751	2140	2.0F
19 Tu O	0301	1321	2.2E
	1851	2228	1.9F
20 W	0254	0621	0.8E
		0833	0.7E
		1527	1.8E
	1951	2313	1.7F
21 Th	0245	0553	1.2E
		1114	*
		1703	1.6E
	2052	2351	1.4F
22 F	0242	0607	1.7E
	1026	1234	0.7F
	1445	1819	1.4E
	2152		
23 Sa		0026	1.2F
	0246	0629	2.3E
	1044	1327	1.5F
	1628	1927	1.3E
	2247		
24 Su		0057	1.0F
	0254	0656	2.9E
	1115	1414	2.2F
	1751	2038	1.1E
	2339		
25 M		0128	0.7F
	0304	0727	3.3E
	1152	1502	2.6F
	1912	2145	0.9E
26 Tu ●	0029	0157	0.4F
	0313	0801	3.5E
	1234	1553	2.7F
	2036	2245	0.6E
27 W		0224	*
		0840	3.5E
	1322	1651	2.6F
	2202	2347	0.4E
28 Th		0245	*
		0925	3.4E
	1417	1759	2.4F
	2334		
29 F		1012	3.2E
	1518	1914	2.3F
30 Sa	0105	1100	2.9E
	1621	2016	2.1F

December

Day	Slack	Max	knots
1 Su	0156	1150	2.6E
	1720	2105	1.9F
2 M	0215	1250	2.2E
	1811	2147	1.6F
3 Tu	0214	0605	0.6E
		0730	0.6E
		1359	1.8E
	1853	2224	1.3F
4 W ◑	0208	0535	0.9E
		0917	0.5E
		1508	1.5E
	1930	2255	1.1F
5 Th	0205	0537	1.2E
		1131	*
		1617	1.1E
	2006	2320	0.9F
6 F	0205	0555	1.7E
	1045	1237	0.4F
	1425	1724	0.9E
	2047	2345	0.7F
7 Sa	0206	0617	2.1E
	1051	1319	1.0F
	1602	1826	0.7E
	2139		
8 Su		0010	0.6F
	0206	0639	2.4E
	1108	1356	1.6F
	1717	1928	0.6E
	2239		
9 M		0034	0.4F
	0204	0659	2.7E
	1130	1431	2.0F
	1825	2037	0.6E
10 Tu		0055	*
		0716	2.9E
	1156	1509	2.3F
	1939	2148	0.5E
11 W		0110	*
		0735	3.0E
	1227	1552	2.5F
	2059	2251	0.4E
12 Th		0116	*
		0758	3.1E
	1304	1640	2.5F
	2219		
13 F		0006	0.3F
		0100	*
		0830	3.2E
	1348	1735	2.5F
	2339		
14 Sa		0916	3.2E
	1440	1835	2.5F
15 Su	0039	1009	3.0E
	1534	1927	2.4F
16 M	0106	1105	2.7E
	1628	2009	2.2F
17 Tu	0109	1213	2.3E
	1722	2046	1.9F
18 W O	0102	0402	0.8E
		0742	0.5E
		1354	1.7E
	1816	2123	1.6F
19 Th	0057	0418	1.3E
		0935	*
		1537	1.3E
	1915	2204	1.1F
20 F	0056	0445	1.8E
	0921	1139	0.6F
	1401	1714	0.9E
	2024	2250	0.8F
21 Sa	0101	0516	2.3E
	0947	1247	1.4F
	1607	1839	0.8E
	2146	2337	0.5F
22 Su	0110	0550	2.8E
	1024	1336	2.1F
	1737	2004	0.7E
23 M		0018	*
		0624	3.2E
	1104	1422	2.6F
	1853	2123	0.6E
24 Tu		0054	*
		0700	3.4E
	1147	1509	2.8F
	2007	2220	0.5E
25 W ●		0126	*
		0739	3.5E
	1232	1558	2.8F
	2119	2309	0.4E
26 Th		0153	*
		0823	3.4E
	1321	1652	2.6F
27 F		0004	*
		0213	*
		0913	3.3E
	1413	1752	2.3F
	2344		
28 Sa		1003	3.1E
	1505	1852	2.1F
29 Su	0027	1050	2.8E
	1554	1939	1.9F
30 M	0032	1135	2.4E
	1636	2011	1.6F
31 Tu	0025	0318	0.5E
		0609	0.4E
		1224	2.0E
	1708	2030	1.4F

Time meridian 90° W. 0000 is midnight. 1200 is noon. Times are not adjusted for Daylight Saving Time.
* Current weak and variable.

Sabine Pass, Texas, 2019

F–Flood, Dir. 321° True   E–Ebb, Dir. 143° True

January

Day	Slack (h m)	Maximum (h m / knots)
1 Tu	0212, 1030, 1915, 2259	0020 0.4F, 0655 1.2E, 1354 1.5F, 2109 0.3E
2 W	0225, 1104, 2147	0048 0.3F, 0715 1.4E, 1429 1.6F
3 Th	0249, 1135, 2210	0112 0.4F, 0735 1.5E, 1503 1.6F
4 F	0318, 1204, 2225	0135 0.4F, 0755 1.6E, 1538 1.6F
5 Sa ●	0349, 1232, 2242	0155 0.4F, 0819 1.7E, 1612 1.5F
6 Su	0417, 1259, 2304	0205 0.4F, 0847 1.7E, 1647 1.5F
7 M	0440, 1330, 2335	0157 0.4F, 0918 1.7E, 1723 1.4F
8 Tu	0459, 1404	0152 0.4F, 0948 1.6E, 1804 1.2F
9 W	0512, 1440	1017 1.4E, 1855 1.0F
10 Th	0519, 1517	1043 1.1E, 2002 0.8F
11 F	0521, 1551	1103 0.8E, 2101 0.5F
12 Sa	0452, 1611	1108 0.4E, 2151 0.3F
13 Su	—	0653 *, 1249 *, 1549 *, 1736 *, 1923† *
14 M ◑	0900	0555 0.4E, 1236 0.5F, 2011 *, 2304 *
15 Tu	0914	0557 0.7E, 1250 1.0F, 2026 *, 2331 *
16 W	0941	0608 1.0E, 1313 1.3F, 2025 *, 2359 *
17 Th	1015	0626 1.3E, 1343 1.7F, 2045 *
18 F	0154, 1052	0027 0.3F, 0653 1.7E, 1419 1.9F, 2115 *
19 Sa	0238, 1133	0055 0.4F, 0725 2.0E, 1501 2.1F, 2148 *
20 Su ○	0322, 1215	0124 0.5F, 0803 2.2E, 1548 2.1F, 2220 *
21 M	0408, 1301	0153 0.6F, 0847 2.2E, 1635 2.1F, 2253 *
22 Tu	0456, 1350	0226 0.6F, 0933 2.1E, 1722 1.8F, 2325 *
23 W	0546, 1444	0311 0.5F, 1018 1.8E, 1811 1.5F
24 Th	0645, 1542	0003 *, 0416 0.4F, 1101 1.3E, 1907 1.1F
25 F	0813, 1652	0140 *, 0553 0.3F, 1154 0.7E, 2008 0.7F
26 Sa	1202, 1842, 2351	0259 0.3F, 0833 0.3E, 1548 0.3E, 2105 0.4F
27 Su ◑	0723, 1600	0350 0.4E, 1112 0.7F, 1831 0.3E, 2205 *
28 M	0825, 1723	0446 0.7E, 1225 1.1F, 1933 0.3E, 2308 *
29 Tu	0916, 1816	0540 1.0E, 1303 1.4F, 2018 0.3E, 2355 *
30 W	1002, 1859, 2249	0621 1.2E, 1336 1.5F, 2053 0.3E
31 Th	0157, 1043	0028 0.3F, 0653 1.3E, 1407 1.6F, 2117 *

February

Day	Slack (h m)	Maximum (h m / knots)
1 F	0241, 1118	0057 0.4F, 0722 1.5E, 1438 1.5F, 2132 *
2 Sa	0321, 1149	0124 0.5F, 0748 1.5E, 1512 1.5F, 2149 *
3 Su	0355, 1217	0150 0.5F, 0815 1.6E, 1547 1.4F, 2212 *
4 M ●	0425, 1246	0213 0.5F, 0842 1.5E, 1622 1.3F, 2238 *
5 Tu	0452, 1314	0228 0.5F, 0911 1.5E, 1655 1.2F, 2302 *
6 W	0519, 1344	0231 0.4F, 0939 1.3E, 1726 0.9F, 2320 *
7 Th	0548, 1412	0237 0.4F, 1006 1.0E, 1751 0.7F, 2312 *
8 F	0623, 1435	0259 0.3F, 1030 0.7E, 1759 0.4F, 2251 *
9 Sa	—	0353 *, 1051 0.4E, 1658 *, 2231 *
10 Su	—	0202 *, 0244 *, 0506 *, 0651 *, 0740† *, 1008 0.4F
11 M	1812	2342 0.4E
12 Tu ◑	0708, 1811	0107 0.3F, 0240 0.4E, 1148 0.8F
13 W	0803	0338 0.7E, 1214 1.1F, 2118 *, 2218 *
14 Th	0851	0439 1.0E, 1243 1.5F, 2019 *, 2328 *
15 F	0938	0540 1.3E, 1317 1.8F, 2024 *
16 Sa	1026	0011 *, 0627 1.7E, 1354 2.0F, 2049 *
17 Su	0226, 1113	0047 0.4F, 0710 1.9E, 1436 2.1F, 2118 *
18 M	0323, 1159	0123 0.6F, 0754 2.0E, 1521 2.0F, 2146 *
19 Tu ○	0422, 1247	0203 0.7F, 0843 2.0E, 1607 1.7F, 2210 *
20 W	0526, 1338	0253 0.8F, 0936 1.7E, 1649 1.4F, 2229 *
21 Th	0637, 1434, 2053	0355 0.8F, 1028 1.3E, 1729 0.9F, 2246 0.3E
22 F	0054, 0809, 1541, 2039	0504 0.8F, 1123 0.7E, 1809 0.5F, 2308 0.5E
23 Sa	0216, 1037	0629 0.8F, 1424 0.3E, 1856 *, 2339 0.6E
24 Su	0357	0827 0.8F, 1748 *, 1958 *
25 M	0547, 1618	0038 0.7E, 1019 1.0F, 1858 0.3E, 2104 *
26 Tu ◑	0721, 1712	0250 0.8F, 1148 1.2F, 1934 0.4E, 2215 *
27 W	0828, 1749	0411 0.9F, 1232 1.4F, 2001 0.3E, 2323 *
28 Th	0923, 1816	0530 1.0E, 1305 1.4F, 2019 0.3E

March

Day	Slack (h m)	Maximum (h m / knots)
1 F	1010, 1836, 2237	0008 *, 0622 1.2E, 1335 1.5F, 2032 0.3E
2 Sa	0233, 1049, 1857, 2252	0043 0.4F, 0700 1.3E, 1406 1.4F, 2048 0.3E
3 Su	0319, 1124, 1922, 2309	0114 0.5F, 0733 1.3E, 1438 1.4F, 2113 0.3E
4 M	0401, 1156, 1950, 2327	0145 0.6F, 0806 1.3E, 1513 1.3F, 2141 0.3E
5 Tu	0441, 1226	0217 0.6F, 0839 1.2E, 1546 1.1F, 2207 *
6 W ●	0522, 1255	0251 0.6F, 0918 1.0E, 1615 0.8F, 2225 *
7 Th	0607, 1320	0330 0.6F, 0945 0.8E, 1635 0.5F, 2223 *
8 F	0703, 1337, 1902	0413 0.5F, 1014 0.5E, 1635 0.3F, 2201 0.3E
9 Sa	0038, 1532, 2146	0458 0.5F, 1041 *, 0.4E
10 Su	0119, 1346, 2157	0558 0.5F, 1113 *, 0.6E
11 M	0231, 1654	0744 0.6F, 2231 0.7E
12 Tu	0402, 1701	0910 0.8F, 2322 0.8E
13 W	0533, 1709	1023 1.1F
14 Th ◑	0656, 1723	0209 0.8E, 1126 1.4F
15 F	0803, 1745	0335 1.1E, 1211 1.7F, 2003 0.3E, 2304 *
16 Sa	0902, 1809	0451 1.3E, 1251 1.9F, 2002 0.3E
17 Su	0958, 1832, 2230	0001 *, 0602 1.5E, 1329 2.0F, 2021 0.3E
18 M	0225, 1052, 1848, 2242	0045 0.4F, 0658 1.6E, 1408 1.9F, 2043 0.3E
19 Tu	0339, 1143, 1852, 2308	0129 0.7F, 0752 1.6E, 1449 1.6F, 2103 0.4E
20 W ○	0457, 1233, 1849, 2343	0217 0.9F, 0853 1.4E, 1529 1.2F, 2117 0.5E
21 Th	0619, 1327, 1839	0314 1.1F, 1000 1.0E, 1606 0.8F, 2131 0.7E
22 F	0024, 0757, 1433, 1821	0417 1.2F, 1103 0.6E, 1639 0.3F, 2152 0.9E
23 Sa	0114	0521 1.3F, 1236 *, 1703 *, 2220 1.1E
24 Su	0214, 1342	0635 1.2F, 2253 1.1E
25 M	0324, 1512	0808 1.2F, 2337 1.0E
26 Tu	0441, 1605	0928 1.2F
27 W ◑	0607, 1641	0057 0.9E, 1044 1.3F, 1923 0.3E, 2116 0.3E
28 Th	0725, 1702	0252 0.9E, 1145 1.3F, 1934 0.3E, 2236 *
29 F	0827, 1716	0409 0.9E, 1225 1.4F, 1940 0.3E, 2342 *
30 Sa	0919, 1731, 2228	0527 1.0E, 1259 1.4F, 1949 0.4E
31 Su	0214, 1006, 1749, 2250	0027 0.4F, 0626 1.0E, 1329 1.3F, 2008 0.4E

Time meridian 90° W. 0000 is midnight. 1200 is noon. Times are not adjusted for Daylight Saving Time.
* Current weak and variable.
† See page 196 for the remaining currents on this day.

Sabine Pass, Texas, 2019

F–Flood, Dir. 321° True   E–Ebb, Dir. 143° True

April

Day	Slack (h m)	Maximum (h m)	knots
1 M	0315	0104	0.5F
	1048	0711	1.0E
	1806	1359	1.2F
	2313	2035	0.5E
2 Tu	0415	0141	0.6F
	1126	0755	0.9E
	1817	1428	1.0F
	2336	2102	0.5E
3 W	0518	0220	0.7F
	1200	0843	0.7E
	1816	1454	0.7F
	2358	2125	0.5E
4 Th	0625	0305	0.8F
	1229	0936	0.5E
	1752	1512	0.4F
		2134	0.6E
5 F ●	0020	0353	0.8F
	0748	1025	0.3E
	1507		*
	2115		0.6E
6 Sa	0045	0440	0.9F
	1110		*
	1403		*
	2104		0.8E
7 Su	0115	0527	1.0F
	1522	2116	0.9E
8 M	0154	0622	1.0F
	1532	2148	1.1E
9 Tu	0246	0734	1.1F
	1543	2231	1.1E
10 W	0349	0840	1.3F
	1553	2324	1.1E
11 Th	0458	0939	1.5F
	1609		
12 F ◑	0612	0115	1.1E
	1630	1040	1.6F
	2103	2019	0.4E
			0.4E
13 Sa	0722	0300	1.1E
	1652	1136	1.8F
	2251	1934	0.4E
			*
14 Su	0827	0415	1.2E
	1709	1222	1.8F
		1935	0.4E
15 M	0929	0000	*
	1718	0545	1.2F
	2238	1301	1.7F
		1948	0.5E
16 Tu	0251	0051	0.5F
	1030	0700	1.1E
	1717	1337	1.4F
	2253	2003	0.6E
17 W	0430	0139	0.9F
	1127	0811	0.9E
	1710	1411	1.0F
	2320	2012	0.8E
18 Th	0611	0232	1.2F
	1223	0932	0.7E
	1658	1443	0.6F
	2353	2022	1.0E
19 F ○	0805	0332	1.4F
		1043	0.4E
		1511	*
		2041	1.2E
20 Sa	0031	0432	1.5F
		1155	*
		1528	*
		2110	1.4E
21 Su	0115	0529	1.6F
	1258	2147	1.5E
22 M	0205	0631	1.5F
	1426	2228	1.4E
23 Tu	0302	0743	1.4F
	1513	2313	1.3E
24 W	0401	0846	1.4F
	1543		
25 Th	0504	0012	1.1F
	1556	0942	1.3F
		1916	0.3E
		2016	0.3E
26 F ◐	0611	0148	1.0E
	1602	1041	1.3F
		1906	0.3E
		2141	*
27 Sa	0714	0306	0.9E
	1612	1135	1.3F
		1901	0.4E
		2305	*
28 Su	0811	0412	0.8E
	1625	1216	1.3F
	2220	1909	0.5E
29 M	0152	0009	0.3F
	0905	0534	0.7E
	1636	1248	1.1F
	2239	1928	0.6E
30 Tu	0320	0055	0.5F
	0956	0645	0.6E
	1641	1315	0.9F
	2302	1952	0.7E

May

Day	Slack (h m)	Maximum (h m)	knots
1 W	0455	0137	0.7F
	1044	0748	0.4E
	1634	1337	0.7F
	2325	2013	0.8E
2 Th	0636	0221	0.9F
	1123	0901	0.3E
	1606	1351	0.4F
	2350	2027	0.9E
3 F		0310	1.1F
		1012	*
		1349	*
		2023	1.0E
4 Sa ●	0016	0400	1.2F
		1108	*
		1310	*
		2021	1.1E
5 Su	0045	0446	1.3F
	1427	2038	1.2E
6 M	0119	0530	1.4F
	1440	2112	1.4E
7 Tu	0201	0620	1.5F
	1452	2156	1.4E
8 W	0250	0719	1.6F
	1457	2242	1.4E
9 Th	0345	0817	1.7F
	1504	2335	1.3E
10 F	0442	0911	1.8F
	1519		
11 Sa ◑	0545	0101	1.2E
	1535	1004	1.8F
		1908	0.5E
		2113	0.4E
12 Su	0650	0241	1.1E
	1548	1059	1.7F
		1848	0.5E
		2252	*
13 M	0755	0358	0.9E
	1552	1148	1.5F
	2219	1856	0.6E
14 Tu	0159	0009	0.3F
	0901	0557	0.7E
	1549	1228	1.2F
	2228	1909	0.8E
15 W	0415	0103	0.8F
	1010	0730	0.5E
	1541	1302	0.9F
	2252	1920	1.0E
16 Th	0634	0154	1.1F
	1118	0903	0.3E
	1529	1331	0.5F
	2323	1927	1.2E
17 F	2357	0249	1.4F
		1028	*
		1354	*
		1941	1.4E
18 Sa ○		0348	1.6F
		1139	*
		1402	*
		2007	1.5E
19 Su	0034	0442	1.7F
	1236	2043	1.6E
20 M	0114	0531	1.7F
	1358	2128	1.6E
21 Tu	0159	0621	1.6F
	1443	2214	1.6E
22 W	0246	0717	1.5F
	1514	2259	1.4E
23 Th	0335	0810	1.5F
	1520	2348	1.3E
24 F	0423	0857	1.4F
	1508		
25 Sa	0512	0055	1.1E
	1507	0943	1.3F
		1835	0.3E
		2056	*
26 Su ◑	0604	0216	0.9E
	1512	1032	1.2F
		1808	0.4E
		2222	*
27 M	0656	0320	0.7E
	1515	1120	1.0F
		1820	0.5E
		2350	*
28 Tu	0746	0430	0.4E
	1513	1158	0.8F
	2209	1841	0.7E
29 W	1500	0046	0.6F
	2233	0624	*
		1223	0.6F
		1902	0.8E
30 Th	1435	0130	0.9F
	2301	0754	*
		1240	0.3F
		1917	1.0E
31 F	2330	0214	1.1F
		0953	*
		1246	*
		1923	1.1E

June

Day	Slack (h m)	Maximum (h m)	knots
1 Sa	1106	0302	1.3F
	1220		*
	1932		*
			1.3E
2 Su	0001	0352	1.5F
	1400	1954	1.5E
3 M	0036	0437	1.6F
	1419	2031	1.6E
4 Tu	0115	0520	1.7F
	1439	2119	1.7E
5 W	0159	0607	1.8F
	1444	2208	1.7E
6 Th	0248	0659	1.9F
	1426	2255	1.6E
7 F	0339	0753	1.9F
	1421	2346	1.4E
8 Sa	0431	0843	1.9F
	1426	1802	0.3E
		1933	0.3E
9 Su ◑	0526	0105	1.1E
	1431	0931	1.7F
		1720	0.5E
		2120	*
10 M	0625	0245	0.8E
	1430	1019	1.4F
		1740	0.6E
		2301	*
11 Tu	0728	0421	0.4E
	1426	1108	1.1F
	2136	1802	0.8E
12 W	1420	0022	0.7F
	2207	0642	*
		1151	0.7F
		1822	1.0E
13 Th	1412	0117	1.1F
	2243	0829	*
		1226	0.4F
		1838	1.2E
14 F	1500	0208	1.4F
	2321	1011	*
		1254	*
		1854	1.4E
15 Sa	2359	0303	1.6F
		1116	*
		1313	*
		1918	1.5E
16 Su	1146	0359	1.6F
		1951	1.6E
17 M ○	0036	0445	1.6F
	1347	2032	1.6E
18 Tu ●	0113	0525	1.6F
	1432	2120	1.6E
19 W	0152	0605	1.6F
	1507	2205	1.6E
20 Th	0231	0650	1.5F
	1524	2247	1.5E
21 F	0312	0736	1.5F
	1454	2329	1.3E
22 Sa	0352	0819	1.4F
	1423		
23 Su	0432	0020	1.0E
		0857	1.2F
		1616	*
		2022	*
24 M	0510	0133	0.7E
	1408	0933	1.0F
		1639	0.4E
		2146	*
25 Tu ◑	0543	0246	0.4E
	1356	1006	0.7F
	2051	1707	0.5E
		2326	0.3E
26 W	1334	0351	*
	2117	1036	0.4F
		1732	0.7E
27 Th	2150	0031	0.7F
		0626	*
		1056	*
		1751	0.9E
28 F	1248	0115	1.0F
	2226	1806	1.1E
29 Sa	1254	0155	1.2F
	2303	1829	1.3E
30 Su	1323	0239	1.4F
	2341	1901	1.5E

Time meridian 90° W. 0000 is midnight. 1200 is noon. Times are not adjusted for Daylight Saving Time.
* Current weak and variable.

Sabine Pass, Texas, 2019

F–Flood, Dir. 321° True   E–Ebb, Dir. 143° True

July

Day	Slack	Maximum	knots	Day	Slack	Maximum	knots
1 M		0328	1.6F	**16 Tu** ○	0032	0433	1.5F
	1401	1941	1.7E		1502	2033	1.5E
2 Tu ●	0021	0415	1.8F	**17 W**	0106	0508	1.5F
	1441	2030	1.8E		1544	2118	1.5E
3 W	0104	0500	1.9F	**18 Th**	0139	0542	1.4F
	1521	2125	1.9E		1624	2200	1.4E
4 Th	0151	0545	2.0F	**19 F**	0214	0618	1.4F
	1600	2217	1.8E		1707	2238	1.3E
5 F	0241	0633	2.0F	**20 Sa**	0250	0657	1.3F
		1443	*			1432	*
		1618	*			1659	*
	2305		1.6E		2316		1.1E
6 Sa	0331	0723	1.8F	**21 Su**	0326	0736	1.1F
		1457	*			1446	*
		1800	*			1816	*
					2359		0.8E
7 Su ◐		0000	1.2E	**22 M**	0400	0808	0.8F
	0422	0811	1.6F			1505	*
	1306	1522	0.4E			1959	*
		1951	*				
8 M		0138	0.8E	**23 Tu**		0104	0.5E
	0514	0856	1.3F		0426	0832	0.6F
	1300	1549	0.6E		1223	1522	0.4E
	1922	2123	0.3F		1836	2117	0.3F
	2352						
9 Tu ◑		0323	0.4E	**24 W** ◑		0233	*
	0611	0938	0.9F			0840	0.3F
	1255	1618	0.8E		1132	1533	0.5E
	2007	2306	0.7F		1923	2245	0.5F
10 W		0532	*	**25 Th**		0346	*
		1022	0.5F			0707	*
	1251	1650	1.0E			1541	0.7E
	2054				2009		
11 Th		0028	1.0F	**26 F**		0005	0.8F
		0742	*		1026	1605	1.0E
		1109	0.3F		2056		
	1249	1725	1.1E				
	2143						
12 F		0121	1.3F	**27 Sa**		0050	1.1F
		0925	*		1048	1647	1.2E
		1152	*		2144		
	1803		1.3E				
	2231						
13 Sa		0210	1.5F	**28 Su**		0128	1.4F
		1029	*		1157	1745	1.4E
		1227	*		2232		
	1839		1.4E				
	2316						
14 Su		0302	1.5F	**29 M**		0208	1.6F
		1112	*		1311	1840	1.6E
		1256	*		2317		
		1913	1.5E				
	2356						
15 M		0353	1.5F	**30 Tu**		0255	1.7F
		1149	*			1047	*
		1318	*			1224	*
		1951	1.5E			1931	1.8E
				31 W ●	0003	0344	1.9F
						1056	*
						1316	0.3F
					1512	2027	1.9E

August

Day	Slack	Maximum	knots	Day	Slack	Maximum	knots
1 Th	0049	0431	1.9F	**16 F**	0120	0508	1.2F
		1121	*			1135	*
		1416	0.3F			1545	*
	1619	2129	1.8E			2201	1.1E
2 F	0137	0515	1.9F	**17 Sa**	0153	0538	1.1F
		1152	*			1200	*
		1545	0.3F			1637	0.3F
	1734	2225	1.6E		1824	2237	1.0E
3 Sa	0229	0559	1.7F	**18 Su**	0228	0606	0.9F
		1229	*			1226	*
		1703	0.4F			1726	0.3F
	1858	2319	1.3E		1935	2313	0.7E
4 Su	0323	0644	1.4F	**19 M**	0302	0631	0.6F
	1058	1313	0.3E			1247	*
	1533	1822	0.5F			1824	0.4F
	2045				2108	2353	0.4E
5 M		0031	0.9E	**20 Tu**	0330	0642	0.3F
	0417	0730	1.0F		0947	1240	0.3E
	1053	1355	0.5E		1555	1941	0.5F
	1645	1953	0.6F				
	2259						
6 Tu		0231	0.5E	**21 W**		0109	*
	0515	0814	0.6F			0544	*
	1050	1431	0.7E			1240	0.4E
	1757	2119	0.9F		1648	2051	0.6F
7 W ◑		0411	*	**22 Th**		0309	*
		0854	0.3F			0522	*
	1047	1504	0.9E			1321	0.6E
	1908	2255	1.1F		1750	2201	0.8F
8 Th		0652	*	**23 F** ○	0751	1416	0.8E
		0934	*		1858	2324	1.0F
		1540	1.1E				
	2014						
9 F		0019	1.3F	**24 Sa**	0829	1506	1.1E
		0818	*		2002		
		1024	*				
	1627		1.2E				
	2116						
10 Sa		0111	1.4F	**25 Su**		0018	1.2F
		0925	*		0919	1601	1.2E
		1126	*		2101		
	1736		1.2E				
	2214						
11 Su		0155	1.4F	**26 M**		0059	1.5F
		1007	*		1035	1711	1.4E
		1216	*		2158		
	1835		1.3E				
	2303						
12 M		0238	1.4F	**27 Tu**		0138	1.7F
		1034	*			1014	*
		1255	*			1152	*
		1919	1.3E			1824	1.6E
	2343						
13 Tu		0322	1.4F	**28 W**		0221	1.8F
		1051	*			0945	*
		1331	*			1254	0.3F
		1958	1.3E		1428	1925	1.7E
					2341		
14 W	0017	0402	1.3F	**29 Th**		0308	1.8F
		1100	*			1004	*
		1407	*			1349	0.4F
		2040	1.3E		1547	2029	1.7E
15 Th ○	0048	0436	1.3F	**30 F** ●	0030	0354	1.7F
		1113	*			1027	*
		1452	*			1454	0.6F
		2122	1.2E		1711	2139	1.5E
				31 Sa	0122	0437	1.5F
					0848	1048	0.3F
					1243	1606	0.8F
					1839	2240	1.3E

September

Day	Slack	Maximum	knots	Day	Slack	Maximum	knots
1 Su	0217	0517	1.1F	**16 M**	0204	0503	0.4F
	0842	1108	0.5E		0750	1101	0.4E
	1342	1713	1.0F		1350	1731	0.7F
	2020	2343	0.9E		2114	2329	0.3E
2 M	0318	0555	0.7F	**17 Tu**		0500	*
	0838	1130	0.7E			1050	0.5E
	1446	1823	1.1F		1423	1819	0.8F
	2218						
3 Tu		0122	0.5E	**18 W**		0020	*
	0423	0633	0.4F			0405	*
	0830	1157	0.9E			1048	0.7E
	1552	1945	1.2F		1504	1921	0.8F
4 W		0314	*	**19 Th**	0526	1100	0.9F
		0712	*		1552	2026	0.9E
		1238	1.0E				
	1700	2105	1.3F				
5 Th ◐		0611	*	**20 F**	0553	1132	1.0F
		0754	*		1650	2128	1.0E
		1340	1.1E				
	1817	2230	1.3F				
6 F		0732	*	**21 Sa** ◑	0626	1237	1.0E
		0841	*		1800	2239	1.2F
		1444	1.1E				
	1934	2356	1.3F				
7 Sa		0820	*	**22 Su**	0656	1418	1.1E
		0942	*		1914	2344	1.4F
		1543	1.1E				
	2044						
8 Su		0048	1.4F	**23 M**	0715	1529	1.2E
		0855	*		2021		
		1107	*				
		1704	1.1E				
	2145						
9 M		0127	1.3F	**24 Tu**		0030	1.6F
		0921	*		0709	1647	1.3E
		1211	*		2124		
		1825	1.1E				
	2235						
10 Tu		0201	1.3F	**25 W**		0110	1.7F
		0938	*			0839	*
		1257	*			1217	*
		1915	1.1E			1818	1.4E
	2315				2224		
11 W		0237	1.3F	**26 Th**		0150	1.7F
		0948	*		0653	0849	0.3E
		1337	0.3F		1056	1313	0.4F
	1530	1959	1.1E		1501	1931	1.3E
	2350				2320		
12 Th		0314	1.2F	**27 F**		0230	1.6F
	0803	1004	0.3E		0646	0909	0.4E
	1205	1420	0.4F		1122	1408	0.4F
	1631	2045	1.0E		1639	2046	1.2E
13 F ○	0023	0349	1.1F	**28 Sa** ●	0013	0312	1.3F
	0814	1023	0.3E		0641	0928	0.6E
	1232	1509	0.5F		1157	1510	1.0F
	1732	2132	0.9E		1815	2159	1.0E
14 Sa	0055	0421	0.9F	**29 Su**	0107	0352	0.9F
	0823	1044	0.4E		0636	0945	0.9E
	1257	1600	0.5F		1238	1614	1.3F
	1835	2214	0.7E		1954	2301	0.8E
15 Su	0129	0446	0.7F	**30 M**	0207	0427	0.5F
	0820	1059	0.4E		0629	1004	1.1E
	1322	1646	0.6F		1324	1714	1.5F
	1948	2252	0.5E		2144		

Time meridian 90° W. 0000 is midnight. 1200 is noon. Times are not adjusted for Daylight Saving Time.
* Current weak and variable.

Sabine Pass, Texas, 2019

F–Flood, Dir. 321° True   E–Ebb, Dir. 143° True

October

Day	Slack (h m)	Maximum (h m)	knots
1 Tu		0009	0.4E
	0457		*
		1028	1.3E
	1417	1816	1.6F
2 W		0217	*
	0516		*
		1058	1.4E
	1515	1928	1.5F
3 Th		1134	1.4E
	1618	2043	1.4F
4 F		1223	1.3E
	1728	2156	1.3F
5 Sa ◖		1342	1.1E
	1847	2320	1.3F
6 Su		0815	*
	0900		*
		1501	1.0E
	1959		
7 M		0016	1.3F
	0819		*
		1051	*
		1617	0.9E
	2100		
8 Tu		0053	1.3F
	0604	0826	0.3E
		1210	*
		1759	0.8E
	2152		
9 W		0124	1.2F
	0603	0833	0.4E
	1110	1259	0.3F
	1450	1903	0.8E
	2237		
10 Th		0154	1.2F
	0608	0848	0.5E
	1133	1342	0.5F
	1611	1955	0.8E
	2317		
11 F		0224	1.0F
	0615	0911	0.6E
	1157	1427	0.7F
	1728	2051	0.7E
	2355		
12 Sa		0254	0.8F
	0619	0934	0.7E
	1220	1515	0.8F
	1840	2146	0.6E
13 Su ○	0031	0319	0.6F
	0611	0952	0.8E
	1242	1603	1.0F
	1958	2232	0.4E
14 M	0101	0335	0.3F
	0542		0.8E
	1305	1645	1.1F
		2313	*
15 Tu		0321	*
		0952	
	1330		0.9E
		1724	1.1F
		2359	*
16 W		0212	*
		0948	1.0E
	1400	1806	1.1F
17 Th	0409	1000	1.2E
	1437	1859	1.2F
18 F	0441	1026	1.3E
	1523	2001	1.2F
19 Sa	0511	1101	1.3E
	1617	2102	1.3F
20 Su	0534	1150	1.3E
	1722	2205	1.4F
21 M ◐	0541	1328	1.1E
	1835	2311	1.5F
22 Tu	0534	1505	1.1E
	1948		
23 W		0003	1.6F
	0527	0809	0.4E
		1129	*
		1640	1.0E
	2057		
24 Th		0044	1.6F
	0520	0754	0.5E
	1058	1237	0.3F
	1411	1841	0.9E
	2203		
25 F		0121	1.5F
	0512	0805	0.7E
	1100	1329	0.7F
	1612	1959	0.9E
	2305		
26 Sa		0156	1.2F
	0506	0818	0.9E
	1122	1422	1.2F
	1758	2116	0.8E
27 Su ●	0001	0229	0.8F
	0500	0832	1.1E
	1153	1519	1.5F
	1937	2221	0.6E
28 M	0055	0301	0.5F
	0452	0850	1.4E
	1229	1615	1.8F
	2119	2318	0.3E
29 Tu		0327	*
		0915	1.6E
	1310	1708	1.8F
30 W		0026	*
		0336	*
		0946	1.7E
	1357	1801	1.8F
31 Th	0339	1020	1.7E
	1448	1903	1.6F

November

Day	Slack (h m)	Maximum (h m)	knots
1 F	0431	1057	1.6E
	1542	2012	1.4F
2 Sa	0510	1138	1.4E
	1640	2118	1.3F
3 Su	0531	1236	1.1E
	1745	2228	1.2F
4 M ◐	0527	1408	0.9E
	1856	2334	1.2F
5 Tu	0500	0750	0.3E
		1034	*
		1532	0.7E
	2001		
6 W		0017	1.2F
	0446	0743	0.5E
		1212	*
		1728	0.6E
	2101		
7 Th		0050	1.1F
	0445	0745	0.6E
	1056	1302	0.4F
	1525	1855	0.5E
	2158		
8 F		0118	1.0F
	0447	0801	0.8E
	1114	1344	0.7F
	1707	1958	0.5E
	2249		
9 Sa		0142	0.8F
	0448	0823	0.9E
	1135	1427	1.0F
	1830	2100	0.4E
	2332		
10 Su		0203	0.6F
	0440	0844	1.0E
	1158	1511	1.2F
	1950	2156	0.3E
11 M	0004	0217	0.3F
	0418	0859	1.1E
	1221	1554	1.3F
		2239	*
12 Tu ○		0212	*
		0902	1.2E
	1246	1632	1.4F
		2317	*
13 W		0138	*
		0902	1.3E
	1314	1709	1.4F
		2357	*
14 Th		0123	*
		0916	1.5E
	1345	1747	1.4F
15 F	0408	0941	1.6E
	1423	1835	1.4F
16 Sa	0434	1012	1.6E
	1507	1934	1.4F
17 Su	0453	1048	1.5E
	1558	2036	1.5F
18 M	0456	1129	1.3E
	1656	2136	1.5F
19 Tu ◐	0438	1241	1.0E
	1807	2239	1.5F
20 W	0421	0755	0.5E
		1005	0.4F
		1500	0.8E
	1926	2336	1.4F
21 Th	0408	0717	0.6E
		1205	*
		1750	0.6E
	2044		
22 F		0020	1.3F
	0357	0717	0.8E
	1033	1258	0.7F
	1601	1922	0.6E
	2159		
23 Sa		0055	1.0F
	0349	0729	1.0E
	1048	1345	1.2F
	1757	2036	0.5E
	2305		
24 Su		0126	0.7F
	0343	0742	1.3E
	1115	1432	1.6F
	1926	2144	0.4E
	2358		
25 M		0153	0.4F
	0339	0756	1.6E
	1147	1522	1.8F
	2054	2238	0.3E
26 Tu ●		0215	*
		0816	1.8E
	1222	1611	1.9F
		2323	*
27 W		0225	*
		0845	1.9E
	1301	1657	1.9F
28 Th		0010	*
		0125	*
		0919	1.9E
	1342	1741	1.7F
29 F	0436	0955	1.9E
	1425	1830	1.5F
30 Sa	0508	1031	1.7E
	1509	1930	1.3F

December

Day	Slack (h m)	Maximum (h m)	knots
1 Su	0530	1108	1.5E
	1555	2033	1.2F
2 M	0533	1150	1.2E
	1643	2133	1.1F
3 Tu	0500	1259	0.8E
	1742	2242	1.0F
4 W ◐	0403	0725	0.4E
		1016	*
		1454	0.5E
	1859	2342	0.9F
5 Th	0345	0706	0.5E
		1216	*
		1719	0.3E
	2021		
6 F	0339	0706	0.7E
	1024	1301	0.6F
	1631	1904	0.3E
	2135		
7 Sa		0047	0.7F
	0335	0722	0.9E
	1043	1339	1.0F
	1806	2010	0.3E
	2236		
8 Su		0107	0.5F
	0326	0742	1.1E
	1106	1417	1.3F
		2110	*
9 M		0121	0.3F
	0312	0801	1.3E
	1132	1455	1.5F
		2155	*
10 Tu		0130	*
		0814	1.4E
	1159	1533	1.6F
		2228	*
11 W ○		0127	*
		0823	1.6E
	1228	1610	1.6F
		2255	*
12 Th		0119	0.3F
	0330	0838	1.7E
	1258	1646	1.7F
		2322	0.3F
13 F		0125	0.4F
	0357	0903	1.8E
	1332	1724	1.6F
		2359	0.4F
14 Sa		0130	0.4F
	0424	0934	1.8E
	1410	1808	1.6F
15 Su	0447	1008	1.8E
	1454	1903	1.6F
16 M	0458	1044	1.6E
	1543	2005	1.5F
17 Tu	0434	1122	1.2E
	1639	2105	1.4F
18 W ◐	0331	1227	0.7E
	1753	2206	1.2F
19 Th	0304	0635	0.5E
		1107	*
		1638	0.4E
	1928	2308	1.0F
20 F	0247	0627	0.7E
	0943	1230	0.6F
	1605	1848	0.4E
	2101	2357	0.8F
21 Sa	0239	0641	1.0E
	1001	1312	1.2F
	1749	2003	0.4E
	2220		
22 Su		0033	0.5F
	0236	0700	1.3E
	1032	1353	1.6F
	1901	2108	0.4E
	2318		
23 M		0103	0.4F
	0239	0719	1.5E
	1106	1435	1.8F
	2011	2201	0.3E
	2353		
24 Tu		0127	0.3F
	0250	0738	1.7E
	1142	1519	1.9F
		2239	*
25 W ●		0147	0.3F
	0311	0801	1.9E
	1218	1601	1.9F
		2304	*
26 Th		0156	0.3F
	0343	0829	1.9E
	1253	1640	1.7F
		2320	0.3F
27 F		0138	0.4F
	0418	0902	1.9E
	1327	1716	1.5F
		2332	0.4F
28 Sa		0132	0.5F
	0453	0936	1.8E
	1401	1753	1.4F
		2347	0.5F
29 Su		0141	0.4F
	0523	1011	1.7E
	1436	1838	1.2F
30 M	0545	1045	1.4E
	1513	1937	1.0F
31 Tu	0549	1121	1.1E
	1555	2041	0.8F

Time meridian 90° W. 0000 is midnight. 1200 is noon. Times are not adjusted for Daylight Saving Time.
* Current weak and variable.

Galveston Bay Entrance (between jetties), Texas, 2019

F–Flood, Dir. 277° True   E–Ebb, Dir. 088° True

January

Day	Slack (h m)	Maximum (h m)	knots
1 Tu	0056	0633	1.4E
	1006	1325	1.7F
	2214		*
2 W		0007	*
		0650	1.5E
	1051	1423	1.8F
	2208		
3 Th		0700	1.6E
	1138	1514	1.9F
	2327		
4 F		0728	1.7E
	1224	1557	1.9F
5 Sa ●	0031	0810	1.7E
	1310	1637	1.9F
6 Su	0127	0857	1.7E
	1354	1718	1.9F
7 M	0221	0942	1.7E
	1435	1803	1.9F
8 Tu	0257	1028	1.6E
	1515	1851	1.8F
9 W	0217	1125	1.3E
	1555	1938	1.6F
10 Th		0428	*
		0549	*
		1247	1.1E
	1635	2021	1.4F
11 F	0127	0340	0.4E
		0730	*
		1351	0.7F
	1713	2057	1.1F
12 Sa	0121	0411	0.6E
	0917		*
		1455	0.3E
	1742	2125	0.8F
13 Su	0110	0440	0.8E
	0820	1127	0.5F
		1644	*
		2148	0.5F
14 M ☽	0044	0503	1.0E
	0838	1150	0.9F
		1824	*
		2207	0.3F
	2351		
15 Tu		0507	1.2E
	0900	1215	1.2F
	2322		
16 W		0449	1.4E
	0927	1250	1.6F
	2222		
17 Th		0508	1.7E
	1000	1337	1.9F
	2230		
18 F		0543	1.9E
	1042	1430	2.2F
	2256		
19 Sa		0628	2.1E
	1132	1522	2.4F
	2330		
20 Su ○		0721	2.3E
	1229	1612	2.6F
21 M	0007	0821	2.3E
	1329	1701	2.6F
22 Tu		0200	*
		0335	*
		0922	2.2E
	1428	1753	2.4F
23 W		0207	*
		0437	*
		1026	1.9E
	1527	1847	2.0F
24 Th		0224	*
		0545	0.3F
	0710	1154	1.5E
	1629	1939	1.5F
25 F	0107	0250	0.3E
	0449	0702	0.5F
	0911	1356	1.0E
	1739	2030	1.0F
26 Sa	0039	0321	0.5E
	0556	0827	0.8F
	1153	1536	0.6E
	1900	2116	0.5F
27 Su ◐	0010	0356	0.8E
	0658	1005	1.1F
	1517	1830	0.3E
		2154	*
28 M		0433	1.0E
	0755	1122	1.4F
	1805	2010	0.3E
		2221	*
29 Tu		0508	1.2E
	0849	1218	1.6F
	1945	2134	0.3E
		2241	*
30 W		0538	1.4E
	0941	1311	1.7F
	2103		
31 Th		0605	1.5E
	1031	1406	1.7F
	2211		

February

Day	Slack (h m)	Maximum (h m)	knots
1 F		0639	1.5E
	1119	1459	1.8F
	2314		
2 Sa		0730	1.6E
	1207	1544	1.8F
3 Su	0004	0832	1.6E
	1253	1623	1.9F
4 M ●	0037	0923	1.6E
	1336	1700	1.9F
5 Tu		0138	*
		0328	*
		1006	1.6E
	1416	1735	1.8F
6 W		0124	*
		0419	*
		1050	1.4E
	1452	1808	1.6F
	2331		
7 Th		0125	0.3E
		0511	*
		1146	1.1E
	1524	1838	1.4F
	2325		
8 F		0149	0.5E
	0431	0611	0.3F
	0755	1252	0.7E
	1551	1904	1.0F
	2316		
9 Sa		0215	0.6E
	0518	0719	0.4F
	1031	1348	0.3E
	1606	1927	0.6F
	2253		
10 Su		0238	0.8E
	0601	0831	0.6F
		1453	*
		1943	0.3F
	2146		
11 M		0243	0.9E
	0638	0950	0.9F
	2105		
12 Tu ◐		0234	1.1E
	0713	1052	1.2F
	2012		
13 W		0251	1.4E
	0751	1135	1.6F
	2022		
14 Th		0325	1.6E
	0834	1221	1.9F
	2048		
15 F		0415	1.8E
	0926	1314	2.1F
	2119		
16 Sa		0516	2.0E
	1024	1415	2.3F
	2154		
17 Su		0618	2.1E
	1126	1513	2.4F
18 M		0021	*
		0130	*
		0726	2.1E
	1229	1603	2.4F
19 Tu ○		0022	*
		0251	*
		0843	2.0E
	1331	1648	2.2F
20 W		0031	*
		0353	0.5F
	0527	1001	1.8E
	1430	1730	1.8F
	2303		
21 Th		0049	0.3E
	0228	0451	0.8F
	0704	1142	1.4E
	1528	1810	1.3F
	2235		
22 F		0112	0.5E
	0311	0553	1.0F
	0850	1311	1.0E
	1628	1846	0.8F
	2201		
23 Sa		0137	0.7E
	0403	0701	1.2F
	1100	1428	0.5E
	1746	1918	0.3F
	2110		
24 Su		0200	0.9E
	0505	0817	1.3F
		1743	*
		1943	*
25 M		0214	1.0E
	0611	0949	1.4F
	1727		
26 Tu ◐		0226	1.2E
	0717	1108	1.5F
	1842		
27 W ◐		0302	1.2E
	0818	1203	1.6F
	1945		
28 Th		0414	1.3E
	0916	1253	1.6F
	2041		

March

Day	Slack (h m)	Maximum (h m)	knots
1 F		0552	1.3E
	1008	1345	1.7F
	2131		
2 Sa		0649	1.4E
	1057	1436	1.7F
	2210		
3 Su		0747	1.5E
	1143	1520	1.8F
	2349		*
4 M		0134	*
		0842	1.5E
	1228	1557	1.8F
	2349		*
5 Tu		0245	*
		0930	1.4E
	1310	1628	1.7F
	2124	2328	0.3F
6 W ●	0156	0339	0.3F
	0525	1015	1.3E
	1349	1653	1.5F
	2115	2347	0.5F
7 Th	0224	0426	0.5F
	0646	1101	1.0E
	1423	1714	1.3F
	2107		
8 F		0012	0.7E
	0254	0512	0.7F
	0812	1158	0.7E
	1449	1733	0.9F
	2051		
9 Sa		0035	0.8E
	0324	0601	0.9F
	0955	1259	0.3E
	1501	1748	0.5F
	2004		
10 Su		0040	0.9E
	0356	0654	1.0F
		1359	*
		1734	0.3F
	1928		
11 M		0019	1.1E
	0430	0751	1.2F
	1847		
12 Tu		0032	1.3E
	0511	0853	1.4F
	1829		
13 W		0101	1.5E
	0559	1003	1.6F
	1843		
14 Th ◐		0144	1.6E
	0656	1106	1.9F
	1907		
15 F		0238	1.7E
	0759	1202	2.1F
	1937		
16 Sa		0348	1.8E
	0907	1259	2.2F
	2008		
17 Su		0510	1.8E
	1016	1400	2.3F
	2035	2233	0.3F
18 M		0037	*
		0631	1.8E
	1122	1457	2.2F
	2052	2237	0.3F
19 Tu ○		0153	*
		0817	1.7E
	1228	1543	2.0F
	2056	2250	0.4F
20 W ○	0047	0302	0.7F
	0509	0949	1.5E
	1331	1620	1.6F
	2037	2310	0.5E
21 Th	0121	0400	1.2F
	0649	1105	1.2E
	1431	1652	1.1F
	2010	2333	0.7E
22 F	0202	0455	1.5F
	0827	1227	0.9E
	1530	1719	0.6F
	1941	2351	0.9E
23 Sa	0246	0551	1.7F
	1030	1349	0.5E
		1741	*
		2335	1.1E
24 Su	0334	0652	1.7F
		1635	*
		1744	*
		2344	1.2E
25 M	0428	0759	1.6F
	1636		
26 Tu		0023	1.3E
	0531	0925	1.5F
	1740		
27 W ◐		0114	1.3E
	0640	1051	1.5F
	1830		
28 Th		0209	1.2E
	0747	1146	1.6F
	1913		
29 F		0323	1.1E
	0846	1231	1.6F
	1948		
30 Sa		0545	1.2E
	0938	1316	1.7F
	2006	2205	0.3E
		2338	*
31 Su		0641	1.2E
	1025	1401	1.7F
	1947	2212	0.3E

Time meridian 90° W. 0000 is midnight. 1200 is noon. Times are not adjusted for Daylight Saving Time.
If three consecutive entries are marked (E) the middle one is not a true maximum but an intermediate value to show the current pattern.
* Current weak and variable.

Galveston Bay Entrance (between jetties), Texas, 2019

F–Flood, Dir. 277° True   E–Ebb, Dir. 088° True

April

Day	Slack (h m)	Maximum (h m)	knots
1 M		0043	*
	1110	0736	1.3E
		1443	1.7F
	1928	2200	0.4E
2 Tu		0152	*
	1154	0831	1.2E
		1517	1.5F
	1920	2156	0.6E
3 W	0049	0254	0.5F
	0516	0923	1.0E
	1236	1541	1.3F
	1917	2215	0.8E
4 Th	0116	0341	0.8F
	0639	1013	0.8E
	1316	1559	1.0F
	1910	2236	0.9E
5 F ●	0142	0421	1.1F
	0803	1106	0.5E
	1349	1616	0.7F
	1846	2243	1.1E
6 Sa	0208	0500	1.3F
		1211	*
		1628	0.4F
	1809	2222	1.2E
7 Su	0233	0541	1.5F
		1319	*
		1620	*
		2223	1.4E
8 M	0300	0627	1.6F
	1716	2233	1.6E
9 Tu	0333	0719	1.7F
	1711	2254	1.8E
10 W	0416	0820	1.8F
	1725	2345	1.8E
11 Th	0514	0933	1.9F
	1744		
12 F ◐		0106	1.8E
	0627	1049	2.1F
	1805		
13 Sa		0221	1.7E
	0743	1149	2.2F
	1827	2120	0.5E
		2216	0.5E
14 Su		0346	1.6E
	0858	1242	2.2F
	1846	2109	0.4E
		2342	*
15 M		0536	1.5E
	1009	1335	2.0F
	1856	2110	0.4E
	2319		
16 Tu		0052	0.4F
	0234	0735	1.4E
	1117	1426	1.7F
	1849	2124	0.6E
	2340		
17 W		0203	0.9F
	0444	0906	1.2E
	1224	1507	1.2F
	1829	2143	0.8E
18 Th	0015	0307	1.4F
	0627	1022	1.0E
	1333	1540	0.8F
	1811	2202	1.0E
19 F ○	0057	0402	1.8F
	0815	1151	0.7E
	1441	1605	0.3F
	1740	2209	1.2E
20 Sa	0141	0452	2.0F
	1033	1329	0.4E
		1623	*
		2157	1.4E
21 Su	0225	0543	2.0F
		1512	*
		1626	*
		2212	1.6E
22 M	0311	0637	1.9F
	1528	2240	1.6E
23 Tu	0401	0739	1.7F
	1640	2320	1.4E
24 W	0459	0859	1.5F
	1726		
25 Th		0027	1.3E
	0605	1028	1.5F
	1759		
26 F ◑		0143	1.2E
	0710	1122	1.6F
	1819		
27 Sa		0308	1.1E
	0808	1203	1.7F
	1812	2057	0.4E
		2247	0.4E
28 Su		0522	1.0E
	0859	1240	1.7F
	1746	2054	0.5E
29 M		0002	*
		0621	1.0E
	0945	1315	1.6F
	1734	2034	0.6E
30 Tu		0101	*
		0718	0.9E
	1029	1347	1.4F
	1731	2034	0.8E
	2344		

May

Day	Slack (h m)	Maximum (h m)	knots
1 W		0203	0.5F
	0448	0819	0.7E
	1112	1414	1.1F
	1730	2054	1.0E
2 Th	0007	0254	0.9F
	0621	0919	0.5E
	1155	1436	0.8F
	1722	2114	1.2E
3 F	0033	0333	1.2F
	0806	1018	0.3E
	1237	1456	0.5F
	1653	2117	1.3E
4 Sa ●	0058	0407	1.6F
		1128	*
		1512	*
		2102	1.5E
5 Su	0124	0441	1.8F
		1340	*
		1512	*
		2108	1.7E
6 M	0150	0519	2.0F
	1529	2124	2.0E
7 Tu	0222	0604	2.1F
	1549	2148	2.1E
8 W	0301	0657	2.1F
	1614	2224	2.1E
9 Th	0352	0800	2.1F
	1637	2325	2.0E
10 F	0458	0915	2.1F
	1654		
11 Sa ◐		0100	1.8E
	0616	1034	2.1F
	1706		
12 Su		0224	1.5E
	0736	1132	2.1F
	1713	1946	0.5E
		2239	*
13 M		0412	1.3E
	0851	1218	1.8F
	1712	1944	0.6E
	2213	2353	0.4E
14 Tu	0153	0637	1.1E
	1002	1300	1.4F
	1657	1958	0.8E
	2234		
15 W		0100	1.0F
	0409	0810	0.9E
	1112	1340	0.9F
	1640	2020	1.0E
	2309		
16 Th		0207	1.5F
	0609	0942	0.7E
	1227	1415	0.5F
	1621	2042	1.3E
	2352		
17 F		0308	1.9F
	0823	1120	0.5E
		1445	*
		2055	1.5E
18 Sa ○	0037	0359	2.1F
	1028	1257	0.4E
		1509	*
		2052	1.7E
19 Su	0124	0446	2.2F
	1227	1420	0.3E
		1521	*
		2109	1.8E
20 M	0210	0532	2.1F
	1408	2137	1.8E
21 Tu	0256	0623	1.9F
	1534	2211	1.7E
22 W	0342	0721	1.7F
	1628	2255	1.5E
23 Th	0433	0833	1.6F
	1659		
24 F		0007	1.3E
	0530	0952	1.6F
	1711		
25 Sa		0135	1.1E
	0628	1047	1.6F
	1647		
26 Su ◐		0300	1.0E
	0722	1126	1.6F
	1612	1938	0.5E
		2337	*
27 M		0452	0.8E
	0811	1157	1.5F
	1559	1907	0.7E
28 Tu		0020	*
		0601	0.7E
	0857	1219	1.2F
	1555	1910	0.9E
	2239		
29 W		0106	0.6E
	0410	0704	0.4E
	0940	1239	0.9F
	1552	1931	1.1E
	2258		
30 Th		0155	0.9F
		0816	0.6E
		1258	0.6F
	1534	1950	1.3E
	2323		
31 F		0238	1.3F
		0936	*
		1317	0.3F
	1451	1950	1.4E
	2348		

June

Day	Slack (h m)	Maximum (h m)	knots
1 Sa		0313	1.6F
	1213		*
		1328	*
	1941		1.6E
2 Su	0015	0346	1.9F
	1243	1956	1.9E
3 M ●	0045	0421	2.1F
	1320	2021	2.1E
4 Tu	0120	0501	2.3F
	1404	2054	2.3E
5 W	0201	0548	2.4F
	1450	2134	2.3E
6 Th	0250	0643	2.3F
	1527	2225	2.2E
7 F	0347	0746	2.2F
	1548	2339	1.9E
8 Sa	0455	0857	2.1F
	1552		
9 Su ◐		0112	1.5E
	0612	1009	1.9F
	1549	1818	0.4E
		2114	*
10 M		0243	1.2E
	0730	1103	1.6F
	1537	1819	0.6E
	2054	2248	0.5E
11 Tu	0104	0532	0.9E
	0847	1143	1.2F
	1513	1835	0.9E
	2122	2358	1.1F
12 W	0330	0712	0.7E
	1002	1216	0.7F
	1454	1857	1.2E
	2201		
13 Th		0101	1.6F
	0602	0906	0.5E
	1121	1244	0.3F
	1423	1921	1.4E
	2246		
14 F		0205	1.9F
	0818	1038	0.4E
		1311	*
		1939	1.6E
	2333		
15 Sa		0305	2.1F
	1010	1212	0.3E
		1334	0.3E
		1948	1.7E
16 Su	0023	0355	2.2F
	1143	2011	1.8E
17 M ○	0112	0439	2.1F
	1301	2045	1.8E
18 Tu	0159	0523	2.0F
	1416	2123	1.7E
19 W	0243	0610	1.8F
	1527	2205	1.6E
20 Th	0326	0702	1.7F
	1609	2255	1.5E
21 F	0408	0758	1.6F
	1616		
22 Sa		0011	1.2E
	0454	0858	1.6F
	1515		
23 Su		0135	1.0E
	0542	0954	1.5F
	1436	1811	0.4E
		2054	*
24 M		0247	0.7E
	0630	1034	1.3F
	1425	1734	0.7E
		2328	*
25 Tu ◑		0427	0.5E
	0716	1058	1.0F
	1421	1748	0.9E
	2124		
26 W		0010	0.6F
		0550	*
		1114	0.7F
	1412	1810	1.1E
	2144		
27 Th		0048	1.0F
		0709	*
		1130	0.4F
	1337	1827	1.3E
	2209		
28 F		0126	1.3F
		0948	*
		1142	*
		1823	1.5E
	2236		
29 Sa		0207	1.6F
	1124	1821	1.6E
	2305		
30 Su		0246	1.9F
	1130	1841	1.9E
	2339		

Time meridian 90° W. 0000 is midnight. 1200 is noon. Times are not adjusted for Daylight Saving Time.
If three consecutive entries are marked (E) the middle one is not a true maximum but an intermediate value to show the current pattern.
* Current weak and variable.

Galveston Bay Entrance (between jetties), Texas, 2019

F–Flood, Dir. 277° True   E–Ebb, Dir. 088° True

July

Day	Slack h m	Maximum h m	knots
1 M	1201	0325	2.1F
		1913	2.1E
2 Tu ●	0019	0405	2.3E
	1238	1956	2.2E
3 W	0105	0448	2.5E
	1316	2046	2.3E
4 Th	0156	0536	2.5F
	1355	2139	2.2E
5 F	0250	0629	2.3F
	1418	2240	2.0E
6 Sa	0348	0727	2.1F
		1545	*
		1810	*
7 Su		0001	1.6E
	0454	0826	1.7F
	1412	1605	0.3E
	1946		*
8 M		0142	1.1E
	0609	0926	1.3F
	1351	1634	0.5E
	1909	2119	0.6F
9 Tu ◐	0008	0406	0.7E
	0731	1019	0.8F
	1327	1705	0.8E
	1956	2250	1.1F
10 W	0249	0624	0.5E
	0900	1057	0.4F
	1306	1736	1.1E
	2045	2357	1.6F
11 Th	0546	0826	0.4E
		1125	*
		1804	1.4E
	2135		
12 F		0057	1.9F
	0752	0952	0.3E
		1147	*
		1830	1.6E
	2227		
13 Sa		0200	2.0F
	0926	1117	0.3E
		1159	0.3F
		1850	1.7E
	2319		
14 Su		0259	2.0F
	1046	1918	1.7E
15 M	0011	0349	2.0F
	1157	2001	1.7E
16 Tu ○	0101	0431	1.9F
	1300	2049	1.7E
17 W	0147	0510	1.9F
	1404	2132	1.6E
18 Th	0227	0549	1.8F
	1614	2216	1.5E
19 F	0304	0630	1.7F
		1509	*
		1633	*
		2308	1.4E
20 Sa	0340	0711	1.6F
		1429	*
		1744	*
21 Su		0026	1.1E
	0416	0750	1.4F
	1248	1451	0.4E
		1909	*
22 M		0136	0.8E
	0454	0826	1.1F
	1242	1525	0.6E
		2041	*
23 Tu		0241	0.4E
	0529	0859	0.8F
	1238	1601	0.8E
	1939	2257	0.6F
24 W ○		0419	*
		0926	0.4F
	1219	1633	1.0E
	2011	2342	1.0F
25 Th		0631	*
		0947	*
		1653	1.2E
	2042		
26 F		0015	1.3F
	0923	1641	1.3E
	2114		
27 Sa		0048	1.5F
	0926	1652	1.5E
	2148		
28 Su		0129	1.8F
	0959	1722	1.8E
	2227		
29 M		0218	2.0F
	1036	1804	1.9E
	2313		
30 Tu		0306	2.2F
	1112	1854	2.1E
31 W ●	0004	0351	2.4F
	1146	1952	2.2E

August

Day	Slack h m	Maximum h m	knots
1 Th	0059	0435	2.4F
		1338	*
		1512	*
		2053	2.1E
2 F	0155	0520	2.3F
		1332	*
		1615	*
		2155	1.9E
3 Sa	0251	0607	2.0F
		1345	*
		1719	0.4F
	1852	2305	1.5E
4 Su	0349	0654	1.6F
	1210	1408	0.4E
	1602	1830	0.7F
	2044		
5 M		0106	1.1E
	0454	0740	1.0F
	1141	1436	0.6E
	1704	1948	0.9F
	2311		
6 Tu		0246	0.6E
	0617	0825	0.5F
	1117	1507	0.8E
	1810	2114	1.2F
7 W ◐	0211	0548	0.3E
		0907	*
		1542	1.1E
	1914	2245	1.6F
8 Th	0519	0745	0.4E
		0946	*
		1626	1.3E
	2015	2352	1.8F
9 F	0701	0914	0.4E
		1017	0.4F
		1715	1.4E
	2115		
10 Sa		0050	1.9F
	0821	1800	1.5E
	2212		
11 Su		0150	1.8F
	0931	1847	1.5E
	2306		
12 M		0248	1.8F
	1037	1944	1.5E
	2357		
13 Tu		0334	1.8F
	1138	2038	1.6E
14 W	0044	0412	1.8F
		1312	*
		1413	*
		2121	1.6E
15 Th ○	0125	0446	1.8F
		1316	*
		1518	*
		2158	1.5E
16 F	0203	0516	1.7F
		1253	*
		1609	0.3F
	1735	2238	1.4E
17 Sa	0237	0545	1.6F
	1044	1250	0.3E
	1503	1700	0.4F
	1851	2331	1.1E
18 Su	0310	0614	1.3F
	1033	1315	0.5E
	1546	1756	0.5F
	2024		
19 M		0038	0.8E
	0339	0641	1.0F
	1030	1343	0.7E
	1633	1900	0.6F
	2233		
20 Tu		0140	0.4E
	0402	0706	0.6F
	1012	1408	0.9E
	1722	2010	0.8F
21 W		0247	*
		0722	0.3F
	0909	1422	1.0E
	1809	2134	1.0F
22 Th	0755	1420	1.1F
	1853	2254	1.3E
23 F ○	0718	1432	1.3F
	1934	2335	1.5E
24 Sa	0745	1459	1.5F
	2018		
25 Su		0013	1.7F
	0820	1543	1.6E
	2106		
26 M		0059	1.9F
	0856	1644	1.8E
	2159		
27 Tu		0152	2.1F
	0929	1748	1.9E
	2256		
28 W		0247	2.2F
		1206	*
		1254	*
		1853	1.9E
	2355		
29 Th		0334	2.3F
		1148	*
		1424	*
		2004	1.9E
30 F ●	0056	0416	2.2F
		1149	*
		1530	0.5F
	1703	2120	1.7E
31 Sa	0155	0455	1.8F
	0959	1208	0.4E
	1401	1628	0.9F
	1842	2242	1.4E

September

Day	Slack h m	Maximum h m	knots
1 Su	0252	0533	1.4F
	0931	1232	0.6E
	1440	1727	1.2F
	2025		
2 M		0033	1.0E
	0352	0609	0.8F
	0909	1257	0.8E
	1528	1831	1.4F
	2225		
3 Tu		0157	0.6E
	0508	0642	0.3F
	0823	1317	1.0E
	1624	1942	1.6F
4 W	0133	0456	0.3E
		0710	*
		1328	1.1E
	1729	2104	1.6F
5 Th ◐	0440	1350	1.3F
	1841	2238	1.7F
6 F	0602	1429	1.3F
	1951	2346	1.8F
7 Sa	0707	1530	1.3F
	2056		
8 Su		0040	1.7F
	0807	1756	1.3E
	2155		
9 M		0132	1.7F
	0900	1851	1.3E
	2245		
10 Tu		0222	1.7F
		1110	*
		1208	*
		1943	1.4E
	2331		
11 W		0305	1.7F
		1124	*
		1321	*
		2032	1.4E
12 Th	0014	0340	1.7F
		1121	*
		1431	*
		2116	1.3E
13 F ○	0054	0408	1.6F
	0845	1053	0.3E
	1324	1527	0.4F
	1734	2159	1.2E
14 Sa	0132	0432	1.5F
	0830	1110	0.6E
	1355	1614	0.7F
	1854	2246	1.0E
15 Su	0208	0454	1.2F
	0827	1136	0.8E
	1428	1700	0.9F
	2016	2343	0.7E
16 M	0240	0514	0.9F
	0817	1200	0.9E
	1500	1748	1.1F
	2154		
17 Tu		0049	0.4E
	0302	0531	0.5F
	0738	1211	1.0E
	1534	1840	1.2F
18 W		0153	*
		0524	*
		1201	1.1E
	1611	1936	1.3F
19 Th	0557	1209	1.3F
	1652	2038	1.4F
20 F	0554	1230	1.4F
	1739	2150	1.5F
21 Sa ○	0617	1309	1.5E
	1833	2257	1.7F
22 Su	0645	1401	1.6E
	1933	2346	1.9F
23 M	0713	1507	1.6E
	2036		
24 Tu		0034	2.1F
	0739	1629	1.6E
	2140		
25 W		0126	2.1F
	0758	1013	0.3E
		1210	*
		1750	1.6E
	2244		
26 Th		0219	2.1F
	0807	1005	0.3E
		1324	*
		1913	1.6E
	2347		
27 F		0306	1.9F
	0803	1013	0.4E
	1223	1435	0.7F
	1641	2103	1.4E
28 Sa ●	0052	0346	1.6F
	0742	1032	0.6E
	1253	1536	1.2F
	1825	2226	1.2E
29 Su	0156	0420	1.1F
	0725	1052	0.8E
	1333	1631	1.6F
	2004	2352	0.9E
30 M	0300	0450	0.6F
	0701	1101	1.1E
	1417	1726	1.9F
	2200		

Time meridian 90° W. 0000 is midnight. 1200 is noon. Times are not adjusted for Daylight Saving Time.
If three consecutive entries are marked (E) the middle one is not a true maximum but an intermediate value to show the current pattern.
* Current weak and variable.

Galveston Bay Entrance (between jetties), Texas, 2019

F–Flood, Dir. 277° True   E–Ebb, Dir. 088° True

October

Day	Slack	Maximum	knots
1 Tu		0123	0.5E
		0515	*
		1052	1.3E
	1505	1825	2.0F
2 W	0055	0334	0.3E
		0527	*
		1111	1.4E
	1558	1931	1.9F
3 Th	0342	1147	1.4E
	1702	2052	1.7F
4 F	0504	1240	1.4E
	1815	2231	1.7F
5 Sa ◐	0559	1341	1.2E
	1928	2334	1.6F
6 Su	0646	1450	1.1E
	2032		
7 M		0020	1.6F
	0725	1740	1.1E
	2125		
8 Tu		0101	1.6F
	0749	0947	0.3E
		1129	*
		1832	1.2E
	2211		
9 W		0141	1.6F
	0732	0954	0.3E
		1231	*
		1920	1.1E
	2253		
10 Th		0219	1.5F
	0656	0939	0.4E
		1336	*
		2012	1.1E
	2334		
11 F		0252	1.4F
	0640	0927	0.6E
	1221	1439	0.6F
	1712	2104	1.0E
12 Sa	0016	0319	1.2F
	0638	0945	0.8E
	1249	1528	0.9F
	1834	2156	0.8E
13 Su ○	0059	0340	1.0F
	0638	1007	1.0E
	1320	1610	1.2F
	1959	2252	0.5E
14 M	0140	0400	0.7F
	0621	1020	1.2E
	1350	1650	1.5F
	2141		
15 Tu		0000	0.3E
	0215	0415	0.4F
	0547	1013	1.3E
	1419	1730	1.6F
16 W		0116	*
		0413	*
		1013	1.5E
	1448	1815	1.7F
17 Th	0430	1017	1.6E
	1521	1904	1.7F
18 F	0441	1024	1.7E
	1559	2002	1.7F
19 Sa	0504	1053	1.8E
	1649	2109	1.8F
20 Su	0527	1205	1.7E
	1753	2225	1.9F
21 M ○	0546	1339	1.6E
	1904	2323	2.0F
22 Tu	0600	1500	1.5E
	2015		
23 W		0010	2.1F
	0610	0850	0.4E
		1114	*
		1635	1.4E
	2125		
24 Th		0055	1.9F
	0611	0837	0.5E
	1103	1224	0.3F
	1350	1825	1.2E
	2233		
25 F		0142	1.6F
	0559	0848	0.7E
	1115	1332	0.5F
	1612	2020	1.1E
	2342		
26 Sa		0226	1.2F
	0545	0908	0.9E
	1147	1439	1.4F
	1800	2146	0.9E
27 Su ●	0055	0305	0.8F
	0533	0927	1.1E
	1227	1537	1.9F
	1950	2314	0.7E
28 M	0212	0336	0.3F
	0506	0936	1.4E
	1313	1629	2.2F
	2202		
29 Tu		0104	0.5E
		0401	*
		0935	1.6E
	1400	1721	2.3F
30 W	0022	0240	0.3E
		0415	*
		0953	1.7E
	1450	1817	2.2F
31 Th	0229	1020	1.7E
	1543	1921	1.9F

November

Day	Slack	Maximum	knots
1 F	0402	1055	1.6E
	1643	2041	1.7F
2 Sa	0459	1152	1.4E
	1750	2213	1.6F
3 Su	0539	1315	1.2E
	1856	2309	1.6F
4 M ◐	0605	1434	1.0E
	1953	2348	1.6F
5 Tu	0606	0842	0.4E
		1029	0.4E
		1702	1.0E
	2041		
6 W		0021	1.6F
	0531	0837	0.4E
		1153	*
		1801	0.9E
	2125		
7 Th		0051	1.5F
	0503	0809	0.6E
	1105	1246	0.3F
	1452	1854	0.8E
	2207		
8 F		0120	1.3F
	0456	0803	0.8E
	1118	1343	0.6F
	1636	1954	0.7E
	2250		
9 Sa		0147	1.0F
	0458	0824	1.1E
	1143	1437	1.0F
	1810	2059	0.5E
	2336		
10 Su		0214	0.7F
	0455	0847	1.3E
	1212	1522	1.4F
	1957	2203	0.3E
11 M	0027	0238	0.4F
	0431	0901	1.4E
	1242	1559	1.7F
		2321	*
12 Tu ○		0257	*
		0856	1.6E
	1312	1634	1.9F
13 W		0158	*
		0300	*
		0900	1.7E
	1342	1710	2.0F
14 Th	0216	0912	1.9E
	1413	1751	2.0F
15 F	0313	0928	2.0E
	1448	1840	2.0F
16 Sa	0353	0955	2.1E
	1531	1936	2.0F
17 Su	0421	1039	2.0E
	1625	2042	2.0F
18 M	0437	1207	1.7E
	1732	2154	2.0F
19 Tu ○	0441	1342	1.5E
	1847	2254	2.0F
20 W	0441	0723	0.5E
		1002	*
		1508	1.2E
	2001	2339	1.8F
21 Th	0431	0709	0.6E
	0953	1123	0.3F
	1306	1733	1.0E
	2115		
22 F		0019	1.4F
	0413	0722	0.8E
	1007	1229	1.0F
	1533	1921	0.8E
	2229		
23 Sa		0058	1.0F
	0400	0743	1.1E
	1040	1334	1.5F
	1737	2103	0.6E
	2347		
24 Su		0136	0.5F
	0342	0806	1.4E
	1122	1438	2.0F
	1954	2246	0.5E
25 M		0212	*
		0821	1.6E
	1209	1536	2.3F
	2156		
26 Tu ●		0031	0.4E
		0244	*
		0830	1.8E
	1300	1627	2.4F
	2348		
27 W		0156	0.4E
		0306	0.3E
		0853	1.9E
	1351	1717	2.3F
28 Th	0123	0922	1.9E
	1442	1811	2.1F
29 F	0251	0956	1.7E
	1533	1912	1.8F
30 Sa	0400	1037	1.5E
	1625	2021	1.6F

December

Day	Slack	Maximum	knots
1 Su	0443	1137	1.3E
	1719	2133	1.5F
2 M	0503	1307	1.1E
	1812	2227	1.5F
3 Tu	0449	1425	0.9E
	1901	2305	1.5F
4 W ◐	0355	0719	0.5E
		1114	*
		1612	0.7E
	1948	2334	1.4F
5 Th	0327	0639	0.6E
		1200	*
		1734	0.6E
	2032	2357	1.2F
6 F	0322	0641	0.9E
	1012	1244	0.7F
	1552	1839	0.4E
	2117		
7 Sa		0017	0.9F
	0322	0702	1.2E
	1034	1333	1.0F
		1952	*
8 Su		0039	0.6F
	0310	0725	1.4E
	1102	1424	1.4F
		2124	*
9 M		0059	*
		0738	1.5E
	1133	1507	1.7F
		2358	*
10 Tu ●		0111	*
		0737	1.6E
	1205	1542	1.9F
	2358		
11 W ○		0747	1.8E
	1238	1616	2.1F
12 Th	0047	0807	2.0E
	1312	1651	2.2F
13 F	0135	0836	2.1E
	1349	1732	2.2F
14 Sa	0224	0911	2.2E
	1431	1820	2.2F
15 Su	0306	0956	2.1E
	1519	1915	2.1F
16 M	0327	1057	1.9E
	1615	2015	2.0F
17 Tu	0322	1227	1.6E
	1721	2117	1.8F
18 W ○	0312	0543	0.4E
		0832	*
		1355	1.2E
	1837	2215	1.5F
19 Th	0252	0540	0.6E
	0822	1008	0.4F
	1215	1554	0.8E
	1956	2301	1.2F
20 F	0231	0558	0.9E
	0849	1124	1.0F
	1446	1822	0.6E
	2119	2338	0.7F
21 Sa	0215	0622	1.2E
	0928	1228	1.6F
	1724	2026	0.4E
	2246		
22 Su		0011	0.3F
	0145	0645	1.5E
	1014	1332	2.0F
	1943	2210	0.4E
23 M		0041	*
		0706	1.7E
	1105	1437	2.3F
	2133	2342	0.4E
24 Tu		0109	0.3E
		0726	1.8E
	1158	1535	2.3F
	2304		
25 W ●		0756	1.9E
	1254	1626	2.3F
26 Th	0023	0834	1.8E
	1347	1714	2.1F
27 F	0136	0914	1.8E
	1436	1802	1.9F
28 Sa	0253	0954	1.6E
	1519	1852	1.7F
29 Su	0357	1039	1.5E
	1600	1941	1.6F
30 M	0418	1143	1.2E
	1639	2029	1.5F
31 Tu	0325	1308	1.0E
	1720	2118	1.3F

Time meridian 90° W. 0000 is midnight. 1200 is noon. Times are not adjusted for Daylight Saving Time.
If three consecutive entries are marked (E) the middle one is not a true maximum but an intermediate value to show the current pattern.
* Current weak and variable.

Bolivar Roads, Galveston Bay, Texas, 2019

F–Flood, Dir. 306° True   E–Ebb, Dir. 116° True

January

Day	Slack (h m)	Maximum (h m)	knots
1 Tu	0024	0632	1.9E
	1040	1410	1.8F
	2013	2221	0.4E
2 W		0029	0.3E
		0646	2.1E
	1111	1447	2.1F
	2108	2330	0.5E
3 Th		0059	0.5E
		0709	2.2E
	1144	1522	2.2F
	2153		
4 F		0742	2.2E
	1220	1558	2.2F
	2237		
5 Sa ●		0822	2.2E
	1300	1637	2.2F
	2321		
6 Su		0906	2.1E
	1343	1720	2.1F
7 M	0005	0952	2.0E
	1427	1808	2.1F
8 Tu	0042	1037	1.9E
	1511	1856	2.0F
9 W	0109	1121	1.6E
	1551	1941	1.8F
10 Th	0125	0511	0.8E
	0610		0.8E
	1204		1.3E
	1627	2019	1.6F
11 F	0129	0512	0.9E
		0819	0.7E
		1255	0.8E
	1657	2046	1.2F
12 Sa	0120	0508	1.0E
		1118	0.3E
		1413	0.4E
	1719	2106	0.9F
13 Su	0055	0500	1.1E
		1151	*
		1556	*
		2123	0.5F
14 M ◗	0009	0457	1.3E
	0904	1207	0.7F
		1835	*
		2131	*
15 Tu		0455	1.5E
	0907	1228	1.2F
	1938		
16 W		0504	1.8E
	0927	1300	1.7F
	1952		
17 Th		0532	2.0E
	1003	1342	2.2F
	2034		
18 F		0615	2.3E
	1052	1430	2.4F
	2134		
19 Sa		0708	2.5E
	1149	1523	2.6F
	2245		
20 Su ○		0809	2.7E
	1251	1619	2.6F
	2359		
21 M		0914	2.7E
	1353	1717	2.6F
22 Tu	0101	1023	2.7E
	1453	1814	2.4F
23 W		0302	*
		0434	*
		1134	2.4E
	1551	1908	2.1F
24 Th	0129	0324	0.3E
		0558	*
		1249	1.9E
	1646	1955	1.7F
25 F	0104	0343	0.6E
		0732	*
		1409	1.3E
	1740	2035	1.2F
26 Sa	0026	0359	0.9E
	0712	0922	0.4F
	1156	1541	0.7E
	1839	2110	0.7F
	2354		
27 Su ◑		0414	1.3E
	0752	1056	0.9F
	1520	1747	0.3E
		2140	*
28 M		0431	1.6E
	0833	1203	1.4F
	1800	2001	0.3E
		2208	*
29 Tu		0453	1.8E
	0914	1256	1.7F
	1919		
30 W		0523	1.9E
	0957	1343	1.9F
	2010		
31 Th		0602	2.0E
	1041	1426	2.0F
	2055		

February

Day	Slack (h m)	Maximum (h m)	knots
1 F		0650	2.0E
		2257	0.6E
2 Sa		0650	2.0E
	1127	1510	2.0F
	2137		
3 Su		0016	0.6E
		0128	0.6E
		0743	2.0E
	1214	1554	2.0F
	2217		
4 M ●		0051	0.6E
		0218	0.6E
		0836	1.9E
	1259	1637	2.0F
	2252		
5 Tu		0128	0.6E
		0303	0.5E
		0926	1.9E
	1341	1719	2.0F
	2320		
6 W		0201	0.6E
		0351	0.5E
		1010	1.8E
	1419	1756	1.9F
	2337		
7 Th		0229	0.7E
		0444	0.5E
		1051	1.5E
	1454	1826	1.7F
	2344		
8 F		0248	0.8E
		0543	0.5E
		1132	1.2E
	1524	1850	1.5F
	2339		
9 Sa		0256	0.9E
		0647	0.3E
		1218	0.9E
	1552	1910	1.2F
	2320		
10 Su		0258	1.0E
		0751	*
		1319	0.5E
	1618	1928	0.8F
	2248		
11 M		0301	1.1E
	0648	0849	0.4F
		1436	*
		1944	0.4F
	2159		
12 Tu ◑		0302	1.2E
	0652	0939	0.8F
		1610	*
		1943	*
13 W		0304	1.4E
	0711	1028	1.3F
	1718		
14 Th		0323	1.6E
	0745	1120	1.6F
	1826		
15 F		0401	1.8E
	0834	1218	1.9F
	1932		
16 Sa		0456	2.1E
	0937	1319	2.1F
	2042		
17 Su		0601	2.3E
	1046	1422	2.3F
	2152		
18 M		0712	2.5E
	1154	1522	2.4F
	2257		
19 Tu ○		0825	2.6E
	1257	1618	2.4F
20 W		0059	*
		0242	*
		0936	2.6E
	1355	1707	2.2F
21 Th		0116	*
		0352	*
		1044	2.3E
	1449	1750	1.9F
22 F		0130	0.3E
	0314	0502	0.4F
	0641	1153	1.9E
	1540	1826	1.5F
	2247		
23 Sa		0140	0.6E
	0404	0615	0.6F
	0837	1305	1.3E
	1632	1858	1.0F
	2202		
24 Su		0151	1.0E
	0454	0731	0.9F
	1055	1427	0.8E
	1730	1925	0.5F
	2131		
25 M		0205	1.3E
	0543	0850	1.2F
	1341	1615	0.3E
		1949	*
26 Tu ◑		0227	1.6E
	0633	1006	1.5F
	1622	1853	0.3E
		1958	*
27 W		0258	1.8E
	0724	1114	1.6F
	1755		
28 Th		0341	1.8E
	0819	1217	1.7F
	1853		

March

Day	Slack (h m)	Maximum (h m)	knots
1 F		0435	1.7E
		0542	1.7E
	1020	1411	1.8F
	2022	2309	0.7E
2 Sa		0104	0.6E
		0654	1.7E
	1117	1502	1.8F
	2059	2335	0.7E
3 Su		0207	0.5E
		0801	1.7E
	1207	1547	1.8F
	2128		
4 M		0003	0.7E
		0256	0.4E
		0857	1.7E
	1250	1625	1.8F
	2146		
5 Tu		0028	0.8E
		0342	0.3E
		0945	1.6E
	1327	1655	1.7F
	2154		
6 W ●		0048	0.8E
		0427	*
		1029	1.3E
	1401	1717	1.5F
	2149		
7 Th		0059	0.9E
		0510	*
		1112	1.1E
	1431	1733	1.2F
	2131		
8 F		0103	1.0E
	0423	0551	0.3F
	0742	1159	0.8E
	1503	1748	0.9F
	2104		
9 Sa		0105	1.1E
	0424	0630	0.6F
	0930	1252	0.5E
	1540	1805	0.6F
	2028		
10 Su		0105	1.2E
	0433	0710	1.0F
	1110	1355	0.3E
		1823	*
11 M		0101	1.3E
	0450	0752	1.3F
	1243	1509	0.3E
		1833	*
12 Tu		0108	1.5E
	0518	0840	1.6F
	1413		
13 W		0136	1.6E
	0600	0937	1.8F
	1559		
14 Th ◗		0224	1.7E
	0658	1043	1.9F
	1753		
15 F		0330	1.9E
	0813	1159	1.9F
	1921		
16 Sa		0448	2.0E
	0933	1315	2.0F
	2030		
17 Su		0612	2.2E
	1048	1421	2.1F
	2123	2324	0.3E
18 M		0046	0.3E
		0734	2.3E
	1154	1515	2.1F
	2156	2334	0.3E
19 Tu		0203	*
		0849	2.2E
	1253	1559	1.9F
	2155	2344	0.3E
20 W ○	0124	0310	0.4F
	0447	0959	2.0E
	1347	1634	1.6F
	2110	2348	0.5E
21 Th	0151	0412	0.8F
	0633	1106	1.6E
	1440	1704	1.1F
	2013	2346	0.8E
22 F	0228	0512	1.2F
	0817	1216	1.2E
	1534	1730	0.7F
	1941	2347	1.2E
23 Sa	0309	0611	1.5F
	1012	1333	0.7E
		1753	*
		2357	1.6E
24 Su	0352	0708	1.7F
	1220	1507	0.4E
		1812	*
25 M		0021	1.8E
	0438	0806	1.8F
	1426		
26 Tu ◑		0057	1.9E
	0527	0909	1.8F
	1608		
27 W		0146	1.8E
	0625	1022	1.7F
	1718		
28 Th		0248	1.6E
	0732	1141	1.6F
	1811		
29 F		0407	1.5E
	0847	1253	1.6F
	1854	2212	0.8E
30 Sa		0031	0.7E
		0534	1.4E
	0957	1353	1.6F
	1928	2223	0.8E
31 Su		0141	0.5E
		0657	1.4E
	1056	1441	1.7F
	1950	2245	0.9E

Time meridian 90° W. 0000 is midnight. 1200 is noon. Times are not adjusted for Daylight Saving Time.
* Current weak and variable.

Bolivar Roads, Galveston Bay, Texas, 2019

F–Flood, Dir. 306° True   E–Ebb, Dir. 116° True

April

Day	Slack (h m)	Maximum (h m)	knots
1 M	1145, 2001	0235, 0806, 1518, 2305	0.3E, 1.4E, 1.6F, 0.9E
2 Tu	1227, 1959	0321, 0904, 1546, 2319	*, 1.2E, 1.4F, 1.0E
3 W	1304, 1942	0401, 0957, 1605, 2323	*, 1.0E, 1.2F, 1.1E
4 Th	0233, 0655, 1341, 1916	0434, 1047, 1616, 2321	0.5F, 0.8E, 0.9F, 1.2E
5 F ●	0235, 0819, 1422, 1843	0500, 1138, 1629, 2318	0.8F, 0.6E, 0.5F, 1.3E
6 Sa	0242, 0934, 1645, 2308	0526, 1231, 1646, —	1.2F, 0.5E, *, 1.4E
7 Su	1039, 1705, 2305	0254, 0557, 1329	1.5F, 0.4E, *, 1.6E
8 M	1139, 1721, 2322	0314, 0633, 1438	1.8F, 0.4E, 0.3F, 1.7E
9 Tu	1246	0345, 0716, 2355	2.0F, 1.8E
10 W	1416	0430, 0809	2.1F
11 Th	0530, 1607	0047, 0914	1.8E, 2.0F
12 F ◐	0646, 1742	0200, 1034	1.8E, 1.9F
13 Sa	0810, 1848	0329, 1200	1.8E, 1.9F
14 Su	0931, 1931	0503, 1311, 2201	1.9E, 2.0F, 0.5E
15 M	1042, 1947	0006, 0634, 1405, 2210	0.4E, 1.9E, 1.9F, 0.5E
16 Tu	1145, 1929	0128, 0758, 1446, 2217	*, 1.8E, 1.6F, 0.6E
17 W	0033, 0433, 1243, 1839	0232, 0915, 1518, 2215	0.5F, 1.6E, 1.2F, 0.8E
18 Th	0051, 0622, 1341, 1803	0328, 1029, 1544, 2205	1.1F, 1.3E, 0.8F, 1.2E
19 F ○	0118, 0806, 1445, 1732	0419, 1142, 1607, 2159	1.6F, 0.9E, 0.3F, 1.6E
20 Sa	0151, 0951, 1628, 2211	0506, 1258, —, —	2.0F, 0.7E, *, 1.9E
21 Su	1131, 1646, 2237	0226, 0551, 1422	2.2F, 0.5E, 0.3F, 2.1E
22 M	1304	0305, 0637, 2314	2.2F, 2.1E
23 Tu	1428	0349, 0727, 2359	2.1F, 2.0E
24 W	1539	0441, 0826	1.9F
25 Th	0543, 1635	0058, 0945	1.7E, 1.7F
26 F ◐	0655, 1716	0214, 1114, 2223, 2314	1.5E, 1.6F, 0.9E, 0.9E
27 Sa	0809, 1745	0344, 1225, 2115	1.3E, 1.6F, 0.9E
28 Su	0917, 1802	0052, 0515, 1318, 2127	0.6E, 1.2E, 1.5F, 1.0E
29 M	1016, 1807	0152, 0641, 1357, 2142	0.3E, 1.0E, 1.4F, 1.1E
30 Tu	1107, 1758	0240, 0801, 1426, 2151	*, 0.8E, 1.2F, 1.2E

May

Day	Slack (h m)	Maximum (h m)	knots
1 W	0118, 0537, 1156, 1736	0319, 0914, 1444, 2150	0.4F, 0.7E, 0.8F, 1.3E
2 Th	0110, 0720, 1247, 1704	0348, 1020, 1454, 2143	0.8F, 0.5E, 0.5F, 1.4E
3 F	0112, 0840, 1505	0408, 1121, —, 2133	1.2F, 0.4E, *, 1.6E
4 Sa ●	0120, 0937, 1522	0427, 1219, —, 2124	1.6F, 0.4E, *, 1.8E
5 Su	0134, 1021, 1542	0452, 1319, —, 2133	2.0F, 0.4E, 0.3F, 1.9E
6 M	0157, 1104, 1600	0525, 1431, —, 2158	2.3F, 0.5E, 0.4F, 2.0E
7 Tu	1202	0231, 0606, 2236	2.4F, 2.1E
8 W	1323	0318, 0657, 2328	2.4F, 2.0E
9 Th	1455	0418, 0758	2.2F
10 F	0530, 1612	0038, 0913	2.0E, 2.1F
11 Sa ◐	0648, 1705	0209, 1038	1.9E, 2.0F
12 Su	0805, 1734	0348, 1151, 2031, 2321	1.7E, 1.9F, 0.7E, 0.5E
13 M	0918, 1738	0524, 1246, 2042	1.6E, 1.7F, 0.8E
14 Tu	1027, 1713, 2338	0052, 0657, 1326, 2050	*, 1.3E, 1.3F, 1.0E
15 W	0422, 1133, 1637, 2354	0154, 0830, 1358, 2048	0.7F, 1.1E, 0.9F, 1.2E
16 Th	0626, 1244, 1606	0245, 0957, 1424, 2039	1.3F, 0.8E, 0.4F, 1.5E
17 F	0018, 0816, 1446	0330, 1115, —, 2035	1.8F, 0.7E, *, 1.9E
18 Sa ○	0047, 0947, 1506	0410, 1230, —, 2049	2.2F, 0.6E, 0.3F, 2.2E
19 Su	0118, 1105, 1523	0448, 1347, —, 2117	2.4F, 0.5E, 0.4F, 2.3E
20 M	0154, 1214	0528, 2153	2.4F, 2.3E
21 Tu	0234, 1320	0611, 2236	2.3F, 2.2E
22 W	0322, 1420	0702, 2328	2.1F, 2.0E
23 Th	0416, 1507	0805	1.9F
24 F	0516, 1542	0031, 0924	1.7E, 1.7F
25 Sa	0618, 1604, 2340	0149, 1042, 2009	1.4E, 1.6F, 1.0E, 0.8E
26 Su	0719, 1615	0316, 1140, 2006	1.1E, 1.5F, 1.1E
27 M	0817, 1615	0053, 0444, 1222, 2015	0.4E, 0.8E, 1.3F, 1.2E
28 Tu	0915, 1603	0145, 0619, 1252, 2017	*, 0.5E, 1.0F, 1.3E
29 W	0006, 0531, 1019, 1538, 2353	0224, 0808, 1309, 2010	0.5F, 0.3E, 0.6F, 1.4E
30 Th	0947, 1318, 2354	0251, —, —, 2003	1.0F, *, *, 1.6E
31 F	0845, 1331	0309, 1103, —, 1955	1.4F, 0.3E, *, 1.8E

June

Day	Slack (h m)	Maximum (h m)	knots
1 Sa	0003, 0929, 1347	0325, 1210, —, 1956	1.8F, 0.4E, 0.3F, 2.0E
2 Su	0021, 1003, 1404	0348, 1316, —, 2015	2.2F, 0.5E, 0.4F, 2.2E
3 M ●	0048, 1044	0421, 2048	2.4F, 2.3E
4 Tu	0128, 1141	0503, 2132	2.6F, 2.4E
5 W	0218, 1255	0553, 2227	2.5F, 2.3E
6 Th	0318, 1407	0652, 2334	2.4F, 2.2E
7 F	0425, 1502	0801	2.3F
8 Sa	0533, 1536	0058, 0915	2.0E, 2.1F
9 Su ◐	0642, 1549	0234, 1024, 1852, 2207	1.8E, 1.9F, 0.8E, 0.4E
10 M	0750, 1542, 2357	0408, 1118, 1906	1.4E, 1.6F, 1.0E, *
11 Tu	0900, 1518, 2231	0545, 1200, 1916	1.0E, 1.1F, 1.2E
12 W	0409, 1015, 1450, 2250	0104, 0735, 1233, 1920	0.8F, 0.7E, 0.7F, 1.5E
13 Th	0632, 1301, 2317	0156, 0918, —, 1921	1.4F, 0.5E, *, 1.8E
14 F	0817, 1325, 2347	0239, 1042, —, 1925	1.9F, 0.5E, *, 2.1E
15 Sa	0318, 0933, 1347	—, 1157, —, 1942	2.2F, 0.5E, 0.4F, 2.3E
16 Su	0020, 1035, 1403	0354, 1312, —, 2012	2.4F, 0.5E, 0.5F, 2.4E
17 M ○	0056, 1133	0431, 2049	2.4F, 2.3E
18 Tu	0137, 1227	0511, 2133	2.3F, 2.3E
19 W	0221, 1315	0558, 2222	2.2F, 2.1E
20 Th	0310, 1353	0652, 2316	2.0F, 1.9E
21 F	0400, 1417	0753	1.9F
22 Sa	0449, 1430	0017, 0855	1.6E, 1.8F
23 Su	0536, 1435	0127, 0949, 1828, 2329	1.2E, 1.6F, 1.0E, 0.6E
24 M	0619, 1431	0248, 1029, 1831	0.8E, 1.3F, 1.2E
25 Tu ◐	0658, 1417, 2247	0031, 0418, 1056, 1827	*, 0.4E, 0.9F, 1.3E
26 W	0611, 1110, 1344, 2228	0112, —, —, 1824	0.5F, *, 0.4F, 1.4E
27 Th	0905, 1119, 2230	0139, —, —, 1822	0.9F, *, *, 1.6E
28 F	0832, 2243	0157, 1821	1.4F, 1.8E
29 Sa	0902, 2307	0214, 1833	1.8F, 2.0E
30 Su	0937, 2342	0241, 1902	2.1F, 2.2E

Time meridian 90° W. 0000 is midnight. 1200 is noon. Times are not adjusted for Daylight Saving Time.
* Current weak and variable.

Bolivar Roads, Galveston Bay, Texas, 2019

F—Flood, Dir. 306° True   E—Ebb, Dir. 116° True

July

Day	Slack h m	Max h m	knots
1 M		0317	2.4F
	1023	1944	2.4E
2 Tu ●	0029	0402	2.5F
	1123	2036	2.5E
3 W	0123	0453	2.6F
	1230	2135	2.6E
4 Th	0223	0551	2.5F
	1328	2242	2.5E
5 F	0325	0653	2.4F
	1404	2359	2.3E
6 Sa	0427	0755	2.2F
	1417	1644	0.5E
		1834	0.4E
7 Su		0125	1.9E
	0527	0853	1.9F
	1413	1700	0.7E
	2028		*
8 M		0254	1.4E
	0628	0943	1.5F
	1354	1717	1.0E
	2041	2228	0.3F
9 Tu ◐	0021	0428	0.9E
	0734	1025	0.9F
	1328	1732	1.3E
	2100	2351	0.9F
10 W	0331	0625	0.5E
	0855	1100	0.4F
	1301	1745	1.6E
	2132		
11 Th		0051	1.5F
	0605	0825	0.4E
		1131	*
		1759	1.9E
	2207		
12 F		0140	1.9F
	0744	0959	0.4E
		1200	0.3F
		1816	2.1E
	2244		
13 Sa		0222	2.1F
	0852	1118	0.5E
		1226	0.5F
		1842	2.2E
	2324		
14 Su		0302	2.2F
	0948	1918	2.2E
15 M	0005	0342	2.1F
	1039	2000	2.2E
16 Tu ○	0049	0423	2.1F
	1127	2047	2.2E
17 W	0133	0507	2.1F
	1207	2137	2.1E
18 Th	0217	0554	2.0F
	1235	2227	1.9E
19 F	0300	0641	2.0F
	1251	1605	0.6E
		1650	0.6E
		2319	1.7E
20 Sa	0340	0725	1.8F
	1257	1615	0.8E
		1824	0.7E
21 Su		0016	1.3E
	0418	0803	1.6F
	1256	1625	0.9E
		2027	0.5E
22 M		0122	0.8E
	0452	0832	1.2F
	1247	1628	1.1E
		2233	*
23 Tu		0241	0.4E
	0522	0853	0.8F
	1227	1630	1.2E
	2048	2326	0.4F
24 W ◐		0412	*
		0905	1635 1.3E
	1139	2039	2357 0.8F
25 Th	0944	1638	1.5E
	2048		
26 F		0019	1.2F
	0737	1644	1.7E
	2110		
27 Sa		0047	1.6F
	0805	1707	1.9F
	2144		
28 Su		0124	1.9F
	0847	1748	2.1E
	2231		
29 M		0209	2.1F
	0942	1840	2.3E
	2327		
30 Tu		0300	2.3F
	1046	1940	2.5E
31 W ●	0028	0355	2.4F
	1151	2045	2.6E

August

Day	Slack h m	Max h m	knots
1 Th	0128	0451	2.4F
	1242	2154	2.6E
2 F	0227	0546	2.3F
		1426	*
		1614	*
		2307	2.4E
3 Sa	0324	0637	2.1F
	1252	1443	0.3E
		1735	*
4 Su		0025	2.0F
	0420	0724	1.7E
	1226	1500	0.6E
	1732	1901	0.3F
	2037		
5 M		0146	1.4E
	0517	0805	1.2F
	1152	1518	0.9E
	1817	2035	0.6F
	2325		
6 Tu		0315	0.9E
	0621	0842	0.7F
	1123	1537	1.3E
	1904	2207	1.1F
7 W ◐	0220	0506	0.5E
		0915	*
		1558	1.6E
	1950	2321	1.5F
8 Th	0457	0721	0.3E
		0946	*
		1623	1.8E
	2038		
9 F		0022	1.8F
	0640	0918	0.4E
		1011	0.4F
		1656	1.9E
	2128		
10 Sa		0115	1.9F
	0747	1737	1.9E
	2219		
11 Su		0205	1.9F
	0842	1827	1.9E
	2311		
12 M		0252	1.9F
	0930	1205	0.6E
		1258	0.6F
		1923	1.9E
13 Tu	0000	0338	1.9F
	1012	1235	0.5E
		1356	0.5F
		2019	1.9E
14 W	0046	0421	1.9F
	1044	1305	0.5E
		1448	0.5F
		2110	1.9E
15 Th ○	0128	0501	1.9F
	1103	1333	0.6E
		1542	0.4E
		2158	1.8E
16 F	0206	0537	1.9F
	1111	1356	0.7E
		1640	0.4E
		2246	1.5E
17 Sa	0242	0609	1.7F
	1110	1412	0.8E
		1741	0.3E
		2336	1.2E
18 Su	0316	0635	1.4F
	1102	1421	0.9E
		1845	*
19 M		0034	0.8E
	0350	0656	1.1F
	1045	1428	1.0E
		1947	*
20 Tu		0140	0.5E
	0425	0713	0.7F
	1015	1436	1.2E
	1814	2041	0.6F
21 W		0256	*
		0725	0.3F
	0913	1441	1.3E
	1827	2126	0.9F
22 Th		0440	*
		0651	*
		1443	1.4E
	1848	2209	1.3F
23 F ○	0513	1457	1.5E
	1921	2257	1.5F
24 Sa	0622	1532	1.7E
	2008	2352	1.7F
25 Su	0727	1625	1.9E
	2110		
26 M		0053	1.9F
	0833	1730	2.1E
	2219		
27 Tu		0155	2.1F
	0938	1841	2.3E
	2326		
28 W		0255	2.2F
	1037	1954	2.5E
29 Th	0029	0349	2.2F
		1232	*
		1419	*
		2107	2.5E
30 F ●	0127	0438	2.1F
		1241	*
		1530	*
		2218	2.3E
31 Sa	0223	0520	1.9F
	1052	1250	0.3E
	1435	1640	0.5F
	1833	2331	1.9E

September

Day	Slack h m	Max h m	knots
1 Su	0318	0558	1.4F
	1001	1300	0.6E
	1522	1749	0.9F
	2026		
2 M		0047	1.4E
	0415	0632	0.9F
	0924	1313	1.0E
	1612	1900	1.2F
	2234		
3 Tu		0211	0.9E
	0522	0702	0.4F
	0853	1330	1.4E
	1702	2012	1.5F
4 W	0100	0353	0.5E
		0729	*
		1354	1.6E
	1754	2126	1.7E
5 Th ◐	0322	0611	0.4E
		0748	0.3E
		1428	1.8E
	1850	2238	1.7F
6 F	0512	1513	1.8E
	1950	2348	1.7F
7 Sa	0626	1611	1.7E
	2056		
8 Su		0052	1.7F
	0722	1721	1.7E
	2201		
9 M		0151	1.7F
	0807	1050	0.6E
		1241	0.6F
		1836	1.6E
	2300		
10 Tu		0243	1.7F
	0843	1112	0.7E
		1349	0.5E
		1944	1.6E
	2351		
11 W		0326	1.7F
	0906	1137	0.7E
		1443	0.3E
		2041	1.6E
12 Th	0034	0403	1.7F
	0916	1200	0.8E
		1532	*
		2132	1.5E
13 F ○	0112	0433	1.6F
	0916	1217	0.8E
		1620	*
		2220	1.3E
14 Sa	0147	0457	1.4F
	0906	1232	0.9E
		1705	*
		2310	1.0E
15 Su	0223	0516	1.1F
	0849	1232	1.1E
	1546	1746	0.5F
	2021		
16 M		0004	0.7E
	0301	0532	0.8F
	0826	1236	1.2E
	1556	1823	0.8F
	2200		
17 Tu		0104	0.5E
	0350	0547	0.4F
	0744	1239	1.3E
	1610	1859	1.1F
	2335		
18 W		0210	0.3E
		0600	*
		1234	1.4E
	1628	1936	1.4F
19 Th		0337	*
		0549	*
		1236	1.5E
	1653	2018	1.6F
20 F	0220	1257	1.6E
	1731	2109	1.7F
21 Sa ○	0353	1341	1.6E
	1826	2212	1.7F
22 Su	0535	1449	1.7E
	1937	2326	1.8F
23 M	0657	1609	1.8E
	2058		
24 Tu		0042	1.9F
	0802	1734	2.0E
	2214		
25 W		0149	2.0F
	0849	1105	0.4E
		1215	0.3E
		1857	2.1E
	2322		
26 Th		0243	2.0F
	0914	1103	0.3E
		1340	*
		2017	2.1E
27 F	0023	0327	1.9F
	0902	1106	0.3E
	1254	1447	0.5F
	1632	2132	2.0E
28 Sa ●	0120	0404	1.5F
	0814	1106	0.6E
	1318	1549	1.0F
	1820	2245	1.7E
29 Su	0218	0436	1.1F
	0731	1106	0.9E
	1354	1648	1.4F
	2004	2359	1.3E
30 M	0320	0505	0.6F
	0703	1108	1.3E
	1435	1745	1.8F
	2154		

Time meridian 90° W. 0000 is midnight. 1200 is noon. Times are not adjusted for Daylight Saving Time.
* Current weak and variable.

Bolivar Roads, Galveston Bay, Texas, 2019

F–Flood, Dir. 306° True   E–Ebb, Dir. 116° True

October

Day	Slack h m	Max h m	knots
1 Tu		0119	0.9E
		0531	*
		1121	1.7E
	1519	1841	2.0F
	2354		
2 W		0253	0.6E
		0553	*
		1147	1.9E
	1606	1938	2.0F
3 Th	0152	0503	0.5E
		0556	0.5E
		1224	1.9E
	1659	2040	1.9F
4 F	0337	1314	1.8E
	1759	2153	1.7F
5 Sa ◐	0456	1419	1.7E
	1909	2316	1.6F
6 Su	0554	1542	1.5E
	2026		
7 M		0032	1.5F
	0635	0951	0.8E
		1205	0.7E
		1712	1.4E
	2136		
8 Tu		0131	1.6F
	0704	0958	0.8E
		1322	0.5E
		1837	1.3E
	2236		
9 W		0217	1.6F
	0719	1017	0.9E
		1418	*
		1949	1.3E
	2325		
10 Th		0253	1.5F
	0722	1035	1.0E
		1507	*
		2052	1.2E
11 F	0009	0322	1.4F
	0715	1048	1.1E
	1401	1550	0.4F
	1745	2150	1.0E
12 Sa	0050	0345	1.1F
	0700	1053	1.2E
	1404	1626	0.7F
	1918	2247	0.8E
13 Su ○	0134	0400	0.8F
	0639	1053	1.3E
	1412	1656	1.1F
	2043	2344	0.6E
14 M	0225	0413	0.4F
	0606	1053	1.4E
	1423	1720	1.4F
	2158		
15 Tu		0044	0.5E
		0426	*
		1046	1.5E
	1437	1746	1.7F
	2300		
16 W		0149	0.4E
		0439	*
		1039	1.6E
	1455	1817	1.9F
	2353		
17 Th		0326	0.4E
		0432	0.4E
		1049	1.7E
	1522	1855	2.0F
18 F	0052	1114	1.8E
	1602	1942	2.0F
19 Sa	0211	1158	1.8E
	1657	2041	1.9F
20 Su	0348	1307	1.8E
	1807	2156	1.9F
21 M ○	0513	1437	1.7E
	1929	2320	1.9F
22 Tu	0612	1615	1.8E
	2049		
23 W		0034	1.9F
	0648	0939	0.6E
		1132	0.5E
		1751	1.7E
	2203		
24 Th		0129	1.8F
	0658	0938	0.6E
		1302	*
		1921	1.7E
	2310		
25 F		0213	1.6F
	0636	0939	0.7E
	1204	1408	0.6F
	1614	2046	1.5E
26 Sa	0014	0248	1.2F
	0557	0934	0.9E
	1220	1504	1.2F
	1806	2206	1.3E
27 Su ●	0120	0317	0.7F
	0527	0928	1.3E
	1248	1555	1.8F
	1950	2324	1.0E
28 M		0343	*
		0927	1.7E
	1321	1642	2.2F
	2132		
29 Tu		0042	0.8E
		0406	*
		0942	2.1E
	1359	1728	2.4F
	2310		
30 W		0207	0.6E
		0426	0.4E
		1009	2.2E
	1441	1815	2.4F
31 Th	0046	1046	2.2E
	1528	1905	2.2F

November

Day	Slack h m	Max h m	knots
1 F	0217	1131	2.1E
	1621	2003	1.9F
2 Sa	0332	1228	1.8E
	1724	2119	1.7F
3 Su	0426	1342	1.6E
	1834	2249	1.6F
4 M ◐	0501	1515	1.3E
	1946		
5 Tu		0000	1.5F
	0521	0849	0.9E
		1229	0.6E
		1650	1.1E
	2052		
6 W		0051	1.5F
	0528	0859	1.0E
		1332	*
		1821	0.9E
	2152		
7 Th		0131	1.4F
	0527	0912	1.2E
		1423	*
		1950	0.8E
	2247		
8 F		0203	1.1F
	0518	0921	1.3E
	1247	1505	0.6F
	1756	2111	0.6E
	2343		
9 Sa		0226	0.8F
	0502	0923	1.5E
	1248	1539	1.1F
	1937	2223	0.5E
10 Su	0046	0241	0.4F
	0435	0922	1.6E
	1256	1604	1.5F
	2054	2329	0.5E
11 M		0252	*
		0919	1.7E
	1307	1624	1.8F
	2152		
12 Tu ○		0033	0.5E
		0304	*
		0912	1.8E
	1321	1644	2.0F
	2236		
13 W		0141	0.5E
		0315	0.4E
		0914	1.9E
	1342	1711	2.2F
	2317		
14 Th		0933	2.0E
	1412	1747	2.3F
15 F	0008	1004	2.1E
	1453	1832	2.3F
16 Sa	0118	1048	2.0E
	1547	1927	2.2F
17 Su	0238	1149	2.0E
	1653	2035	2.1F
18 M	0345	1310	1.9E
	1805	2153	2.0F
19 Tu ◑	0430	1450	1.7E
	1920	2308	1.9F
20 W	0454	0807	0.7E
		1032	0.6E
		1633	1.5E
	2034		
21 Th		0006	1.7F
	0454	0809	0.8E
		1220	*
		1815	1.2E
	2148		
22 F		0052	1.3F
	0432	0812	1.0E
	1109	1326	0.7F
	1556	1956	1.0E
	2303		
23 Sa		0128	0.9F
	0404	0810	1.3E
	1123	1419	1.4F
	1803	2131	0.9E
24 Su	0023	0158	0.4F
	0335	0808	1.6E
	1149	1505	2.0F
	1951	2255	0.8E
25 M		0224	*
		0810	2.0E
	1220	1547	2.4F
	2123		
26 Tu ●		0011	0.7E
		0247	0.4E
		0827	2.3E
	1255	1628	2.6F
	2243		
27 W		0128	0.6E
		0306	0.5E
		0855	2.4E
	1334	1709	2.5F
28 Th	0001	0932	2.4E
	1418	1753	2.4F
29 F	0116	1015	2.3E
	1507	1843	2.1F
30 Sa	0221	1106	2.1E
	1600	1943	1.9F

December

Day	Slack h m	Max h m	knots
1 Su	0306	1205	1.8E
	1657	2055	1.7F
2 M	0331	1317	1.5E
	1755	2210	1.6F
3 Tu	0341	0743	0.9E
		1055	0.8E
		1444	1.1E
	1853	2309	1.5F
4 W ◐	0342	0735	1.1E
		1227	0.4E
		1620	0.7E
	1950	2354	1.3F
5 Th	0339	0743	1.2E
		1324	*
		1806	0.4E
	2053		
6 F		0029	0.9F
	0329	0747	1.4E
	1136	1408	0.7F
	1748	2013	0.3E
	2212		
7 Sa		0054	0.5F
	0310	0747	1.6E
	1133	1442	1.2F
	1940	2152	0.3E
8 Su		0109	*
		0749	1.7E
	1141	1507	1.6F
	2046	2309	0.4E
9 M		0119	*
		0749	1.8E
	1154	1525	1.9F
	2131		
10 Tu		0021	0.5E
		0128	0.5E
		0749	2.0E
	1212	1544	2.1F
	2210		
11 W		0802	2.1E
	1238	1610	2.3F
	2252		
12 Th ○		0829	2.2E
	1312	1646	2.4F
	2343		
13 F		0908	2.3E
	1358	1731	2.4F
14 Sa	0046	0957	2.3E
	1451	1824	2.4F
15 Su	0148	1056	2.2E
	1551	1925	2.3F
16 M	0235	1207	2.1E
	1654	2031	2.1F
17 Tu	0302	1336	1.8E
	1759	2137	1.9F
18 W ○	0311	0618	0.7E
		0906	0.5E
		1516	1.4E
	1906	2234	1.6F
19 Th	0303	0627	0.9E
		1112	*
		1659	1.0E
	2019	2322	1.1F
20 F	0243	0636	1.2E
	0956	1230	0.8F
	1530	1856	0.7E
	2144		
21 Sa		0001	0.6F
	0219	0644	1.5E
	1017	1326	1.4F
	1758	2050	0.6E
22 Su		0035	*
		0651	1.8E
	1047	1413	2.0F
	1944	2220	0.6E
23 M		0104	0.3E
		0702	2.1E
	1121	1456	2.3F
	2103	2336	0.6E
24 Tu		0130	0.5E
		0723	2.3E
	1159	1535	2.5F
	2212		
25 W ●		0049	0.6E
		0151	0.6E
		0754	2.4E
	1240	1615	2.4F
	2317		
26 Th		0834	2.4E
	1324	1657	2.3F
27 F	0020	0918	2.3E
	1410	1742	2.2F
28 Sa	0113	1007	2.2E
	1457	1832	2.0F
29 Su	0148	1059	2.0E
	1544	1927	1.9F
30 M	0203	1156	1.7E
	1629	2021	1.8F
31 Tu	0203	0547	0.8E
		0704	0.8E
		1302	1.3E
	1713	2112	1.6F

Time meridian 90° W. 0000 is midnight. 1200 is noon. Times are not adjusted for Daylight Saving Time.
* Current weak and variable.

Aransas Pass (between jetties), Texas, 2019

F–Flood, Dir. 300° True   E–Ebb, Dir. 120° True

January

Day	Slack (h m)	Maximum (h m)	knots
1 Tu	0956 2331	0536 1450	1.4E 1.4F
2 W	1035 2330	0553 1518	1.7E 1.7F
3 Th	1115 2345	0617 1553	1.8E 1.8F
4 F	1154	0644 1636	1.9E 1.9F
5 Sa ●	0015 1231	0713 1719	1.9E 1.9F
6 Su	0056 1307	0743 1754	1.9E 1.8F
7 M	0141 1341	0814 1821	1.8E 1.7F
8 Tu	0220 1416	0848 1846	1.7E 1.6F
9 W	0252 1449	0928 1914	1.5E 1.5F
10 Th	0315 1521	1013 1943	1.3E 1.3F
11 F	0328 1547	1051 2012	1.0E 1.1F
12 Sa	0320 1552	0615 0724 1122 2038	0.3E 0.3E 0.7F 0.8F
13 Su	0214 2346	0535 0915 1147 2058	0.3E * * 0.5F
14 M ◑	0825	0458 1030 1203 1452 1921†	0.5E 0.3F 0.3F 0.4F 0.3F
15 Tu	0837 2217	0424 1415	0.8E 0.8F
16 W	0906 2149	0423 1409	1.2E 1.3F
17 Th	0945 2215	0445 1428	1.6E 1.8F
18 F	1031 2257	0520 1501	2.0E 2.1F
19 Sa	1122 2348	0604 1545	2.3E 2.3F
20 Su ○	1212	0653 1639	2.4E 2.3F
21 M	0050 1301	0743 1730	2.4E 2.2F
22 Tu	0158 1348	0832 1809	2.3E 2.0F
23 W	0253 1433	0930 1841	1.9E 1.7F
24 Th	0325 1515	1034 1907	1.4E 1.3F
25 F	1546	0448 0540 1122 1931	* * 0.8F 1.0F
26 Sa	0033 2259	0405 0752 1151 1951	0.3E * * 0.6F
27 Su ◐	0715	0358 0946 1142 1404 1713†	0.6E 0.4F 0.4F 0.4F 0.3F
28 M	0756 2212	0407 1354	1.0E 0.9F
29 Tu	0839 2216	0426 1413	1.3E 1.3F
30 W	0924 2231	0451 1438	1.5E 1.6F
31 Th	1009 2256	0521 1507	1.7E 1.7F

February

Day	Slack (h m)	Maximum (h m)	knots
1 F	1055 2331	0556 1539	1.8E 1.8F
2 Sa	1139	0634 1617	1.8E 1.7F
3 Su	0017 1219	0710 1657	1.8E 1.6F
4 M ●	0119 1256	0742 1724	1.7E 1.5F
5 Tu	0216 1330	0814 1740	1.6E 1.4F
6 W	0257 1401	0847 1759	1.4E 1.2F
7 Th	0330 1430	0926 1822	1.2E 1.0F
8 F	0356 1456	1015 1847	0.9E 0.8F
9 Sa	1506	0458 0544 1058 1912	* * 0.6E 0.6F
10 Su		0036 0208 0409 0734 1131†	* * * * *
11 M	0607 2104	0031 0904 1158 1423	0.4E 0.4F 0.3F 0.3F
12 Tu ◐	0647 1936	0052 1013 1216 1345	0.7E 0.8F 0.7F 0.7F
13 W	0733 1959	0143 1335	1.1E 1.2F
14 Th	0823 2049	0316 1350	1.4E 1.6F
15 F	0916 2146	0410 1416	1.8E 1.9F
16 Sa	1012 2246	0500 1448	2.0E 2.1F
17 Su	1109 2353	0555 1524	2.2E 2.1F
18 M	1204	0653 1605	2.2E 2.0F
19 Tu ○	0136 1254	0749 1644	2.0E 1.7F
20 W	0317 1340	0846 1715	1.7E 1.3F
21 Th ●	0451 1422	0104 0231 1001 1740	* 0.3F 1.2F 1.0F
22 F	0650 1459 2149	0033 0443 1117 1801	* 0.3E 0.7E 0.6F
23 Sa	0316 2027	0019 0625 1215 1819	0.3E 0.5F * 0.3F
24 Su	0449	0023 0807 1701 1822	0.7E 0.7F * *
25 M	0555 1937	0041 0948	1.0E 1.0F
26 Tu ◐	0655 1944	0117 1255	1.2E 1.2F
27 W	0751 2026	0306 1340	1.3E 1.4F
28 Th	0844 2121	0407 1412	1.4E 1.6F

March

Day	Slack (h m)	Maximum (h m)	knots
1 F	0936 2218	0453 1440	1.5E 1.6F
2 Sa	1027 2317	0538 1506	1.5E 1.5F
3 Su	1117	0626 1527	1.5E 1.4F
4 M	0048 1201	0708 1541	1.4E 1.2F
5 Tu	0222 1240	0745 1558	1.3E 1.1F
6 W ●	1315	0033 0147 0820 1622	* * 1.1F 0.9F
7 Th	0430 1348	0026 0230 0901 1649	* 0.3F 0.9F 0.7F
8 F	0550 1421	0006 0323 1014 1716 2322	* 0.3F 0.6F 0.5F *
9 Sa	0734	0454 1118 1739 2252	0.4F 0.4F * 0.3E
10 Su	0137	0614 1206 1420 1621 1749†	0.6F * * * *
11 M	0259 1604	0731 2325	0.8F 0.9F
12 Tu	0423 1654	0849 2357	1.1F 1.2F
13 W	0532 1750	0953	1.3F
14 Th ◑	0639 1849	0039 1102	1.5E 1.5F
15 F	0743 1954	0147 1309	1.6E 1.7F
16 Sa	0846 2108	0338 1349	1.7E 1.9F
17 Su	0947 2228	0445 1418	1.8E 1.8F
18 M	1049	0550 1443	1.7E 1.6F
19 Tu	0100 1149 2334	0659 1508	1.5E 1.3F *
20 W ○	0321 1242 2301	0141 0806 1531	0.3F 1.2F 1.0F *
21 Th	0514 1331	0245 0938 1554 2233	0.6F 0.8F 0.6F *
22 F	0746	0356 1128 1613 2224	0.8F 0.4F * 0.6F
23 Sa	0135	0520 1251 1618 2241	1.0F * * 0.9F
24 Su	0239 1513	0638 2308	1.1F 1.2F
25 M	0347 1606	0804 2336	1.3F 1.3E
26 Tu	0452 1655	0922	1.4F
27 W ◐	0554 1746	0006 1020	1.4E 1.4F
28 Th	0655 1838	0042 1236	1.3E 1.4F
29 F	0755 1933	0206 1332	1.2E 1.4F
30 Sa	0851 2040	0416 1401	1.2E 1.3F
31 Su	0945 2228	0512 1418	1.1E 1.2F

Time meridian 90° W. 0000 is midnight. 1200 is noon. Times are not adjusted for Daylight Saving Time.
If three or more consecutive entries are marked (F) or (E) the middle ones are not true maximums but intermediate values to show the current pattern.
* Current weak and variable.
† See page 196 for the remaining currents on this day.

Aransas Pass (between jetties), Texas, 2019

F–Flood, Dir. 300° True   E–Ebb, Dir. 120° True

April

Day	Slack (h m)	Maximum (h m)	knots
1 M	1038	0609	1.0E
		1424	1.0F
		2250	*
2 Tu	1130, 2241	0035	*
		0705	0.9E
		1433	0.8F
3 W	0327, 1218, 2219	0137	0.3F
		0756	0.7E
		1449	0.6F
4 Th	0455, 1303, 2024	0223	0.5F
		0902	0.5E
		1508	0.4F
5 F ●	0652, 1525	0310	0.7F
		1111	0.3E
		2012	0.4E
6 Sa	0017, 1524	0408	0.8F
		1220	*
		2027	0.7E
7 Su	0059, 1221	0516	1.0F
		2059	1.0E
8 M	0143, 1420	0620	1.3F
		2145	1.3E
9 Tu	0236, 1517	0726	1.5F
		2237	1.5E
10 W	0340, 1608	0835	1.6F
		2323	1.7E
11 Th	0450, 1701	0934	1.8F
12 F ☽	0558, 1758	0008	1.7E
		1028	1.8F
13 Sa	0706, 1853	0101	1.6E
		1132	1.7F
14 Su	0811, 1945	0300	1.4E
		1248	1.6F
15 M	0912, 2149, 2324	0432	1.3E
		1323	1.4F
16 Tu	1015	0552	1.0E
		1346	1.0F
		2053	*
17 W	0321, 1121, 1730, 2313	0120	0.3F
		0729	0.7E
		1405	0.7F
		2022	0.3E
18 Th	0612, 1228, 1609, 2359	0221	0.8F
		0931	0.3E
		1421	0.3F
		2009	0.7E
19 F ○	1142, 1431	0318	1.1F
		2018	1.1E
20 Sa	0044, 1150	0426	1.4F
		2040	1.3E
21 Su	0128, 1336	0538	1.6F
		2113	1.5E
22 M	0215, 1436	0642	1.7F
		2157	1.6E
23 Tu	0306, 1521	0748	1.7F
		2244	1.6E
24 W	0402, 1602	0851	1.7F
		2322	1.5E
25 Th	0500, 1643	0936	1.6F
		2357	1.4E
26 F ○	0558, 1724	1015	1.4F
27 Sa	0656, 1801	0032	1.1E
		1056	1.3F
28 Su	0751	0126	0.9E
		1151	1.1F
		2032	*
		2158	*
29 M	0842	0431	0.7E
		1241	0.9F
		2028	*
		2327	*
30 Tu	0933	0542	0.5E
		1305	0.7F
		2016	*

May

Day	Slack (h m)	Maximum (h m)	knots
1 W	0327, 1031, 1622, 2251	0105	0.3F
		0719	0.3E
		1326	0.5F
		1947	0.3E
2 Th	2317	0157	0.6F
		0908	*
		1345	*
		1915	0.6E
3 F	2347	0240	0.9F
		1135	*
		1359	*
		1910	0.9E
4 Sa ●		0326	1.2F
		1303	*
		1342	*
		1925	1.2E
5 Su	0020, 1201	0423	1.4F
		1950	1.5E
6 M	0057, 1307	0524	1.7F
		2024	1.7E
7 Tu	0138, 1407	0622	1.9F
		2110	1.9E
8 W	0227, 1458	0721	2.0F
		2207	2.0E
9 Th	0324, 1545	0822	2.0F
		2302	1.9E
10 F	0426, 1629	0914	2.0F
		2348	1.8E
11 Sa ☾	0528, 1706	0956	1.9F
12 Su	0627, 1728	0032	1.4E
		1034	1.6F
13 M	0722, 1713	0133	1.0E
		1111	1.2F
		1949	0.4E
		2247	*
14 Tu	0812, 1612, 2228	0431	0.5E
		1147	0.9F
		1926	0.5E
15 W	1501, 2245	0056	0.3F
		0648	*
		1219	0.5F
		1909	0.8E
16 Th	0933, 2320	0204	0.9F
		1241	*
		1905	1.1E
17 F	1137, 2358	0253	1.3F
		1916	1.5E
18 Sa ○	1157	0347	1.6F
		1936	1.7E
19 Su	0037, 1242	0451	1.8F
		2002	1.9E
20 M	0116, 1331	0550	1.9F
		2032	1.9E
21 Tu	0157, 1415	0639	1.9F
		2111	1.8E
22 W	0240, 1455	0729	1.9F
		2200	1.7E
23 Th	0327, 1531	0819	1.8F
		2248	1.6E
24 F	0416, 1603	0858	1.6F
		2325	1.4E
25 Sa	0505, 1628	0928	1.4F
		2356	1.1E
26 Su ☾	0551, 1642	0956	1.2F
		1939	0.4E
		2059	0.4E
27 M	0633, 1633	0024	0.7E
		1023	1.0F
		1925	0.4E
		2216	*
28 Tu	0707, 1547	0054	0.3E
		1051	0.7F
		1911	0.4E
		2358	*
29 W	1432, 2217	0534	*
		1117	0.4F
		1846	0.6E
30 Th	2234	0139	0.5F
		0834	*
		1136	*
		1815	0.8E
31 F	1110, 2301	0214	1.0F
		1813	1.2E

June

Day	Slack (h m)	Maximum (h m)	knots
1 Sa	1100, 2335	0251	1.4F
		1829	1.5E
2 Su	1133	0334	1.7F
		1857	1.8E
3 M ●	0012, 1217	0429	1.9F
		1931	2.1E
4 Tu	0052, 1311	0528	2.1F
		2010	2.2E
5 W	0135, 1404	0621	2.2F
		2057	2.2E
6 Th	0223, 1451	0713	2.2F
		2154	2.1E
7 F	0315, 1530	0804	2.2F
		2251	1.9E
8 Sa	0408, 1557	0846	1.9F
		2335	1.5E
9 Su ☽	0458, 1602	0918	1.6F
10 M	0539, 1530	0008	1.0E
		0944	1.3F
		1832	0.5E
		2156	*
11 Tu	0554, 1420, 2142	0030	0.4E
		1005	0.9F
		1811	0.7E
12 W	1306, 2158	0216	0.3F
		0558	*
		1018	0.5F
		1803	1.1E
13 Th	1229, 2231	0224	0.9F
		1806	1.4E
14 F	1157, 2309	0252	1.4F
		1822	1.7E
15 Sa	1144, 2349	0329	1.7F
		1845	1.9E
16 Su	1206	0417	1.9F
		1913	2.0E
17 M ○	1242	0511	2.0F
		1943	2.1E
18 Tu	0106, 1325	0555	2.0F
		2014	2.0E
19 W	0143, 1407	0633	2.0F
		2050	1.9E
20 Th	0222, 1443	0708	1.8F
		2134	1.7E
21 F	0301, 1513	0743	1.7F
		2222	1.5E
22 Sa	0341, 1535	0815	1.5F
		2301	1.2E
23 Su	0419, 1545	0843	1.3F
		2330	0.9E
24 M	0448, 1533	0908	1.1F
		1833	0.4E
		2102	0.3E
		2354	0.5E
25 Tu ○	0455, 1438	0931	0.8F
		1812	0.5E
		2218	*
26 W	1252, 2122	0011	*
		0948	0.6F
		1744	0.6E
27 Th	1202, 2136	0238	0.5F
		0750	0.3E
		0945	0.3F
		1716	0.9E
28 F	1113, 2202	0216	0.9F
		1714	1.3E
29 Sa	1038, 2238	0226	1.3F
		1731	1.6E
30 Su	1057, 2319	0254	1.7F
		1802	1.9E

Time meridian 90° W. 0000 is midnight. 1200 is noon. Times are not adjusted for Daylight Saving Time.
If three or more consecutive entries are marked (F) or (E) the middle ones are not true maximums but intermediate values to show the current pattern.
* Current weak and variable.

Aransas Pass (between jetties), Texas, 2019

F–Flood, Dir. 300° True   E–Ebb, Dir. 120° True

July

Day	Slack (h m)	Maximum (h m / knots)
1 M	1134	0335 2.0F; 1841 2.2E
2 Tu ●	0003; 1222	0429 2.2F; 1923 2.4E
3 W	0047; 1318	0525 2.3F; 2008 2.4E
4 Th	0133; 1411	0613 2.3F; 2057 2.2E
5 F	0219; 1454	0655 2.1F; 2156 2.0E
6 Sa	0306; 1519	0732 1.9F; 2252 1.5E
7 Su	0350; 1510	0803 1.5F; 2332 1.0E
8 M	0423; 1407; 2050; 2354	0829 1.2F; 1709 0.5E; 2050 *; 0.3E
9 Tu ◑	0403; 1218; 2025; 2341	0849 0.8F; 1654 0.7E; 2231 0.3F; 0.3E
10 W	1126; 2050	0225 0.4F; 0522 0.3F; 0901 0.3E; 1654 1.1E
11 Th	1108; 2127	0215 1.0F; 1705 1.5E
12 F	1102; 2209	0235 1.4F; 1726 1.7E
13 Sa	1108; 2253	0303 1.8F; 1754 1.9E
14 Su	1130; 2336	0337 1.9F; 1828 2.0E
15 M	1203	0421 2.0F; 1902 2.0E
16 Tu ○	0017; 1245	0509 1.9F; 1935 2.0E
17 W	0056; 1332	0547 1.8F; 2008 1.8E
18 Th	0132; 1414	0615 1.7F; 2041 1.7E
19 F	0207; 1447	0636 1.6F; 2120 1.5E
20 Sa	0240; 1510	0658 1.4F; 2206 1.2E
21 Su	0312; 1520	0723 1.2F; 2247 0.9E
22 M	0338; 1506; 2317	0750 1.0F; 1735 0.3E; 1908 *; 0.6E
23 Tu	0341; 1327	0816 0.7F; 1707 0.3E; 2055 *; 2341 *
24 W ◑	1115; 1957	0838 0.5F; 1638 0.5E; 2208 0.3F; 2358 0.3E
25 Th	1039; 2016	0242 0.4F; 0708 *; 0843 0.3F; 1607 0.8E
26 F	1002; 2047	0214 0.8F; 1606 1.1E
27 Sa	0936; 2126	0208 1.2F; 1628 1.5E
28 Su	1000; 2212	0220 1.6F; 1701 1.8E
29 M	1042; 2302	0247 1.9F; 1743 2.1E
30 Tu	1131; 2353	0325 2.1F; 1833 2.3E
31 W ●	1231	0413 2.2F; 1923 2.3E

August

Day	Slack (h m)	Maximum (h m / knots)
1 Th	0041; 1342	0504 2.1F; 2012 2.2E
2 F	0128; 1449	0544 1.9F; 2106 1.8E
3 Sa	0213; 1543	0615 1.6F; 2215 1.4E
4 Su	0255; 1548	0641 1.2F; 2315 0.8E
5 M	0330	0704 0.9F; 1519 *; 1918 *; 2358 *
6 Tu	1016; 1823	0723 0.5F; 1501 0.6E; 2113 0.5F
7 W ◑	0939	0026 0.4F; 0139 0.4F; 0506 *; 0734 0.3F; 1518† 1.0E
8 Th	0930; 2004	0121 1.0F; 1548 1.3E
9 F	0936; 2053	0148 1.4F; 1621 1.6E
10 Sa	1000; 2143	0217 1.7F; 1657 1.7E
11 Su	1035; 2232	0247 1.8F; 1736 1.8E
12 M	1115; 2320	0319 1.8F; 1818 1.8E
13 Tu	1205	0353 1.7F; 1859 1.7E
14 W	0004; 1314	0432 1.6F; 1935 1.6E
15 Th ○	0043; 1421	0504 1.5F; 2007 1.5E
16 F	0118; 1511	0520 1.3F; 2041 1.3E
17 Sa	0151; 1559	0538 1.1F; 2122 1.1E
18 Su	0222; 1704	0600 0.9F; 2218 0.8E
19 M	0251	0625 0.7F; 1607 *; 1741 *; 2305 0.5E
20 Tu	0308	0649 0.5F; 1209 *; 1913 0.3F; 2339 *
21 W	1723	0307 *; 0353 *; 0709 *; 1208 0.4E; 2041 0.5F
22 Th	0803; 1813	0006 0.3F; 0200 0.3F; 1226 0.7E; 2150 0.8F
23 F ◑	0640; 1904	1301 1.0E; 2300 1.1F
24 Sa	0720; 1956	1423 1.3E
25 Su	0814; 2050	0132 1.5F; 1545 1.6E
26 M	0917; 2145	0158 1.8F; 1637 1.8E
27 Tu	1022; 2242	0227 1.9F; 1730 2.0E
28 W	1130; 2339	0258 2.0F; 1829 2.0E
29 Th	1320	0333 1.8F; 1927 1.9E
30 F ●	0032; 1513	0408 1.6F; 2024 1.6E
31 Sa	0120; 1652	0441 1.2F; 1224 0.3F; 1439 0.4F; 2141 1.1E

September

Day	Slack (h m)	Maximum (h m / knots)
1 Su	0205; 1857	0508 0.8F; 1155 *; 1621 0.5F; 2316 0.6E
2 M	0249; 0829; 1419	0531 0.5F; 1141 0.3E; 1802 0.7F
3 Tu	1557	0029 *; 0547 *; 1148 0.8E; 1936 0.9F
4 W	0615; 1711	1209 1.1F; 2119 1.2E
5 Th ◑	0547; 1816	1239 1.3F; 2238 1.4E
6 F	0635; 1917	1332 1.4E
7 Sa	0729; 2014	0102 1.5F; 1533 1.4E
8 Su	0832; 2108	0147 1.6F; 1631 1.5E
9 M	0944; 2201	0218 1.6F; 1720 1.5E
10 Tu	1054; 2253	0244 1.5F; 1810 1.4E
11 W	1236; 2341	0303 1.4F; 1857 1.3E
12 Th		0314 1.2F; 1203 *; 1300 *; 1938 1.2E
13 F ○	0024; 1533	0329 1.0F; 1156 *; 1354 0.3E; 2015 1.0E
14 Sa	0102; 1643	0350 0.8F; 1151 *; 1437 0.4F; 2103 0.7E
15 Su	0138; 1809	0416 0.6F; 1132 *; 1529 0.4F; 2244 0.5E
16 M	0216; 2011	0443 0.3F; 1022 *; 1644 0.5F; 2345 0.3E
17 Tu	1327	0506 *; 0952 0.4E; 1759 0.7F
18 W	0028; 1429	1023 0.7E; 1909 0.9F
19 Th	0326; 1544	1058 0.9E; 2024 1.1F
20 F	0416; 1656	1133 1.2E; 2129 1.3F
21 Sa ◍	0509; 1804	1212 1.4E; 2227 1.5F
22 Su	0608; 1909	1303 1.5E; 2347 1.6F
23 M	0710; 2013	1451 1.6E
24 Tu	0820; 2114	0117 1.7F; 1616 1.6E
25 W	0946; 2215	0150 1.7F; 1720 1.6E
26 Th	1220; 2318	0216 1.5F; 1831 1.4E
27 F	1512	0239 1.2F; 1101 *; 1329 *; 1944 1.1E
28 Sa ●	0018; 1713	0301 0.9F; 0956 *; 1432 0.6F; 2116 0.7E
29 Su	0113; 0609; 1206; 2004	0320 0.5F; 0903 0.3E; 1538 0.9F; 2329 0.4E
30 M	1309	0334 *; 0912 0.7E; 1659 1.1F

Time meridian 90° W. 0000 is midnight. 1200 is noon. Times are not adjusted for Daylight Saving Time.
If three or more consecutive entries are marked (F) or (E) the middle ones are not true maximums but intermediate values to show the current pattern.
* Current weak and variable.
† See page 196 for the remaining currents on this day.

Aransas Pass (between jetties), Texas, 2019

F–Flood, Dir. 300° True   E–Ebb, Dir. 120° True

October

Day	Slack (h m)	Maximum (h m)	knots
1 Tu	1409	0107 / 0304 / 0947 / 1819	* / * / 1.1E / 1.4F
2 W	0233 / 1513	1031 / 1940	1.4E / 1.5F
3 Th	0333 / 1619	1110 / 2103	1.5E / 1.6F
4 F	0422 / 1724	1146 / 2159	1.6E / 1.6F
5 Sa ◐	0511 / 1826	1222 / 2258	1.5E / 1.5F
6 Su	0600 / 1926	1311	1.3E
7 M	0648 / 2023	0055 / 1553	1.4F / 1.1E
8 Tu	0735 / 2116	0135 / 1655	1.3F / 1.0E
9 W	0823 / 2209	0154 / 1754	1.2F / 0.9E
10 Th	2302	0200 / 0938 / 1230 / 1857	1.0F / * / * / 0.8E
11 F	1538 / 2355	0208 / 0930 / 1334 / 1955	0.8F / * / 0.3F / 0.6E
12 Sa	1724	0223 / 0848 / 1419 / 2124	0.6F / * / 0.6F / 0.4E
13 Su O	0046 / 0450 / 1140 / 2327	0241 / 0757 / 1504	0.3F / 0.3E / 0.8F
14 M	1215	0255 / 0750 / 1557	* / 0.6E / 0.9F
15 Tu	1250	0039 / 0245 / 0803 / 1701	* / * / 0.8E / 1.1F
16 W	0029 / 1328	0830 / 1802	1.1E / 1.3F
17 Th	0159 / 1413	0910 / 1903	1.3E / 1.5F
18 F	0253 / 1509	1002 / 2009	1.5E / 1.6F
19 Sa	0340 / 1615	1055 / 2109	1.6E / 1.7F
20 Su	0429 / 1722	1141 / 2200	1.7E / 1.8F
21 M O	0519 / 1828	1228 / 2250	1.6E / 1.7F
22 Tu	0610 / 1932	1336 / 2348	1.4E / 1.5F
23 W	0654 / 2033	1555	1.2E
24 Th	2133	0042 / 0900 / 1103 / 1716	1.3F / * / * / 0.9E
25 F	1510 / 2240	0113 / 0816 / 1302 / 1901	1.0F / * / 0.3F / 0.6E
26 Sa	0432 / 1051	0136 / 0745 / 1407 / 2107	0.6F / 0.4E / 0.8F / *
27 Su ●	0325 / 1136	0153 / 0736 / 1503 / 2346	0.3F / 0.8E / 1.2F / *
28 M	1221 / 2351	0200 / 0748 / 1607	* / 1.3E / 1.5F
29 Tu	1307	0812 / 1720	1.6E / 1.8F
30 W	0116 / 1354	0844 / 1826	1.8E / 1.9F
31 Th	0217 / 1444	0927 / 1932	1.8E / 1.9F

November

Day	Slack (h m)	Maximum (h m)	knots
1 F	0303 / 1540	1020 / 2037	1.8E / 1.9F
2 Sa	0344 / 1638	1105 / 2124	1.7E / 1.7F
3 Su	0421 / 1735	1142 / 2159	1.5E / 1.6F
4 M ◐	0456 / 1830	1215 / 2233	1.2E / 1.4F
5 Tu	0524 / 1922	1252 / 2308	0.9E / 1.1F
6 W	0540 / 2012	0802 / 0958 / 1616 / 2348	0.3E / * / 0.6E / 0.9F
7 Th	0534 / 2057	0759 / 1121 / 1733	0.3E / * / 0.4E
8 F	0448 / 1038	0026 / 0750 / 1305 / 1920	0.6F / 0.3E / 0.3F / *
9 Sa	0336 / 1050	0054 / 0729 / 1355 / 2119	0.4F / 0.5E / 0.6F / *
10 Su	1114	0117 / 0703 / 1435 / 2343	* / 0.7E / 1.0F / *
11 M	1141 / 2312	0131 / 0658 / 1517	* / 1.0E / 1.2F
12 Tu O	1212	0710 / 1608	1.3E / 1.5F
13 W	0001 / 1245	0734 / 1707	1.5E / 1.7F
14 Th	0056 / 1322	0804 / 1803	1.7E / 1.8F
15 F	0150 / 1405	0843 / 1858	1.9E / 1.9F
16 Sa	0239 / 1456	0934 / 1956	1.9E / 2.0F
17 Su	0323 / 1553	1032 / 2049	1.9E / 2.0F
18 M	0403 / 1652	1121 / 2131	1.8E / 1.9F
19 Tu O	0438 / 1749	1204 / 2206	1.5E / 1.6F
20 W	0458 / 1842	1248 / 2239	1.0E / 1.3F
21 Th	0443 / 1928	0732 / 1024 / 1546 / 2309	0.4E / * / 0.5E / 0.9F
22 F	0342 / 1012 / 1808	0703 / 1229 / 2335	0.5E / 0.3F / 0.5F
23 Sa	0227 / 1022	0641 / 1353 / 2109 / 2348	0.8E / 0.9F / * / *
24 Su	1055 / 2346	0637 / 1440	1.3E / 1.4F
25 M	1136 / 2348	0651 / 1530	1.6E / 1.8F
26 Tu ●	1217	0716 / 1632	1.9E / 2.0F
27 W	0029 / 1259	0745 / 1734	2.1E / 2.1F
28 Th	0118 / 1341	0818 / 1826	2.1E / 2.1F
29 F	0204 / 1425	0856 / 1916	2.0E / 2.0F
30 Sa	0244 / 1511	0943 / 2006	1.9E / 1.9F

December

Day	Slack (h m)	Maximum (h m)	knots
1 Su	0319 / 1559	1033 / 2045	1.7E / 1.7F
2 M	0347 / 1646	1111 / 2114	1.4E / 1.5F
3 Tu	0408 / 1729	1141 / 2138	1.1E / 1.3F
4 W ◐	0416 / 1805	0716 / 0848 / 1205 / 2203	0.5E / 0.4F / 0.7E / 1.0F
5 Th	0402 / 1826	0702 / 1008 / 1225 / 2226	0.5E / * / 0.3E / 0.7F
6 F	0315	0651 / 1428 / 1757 / 2246	0.5E / * / * / 0.5F
7 Sa	0158 / 1009	0632 / 1406 / 2036 / 2247	0.7E / 0.6F / * / *
8 Su	1027 / 2346	0609 / 1418	0.9E / 1.0F
9 M	1054 / 2306	0605 / 1447	1.2E / 1.3F
10 Tu	1126 / 2330	0620 / 1524	1.5E / 1.6F
11 W O	1201	0645 / 1613	1.8E / 1.9F
12 Th	0009 / 1239	0717 / 1709	2.0E / 2.0F
13 F	0057 / 1319	0753 / 1801	2.1E / 2.1F
14 Sa	0149 / 1402	0835 / 1849	2.2E / 2.2F
15 Su	0235 / 1449	0925 / 1936	2.1E / 2.1F
16 M	0314 / 1538	1022 / 2019	1.9E / 1.9F
17 Tu	0341 / 1626	1111 / 2053	1.6E / 1.6F
18 W O	0348 / 1705	1147 / 2120	1.1E / 1.3F
19 Th	0316 / 1716	0618 / 0930 / 1213 / 2141	0.5E / * / 0.4E / 0.9F
20 F	0153 / 1427	0549 / 1113 / 1204 / 1724†	0.7E / * / * / 0.3F
21 Sa	0032 / 0932 / 2356	0536 / 1418	1.0E / 0.9F
22 Su	1004 / 2328	0539 / 1439	1.4E / 1.5F
23 M	1044 / 2325	0557 / 1512	1.8E / 1.8F
24 Tu	1127 / 2351	0625 / 1556	2.1E / 2.1F
25 W ●	1210	0658 / 1650	2.2E / 2.1F
26 Th	0030 / 1251	0732 / 1739	2.2E / 2.1F
27 F	0116 / 1330	0806 / 1819	2.1E / 2.0F
28 Sa	0200 / 1409	0842 / 1854	2.0E / 1.9F
29 Su	0236 / 1448	0923 / 1926	1.8E / 1.7F
30 M	0305 / 1527	1009 / 1956	1.5E / 1.5F
31 Tu	0324 / 1602	1049 / 2023	1.2E / 1.3F

Time meridian 90° W. 0000 is midnight. 1200 is noon. Times are not adjusted for Daylight Saving Time.
If three or more consecutive entries are marked (F) or (E) the middle ones are not true maximums but intermediate values to show the current pattern.
* Current weak and variable.
† See page 196 for the remaining currents on this day.

Vieques Passage, Puerto Rico, 2019

F–Flood, Dir. 250° True   E–Ebb, Dir. 055° True

January

Date	Slack (h m)	Maximum (h m)	knots
1 Tu		0044	0.5E
	0335	0711	0.8F
	1037	1401	0.8E
	1752	2010	0.3F
	2239		
2 W		0138	0.5E
	0419	0801	0.8F
	1126	1455	0.9E
	1853	2111	0.3F
	2342		
3 Th		0231	0.4E
	0504	0849	0.8F
	1212	1545	0.9E
	1945	2206	0.4F
4 F	0043	0322	0.4E
	0548	0934	0.8F
	1254	1630	0.9E
	2031	2255	0.4F
5 Sa ●	0139	0412	0.3E
	0633	1018	0.8F
	1334	1712	0.9E
	2111	2340	0.4F
6 Su	0231	0459	0.3E
	0719	1100	0.7F
	1412	1751	0.9E
	2147		
7 M		0022	0.4F
	0319	0546	0.3E
	0806	1141	0.7F
	1449	1829	0.9E
	2220		
8 Tu		0101	0.5F
	0405	0631	0.3E
	0854	1222	0.6F
	1525	1905	0.9E
	2252		
9 W		0138	0.5F
	0447	0717	0.3E
	0946	1304	0.6F
	1602	1941	0.8E
	2323		
10 Th		0216	0.5F
	0529	0804	0.4E
	1041	1349	0.5F
	1640	2018	0.8E
	2353		
11 F		0253	0.6F
	0610	0852	0.4E
	1140	1436	0.4F
	1721	2056	0.7E
12 Sa	0024	0331	0.6F
	0651	0942	0.5E
	1243	1527	0.4F
	1803	2136	0.6E
13 Su	0055	0410	0.6F
	0734	1033	0.5E
	1351	1621	0.3F
	1850	2218	0.6E
14 M ◐	0127	0452	0.7F
	0818	1127	0.6E
	1500	1720	0.3F
	1942	2303	0.5E
15 Tu	0203	0536	0.7F
	0904	1222	0.7E
	1608	1821	0.3F
	2039	2353	0.5E
16 W	0242	0623	0.8F
	0952	1316	0.7E
	1712	1922	0.3F
	2142		
17 Th		0046	0.4E
	0327	0713	0.8F
	1041	1410	0.8E
	1810	2022	0.3F
	2247		
18 F		0142	0.4E
	0417	0805	0.9F
	1131	1503	0.9E
	1901	2120	0.4F
	2351		
19 Sa		0241	0.4E
	0513	0859	0.9F
	1222	1554	1.0E
	1949	2214	0.4F
20 Su	0053	0340	0.5E
	0612	0954	0.9F
	1313	1644	1.0E
	2033	2306	0.5F
21 M ○	0152	0439	0.5E
	0714	1049	0.9F
	1404	1734	1.1E
	2116	2356	0.6F
22 Tu	0249	0537	0.6E
	0818	1144	0.9F
	1454	1822	1.1E
	2159		
23 W		0046	0.7F
	0345	0636	0.6E
	0923	1240	0.8F
	1545	1911	1.0E
	2241		
24 Th		0135	0.7F
	0440	0734	0.7E
	1029	1336	0.7F
	1636	1959	1.0E
	2323		
25 F		0225	0.8F
	0536	0834	0.7E
	1137	1434	0.7F
	1727	2048	0.9E
26 Sa	0005	0315	0.8F
	0631	0934	0.7E
	1247	1533	0.6F
	1819	2138	0.8E
27 Su ◑	0048	0405	0.8F
	0726	1034	0.7E
	1400	1635	0.5F
	1913	2229	0.7E
28 M	0131	0457	0.8F
	0821	1136	0.8E
	1513	1738	0.4F
	2010	2321	0.6E
29 Tu	0216	0549	0.8F
	0915	1236	0.8E
	1625	1843	0.3F
	2111		
30 W		0015	0.5E
	0301	0641	0.8F
	1007	1334	0.8E
	1730	1946	0.3F
	2214		
31 Th		0110	0.4E
	0349	0732	0.8F
	1057	1428	0.8E
	1828	2046	0.3F
	2319		

February

Date	Slack (h m)	Maximum (h m)	knots
1 F		0206	0.4E
	0437	0822	0.7F
	1143	1518	0.8E
	1918	2140	0.3F
2 Sa	0020	0300	0.3E
	0527	0909	0.7F
	1227	1603	0.8E
	2000	2228	0.4F
3 Su	0115	0351	0.3E
	0617	0955	0.7F
	1308	1645	0.8E
	2037	2311	0.4F
4 M ●	0205	0440	0.3E
	0707	1039	0.6F
	1347	1723	0.8E
	2110	2350	0.5F
5 Tu	0249	0526	0.4E
	0757	1121	0.6F
	1425	1800	0.8E
	2141		
6 W		0027	0.5F
	0330	0610	0.4E
	0848	1203	0.6F
	1503	1835	0.8E
	2211		
7 Th		0102	0.5F
	0408	0653	0.4E
	0939	1246	0.5F
	1540	1910	0.7E
	2239		
8 F		0136	0.6F
	0446	0737	0.5E
	1032	1329	0.5F
	1619	1945	0.7E
	2307		
9 Sa		0211	0.6F
	0524	0821	0.5E
	1127	1414	0.4F
	1658	2021	0.6E
	2336		
10 Su		0247	0.6F
	0604	0908	0.6E
	1225	1502	0.4F
	1740	2100	0.6E
11 M	0006	0326	0.7F
	0646	0957	0.6E
	1327	1554	0.3F
	1825	2141	0.5E
12 Tu ◑	0040	0409	0.7F
	0733	1049	0.7E
	1431	1650	0.3F
	1915	2227	0.5E
13 W	0119	0456	0.7F
	0822	1144	0.7E
	1535	1750	0.3F
	2012	2319	0.5E
14 Th	0205	0547	0.8F
	0915	1241	0.7E
	1637	1851	0.3F
	2116		
15 F		0017	0.4E
	0259	0643	0.8F
	1009	1338	0.8E
	1734	1953	0.3F
	2222		
16 Sa		0120	0.5E
	0359	0742	0.8F
	1105	1434	0.9E
	1825	2051	0.4F
	2328		
17 Su		0223	0.5E
	0504	0841	0.9F
	1201	1528	0.9E
	1912	2146	0.5F
18 M	0031	0326	0.6E
	0610	0940	0.9F
	1255	1620	1.0E
	1957	2239	0.6F
19 Tu ○	0130	0427	0.6E
	0716	1038	0.9F
	1348	1711	1.0E
	2040	2329	0.7F
20 W	0226	0525	0.7E
	0821	1134	0.8F
	1440	1800	1.0E
	2122		
21 Th		0018	0.8F
	0320	0622	0.8E
	0925	1230	0.8F
	1531	1848	0.9E
	2204		
22 F		0106	0.8F
	0413	0719	0.8E
	1028	1325	0.7F
	1621	1935	0.8E
	2246		
23 Sa		0155	0.9F
	0506	0814	0.8E
	1132	1420	0.6F
	1711	2023	0.8E
	2328		
24 Su		0243	0.9F
	0559	0911	0.8E
	1236	1516	0.5F
	1802	2111	0.7E
25 M	0011	0333	0.8F
	0652	1007	0.8E
	1341	1614	0.5F
	1855	2201	0.6E
26 Tu ◑	0056	0423	0.8F
	0745	1105	0.8E
	1447	1714	0.4F
	1951	2253	0.5E
27 W	0142	0515	0.8F
	0837	1202	0.8E
	1552	1816	0.3F
	2051	2349	0.4F
28 Th	0232	0608	0.7F
	0930	1259	0.7E
	1652	1917	0.3F
	2155		

March

Date	Slack (h m)	Maximum (h m)	knots
1 F		0046	0.4E
	0325	0702	0.7F
	1020	1352	0.7E
	1746	2014	0.3F
	2257		
2 Sa		0144	0.4E
	0420	0754	0.6F
	1109	1442	0.7E
	1832	2106	0.4F
	2355		
3 Su		0240	0.4E
	0516	0845	0.6F
	1155	1528	0.7E
	1913	2152	0.4F
4 M	0046	0332	0.4E
	0612	0934	0.6F
	1240	1610	0.7E
	1949	2233	0.5F
5 Tu	0131	0420	0.4E
	0705	1020	0.6F
	1322	1650	0.7E
	2022	2311	0.5F
6 W ●	0211	0505	0.5E
	0757	1104	0.6F
	1403	1727	0.7E
	2052	2346	0.5F
7 Th	0249	0547	0.5E
	0846	1147	0.5F
	1443	1802	0.7E
	2121		
8 F		0020	0.6F
	0325	0628	0.6E
	0936	1230	0.5F
	1522	1837	0.6E
	2149		
9 Sa		0054	0.6F
	0401	0709	0.6E
	1025	1313	0.5F
	1602	1912	0.6E
	2217		
10 Su		0128	0.7F
	0438	0752	0.7E
	1116	1357	0.4F
	1642	1949	0.6E
	2246		
11 M		0205	0.7F
	0519	0836	0.7E
	1209	1443	0.4F
	1724	2028	0.5E
	2320		
12 Tu		0246	0.7F
	0603	0924	0.7E
	1305	1533	0.4F
	1810	2112	0.5E
	2359		
13 W		0331	0.7F
	0651	1016	0.8E
	1402	1627	0.4F
	1902	2201	0.5E
14 Th ◐	0046	0422	0.7F
	0744	1111	0.8E
	1501	1725	0.4F
	2000	2258	0.4E
15 F	0142	0519	0.7F
	0841	1209	0.8E
	1558	1825	0.4F
	2104		
16 Sa		0002	0.5E
	0245	0621	0.7F
	0940	1308	0.8E
	1652	1926	0.4F
	2209		
17 Su		0108	0.5E
	0355	0725	0.8F
	1040	1406	0.8E
	1743	2023	0.5F
	2313		
18 M		0214	0.6E
	0507	0828	0.8F
	1140	1501	0.8E
	1830	2118	0.6F
19 Tu	0013	0317	0.7E
	0616	0930	0.8F
	1237	1555	0.9E
	1915	2210	0.7F
20 W ○	0109	0417	0.8E
	0722	1029	0.8F
	1333	1645	0.8E
	1959	2300	0.8F
21 Th	0203	0513	0.8E
	0826	1125	0.7F
	1425	1734	0.8E
	2042	2348	0.8F
22 F	0254	0608	0.9E
	0926	1219	0.7F
	1517	1822	0.8E
	2124		
23 Sa		0036	0.9F
	0345	0700	0.9E
	1025	1312	0.7F
	1607	1909	0.7E
	2206		
24 Su		0123	0.9F
	0434	0752	0.9E
	1122	1405	0.6F
	1657	1956	0.6E
	2249		
25 M		0210	0.8F
	0523	0844	0.9E
	1220	1458	0.5F
	1747	2044	0.6E
	2333		
26 Tu		0257	0.8F
	0612	0936	0.9E
	1317	1552	0.5F
	1840	2134	0.5E
27 W	0020	0347	0.7F
	0702	1029	0.8E
	1414	1648	0.4F
	1937	2227	0.4E
28 Th ◑	0110	0438	0.7F
	0752	1122	0.8E
	1509	1745	0.4F
	2036	2324	0.4E
29 F	0205	0532	0.6F
	0843	1216	0.7E
	1602	1842	0.4F
	2137		
30 Sa		0024	0.4E
	0305	0628	0.5F
	0935	1308	0.7E
	1650	1935	0.4F
	2234		
31 Su		0123	0.4E
	0408	0724	0.5F
	1027	1358	0.7E
	1734	2024	0.4F
	2326		

Time meridian 60° W. 0000 is midnight. 1200 is noon. Times are not adjusted for Daylight Saving Time.

Vieques Passage, Puerto Rico, 2019

F–Flood, Dir. 250° True   E–Ebb, Dir. 055° True

April

Day	Slack (h m)	Maximum (h m)	knots	Day	Slack (h m)	Maximum (h m)	knots
1 M		0219	0.4E	**16** Tu		0208	0.7E
	0510	0819	0.5F		0516	0818	0.6F
	1118	1446	0.6E		1118	1433	0.7E
	1814	2109	0.5F		1746	2051	0.7F
					2356		
2 Tu	0012	0310	0.5E	**17** W		0309	0.8E
	0609	0911	0.5F		0625	0921	0.6F
	1207	1529	0.6E		1218	1527	0.7E
	1850	2149	0.5F		1831	2142	0.8F
3 W	0054	0357	0.5E	**18** Th	0049	0406	0.9E
	0704	1000	0.5F		0729	1020	0.7F
	1254	1611	0.6E		1315	1618	0.7E
	1924	2227	0.6F		1915	2231	0.8F
4 Th	0131	0441	0.6E	**19** F ○	0140	0500	0.9E
	0755	1046	0.5F		0829	1115	0.6F
	1339	1649	0.6E		1409	1707	0.7E
	1955	2302	0.6F		1959	2318	0.9F
5 F ●	0207	0522	0.7E	**20** Sa	0229	0552	1.0E
	0844	1131	0.5F		0925	1208	0.6F
	1423	1726	0.6E		1501	1755	0.6E
	2024	2337	0.7F		2042		
6 Sa	0243	0603	0.7E	**21** Su		0004	0.9F
	0931	1214	0.5F		0316	0641	1.0E
	1505	1803	0.5E		1019	1259	0.6F
	2054				1552	1842	0.6E
					2125		
7 Su		0012	0.7F	**22** M		0050	0.9F
	0320	0643	0.8E		0402	0729	1.0E
	1018	1257	0.5F		1110	1349	0.6F
	1547	1840	0.5E		1643	1929	0.5E
	2125				2209		
8 M		0048	0.7F	**23** Tu		0135	0.8F
	0359	0725	0.8E		0447	0816	0.9E
	1105	1341	0.5F		1200	1439	0.5F
	1629	1919	0.5E		1734	2017	0.5E
	2200				2255		
9 Tu		0128	0.7F	**24** W		0221	0.7F
	0441	0809	0.8E		0532	0903	0.9E
	1154	1427	0.4F		1249	1529	0.5F
	1714	2002	0.4E		1828	2108	0.4E
	2241				2344		
10 W		0212	0.7F	**25** Th		0309	0.6F
	0527	0857	0.8E		0617	0951	0.8E
	1244	1516	0.4F		1337	1620	0.5F
	1803	2051	0.4E		1923	2202	0.4E
	2329						
11 Th		0301	0.7F	**26** F ○	0039	0359	0.6F
	0617	0947	0.8E		0703	1039	0.8E
	1335	1609	0.4F		1423	1712	0.5F
	1857	2146	0.4E		2020	2300	0.4E
12 F ◐	0025	0357	0.7F	**27** Sa	0140	0454	0.5F
	0711	1042	0.8E		0752	1129	0.7E
	1427	1705	0.4F		1508	1803	0.5F
	1956	2248	0.4E		2115	2359	0.4E
13 Sa	0131	0458	0.7F	**28** Su	0247	0551	0.4F
	0810	1139	0.8E		0844	1219	0.6E
	1519	1803	0.5F		1551	1852	0.5F
	2059	2355	0.5E		2206		
14 Su	0245	0604	0.7F	**29** M		0058	0.4E
	0912	1238	0.8E		0356	0651	0.4F
	1610	1901	0.6F		0938	1309	0.6E
	2201				1632	1939	0.5F
					2253		
15 M		0102	0.6E	**30** Tu		0153	0.5E
	0401	0712	0.6F		0502	0749	0.4F
	1016	1337	0.8E		1033	1357	0.6E
	1659	1957	0.6F		1711	2022	0.6F
	2300				2335		

May

Day	Slack (h m)	Maximum (h m)	knots	Day	Slack (h m)	Maximum (h m)	knots
1 W		0244	0.6E	**16** Th		0259	0.8E
	0602	0845	0.4F		0632	0911	0.5F
	1128	1442	0.5E		1157	1458	0.6E
	1747	2102	0.6F		1748	2115	0.9F
2 Th	0015	0330	0.6E	**17** F	0030	0354	0.9E
	0658	0936	0.4F		0734	1010	0.5F
	1221	1526	0.5E		1256	1550	0.6E
	1821	2141	0.7F		1833	2203	0.9F
3 F	0052	0414	0.7E	**18** Sa ○	0118	0446	1.0E
	0748	1025	0.4F		0830	1104	0.5F
	1311	1607	0.5E		1352	1640	0.5E
	1854	2218	0.7F		1917	2249	0.9F
4 Sa ●	0129	0456	0.8E	**19** Su	0204	0534	1.0E
	0836	1111	0.4F		0921	1156	0.5F
	1359	1648	0.5E		1446	1728	0.5E
	1927	2255	0.7F		2001	2334	0.9F
5 Su	0207	0537	0.9E	**20** M	0248	0620	1.0E
	0922	1156	0.5F		1009	1244	0.5F
	1445	1728	0.4E		1538	1815	0.4E
	2002	2334	0.8F		2046		
6 M	0246	0619	0.9E	**21** Tu		0018	0.8F
	1007	1240	0.5F		0331	0705	1.0E
	1530	1810	0.4E		1054	1332	0.5F
	2040				1629	1903	0.4E
					2131		
7 Tu		0014	0.8F	**22** W		0102	0.7F
	0328	0701	0.9E		0412	0748	0.9E
	1052	1325	0.5F		1137	1418	0.5F
	1617	1854	0.4E		1720	1952	0.4E
	2123				2219		
8 W		0059	0.8F	**23** Th		0147	0.7F
	0412	0746	1.0E		0452	0830	0.9E
	1137	1412	0.5F		1218	1504	0.5F
	1705	1943	0.4E		1812	2043	0.3E
	2213				2312		
9 Th		0147	0.8F	**24** F		0233	0.6F
	0459	0834	0.9E		0533	0913	0.8E
	1222	1501	0.5F		1258	1550	0.5F
	1758	2037	0.4E		1904	2136	0.3E
	2311						
10 F		0240	0.7F	**25** Sa	0010	0322	0.5F
	0550	0924	0.9E		0616	0957	0.8E
	1308	1553	0.5F		1337	1636	0.5F
	1853	2137	0.4E		1955	2232	0.4E
11 Sa ◐	0018	0339	0.7F	**26** Su ◐	0115	0416	0.4F
	0645	1017	0.9E		0702	1042	0.7E
	1355	1647	0.6F		1416	1722	0.6F
	1952	2242	0.5E		2044	2330	0.4E
12 Su	0132	0443	0.6F	**27** M	0226	0513	0.4F
	0744	1113	0.8E		0752	1129	0.6E
	1442	1742	0.6F		1454	1807	0.6F
	2052	2350	0.6E		2130		
13 M	0251	0552	0.6F	**28** Tu		0026	0.5E
	0846	1210	0.7E		0337	0614	0.3F
	1530	1838	0.7F		0846	1217	0.6E
	2150				1531	1851	0.6F
					2214		
14 Tu		0057	0.6E	**29** W		0121	0.5E
	0410	0701	0.5F		0446	0714	0.3F
	0951	1308	0.7E		0944	1305	0.5E
	1617	1932	0.8F		1608	1934	0.7F
	2246				2255		
15 W		0200	0.7E	**30** Th		0211	0.6E
	0525	0808	0.5F		0548	0813	0.3F
	1055	1404	0.6E		1043	1352	0.5E
	1703	2025	0.8F		1644	2016	0.7F
	2340				2336		
				31 F		0259	0.7E
					0644	0908	0.3F
					1141	1439	0.4E
					1720	2056	0.7F

June

Day	Slack (h m)	Maximum (h m)	knots	Day	Slack (h m)	Maximum (h m)	knots
1 Sa	0015	0344	0.8E	**16** Su	0057	0430	1.0E
	0735	0959	0.4F		0825	1051	0.4F
	1237	1524	0.4E		1334	1614	0.4E
	1758	2137	0.8F		1842	2223	0.9F
2 Su	0055	0428	0.9E	**17** M ○	0141	0516	1.0E
	0823	1048	0.4F		0912	1141	0.4F
	1330	1610	0.4E		1430	1703	0.4E
	1837	2219	0.8F		1928	2308	0.8F
3 M ●	0137	0512	1.0E	**18** Tu	0223	0559	1.0E
	0907	1135	0.4F		0954	1227	0.5F
	1420	1656	0.4E		1522	1752	0.4E
	1921	2303	0.8F		2014	2351	0.8F
4 Tu	0219	0555	1.0E	**19** W	0302	0640	1.0E
	0950	1221	0.5F		1033	1311	0.5F
	1510	1744	0.4E		1612	1839	0.3E
	2008	2349	0.8F		2102		
5 W	0304	0640	1.0E	**20** Th		0034	0.7F
	1033	1307	0.5F		0340	0719	0.9E
	1601	1835	0.4E		1109	1353	0.5F
	2102				1700	1928	0.3E
					2153		
6 Th		0038	0.8F	**21** F		0117	0.6F
	0350	0726	1.0E		0418	0758	0.9E
	1115	1354	0.6F		1144	1434	0.5F
	1653	1930	0.4E		1748	2017	0.3E
	2201				2247		
7 F		0130	0.8F	**22** Sa		0202	0.5F
	0439	0813	1.0E		0457	0837	0.8E
	1157	1443	0.6F		1218	1515	0.6F
	1747	2028	0.5E		1834	2108	0.4E
	2306				2347		
8 Sa		0226	0.7F	**23** Su		0250	0.5F
	0530	0903	0.9E		0537	0917	0.8E
	1240	1534	0.6F		1252	1556	0.6F
	1843	2130	0.5E		1919	2200	0.4E
9 Su	0018	0327	0.6F	**24** M	0051	0341	0.4F
	0624	0955	0.9E		0620	0959	0.7E
	1323	1626	0.7F		1326	1638	0.6F
	1940	2235	0.6E		2003	2254	0.4E
10 M ◐	0136	0432	0.6F	**25** Tu	0200	0436	0.3F
	0722	1048	0.8E		0707	1042	0.6E
	1408	1720	0.7F		1400	1720	0.6F
	2038	2341	0.6E		2047	2349	0.5E
11 Tu	0256	0539	0.5F	**26** W	0311	0536	0.3F
	0822	1144	0.7E		0759	1128	0.5E
	1453	1813	0.8F		1435	1803	0.7F
	2134				2130		
12 W		0046	0.7E	**27** Th		0042	0.6E
	0414	0648	0.4F		0421	0636	0.3F
	0926	1240	0.6E		0856	1215	0.5E
	1539	1907	0.8F		1511	1847	0.7F
	2229				2213		
13 Th		0148	0.8E	**28** F		0134	0.7E
	0528	0755	0.4F		0525	0737	0.3F
	1031	1335	0.6E		0957	1304	0.4E
	1625	1959	0.9F		1549	1931	0.8F
	2321				2257		
14 F		0246	0.9E	**29** Sa		0225	0.8E
	0634	0858	0.4F		0622	0835	0.3F
	1134	1430	0.5E		1059	1354	0.4E
	1710	2049	0.9F		1630	2016	0.8F
					2341		
15 Sa	0011	0340	0.9E	**30** Su		0313	0.9E
	0732	0957	0.4F		0713	0929	0.3F
	1236	1523	0.5E		1159	1446	0.4E
	1756	2137	0.9F		1714	2103	0.8F

Time meridian 60° W. 0000 is midnight. 1200 is noon. Times are not adjusted for Daylight Saving Time.

Vieques Passage, Puerto Rico, 2019

F—Flood, Dir. 250° True   E—Ebb, Dir. 055° True

July

Day	Slack (h m)	Maximum (h m)	knots
1 M	0025	0400	0.9E
	0800	1021	0.4F
	1257	1538	0.4E
	1803	2150	0.9F
2 Tu ●	0111	0446	1.0E
	0844	1109	0.4F
	1353	1631	0.4E
	1856	2240	0.9F
3 W	0157	0532	1.0E
	0925	1157	0.5F
	1446	1725	0.5E
	1954	2331	0.9F
4 Th	0245	0619	1.1E
	1006	1244	0.6F
	1540	1821	0.5E
	2055		
5 F		0024	0.8F
	0334	0705	1.0E
	1046	1332	0.6F
	1633	1918	0.5E
	2159		
6 Sa		0119	0.8F
	0423	0753	1.0E
	1127	1421	0.7F
	1728	2017	0.6E
	2307		
7 Su		0216	0.7F
	0515	0842	0.9E
	1209	1511	0.8F
	1824	2119	0.6E
8 M	0019	0316	0.6F
	0607	0932	0.8E
	1251	1602	0.8F
	1920	2222	0.7E
9 Tu ◐	0135	0419	0.5F
	0703	1024	0.8E
	1335	1654	0.8F
	2017	2325	0.7E
10 W	0252	0525	0.4F
	0801	1118	0.7E
	1419	1748	0.9F
	2113		
11 Th		0029	0.8E
	0408	0632	0.4F
	0903	1213	0.6E
	1505	1841	0.9F
	2207		
12 F		0130	0.8E
	0520	0739	0.4F
	1007	1309	0.5E
	1552	1934	0.9F
	2259		
13 Sa		0228	0.9E
	0624	0842	0.3F
	1113	1405	0.4E
	1640	2025	0.8F
	2349		
14 Su		0321	0.9E
	0720	0940	0.4F
	1216	1500	0.4E
	1729	2114	0.8F
15 M	0035	0410	0.9E
	0809	1033	0.4F
	1316	1553	0.4E
	1818	2201	0.8F
16 Tu O	0118	0454	0.9E
	0851	1121	0.4F
	1410	1643	0.4E
	1907	2245	0.7F
17 W	0158	0535	0.9E
	0928	1204	0.5F
	1500	1731	0.3E
	1956	2328	0.7F
18 Th	0237	0614	0.9E
	1002	1244	0.5F
	1546	1818	0.4E
	2046		
19 F		0011	0.6F
	0314	0651	0.9E
	1034	1322	0.5F
	1630	1904	0.4E
	2138		
20 Sa		0053	0.6F
	0350	0727	0.8E
	1105	1359	0.6F
	1711	1950	0.4E
	2232		
21 Su		0137	0.5F
	0428	0803	0.8E
	1135	1436	0.6F
	1752	2037	0.4E
	2329		
22 M		0223	0.4F
	0507	0840	0.7E
	1206	1514	0.6F
	1834	2125	0.5E
23 Tu	0029	0311	0.4F
	0548	0919	0.6E
	1237	1552	0.6F
	1915	2216	0.5E
24 W O	0133	0404	0.3F
	0633	1000	0.6E
	1309	1633	0.7F
	1959	2308	0.6E
25 Th	0240	0500	0.3F
	0722	1044	0.5E
	1344	1716	0.7F
	2044		
26 F		0001	0.6F
	0348	0559	0.3F
	0817	1131	0.5E
	1421	1802	0.7F
	2130		
27 Sa		0055	0.7E
	0452	0700	0.3F
	0917	1223	0.4E
	1504	1851	0.8F
	2219		
28 Su		0148	0.8E
	0549	0800	0.3F
	1021	1318	0.4E
	1553	1942	0.8F
	2308		
29 M		0240	0.9E
	0641	0856	0.4F
	1125	1416	0.4E
	1648	2035	0.8F
	2358		
30 Tu		0331	0.9E
	0727	0950	0.4F
	1227	1514	0.4E
	1747	2129	0.9F
31 W ●	0049	0420	1.0E
	0810	1040	0.5F
	1325	1612	0.5E
	1848	2223	0.9F

August

Day	Slack (h m)	Maximum (h m)	knots
1 Th	0139	0508	1.0E
	0851	1129	0.6F
	1421	1710	0.6E
	1952	2318	0.9F
2 F	0229	0556	1.0E
	0932	1218	0.7F
	1515	1808	0.6E
	2056		
3 Sa		0013	0.8F
	0320	0644	1.0E
	1012	1306	0.7F
	1609	1905	0.7E
	2201		
4 Su		0109	0.8F
	0410	0731	0.9E
	1053	1354	0.8F
	1703	2003	0.7E
	2308		
5 M		0206	0.7F
	0501	0820	0.9E
	1135	1444	0.8F
	1757	2102	0.8E
6 Tu	0016	0304	0.6F
	0553	0909	0.8E
	1218	1534	0.9F
	1853	2202	0.8E
7 W ◐	0126	0405	0.5F
	0647	1000	0.7E
	1302	1626	0.9F
	1949	2303	0.8E
8 Th	0239	0508	0.4F
	0743	1053	0.6E
	1348	1720	0.8F
	2044		
9 F		0005	0.8E
	0350	0613	0.4F
	0844	1149	0.5E
	1436	1814	0.8F
	2139		
10 Sa		0105	0.8E
	0458	0718	0.3F
	0949	1246	0.4E
	1527	1908	0.8F
	2232		
11 Su		0202	0.8E
	0559	0820	0.3F
	1054	1344	0.4E
	1619	2001	0.7F
	2322		
12 M		0255	0.8E
	0652	0917	0.4F
	1157	1441	0.4E
	1713	2052	0.7F
13 Tu	0009	0343	0.8E
	0737	1007	0.4F
	1255	1535	0.4E
	1807	2141	0.7F
14 W	0053	0427	0.8E
	0816	1052	0.4F
	1345	1626	0.4E
	1859	2226	0.6F
15 Th O	0134	0507	0.8E
	0850	1132	0.5F
	1431	1713	0.4E
	1951	2310	0.6F
16 F	0213	0544	0.8E
	0922	1209	0.5F
	1512	1757	0.4E
	2041	2353	0.6F
17 Sa	0251	0620	0.8E
	0951	1245	0.5F
	1550	1840	0.5E
	2131		
18 Su		0035	0.5F
	0328	0655	0.7E
	1020	1319	0.6F
	1628	1923	0.5E
	2222		
19 M		0117	0.5F
	0406	0730	0.7E
	1048	1354	0.6F
	1705	2006	0.5E
	2315		
20 Tu		0201	0.4F
	0445	0805	0.6E
	1117	1429	0.6F
	1744	2050	0.6E
21 W	0010	0247	0.4F
	0526	0843	0.6E
	1147	1507	0.7F
	1825	2137	0.6E
22 Th	0108	0336	0.3F
	0609	0923	0.5E
	1220	1548	0.7F
	1910	2227	0.7E
23 F O	0209	0430	0.3F
	0657	1007	0.5E
	1258	1633	0.7F
	1957	2320	0.7E
24 Sa	0311	0527	0.3F
	0751	1056	0.4E
	1342	1722	0.7F
	2048		
25 Su		0015	0.7E
	0411	0626	0.3F
	0852	1152	0.4E
	1433	1817	0.8F
	2142		
26 M		0111	0.8E
	0507	0726	0.3F
	0956	1253	0.4E
	1533	1915	0.8F
	2237		
27 Tu		0207	0.8E
	0557	0823	0.4F
	1101	1356	0.5E
	1637	2014	0.8F
	2333		
28 W		0301	0.9E
	0644	0918	0.5F
	1202	1459	0.5E
	1744	2113	0.8F
29 Th	0028	0353	0.9E
	0728	1010	0.6F
	1300	1559	0.6E
	1851	2211	0.8F
30 F ●	0122	0443	0.9E
	0810	1100	0.7F
	1355	1658	0.7E
	1956	2308	0.8F
31 Sa	0214	0532	0.9E
	0852	1148	0.8F
	1449	1754	0.8E
	2059		

September

Day	Slack (h m)	Maximum (h m)	knots
1 Su		0004	0.8F
	0306	0620	0.9E
	0934	1237	0.8F
	1542	1850	0.8E
	2202		
2 M		0059	0.7F
	0357	0708	0.8E
	1016	1325	0.9F
	1635	1946	0.9E
	2305		
3 Tu		0154	0.7F
	0448	0756	0.8E
	1059	1414	0.9F
	1727	2041	0.9E
4 W	0008	0251	0.6F
	0540	0845	0.7E
	1143	1504	0.9F
	1821	2138	0.9E
5 Th ◐	0112	0348	0.5F
	0633	0936	0.6E
	1230	1556	0.8F
	1915	2236	0.8E
6 F	0217	0448	0.4F
	0730	1030	0.5E
	1319	1649	0.8F
	2009	2334	0.8E
7 Sa	0321	0550	0.4F
	0831	1127	0.5E
	1411	1744	0.7F
	2104		
8 Su		0032	0.8E
	0422	0651	0.4F
	0934	1226	0.4E
	1507	1840	0.7F
	2157		
9 M		0128	0.8E
	0518	0750	0.4F
	1038	1327	0.4E
	1606	1936	0.6F
	2249		
10 Tu		0221	0.7E
	0606	0844	0.4F
	1136	1425	0.4E
	1706	2030	0.6F
	2338		
11 W		0309	0.7E
	0649	0932	0.4F
	1228	1519	0.4E
	1804	2121	0.6F
12 Th	0024	0353	0.7E
	0726	1014	0.5F
	1314	1607	0.5E
	1859	2208	0.5F
13 F	0108	0433	0.7E
	0800	1053	0.5F
	1355	1652	0.5E
	1951	2253	0.5F
14 Sa O	0150	0511	0.7E
	0831	1129	0.6F
	1432	1734	0.6E
	2040	2336	0.5F
15 Su	0230	0546	0.6E
	0900	1203	0.6F
	1508	1815	0.6E
	2128		
16 M		0018	0.5F
	0310	0621	0.6E
	0928	1236	0.6F
	1543	1855	0.6E
	2215		
17 Tu		0100	0.5F
	0349	0656	0.6E
	0957	1310	0.6F
	1619	1936	0.7E
	2304		
18 W		0143	0.4F
	0429	0732	0.5E
	1026	1346	0.7F
	1658	2018	0.7E
	2353		
19 Th		0227	0.4F
	0510	0810	0.5E
	1059	1424	0.7F
	1739	2103	0.7E
20 F ◐	0045	0315	0.4F
	0555	0851	0.4E
	1136	1507	0.7F
	1825	2151	0.7E
21 Sa	0139	0405	0.4F
	0643	0939	0.4E
	1221	1555	0.7F
	1915	2243	0.8E
22 Su	0234	0500	0.4F
	0738	1033	0.4E
	1314	1650	0.7F
	2009	2339	0.8E
23 M	0328	0557	0.4F
	0839	1134	0.4E
	1417	1750	0.7F
	2107		
24 Tu		0036	0.8E
	0420	0656	0.4F
	0942	1239	0.5E
	1527	1854	0.7F
	2208		
25 W		0134	0.8E
	0510	0752	0.5F
	1044	1345	0.5E
	1639	1958	0.7F
	2308		
26 Th		0230	0.8E
	0557	0847	0.6F
	1143	1448	0.6E
	1750	2101	0.7F
27 F	0007	0323	0.8E
	0642	0939	0.7F
	1239	1548	0.6E
	1857	2201	0.7F
28 Sa ●	0104	0415	0.8E
	0726	1029	0.8F
	1332	1645	0.7E
	2001	2258	0.7F
29 Su	0158	0505	0.8E
	0809	1118	0.8F
	1424	1740	0.9E
	2101	2354	0.7F
30 M	0251	0554	0.8E
	0853	1206	0.9F
	1515	1834	1.0E
	2200		

Time meridian 60° W. 0000 is midnight. 1200 is noon. Times are not adjusted for Daylight Saving Time.

Vieques Passage, Puerto Rico, 2019

F–Flood, Dir. 250° True   E–Ebb, Dir. 055° True

October

Day	Slack	Maximum	knots
1 Tu		0048	0.7F
	0343	0643	0.7E
	0937	1255	0.9F
	1605	1926	1.0E
	2258		
2 W		0142	0.6F
	0435	0731	0.7E
	1022	1343	0.9F
	1656	2019	1.0E
	2355		
3 Th		0235	0.6F
	0527	0821	0.6E
	1108	1432	0.8F
	1746	2111	0.9E
4 F	0052	0330	0.5F
	0622	0913	0.5E
	1157	1523	0.8F
	1837	2204	0.9E
5 Sa ☽	0148	0426	0.5F
	0719	1008	0.5E
	1250	1616	0.7F
	1928	2258	0.8E
6 Su	0243	0523	0.4F
	0819	1106	0.4E
	1348	1712	0.6F
	2021	2353	0.7E
7 M	0336	0620	0.4F
	0920	1207	0.4E
	1451	1809	0.5F
	2114		
8 Tu		0046	0.7E
	0425	0714	0.5F
	1018	1308	0.4E
	1557	1908	0.5F
	2207		
9 W		0137	0.7E
	0509	0804	0.5F
	1110	1405	0.4E
	1702	2004	0.5F
	2259		
10 Th		0226	0.6E
	0550	0850	0.5F
	1157	1458	0.5E
	1802	2058	0.5F
	2350		
11 F		0310	0.6E
	0627	0931	0.6F
	1238	1545	0.6E
	1857	2148	0.5F
12 Sa	0038	0352	0.6E
	0701	1009	0.6F
	1316	1629	0.6E
	1948	2235	0.5F
13 Su ○	0124	0432	0.6E
	0733	1045	0.6F
	1352	1710	0.7E
	2036	2319	0.5F
14 M	0209	0509	0.5E
	0803	1119	0.7F
	1427	1749	0.7E
	2122		
15 Tu		0002	0.5F
	0251	0546	0.5E
	0833	1154	0.7F
	1503	1828	0.8E
	2207		
16 W		0044	0.5F
	0333	0623	0.5E
	0903	1229	0.7F
	1539	1908	0.8E
	2252		
17 Th		0127	0.4F
	0416	0701	0.4E
	0937	1307	0.7F
	1619	1950	0.8E
	2338		
18 F		0210	0.4F
	0459	0742	0.4E
	1015	1348	0.7F
	1701	2034	0.8E
19 Sa	0024	0256	0.4F
	0545	0828	0.4E
	1101	1434	0.7F
	1748	2121	0.8E
20 Su	0111	0345	0.4F
	0636	0920	0.4E
	1156	1527	0.7F
	1839	2212	0.8E
21 M ○	0159	0438	0.4F
	0732	1019	0.4E
	1300	1626	0.6F
	1936	2307	0.8E
22 Tu	0247	0533	0.5F
	0831	1124	0.5E
	1413	1730	0.6F
	2036		
23 W		0004	0.8E
	0335	0629	0.5F
	0931	1231	0.5E
	1530	1838	0.6F
	2139		
24 Th		0102	0.7E
	0423	0724	0.5F
	1029	1337	0.6E
	1646	1946	0.6F
	2243		
25 F		0158	0.7E
	0510	0818	0.7F
	1126	1439	0.8E
	1757	2050	0.6F
	2345		
26 Sa		0253	0.7E
	0556	0910	0.8F
	1219	1538	0.9E
	1903	2151	0.6F
27 Su ●	0044	0346	0.7E
	0641	1000	0.9F
	1311	1633	1.0E
	2004	2248	0.6F
28 M	0141	0438	0.7E
	0727	1049	0.9F
	1401	1725	1.0E
	2102	2343	0.6F
29 Tu	0236	0528	0.6E
	0812	1137	0.9F
	1450	1816	1.1E
	2156		
30 W		0036	0.6F
	0329	0617	0.6E
	0858	1225	0.9F
	1537	1906	1.0E
	2248		
31 Th		0128	0.6F
	0422	0707	0.5E
	0945	1312	0.9F
	1624	1954	1.0E
	2339		

November

Day	Slack	Maximum	knots
1 F		0219	0.6F
	0516	0757	0.5E
	1033	1400	0.8F
	1710	2043	0.9E
2 Sa	0028	0310	0.5F
	0611	0850	0.4E
	1126	1450	0.7F
	1757	2131	0.9E
3 Su	0116	0401	0.5F
	0707	0945	0.4E
	1223	1541	0.6F
	1844	2220	0.8E
4 M ☽	0202	0453	0.5F
	0804	1044	0.4E
	1326	1636	0.5F
	1932	2309	0.7E
5 Tu	0246	0544	0.5F
	0859	1144	0.4E
	1434	1734	0.4F
	2023	2359	0.7E
6 W	0328	0633	0.5F
	0951	1243	0.4E
	1545	1834	0.4F
	2117		
7 Th		0048	0.6E
	0409	0720	0.6F
	1038	1339	0.5E
	1652	1933	0.4F
	2212		
8 F		0136	0.6E
	0448	0804	0.6F
	1121	1430	0.6E
	1754	2030	0.4F
	2308		
9 Sa		0223	0.5E
	0524	0845	0.6F
	1200	1517	0.6E
	1850	2123	0.4F
10 Su	0002	0307	0.5E
	0559	0924	0.7F
	1238	1601	0.7E
	1940	2212	0.4F
11 M	0054	0349	0.4E
	0632	1001	0.7F
	1314	1642	0.8E
	2027	2259	0.4F
12 Tu ○	0143	0430	0.4E
	0705	1038	0.7F
	1351	1723	0.9E
	2112	2343	0.4F
13 W	0230	0510	0.4E
	0739	1115	0.7F
	1428	1803	0.9E
	2155		
14 Th		0026	0.4F
	0316	0551	0.4E
	0816	1154	0.8F
	1507	1843	0.9E
	2237		
15 F		0109	0.4F
	0401	0633	0.4E
	0858	1236	0.8F
	1549	1926	0.9E
	2319		
16 Sa		0153	0.5F
	0447	0720	0.4E
	0945	1321	0.7F
	1633	2010	0.9E
17 Su	0001	0239	0.5F
	0536	0812	0.4E
	1041	1412	0.7F
	1721	2057	0.9E
18 M	0043	0327	0.5F
	0628	0909	0.4E
	1145	1508	0.7F
	1812	2147	0.9E
19 Tu ◐	0126	0417	0.6F
	0724	1011	0.5E
	1258	1609	0.6F
	1908	2239	0.8E
20 W	0210	0510	0.6F
	0821	1117	0.5E
	1416	1716	0.5F
	2009	2335	0.7E
21 Th	0255	0604	0.7F
	0918	1223	0.6E
	1536	1825	0.5F
	2112		
22 F		0032	0.7E
	0341	0658	0.8F
	1014	1327	0.7E
	1653	1933	0.5F
	2217		
23 Sa		0128	0.6E
	0427	0751	0.8F
	1109	1428	0.8E
	1803	2039	0.5F
	2322		
24 Su		0224	0.6E
	0514	0843	0.7F
	1201	1525	0.9E
	1907	2140	0.5F
25 M	0024	0318	0.6E
	0601	0934	0.9F
	1319	1619	1.0E
	2005	2237	0.5F
26 Tu ●	0123	0411	0.5E
	0648	1023	0.9F
	1339	1710	1.1E
	2058	2331	0.5F
27 W ○	0220	0502	0.5E
	0735	1111	0.9F
	1426	1758	1.1E
	2148		
28 Th		0022	0.5F
	0315	0553	0.5E
	0823	1157	0.9F
	1511	1845	1.0E
	2234		
29 F		0112	0.5F
	0409	0643	0.4E
	0912	1244	0.8F
	1554	1929	1.0E
	2318		
30 Sa		0159	0.5F
	0502	0734	0.4E
	1003	1330	0.7F
	1636	2013	0.9E

December

Day	Slack	Maximum	knots
1 Su	0000	0246	0.5F
	0555	0827	0.4E
	1058	1418	0.6F
	1718	2056	0.9E
2 M	0040	0332	0.6F
	0647	0921	0.4E
	1157	1507	0.5F
	1801	2140	0.8E
3 Tu	0118	0418	0.6F
	0738	1017	0.4E
	1303	1600	0.4F
	1845	2225	0.7E
4 W ◐	0156	0504	0.6F
	0828	1114	0.4E
	1413	1657	0.4F
	1933	2310	0.6E
5 Th	0234	0549	0.6F
	0915	1211	0.5E
	1524	1756	0.3F
	2025	2357	0.6E
6 F	0311	0633	0.6F
	0959	1305	0.5E
	1633	1857	0.3F
	2122		
7 Sa		0045	0.5E
	0347	0716	0.7F
	1041	1357	0.6E
	1737	1956	0.3F
	2221		
8 Su		0132	0.5E
	0424	0758	0.7F
	1121	1445	0.7E
	1834	2052	0.3F
	2320		
9 M		0219	0.4E
	0500	0839	0.7F
	1200	1530	0.8E
	1925	2145	0.3F
10 Tu	0018	0305	0.4E
	0537	0920	0.8F
	1239	1613	0.9E
	2012	2234	0.4F
11 W	0112	0351	0.4E
	0615	1001	0.8F
	1319	1656	0.9E
	2055	2320	0.4F
12 Th ○	0203	0436	0.4E
	0657	1043	0.8F
	1400	1738	1.0E
	2136		
13 F		0004	0.4F
	0252	0523	0.4E
	0744	1127	0.8F
	1442	1820	1.0E
	2216		
14 Sa		0048	0.5F
	0341	0612	0.4E
	0835	1214	0.8F
	1526	1903	1.0E
	2255		
15 Su		0132	0.5F
	0430	0704	0.4E
	0932	1304	0.8F
	1613	1948	1.0E
	2333		
16 M		0218	0.6F
	0521	0800	0.5E
	1036	1357	0.7F
	1701	2035	0.9E
17 Tu	0013	0305	0.6F
	0614	0859	0.5E
	1145	1455	0.6F
	1753	2124	0.9E
18 W	0054	0355	0.7F
	0709	1001	0.6E
	1300	1557	0.6F
	1848	2215	0.8E
19 Th ○	0136	0447	0.7F
	0805	1106	0.6E
	1419	1703	0.5F
	1946	2309	0.7E
20 F	0219	0540	0.8F
	0901	1211	0.7E
	1538	1812	0.4F
	2048		
21 Sa		0004	0.6E
	0305	0633	0.8F
	0957	1314	0.8E
	1653	1920	0.4F
	2153		
22 Su		0101	0.6E
	0352	0727	0.9F
	1051	1415	0.9E
	1802	2026	0.4F
	2259		
23 M		0158	0.5E
	0439	0819	0.9F
	1143	1511	0.9E
	1904	2127	0.4F
24 Tu		0253	0.5E
	0528	0910	0.9F
	1232	1604	1.0E
	1959	2224	0.4F
25 W	0106	0348	0.4E
	0618	1000	0.9F
	1319	1653	1.0E
	2048	2317	0.5F
26 Th ●	0204	0441	0.4E
	0707	1048	0.9F
	1404	1739	1.0E
	2133		
27 F ○		0006	0.5F
	0259	0532	0.4E
	0758	1134	0.8F
	1446	1822	1.0E
	2213		
28 Sa		0052	0.5F
	0351	0623	0.4E
	0849	1219	0.7F
	1526	1903	0.9E
	2251		
29 Su		0135	0.5F
	0441	0712	0.4E
	0941	1304	0.6F
	1605	1943	0.9E
	2326		
30 M		0217	0.6F
	0529	0802	0.4E
	1037	1349	0.6F
	1644	2022	0.8E
31 Tu	0000	0258	0.6F
	0616	0853	0.4E
	1136	1437	0.5F
	1724	2102	0.8E

Time meridian 60° W. 0000 is midnight. 1200 is noon. Times are not adjusted for Daylight Saving Time.

EXTRA CURRENTS, 2019

Bucksport, Maine

January

	Slack h m	Maximum h m	knots
12	1503	1926	1.7E
	2156		
13	1553	1717	1.1E
		1817	1.0E
		2019	1.6E
	2243		
14	1644	1805	1.1E
		1907	0.9E
		2112	1.6E
	2332		
15		2203	1.7E

February

	Slack h m	Maximum h m	knots
10		1853	1.7E
	2117		
11		1944	1.6E
	2205		
12	1614	1739	1.2E
		1846	1.1E
		2039	1.5E
	2255		
13	1707	2133	1.6E
	2348		
14	1804	2224	1.7E

March

	Slack h m	Maximum h m	knots
11	1408	1824	1.7E
	2044		
12	1456	1913	1.6E
	2132		
13	1548	1715	1.3E
		1818	1.1E
		2008	1.6E
	2225		
14	1642	1805	1.1E
		1904	1.0E
		2105	1.6E
	2321		
15		2159	1.8E

April

	Slack h m	Maximum h m	knots
9	2017		
10		1847	1.7E
	2106		
11		1941	1.7E
	2202		

May

	Slack h m	Maximum h m	knots
27		2136	1.7E

June

	Slack h m	Maximum h m	knots
24		2009	1.7E
	2245		
26	1727	2152	1.8E
27	1819	2240	1.9E

July

	Slack h m	Maximum h m	knots
23	1513	1933	1.7E
	2204		
24	1601	1723	1.0E
		1814	0.9E
		2026	1.7E
	2255		
25	1651	1810	1.0E
		1905	0.9E
		2119	1.7E
	2348		
26		2208	1.8E

August

	Slack h m	Maximum h m	knots
21		1859	1.7E
	2126		
22		1951	1.6E
	2218		
23	1617	1743	1.2E
		1845	1.1E
		2046	1.7E
	2311		
24	1709	2138	1.8E
25	1804	2229	1.9E

September

	Slack h m	Maximum h m	knots
19	1408	1828	1.8E
	2054		
20	1456	1918	1.7E
	2145		
21	1547	1717	1.3E
		1820	1.2E
		2014	1.7E
	2240		
22	1641	1808	1.3E
		1905	1.1E
		2110	1.8E
	2338		
23		2203	2.0E

October

	Slack h m	Maximum h m	knots
18		1602	1.4E
		1800	1.9E
	2027		
19		1850	1.8E
	2119		
20		1945	1.8E
	2216		
21	1616	2043	1.9E
	2315		
22	1714	2138	2.1E

November

	Slack h m	Maximum h m	knots
17	1407	1825	2.1E
	2059		

Portsmouth Harbor Entrance

January

	Slack h m	Maximum h m	knots
30	2102	2321	1.3E

March

	Slack h m	Maximum h m	knots
29	2008	2222	1.2E
30	2100	2315	1.2E

September

	Slack h m	Maximum h m	knots
8	2029	2306	1.4E

October

	Slack h m	Maximum h m	knots
10	1626	1826	0.9F
	2236		

Woods Hole, Massachusetts

March

	Slack h m	Maximum h m	knots
29	1738	1957	2.0E
	2352		

April

	Slack h m	Maximum h m	knots
27		2049	1.9E
	2322		
29	1847	2225	2.1E

November

	Slack h m	Maximum h m	knots
5		2056	2.1E
	2337		
6		2148	2.1E

December

	Slack h m	Maximum h m	knots
6	1803	2008	2.2E

Quonset Point, Massachusetts

January

	Slack h m	Maximum h m	knots
26	1750	2242	0.3F
27	1849	2337	0.3F

February

	Slack h m	Maximum h m	knots
10		2154	*
11		2245	*
24		1811	*
		1923	*
		2219	0.3F
25		1853	*
		2013	*
		2315	0.3F
26		1947	*
		2058	*
27		1700	0.3E
		2056	*
		2139	*

March

	Slack h m	Maximum h m	knots
10		2028	*
11		2124	*
12		2219	*
13		2316	*
24		2101	0.3F
	2259		
25		2156	0.3F
	2352		
26		1828	*
		1958	*
		2251	*
27		1917	*
		2043	*
		2345	*
28		2019	*
		2124	*

April

	Slack h m	Maximum h m	knots
9		2100	*
10		2158	*
23		1729	*
		1847	*
		2130	0.3F
	2326		
24		1808	*
		1939	*
		2223	*
25		1853	*
		2023	*
		2315	*
26		1950	*
		2101	*

EXTRA CURRENTS, 2019

Quonset Point, Massachusetts

(Continued)

May

Slack h m	Maximum h m	knots
8	2041	0.3F
2241		
9	2140	0.3F
2336		
10	2238	0.3F
22	2059	*
23	1753	*
	1915	*
	2149	*
24	1835	*
	1958	*
	2237	*
25	1927	*
	2035	*
	2323	*

June

Slack h m	Maximum h m	knots
7	2122	0.3F
2321		
21	2109	*
22	1822	*
	1929	*
	2154	*
23	1908	*
	2004	*
	2239	*

July

Slack h m	Maximum h m	knots
23	2246	*

August

Slack h m	Maximum h m	knots
6 1754	2240	0.3F
7 2054	2337	0.3F
8 2204		
20	2121	*
21	2211	*
22	2303	*
23 2354	*	

September

Slack h m	Maximum h m	knots
4	1816	*
	1917	*
	2220	0.3F
5	1857	*
	2006	*
	2317	0.3F
6	1951	*
	2049	*
7 1439	1717	0.3E
18	2049	*
19	2142	*
20	2235	*
21	2329	*

October

Slack h m	Maximum h m	knots
3	1752	*
	1859	*
	2159	0.3F
2350		
4	1830	*
	1950	*
	2255	*
5	1918	*
	2034	*
	2349	*
18	2116	*
19	2211	*
20	2306	*

November

Slack h m	Maximum h m	knots
1	1733	*
	1836	*
	2135	*
2	1810	*
	1929	*
	2229	*
3	1855	*
	2014	*
	2321	*
4	1957	*
	2050	*
17 1711	2149	0.3F
2339		
18 1809	2244	0.3F
30	2107	*

December

Slack h m	Maximum h m	knots
1	1757	*
	1904	*
	2158	*
2	1840	*
	1950	*
	2247	*
3	2334	*
31	2205	*

Philadelphia, Pennsylvania

April

Slack h m	Maximum h m	knots
13 2109		
17 2013	2238	1.9F
18 2058	2321	2.1F

June

Slack h m	Maximum h m	knots
9 1929	2212	1.5E

July

Slack h m	Maximum h m	knots
3 2146		
4 1516	1801	2.0E
2237		
10 2116		

August

Slack h m	Maximum h m	knots
27 1843	2053	1.6F
2352		

September

Slack h m	Maximum h m	knots
28 2115	2330	2.0F
30	2012	2.1E
2252		

October

Slack h m	Maximum h m	knots
24 1818	2023	1.2F
2304		
25 1919	2140	1.5F

Charleston Harbor, South Carolina

January

Slack h m	Maximum h m	knots
31 1713	2041	1.8E
2344		

February

Slack h m	Maximum h m	knots
1 1804	2130	1.8E

Johns Pass, Florida

April

Slack h m	Maximum h m	knots
17 1750	2035	0.5F
2310		
26	2148	1.2E

May

Slack h m	Maximum h m	knots
14 2102		
15 1650	1951	0.4F
2217		
25	2048	1.0E

October

Slack h m	Maximum h m	knots
5	2327	*
24	1939	0.4F
2212		

EXTRA CURRENTS, 2019

St. Andrew Bay, Florida

January
	Slack h m	Maximum h m	knots
26	2137	2320	0.3F

February
	Slack h m	Maximum h m	knots
22	1854	2119	1.0F
24		2330	*

March
	Slack h m	Maximum h m	knots
11		2318	*
21	1722	1951	1.2F

April
	Slack h m	Maximum h m	knots
7		2257	0.4F

May
	Slack h m	Maximum h m	knots
15		1811	*
		2005	0.3F
		2356	*
29		2105	0.4E
	2356		
30		2157	*

June
	Slack h m	Maximum h m	knots
12		2213	*

August
	Slack h m	Maximum h m	knots
6		1451	*
		1745	0.4E
	1946	2311	0.9F
21	1846	2308	1.1F

September
	Slack h m	Maximum h m	knots
1		2312	*
3		2129	1.2F
4		2201	1.4F
18		2119	1.3F
19		2139	1.3F
28		2215	0.4F
	2359		
30		1952	1.1F
	2244		

October
	Slack h m	Maximum h m	knots
1		2016	1.5F
	2318		
15		1954	1.5F
	2308		

November
	Slack h m	Maximum h m	knots
9	1303	1723	1.2F
	2143		
22	2113		
23		1602	1.0F
	2055		

December
	Slack h m	Maximum h m	knots
21	1937	2338	1.7E

Mobile Bay, Alabama

February
	Slack h m	Maximum h m	knots
11		2226	0.8E
12		2329	1.2E
22		2105	*
		2235	0.4E

March
	Slack h m	Maximum h m	knots
9		2037	*
		2357	*
22		2135	*
		2306	*

April
	Slack h m	Maximum h m	knots
17		2228	*
30		2300	*

May
	Slack h m	Maximum h m	knots
14		2034	*

June
	Slack h m	Maximum h m	knots
11	2049		

August
	Slack h m	Maximum h m	knots
21		2341	0.6F

September
	Slack h m	Maximum h m	knots
1		2114	0.5E
2		2310	*
29	1849	2216	0.3E
		2355	0.3E

October
	Slack h m	Maximum h m	knots
25		2318	*

November
	Slack h m	Maximum h m	knots
8		1722	*
		2213	*
		2323	*
22		1735	*

Sabine Pass, Texas

January
	Slack h m	Maximum h m	knots
13		2236	*

February
	Slack h m	Maximum h m	knots
10		1109	*
		1629	*
		2246	*

Aransas Pass, Texas

January
	Slack h m	Maximum h m	knots
14		2100	0.3F
	2302		
27		2005	0.4F
	2221		

February
	Slack h m	Maximum h m	knots
10		1932	0.3F
	2151		

March
	Slack h m	Maximum h m	knots
10		2301	0.6E

August
	Slack h m	Maximum h m	knots
7	1914		

December
	Slack h m	Maximum h m	knots
20		2153	0.6F

TABLE 2. — CURRENT DIFFERENCES AND OTHER CONSTANTS AND ROTARY TIDAL CURRENTS

EXPLANATION OF TABLE

In this publication, reference stations are those for which daily predictions are listed in Table 1. Those stations appearing in Table 2 are called subordinate stations. The principal purpose of Table 2 is to present data that will enable one to determine the approximate times of minimum currents (slack waters) and the times and speeds of maximum currents at numerous subordinate stations on the Atlantic Coast of North America. By applying specific corrections given in Table 2 to the predicted times and speeds of the current at the appropriate reference station, reasonable approximations of the current at the subordinate station may be compiled.

Locations and Depths

Because the latitude and longitude are listed according to the exactness recorded in the original survey records, the locations of the subordinate stations are presented in varying degrees of accuracy. Since a minute of latitude is nearly equivalent to a mile, a location given to the nearest minute may not indicate the exact position of the station. This should be noted, especially in the case of a narrow stream, where the nearest minute of latitude or longitude may locate a station inland. In such cases, unless the description locates the station elsewhere, reference is made to the current in the center of the channel. In some instances, the charts may not present a convenient name for locating a station. In those cases, the position may be described by a bearing from some prominent place on the chart.

Although current measurements may have been recorded at various depths in the past, the data listed here for most of the subordinate stations are mean values determined to have been representative of the current at each location. For that reason, no specific current meter depths for those stations are given in Table 2. Beginning with the Boston Harbor tidal current survey in 1971, data for individual meter depths were published and subsequent new data may be presented in a similar manner.

Since most of the current data in Table 2 came from meters suspended from survey vessels or anchored buoys, the listed depths are those measured downward from the surface. Some later data have come from meters anchored at fixed depths from the bottom. Those meter positions were defined as depths below chart datum. Such defined depths in this and subsequent editions will be accompanied by the small letter "d."

Minimum Currents

The reader may note that at many locations the current may not diminish to a true slack water or zero speed stage. For that reason, the phrases, "minimum before flood" and "minimum before ebb" are used in Table 2 rather than "slack water" although either or both minimums may actually reach a zero speed value at some locations. Table 2 lists the average speeds and directions of the minimums.

Maximum Currents

Near the coast and in inland tidal waters, the current increases from minimum current (slack water) for a period of about 3 hours until the maximum speed or the strength of the current is reached. The speed then decreases for another period of about 3 hours when minimum current is again reached and the current begins a similar cycle in the opposite direction. The current that flows toward the coast or up a stream is known as the flood current; the opposite flow is known as the ebb current. Table 2 lists the average speeds and directions of the maximum floods and maximum ebbs. The directions are given in degrees, true, reading clockwise from 000° at north to 359° and are the directions toward which the current flows.

TABLE 2. — CURRENT DIFFERENCES AND OTHER CONSTANTS AND ROTARY TIDAL CURRENTS

Differences and Speed Ratios

Table 2 contains mean time differences by which the reader can compile approximate times for the minimum and maximum current phases at the subordinate stations. Time differences for those phases should be applied to the corresponding phases at the reference station. It will be seen upon inspection that some subordinate stations exhibit either a double flood or a double ebb stage, or both. Explanations of these stages can be found in the glossary located elsewhere in this publication. In those cases, a separate time difference is listed for each of the three flood (or ebb) phases and these should be applied only to the daily maximum flood (or ebb) phase at the reference station. The results obtained by the application of the time differences will be based upon the time meridian shown above the name of the subordinate station. Differences of time meridians between a subordinate station and its reference station have been accounted for and no further adjustment by the reader is needed. Summer or daylight -saving time is not used in this publication.

The speed ratios are used to compile approximations of the daily current speeds at the subordinate stations and refer only to the maximum floods and ebbs. No attempt is made to predict the speeds of the minimum currents. Normally, the ratios should be applied to the corresponding maximum current phases at the reference station. As mentioned above, however, some subordinate stations may exhibit either a double flood or a double ebb or both. As with the time differences, separate ratios are listed for each of the three flood (or ebb phases) and should be applied only to the daily maximum flood (or ebb) speed at the reference station. It should be noted that although the speed of a given current phase at a subordinate station is obtained by reference to the corresponding phase at the reference station, the directions of the current at the two places may differ considerably. Table 2 lists the average directions of the various current phases at the subordinate stations.

Rotary Tidal Currents

Table 5 contains listings of data for those stations which exhibit rotary current patterns. Briefly, a rotary current can be described as one which flows continually with the direction of flow changing through all points of the compass during the tidal period. A more complete description can be found in the glossary located elsewhere in this publication. The average speeds and directions are listed in hourly increments as referred to the predicted times of a particular current phase at a reference station in Table 1. The Moon, at times of new, full, or perigee may increase speeds 15 to 20 percent above average; or 30 to 40 percent if perigee occurs at or near the time of new or full Moon. Conversely, the Moon at times of quadrature or apogee may decrease the speeds 15 to 20 percent or 30 to 40 percent if they occur together. Near average speeds may be expected when apogee occurs near or at new or full Moon, or when perigee occurs at or near quadrature. The directions of the currents are given in degrees true, reading clockwise from 000° at north to 359° and are the directions toward which the current flows.

TABLE 2. — CURRENT DIFFERENCES AND OTHER CONSTANTS AND ROTARY TIDAL CURRENTS

EXAMPLE OF THE USE OF TABLE 2

Suppose we wish to calculate the times of the minimum currents and the times and speeds of the maximum currents on a particular morning at the location listed in Table 2 as Winthrop Head, 1.1 n. mi. east of. From Table 2 we learn that the reference station is Boston Harbor whose morning currents are listed below. Currents for Winthrop Head can be approximated by using the Table 2 corrections as indicated.

	Minimum before Flood	Maximum flood		Minimum before ebb	Maximum ebb	
	h.m.	h.m.	kn.	h.m.	h.m.	kn.
Boston Harbor	0052	0419	1.2	0645	1109	1.4
Table 2 corrections.............	-0112	+0019	x0.4 ratio	+0031	-0146	x0.3 ratio
Winthrop Point....................	2340*	0438	0.5	0716	0923	0.4

* this minimum current phase is seen to occur just before midnight of the previous day.

Table 2 states that the average speeds and directions of the minimums before flood and ebb are 0.3 knots at 103° and 0.2 knots at 297°, respectively. The average directions of the maximum flood and maximum ebb are 205° and 019°; respectively.

TABLE 2. – CURRENT DIFFERENCES AND OTHER CONSTANTS

No.	PLACE	Meter Depth (ft)	Latitude North	Longitude West	Min. before Flood (h m)	Flood (h m)	Min. before Ebb (h m)	Ebb (h m)	Speed Ratio Flood	Speed Ratio Ebb	Min. before Flood knots	Dir.	Max. Flood knots	Dir.	Min. before Ebb knots	Dir.	Max. Ebb knots	Dir.
	BAY OF FUNDY Time meridian, 60°W																	
					on Portland Harbor Entrance, p.20													
1	Brazil Rock, 6 miles east of		43°22'	65°18'	-2 12	-1 36	-0 27	-1 31	1.5	0.9	—	—	1.0	275°	—	—	1.0	050°
3	Cape Sable, 3 miles south of		43°20'	65°38'	-3 12	-1 46	-0 58	-1 41	3.3	1.8	—	—	2.2	275°	—	—	2.0	095°
5	Cape Sable, 12 miles south of		43°11'	65°37'	-1 22	-0 36	-0 23	-0 37	2.5	1.5	—	—	1.7	285°	—	—	1.6	090°
7	Blonde Rock, 5 miles south of		43°15'	65°59'	-1 22	-0 26	-0 13	-0 21	3.0	1.8	—	—	2.6	310°	—	—	2.0	125°
9	Seal Island, 13 miles southwest of		43°16'	66°15'	-0 27	+0 34	+1 02	+0 39	1.8	1.5	—	—	1.2	325°	—	—	1.6	140°
11	Cape Fourchu, 17 miles southwest of		43°34'	66°24'	+0 28	+1 09	+1 07	+1 14	3.0	1.1	—	—	2.0	355°	—	—	1.2	145°
13	Cape Fourchu, 4 miles west of		43°47'	66°15'	-0 22	+0 24	+0 32	+0 29	3.0	1.6	—	—	2.0	000°	—	—	1.7	175°
15	Lurcher Shoal, 6 miles east of		43°52'	66°21'	-0 02	+0 54	+1 02	+0 59	3.0	1.7	—	—	2.0	355°	—	—	1.8	175°
17	Lurcher Shoal, 10 miles west of		43°46'	66°42'	+0 13	+0 54	-0 11	+0 59	2.1	1.5	—	—	1.4	000°	—	—	1.6	160°
19	Lurcher Shoal, 10 miles northwest of		43°59'	66°37'	-0 12	+0 54	+1 12	+0 59	2.7	1.1	—	—	1.8	005°	—	—	1.2	175°
21	Brier Island, 5 miles west of		44°13'	66°30'	+0 33	+1 14	+1 17	+1 19	4.0	2.3	—	—	2.7	005°	—	—	2.5	185°
23	Brier Island, 15 miles west of		44°17'	66°44'	-0 52	+0 09	+0 37	+0 14	2.1	1.2	—	—	1.4	060°	—	—	1.2	250°
25	Gannet Rock, 5 miles southeast of		44°29'	66°41'	+0 28	+0 54	+0 32	+0 59	3.8	3.6	—	—	2.6	040°	—	—	3.9	230°
27	Boars Head, 10 miles northwest of		44°31'	66°23'	+0 38	+1 19	+1 22	+1 24	2.8	1.8	—	—	1.9	020°	—	—	2.0	205°
29	Prim Point, 20 miles west of		44°44'	66°15'	+0 28	+1 19	+1 17	+1 14	2.4	1.3	—	—	1.6	040°	—	—	1.4	235°
31	Cape Spencer, 14 miles south of		44°58'	65°57'	+0 28	+1 19	+1 17	+1 14	2.5	1.5	—	—	1.7	050°	—	—	1.6	245°
33	BAY OF FUNDY ENTRANCE		44°45.2'	66°55.9'	+0 41	+1 19	+1 20	+1 24	2.5	1.5	—	—	2.3	032°	—	—	2.4	212°
	MAINE COAST Time meridian, 75°W																	
					Daily predictions on Estes Head, p.8													
35	ESTES HEAD, EASTPORT	32d	44°53.28'	66°59.74'	Daily predictions				1.0	1.1	0.1	175°	2.2	263°	—	—	2.4	088°
	do.	13d	44°53.28'	66°59.74'	+0 00	+0 00	+0 00	-0 04	1.0	0.9	0.1	174°	2.3	260°	—	—	2.6	090°
	do.	52d	44°53.28'	66°59.74'	-0 03	-0 02	+0 01	+0 01	0.9	0.8	—	—	2.1	266°	0.1	354°	2.3	085°
	do.	78d	44°53.28'	66°59.74'	-0 06	-0 01	+0 01	+0 00	1.2	1.2	—	—	2.0	271°	0.1	355°	2.0	079°
37	Eastport, Friar Roads	12d	44°54'	66°59'	+0 00	+0 00	+0 00	+0 00	0.5	0.5	—	—	3.0	210°	—	—	3.0	040°
39	Robbinston, St. Croix River	32d	45°04.58'	67°06.06'	-0 27	-0 10	-0 17	-0 13	0.5	0.4	—	—	1.0	349°	—	—	1.1	165°
	do.	58d	45°04.58'	67°06.06'	-0 19	-0 07	-0 07	+0 00	0.4	0.3	—	—	1.1	344°	—	—	0.9	166°
41	Western Passage, off Kendall Head		44°55.9'	67°00.0'	-0 54	-0 24	-0 21	-1 06	1.4	1.3	—	—	3.2	319°	—	—	3.1	142°
43	Western Passage, off Frost Ledge		44°57.9'	67°01.9'	+0 27	+0 11	+0 13	+0 40	0.9	0.7	—	—	2.1	330°	—	—	1.7	150°
					on Portland Harbor Entrance, p.20													
45	Pond Point, 7.6 miles SSE of		44°20.1'	67°30.2'	+0 03	+0 04	-1 10	+0 24	0.7	1.1	—	—	0.5	015°	—	—	1.2	215°
47	Moosabec Reach, east end		44°31.71'	67°34.36'	-2 55	-2 44	-2 50	-3 10	1.5	0.9	—	—	1.0	110°	—	—	1.0	253°
49	Moosabec Reach, west end <1>		44°31.25'	67°39.00'	-1 53	-1 19	-1 37	-1 15	1.5	1.1	—	—	1.0	092°	—	—	1.2	253°
51	Bar Harbor, 1.2 miles east of <1>		44°23.0'	68°10.0'	—	+0 54	—	+1 17	0.3	0.6	—	—	0.2	328°	—	—	0.7	148°
53	Casco Passage, east end, Blue Hill Bay		44°11.7'	68°27.9'	-1 59	-1 20	-0 39	-0 51	1.3	1.2	—	—	0.7	086°	—	—	0.7	284°
55	Hat Island, SE of, Jericho Bay		44°08.0'	68°29.7'	-1 12	-0 11	-0 27	-2 17	1.3	1.2	—	—	0.9	318°	—	—	1.3	124°
57	Clam I., NW of, Deer I. Thorofare	14	44°09.87'	68°36.23'	-2 24	+0 09	-0 34	-3 02	0.3	0.2	—	—	0.2	004°	—	—	0.2	199°
59	Grog Island, E of, Deer Island Thorofare	14	44°09.72'	68°37.23'	-2 26	-1 58	-2 04	-2 17	0.3	0.3	—	—	0.2	020°	0.1	302°	0.2	235°
61	Russ Island, N of, Deer Island Thorofare	14	44°09.18'	68°38.78'	-2 22	-1 46	-2 06	-2 47	0.6	0.6	—	—	0.4	074°	—	—	0.6	265°
63	Crotch Island–Moose Island, between <49>	14	44°08.85'	68°40.58'	Currents are unidirectional													
65	Isle au Haut, 0.8 mile E of Rich's Pt	11	44°05'	68°35'	-1 03	-0 43	-0 44	-0 50	2.1	1.4	—	—	1.4	336°	—	—	1.5	139°
	East Penobscot Bay																	
67	Mark Island, north of	14	44°08.20'	68°42.17'	-0 28	-0 37	-0 28	+0 07	0.4	0.4	—	—	0.3	013°	0.1	300°	0.4	164°
69	Widow Island–Stimpson Island, between	14	44°07.95'	68°49.50'	-0 53	-0 25	-0 53	-0 39	0.9	0.5	—	—	0.6	302°	—	—	0.5	118°
71	Eagle Island, 0.4 nautical mile S of	14	44°11.63'	68°46.93'	-0 28	-0 31	-2 04	-1 17	1.3	0.9	0.2	030°	0.9	336°	0.3	050°	1.0	147°
73	Burnt Island–Oak Island, between	14	44°11.47'	68°49.13'	-0 28	-0 55	-1 59	-0 28	0.9	0.6	0.1	347°	0.7	290°	—	—	0.6	098°
75	Butter I., 0.3 nautical mile SE of	14	44°13.33'	68°46.67'	-2 53	-1 50	-0 02	-1 07	0.4	0.6	—	—	0.3	050°	0.1	150°	0.6	194°
77	Bradbury Island, ESE of	14	44°14.03'	68°44.07'	+0 01	+0 07	-0 30	-0 27	0.7	0.6	0.2	305°	0.5	025°	0.1	304°	0.7	225°
79	Compass Island, 0.4 nmi. ENE of	14	44°13.00'	68°51.33'	-1 54	-0 58	-1 02	-0 32	0.4	0.7	0.2	092°	0.3	015°	—	—	0.7	175°
81	Scrag Island, 0.3 nautical mile SW of	14	44°13.33'	68°50.62'	-0 55	-0 03	-0 33	-0 26	0.6	0.3	—	—	0.4	010°	0.1	078°	0.3	197°
83	Great Spruce Head Island, west of	14	44°14.30'	68°50.18'	-1 24	-0 30	-0 03	-0 50	0.4	0.3	—	—	0.3	003°	—	—	0.3	174°
85	Horse Head Island, 0.2 nmi. ENE of	14	44°15.07'	68°50.67'	Current weak and variable													
87	Pickering Island, south of	14	44°15.63'	68°45.38'	-2 55	-1 13	-1 33	-2 08	0.9	0.6	0.2	203°	0.6	300°	0.3	201°	0.6	150°

Endnotes can be found at the end of table 2.

TABLE 2. – CURRENT DIFFERENCES AND OTHER CONSTANTS

No.	PLACE	Meter Depth (ft)	Latitude North	Longitude West	TIME DIFF. Min. before Flood (h m)	Flood (h m)	Min. before Ebb (h m)	Ebb (h m)	SPEED RATIO Flood	SPEED RATIO Ebb	Min. before Flood (knots, Dir.)	Maximum Flood (knots, Dir.)	Min. before Ebb (knots, Dir.)	Maximum Ebb (knots, Dir.)
	MAINE COAST Time meridian, 75°W													
	East Penobscot Bay-cont.				on Portland Harbor Entrance, p.20									
89	Little Eaton Island, NNE of	14	44°16.45'	68°43.87'	−0 53	+0 36	+0 25	+0 10	0.6	0.3	-- --	0.4 300°	0.2 224°	0.3 106°
91	Pickering Island, north of	14	44°16.48'	68°45.28'	See Table 5.									
93	Hog Island, ESE of	14	44°16.52'	68°46.87'	−0 23	+0 22	−0 10	−0 22	0.4	0.5	-- --	0.3 024°	0.2 105°	0.5 180°
95	Little Deer I.–Sheep I., between	14	44°16.78'	68°43.43'	−0 23	−0 13	+0 56	−0 23	0.9	0.6	0.1 231°	0.6 310°	-- --	0.6 124°
97	Swains Ledge, WSW of	14	44°16.97'	68°45.28'	See Table 5.									
99	Swains Ledge, 0.3 nautical mile SW of	14	44°17.13'	68°43.87'	−0 56	+0 02	−0 32	−0 38	0.7	0.4	-- --	0.5 358°	-- --	0.4 170°
101	Pond Island–Western Island, between	14	44°17.58'	68°49.00'	−1 54	−0 49	−1 33	−1 05	0.6	0.6	-- --	0.4 356°	-- --	0.6 172°
103	Birch Island, northwest of	14	44°18.17'	68°45.35'	−1 54	−1 07	−0 33	−1 01	0.4	0.2	-- --	0.3 022°	-- --	0.2 200°
105	Pond Island, north of	14	44°18.17'	68°48.60'	Current weak and variable									
107	Howard Ledges, ENE of, Eggemoggin Reach	14	44°18.28'	68°42.63'	Current weak and variable									
109	Howard Ledges, NE of, Eggemoggin Reach	14	44°18.30'	68°42.08'	Current weak and variable									
111	Spectacle Island, 0.2 nmi. NW of	14	44°18.47'	68°47.33'	Current weak and variable									
113	Pumpkin Island, north of	14	44°18.80'	68°44.42'	−3 24	−1 46	−1 31	−2 14	0.4	0.3	-- --	0.3 290°	0.1 340°	0.3 090°
115	Islesboro Harbor, Penobscot Bay	14	44°18.86'	68°53.35'	See Table 5.									
117	Islesboro Harbor, NE of, Penobscot Bay	75	44°18.97'	68°52.78'	−1 14	−0 36	−1 13	−0 56	0.4	0.3	-- --	0.3 004°	-- --	0.3 166°
119	Islesboro Harbor, NE of, Penobscot Bay	15	44°19.03'	68°52.67'	+0 16	−0 30	−0 59	−0 54	0.1	0.3	-- --	0.1 334°	0.1 248°	0.3 154°
121	Islesboro Ledge	–	44°21.00'	68°50.57'	See Table 5.									
123	Thrum Cap I., E of, East Penobscot Bay	14	44°19.40'	68°44.80'	Current weak and variable									
					on Bucksport, p.12									
125	Turtle Head Pt., ESE of, Penobscot Bay	15	44°22.57'	68°51.28'	−0 36	−1 18	+0 24	−1 02	0.3	0.4	-- --	0.7 338°	-- --	0.8 171°
127	Hosmer Ledge, Castine Harbor	40	44°22.57'	68°51.28'	−0 55	−1 18	−0 31	−0 32	0.2	0.4	-- --	0.4 319°	-- --	0.8 155°
	do.	13d	44°23.01'	68°47.40'	+0 15	−0 10	+0 37	−0 08	0.5	0.6	0.1 330°	1.2 061°	-- --	1.2 240°
	do.	33d	44°23.01'	68°47.40'	+0 02	−0 17	+0 41	−0 03	0.5	0.5	0.1 332°	1.2 060°	-- --	1.1 241°
129	Dice Head, west of, Penobscot Bay	52d	44°23.01'	68°47.40'	−0 12	−0 31	+0 38	−0 14	0.5	0.5	-- --	1.3 052°	-- --	1.1 245°
	do.	15	44°22.77'	68°50.72'	−1 52	−1 23	−0 27	−0 48	0.2	0.3	-- --	0.5 028°	-- --	0.5 198°
	do.	58	44°22.77'	68°50.72'	−0 09	−0 39	+0 25	+0 34	0.3	0.3	-- --	0.6 334°	-- --	0.5 178°
	do.	96	44°22.77'	68°50.72'	+0 37	−0 32	+0 34	+0 24	0.2	0.3	-- --	0.4 312°	-- --	0.6 135°
131	Sears Island, S of, Penobscot Bay <53>	15	44°25.12'	68°53.25'	---	−1 50	---	+0 27	0.2	0.2	-- --	0.4 012°	-- --	0.4 237°
	do.	40	44°25.12'	68°53.25'	---	+0 04	---	−0 15	1.8	2.1	-- --	4.2 080°	-- --	4.2 270°
133	Jones Point, Bagaduce River <51>	15	44°25.55'	68°45.50'	−0 13	−0 03	+0 21	+0 21	0.5	0.4	-- --	1.2 053°	-- --	0.9 237°
135	Fort Point Ledge, Penobscot Bay	25d	44°27.85'	68°48.69'	−0 44	−0 35	+0 28	−0 15	0.5	0.4	0.1 323°	1.2 053°	0.1 332°	0.8 248°
	do.	45d	44°27.85'	68°48.69'	−1 26	−0 46	+0 25	−0 06	0.5	0.4	0.1 346°	1.3 052°	0.1 330°	0.7 258°
	do.	71d	44°27.85'	68°48.69'	−1 46	−0 55	+0 46	−0 41	0.4	0.4	0.1 349°	1.1 062°	0.1 342°	0.8 273°
137	Odom Ledge, Penobscot River	16d	44°31.00'	68°48.19'	−0 21	−0 10	−0 12	−0 05	0.5	0.5	0.1 276°	1.3 358°	-- --	1.1 177°
	do.	29d	44°31.00'	68°48.19'	−1 22	−0 44	+0 33	−0 05	0.5	0.2	0.2 282°	1.1 007°	-- --	0.4 193°
139	Verona I., N of, Easter Ch., Penobscot R <52>	10	44°34.07'	68°46.87'	+2 18	+0 07	+0 10	+0 18	1.2	0.9	-- --	2.8 273°	-- --	1.8 116°
141	Penobscot Narrows Bridge	13d	44°33.74'	68°48.03'	+0 27	−0 01	+0 10	+0 22	1.2	1.2	0.1 106°	2.7 034°	-- --	2.4 210°
	do.	26d	44°33.74'	68°48.03'	−0 17	−0 20	+0 13	+0 03	1.1	1.1	-- --	2.5 033°	-- --	2.1 201°
	do.	36d	44°33.74'	68°48.03'	−0 44	−0 37	+0 17	+0 04	1.0	1.0	0.1 113°	2.4 029°	-- --	1.9 201°
143	BUCKSPORT, Penobscot River	12d	44°34.28'	68°48.46'	Daily Predictions				1.1	0.9	-- --	2.5 292°	0.1 202°	2.0 113°
	do.	32d	44°34.28'	68°48.46'	−0 23	−0 04	−0 05	−0 21	1.0	0.9	-- --	2.4 290°	0.2 204°	1.8 118°
	do.	45d	44°34.28'	68°48.46'	−0 34	−0 01	−0 03	−0 23	0.3	0.8	-- --	0.7 300°	-- --	1.8 123°
145	Frankfort Flats at Marsh River, Penobscot River	11d	44°36.29'	68°50.80'	−0 25	+0 04	−0 06	+0 42	0.7	0.5	0.1 015°	1.6 273°	-- --	1.0 109°
147	Winterport, Penobscot River <51>	7d	44°37.88'	68°50.54'	−0 15	+0 10	+0 16	−0 06	0.7	0.5	-- --	1.5 033°	-- --	1.6 212°
	do.	14d	44°37.88'	68°50.54'	−0 27	+0 10	+0 43	+0 04	0.6	0.9	-- --	1.6 036°	-- --	1.0 210°
149	Oak Point, Penobscot River <51>	15	44°40.10'	68°48.78'	+0 05	+0 16	+0 01	+1 09	0.6	0.9	-- --	1.5 026°	-- --	1.8 219°
	do.	35	44°40.10'	68°48.78'	−0 53	+0 10	+0 21	+1 50	0.7	0.9	-- --	1.6 337°	-- --	1.7 258°
151	Snub Point, Penobscot River <51>	7d	44°42.57'	68°50.46'	+0 31	+0 22	−0 06	−0 26	0.7	0.7	-- --	1.7 002°	-- --	1.3 182°
	do.	17d	44°42.57'	68°50.46'	+0 18	+0 17	−0 05	−0 47	0.5	0.5	-- --	1.3 003°	-- --	1.0 179°
	do.	26d	44°42.57'	68°50.46'	+0 04	+0 22	+0 53	−0 08	0.3	0.4	-- --	0.8 003°	-- --	0.9 176°

Endnotes can be found at the end of table 2.

TABLE 2. – CURRENT DIFFERENCES AND OTHER CONSTANTS

No.	PLACE	Meter Depth (ft)	Position Latitude (North)	Position Longitude (West)	Min. before Flood (h m)	Flood (h m)	Min. before Ebb (h m)	Ebb (h m)	Speed Ratio Flood	Speed Ratio Ebb	Min. before Flood (knots)	Min. before Flood (Dir.)	Maximum Flood (knots)	Maximum Flood (Dir.)	Min. before Ebb (knots)	Min. before Ebb (Dir.)	Maximum Ebb (knots)	Maximum Ebb (Dir.)
	MAINE COAST Time meridian, 75°W				**on Portland Harbor Entrance, p.20**													
	West Penobscot Bay																	
153	Andrews Island, ESE of	15	43°59.65'	69°00.78'	−0.30	−0.20	−0.32	−0.45	0.6	0.6	–	–	0.4	011°	–	–	0.7	155°
	do	75	43°59.65'	69°00.78'	−1.25	−0.32	+0.03	−0.38	1.2	0.6	–	–	0.8	342°	–	–	0.6	188°
155	Little Hurricane Island, southwest of	15	44°01.38'	68°55.07'	−0.15	−0.26	+0.05	+0.16	0.7	0.7	–	–	0.5	331°	–	–	0.8	157°
	do	40	44°01.38'	68°55.07'	−0.28	−0.11	−0.04	−0.06	0.9	0.6	–	–	0.6	300°	–	–	0.7	125°
157	Heron Neck, Green Island	14	44°01.78'	68°52.38'	−1.57	−0.35	−0.35	−1.14	1.5	0.6	–	–	1.0	344°	0.2	218°	0.6	165°
159	The Reach, Norton Point	14	44°02.25'	68°50.90'	Current weak and variable													
	Isle au Haut Bay																	
161	Triangle Ledge, SSE of	15	44°02.47'	68°45.48'	+0.04	+0.07	−0.03	+0.12	1.0	0.9	–	–	0.7	354°	–	–	1.0	197°
	do	40	44°02.47'	68°45.48'	−1.30	+0.15	−0.09	−0.46	0.9	0.6	–	–	0.6	317°	–	–	0.6	180°
163	Moore Harbor, W of	15	44°02.53'	68°41.55'	−0.10	+0.44	+0.07	−0.09	0.9	1.0	–	–	0.4	344°	0.1	063°	1.1	135°
	do	75	44°02.53'	68°41.55'	−1.43	−0.31	−0.17	−0.25	0.9	0.5	–	–	0.6	337°	–	–	0.5	165°
	do	120	44°02.53'	68°41.55'	−2.44	−0.19	−1.02	−0.50	1.0	0.3	–	–	0.7	345°	–	–	0.3	215°
	West Penobscot Bay																	
165	The Reach, NNE of, Green Island	14	44°02.57'	68°51.58'	−3.33	−0.46	−1.32	−2.26	0.6	0.4	0.2	262°	0.4	284°	0.1	150°	0.4	111°
167	White Islands, northeast of	14	44°03.00'	68°54.40'	−1.58	−1.54	−1.32	−1.39	0.6	0.6	0.1	136°	0.4	322°	0.3	258°	0.6	165°
169	Fisherman Island Passage	14	44°03.12'	69°02.70'	−0.59	−2.13	−2.03	−1.59	1.8	0.6	–	–	0.6	053°	0.2	312°	0.7	240°
171	Crotch Island, east of	14	44°03.62'	68°54.43'	−0.58	−0.31	−0.58	−0.40	1.8	1.8	–	–	1.9	343°	–	–	2.0	163°
173	Laireys Island, south of	14	44°03.62'	68°53.78'	−0.58	+0.06	−0.28	−1.22	0.7	0.8	0.1	073°	0.4	335°	–	–	0.9	155°
175	Sheep Island	14	44°03.88'	69°03.47'	−0.54	−0.55	−1.34	−1.47	0.6	0.7	–	–	0.5	023°	–	–	0.8	220°
177	Leadbetter I., SSW of southern tip	14	44°04.07'	68°53.90'	−0.53	−0.15	−0.05	−1.03	2.1	1.2	–	–	1.4	320°	–	–	1.3	126°
179	Leadbetter Island, E of southern tip	14	44°04.15'	68°53.62'	−0.28	−0.19	+1.00	+0.16	0.6	0.6	0.1	214°	0.4	360°	0.1	105°	0.6	175°
181	Leadbetter Island, northwest tip of	14	44°05.03'	68°54.67'	−0.58	−0.17	−0.32	−0.43	1.2	0.9	–	–	0.8	016°	0.1	135°	1.0	214°
183	Dodge Point-Monroe Island, between	14	44°05.12'	69°02.62'	−3.53	−1.19	−2.32	−2.38	0.6	0.5	0.2	267°	0.8	015°	0.1	092°	0.5	205°
185	Dogfish Island, NNE of	14	44°05.52'	68°54.80'	−2.24	−2.03	−2.32	−1.37	0.7	0.4	0.1	244°	0.5	325°	–	–	0.4	147°
187	Rockland Harbor Breakwater	14	44°06.13'	69°04.67'	−1.28	−0.06	−0.41	−0.10	0.4	0.4	0.1	215°	0.3	315°	–	–	0.4	097°
189	Browns Head, Vinalhaven Island, NNW of	14	44°06.78'	68°54.73'	−1.58	−0.58	−0.32	−0.27	0.3	0.2	0.1	325°	0.2	016°	0.2	100°	0.2	221°
191	Crabtree Pt., North Haven I., NNE of	14	44°06.90'	68°55.42'	−3.23	−0.54	−3.02	−0.32	0.3	0.2	0.2	287°	0.3	003°	0.1	150°	0.2	228°
193	Fox Island Thorofare	14	44°07.62'	68°53.58'	−3.23	−2.17	−3.02	−2.56	0.3	0.5	–	–	0.2	070°	–	–	0.4	278°
195	Saddle Island, northwest of	14	44°10.00'	68°58.83'	−3.51	−1.07	−1.36	−0.57	0.6	0.4	0.2	331°	0.4	044°	0.1	163°	0.5	246°
197	Mark Island, 0.3 nmi., SSE of	14	44°10.85'	68°57.30'	−3.53	−2.07	−3.33	−1.44	0.4	0.4	0.2	272°	0.3	010°	0.1	101°	0.4	225°
199	Mark Island, 0.3 nautical mile, N of	14	44°10.87'	68°58.92'	See Table 5.													
201	Lasell Island, SSW of	14	44°11.20'	68°56.82'	−1.57	−1.07	−2.31	−1.17	0.4	0.4	–	–	0.4	022°	–	–	0.4	217°
203	East Goose Rock, NNE of	14	44°11.37'	68°58.08'	−3.55	−2.19	−2.44	−2.44	0.6	0.4	–	–	0.4	000°	0.2	112°	0.4	210°
205	Camden Harbor Entrance	14	44°12.17'	69°02.80'	−2.54	−3.42	−2.03	−1.27	0.3	0.3	–	–	0.2	354°	0.1	325°	0.3	190°
207	Ensign Island, SSE of	14	44°13.40'	68°57.52'	−1.40	−0.36	+0.55	−0.56	0.4	0.3	–	–	0.3	022°	–	–	0.3	220°
209	Warren Island, northwest of	14	44°16.55'	68°57.22'	−2.27	−0.28	−1.00	−0.44	0.7	0.4	–	–	0.5	036°	–	–	0.3	248°
211	Ducktrap Harbor, northeast of	15	44°18.00'	68°56.38'	−1.17	−0.34	−1.24	−0.12	0.6	0.4	–	–	0.5	355°	–	–	0.4	185°
213	Ducktrap Harbor, NNE of	40	44°18.27'	68°56.38'	−2.39	−0.56	−1.24	−1.20	0.6	0.3	–	–	0.4	014°	–	–	0.3	237°
	do	90	44°18.27'	68°57.35'	−1.09	−0.04	+0.04	−0.04	0.6	0.4	–	–	0.4	014°	–	–	0.3	203°
215	Ducktrap Harbor, NNE of	160	44°18.30'	68°57.35'	−1.12	−0.05	+0.13	−0.06	0.6	0.3	–	–	0.5	038°	–	–	0.3	233°
	do	130	44°18.30'	68°57.55'	+0.23	+0.11	−0.33	+0.02	0.6	0.5	–	–	0.5	058°	–	–	0.3	202°
217	Flat Island, SSW of	14	44°18.83'	68°57.55'	−1.24	−0.28	−0.25	−0.42	0.9	0.5	–	–	0.6	013°	–	–	0.5	193°
219	Head of the Cape, 0.8 nmi. W, of Penobscot Bay	15	44°19.25'	68°55.45'	−1.23	+0.01	−0.32	−1.38	0.6	0.4	–	–	0.4	045°	0.1	135°	0.4	230°
	do	130	44°19.25'	68°50.80'	−0.34	+0.10	−0.01	+0.01	0.6	0.4	–	–	0.4	325°	–	–	0.3	166°
221	Head of the Cape, NNW of, Penobscot Bay	15	44°19.07'	68°50.17'	−1.24	−0.35	−0.18	−0.22	0.9	0.3	–	–	0.4	015°	–	–	0.4	163°
	do	30	44°19.07'	68°50.17'	−0.56	−0.15	+0.05	−0.24	0.7	0.4	–	–	0.6	332°	–	–	0.3	176°
	do	130	44°19.07'	68°50.17'	−1.32	−0.23	−0.01	−0.30	0.7	0.3	–	–	0.5	356°	–	–	0.3	172°
223	Ram Island, west of, West Penobscot Bay	14	44°21.28'	68°54.95'	−1.09	−0.56	−0.48	−0.30	0.4	0.4	–	–	0.3	353°	–	–	0.3	189°
225	Temple Heights, NE of, W Penobscot Bay	15	44°21.38'	68°55.33'	−3.53	−1.31	−2.30	−1.47	0.6	0.4	–	–	0.4	004°	–	–	0.4	189°
227	Temple Heights, NNE of, W Penobscot Bay	65	44°21.45'	68°56.62'	−1.12	−0.59	−1.40	−0.49	0.6	0.3	–	–	0.4	000°	–	–	0.3	175°
	do	15	44°21.45'	68°56.62'	−1.56	−0.48	−1.13	−1.04	0.9	0.4	–	–	0.4	354°	–	–	0.4	175°
	do	30	44°21.45'	68°56.62'	−0.44	+0.03	−0.12	−0.36	0.9	0.6	–	–	0.6	005°	–	–	0.7	188°
229	Muscongus Sound	50	43°56.5'	69°26.9'	−1.01	−0.02	+0.08	−0.14	0.9	0.4	–	–	0.4	344°	–	–	0.4	188°
					−0.38	−0.06	−0.24	−0.10	0.7	0.5	–	–	0.5	333°	0.0	–	0.5	164°
	Current weak and variable																	

Endnotes can be found at the end of table 2.

TABLE 2. – CURRENT DIFFERENCES AND OTHER CONSTANTS

No.	PLACE	Meter Depth (ft)	Lat. North	Long. West	Min. before Flood (h m)	Flood (h m)	Min. before Ebb (h m)	Ebb (h m)	Flood ratio	Ebb ratio	Min. bef. Flood knots	dir	Max. Flood knots	dir	Min. bef. Ebb knots	dir	Max. Ebb knots	dir
	MAINE COAST Time meridian, 75°W				**on Bath Iron Works, p.16**													
231	Damariscotta River, off Cavis Point		43°52.5'	69°35.0'	-1 27	-1 55	-2 10	-1 58	0.3	0.5	--	--	0.6	350°	--	--	1.0	215°
233	Sheepscot River, off Barter Island		43°54.0'	69°41.5'	-1 26	-2 13	-2 01	-1 13	0.4	0.5	--	--	0.8	005°	--	--	1.1	200°
235	Lowe Point, NE of, Sasanoa River		43°51.1'	69°43.3'	-1 26	-1 02	-1 32	-1 07	0.9	0.9	--	--	1.7	327°	--	--	1.8	152°
237	Lower Hell Gate, Knubble Bay <2>		43°52.6'	69°43.8'	-1 01	-0 34	-1 32	-0 34	1.6	1.7	--	--	3.0	290°	--	--	3.5	155°
239	Upper Hell Gate, Sasanoa River		43°53.7'	69°46.3'	+2 53	+1 37	+0 34	+1 23	0.5	0.4	--	--	1.0	307°	--	--	0.8	142°
	KENNEBEC RIVER																	
241	Hunniwell Point, northeast of		43°45.4'	69°46.9'	-0 33	-0 59	-0 41	-0 16	1.3	1.4	--	--	2.4	332°	--	--	2.9	151°
243	Bald Head, 0.3 mile southwest of		43°48.1'	69°47.6'	-0 15	-0 43	-0 50	-0 17	0.8	1.1	--	--	1.6	321°	--	--	2.3	153°
245	Bluff Head, west of		43°51.3'	69°47.8'	-0 05	-0 18	-0 20	-0 16	1.2	1.7	--	--	2.3	014°	--	--	3.4	184°
247	Fiddler Ledge, north of		43°52.8'	69°47.8'	+0 09	+0 01	-0 24	+0 08	1.0	1.3	--	--	1.9	267°	--	--	2.6	113°
249	Doubling Point, south of		43°52.8'	69°48.4'	-0 10	-0 22	-0 23	+0 13	1.4	1.5	--	--	2.6	300°	--	--	3.0	127°
251	Bath Iron Works	16d	43°54.23'	69°48.56'	Daily Predictions				1.0	1.2	--	--	1.9	001°	0.1	085°	2.1	178°
	....do	3d	43°54.23'	69°48.56'	+0 02	-0 01	-0 11	-0 14	0.7	0.6	--	--	1.9	004°	0.2	090°	2.5	178°
	....do	39d	43°54.23'	69°48.56'	+0 01	-0 05	-0 06	+0 35	1.3	1.5	--	--	1.3	354°	0.1	274°	1.3	176°
253	Goose Cove, south of Chops Passage	4d	43°58.51'	69°49.60'	+0 31	+0 17	+0 05	+0 41	1.2	1.5	--	--	2.4	343°	0.1	252°	3.0	154°
	....do	14d	43°58.51'	69°49.60'	+0 31	+0 17	+0 07	+0 41	1.0	1.3	0.1	072°	2.3	342°	0.1	252°	3.0	154°
	....do	27d	43°58.51'	69°49.60'	+0 32	+0 19	+0 08	+0 39	0.9	0.4	0.1	070°	2.0	338°	0.1	252°	2.6	158°
255	Merrymeeting Bay, north of Chops Passage	4d	43°59.06'	69°50.17'	+0 22	+0 48	+0 22	+0 09	0.7	0.4	--	--	1.7	306°	0.1	031°	0.9	108°
	....do	20d	43°59.06'	69°50.17'	+0 23	+0 51	+0 26	+0 23	0.6	0.7	--	--	1.3	306°	--	--	0.9	120°
	....do	40d	43°59.06'	69°50.17'	+0 26	+0 52	+0 24	+0 09	0.5	0.6	--	--	1.2	307°	--	--	0.9	137°
257	Maine Kennebec Bridge, 0.2nm south of	4d	44°05.28'	69°47.11'	+1 40	+1 01	+0 24	+2 01	0.7	0.7	0.1	219°	1.3	016°	0.1	291°	1.5	208°
	....do	19d	44°05.28'	69°47.11'	+1 40	+1 04	+0 23	+2 02	0.6	0.6	0.1	292°	0.9	025°	--	--	1.2	202°
	CASCO BAY				**on Portland Harbor Entrance, p.20**													
259	Broad Sound, west of Eagle Island	19d	43°42.60'	70°03.77'	-0 45	-0 37	-0 21	-0 16	1.6	1.0	0.1	263°	1.0	351°	--	--	1.1	187°
	....do	39d	43°42.60'	70°03.77'	-0 33	-0 22	-0 22	-0 10	1.4	1.0	0.1	271°	1.0	356°	--	--	1.0	187°
	....do	91d	43°42.60'	70°03.77'	-1 38	-0 28	+0 12	-0 14	1.9	0.6	0.1	271°	1.3	340°	--	--	0.6	191°
261	Littlejohn Island, S. of Town Ledge	6d	43°45.25'	70°07.66'	-2 19	-0 48	+0 00	-0 58	0.6	0.3	0.1	296°	0.4	025°	--	--	0.3	221°
	....do	20d	43°45.25'	70°07.66'	-2 51	-0 25	+0 03	-1 03	0.5	0.3	--	--	0.3	025°	0.1	299°	0.3	214°
	....do	36d	43°45.25'	70°07.66'	-3 09	-1 09	-1 03	-1 15	0.4	0.2	--	--	0.3	033°	--	--	0.3	210°
263	Luckse Sound, between Hope & Cliff Is.	14d	43°41.90'	70°06.94'	-0 48	-0 44	-0 24	-1 12	0.6	0.5	0.1	322°	0.4	050°	--	--	0.5	227°
	....do	27d	43°41.90'	70°06.94'	+0 48	+0 53	+1 01	+1 13	0.6	0.5	--	--	0.4	052°	--	--	0.5	228°
	....do	40d	43°41.90'	70°06.94'	+0 09	+0 34	+0 59	+0 56	0.7	0.5	--	--	0.5	051°	--	--	0.5	227°
265	Stepping Stones	6d	43°41.75'	70°07.96'	+0 13	+0 02	+0 58	-0 21	0.7	0.7	--	--	0.5	018°	--	--	0.8	197°
	....do	19d	43°41.75'	70°07.96'	+0 09	+0 01	+0 02	-0 10	0.5	0.7	--	--	0.5	013°	--	--	0.8	191°
267	Chandler Cove, south entrance	42d	43°42.42'	70°07.94'	-0 53	-0 46	-0 03	-0 14	1.0	0.4	--	--	0.7	355°	--	--	0.4	169°
	....do	4d	43°42.42'	70°07.94'	-1 26	-0 26	-0 38	-1 18	0.9	0.8	--	--	0.6	354°	--	--	0.8	179°
	....do	17d	43°42.42'	70°07.94'	-1 19	-0 58	-0 37	-1 08	0.7	0.8	--	--	0.6	357°	--	--	0.8	180°
269	Long Island, Mariner Ledge	37d	43°42.12'	70°09.85'	-1 27	-0 19	-0 19	-0 43	0.7	0.3	--	--	0.3	001°	--	--	0.7	187°
	....do	9d	43°42.12'	70°09.85'	-0 51	-0 45	+1 53	+0 29	0.4	0.2	--	--	0.3	017°	--	--	0.3	182°
271	Cow Island, northeast of	26d	43°41.65'	70°10.86'	-0 54	+0 15	+2 08	-0 30	0.4	0.8	0.1	067°	0.4	026°	0.1	133°	0.9	194°
	....do	13d	43°41.65'	70°10.86'	-1 27	-1 21	-0 35	-0 14	0.6	0.9	--	--	0.4	000°	--	--	0.9	144°
273	Hussey Sound, Cow Island	39d	43°41.39'	70°10.70'	-1 23	-1 27	-1 07	-0 25	0.8	0.8	0.1	087°	0.5	002°	--	--	0.9	152°
	....do	11d	43°41.39'	70°10.70'	-1 19	+0 15	+0 16	-0 21	1.6	0.8	0.1	098°	1.1	012°	0.1	283°	0.8	178°
	....do	30d	43°41.39'	70°10.70'	-1 02	+0 05	+0 10	-0 12	1.2	0.9	0.1	097°	0.8	012°	0.1	281°	0.9	185°
275	Hussey Sound, between Long & Peaks Islands	57d	43°40.25'	70°10.58'	-0 44	-0 34	-0 03	-0 06	1.0	1.0	--	--	0.7	018°	0.1	226°	1.1	195°
	....do	11d	43°40.25'	70°10.58'	-0 29	-0 08	+0 16	-0 07	1.5	1.1	--	--	0.9	325°	0.2	229°	1.2	145°
	....do	31d	43°40.25'	70°10.58'	-0 26	-0 03	+0 00	-0 06	1.4	1.0	--	--	1.0	311°	--	--	1.1	147°
277	Diamond Island Roads	70d	43°39.75'	70°12.94'	-1 14	-0 55	+0 14	+0 06	1.5	0.6	0.1	230°	1.0	327°	0.1	065°	0.7	140°
	....do	7d	43°39.75'	70°12.94'	-0 51	-0 23	-1 17	-0 28	0.6	0.8	0.1	250°	0.4	342°	0.2	070°	0.8	164°
	....do	17d	43°39.75'	70°12.94'	-0 46	+0 08	-0 58	-0 34	0.5	0.7	0.1	233°	0.3	023°	0.1	108°	0.7	165°
279	**PORTLAND HARBOR ENTRANCE**	34d	43°37.68'	70°12.57'	Daily Predictions						--	--			--	--	0.5	168°
	....do	9d	43°37.68'	70°12.57'	-1 00	-0 55	-1 17	-0 28	0.5	0.5	0.1	234°	0.7	310°	0.1	226°	1.1	138°
	....do	19d	43°37.68'	70°12.57'	-0 18	-0 02	-0 09	+0 03	1.0	1.0	--	--	0.7	313°	--	--	1.1	137°
	....do	38d	43°37.68'	70°12.57'	-0 39	-0 07	-0 39	+0 03	0.8	0.9	--	--	0.5	308°	--	--	0.9	140°

Endnotes can be found at the end of table 2.

TABLE 2. – CURRENT DIFFERENCES AND OTHER CONSTANTS

Time differences for CASCO BAY are referred to **Portland Harbor Entrance, p.20**.
Time differences for PORTSMOUTH HARBOR and PISCATAQUA RIVER are referred to **Portsmouth Harbor Entrance, p.24**.

No.	Place	Meter Depth (ft)	Lat. North	Long. West	Min. before Flood (h m)	Flood (h m)	Min. before Ebb (h m)	Ebb (h m)	Speed Ratio Flood	Speed Ratio Ebb	Min. bef. Flood knots	Min. bef. Flood Dir.	Max. Flood knots	Max. Flood Dir.	Min. bef. Ebb knots	Min. bef. Ebb Dir.	Max. Ebb knots	Max. Ebb Dir.
	CASCO BAY — Time meridian, 75°W																	
281	Spring Point, east of	7d	43°39.22'	70°13.36'	-0 38	-0 22	-0 37	-0 22	1.5	0.8	—	—	1.0	343°	0.1	060°	0.9	124°
	do.	20d	43°39.22'	70°13.36'	-0 57	-0 03	-0 19	-0 32	1.7	0.7	—	—	1.1	344°	0.1	056°	0.8	123°
	do.	36d	43°39.22'	70°13.36'	-1 15	-0 05	-0 06	-0 36	1.4	0.6	—	—	1.0	337°	0.1	053°	0.6	113°
283	Portland Breakwater Light, 0.3nm east of	6d	43°39.32'	70°13.67'	—	—	—	-0 45	—	0.5	—	—	—	—	—	—	0.5	114°
	do.	20d	43°39.32'	70°13.67'	—	—	—	-1 00	—	0.4	—	—	—	—	—	—	0.4	121°
285	Ocean Gate Terminal	36d	43°39.32'	70°14.40'	-2 11	+1 01	+0 40	-0 28	0.5	0.3	—	—	0.4	230°	—	—	0.3	050°
	do.	3d	43°39.66'	70°14.40'	—	—	—	—	0.6	—	—	—	0.4	209°	—	—	—	—
287	Portland Harbor, State Pier	21d	43°39.28'	70°14.70'	-0 06	+1 15	-0 09	+0 26	0.6	0.6	—	—	0.4	214°	0.1	127°	0.6	054°
	do.	3d	43°39.28'	70°14.70'	-0 49	+0 05	+0 21	+0 03	0.6	0.2	—	—	0.4	221°	—	—	0.3	056°
	do.	17d	43°39.28'	70°14.70'	—	+0 14	—	—	0.6	—	—	—	0.4	221°	—	—	—	—
289	Fore River, Portland River Bridge	30d	43°38.75'	70°15.44'	-0 12	-0 01	-0 15	-0 13	0.8	0.4	—	—	0.5	229°	—	—	0.4	065°
	do.	5d	43°38.75'	70°15.44'	-1 57	-0 16	-0 04	-0 46	0.7	0.4	—	—	0.5	227°	—	—	0.5	064°
291	Seal Cove, Cape Elizabeth	21d	43°33.14'	70°13.06'	+1 28	+2 10	+2 35	+2 03	0.4	0.2	0.1	149°	0.3	286°	0.1	196°	0.3	112°
	do.	3d	43°33.14'	70°13.06'	*Current weak and variable*													
293	Saco River Entrance	19d	43°27.73'	70°21.07'	+0 00	-0 26	-0 14	+0 51	0.4	0.5	0.1	021°	0.3	262°	—	—	0.5	078°
	do.	1d	43°27.73'	70°21.07'	*Current weak and variable*													
	do.	13d	43°27.73'	70°21.07'	*Current weak and variable*													
	PORTSMOUTH HARBOR																	
295	Odiornes Point, NNE of	15	43°02.60'	70°42.30'	+1 23	+1 54	+0 41	+2 13	0.4	0.6	—	—	0.5	339°	—	—	0.8	183°
297	Odiornes Point, northeast of	15	43°03.00'	70°42.10'	+0 09	+0 14	+0 29	+1 03	0.5	0.7	0.1	238°	0.6	320°	—	—	1.0	156°
299	Kitts Rocks, WSW of <55>	15	43°03.10'	70°41.80'	—	-0 04	+0 00	-0 04	0.6	0.5	0.2	191°	0.7	314°	0.1	058°	0.8	133°
301	Little Harbor entrance	3d	43°03.32'	70°42.94'	-1 05	-0 30	-1 04	-1 19	0.7	0.8	—	—	0.8	321°	—	—	1.2	107°
303	Whaleback Reef, west of	12d	43°03.50'	70°42.27'	-1 58	-0 36	-1 09	-1 23	0.6	0.7	—	—	0.7	316°	—	—	1.0	122°
305	PORTSMOUTH HARBOR ENTRANCE	15	43°03.74'	70°42.32'	*Daily predictions*				1.0	1.0	—	—	0.7	340°	—	—	1.5	144°
	do.	8d	43°03.74'	70°42.32'	+0 09	+0 27	+0 03	+0 10	1.0	0.9	0.1	282°	1.2	342°	0.1	092°	1.5	194°
	do.	25d	43°03.74'	70°42.32'	-0 34	-0 30	-0 03	+0 07	0.9	0.6	0.1	282°	1.0	346°	—	—	1.3	196°
	do.	44d	43°03.95'	70°42.30'	-1 03	-0 49	-0 03	+0 04	1.0	0.8	0.2	291°	1.0	007°	—	—	0.9	178°
307	Wood Island, northwest of	15	43°04.47'	70°42.40'	+0 12	+0 09	+0 23	-0 44	1.4	1.3	—	—	1.2	358°	0.1	278°	1.3	199°
309	Fort Point	6d	43°04.47'	70°42.40'	+0 24	+0 43	-0 01	+0 20	1.3	1.1	0.2	213°	1.6	328°	0.1	043°	2.0	098°
	do.	19d	43°04.47'	70°42.40'	-0 14	+0 19	+0 00	+0 15	1.4	0.5	0.2	221°	1.7	328°	0.2	052°	1.6	104°
	do.	39d	43°04.47'	70°42.40'	-0 44	-0 29	-0 09	+0 07	1.2	0.6	0.1	255°	1.6	323°	0.1	047°	0.7	138°
311	Salamander Point, north of	15	43°04.58'	70°43.02'	+0 24	+0 44	+0 26	+0 45	1.4	1.5	—	—	1.4	257°	0.2	167°	0.8	091°
313	Clark Island, south of	15	43°04.43'	70°43.48'	+0 33	+0 31	+0 28	+0 31	0.6	0.6	—	—	1.6	270°	—	—	2.3	085°
315	Clark Island, southwest of	15	43°04.50'	70°43.67'	+0 31	-0 05	+0 26	-0 06	1.4	1.2	—	—	0.7	263°	—	—	0.8	070°
317	Henderson Point, SSW of	15	43°04.49'	70°44.32'	+0 14	+1 20	+0 07	+0 36	2.1	1.9	0.1	228°	1.6	306°	—	—	1.8	133°
319	Henderson Point, west of	10d	43°04.49'	70°44.30'	+0 11	+0 30	+0 05	+0 08	1.5	1.7	—	—	2.4	285°	—	—	2.8	138°
	do.	32d	43°04.49'	70°44.30'	+0 03	+0 30	+0 06	+0 00	0.7	0.4	—	—	2.6	293°	0.2	218°	2.5	147°
	do.	59d	43°04.49'	70°44.30'	-0 14	+0 21	+0 08	+0 04	2.4	0.8	—	—	1.8	340°	0.2	219°	1.7	160°
321	Shapleigh Island Bridge, south of	15	43°04.18'	70°44.30'	-0 40	-0 18	-1 01	-0 37	0.7	0.4	0.1	244°	0.8	178°	0.2	240°	0.7	348°
323	Pierces Island, northeast of	15	43°04.55'	70°44.48'	-0 08	+0 34	+0 31	-0 21	2.4	0.8	0.1	243°	2.8	325°	—	—	1.3	144°
	PISCATAQUA RIVER and tributaries																	
325	Memorial Bridge	8d	43°04.76'	70°45.12'	+0 06	+0 28	+0 09	+0 03	2.3	2.2	—	—	2.6	277°	—	—	3.2	105°
	do.	31d	43°04.76'	70°45.12'	+0 04	+0 39	+0 15	+0 03	2.4	2.4	—	—	2.8	275°	—	—	3.1	101°
	do.	58d	43°04.76'	70°45.12'	+0 01	+0 46	+0 16	+0 03	2.1	1.6	—	—	2.4	275°	—	—	2.4	093°
327	Sara Long Bridge	6d	43°05.32'	70°45.72'	+0 11	+0 40	+0 08	+0 18	1.9	2.1	—	—	2.2	331°	0.1	242°	3.1	153°
	do.	19d	43°05.32'	70°45.72'	+0 07	+0 41	+0 11	+0 15	1.9	1.9	—	—	2.2	332°	0.1	245°	2.9	155°
	do.	33d	43°05.32'	70°45.72'	+0 04	+0 41	+0 13	+0 16	1.8	1.7	0.1	244°	2.1	333°	—	—	2.6	158°
329	I-95 Bridge	6d	43°05.57'	70°46.02'	+0 13	+0 42	+0 08	+0 14	2.8	2.9	0.2	033°	3.3	309°	—	—	4.3	123°
	do.	29d	43°05.57'	70°46.02'	+0 06	+0 41	+0 11	+0 13	2.9	2.9	0.1	042°	3.4	317°	—	—	3.4	129°
	do.	48d	43°05.57'	70°46.02'	+0 01	+0 37	+0 12	+0 10	2.2	1.6	0.1	233°	2.6	313°	—	—	2.5	142°
331	Schiller Station	9d	43°05.84'	70°46.86'	+0 13	+1 00	+0 17	+0 10	3.4	2.4	—	—	4.0	329°	0.1	226°	3.6	157°
	do.	29d	43°05.84'	70°46.86'	+0 10	+0 55	+0 20	+0 15	3.3	2.3	—	—	3.8	337°	0.1	243°	3.5	162°
	do.	52d	43°05.84'	70°46.86'	+0 10	+0 51	+0 23	+0 19	3.0	1.9	—	—	3.5	353°	0.1	249°	2.9	168°

Endnotes can be found at the end of table 2.

TABLE 2. – CURRENT DIFFERENCES AND OTHER CONSTANTS

No.	PLACE	Latitude North	Longitude West	Meter Depth (ft)	Min. before Flood (h m)	Flood (h m)	Min. before Ebb (h m)	Ebb (h m)	Speed Ratio Flood	Speed Ratio Ebb	Min. before Flood knots	Dir.	Max. Flood knots	Dir.	Min. before Ebb knots	Dir.	Max. Ebb knots	Dir.
	PISCATAQUA RIVER and tributaries Time meridian, 75°W																	
	on Portsmouth Harbor Entrance, p.24																	
333	Frankfort Island, south of	43°06.85'	70°48.32'	7d	+0 15	+0 56	+0 21	+0 43	2.5	2.3	0.1	218°	2.9	304°	0.1	219°	3.4	130°
	do.	43°06.85'	70°48.32'	24d	+0 15	+0 55	+0 26	+0 42	2.4	2.2	--	--	2.8	305°	0.1	218°	3.2	130°
	do.	43°06.85'	70°48.32'	37d	+0 15	+0 58	+0 24	+0 42	2.0	1.9	--	--	2.3	303°	--	--	2.8	129°
335	General Sullivan Bridge	43°07.07'	70°49.56'	8d	+0 19	+0 42	+0 24	+1 06	3.6	2.8	0.2	158°	4.0	238°	0.1	159°	4.2	078°
	do.	43°07.07'	70°49.56'	15d	+0 19	+0 39	+0 24	+1 09	3.4	2.6	0.2	157°	3.2	238°	--	--	3.9	075°
337	Dover Point, west of	43°07.15'	70°50.23'	15d	+0 19	+0 40	+0 25	+1 11	2.8	2.1	0.1	156°	1.4	243°	--	--	3.2	071°
339	Goat Island, north of	43°07.62'	70°51.37'	15d	+0 07	+0 18	+0 23	-0 02	1.0	0.4	0.1	191°	1.2	283°	--	--	0.6	119°
341	Goat Island and Fox Point, between	43°07.37'	70°51.42'	15d	+0 52	+1 05	+0 20	+0 49	1.0	0.8	0.1	352°	1.1	272°	--	--	1.3	077°
343	Knight Hill Township, west of	43°06.47'	70°51.50'	4d	+0 34	+1 39	+0 51	+2 30	0.6	0.5	0.1	219°	0.7	303°	0.1	286°	0.8	142°
345	Furber Strait	43°05.47'	70°51.68'	14d	+0 39	+0 41	+0 54	+0 21	1.8	0.4	0.1	289°	2.0	205°	0.1	288°	2.1	015°
	do.	43°05.47'	70°51.68'	25d	+0 30	+1 10	+0 24	+1 05	1.8	1.4	0.1	285°	2.0	201°	0.1	285°	2.1	007°
	do.	43°05.47'	70°51.68'		+0 27	+1 00	+0 30	+0 55	1.6	1.3	0.2	279°	1.8	198°	--	--	1.9	001°
	MASSACHUSETTS COAST																	
	on Boston Harbor, p.28																	
347	Merrimack River entrance	42°49.1'	70°48.6'		+0 55	+1 20	+1 08	-0 46	1.7	1.1	--	--	2.2	285°	--	--	1.4	105°
349	Newburyport, Merrimack River	42°48.8'	70°52.1'		+1 19	+1 53	+1 42	+0 23	1.2	1.1	--	--	1.5	288°	--	--	1.4	098°
351	Plum Island Sound entrance	42°42.3'	70°47.3'		+0 27	+0 55	+0 43	-0 19	1.2	1.2	--	--	1.6	316°	--	--	1.5	184°
353	Annisquam Harbor Light	42°40.1'	70°41.1'		+0 33	+0 54	+0 53	-0 09	0.8	1.1	--	--	1.6	200°	--	--	1.3	013°
355	Gloucester Harbor entrance	42°34.9'	70°40.5'		-0 37	+0 06	-0 34	-0 48	0.2	0.2	--	--	0.3	340°	--	--	0.3	195°
357	Blynman Canal ent., Gloucester Harbor	42°36.6'	70°40.4'		-0 15	+0 10	-0 20	-0 51	2.3	2.7	--	--	3.0	310°	--	--	3.3	130°
	Salem Sound																	
359	Little Misery Island	42°32.53'	70°48.01'	5d	-0 49	-0 19	+0 18	-0 32	0.4	0.3	0.1	185°	0.5	249°	0.1	169°	0.4	105°
	do.	42°32.53'	70°48.01'	18d	-0 32	-0 03	+0 27	-0 17	0.4	0.3	0.1	185°	0.3	258°	0.1	174°	0.4	102°
	do.	42°32.53'	70°48.01'	50d	-0 33	-1 03	-0 29	-0 38	0.2	0.3	--	--	0.3	275°	--	--	0.4	090°
361	Haste Shoal	42°32.36'	70°50.70'	4d	-0 34	+0 29	+0 57	+0 39	0.3	0.3	--	--	0.4	273°	--	--	0.4	093°
	do.	42°32.36'	70°50.70'	15d	-0 12	-0 17	+0 43	+0 04	0.3	0.3	0.1	345°	0.3	268°	--	--	0.3	067°
363	Abbot Rock	42°31.78'	70°51.60'	6d	Current weak and variable													
365	Fort Pickering, 0.2nm south of	42°31.34'	70°52.08'	6d	+0 05	+0 06	+0 50	+0 03	0.2	0.2	--	--	0.3	264°	--	--	0.3	080°
	do.	42°31.34'	70°52.08'	16d	-0 31	-0 50	+0 07	-0 11	0.2	0.2	--	--	0.3	268°	--	--	0.3	081°
	do.	42°31.34'	70°52.08'	29d	Current weak and variable													
367	Marblehead Channel	42°30.04'	70°49.21'	4d	+0 41	+0 10	+0 26	+1 31	0.2	0.3	0.2	228°	0.3	280°	0.1	005°	0.3	171°
	do.	42°30.04'	70°49.21'	17d	Current weak and variable													
	do.	42°30.04'	70°49.21'	30d	Current weak and variable													
369	Ram Island, 0.2 n.mi. NNE of	42°28.75'	70°51.68'	10	See Table 5.													
371	Ram Island, 0.2 n.mi. southeast of	42°28.45'	70°51.55'	10	See Table 5.													
373	Great Pig Rocks, southeast of	42°27.53'	70°50.70'	10	See Table 5.													
375	Galloupes Point, 0.4 n.mi. south of	42°27.24'	70°53.70'	10	See Table 5.													
377	Little Nahant, 0.9 n.mi. northeast of	42°26.85'	70°54.84'	10	See Table 5.													
379	Egg Rock, 0.2 n.mi. north of	42°26.25'	70°53.93'	10	See Table 5.													
381	Egg Rock, southwest of	42°25.85'	70°54.20'	10	See Table 5.													
383	Nahant, 1.8 n.mi. NE of East Point	42°26.00'	70°52.02'	10	+0 23	+0 54	+0 10	+0 48	0.5	0.1	--	--	0.7	252°	0.1	291°	0.7	144°
	do.	42°26.00'	70°52.02'	45	-0 30	+1 09	+1 10	-0 43	0.2	0.2	--	--	0.3	250°	--	--	0.2	070°
	do.	42°26.00'	70°52.00'	80	-0 34	+1 09	+1 09	-0 43	0.2	0.2	0.1	329°	0.2	238°	--	--	0.2	077°
385	Nahant, 0.4 n.mi. east of East Point	42°25.23'	70°53.63'	15	-0 05	-0 36	+0 10	+0 10	0.4	0.5	0.2	118°	0.4	205°	0.1	282°	0.6	045°
	do.	42°25.23'	70°53.63'	25	-0 06	-0 21	+0 03	+0 17	0.3	0.4	0.1	102°	0.3	198°	--	--	0.5	027°
387	Nahant, 1 n.mi. SE of East Point	42°23.83'	70°51.17'	45	-0 31	+0 01	+0 14	-1 13	0.2	0.2	--	--	0.3	253°	--	--	0.3	074°
	do.	42°23.83'	70°51.17'	70	-0 05	+1 09	+1 08	-0 02	0.4	0.4	--	--	0.5	261°	--	--	0.5	090°
389	Pea Island, 0.4 n.mi. southeast of	42°24.63'	70°54.13'	15	+0 44	+1 00	+1 07	-0 13	0.4	0.3	--	--	0.5	239°	0.1	161°	0.5	063°
	do.	42°24.63'	70°54.13'	25	+0 25	+0 39	+0 52	+0 17	0.4	0.3	--	--	0.5	224°	--	--	0.4	048°
	do.	42°24.63'	70°54.13'	65	-0 46	-0 54	+0 09	-0 23	0.4	0.3	0.1	332°	0.5	271°	--	--	0.3	035°
391	Bass Point, 1.2 n.mi. southeast of	42°24.12'	70°55.07'	10	-0 31	+1 25	+0 53	-0 26	0.6	0.6	0.1	351°	0.7	259°	--	--	0.7	066°
	do.	42°24.12'	70°55.07'	45	-0 38	-0 05	+0 47	-0 41	0.3	0.2	--	--	0.4	251°	--	--	0.3	086°
	do.	42°24.12'	70°55.07'	60	-0 38	-0 05	+0 26	-1 11	0.2	0.2	--	--	0.3	250°	--	--	0.2	091°
393	Bass Point, 0.5 n.mi. SSW of	42°24.57'	70°56.53'	15	See Table 5.													
395	Bass Point, 0.7 n.mi. west of	42°25.13'	70°57.25'	10	See Table 5.													

Endnotes can be found at the end of table 2.

TABLE 2. – CURRENT DIFFERENCES AND OTHER CONSTANTS

No.	PLACE	Meter Depth (ft)	Position Lat. North	Position Long. West	Min. before Flood (h m)	Flood (h m)	Min. before Ebb (h m)	Ebb (h m)	Speed Ratio Flood	Speed Ratio Ebb	Min. before Flood (kn)	Dir.	Max Flood (kn)	Dir.	Min. before Ebb (kn)	Dir.	Max Ebb (kn)	Dir.
	MASSACHUSETTS COAST Time meridian, 75°W				on Boston Harbor, p.28													
397	Little Nahant Cupola, 0.6 n.mi. west of	10	42°25.87'	70°56.83'	-0 11	-0 21	+1 27	+0 34	0.3	0.4	--	--	0.4	033°	0.1	137°	0.5	219°
399	Sand Point, Black Marsh Channel	10	42°26.58'	70°56.52'	-0 05	-0 12	+1 15	+1 15	0.4	0.4	--	--	0.5	013°	--	--	0.5	203°
401	Lynn Harbor	10	42°27.27'	70°56.78'	+0 20	-0 21	+2 30	+1 12	0.2	0.2	--	--	0.3	274°	--	--	0.2	090°
403	Point of Pines, 0.5 n.mi. south of	6	42°25.97'	70°57.53'	-0 04	+0 24	+1 03	-0 29	0.4	0.5	--	--	0.9	009°	--	--	0.6	198°
405	Point of Pines, 0.1 n.mi. northeast of	6	42°26.52'	70°55.42'	+0 34	+0 24	+0 45	+0 22	0.7	1.0	--	--	0.9	296°	--	--	1.2	131°
407	Finn's Ledge Bell, 0.2 n.mi. west of	10	42°22.17'	70°55.42'	-0 10	+1 10	+0 21	-0 14	0.4	0.6	--	--	0.6	226°	0.2	295°	0.8	035°
409	Winthrop Head, 1.1 n.mi. east of	25	42°22.17'	70°56.52'	-0 20	+0 55	+0 31	+0 16	0.3	0.4	--	--	0.6	229°	--	--	0.5	033°
411	Lovell Island, 1.3nm north of	10	42°21.93'	70°56.52'	-1 21	+0 24	+0 26	-1 58	0.4	0.3	0.3	103°	0.5	205°	0.2	297°	0.4	019°
	do.	4d	42°21.30'	70°55.91'	+0 01	+0 02	+0 38	+0 19	0.8	1.1	0.2	110°	1.0	198°	0.1	298°	1.4	029°
	do.	20d	42°21.30'	70°55.91'	-0 16	-0 17	+0 43	+0 26	0.7	0.9	0.2	108°	0.9	192°	0.1	111°	1.1	027°
	do.	30d	42°21.30'	70°55.91'	-0 23	-0 19	+0 45	+0 22	0.6	0.6	0.2	107°	0.8	187°	--	--	0.8	027°
	BOSTON HARBOR APPROACHES																	
413	Stellwagen Bank, 15nm NNE of Race Point	27d	42°18.73'	70°06.72'	+0 55	+0 07	-0 18	+0 16	0.3	0.4	0.3	197°	0.4	254°	0.1	201°	0.5	121°
	do.	105d	42°18.73'	70°06.72'	+0 01	+0 07	-0 01	-0 48	0.4	0.6	0.3	199°	0.5	265°	0.1	193°	0.7	125°
	do.	210d	42°18.73'	70°06.72'	-0 05	-0 07	-0 11	-0 53	0.3	0.6	0.3	214°	0.5	275°	0.1	193°	0.8	121°
415	Stellwagen Bank, 16nm North of Race Point	8d	42°19.44'	70°17.64'	-0 12	-0 33	-0 38	-0 32	0.4	0.8	0.3	178°	0.5	253°	0.1	352°	0.9	100°
	do.	51d	42°19.44'	70°17.64'	+0 16	+0 13	+0 09	-0 29	0.5	0.8	0.2	171°	0.7	262°	0.2	353°	1.0	086°
	do.	90d	42°19.44'	70°17.64'	-0 26	-0 42	-0 14	-0 54	0.3	0.4	--	--	0.4	268°	--	--	0.5	092°
417	Stellwagen Bank, 17nm ESE of Eastern Pt. Light	52d	42°28.38'	70°18.72'	+0 35	+0 28	+0 21	+0 06	0.2	0.3	0.1	184°	0.3	269°	--	--	0.5	091°
	do.	150d	42°28.38'	70°18.72'	-0 54	-0 59	-1 11	-1 04	0.3	0.3	--	--	0.3	311°	--	--	0.4	095°
419	Stellwagen Bank, 13.4nm SE of Eastern Pt. Light	308d	42°25.34'	70°26.99'	-0 03	-0 22	+0 19	-0 18	0.2	0.3	0.1	170°	0.3	252°	--	--	0.3	108°
	do.	12d	42°25.34'	70°26.99'	-0 03	+1 15	+1 03	-0 25	0.3	0.3	0.1	158°	0.4	236°	--	--	0.3	093°
	do.	38d	42°25.34'	70°26.99'	+0 19	+1 15	+1 34	+0 32	0.3	0.4	0.1	140°	0.2	223°	--	--	0.4	070°
421	Stellwagen Basin, 13.8nm SE of Eastern Pt. Light	71d	42°23.29'	70°28.98'	-4 51	-4 20	-4 42	-5 21	0.2	0.3	0.1	131°	0.2	059°	0.1	130°	0.5	049°
	do.	35d	42°23.29'	70°28.98'	--	-0 30	--	--	0.2	0.4	--	--	0.3	305°	--	--	0.3	195°
	do.	100d	42°23.29'	70°28.98'	--	-0 23	--	--	0.2	0.2	--	--	0.2	296°	--	--	--	--
423	Stellwagen Basin, east end	245d	42°20.29'	70°31.92'	-2 23	-3 16	-3 23	-3 59	0.2	0.3	0.1	081°	0.2	033°	0.1	084°	0.4	147°
	do.	30d	42°20.29'	70°31.92'	--	--	--	-0 44	0.2	0.3	--	--	--	--	--	--	0.3	093°
	do.	122d	42°20.29'	70°31.92'	--	--	--	-0 59	--	0.2	--	--	--	--	--	--	0.3	097°
	do.	240d	42°20.29'	70°31.92'	--	--	--	--	--	--	--	--	--	--	--	--	--	--
425	Minots Ledge Light, 6.5 miles north of	8d	42°21.80'	70°44.28'	Current weak and variable				--	--	--	--	--	--	--	--	--	--
427	Minots Ledge Light, 3.3 miles north of	25d	42°19.21'	70°45.05'	Current weak and variable				--	--	--	--	--	--	--	--	--	--
429	Northeast Grave	45d	42°22.31'	70°51.71'	+1 14	+0 50	+0 42	+1 06	0.2	0.3	0.1	175°	0.3	251°	--	--	0.4	086°
	do.	10	42°22.31'	70°51.71'	+0 21	+0 15	-0 01	+0 25	0.2	0.3	--	--	0.3	266°	--	--	0.5	090°
	do.	45	42°22.31'	70°51.71'	-1 12	-1 17	-1 02	-1 41	0.2	0.4	--	--	0.3	301°	--	--	0.6	114°
431	The Graves, 0.3 n.mi. SSE of	10	42°21.60'	70°52.00'	+0 07	+1 13	+1 16	+0 07	0.5	0.5	0.3	171°	0.6	227°	0.1	135°	0.5	103°
	do.	45	42°21.60'	70°52.00'	-0 46	-0 47	-0 15	-1 10	0.3	0.4	0.1	186°	0.4	262°	--	--	0.4	085°
	do.	60	42°21.60'	70°52.00'	-0 58	-0 01	-0 21	-1 35	0.2	0.3	--	--	0.4	252°	--	--	0.3	070°
433	Thieves Ledge	35	42°19.28'	70°50.28'	-0 24	-0 01	-0 45	-1 49	0.5	0.9	--	--	0.6	304°	--	--	0.3	128°
435	Little Brewster Island, 1.5 n.mi. E of	10	42°19.68'	70°51.43'	+2 10	+0 46	-0 45	+0 43	0.5	0.4	0.4	030°	0.6	285°	0.6	337°	1.0	080°
	do.	35	42°19.68'	70°51.43'	+0 44	-0 44	-0 02	+1 15	0.3	0.9	0.4	028°	0.3	236°	0.2	212°	0.5	076°
	do.	60	42°19.68'	70°51.43'	-1 23	-1 18	+1 26	-0 57	0.7	0.4	--	--	0.9	225°	--	--	0.2	047°
437	Hypocrite Channel	10	42°20.95'	70°53.63'	+0 44	+0 24	+0 44	-0 43	0.7	0.8	0.2	265°	0.9	262°	--	--	0.7	070°
439	Little Calf Island, 0.4 n.mi. NW of	10	42°21.05'	70°54.00'	+0 14	+0 09	-0 20	-0 30	0.5	0.6	0.1	345°	0.5	220°	0.1	351°	1.0	048°
441	Boston Light, 0.2 n.mi. south of	10	42°19.52'	70°53.40'	+0 05	+0 28	+0 36	+0 28	1.0	1.1	--	--	1.0	267°	0.1	290°	1.4	100°
443	Point Allerton, 0.65 n.mi. NNW of	4d	42°19.16'	70°53.22'	-0 03	-0 04	+0 47	-0 03	0.8	0.7	0.1	203°	1.0	266°	--	--	1.6	072°
	do.	17d	42°19.16'	70°53.22'	-0 09	+0 39	+0 39	+0 21	1.0	1.3	--	--	1.3	253°	--	--	1.3	071°
	do.	30d	42°19.16'	70°53.23'	-0 18	-0 10	+0 19	+0 33	0.8	1.1	--	--	1.3	236°	--	--	0.9	071°
445	Point Allerton, 0.4 n.mi. northwest of	10	42°18.88'	70°53.23'	+0 07	+0 58	+0 12	-1 23	0.8	0.7	--	--	0.7	265°	0.2	353°	0.8	080°
447	Calf Island, 0.4 n.mi. west of	10	42°20.33'	70°54.38'	-0 37	+0 28	+0 05	+0 01	0.4	0.5	--	--	0.6	198°	--	--	0.6	037°
	do.	25	42°20.33'	70°54.38'	-1 37	+0 05	+0 11	-1 48	0.4	0.3	--	--	0.5	203°	--	--	0.3	052°
	do.	45	42°20.33'	70°54.38'	--	+0 09	+0 00	-2 27	0.3	0.3	--	--	0.4	209°	--	--	0.3	020°
449	South Channel Aldridge Ledge	4d	42°20.97'	70°54.77'	+0 28	+0 58	+0 55	+0 22	0.6	1.0	0.1	143°	0.4	229°	0.1	130°	1.2	057°
	do.	20d	42°20.97'	70°54.77'	+0 15	+0 32	+0 57	+0 34	0.5	0.7	--	--	0.8	222°	--	--	0.8	045°
	do.	30d	42°20.97'	70°54.77'	+0 03	+0 20	+1 01	+0 36	0.4	0.5	--	--	0.5	219°	--	--	0.6	039°

Endnotes can be found at the end of table 2.

TABLE 2. – CURRENT DIFFERENCES AND OTHER CONSTANTS

No.	PLACE	Meter Depth (ft)	POSITION Latitude North	POSITION Longitude West	TIME DIFFERENCES Min. before Flood	TIME DIFFERENCES Flood	TIME DIFFERENCES Min. before Ebb	TIME DIFFERENCES Ebb	SPEED RATIOS Flood	SPEED RATIOS Ebb	Minimum before Flood knots	Minimum before Flood Dir.	Maximum Flood knots	Maximum Flood Dir.	Minimum before Ebb knots	Minimum before Ebb Dir.	Maximum Ebb knots	Maximum Ebb Dir.
	BOSTON HARBOR APPROACHES Time meridian, 75°W					**on Boston Harbor, p.28**												
451	Commissioners Ledge	6d	42°20.15'	70°54.78'	−0 18	+0 48	+0 57	+0 26	0.5	0.7	0.1	129°	0.7	222°	0.1	310°	0.8	037°
	...do.	16d	42°20.15'	70°54.78'	−0 07	+0 05	+0 31	+0 19	0.4	0.4	--	--	0.5	215°	0.1	123°	0.5	029°
453	Black Rock Channel	10	42°19.73'	70°54.93'	−0 17	−0 06	+0 19	−0 13	0.5	0.8	0.1	325°	0.6	247°	0.2	122°	0.9	046°
455	Deer Island Light, 0.4 n.mi. NW of	35	42°20.58'	70°55.70'	−0 24	−2 05	−4 16	−1 58	0.2	0.5	--	--	0.2	307°	--	--	0.6	116°
457	Lovell Island, 0.4 n.mi. north of	10	42°20.45'	70°55.80'	0 00	−0 06	+0 17	−0 41	0.9	1.0	0.1	330°	1.2	259°	0.1	337°	1.2	064°
	...do.	25	42°20.45'	70°55.80'	−0 17	−0 09	+0 21	−0 23	0.9	0.8	--	--	1.2	264°	--	--	0.9	074°
459	Deer Island, 0.7 nm ESE of	7d	42°20.65'	70°56.33'	+0 18	+0 17	+0 37	+0 04	1.1	1.3	--	--	1.4	220°	0.1	320°	1.6	046°
	...do.	16d	42°20.65'	70°56.33'	+0 06	+0 13	+0 39	+0 08	1.1	1.2	0.1	126°	1.4	220°	0.1	313°	1.5	047°
	...do.	36d	42°20.65'	70°56.33'	−0 24	−0 07	+1 06	+0 23	0.8	0.8	0.1	138°	1.1	219°	0.1	109°	1.0	035°
461	Deer Island Light, 0.8 n.mi. ESE of	10	42°20.22'	70°56.28'	−0 13	−0 15	+0 15	−1 35	0.7	0.8	0.2	138°	0.9	233°	--	--	0.9	066°
463	Deer Island Light, 0.4 n.mi. east of	10	42°20.45'	70°56.77'	−0 01	−1 08	+0 12	−0 28	0.9	0.6	0.3	319°	0.9	240°	0.2	138°	1.0	057°
	...do.	35	42°20.45'	70°56.77'	−0 41	+0 57	+0 39	+0 04	0.9	0.6	--	--	1.1	264°	--	--	0.8	053°
465	Deer Island Light, 0.7 n.mi. ESE of	35	42°20.25'	70°56.38'	−0 32	−0 05	+0 20	−1 13	0.7	0.5	0.1	312°	1.0	233°	--	--	0.6	062°
	BOSTON HARBOR-PRESIDENT ROADS																	
467	BOSTON HARBOR (Deer Island Light)	8d	42°20.27'	70°57.35'	−0 11	−0 02	−0 20	+0 05	1.0	1.0	0.1	008°	1.3	264°	0.2	188°	1.2	112°
	...do.	28d	42°20.27'	70°57.35'	−0 15	−0 05	+0 42	−0 03	0.8	0.9	0.1	187°	1.3	265°	0.1	187°	1.2	100°
	...do.	51d	42°20.27'	70°57.35'	−0 07	+0 49	+0 10	+0 16	1.1	0.9	0.1	189°	1.0	273°	0.4	010°	1.1	102°
469	Deer Island Light, 0.3 n.mi. SSE of	10	42°20.12'	70°57.42'	−0 20	+0 51	+0 44	+0 18	1.1	0.8	--	--	1.4	265°	--	--	1.0	082°
	...do.	35	42°20.12'	70°57.42'	−0 03	+0 58	+0 38	+0 21	1.2	0.9	--	--	1.5	265°	0.2	178°	1.2	090°
471	Deer Island Light, 0.4 n.mi. SSE of	10	42°19.97'	70°57.42'	−0 11	−0 21	+0 47	−1 20	1.1	0.9	--	--	1.4	269°	--	--	1.0	073°
	...do.	25	42°19.97'	70°57.42'	−0 05	+0 35	−2 03	−0 56	1.1	0.5	--	--	0.4	351°	0.3	065°	0.6	081°
473	Deer Island, southwest of	10	42°20.63'	70°57.78'	−0 17	+1 26	−0 04	+0 13	0.5	0.5	0.1	175°	0.6	302°	--	--	0.6	137°
475	Long Island Head, 0.9 n.mi. NW of	10	42°20.40'	70°58.43'	−0 10	−1 06	−0 45	−0 21	0.5	0.3	--	--	0.4	304°	--	--	0.4	103°
	...do.	35	42°20.40'	70°58.43'	−0 36	−1 37	−1 37	−3 16	0.4	0.4	--	--	0.4	327°	0.4	049°	0.5	079°
477	Deer Island Flats	10	42°20.83'	70°58.65'	See Table 5.				0.4	0.4	--	--	0.4	312°	--	--	0.5	107°
479	Deer Island Light, 1.3 n.mi. NW of	10	42°21.12'	70°58.74'	−0 14	+0 24	+0 26	+0 01	0.3	0.7	--	--	0.4	312°	--	--	0.5	134°
481	Snake Island, southwest of	10	42°19.97'	70°59.22'	+0 43	+1 13	+2 05	+0 53	1.0	0.7	--	--	1.3	254°	--	--	0.8	086°
483	Deer Island Light, 1.0 n.mi. WSW of	35	42°19.97'	70°58.43'	−0 05	+1 38	+1 41	+0 11	1.0	0.3	--	--	1.2	273°	--	--	0.6	082°
	...do.	10	42°19.35'	70°58.45'	−0 13	+1 09	−0 39	−0 34	0.4	0.5	--	--	0.5	217°	0.4	121°	0.6	038°
485	Spectacle I. and Long I., between	10	42°18.98'	70°59.15'	−0 22	−1 00	−0 57	−1 58	0.4	0.4	--	--	0.5	244°	0.1	180°	0.4	098°
487	Spectacle Island, 0.2 n.mi. south of	10	42°20.05'	70°59.16'	−0 42	+0 59	+1 40	+0 26	0.7	0.6	0.1	349°	0.5	284°	0.2	008°	0.8	091°
489	Spectacle Island, 0.4nm north of	3d	42°20.05'	70°59.16'	+0 11	+0 25	+1 37	+0 27	0.6	0.6	--	--	0.8	283°	0.1	000°	0.7	086°
	...do.	16d	42°20.05'	70°59.16'	−0 26	−3 49	+1 16	+0 13	0.4	0.3	--	--	0.2	275°	0.1	181°	0.4	099°
	...do.	33d	42°20.05'	70°59.57'	−1 49	−0 37	−2 35	−3 08	0.2	0.3	0.2	227°	0.2	306°	0.2	045°	0.6	127°
491	Spectacle I. and Thompson I., between	10	42°19.25'	70°59.57'	−0 37	+1 36	+1 05	−0 32	0.6	0.5	--	--	0.5	281°	0.2	003°	0.4	086°
493	Thompson Island, 0.7 n.mi. NNE of	10	42°19.97'	70°59.90'	−1 13	+1 36	+0 43	−0 52	0.4	0.2	--	--	0.8	277°	--	--	0.6	091°
	...do.	35	42°19.97'	70°59.90'	+0 20	+1 21	+1 48	+0 12	0.4	0.4	0.1	190°	0.6	283°	0.1	009°	0.5	104°
495	Boston Channel Light No.5	3d	42°20.15'	71°00.02'	−0 04	+1 48	+1 57	+0 10	0.4	0.3	--	--	0.5	276°	0.1	034°	0.4	095°
	...do.	15d	42°20.15'	71°00.02'	−0 15	+1 57	+2 42	+0 41	0.2	0.2	0.1	213°	0.3	297°	0.2	061°	0.3	119°
	...do.	33d	42°20.33'	71°00.02'	+0 27	+2 42	+1 25	+1 00	0.5	0.5	--	--	0.6	303°	0.1	294°	0.6	125°
497	Fort Independence, 0.3 n.mi. east of	10	42°20.51'	71°00.54'	+0 43	+1 25	+0 58	+0 27	0.3	0.4	--	--	0.6	294°	0.1	034°	0.6	108°
499	Fort Independence, 0.1nm north of	6d	42°20.51'	71°00.54'	+0 04	+0 58	+2 01	+0 38	0.4	0.4	0.1	192°	0.5	297°	0.1	030°	0.4	108°
	...do.	16d	42°20.51'	71°00.54'	−0 21	+2 01	+1 17	+0 32	0.4	0.3	--	--	0.5	300°	0.1	034°	0.3	103°
	...do.	26d	42°20.57'	71°01.57'	+0 25	+1 02	+1 17	+0 33	0.5	0.2	--	--	0.5	312°	--	--	0.3	124°
501	Ted William Tunnel	7d	42°20.57'	71°01.57'	−0 19	+1 07	+1 34	+0 23	0.4	0.2	--	--	0.5	315°	--	--	0.3	136°
	...do.	16d	42°20.57'	71°01.57'	−0 34	+0 44	+1 22	+0 08	0.4	0.2	--	--	0.3	309°	--	--	0.3	125°
	...do.	26d	42°21.13'	71°01.85'	−0 11	+1 34	+1 01	+1 01	0.3	0.2	--	--	0.4	299°	--	--	0.3	118°
503	South Boston, Pier 4, 0.2 n.mi. NNE of	10	42°21.13'	71°03.11'	−0 29	+1 22	+1 22	+0 03	0.3	0.1	0.1	--	0.4	030°	0.1	--	0.2	120°
	...do.	25			−0 23	+0 24	+1 37											
505	Charles River Entrance	10	42°22.23'	71°02.80'	Current weak and variable				0.2	0.3	--	--	0.2	017°	--	--	0.4	194°
507	East Boston, Pier 10, southeast of	25	42°22.55'	71°02.80'	Current weak and variable				0.3	0.2	--	--	0.3	030°	--	--	0.2	193°
509	Charlestown Pier 1	8d	42°22.80'	71°02.70'	+1 26	+0 55	+0 23	+0 04										
	...do.	31d	42°22.80'	71°02.70'	−0 08	+1 10	+1 18	+0 39	0.1	0.3	--	--	0.1	356°	--	--	0.3	188°
	...do.	57d	42°22.80'	71°02.70'	+0 27	+1 20	+0 36	+0 15										

Note at 467: Daily predictions

Endnotes can be found at the end of table 2.

TABLE 2. – CURRENT DIFFERENCES AND OTHER CONSTANTS

No.	PLACE	Meter Depth (ft)	Latitude North	Longitude West	TIME DIFFERENCES Min. before Flood (h m)	Flood (h m)	Min. before Ebb (h m)	Ebb (h m)	SPEED RATIOS Flood	Ebb	Min. before Flood knots	Dir.	Max. Flood knots	Dir.	Min. before Ebb knots	Dir.	Max. Ebb knots	Dir.
	BOSTON HARBOR–PRESIDENT ROADS Time meridian, 75°W				on Boston Harbor, p.28													
511	Chelsea River, west of bascule bridge	10	42°23.07'	71°02.53'	-0 07	-0 21	+0 38	-0 58	0.2	0.2	--	--	0.2	048°	--	--	0.2	240°
513	Chelsea River, below bascule bridge	10	42°23.03'	71°01.70'	+0 20	-0 10	+0 32	-0 16	0.2	0.2	--	--	0.2	088°	--	--	0.3	272°
515	Mystic River Bridge, 0.1 n.mi. west of	10	42°23.15'	71°03.02'	+0 22	-0 05	-0 51	-0 28	0.1	0.1	--	--	0.1	267°	--	--	0.1	093°
517	Mystic River Bridge, northwest of	10	42°23.15'	71°02.95'	-0 29	+1 09	+0 17	-0 56	0.1	0.1	--	--	0.1	300°	0.1	170°	0.1	098°
519	City Point, 0.8 n.mi. SSE of	10	42°19.22'	71°00.88'	+0 04	+0 39	+1 14	-0 51	0.5	0.5	--	--	0.6	248°	--	--	0.6	069°
521	Squantum Point, 0.8 n.mi. northeast of	10	42°18.63'	71°01.70'	+0 09	+0 40	+1 11	+0 39	0.3	0.4	--	--	0.4	216°	--	--	0.5	036°
523	Squantum Point, 0.4 n.mi. NNE of	10	42°18.38'	71°02.23'	+0 05	-0 01	+0 36	+0 40	0.3	0.4	--	--	0.4	266°	--	--	0.5	091°
525	Neponset River	10	42°18.25'	71°02.58'	-0 34	-0 27	+0 40	+0 23	0.3	0.4	--	--	0.4	218°	--	--	0.4	025°
	BOSTON HARBOR–NANTASKET ROADS																	
527	Nixes Mate	4d	42°19.95'	70°56.36'	-0 18	+0 05	+0 48	-0 18	0.4	0.4	0.1	285°	0.5	180°	0.1	107°	0.5	023°
	do.	14d	42°19.95'	70°56.36'	-0 06	+0 18	+0 49	-0 24	0.4	0.4	0.2	277°	0.5	176°	0.1	100°	0.5	012°
	do.	27d	42°19.95'	70°56.36'	+0 27	+0 49	+0 55	-0 32	0.4	0.9	0.2	246°	0.7	147°	0.1	051°	0.5	352°
529	Lovell Island, 0.1 n.mi. south of	10	42°19.40'	70°55.48'	-0 01	-0 49	-0 35	+0 05	0.6	0.9	0.2	205°	0.7	275°	0.2	169°	1.0	092°
	do.	24	42°19.40'	70°55.48'	-0 34	-2 12	-0 25	-1 13	0.6	0.7	--	--	0.7	294°	0.2	183°	0.9	095°
531	Georges Island, northeast of	25	42°19.37'	70°55.53'	-0 22	-1 42	-0 34	-2 22	0.6	0.6	0.2	191°	0.8	279°	--	--	0.8	100°
533	Georges Island, north of	10	42°19.38'	70°55.67'	-1 34	-1 36	-0 06	-1 58	0.6	0.8	--	--	0.8	298°	--	--	0.9	112°
535	Gallops Island, 0.2 n.mi. SSE of	10	42°19.42'	70°55.93'	-0 08	+0 21	-0 04	+0 09	0.9	0.9	--	--	1.1	243°	0.2	130°	1.0	062°
537	Gallops Island, 0.1 n.mi. southeast of	10	42°19.45'	70°55.90'	-0 10	-0 33	-0 01	+0 15	0.7	0.9	--	--	0.9	225°	--	--	1.0	063°
539	Gallops Island, The Narrows	35	42°19.45'	70°55.90'	-0 07	-0 38	+0 17	-0 15	0.8	0.7	--	--	0.9	255°	--	--	0.9	052°
541	Lovell Island Narrows	20	42°19.62'	70°56.03'	-1 34	-0 06	+1 08	-0 58	0.4	0.1	0.1	233°	0.5	135°	--	--	0.2	262°
	do.	14d	42°19.69'	70°55.99'	+0 28	-0 13	+1 03	+0 14	0.3	0.7	--	--	0.5	142°	--	--	0.8	326°
543	Lovell Island, west of	25d	42°19.69'	70°55.99'	+0 23	+0 19	+1 34	+0 17	0.4	0.8	0.1	062°	0.4	139°	--	--	1.0	320°
	do.	10	42°19.72'	70°55.97'	+0 10	+0 33	+1 37	+0 19	0.3	0.8	0.2	232°	0.4	149°	--	--	0.9	320°
545	Fort Warren, Georges Island, 0.2nm east of	24	42°19.31'	70°55.26'	-0 13	+0 19	+1 17	-0 10	0.3	1.0	--	--	0.4	136°	--	--	1.2	299°
547	Georges Island, 0.5 n.mi. ESE of	10	42°19.17'	70°54.97'	Current weak and variable						0.2	165°	1.0	244°	--	--	1.2	313°
549	Georges Island, 0.4 n.mi. east of	7d	42°19.12'	70°55.20'	+0 23	+0 51	+0 55	+0 01	0.8	1.0	0.3	180°	1.0	248°	--	--	1.2	065°
551	Georges Island, 0.4nm southeast of	33d	42°18.78'	70°55.20'	-0 26	+0 09	+0 03	-0 23	0.8	0.9	0.1	145°	1.4	233°	0.2	137°	1.1	057°
	do.	72d	42°18.78'	70°55.20'	+0 10	+0 43	+0 39	+0 16	1.1	1.3	--	--	1.4	234°	0.1	331°	1.6	051°
553	Georges Island, 0.3 n.mi. SSE of	10	42°18.78'	70°55.55'	+0 04	+0 27	+0 46	+0 29	1.0	1.2	0.1	159°	1.5	235°	0.4	126°	1.5	056°
	do.	35	42°18.78'	70°55.53'	-0 02	+0 14	+0 57	+0 17	0.8	1.0	0.1	159°	1.1	234°	0.2	346°	1.2	076°
555	Georges Island, 0.4 n.mi. SSE of	10	42°18.78'	70°55.55'	+0 12	+0 29	+0 29	+0 29	0.9	1.0	--	--	1.1	237°	0.3	161°	1.2	069°
	do.	35	42°18.67'	70°55.53'	-0 01	+0 40	+0 53	-0 10	0.8	0.7	0.2	145°	1.0	236°	0.2	347°	0.8	073°
557	Nubble Channel	10	42°18.67'	70°55.53'	+0 05	+0 58	+0 27	-2 15	1.0	0.8	--	--	1.3	240°	0.3	347°	0.9	046°
559	Georges Island, 0.2 n.mi. WSW of	10	42°19.73'	70°56.93'	-0 21	+1 01	+0 51	-0 12	1.0	0.8	0.1	282°	1.2	240°	0.1	347°	1.0	065°
	do.	20	42°19.02'	70°56.10'	See Table 5.	See Table 5.	+0 40	+0 31	0.6	0.6	--	--	0.8	187°	0.2	139°	0.8	006°
561	Hull Gut	9d	42°18.20'	70°55.50'	-0 21	-0 28	-0 16	-0 02	1.4	2.0	0.1	068°	1.9	162°	--	--	2.5	340°
	do.	22d	42°18.20'	70°55.50'	-0 23	-0 30	-0 06	-0 05	1.4	2.0	--	--	1.9	159°	0.1	062°	2.5	341°
	do.	35d	42°18.20'	70°55.50'	+0 36	-0 25	+0 01	-0 04	1.4	1.8	--	--	1.8	152°	0.1	064°	2.2	343°
563	Peddocks Island, 0.2 n.mi. north of	25	42°18.32'	70°56.00'	-0 28	+1 27	+1 15	-0 41	0.8	0.6	--	--	1.0	246°	--	--	0.7	257°
	do.	10	42°18.40'	70°56.13'	-0 02	+1 09	+1 25	-1 05	0.8	0.5	0.1	337°	1.0	255°	0.1	178°	0.6	060°
565	Peddocks Island, 0.3 n.mi. northwest of	25	42°18.40'	70°56.13'	+0 42	+1 30	+1 20	+0 44	0.9	0.5	--	--	1.1	245°	--	--	1.0	060°
	do.	40	42°18.40'	70°56.13'	+0 12	+1 11	+1 27	+0 03	0.8	0.4	0.2	342°	1.0	250°	--	--	0.6	055°
	do.	10	42°18.52'	70°56.32'	-0 17	+1 40	+1 40	-0 59	0.8	0.4	--	--	1.0	261°	--	--	0.5	060°
567	Rainsford I. and Windmill Pt., between	10	42°18.52'	70°56.32'	+0 28	+0 59	+0 29	+0 34	0.6	0.4	--	--	0.8	251°	0.3	168°	0.5	056°
569	Gallops Island, 0.5 n.mi. southwest of	25	42°19.13'	70°56.82'	+0 13	+0 24	+1 31	-0 07	0.6	0.6	0.2	165°	0.8	256°	0.2	329°	1.0	053°
	do.	10	42°18.90'	70°56.82'	+0 41	+0 19	-1 02	+0 35	0.5	0.6	--	--	0.6	238°	0.3	204°	0.7	074°
571	Rainsford Island, 0.2 n.mi. NE of	25	42°18.90'	70°56.95'	+0 08	+0 22	-0 33	+0 58	0.4	0.3	0.1	143°	0.5	237°	0.1	143°	0.4	072°
	do.	10	42°18.50'	70°56.62'	-0 26	+0 23	+0 14	-1 13	0.4	0.2	--	--	0.5	239°	--	--	0.3	084°
573	Rainsford Island, 0.4 n.mi. SE of	20	42°18.50'	70°57.78'	-2 01	-0 44	+0 12	-1 24	0.5	0.6	--	--	0.5	237°	0.2	127°	0.3	086°
575	Long I. and Rainsford I., between	10	42°18.70'	70°57.78'	-0 08	+0 18	+0 57	-0 11	0.6	0.7	0.2	127°	0.7	225°	--	--	0.8	055°
	do.	25	42°18.70'	70°57.78'	+0 13	+0 43	+0 38	-0 13	0.5	0.6	--	--	0.6	229°	0.1	322°	0.8	049°

Endnotes can be found at the end of table 2.

TABLE 2. – CURRENT DIFFERENCES AND OTHER CONSTANTS

No.	PLACE	Meter Depth (ft)	Latitude North	Longitude West	Time Diff. Min. before Flood (h m)	Time Diff. Flood (h m)	Time Diff. Min. before Ebb (h m)	Time Diff. Ebb (h m)	Speed Ratio Flood	Speed Ratio Ebb	Min. before Flood (knots)	Min. before Flood (Dir.)	Max Flood (knots)	Max Flood (Dir.)	Min. before Ebb (knots)	Min. before Ebb (Dir.)	Max Ebb (knots)	Max Ebb (Dir.)
	BOSTON HARBOR–NANTASKET ROADS Time meridian, 75°W *on Boston Harbor, p.28*																	
577	West Head, Peddocks I., 0.1 n.mi. W of	10	42°17.45'	70°57.22'	-1 30	+1 02	+1 24	-1 16	0.8	0.7	--	--	1.1	208°	--	--	0.9	018°
	....do....	30	42°17.45'	70°57.22'	-1 35	+1 08	+1 15	-1 00	0.7	0.5	--	--	0.9	198°	--	--	0.6	038°
579	Sunken Ledge, 0.2 n.mi. northwest of	10	42°17.87'	70°57.87'	+0 17	-0 31	+0 28	+0 44	0.3	0.5	0.3	304°	0.4	223°	0.1	307°	0.7	016°
	....do....	20	42°17.87'	70°57.87'	+0 19	+0 29	+0 33	-0 14	0.3	0.4	0.2	299°	0.3	236°	0.2	335°	0.5	030°
581	West Head, Long I., 0.4 n.mi. south of	10	42°18.32'	70°58.28'	+0 24	+0 51	+1 00	+0 17	0.5	0.5	--	--	0.7	231°	--	--	0.6	060°
	....do....	20	42°18.32'	70°58.28'	+0 06	+1 05	+0 55	+0 13	0.4	0.4	0.3	310°	0.5	231°	--	--	0.5	043°
583	Moon Head, 0.4 n.mi. east of	10	42°18.38'	70°58.73'	-0 18	-1 49	-0 30	-1 43	0.3	0.3	--	--	0.3	259°	--	--	0.4	080°
585	West Head, 0.2 n.mi. southwest of	10	42°17.15'	70°57.18'	-0 13	+0 26	+1 00	-0 03	1.1	1.2	0.2	220°	1.4	167°	--	--	1.4	322°
587	Nut Island, 0.4 n.mi. NNE of	10	42°17.08'	70°57.22'	+0 11	+0 30	+1 01	+0 31	1.0	1.2	0.1	245°	1.3	158°	--	--	1.4	312°
	....do....	20	42°17.08'	70°57.22'	+0 11	+0 34	+1 08	+0 29	0.9	1.2	0.1	216°	1.2	155°	--	--	1.4	321°
589	Nut Island, 0.2 n.mi. NNE of	10	42°16.98'	70°57.32'	+0 31	+0 40	+1 15	+0 31	0.9	1.0	0.2	305°	1.2	146°	--	--	1.2	309°
	....do....	20	42°16.98'	70°57.32'	+0 30	+0 43	+1 25	+0 16	0.8	0.8	0.2	314°	1.2	131°	--	--	1.0	303°
591	Peddocks Island, west of	10	42°17.23'	70°57.92'	-0 42	+0 20	-0 04	-0 43	0.4	0.3	--	--	0.5	187°	--	--	0.4	358°
593	Moon Head, 0.9 n.mi. southeast of	20	42°17.50'	70°58.93'	+0 30	+1 09	+1 27	+0 32	0.3	0.3	--	--	0.3	227°	0.2	112°	0.3	033°
595	Squantum, 0.3 n.mi. southeast of	8	42°17.40'	71°00.10'	Current weak and variable													
	BOSTON HARBOR–HINGHAM BAY																	
597	Weir River entrance	10	42°16.53'	70°52.83'	+0 09	+0 39	+0 42	+0 30	0.6	0.6	--	--	0.7	076°	--	--	0.8	272°
599	Strawberry Hill, 0.4 n.mi. west of	6	42°17.40'	70°53.60'	Current weak and variable													
601	Crow Point, 0.2 n.mi. north of	10	42°15.97'	70°53.70'	+0 05	-0 36	+0 04	+1 30	0.2	0.2	--	--	0.3	146°	0.2	241°	0.3	319°
603	Bumkin Island, 0.1 n.mi. west of	10	42°16.85'	70°54.37'	-0 02	+1 18	+0 37	+0 52	0.5	0.6	--	--	0.6	166°	0.1	274°	0.8	320°
	....do....	20	42°16.85'	70°54.37'	-0 23	+1 16	+0 57	+0 41	0.4	0.5	0.1	248°	0.5	161°	0.4	083°	0.6	316°
605	Windmill Point, 0.7 n.mi. SSE of	10	42°17.55'	70°54.97'	-0 02	+0 40	+0 11	-1 41	0.8	0.4	--	--	1.1	128°	0.1	015°	0.4	350°
	....do....	25	42°17.55'	70°54.97'	-0 07	+0 51	+1 41	-0 49	0.8	0.2	--	--	1.0	136°	0.2	263°	0.2	315°
607	Bumkin Island, 0.4 n.mi. west of	10	42°16.83'	70°54.75'	-0 23	See Table 5.	+1 23	-2 58	0.4	0.2	--	--	0.5	195°	--	--	0.3	303°
609	Peddocks Island, east of	20	42°17.50'	70°55.52'		See Table 5.												
611	Sheep Island, 0.3 n.mi. west of	10	42°16.87'	70°55.98'	+0 11	+1 14	+1 15	+0 49	0.8	0.4	0.2	245°	1.0	075°	0.3	328°	0.4	305°
	....do....	25	42°16.87'	70°55.98'	+1 10	+1 14	+1 32	-0 22	0.7	0.3	0.2	150°	0.8	082°	0.1	132°	0.3	300°
613	The Piglets, 0.4 n.mi. northeast of	7d	42°17.00'	70°55.86'	-3 15	-3 54	-5 02	-4 21	0.1	0.3	0.1	298°	0.3	224°	0.1	121°	0.3	041°
	....do....	17d	42°17.00'	70°55.86'	-4 23	-3 54	-4 03	-5 31	0.2	0.4	--	--	0.3	213°	--	--	0.5	041°
	....do....	30d	42°17.00'	70°55.86'	-4 48	-3 21	-4 03	-5 22	0.3	0.4	--	--	0.3	207°	--	--	0.5	036°
615	Pig Rock, north of	10	42°16.93'	70°56.45'	+0 40	-0 15	-0 36	+0 47	0.5	0.8	--	--	0.7	078°	--	--	0.8	290°
	....do....	25	42°16.93'	70°56.45'	+0 35	+0 24	+1 21	+0 22	0.5	0.6	--	--	0.6	082°	0.1	019°	0.8	293°
617	Pig Rock, northwest of	20	42°16.88'	70°56.55'	+1 04	+0 52	+1 53	+1 00	0.8	0.7	--	--	1.0	085°	--	--	0.9	283°
619	Grape Island and Lower Neck, between	10	42°15.87'	70°55.50'	-0 23	-1 16	+0 06	+0 11	0.6	0.7	--	--	0.7	094°	--	--	0.7	281°
621	Grape Island	10	42°16.08'	70°55.88'	-0 47	+0 13	+0 38	-0 18	0.4	0.3	--	--	0.7	203°	--	--	0.4	345°
623	Stodders Neck, Weymouth Back River	10	42°15.20'	70°55.65'	-0 32	+0 54	+0 34	-0 43	0.4	0.2	--	--	0.4	268°	--	--	0.2	093°
625	Jacknife Ledge	6d	42°15.53'	70°56.46'	-0 03	+0 29	+0 59	+0 43	0.4	0.4	0.1	294°	0.5	219°	--	--	0.5	024°
	....do....	16d	42°15.53'	70°56.46'	-0 13	+0 05	+1 09	+0 01	0.4	0.4	--	--	0.5	216°	--	--	0.5	017°
	....do....	32d	42°15.53'	70°56.46'	-0 51	-0 19	+0 59	-0 05	0.3	0.3	--	--	0.5	203°	--	--	0.4	030°
627	Gull Point, 0.4 n.mi. ESE of	10	42°15.18'	70°56.82'	-0 19	-0 32	+0 08	+0 07	0.3	0.4	--	--	0.4	229°	--	--	0.4	069°
	....do....	25	42°15.18'	70°56.82'	-0 49	-0 42	+0 42	+0 07	0.4	0.5	--	--	0.4	235°	--	--	0.5	042°
629	Weymouth Harbor Entrance	6d	42°14.89'	70°57.64'	+0 22	+0 44	+0 55	+0 10	0.6	0.4	--	--	0.5	250°	--	--	0.6	076°
	....do....	16d	42°14.89'	70°57.64'	+0 01	+0 32	+1 06	+0 29	0.6	0.3	--	--	0.7	250°	--	--	0.5	073°
	....do....	29d	42°14.89'	70°57.64'	-0 24	+0 24	+1 13	+0 01	0.3	0.3	--	--	0.3	249°	--	--	0.4	065°
631	Germantown Point	20	42°14.78'	70°57.88'	+0 05	+0 54	+0 49	+0 01	0.3	0.3	--	--	0.4	269°	--	--	0.4	070°
633	Pine Point, southeast of	10	42°14.28'	70°58.08'	Current weak and variable													
635	Philip Head, Town River Bay	10	42°15.00'	70°58.22'	+0 11	+1 33	+1 11	+0 17	0.3	0.2	0.1	294°	0.4	289°	--	--	0.3	095°
637	Hole Point Reach, Town River	10	42°15.23'	70°58.78'	Negligible current													
	CAPE COD BAY																	
639	Barnstable Harbor	7	41°43.6'	70°16.4'	+0 10	+1 03	+0 17	+0 17	0.9	1.1	--	--	1.2	192°	--	--	1.4	004°
641	Sandwich Harbor		41°46'	70°29'	Current weak and variable													

Endnotes can be found at the end of table 2.

TABLE 2. – CURRENT DIFFERENCES AND OTHER CONSTANTS

No.	PLACE	Meter Depth (ft)	Pos. Lat. North	Pos. Long. West	Min. before Flood	Flood	Min. before Ebb	Ebb	Speed Ratio Flood	Speed Ratio Ebb	Min. before Flood (knots)	Dir.	Max. Flood (knots)	Dir.	Min. before Ebb (knots)	Dir.	Max. Ebb (knots)	Dir.
	CAPE COD BAY Time meridian, 75°W																	
643	Sagamore Beach		41°48'	70°31'	on Boston Harbor, p.28													
	MASSACHUSETTS COAST-cont.				Current weak and variable													
					on Pollock Rip Channel, p.44													
645	Nauset Beach Light, 5 miles northeast of		41°56'	69°54'	See table 5.													
647	Georges Bank and vicinity		---	---	See table 5.													
649	Davis Bank		---	---	See table 5.													
651	Monomoy Point, 23 miles east of		41°35'	69°30'	See table 5.													
653	Nantucket Shoals		40°37'	69°37'	See table 5.													
655	Nantucket Island, 28 miles east of		41°20'	69°21'	See table 5.													
657	Old Man Shoal, Nantucket Shoals		41°13.6'	69°59.0'	+1 23	+1 03	+1 17	+1 14	0.9	0.9	--	--	1.9	080°	--	--	1.6	225°
659	Miacomet Pond, 3.0 miles SSE of		41°11.4'	70°05.8'	+2 19	+2 03	+2 22	+2 16	0.6	0.8	--	--	1.3	080°	--	--	1.4	280°
661	Tuckernuck Island, 4.2 miles SSW of		41°13.57'	70°16.90'	+4 08	+3 13	+2 17	+3 56	0.3	0.6	--	--	0.5	090°	--	--	1.0	280°
663	Martha's Vineyard, 1.4 miles S of <1>		41°19.50'	70°39.90'	---	-2 53	---	-2 47	0.1	0.1	--	--	0.3	230°	--	--	0.3	095°
	NANTUCKET SOUND ENTRANCE																	
665	Pollock Rip Channel, east end		41°33.9'	69°55.4'	-0 14	-0 39	-0 23	-0 38	1.0	1.1	--	--	2.0	053°	--	--	1.8	212°
667	POLLOCK RIP CHANNEL (Butler Hole)		41°33'	69°59'	Daily predictions See table 5.								2.0	037°			1.8	226°
669	Great Round Shoal Channel		---	---														
	NANTUCKET SOUND																	
671	Monomoy Pt., channel 0.2 mile west of		41°33.0'	70°01.3'	+0 00	+0 39	+0 18	-0 23	0.8	1.2	--	--	1.7	170°	--	--	2.0	346°
673	Chatham Roads		41°38.6'	70°01.7'	Current weak and variable													
675	Stage Harbor, west of Morris Island		41°39.4'	69°58.5'	+3 07	+1 29	+2 24	+4 28	0.3	0.6	--	--	0.5	335°	--	--	1.0	144°
677	Dennis Port, 2.2 miles south of		41°37.0'	70°06.9'	+1 28	+0 52	+0 27	+1 04	0.2	0.2	0.1	138°	0.3	077°	0.1	052°	0.3	269°
679	Monomoy Point, 6 miles west of		41°33.5'	70°09.0'	+1 22	+1 52	+1 09	+1 22	0.6	0.3	0.1	194°	0.5	090°	0.1	256°	0.5	275°
681	Handkerchief Lighted Whistle Buoy 'H'		41°29.3'	70°04.0'	+1 08	+1 10	+0 49	+0 59	0.6	0.8	--	--	1.3	080°	--	--	1.3	251°
683	Halfmoon Shoal, 1.9 miles northeast of		41°29.05'	70°11.55'	+1 42	+1 49	+1 24	+1 44	0.4	0.3	--	--	0.8	110°	--	--	0.6	265°
685	Halfmoon Shoal, 3.5 miles east of		41°28.1'	70°09.2'	+1 13	+1 23	+1 06	+1 11	0.5	0.6	--	--	1.1	088°	--	--	1.2	295°
687	Great Point, 0.5 mile west of		41°23.6'	70°03.7'	+0 25	+1 37	+0 51	+0 33	0.5	0.7	--	--	1.1	029°	--	--	1.2	195°
689	Great Point, 3 miles west of		41°23.4'	70°06.8'	+1 15	+1 23	+1 13	+1 08	0.4	0.5	--	--	0.8	066°	--	--	0.8	248°
691	Tuckernuck Shoal, off east end		41°24.3'	70°10.4'	+1 22	+1 34	+1 09	+1 10	0.4	0.5	--	--	0.9	113°	0.3	186°	0.8	287°
693	Brant Point, 2 miles NNW of <1>		41°19.25'	70°06.30'	---	+1 43	---	+2 36	0.2	0.2	0.3	000°	0.3	090°	--	--	0.3	275°
695	Nantucket Harbor entrance channel		41°18.4'	70°06.0'	+3 22	+1 55	+2 44	+3 58	0.5	0.9	--	--	1.2	171°	--	--	1.5	350°
697	Eel Pt., Nantucket I. 2.5 miles NE of		41°19.3'	70°10.2'	+1 13	+1 12	+1 02	+1 15	0.3	0.2	--	--	0.6	094°	--	--	0.4	284°
699	Muskeget I., channel 1 mile northeast of		41°21.0'	70°17.1'	+1 29	+0 45	+0 57	+0 56	0.6	0.9	0.2	000°	1.1	108°	--	--	1.5	295°
701	Muskeget Rock, 1.3 miles southwest of		41°19.2'	70°23.6'	+1 10	+0 23	+0 57	+0 18	0.6	0.6	--	--	1.3	024°	--	--	1.0	192°
703	Muskeget Channel		41°20.9'	70°25.2'	+1 40	+0 38	+1 29	+1 02	1.9	1.9	--	--	3.8	021°	--	--	3.3	200°
705	Wasque Point, 2.0 miles southwest of		41°19.90'	70°29.25'	+1 30	+1 04	+1 11	+0 32	0.6	0.6	--	--	1.3	075°	--	--	1.2	280°
707	Long Shoal–Norton Shoal, between		41°24.50'	70°20.00'	+1 31	+1 12	+1 26	+1 13	0.7	0.6	--	--	1.4	100°	--	--	0.9	280°
709	Cape Poge Lt., 1.7 miles SSE of		41°24.0'	70°25.6'	+0 58	-0 07	+0 49	+0 48	0.8	0.7	--	--	1.6	025°	--	--	1.1	260°
711	Cross Rip Channel		41°26.9'	70°17.5'	+1 48	+1 48	+1 55	+1 59	0.6	0.5	--	--	1.3	091°	--	--	0.9	215°
713	Cape Poge Lt., 3.2 miles northeast of		41°27.5'	70°24.0'	+2 42	+2 03	+2 33	+2 37	0.8	0.7	--	--	1.6	095°	--	--	1.2	272°
715	Broken Ground–Horseshoe Shoal, between		41°33.0'	70°17.1'	+1 46	+1 55	+1 15	+1 20	0.5	0.5	--	--	1.1	107°	--	--	0.9	300°
717	Point Gammon, 1.2 miles south of		41°35.3'	70°15.4'	+1 15	+1 03	+1 06	+1 02	0.5	0.6	--	--	1.1	105°	0.1	224°	1.0	276°
719	Hyannis Harbor, entrance off breakwater		41°37.4'	70°17.5'	Current weak and variable													
721	Lewis Bay entrance channel		41°37.9'	70°16.4'	+2 46	+0 53	+2 44	+4 22	0.5	0.8	--	--	0.9	004°	--	--	1.3	184°
723	Cotuit Bay entrance (Bluff Point)		41°36.6'	70°25.8'	+2 44	+2 33	+2 51	+3 35	0.3	0.4	--	--	0.5	035°	--	--	0.7	218°
725	Wreck Shoal–Eldridge Shoal, between		41°32.0'	70°25.7'	+1 47	+1 32	+1 44	+1 45	0.8	0.8	--	--	1.7	062°	--	--	1.4	245°
727	Hedge Fence Lighted Gong Buoy 22		41°28.3'	70°29.00'	+2 48	+2 34	+2 38	+2 44	0.7	0.7	--	--	1.4	108°	--	--	1.2	268°
729	Cape Poge Light, 1.4 miles west of		41°25.45'	70°29.00'	+2 13	+1 54	+1 26	+1 39	0.2	0.1	--	--	0.3	095°	--	--	0.2	250°
731	Edgartown, Inner Harbor		41°23.4'	70°30.5'	+0 25	-1 04	+0 35	-0 20	0.6	0.6	--	--	1.1	075°	--	--	1.1	270°

Endnotes can be found at the end of table 2.

TABLE 2. – CURRENT DIFFERENCES AND OTHER CONSTANTS

No.	PLACE	Meter Depth (ft)	POSITION Latitude North	POSITION Longitude West	TIME DIFFERENCES Min. before Flood	Flood	Min. before Ebb	Ebb	SPEED RATIOS Flood	Ebb	Min. before Flood knots	Dir.	Maximum Flood knots	Dir.	Min. before Ebb knots	Dir.	Maximum Ebb knots	Dir.
	NANTUCKET SOUND Time meridian, 75°W																	
					h m	h m	h m	h m										
					on Pollock Rip Channel, p.44													
733	Katama Pt., 0.6 mi. NNW of, Katama Bay		41°21.9'	70°30.3'	+0 12	−0 43	+0 20	−0 31	0.3	0.3	– –	– –	0.6	325°	– –	– –	0.5	180°
735	East Chop–Squash Meadow, between		41°27.9'	70°32.2'	+2 07	+0 47	+1 43	+1 12	0.2	0.1	– –	– –	0.3	325°	– –	– –	0.2	195°
737	East Chop, 1 mile north of		41°29.1'	70°33.5'	+2 40	+1 46	+2 17	+1 57	0.2	0.2	– –	– –	0.4	325°	– –	– –	0.3	175°
739	Vineyard Haven		41°28.1'	70°35.2'	Current weak and variable				0.7	1.1	– –	– –	1.4	131°	– –	– –	1.8	329°
741	West Chop, 0.8 mile north of		41°29.6'	70°35.7'	+2 49	+1 58	+1 58	+2 04	1.1	1.3	– –	– –	2.2	116°	– –	– –	2.2	297°
743	Hedge Fence–L'Hommedieu Shoal, between		41°30.3'	70°32.2'	+2 27	+1 38	+2 20	+2 35	1.6	1.8	– –	– –	3.1	096°	– –	– –	3.0	282°
745	Waquoit Bay entrance		41°32.9'	70°31.8'	+3 21	+2 14	+3 40	+2 11	1.0	1.3	– –	– –	2.1	106°	– –	– –	2.2	276°
747	L'Hommedieu Shoal, north of west end		41°31.6'	70°34.6'	+2 30	+2 03	+2 12	+4 01	0.8	0.8	– –	– –	1.5	348°	– –	– –	1.4	203°
749	Nobska Point, 1.8 miles east of		41°31.1'	70°37.1'	+2 13	+1 45	+1 55	+1 49	1.2	1.0	– –	– –	2.3	080°	– –	– –	2.3	268°
	VINEYARD SOUND																	
751	West Chop, 0.2 mile west of		41°29.0'	70°36.6'	+1 19	+1 34	+1 50	+1 16	1.3	0.8	– –	– –	2.7	059°	– –	– –	1.4	241°
753	Nobska Point, 1 mile southeast of		41°30.1'	70°38.6'	+2 33	+2 15	+2 25	+2 19	1.3	1.4	– –	– –	2.6	071°	– –	– –	2.4	259°
755	Norton Point, 0.5 mile north of		41°28.1'	70°39.9'	+1 55	+1 44	+2 01	+1 12	1.7	1.4	– –	– –	3.4	050°	– –	– –	2.4	240°
757	Tarpaulin Cove, 1.5 miles east of		41°28.3'	70°43.5'	+2 49	+2 07	+2 12	+2 33	1.0	1.4	– –	– –	1.9	055°	– –	– –	2.3	232°
759	Robinsons Hole, 1.2 miles southeast of		41°26.1'	70°46.8'	+2 30	+1 51	+2 11	+2 02	1.0	1.2	– –	– –	1.9	060°	– –	– –	2.1	240°
761	Gay Head, 3 miles northeast of		41°23.1'	70°47.0'	+2 25	+1 50	+1 42	+2 11	0.5	0.8	– –	– –	0.9	081°	– –	– –	1.3	238°
763	Menemsha Bight <6>		41°24.1'	70°46.3'														
765	Gay Head, 3 miles north of		41°24.1'	70°51.2'	+2 13	+1 24	+1 55	+1 17	0.6	0.7	– –	– –	1.1	074°	– –	– –	1.2	255°
767	Gay Head, 1.5 miles northwest of		41°21.8'	70°51.8'	+1 30	+0 54	+1 42	+1 16	1.0	1.2	– –	– –	2.0	012°	– –	– –	2.0	249°
769	Cuttyhunk Island, 3.2 miles southwest of		41°23'	71°00'	See table 5.		See table 5.											
771	Browns Ledge		41°19.8'	71°05.9'	See table 5.		See table 5.											
	VINEYARD SOUND–BUZZARDS BAY <59>																	
					on Woods Hole, p.32													
773	*Woods Hole,* Juniper Point	5d	41°30.95'	70°40.30'	+0 10	+0 10	+0 06	+0 26	0.8	0.4	0.1	074°	1.6	165°	0.1	247°	1.2	331°
	…do.	15d	41°30.95'	70°40.30'	+0 10	+0 10	+0 06	+0 28	0.7	0.4	0.1	076°	1.6	166°	0.1	247°	1.2	333°
	…do.	29d	41°30.95'	70°40.30'	+0 06	+0 10	+0 06	+0 12	0.7	0.4	– –	– –	1.6	169°	0.1	249°	1.1	333°
775	**WOODS HOLE, THE STRAIT**	14d	41°31.16'	70°40.97'	Daily predictions				1.6	1.2	– –	– –	2.2	079°	0.1	354°	2.9	267°
	…do.	5d	41°31.16'	70°40.97'	−0 06	−0 03	−0 06	+0 06	0.3	0.8	– –	– –	3.4	077°	0.1	350°	3.4	261°
	…do.	21d	41°31.16'	70°40.97'	+0 18	+0 14	−0 17	+0 01	0.6	0.5	0.1	277°	0.7	096°	– –	– –	2.4	274°
777	North end	4d	41°31.38'	70°41.58'	−0 21	−0 02	−0 08	−0 05	0.6	0.4	– –	– –	1.2	195°	– –	– –	1.3	004°
	…do.	17d	41°31.38'	70°41.58'	−0 17	−0 09	+0 01	+0 26	0.4	1.0	0.1	283°	0.9	197°	– –	– –	1.1	013°
779	Robinsons Hole, Nashuon Point	4d	41°26.98'	70°48.40'	+0 39	+0 15	+0 40	+0 24	1.4	1.0	– –	– –	3.0	151°	– –	– –	2.9	332°
	…do.	14d	41°26.98'	70°48.40'	+0 36	+0 16	+0 40	+0 25	1.3	1.0	– –	– –	2.8	153°	– –	– –	2.6	330°
	…do.	24d	41°26.98'	70°48.40'	+0 31	+0 16	+0 40	+0 25	1.1	0.9	– –	– –	2.4	157°	– –	– –	2.6	329°
781	*Quicks Hole,* South end	7d	41°26.3'	70°50.5'	+1 17	+1 07	+0 29	+0 09	0.9	0.7	– –	– –	1.9	140°	– –	– –	2.0	300°
783	Middle	17d	41°26.56'	70°50.89'	+1 29	+1 05	+0 59	+0 52	1.1	0.6	0.1	242°	2.3	157°	0.2	244°	1.8	327°
	…do.	40d	41°26.56'	70°50.89'	+1 27	+1 02	+0 58	+0 51	1.0	0.6	0.1	244°	2.1	156°	0.1	243°	1.7	329°
785	…do.		41°26.56'	70°50.89'	+1 20	+1 02	+0 57	+0 47	0.7	0.4	– –	– –	2.0	153°	– –	– –	1.2	336°
787	North end	4d	41°27.1'	70°51.0'	+1 41	+0 36	+0 56	−0 21	0.9	0.9	– –	– –	2.0	165°	– –	– –	2.6	002°
	Canapitsit Channel	4d	41°25.45'	70°54.47'	+1 02	+0 57	+0 14	−0 18	0.8	0.5	– –	– –	1.7	131°	– –	– –	1.6	312°
	BUZZARDS BAY <7>																	
789	Westport River entrance		41°30.5'	71°05.3'	−1 15	−1 23	−1 26	−1 49	1.0	0.9	– –	– –	2.2	290°	– –	– –	2.5	108°
791	Gooseberry Neck, 2 miles SSE of		41°27'	71°01'	See table 5.													
793	Ribbon Reef–Sow & Pigs Reef, between		41°25.3'	70°58.2'	−1 43	−2 49	−2 30	−2 30	0.4	0.4	– –	– –	0.8	062°	– –	– –	1.2	237°
795	Penikese Island, 0.8 mile northwest of		41°27.9'	70°56.2'	−3 01	−1 43	−1 55	−1 33	0.6	0.6	– –	– –	1.2	050°	– –	– –	1.1	254°
797	Penikese Island, 0.2 mile south of		41°26.6'	70°55.5'	−3 07	−1 33	−2 30	−3 15	0.3	0.3	– –	– –	0.7	093°	– –	– –	0.9	287°
799	Gull I. and Nashawena I., between		41°26.2'	70°54.2'	−3 39	−2 15	−3 01	−3 17	0.4	0.4	– –	– –	0.9	091°	– –	– –	1.1	247°
801	Weepecket Island, south of		41°30.4'	70°44.3'	−4 40	−2 25	−2 28	−3 03	0.4	0.2	– –	– –	0.8	069°	– –	– –	0.6	255°

Endnotes can be found at the end of table 2.

TABLE 2. – CURRENT DIFFERENCES AND OTHER CONSTANTS

No.	PLACE	Meter Depth (ft)	Latitude North	Longitude West	Min. before Flood (h m)	Flood (h m)	Min. before Ebb (h m)	Ebb (h m)	SR Flood	SR Ebb	Min. before Flood knots	Dir.	Max. Flood knots	Dir.	Min. before Ebb knots	Dir.	Max. Ebb knots	Dir.
	BUZZARDS BAY <7> Time meridian, 75°W					on Woods Hole, p.32												
803	Quamquisset Harbor entrance		41°32.4'	70°39.8'	Current weak and variable						--	--	0.4	--	--	--	0.3	--
805	West Falmouth Harbor entrance		41°36.5'	70°39.3'	Current weak and variable						--	--	--	--	--	--	1.1	--
807	Dumpling Rocks, 0.2 mile southeast of		41°32.0'	70°55.1'	-3 07	-2 21	-2 32	-2 45	0.4	0.4	--	--	0.8	066°	--	--	1.1	190°
809	Apponagansett Bay		41°35'	70°57'	Current weak and variable						--	--	--	--	--	--	--	--
811	Clarks Cove		41°36'	70°55'	Current weak and variable						--	--	--	--	--	--	1.2	134°
813	New Bedford Hurricane Barrier <65>	4d	41°37.39'	70°54.31'	-2 08	-2 00	-2 46	-2 22	0.2	0.4	--	--	0.3	320°	--	--	1.2	134°
	do.	14d	41°37.39'	70°54.31'	-2 40	-2 15	-2 17	-2 17	0.2	0.3	--	--	0.4	319°	--	--	1.0	134°
	do.	24d	41°37.39'	70°54.31'	-3 15	-2 34	-1 51	-2 10	0.2	0.3	--	--	0.4	318°	--	--	0.8	134°
815	West Island and Long Island, between		41°35.6'	70°50.4'	Current weak and variable						--	--	--	--	--	--	0.4	--
817	West Island, 1 mile Southeast of	4d	41°33.94'	70°48.66'	-1 48	-1 55	-2 26	-2 11	0.3	0.3	0.1	139°	0.6	072°	0.2	149°	0.9	225°
	do.	15d	41°33.94'	70°48.66'	-2 05	-2 03	-2 26	-2 19	0.3	0.2	0.1	147°	0.6	069°	0.1	152°	0.7	233°
	do.	27d	41°33.94'	70°48.66'	-3 12	-2 17	-2 39	-2 28	0.2	0.1	--	--	0.4	066°	--	--	0.4	243°
819	Nasketucket Bay		41°37.1'	70°50.2'	Current weak and variable						--	--	0.3	--	--	--	0.3	--
821	Mattapoisett Harbor		41°38'	70°47'	Current weak and variable						--	--	--	--	--	--	--	--
						on Cape Cod Canal, p.36												
823	Cleveland Ledge	8d	41°37.93'	70°41.81'	-0 19	-0 25	-1 06	+0 05	0.1	0.1	--	--	0.4	037°	--	--	0.4	212°
	do.	15d	41°37.93'	70°41.81'	-0 36	-0 30	-1 12	-1 03	0.1	0.1	--	--	0.4	041°	--	--	0.4	213°
	do.	34d	41°37.93'	70°41.81'	-2 01	-1 04	-1 43	-1 47	0.1	0.1	--	--	0.3	033°	--	--	0.3	217°
825	Megansett Harbor		41°38.8'	70°39.2'	Current weak and variable						--	--	--	--	--	--	--	--
827	Abiels ledge	3d	41°41.38'	70°40.25'	+0 08	-0 14	-0 20	+0 02	0.3	0.4	0.2	155°	1.3	069°	0.1	159°	1.8	236°
	do.	15d	41°41.38'	70°40.25'	+0 15	-0 16	-0 19	+0 02	0.3	0.4	--	--	1.3	063°	0.1	155°	1.7	235°
	do.	31d	41°41.38'	70°40.25'	+0 17	-0 10	-0 15	+0 03	0.2	0.3	--	--	1.0	059°	0.1	326°	1.4	235°
829	Sippican Harbor		41°41'	70°44'	Current weak and variable						--	--	0.4	--	--	--	0.4	--
831	Wareham River, off Long Beach Point		41°44.0'	70°43.0'	-2 09	-0 33	-1 38	-1 24	0.1	0.1	--	--	0.6	022°	--	--	0.6	202°
833	Wareham River, off Barneys Point		41°44.7'	70°42.4'	-2 17	-0 29	-1 38	-1 32	0.2	0.1	--	--	0.7	010°	--	--	0.6	185°
835	Hog Neck	2d	41°43.43'	70°38.36'	-0 03	-0 04	-0 08	-0 11	0.8	0.6	--	--	3.4	035°	0.2	123°	3.0	210°
	do.	15d	41°43.43'	70°38.36'	+0 00	-0 07	-0 10	-0 03	0.8	0.6	--	--	3.2	038°	0.2	122°	2.9	209°
	do.	28d	41°43.43'	70°38.36'	+0 02	-0 05	-0 12	-0 05	0.6	0.5	--	--	2.6	038°	0.2	120°	2.4	208°
	CAPE COD CANAL					Daily predictions												
837	CAPE COD CANAL, Railroad Bridge, midchannel	13d	41°44.52'	70°36.83'	-0 03	+0 11	-0 02	-0 05	0.8	0.8	0.1	336°	4.3	066°	0.1	337°	4.9	248°
	Cape Cod Canal, RR Bridge, 70ft from N shore	13d	41°44.55'	70°36.84'	-0 01	+0 38	+0 02	-0 14	0.7	0.8	--	--	3.4	068°	--	--	3.9	248°
	Cape Cod Canal, RR Bridge, 400ft from N shore	13d	41°44.50'	70°36.81'	-0 08	-0 15	+0 02	-0 13	0.7	0.8	0.1	332°	3.2	060°	0.1	332°	4.1	244°
839	Bourne Highway bridge		41°45'	70°35'	-0 01	+0 01	-0 07	+0 01	0.7	0.8	--	--	3.3	065°	--	--	4.0	245°
841	Bournedale	13d	41°45.99'	70°34.02'	+0 00	+0 01	-0 08	+0 00	0.7	0.7	--	--	3.2	037°	--	--	3.7	219°
	do.	30d	41°45.99'	70°34.02'	+0 00	+0 02	-0 09	-0 01	0.6	0.6	--	--	2.9	037°	--	--	3.5	217°
	do.	46d	41°45.99'	70°34.02'	-0 05	+0 05	-0 06	+0 00	0.6	0.6	--	--	2.4	037°	--	--	2.9	214°
843	Sagamore Bridge	6d	41°46.57'	70°32.60'	-0 05	+0 01	-0 07	+0 02	0.7	0.7	--	--	3.6	077°	--	--	3.7	260°
	do.	26d	41°46.57'	70°32.60'	-0 06	+0 00	-0 07	+0 03	0.6	0.7	--	--	3.1	079°	--	--	3.2	259°
	do.	42d	41°46.57'	70°32.60'	-0 13	-0 14	-0 12	-0 05	0.6	0.6	0.1	169°	2.7	082°	--	--	2.8	256°
845	Cape Cod Canal, east end	8d	41°46.53'	70°29.96'	-0 14	-0 16	-0 13	-0 06	0.8	0.7	--	--	3.4	053°	--	--	3.3	233°
	do.	15d	41°46.53'	70°29.96'	-0 10	-0 08	-0 18	-0 06	0.8	0.7	--	--	3.3	053°	--	--	3.3	232°
	do.	34d	41°46.53'	70°29.96'					0.5	0.6	--	--	2.0	048°	--	--	2.7	231°
	NARRAGANSETT BAY <8>					on Pollock Rip Channel, p.44												
847	Sakonnet River (except Narrows)		- - -	- - -	Current weak and variable						--	--	--	--	--	--	--	--
849	Black Point, SW of, Sakonnet River	15	41°30.4'	71°13.2'	-2 54	-1 55	-2 13	-2 26	0.2	0.2	--	--	0.4	012°	--	--	0.4	194°
851	Almy Point Bridge, south of, Sakonnet River	15	41°37.3'	71°13.2'	-3 00	-2 10	-2 30	-3 13	0.8	0.8	--	--	0.4	034°	--	--	1.5	180°
853	Tiverton, Stone bridge, Sakonnet R. <9>		41°37.5'	71°13.0'	-2 58	-2 02	-2 26	-3 06	1.4	1.6	--	--	2.7	010°	--	--	2.7	190°
						-2 54			0.3		--	--	0.6	010°	--	--		
						-0 36			1.3		--	--	2.5	010°	--	--		
855	Tiverton, RR. bridge, Sakonnet R. <10>		41°38.3'	71°12.9'	-3 26	-5 06	-2 48	-3 41	1.2	1.4	--	--	2.3	000°	--	--	2.4	180°

Endnotes can be found at the end of table 2.

TABLE 2. – CURRENT DIFFERENCES AND OTHER CONSTANTS

No.	PLACE	Meter Depth (ft)	Position Latitude North	Position Longitude West	Time Diff. Min. before Flood (h m)	Time Diff. Flood (h m)	Time Diff. Min. before Ebb (h m)	Time Diff. Ebb (h m)	Speed Ratio Flood	Speed Ratio Ebb	Avg Min. before Flood (knots)	Dir.	Avg Max Flood (knots)	Dir.	Avg Min. before Ebb (knots)	Dir.	Avg Max Ebb (knots)	Dir.
	NARRAGANSETT BAY <8> Time meridian, 75°W																	
857	Common Fence Point, northeast of	10	41° 39.5'	71° 12.5'	**on Pollock Rip Channel, p.44**													
857					-2 38	-4 50	-2 32	-2 41	0.1	0.2	--	--	0.2	026°	--	--	0.3	210°
859	Brenton Point, 1.4 n.mi. southwest of	7	41° 25.9'	71° 22.6'	-1 03	-0 58	-1 20	-1 04	0.1	0.4	--	--	0.1	058°	--	--	0.6	170°
861	Castle Hill, west of, East Passage	15	41° 27.4'	71° 22.7'	-0 06	-0 42	-1 07	-0 29	0.1	0.7	--	--	0.1	046°	--	--	1.2	237°
863	Bull Point, east of	10	41° 28.8'	71° 21.0'	-1 10	-0 47	-1 10	-1 33	0.2	0.8	--	--	0.4	347°	--	--	1.5	206°
865	Mackerel Cove		41° 28.5'	71° 22.8'	Current weak and variable				0.4		--	--	0.7	013°	--	--	--	--
867	Newport Harbor, S and E of Goat Island		41° 29'	71° 20'	Current weak and variable				0.6		--	--	1.2	001°	--	--	--	--
869	Rose Island, northeast of	15	41° 30.2'	71° 19.9'	-1 57	-0 07	-1 17	-2 08	0.4	0.5	0.1	105°	0.8	310°	0.1	102°	1.0	124°
871	Rose Island, northwest of	15	41° 30.4'	71° 21.1'	-1 38	-0 26	-1 38	-1 39	0.4	0.5	--	--	0.7	007°	--	--	1.0	190°
873	Rose Island, west of		41° 29.8'	71° 21.0'	-0 42	-0 34	-1 20	-1 28	0.4	0.6	--	--	0.7	001°	--	--	1.0	172°
875	Gould Island, southeast of	7	41° 31.5'	71° 20.2'	-1 40	-1 28	-1 14	-1 16	0.3	0.4	--	--	0.5	033°	--	--	0.7	217°
877	Gould Island, west of	15	41° 31.9'	71° 21.5'	-0 16	-0 32	-1 13	-1 07	0.3	0.4	--	--	0.6	351°	0.1	279°	0.8	193°
879	Dyer Island–Carrs Point (between)		41° 34.5'	71° 17.8'	-1 56	-1 13	-0 50	-1 37	0.4	0.4	--	--	0.8	040°	--	--	0.6	236°
881	Conanicut Point, ENE of	15	41° 34.5'	71° 20.5'	-2 05	-0 24	-1 18	-1 13	0.2	0.2	0.1	111°	0.4	018°	0.1	106°	0.4	183°
883	Dyer Island, west of	7	41° 35.2'	71° 18.5'	-1 04	-0 46	-0 53	-1 34	0.4	0.6	--	--	0.8	023°	--	--	1.0	216°
885	QUONSET POINT	16	41° 35.01'	71° 23.74'	**Daily Predictions, p.40**				0.6	0.8	--	--	0.3	021°	--	--	1.4	200°
887	Mount Hope Bridge		41° 38.4'	71° 15.5'	-1 22	-1 34	-1 08	-0 58	0.6	0.8	0.1	282°	1.1	047°	--	--	0.4	230°
889	Hog Island, northwest of	10	41° 39.0'	71° 17.7'	-2 16	-0 04	-0 30	-1 04	0.2	0.2	--	--	0.4	011°	0.1	133°	0.7	199°
891	Common Fence Point, west of	10	41° 40.8'	71° 14.7'	-1 13	+0 08	-1 00	-0 57	0.2	0.4	--	--	0.5	050°	--	--	0.4	224°
893	Mount Hope Point, northeast of	10	41° 41.9'	71° 12.7'	-2 01	-0 20	-1 03	-0 37	0.2	0.2	--	--	0.4	038°	0.1	121°	0.4	217°
895	Kickamuit R. (Narrows), Mt. Hope Bay			71° 14.7'	-2 04	-3 34	-1 19	-0 48	0.7	1.0	--	--	1.4	000°	--	--	1.7	191°
897	Warren River entrance		41° 42.7'	71° 17.8'	Current weak and variable				0.5	0.5	--	--	0.9	000°	--	--	0.3	200°
899	Warren, Warren River		41° 43.7'	71° 23.6'	Current weak and variable				0.3	0.6	--	--	1.0	358°	--	--	0.9	171°
901	Beavertail Point, 0.8 mile northwest of		41° 27.5'	71° 24.7'	-0 14	+0 11	-1 05	-1 05	0.2	0.5	--	--	0.4	003°	--	--	1.0	188°
903	Dutch Island, east of, West Passage	15	41° 30.2'	71° 23.7'	-0 11	-0 54	-1 31	-0 19	0.2	0.6	0.1	103°	0.4	035°	0.2	126°	0.9	186°
905	Dutch Island and Beaver Head, between	7	41° 29.8'	71° 24.2'	-3 02	-5 10	-2 37	-2 46	0.3	0.5	--	--	0.6	032°	--	--	1.0	233°
907	Dutch Island, west of	15	41° 30.3'	71° 24.6'	-1 56	-1 32	-1 58	-1 47	0.3	0.6	--	--	0.6	038°	--	--	1.2	206°
909	Jamestown–North Kingstown Bridge		41° 31.8'	71° 23.8'	-1 33	-1 49	-1 21	-1 16	0.7	0.7	0.1	112°	1.3	030°	0.1	097°	1.3	176°
911	Wickford Harbor		41° 34'	71° 26'	Current weak and variable				0.4	0.5	--	--	0.3	--	--	--	0.3	--
913	Greenwich Bay entrance		41° 40.0'	71° 23.6'	Current weak and variable				0.3	0.5	--	--	0.3	--	--	--	0.4	--
915	Patience Island, narrows east of		41° 39.5'	71° 21.2'	-2 41	-2 29	-2 44	-2 37	0.4	0.5	--	--	0.7	354°	--	--	0.9	157°
917	Patience I. and Warwick Neck, between		41° 39.8'	71° 22.4'	-1 40	-1 21	-1 18	-1 13	0.3	0.5	--	--	0.6	040°	--	--	0.8	224°
919	Nayatt Point, WNW of	10	41° 43.7'	71° 21.6'	-2 24	+0 47	-1 00	-1 11	0.1	0.1	--	--	0.2	325°	--	--	0.2	128°
921	India Point RR. bridge, Seekonk River <9>		41° 49.0'	71° 23.3'	-1 48	-4 02	-1 31	-1 06	0.5	0.8	0.1	--	1.0	020°	--	--	1.4	180°
923	Fox Point, south of, Providence River	10	41° 48.8'	71° 24.0'	-3 02	+0 08	-0 27	-1 34	0.7	0.1	--	--	1.3	020°	--	--	0.1	166°
925	Cold Spring Pt., Seekonk River <10>		41° 49.6'	71° 22.8'	-1 48	-4 14	-1 31	-1 02	0.4	0.8	--	--	0.8	343°	--	--	1.4	210°
	BLOCK ISLAND SOUND				**on The Race, p.48**													
	Point Judith																	
927	Harbor of Refuge, south entrance		41° 21.48'	71° 29.75'	-2 25	-2 53	-2 47	-3 02	0.2	0.2	--	--	0.6	335°	--	--	0.7	181°
929	Harbor of Refuge, west entrance		41° 22'	71° 31'	See table 5.													
931	Pond entrance – Point Judith		41° 23'	71° 31'	-3 15	-3 06	-3 06	-4 04	0.6	0.4	--	--	1.8	351°	--	--	1.5	186°
933	2.4 miles southwest of		41° 19.87'	71° 30.65'	-0 40	+0 06	+0 28	-0 36	0.2	0.1	--	--	0.7	258°	--	--	0.6	090°
935	4.5 miles southwest of		41° 18'	71° 33'	See table 5.													

Endnotes can be found at the end of table 2.

TABLE 2. – CURRENT DIFFERENCES AND OTHER CONSTANTS

No.	PLACE	Meter Depth (ft)	Latitude North	Longitude West	TIME DIFFERENCES Min. before Flood (h m)	Flood (h m)	Min. before Ebb (h m)	Ebb (h m)	SPEED RATIOS Flood	Ebb	AVG Min. before Flood knots	Dir.	Max. Flood knots	Dir.	Min. before Ebb knots	Dir.	Max. Ebb knots	Dir.
	BLOCK ISLAND SOUND Time meridian, 75°W						**on The Race, p.48**											
	Block Island																	
937	4 miles north of		41° 18'	71° 32'	−0 32	−0 05	+0 31	+0 06	0.2	0.2			0.8	285°			0.8	076°
939	Sandy Point, 2.1 miles NNE of	15	41° 15.85'	71° 34.00'	+0 17	−0 58	−0 20	−0 55	0.3	0.4			1.0	296°			1.7	066°
941	Sandy Pt., 1.5 miles north of	7	41° 15.35'	71° 34'	−0 24	−0 38	−1 07	−1 05	0.6	0.5			1.9	315°			2.1	063°
943	Clay Head, 1.2 miles ENE of	15	41° 13.35'	71° 31.85'	−2 20	−1 37	+0 49	−1 07	0.2	0.1			0.7	298°			0.5	164°
945	Old Harbor Pt., 0.5 mile southeast of		41° 09'	71° 32'	−0 12	−0 37	−0 38	−0 06	0.1	0.1			0.2	336°			0.6	175°
947	Lewis Pt., 1.0 mile southwest of		41° 08.20'	71° 37.30'	−1 29	−1 13	−0 24	−1 25	0.6	0.4			1.9	298°			1.8	136°
949	Lewis Pt., 1.5 miles west of		41° 09'	71° 38'	−1 33	−1 23	−0 48	−1 12	0.4	0.4			1.4	318°			1.7	170°
951	Great Salt Pond entrance		41° 11.97'	71° 35.50'	−4 10	−3 40	−3 24	−4 34	0.1	0.1			0.3	165°			0.3	326°
953	Great Salt Pond ent., 1 mile NW of <1>	7	41° 12'	71° 36'	−0 54	−1 06	−1 54	−0 47	0.1	0.1			0.4	158°			0.4	035°
955	Sandy Point, 0.4 mile west of <1>		41° 13.80'	71° 35.13'		−1 29		−1 47		0.2							0.7	011°
957	Green Hill Point, 1.1 miles south of		41° 20.90'	71° 35.77'	−0 58	−0 52	−0 24	−1 07	0.2	0.1			0.6	258°			0.4	070°
959	Sandy Point, 4.1 miles northwest of	15	41° 17.60'	71° 38.00'	+0 04	+0 06	+0 32	−0 08	0.2	0.2			0.7	270°			0.6	084°
961	Grace Point, 2.0 miles northwest of		41° 12'	71° 38'	See table 5.													
963	Quonochontaug Beach, 1.1 miles S of		41° 18.80'	71° 42.82'	−0 43	+0 01	+0 47	−0 32	0.3	0.2			1.1	248°			0.4	078°
965	Quonochontaug Beach, 3.8 miles S of	15	41° 16.35'	71° 43'	+0 03	+0 11	+0 39	−0 04	0.2	0.2			0.7	243°			0.6	058°
967	Lewis Point, 6.0 miles WNW of	15	41° 11.60'	71° 44.20'	+0 59	+0 35	+0 16	+0 23	0.5	0.3			0.6	286°			1.2	097°
969	Southwest Ledge		41° 07'	71° 42'	−0 35	−0 41	−0 14	−0 23	0.4	0.5			1.5	321°			2.1	141°
971	Southwest Ledge, 2.0 miles west of	15	41° 06.80'	71° 43.00'	+0 10	+0 05	+0 11	−0 53	0.4	0.2			1.5	354°			1.9	168°
973	Watch Hill Point, 2.2 miles east of		41° 18.16'	71° 48.60'	−0 29	−0 13	+0 45	−0 33	0.4	0.3			1.2	260°			0.7	086°
975	Watch Hill Point, 5.2 miles SSE of	15d	41° 13.20'	71° 49.00'	+0 35	+0 13	+0 39	+0 00	0.3	0.4			0.7	265°			1.2	064°
977	Watch Hill Point, 5.3 n.mi. SE of	15	41° 14.65'	71° 46.43'	−0 08	−0 11	−0 17	−0 03	0.3	0.2	0.1	176°	1.1	279°			0.9	092°
979	Montauk Point, 5.4 miles NNE of		41° 09.55'	71° 49.48'	+0 33	−0 08	−0 38	−0 04	0.3	0.4			2.8	346°			1.6	079°
981	Montauk Point, 1.2 miles east of		41° 04.50'	71° 49.80'	−1 22	−1 14	−0 38	−2 05	0.8	0.7			2.4	356°			2.8	162°
983	Montauk Point, 1 mile northeast of		41° 05'	71° 51'	−2 04	−1 37	−1 14	−1 56	0.7	0.5			1.7	321°			1.9	145°
985	Wicopesset Island, NE of	8d	41° 17.90'	71° 54.06'	−0 55	−1 18	−0 58	−1 15	0.5	0.6	0.1	036°	1.6	342°			2.4	125°
985	do.	25d	41° 17.90'	71° 54.06'	−1 13	−1 20	−1 03	−1 24	0.5	0.5	0.1	225°	0.9	327°	0.1	048°	1.9	132°
985	do.	44d	41° 17.90'	71° 54.06'	−1 27	−1 08	−0 59	−1 26	0.3	0.3	0.1	238°	1.1	236°	0.2	048°	1.4	141°
987	East Pt., 4.1 miles S of Fishers Island	15	41° 13.40'	71° 55.50'	+0 50	+0 27	+0 19	+0 00	0.5	0.4			1.9	256°			1.8	073°
989	Cerberus Shoal, 1.5 miles east of	15	41° 10.45'	71° 55.17'	−0 15	+0 20	−0 23	−1 04	0.3	0.4			1.2	241°			1.8	092°
991	Shagwong Reef & Cerberus Shoal, between		41° 07.90'	71° 55.50'	−0 30	−0 52	−0 25	−1 10	0.6	0.6			1.2	226°			1.8	056°
993	Montauk Harbor entrance	6	41° 04.78'	71° 56.35'	−2 17	−2 52	−3 02	−5 01	0.4	0.1							0.6	033°
								−2 44		0.1							0.5	024°
								−0 56		0.1							0.2	353°
995	Mt. Prospect, 0.6 mile SSE of	15	41° 14.75'	71° 59.80'	−0 34	−0 11	+0 10	−1 11	0.5	0.4			1.7	275°			1.6	054°
997	Cerberus Shoal and Fishers I., between	7	41° 13'	71° 58'	−0 59	−0 13	+0 07	−0 21	0.4	0.3			1.3	264°			1.3	096°
999	Little Gull Island, 3.7 miles ESE of		41° 10.7'	72° 02.1'	See table 5.													
1001	Gardiners Island, 3 miles northeast of	10	41° 07.9'	72° 02.0'	−0 47	−1 04	−0 25	−0 41	0.3	0.2			0.9	305°			1.0	138°
1003	Eastern Plain Pt., 3.9 miles ENE of		41° 07.05'	71° 59.80'	−1 01	−1 30	−0 22	−1 13	0.4	0.2			1.0	246°			0.6	096°
1005	Little Gull Island, 0.8 mile SSE of <43>		41° 11.67'	72° 06.23'	−2 10	−0 55	−0 23	−3 14	0.4	0.1			1.3	331°			0.1	105°
								−2 06									0.6	252°
								−0 44									0.1	174°
1007	Rocky Point, 2 miles WNW of	15	41° 03.55'	72° 01.80'	−1 22	−1 06	−0 49	−1 11	0.1	0.1	0.1	192°	0.3	255°	0.2	340°	0.3	065°
	GARDINERS BAY, etc.																	
1009	Goff Point, 0.4 mile northwest of		41° 01.49'	72° 03.75'	−1 46	−2 30	−1 25	−2 43	0.4	0.4			1.2	225°			1.6	010°
1011	Acabonack Hbr. ent., 0.6 mile ESE of		41° 01.30'	72° 07.40'	−1 34	−2 15	−1 05	−2 42	0.4	0.3			1.4	345°			1.2	140°
1013	Hog Creek Point, north of		41° 04.10'	72° 09.70'	−0 56	−0 54	−1 21	−2 04	0.1	0.1			0.3	281°			0.3	067°
1015	Ram Island, 2.2 miles east of		41° 04.70'	72° 13.80'	−0 19	−0 29	−0 14	−0 24	0.1	0.1			0.2	250°			0.3	090°
1017	Orient Point, 2.4 miles SSE of		41° 07.50'	72° 12.30'	+0 19	−0 39	+1 11	−0 43	0.4	0.4			0.4	250°			0.3	025°
1019	Gardiners Pt. Ruins, 1.1 miles N of		41° 09.50'	72° 08.83'	−0 12	−0 22	−0 09	−0 09	0.4	0.3			1.2	270°			1.8	066°
1021	Gardiners Point & Plum Island, between	15	41° 09.33'	72° 09.52'	−0 18	−0 36	−0 32	−0 42	0.4	0.4			1.4	288°			0.6	100°
1023	Ram Island, 1.4 miles NNE of		41° 05.8'	72° 15.8'	+0 01	−0 07	+0 07	+0 05	0.1	0.1			0.4	240°			1.8	075°
1025	Long Beach Pt., 0.7 mile southwest of	15	41° 06.25'	72° 18.40'	+0 33	−0 16	+0 44	−0 12	0.4	0.4			1.3	307°			0.6	101°
1027	Hay Beach Point, 0.3 mile NW of <44>		41° 06.65'	72° 20.43'	+0 40	+0 15	+1 01	−1 03	0.5	0.3			1.5	210°			1.2	025°

Endnotes can be found at the end of table 2.

TABLE 2. – CURRENT DIFFERENCES AND OTHER CONSTANTS

No.	PLACE	Meter Depth (ft)	Lat. North	Long. West	Min. before Flood (h m)	Flood (h m)	Min. before Ebb (h m)	Ebb (h m)	Speed Ratio Flood	Speed Ratio Ebb	Min. before Flood knots	Min. before Flood Dir.	Max. Flood knots	Max. Flood Dir.	Min. before Ebb knots	Min. before Ebb Dir.	Max. Ebb knots	Max. Ebb Dir.
	GARDINERS BAY, etc. Time meridian, 75°W					on The Race, p.48												
1029	Jennings Point, 0.2 mile NNW of	13	41° 04.48'	72° 22.95'	+0 32	+0 04	+0 37	-0 09	0.5	0.4	--	--	1.6	290°	--	--	1.5	055°
1031	Cedar Point, 0.2 mile west of		41° 02.38'	72° 16.07'	-0 11	-0 21	+0 29	-0 53	0.7	0.5	--	--	1.8	195°	--	--	1.6	005°
1033	North Haven Peninsula, north of		41° 02.47'	72° 19.25'	+0 12	-0 35	+0 39	-0 46	0.7	0.5	--	--	2.4	230°	--	--	2.1	035°
1035	Paradise Point, 0.4 mile east of		41° 02.88'	72° 22.57'	+0 26	-0 02	+0 45	-0 06	0.5	0.4	--	--	1.5	145°	--	--	1.5	345°
1037	Little Peconic Bay entrance	13	41° 01.58'	72° 23.08'	+0 35	-0 04	+0 53	+0 09	0.5	0.4	--	--	1.6	240°	--	--	1.5	015°
1039	Robins Island, 0.5 mile south of	19	40° 56.98'	72° 27.18'	+0 32	-0 17	+0 56	+0 23	0.3	0.1	--	--	1.7	245°	--	--	0.6	065°
	FISHERS ISLAND SOUND																	
1041	Edwards Pt. and Sandy Pt., between	4	41° 19.90'	71° 53.88'	-2 26	-3 22	-2 15	-3 53	0.3	0.3	--	--	1.1	035°	--	--	1.0	227°
1043	Napatree Point, 0.7 mile southwest of	6	41° 17.92'	71° 54.00'	-0 48	-1 12	-0 47	-1 30	0.5	0.5	--	--	1.7	284°	--	--	2.2	113°
1045	Little Narragansett Bay entrance		41° 20'	71° 53'	-1 58	-2 07	-2 13	-2 50	0.4	0.3	--	--	1.3	092°	--	--	1.3	268°
1047	Avondale, Pawcatuck River <43>		41° 19.90'	71° 50.73'	-1 48	-2 47	-2 07	-3 52	0.2	0.1	--	--	0.6	058°	--	--	0.5	265°
1049	Ram Island Reef, south of	7	41° 18.1'	71° 58.5'	-0 54	-0 55	-0 45	-1 05	0.4	0.4	--	--	1.3	255°	--	--	1.6	088°
1051	Noank <43>	4	41° 19.12'	71° 59.30'	-1 28	-3 21	-4 00	-4 42	0.2	0.1	--	--	0.5	340°	--	--	0.3	173°
1053	Mystic, Highway Bridge, Mystic River	6	41° 21.25'	71° 58.18'	-1 54	-2 55	-1 57	-3 51	0.2	0.1	--	--	0.5	039°	--	--	0.5	162°
1055	Clay Point, 1.3 miles NNE of	15	41° 17.88'	71° 58.53'	-0 34	-0 54	-0 30	-1 27	0.4	0.4	--	--	1.4	264°	--	--	1.9	035°
1057	North Hill Point, 1.1 miles NNW of		41° 17.57'	72° 01.68'	-0 57	-0 31	-0 08	-1 49	0.5	0.3	--	--	1.5	258°	--	--	1.2	082°
	LONG ISLAND SOUND *The Race*																	
1059	Race Point, 0.4 mile southwest of	6d	41° 14.70'	72° 02.60'	-0 16	-0 40	-0 33	-0 57	0.8	0.8	0.3	--	2.6	288°	0.2	195°	3.5	135°
1061	THE RACE	25d	41° 13.69'	72° 03.75'	Daily predictions				1.0	0.8	0.1	024°	3.3	291°	0.2	200°	4.2	106°
	...do.	45d	41° 13.69'	72° 03.75'					0.9	0.4	0.1	016°	3.3	292°	0.5	205°	3.2	108°
	...do.	45d	41° 13.53'	72° 03.75'					0.4	0.4	--	--	2.9	295°	0.5	036°	1.9	105°
1063	Little Gull Island, 1.4 n.mi. NNE of	15	41° 13.10'	72° 05.10'	-0 12	-0 14	+0 00	+0 02	1.2	1.1	0.1	011°	1.5	304°	--	--	1.6	100°
1065	Little Gull Island, 1.1 miles ENE of	3d	41° 11.67'	72° 06.93'	-0 24	+0 12	+0 08	+0 05	0.6	0.7	--	--	4.0	301°	--	--	4.7	130°
1067	Little Gull Island, 0.8 mile NNW of	16d	41° 11.67'	72° 08.02'	+0 02	-0 16	+0 11	-0 34	0.7	0.8	0.2	226°	2.3	258°	0.3	055°	2.9	043°
1069	Great Gull Island, SW of	29d	41° 11.67'	72° 08.02'	+0 01	-0 24	+0 19	-0 57	0.6	0.8	0.3	236°	2.0	320°	0.3	061°	3.3	147°
	...do.	2d	41° 11.67'	72° 08.02'	+0 25	-0 39	-0 36	-1 33	0.6	0.6	0.3	241°	1.6	326°	0.2	067°	2.5	157°
	...do.	15d	41° 19.13'	72° 04.90'	-0 40	-0 25	-0 34	-1 23	0.5	0.4	0.1	241°	0.3	332°	--	--	1.6	164°
1071	New London Harbor entrance	31d	41° 19.13'	72° 04.90'	-0 46	-0 18	-0 33	-1 19	0.5	0.4	--	--	0.3	316°	--	--	0.3	167°
	...do.	5d	41° 19.13'	72° 04.90'	-0 54	-2 04	-1 40	-0 50	0.1	0.1	--	--	0.3	335°	--	--	--	--
	...do.	15d	41° 17.63'	72° 04.71'	-1 10	-2 36	-2 14	--	0.1	--	--	--	0.3	353°	--	--	--	--
	Thames River																	
1073	Thames River Approach	35d	41° 17.63'	72° 04.71'	-2 06	-2 59	-2 06	-2 09	0.3	0.2	0.1	166°	0.9	268°	--	--	0.8	071°
	...do.	5d	41° 17.63'	72° 04.71'	-2 43	-1 29	-1 08	-1 58	0.3	0.2	0.1	357°	0.8	271°	--	--	0.8	065°
1075	Fort Trumbull State Park	14d	41° 20.73'	72° 05.18'	-2 04	-1 30	-1 09	-1 27	0.2	0.2	0.2	346°	0.6	267°	0.1	171°	0.6	051°
	...do.	31d	41° 20.73'	72° 05.18'	-2 09	-2 26	-1 38	-1 05	0.2	0.1	--	--	0.3	357°	--	--	0.3	169°
	...do.	14d	41° 21.44'	72° 05.20'	-1 07	-1 59	-1 39	-0 30	0.1	0.1	--	--	0.3	349°	--	--	--	--
1077	New London State Pier	31d	41° 21.44'	72° 05.20'	-1 45	-2 03	-1 20	-1 13	0.1	0.1	--	--	0.5	347°	--	--	0.4	178°
	...do.	57d	41° 21.44'	72° 05.20'	-2 30	-2 17	-1 12	-3 21	0.1	0.2	--	--	0.4	358°	--	--	0.3	172°
	...do.	9d	41° 22.42'	72° 05.37'	-1 37	-2 20	-1 48	-0 43	0.2	0.2	--	--	0.5	351°	--	--	0.3	164°
1079	U.S. Coast Guard Academy	16d	41° 22.42'	72° 05.37'	-2 03	-2 22	-1 11	-0 19	0.1	0.1	--	--	0.3	346°	--	--	0.3	182°
	...do.	32d	41° 22.42'	72° 05.37'	-4 03	-2 35	-1 15	-1 52	0.1	0.1	--	--	0.5	358°	--	--	0.3	179°
	...do.		41° 22.42'	72° 05.37'	-1 45	-1 47	-2 04	-3 43	0.1	0.1	--	--	0.3	002°	--	--	0.3	184°
1081	Groton, Pier 6	42d	41° 23.51'	72° 05.54'	-2 07	-2 53	-2 06	--	0.1	0.1	--	--	0.5	004°	--	--	0.3	132°

Endnotes can be found at the end of table 2.

TABLE 2. – CURRENT DIFFERENCES AND OTHER CONSTANTS

LONG ISLAND SOUND — Time meridian, 75°W

Time differences referred to *The Race, p.48*

No.	PLACE	Meter Depth (ft)	Latitude North	Longitude West	Min. before Flood (h m)	Flood (h m)	Min. before Ebb (h m)	Ebb (h m)	SR Flood	SR Ebb	Min. bef. Flood knots	Dir.	Max. Flood knots	Dir.	Min. bef. Ebb knots	Dir.	Max. Ebb knots	Dir.
	Thames River—cont.																	
1083	Smith Cove	5d	41°23.79'	72°05.76'	-1 03	-2 23	-2 09	-0 57	0.1	0.2	—	—	0.4	355°	—	—	0.7	181°
	...do.	14d	41°23.79'	72°05.76'	-1 15	-2 15	-1 56	-0 23	0.1	0.1	—	—	0.4	359°	—	—	0.4	184°
	...do.	31d	41°23.79'	72°05.76'	-2 41	-2 53	-1 47	-2 52	0.1	0.1	—	—	0.4	357°	—	—	0.3	179°
1085	Allyn Point	4d	41°26.58'	72°05.14'	-1 31	-2 25	-2 10	-1 41	0.3	0.2	—	—	0.8	002°	—	—	0.6	195°
	...do.	12d	41°26.58'	72°05.14'	-1 22	-1 54	-1 04	-0 53	0.1	0.2	—	—	0.4	002°	—	—	0.6	182°
	...do.	19d	41°26.58'	72°05.14'	-1 33	-2 23	-1 16	-1 16	0.1	0.1	—	—	0.3	005°	—	—	0.4	184°
1087	Lower Coal Dock	15	41°30.88'	72°04.72'		*Current weak and variable*												
1089	Goshen Point, 1.9 miles SSE of	15	41°16.00'	72°08'	-0 57	-1 05	-0 53	-2 01	0.4	0.4	—	—	1.2	285°	—	—	1.6	062°
1091	Bartlett Reef, 0.2 mile south of	15	41°16'	72°08'	-2 03	-0 58	-0 53	-1 46	0.4	0.3	—	—	1.4	255°	—	—	1.3	090°
1093	Twotree Island Channel	11	41°17.90'	72°08.50'	-0 58	-1 32	-0 33	-1 54	0.5	0.4	—	—	1.2	267°	—	—	1.6	099°
1095	Niantic (Railroad Bridge)	5	41°19.60'	72°10.60'	-0 45	-1 08	-0 43	-0 52	0.5	0.3	—	—	1.6	352°	—	—	0.8	178°
1097	Black Point, 0.8 mile south of	15	41°16.40'	72°12.50'	-0 42	-1 16	-0 15	-1 22	0.4	0.3	—	—	1.3	260°	—	—	1.4	073°
	Black Point and Plum Island, between	15	41°14.00'	72°12.30'	+0 33	-0 01	+0 39	+0 14	0.7	0.6	—	—	2.1	236°	—	—	2.4	076°
1099	Plum Island, 3nm. North of, Buoy Pl	20d	41°13.35'	72°10.63'	+0 08	-0 02	+0 10	-0 18	0.6	0.6	0.3	185°	2.0	259°	0.2	342°	2.4	081°
	...do.	79d	41°13.35'	72°10.63'	-0 08	-0 42	-0 10	+0 05	0.6	0.4	0.1	352°	1.8	258°	0.1	162°	1.8	079°
1101	...do.	131d	41°13.35'	72°10.63'	-0 30	-0 21	-0 02	-0 09	0.6	0.3	0.3	347°	1.7	253°	0.3	170°	1.3	082°
1103	Plum Island, 0.8 mile NNW of	15	41°11.90'	72°12.45'	+0 12	-1 07	-1 03	-0 53	0.6	0.6	0.1	033°	1.9	306°	0.1	032°	2.4	065°
1105	Plum Gut	25d	41°09.55'	72°12.45'	-1 00	-1 28	-0 59	-1 43	0.6	0.7	0.1	031°	2.0	305°	0.1	039°	3.0	116°
	...do.	99d	41°09.55'	72°12.45'	-1 06	-1 36	-1 01	-1 30	0.5	0.5	0.1	021°	1.7	317°	0.2	043°	2.5	124°
	...do.	158d	41°09.55'	72°12.45'	-1 13	-1 07	-0 27	-1 34	0.5	0.4	0.1	160°	1.7	255°	0.1	336°	1.9	121°
1107	Hatchett Point, 1.6 n.mi. S of	15	41°15.37'	72°15.37'	-0 59	-1 16	-0 42	-1 04	0.5	0.4	—	—	1.7	240°	—	—	1.9	075°
1109	Hatchett Point, 1.1 miles WSW of		41°16.35'	72°16.92'	-2 29	-2 07	-0 23	-2 49	0.4	0.3	—	—	1.3	240°	—	—	1.2	045°
1111	Orient Point, 1 mile WNW of		41°10.00'	72°15.10'	-1 01	-2 07	-0 23	-1 27	0.4	0.7	—	—	1.4	245°	—	—	3.1	055°
1113	Saybrook Breakwater, 1.5 miles SE of	15	41°14.78'	72°19.05'	-1 22	-1 16	-0 45	-2 09	0.6	0.5	—	—	1.9	260°	—	—	2.0	070°
	Connecticut River																	
1115	Saybrook Breakwater Light	5d	41°15.49'	72°20.52'	-1 52	-2 08	-1 33	-1 55	0.4	0.4	0.4	183°	1.3	249°	—	—	1.8	103°
	...do.	14d	41°15.49'	72°20.52'	-1 30	-2 06	-1 25	-2 01	0.4	0.3	0.1	024°	1.4	286°	—	—	1.4	105°
	...do.	19d	41°15.49'	72°20.52'	-1 31	-1 59	-1 26	-2 05	0.4	0.3	0.1	025°	1.2	287°	—	—	1.2	104°
1117	Saybrook Channel	2d	41°17.00'	72°20.85'	-0 10	+0 49	+0 37	+0 42	0.4	0.5	—	—	1.2	000°	—	—	2.0	180°
	...do.	13d	41°17.00'	72°20.85'	+1 12	+0 11	+0 40	+0 06	0.3	0.2	—	—	1.1	003°	—	—	0.8	186°
1119	I-95 Bridge	3d	41°19.09'	72°20.75'	+1 15	+0 38	+0 18	+0 38	0.3	0.4	—	—	0.9	356°	—	—	1.8	166°
	...do.	14d	41°19.09'	72°20.75'	+0 32	+0 48	+0 44	+0 45	0.3	0.3	—	—	1.1	000°	—	—	1.2	169°
	...do.	23d	41°19.09'	72°20.75'	+0 09	+0 55	+0 57	+0 46	0.3	0.2	—	—	0.9	352°	—	—	0.6	182°
1121	Eustasia Island, 0.6 mile ESE of	15	41°23.30'	72°24.23'	+2 01	+1 33	+1 33	+1 14	0.3	0.3	—	—	1.9	290°	—	—	1.4	070°
1123	Eddy Rock Shoal, west of	15	41°26.57'	72°27.78'	+1 49	+2 11	+2 11	+1 08	0.2	0.1	—	—	0.8	350°	—	—	0.6	155°
1125	Higganum Creek, 0.5 mile ESE of		41°30.02'	72°32.62'	+3 14	+2 47	+2 45	+2 49	0.2	0.2	—	—	0.8	270°	—	—	1.0	080°
1127	Wilcox Island Park, east of		41°34.33'	72°38.88'	+4 14	+3 31	+3 17	+3 23	0.2	0.2	—	—	0.9	355°	—	—	1.0	160°
1129	Rocky Hill	9	41°39.82'	72°37.73'	+4 51	+3 32	+3 31	+3 18	0.2	0.2	—	—	0.6	335°	—	—	0.8	135°
1131	Hartford Jetty <35>	9	41°45.07'	72°39.02'	+5 53	+4 34	+3 32	+4 17	0.0	0.5	—	—	0.1	290°	—	—	0.7	095°
	Mulford Point, 3.1 miles northwest of	15	41°12.00'	72°19.10'	+0 02	-1 10	+0 05	-0 36	0.5	0.5	—	—	1.9	269°	—	—	2.3	066°
1135	Rocky Point, 0.3 mile north of	15	41°08.63'	72°21.42'	-0 19	-1 07	-0 51	-0 40	0.5	0.5	—	—	1.8	279°	—	—	2.1	041°
1137	Cornfield Point, 2.8 n.mi. SE of	15d	41°13.95'	72°20.33'	-1 27	-1 02	-0 32	-1 44	0.5	0.3	0.1	170°	1.9	249°	—	—	1.4	085°
1139	Cornfield Point, 4 miles south of, Buoy CF	19d	41°11.37'	72°22.18'	-0 06	+0 00	-0 06	+0 04	0.6	0.6	0.4	157°	2.0	245°	0.4	332°	2.3	065°
	...do.	71d	41°11.37'	72°22.18'	-0 25	-0 31	-0 11	-0 20	0.5	0.4	—	—	1.6	244°	0.1	155°	1.6	067°
	...do.	124d	41°11.37'	72°22.18'	-0 51	-0 41	-0 26	-0 25	0.4	0.2	0.4	338°	1.2	240°	0.4	169°	1.0	069°
1141	Cornfield Point, 1.1 miles south of	15	41°14.65'	72°23.40'	-0 53	-1 39	-0 52	-1 23	0.4	0.4	—	—	1.4	293°	—	—	1.5	108°
1143	Cornfield Point, 1.9 n.mi. SW of	15d	41°14.48'	72°25.30'	-1 09	-1 40	-1 24	-1 12	0.4	0.4	0.1	174°	1.3	272°	—	—	1.5	091°
1145	Kelsey Point, 2.1 miles southeast of		41°14.10'	72°27.93'	-0 27	-1 07	-1 07	-2 06	0.6	0.5	—	—	1.5	260°	—	—	1.8	070°
1147	Kelsey Point, 1 mile south of	14'	41°14'	72°30'	-1 34	-1 08	-2 06	-0 53	0.6	0.3	—	—	2.0	249°	—	—	1.3	118°
1149	Six Mile Reef, 1.5 miles north of		41°12.67'	72°28.87'	-0 09	-0 17	-0 13	-0 47	0.3	0.5	—	—	1.0	290°	—	—	2.1	095°
1151	Six Mile Reef, 2 miles east of		41°10.83'	72°26.90'	-0 28	-0 17	+0 03	-0 37	0.5	0.4	—	—	1.6	235°	—	—	1.4	040°
1153	Six Mile Reef, 1 mile south of	15d	41°10.10'	72°29.96'	-0 21	-0 35	-0 31	-0 37	0.5	0.3	0.3	164°	1.8	250°	0.1	166°	1.0	077°
	...do.	35d	41°10.10'	72°29.96'	-0 39	-0 46	-0 36	-0 45	0.5	0.4	0.1	164°	1.5	257°	0.2	169°	1.8	075°
	...do.	58d	41°10.10'	72°29.36'	-0 54	-0 40	-0 45	-0 27	0.6	0.4	—	—	1.1	258°	—	338°	1.5	073°
1155	Six Mile Reef, 2 miles south of, Buoy TE	16d	41°08.07'	72°29.36'	-0 15	-0 08	+0 01	+0 02	0.6	0.4	0.5	166°	1.8	255°	—	—	1.0	073°
	...do.	49d	41°08.07'	72°29.36'	-0 26	-0 09	+0 17	+0 02	0.5	0.4	0.1	159°	1.7	252°	0.4	338°	1.5	074°
	...do.	88d	41°08.07'	72°29.36'	-0 54	-0 07	+0 00	-0 35	0.4	0.2	0.3	342°	1.2	247°	0.3	168°	0.8	082°

Endnotes can be found at the end of table 2.

TABLE 2. – CURRENT DIFFERENCES AND OTHER CONSTANTS

No.	PLACE	Meter Depth (ft)	Position Latitude (North)	Position Longitude (West)	Time Diff. Min. before Flood (h m)	Time Diff. Flood (h m)	Time Diff. Min. before Ebb (h m)	Time Diff. Ebb (h m)	Speed Ratio Flood	Speed Ratio Ebb	Min. before Flood (knots)	Min. before Flood Dir.	Maximum Flood (knots)	Maximum Flood Dir.	Min. before Ebb (knots)	Min. before Ebb Dir.	Maximum Ebb (knots)	Maximum Ebb Dir.
	LONG ISLAND SOUND Time meridian, 75°W					on The Race, p.48												
1157	Six Mile Reef, 1 mile west of	13d	41° 10.78'	72° 33.11'	-0 16	-0 43	-0 31	-0 21	0.5	0.4	0.1	182°	1.6	275°	0.1	001°	1.7	087°
	...do.	26d	41° 10.78'	72° 33.11'	-0 34	-0 49	-0 32	-0 31	0.4	0.4	—	—	1.4	277°	0.1	002°	1.5	086°
	...do.	36d	41° 10.78'	72° 33.11'	-0 43	-0 49	-0 33	-0 30	0.4	0.3	0.1	004°	1.2	278°	0.1	003°	1.2	087°
1159	Horton Point, 1.4 miles NNW of	15	41° 06.30'	72° 27.40'	+0 12	+0 03	+0 07	-0 30	0.4	0.5	—	—	1.4	260°	—	—	2.0	040°
1161	Hammonasset Point, 1.2 miles SW of	15	41° 14.22'	72° 34.00'	-0 51	-1 20	-0 34	-1 43	0.3	0.2	—	—	1.0	287°	—	—	1.5	106°
1163	Hammonasset Point, 5 miles south of	15d	41° 09.80'	72° 34.17'	+0 05	-0 08	-0 14	-0 18	0.4	0.4	—	—	1.2	284°	—	—	1.5	090°
1165	Duck Pond Point, 3.2 n.mi. NW of	15	41° 04.73'	72° 33.91'	-0 25	-0 14	-0 06	-0 15	0.3	0.3	0.2	161°	1.2	253°	0.1	343°	1.2	071°
1167	Mattituck Inlet, 1 mile northwest of	15	41° 01.68'	72° 34.22'	-0 13	-0 20	+0 02	-0 38	0.3	0.2	—	—	0.9	241°	—	—	1.0	053°
1169	Sachem Head, 1 mile SSE of	15	41° 13.65'	72° 42.30'	-0 30	-0 41	-0 25	-1 14	0.3	0.2	—	—	1.1	255°	—	—	1.0	065°
1171	Sachem Head, 6.2 miles south of	15	41° 08.73'	72° 42.30'	+0 37	+0 19	-0 02	-0 16	0.3	0.2	—	—	0.6	255°	—	—	0.9	065°
1173	Roanoke Point, 5.6 miles north of	16d	41° 04.37'	72° 42.53'	+0 06	-0 07	-0 05	-0 36	0.2	0.2	—	—	0.7	255°	—	—	0.9	050°
1175	Roanoke Point, 2 miles NE of	39d	41° 00.42'	72° 39.79'	-0 28	-0 20	-0 29	-0 27	0.2	0.2	0.1	178°	0.7	271°	0.1	009°	0.7	093°
	...do.	62d	41° 00.42'	72° 39.79'	-0 45	-0 25	-0 15	-0 30	0.2	0.2	0.1	187°	0.7	277°	0.1	011°	0.8	106°
	...do.	15	41° 00.42'	72° 39.79'	-1 39	-1 46	-0 45	-1 12	0.2	0.2	—	—	0.6	287°	—	—	0.7	103°
1177	Roanoke Point, 2.3 miles NNW of	6d	41° 00.92'	72° 42.97'	-1 11	-0 27	+0 00	-0 41	0.3	0.2	—	—	0.9	270°	—	—	0.7	070°
1179	Branford Reef, 1.5 miles southwest of	39d	41° 12.57'	72° 49.83'	-0 05	-0 19	+0 01	-0 30	0.3	0.2	—	—	0.8	272°	—	—	0.7	068°
1181	Branford Reef, 5.0 miles south of	69d	41° 08.67'	72° 49.68'	+0 03	+0 07	+0 15	+0 17	0.3	0.2	—	—	0.9	262°	—	—	0.7	084°
	...do.	15	41° 08.67'	72° 49.68'	-0 36	-0 20	+0 03	-0 09	0.3	0.2	0.1	184°	0.6	273°	—	—	0.5	096°
	...do.	15	41° 08.67'	72° 49.68'	-1 00	-0 43	-0 24	-0 42	0.2	0.1	0.1	013°	0.9	277°	0.1	187°	0.6	106°
	...do.	15d	41° 04.65'	72° 49.80'	-0 19	+0 01	+0 22	-0 19	0.3	0.2	—	—	0.4	254°	—	—	0.7	070°
1183	Herod Point, 6.5 miles north of	4d	41° 00.97'	72° 54.73'	-0 21	-0 22	-0 17	-0 18	0.1	0.2	0.1	020°	0.4	290°	0.1	020°	0.5	090°
1185	Herod Point, 2.8 miles north of	14d	41° 01.64'	72° 54.56'	-0 09	-0 22	-0 27	-0 01	0.2	0.2	0.1	179°	0.7	271°	—	—	0.6	089°
1187	Herod Point, 5.0 n.mi. NW of	31d	41° 13.34'	72° 54.56'	-0 12	-0 11	+0 06	+0 20	0.2	0.1	0.1	215°	0.7	277°	0.1	192°	0.7	122°
1189	New Haven Harbor entrance	8d	41° 13.34'	72° 54.56'	-0 25	-0 49	-0 20	-0 05	0.2	0.1	0.1	221°	0.6	288°	0.1	194°	0.5	117°
	...do.	18d	41° 16.96'	72° 54.72'	-0 51	-1 49	-1 05	-0 30	0.1	0.1	—	—	0.6	295°	—	—	0.4	106°
	...do.	31d	41° 16.96'	72° 54.72'					0.2	—	—	—	0.3	—	—	—	—	—
1191	New Haven Harbor, Gateway Terminal Approach	11d	41° 16.96'	72° 54.72'		+0 31			0.2	—	—	—	0.5	015°	—	—	—	—
	...do.	21d	41° 17.70'	72° 54.54'		-0 05		+0 12	—	—	—	—	0.6	015°	—	—	—	—
1193	New Haven Harbor, Tanker Terminal	30d	41° 17.70'	72° 54.54'		-1 14		-0 14	—	0.1	—	—	—	—	—	—	0.5	218°
	...do.		41° 17.70'	72° 54.54'		Current weak and variable			—	0.1	—	—	—	—	—	—	0.3	209°
1195	Oyster River Pt., 1.3 miles SSE of <1>	10	41° 12.87'	72° 58.00'	-0 12	-0 20	+0 06	-0 59	0.1	0.1	—	—	0.3	255°	—	—	0.3	060°
1197	Pond Point, 4.2 miles SSE of	5	41° 08.60'	72° 58.08'	+0 05	-0 01	-0 05	-0 26	0.2	0.1	—	—	0.6	265°	—	—	0.6	065°
1199	Sound Beach, 2.2 miles north of	5	41° 00.33'	72° 58.45'	-0 43	-0 11	-0 11	-0 37	0.3	0.2	—	—	0.9	270°	—	—	0.9	075°
1201	Charles Island, 0.8 mile SSE of	5	41° 10.77'	73° 02.63'		-0 41	-0 20	-1 06	0.1	0.1	—	—	0.4	250°	—	—	0.4	070°
	Housatonic River																	
1203	Milford Point, 0.2 mile west of	15	41° 10.35'	73° 06.82'	+0 02	-0 04	+0 25	-1 07	0.4	0.3	—	—	1.2	330°	—	—	1.2	135°
1205	Railroad drawbridge, above	6d	41° 12.53'	73° 06.67'	+0 42	+0 08	+0 39	-1 07	0.3	0.3	—	—	1.1	350°	—	—	1.3	185°
1207	Fowler Island, 0.1 mile NNW of	16d	41° 14.40'	73° 06.23'	+0 56	+0 05	+0 30	+0 10	0.2	0.2	—	—	1.1	040°	—	—	1.1	270°
1209	Wooster Island, 0.1 mile southwest of	43d	41° 16.47'	73° 04.78'	+1 27	+0 28		+0 36	0.2	0.1	—	—	0.6	020°	—	—	0.7	220°
1211	Derby–Shelton Bridge, below <13>	15	41° 18.73'	73° 07.13'	-0 22	-0 11	+0 02	-0 18	0.1	0.1	—	—	—	—	—	—	0.4	095°
1213	Point No Point, 2.1 miles south of	60	41° 06.75'	73° 06.27'	-0 01	-0 04	+0 14	-0 13	0.4	0.3	—	—	1.3	251°	—	—	1.2	074°
1215	Stratford Point, 3.5 miles south of	15	41° 05.40'	73° 06.27'	-0 21	-0 01	+0 09	+0 05	0.4	0.3	0.2	154°	1.2	247°	—	—	1.0	070°
	...do.	51	41° 05.40'	73° 06.27'	-0 03	-0 19	-0 12	-0 17	0.3	0.2	0.1	157°	1.0	251°	—	—	1.0	071°
1217	Stratford Point, 4.3 miles south of		41° 04.77'	73° 06.67'	+0 20	+0 14	+0 15	+0 02	0.2	0.2	0.1	338°	0.8	249°	0.2	166°	0.7	067°
1219	Stratford Point, 6.1 miles south of		41° 04.77'	73° 06.67'	-0 28	-0 14	-0 13	+0 03	0.3	0.2	—	—	1.0	254°	—	—	1.0	075°
	...do.		41° 02.97'	73° 05.80'	-0 10	-0 02	+0 26	+0 18	0.3	0.3	—	—	0.6	291°	—	—	0.8	078°
1221	Stratford Shoal, 6 miles east of	22d	41° 04.52'	72° 58.43'	-0 35	-0 36	-0 24	-0 24	0.2	0.2	0.1	172°	1.0	267°	0.2	356°	0.8	080°
1223	Stratford Shoal, 2 miles south of	68d	41° 01.38'	73° 06.29'	+0 09	-0 07	+0 03	+0 15	0.2	0.1	0.1	176°	0.6	279°	—	—	0.9	087°
	...do.	114d	41° 01.38'	73° 06.29'	+0 18	+0 11	+0 22	-0 10	0.3	0.2	—	—	0.9	265°	—	—	0.6	060°
	...do.	15d	41° 01.38'	73° 06.29'	-0 26	-0 05	-0 18	-0 30	0.3	0.2	—	—	0.8	272°	—	—	0.9	079°
1225	Old Field Point, 2.9 n.mi. NNW of	40	41° 01.32'	73° 08.37'	-1 03	-0 10	+0 09	-0 15	0.2	0.2	—	—	0.5	263°	—	—	0.7	093°
1227	Old Field Point, 2 miles northeast of	15	41° 00.23'	73° 05.70'	+0 27	-0 16	-0 35	+0 46	0.2	0.2	—	—	0.5	261°	—	—	0.6	099°
	...do.	22	41° 00.23'	73° 05.80'	+0 41	+0 03	-0 01	+0 29	0.2	0.2	0.1	182°	0.5	254°	0.1	182°	0.6	076°
	...do.		40° 58.47'	73° 05.80'	+3 34	+2 26	+2 35	+1 44	0.1	0.2	0.1	338°	1.0	266°	0.1	338°	1.1	092°
1229	Old Field Point, 1 mile east of		40° 58.47'	73° 05.80'	+2 38	+1 49	+2 27	+1 32	0.1	0.1	—	—	0.5	236°	—	—	0.6	081°

Endnotes can be found at the end of table 2.

TABLE 2. – CURRENT DIFFERENCES AND OTHER CONSTANTS

No.	PLACE	POSITION Latitude North	POSITION Longitude West	Meter Depth (ft)	TIME DIFFERENCES Min. before Flood (h m)	Flood (h m)	Min. before Ebb (h m)	Ebb (h m)	SPEED RATIOS Flood	Ebb	AVG Minimum before Flood (knots)	Dir.	Maximum Flood (knots)	Dir.	Minimum before Ebb (knots)	Dir.	Maximum Ebb (knots)	Dir.
	LONG ISLAND SOUND Time meridian, 75°W																	
1231	Port Jefferson Harbor entrance	40°58.19'	73°05.50'	3d	-0 18	-0 05	-0 05	-0 05	0.5	0.2	–	–	1.6	150°	0.1	060°	1.0	336°
	do.	40°58.19'	73°05.50'	15d	-0 24	-0 09	-0 02	-0 03	0.5	0.2	–	–	1.7	149°	0.1	065°	1.0	342°
	do.	40°58.19'	73°05.50'	31d	-0 29	-0 09	+0 04	-0 01	0.4	0.2	–	–	1.3	154°	–	–	0.9	001°
1233	Crane Neck Point, 0.5 mile northwest of	40°58'	73°10'		on The Race, p.48													
1235	Bridgeport Harbor Entrance	41°07.28'	73°11.37'	5d	-0 47	-1 32	-1 42	-1 49	0.4	0.4	–	–	1.3	256°	–	–	1.5	016°
	do.	41°07.28'	73°11.37'	15d	+0 06	+0 01	-0 07	-0 06	0.2	0.1	–	–	0.5	256°	0.2	345°	0.6	058°
	do.	41°07.28'	73°11.37'	31d	-0 09	-0 25	-0 34	-0 28	0.2	0.1	–	–	0.5	256°	0.1	342°	0.5	058°
1237	Bridgeport Harbor, Tongue Point	41°10.00'	73°10.52'	4d	-0 51	-1 00	-1 27	-0 54	0.1	0.1	0.1	337°	0.3	254°	–	–	0.4	062°
	do.	41°10.00'	73°10.52'	15d	–	+1 01	+0 50	–	0.1	–	–	–	0.3	043°	–	–	–	–
	do.	41°10.00'	73°10.52'	30d	–	+0 50	+0 31	–	0.1	–	–	–	0.2	040°	–	–	–	–
1239	Pine Creek Point, 2.3 miles SSE of	41°05.05'	73°14.40'	15	-0 12	+0 01	+0 52	+0 11	0.2	0.1	–	–	0.7	272°	–	–	0.6	084°
1241	Shoal Point, 6 miles south of	41°01.70'	73°14.03'	15	+0 30	+0 23	-0 15	+0 43	0.2	0.1	–	–	0.4	232°	–	–	0.4	047°
1243	Crane Neck Point, 3.4 miles WNW of	40°59.00'	73°13.87'	15	-0 04	-0 03	-0 14	-0 03	0.2	0.1	–	–	0.5	261°	–	–	0.6	079°
1245	Crane Neck Point, 3.7 miles WSW of	40°56.30'	73°13.87'	15	-1 24	-0 36	+0 30	-0 30	0.2	0.1	–	–	0.4	066°	–	–	0.4	232°
1247	Saugatuck River, 0.3 mi. NW of Bluff Pt	41°06.27'	73°21.92'	15	-0 04	-0 46	+0 13	-0 02	0.1	–	–	–	0.5	265°	–	–	–	–
1249	Saugatuck R., 0.5 mile above Bluff Pt	41°06'	73°23'		Current weak and variable													
1251	Norwalk Harbor	41°05.12'	73°24.14'	2d	-0 10	-0 46	+0 25	+0 43	0.2	0.1	–	–	0.5	339°	–	–	0.4	080°
1253	Sheffield I. Hbr. 0.5 mile southeast of	41°05.12'	73°25.25'	11d	-0 43	-1 06	-3 26	-2 24	0.1	0.1	–	–	0.5	329°	–	–	0.4	148°
1255	Sheffield I. Tower, 1.1 miles SE of	41°03.32'	73°24.33'	12	-2 33	-3 59	+1 09	+0 21	0.3	0.2	–	–	0.2	229°	–	–	0.4	151°
1257	Eatons Neck, 3 miles north of	41°01.97'	73°24.30'	15	+0 41	+0 34	+1 10	+0 24	0.2	0.1	–	–	0.9	283°	–	–	0.8	042°
	do.	41°00.30'	73°24.30'	60	-0 19	+0 19	+0 35	+0 18	0.3	0.2	–	–	0.6	269°	–	–	0.5	081°
	do.	41°00.30'	73°24.30'	10d	+0 00	+0 07	+0 35	+0 02	0.3	0.1	0.1	173°	0.8	267°	0.1	351°	0.7	076°
	do.	41°00.30'	73°24.60'	49d	-0 15	-0 02	-2 06	-0 20	0.3	0.1	–	–	0.9	264°	0.2	347°	0.7	080°
	do.	40°59.73'	73°24.60'	92d	-1 51	-2 02	+0 13	-2 21	0.4	0.3	0.1	341°	0.8	249°	0.1	341°	0.5	083°
1259	Eatons Neck Pt., 2.5 n.mi. NNW of	40°58.60'	73°23.77'	15d	+0 29	+0 16	-0 06	+0 09	0.2	0.1	0.1	164°	0.6	263°	–	–	0.6	073°
1261	Eatons Neck Pt., 1.3 miles north of	40°57.45'	73°20.52'	15	-0 49	-0 25	-0 11	-0 14	0.4	0.3	–	–	1.4	283°	–	–	1.4	075°
1263	Eatons Neck, 2.5 miles east of	40°57.45'	73°20.52'	5d	-0 48	-0 34	-0 59	-0 15	0.2	0.1	0.1	207°	0.5	276°	–	–	0.5	125°
	do.	40°57.45'	73°20.52'	18d	-1 13	-0 45	-0 32	-0 54	0.2	0.1	0.2	207°	0.5	279°	–	–	0.5	128°
	do.	40°57'	73°20.52'	41d	-1 11	-1 09	-0 24	-0 44	0.2	0.1	0.1	201°	0.4	291°	–	–	0.4	122°
1265	Eatons Neck Pt., 1.8 miles west of	40°57'	73°26'	15	+0 02	+0 05	+0 15	-0 39	0.2	0.1	–	–	0.5	199°	0.1	209°	0.6	068°
1267	Huntington Bay, off East Fort Point	40°55.60'	73°25.05'	30	-0 46	+0 09	+0 08	-0 28	0.2	0.1	–	–	0.4	190°	–	–	0.5	014°
	do.	40°55.60'	73°25.05'	15	-0 03	+0 46	+1 24	+0 18	0.1	0.1	–	–	0.4	179°	–	–	0.6	007°
1269	Northport Bay entrance (in channel)	40°54.53'	73°24.45'	15	+0 29	+0 09	+1 22	-0 20	0.1	0.1	–	–	0.4	100°	–	–	0.5	267°
1271	Northport Bay, south of Duck I. Bluff	40°55'	73°23'	27	-1 12	-0 10	+1 30	-0 01	0.1	0.1	–	–	0.4	007°	–	–	0.3	286°
1273	Long Neck Point, 0.6 mile south of	41°01.58'	73°28.68'	15	-0 57	-0 13	+1 17	-0 03	0.3	0.2	–	–	0.8	252°	–	–	0.4	073°
	do.	41°01.58'	73°28.68'	40	+1 24	+0 49	+0 23	+0 53	0.3	0.2	–	–	0.8	257°	–	–	0.5	080°
	do.	40°57.95'	73°29.70'	15	+0 00	+0 08	+0 56	+0 25	0.3	0.2	–	–	1.0	255°	–	–	0.5	055°
1275	Lloyd Point, 1.3 miles NNW of	40°57.95'	73°29.70'	15	+0 36	+0 02	+0 42	+0 04	0.3	0.2	–	–	0.9	269°	–	–	0.5	053°
1277	Shippan Point, 1.3 miles SSE of	40°59.90'	73°31.03'	40	+0 18	+0 06	+0 37	-0 22	0.3	0.1	–	–	0.7	239°	–	–	0.9	055°
	do.	40°59.98'	73°29.75'	15	+0 39	-0 03	+0 13	+0 17	0.3	0.2	–	–	0.7	247°	–	–	0.7	071°
1279	The Cows, 2 miles SE of	40°59.31'	73°29.75'	15	+0 03	+0 11	+0 13	+0 14	0.2	0.1	–	–	0.6	243°	–	–	0.9	072°
	do.	40°59.31'	73°29.75'	14d	-0 25	-0 24	-2 11	+0 00	0.2	0.2	–	–	0.7	253°	–	–	0.8	080°
	do.	40°59.31'	73°29.75'	47d	-1 19	-1 31	-1 53	-0 46	0.2	0.1	–	–	0.6	263°	–	–	0.6	081°
1281	Stamford Harbor entrance	41°00.92'	73°32.22'	86d	-1 27	-1 26	+0 24	-0 49	0.2	0.1	0.1	354°	0.7	015°	–	–	0.5	175°
	do.	41°00.92'	73°32.22'	3d	+0 19	+0 15	+0 00	+0 13	0.2	0.2	–	–	0.5	023°	0.2	107°	0.4	174°
	do.	41°01'	73°36'	14d	-0 06	-0 01	-0 03	+0 14	0.2	0.1	–	–	0.6	117°	0.1	113°	0.4	306°
	Oyster Bay																	
1283	Rocky Point, 1 mile east of	40°55.15'	73°30.03'	15	+0 24	+0 20	+0 24	+0 30	0.2	0.1	–	–	0.6	244°	–	–	0.5	054°
1285	Harbor ent., south of Plum Point	40°54'	73°31'	7	+1 21	+0 58	+1 49	-0 11	0.2	0.2	–	–	0.7	333°	–	–	0.7	140°
1287	Harbor, west of Soper Point	40°53'	73°32'	7	+1 24	+0 51	+0 57	+0 11	0.2	0.1	–	–	0.6	258°	–	–	0.4	073°
1289	Cold Spring Harbor	40°53'	73°29'		Current weak and variable													
1291	Greenwich Point, 1.1 miles south of	40°59.02'	73°34.02'	15	+0 47	+0 10	-0 27	+1 01	0.2	0.2	–	–	0.7	265°	–	–	0.8	069°
	do.	40°59.02'	73°34.02'	55	-1 07	-0 04	-0 17	+1 03	0.2	0.1	–	–	0.6	242°	–	–	0.4	052°
1293	Greenwich Point, 2.5 miles south of	40°57.60'	73°33.68'	15	+2 51	+1 58	+2 25	+0 29	0.2	0.2	–	–	0.7	256°	–	–	0.7	079°
	do.	40°57.60'	73°34.02'	55	+0 54	+1 35	+1 41	+1 51	0.2	0.1	–	–	0.5	260°	–	–	0.4	072°
1295	Oak Neck Point, 0.6 mile south of	40°55.50'	73°34.02'	15	+0 11	+1 35	+1 41	+1 51	0.2	0.2	–	–	0.5	300°	–	–	0.6	090°
1297	Coscob Harbor, off Goose Island	41°01'	73°36'	30	+0 11	-0 15	+0 00	-0 55	0.2	0.1	–	–	0.5	013°	–	–	0.5	188°

Endnotes can be found at the end of table 2.

TABLE 2. – CURRENT DIFFERENCES AND OTHER CONSTANTS

No.	PLACE	Meter Depth (ft)	Position Lat. North	Position Long. West	Min. before Flood	Flood	Min. before Ebb	Ebb	Speed Ratio Flood	Speed Ratio Ebb	Min. before Flood knots	Min. before Flood Dir.	Max. Flood knots	Max. Flood Dir.	Min. before Ebb knots	Min. before Ebb Dir.	Max. Ebb knots	Max. Ebb Dir.
	LONG ISLAND SOUND Time meridian, 75°W																	
1299	Captain Hbr. Ent., 0.6 mile southwest of	15	40°59.65'	73°35.67'	+1 32	+1 44	+1 49	+2 00	0.2	0.2	—	—	0.6	312°	—	—	0.7	118°
	do.	30	40°59.65'	73°35.67'	+1 22	+1 14	+0 58	+1 58	0.2	0.2	—	—	0.5	319°	—	—	0.7	142°
1301	Parsonage Point, 1.3 n.mi. ESE of	15d	40°56.25'	73°39.49'	+0 47	+0 24	+1 10	+1 00	0.2	0.1	—	—	0.5	230°	—	—	0.4	051°
1303	Peningo Neck, 0.6 mi. off Parsonage Pt	15	40°56.32'	73°40.50'	+1 09	+0 23	+1 16	+0 27	0.2	0.2	—	—	0.7	226°	—	—	0.7	035°
1305	Matinecock Point, 1.7 miles northwest of	10d	40°55.47'	73°39.35'	+0 58	+0 19	+1 01	+0 49	0.2	0.1	0.1	147°	0.5	233°	—	—	0.5	055°
	do.	30d	40°55.47'	73°39.35'	+0 18	-0 10	+0 43	+0 32	0.1	0.1	—	—	0.5	244°	0.1	163°	0.4	063°
	do.	46d	40°55.47'	73°39.35'	-0 57	-0 29	-0 08	-0 17	0.1	0.1	0.1	351°	0.4	251°	0.1	166°	0.3	072°
1307	Matinecock Point, 0.7 mile NNW of	15	40°54.80'	73°38.40'	+1 14	+0 27	+1 34	+0 36	0.2	0.1	—	—	0.6	233°	—	—	0.6	046°
	do.	40	40°54.80'	73°38.40'	+0 35	+0 07	+1 33	+0 20	0.2	0.1	—	—	0.7	262°	—	—	0.5	053°
1309	Hempstead Harbor, 0.3 mile north of	15	40°51.72'	73°40.47'	—	+0 00	—	-0 31	0.1	—	—	—	0.3	157°	—	—	0.1	331°
1311	Hempstead Harbor, 0.5 mile east of	15	40°51.50'	73°39.98'	-0 38	-0 19	+0 03	-0 59	0.3	0.2	—	—	0.9	138°	—	—	0.7	320°
1313	Hempstead Harbor, off Glenwood Landing	10	40°49.68'	73°39.08'	—	-0 27	—	—	0.1	—	—	—	0.4	196°	—	—	—	—
1315	Old Town Wharf, 0.5 mile north of	5	40°55.00'	73°42.73'	+0 45	+0 09	+1 14	-0 05	0.2	0.1	—	—	0.5	244°	—	—	0.4	059°
1317	Delancey Point, 1 mile southeast of	15	40°55.00'	73°42.73'	—	+0 06	+1 09	-0 39	0.1	0.1	—	—	0.4	239°	—	—	0.3	069°
1319	Mamaroneck Harbor	33	40°56'	73°43'	Current weak and variable													
1321	Echo Bay entrance		40°54'	73°46'	Current weak and variable													
	on Throgs Neck, p.52																	
1323	Davids Island, channel 0.1 mile east of	15	40°53.43'	73°46'	-3 25	-4 16	-3 21	-3 40	0.1	0.2	—	—	0.2	069°	—	—	0.2	234°
1325	Huckleberry Island, 0.2 mile NW of	15	40°53.80'	73°45.43'	-2 35	-0 33	-1 53	-2 24	0.3	0.2	—	—	0.4	025°	—	—	0.4	226°
1327	Huckleberry Island, 0.6 mile SE of	11d	40°52.80'	73°44.75'	-2 30	-2 18	-2 14	-2 02	0.3	0.4	—	—	0.5	043°	—	—	0.4	232°
1329	Execution Rocks	50d	40°52.39'	73°44.00'	-2 40	-2 33	-2 45	-2 53	0.3	0.5	—	—	0.4	058°	—	—	0.5	232°
	do.	96d	40°52.39'	73°44.00'	-2 36	-2 51	-3 10	-2 52	0.2	0.4	—	—	0.4	057°	—	—	0.4	219°
1331	Manhasset Bay entrance	15	40°49.75'	73°43.78'	+2 48	+2 18	+2 48	+3 04	0.1	0.3	—	—	0.2	115°	—	—	0.3	307°
1333	Hart Island, 0.2 mile north of	15	40°51.82'	73°46.26'	-2 33	-4 04	-3 56	-3 10	0.1	0.1	—	—	0.2	098°	—	—	0.1	264°
1335	Hart Island, southeast of	13d	40°50.59'	73°45.73'	-1 47	-0 10	-1 11	-0 42	0.5	0.5	0.1	122°	0.7	035°	0.2	125°	0.7	201°
	do.	59d	40°50.59'	73°45.73'	-1 10	-0 46	-2 09	-1 10	0.3	0.6	—	—	0.5	030°	0.1	115°	0.6	194°
	do.	98d	40°50.59'	73°45.73'	-1 12	-0 58	-1 58	-1 36	0.3	0.5	—	—	0.4	009°	—	—	0.5	189°
1337	Hart Island, 0.3 n.mi. SSE of	15d	40°50.43'	73°45.94'	-1 37	-1 28	-1 46	-1 10	0.3	0.5	0.1	114°	0.4	040°	0.2	119°	0.5	201°
1339	Hart Island and City Island, between	15	40°51.37'	73°46.73'	-1 58	-3 00	-1 58	-2 27	0.1	0.2	—	—	0.2	349°	—	—	0.2	143°
1341	City Island Bridge	10	40°51.47'	73°47.60'	-3 09	-5 01	-4 06	-4 13	0.1	0.4	—	—	0.3	349°	—	—	0.3	150°
1343	Eastchester Bay, near Big Tom	5	40°50.20'	73°47.72'	-3 15	-4 00	-3 46	-3 14	0.1	0.4	—	—	0.3	352°	—	—	0.5	198°
1345	Hutchinson R., Pelham Highway Bridge	5	40°51.70'	73°49.00'	+2 31	+2 28	+2 12	+2 13	0.5	0.4	—	—	0.8	097°	—	—	0.4	294°
1347	City Island, 0.6 mile southeast of	15	40°49.72'	73°46.47'	-1 27	-0 54	-2 38	-3 27	0.3	0.4	—	—	0.5	038°	—	—	0.4	078°
1349	Elm Point, 0.2 mile west of	15	40°48.92'	73°46.02'	-1 43		-1 27		0.2	0.5	—	—	0.6	024°	—	—	0.6	213°
1351	Throgs Neck, 0.3 n.mi. NE of	15d	40°48.64'	73°47.13'	-0 31	-0 40	-0 52	+0 08	0.6	0.6	0.1	312°	1.0	015°	0.1	286°	0.6	193°
1353	Throgs Neck, 0.4 mile south of	15	40°47.90'	73°47.45'	-0 26	+0 09	+0 41	+0 19	0.5	0.6	—	—	0.8	090°	—	—	0.6	278°
1355	Throgs Neck, 0.2 mile S of (Willets Point)	15	40°48.12'	73°47.48'	-0 10	-0 09	+0 21	+0 13	0.4	0.7	—	—	1.6	090°	—	—	0.8	289°
1357	THROGS NECK BRIDGE **Daily predictions**	14d	40°48.06'	73°47.53'		+0 02	-0 35	-0 05	0.8	0.8	0.1	182°	1.6	106°	—	—	1.0	262°
	do.	36d	40°48.06'	73°47.53'	-0 30	-0 08	-0 53	+0 10	0.6	0.8	0.1	353°	1.3	105°	—	—	0.9	268°
	do.	59d	40°48.06'	73°47.53'	-0 41						0.1	008°	0.9	082°	—	—	0.8	289°

Endnotes can be found at the end of table 2.

TABLE 2. – CURRENT DIFFERENCES AND OTHER CONSTANTS

222

No.	PLACE	Meter Depth (ft)	POSITION Latitude North	POSITION Longitude West	TIME DIFFERENCES Min. before Flood (h m)	Flood (h m)	Min. before Ebb (h m)	Ebb (h m)	SPEED RATIOS Flood	Ebb	Min. before Flood knots	Dir.	Maximum Flood knots	Dir.	Min. before Ebb knots	Dir.	Maximum Ebb knots	Dir.
	EAST RIVER Time meridian, 75°W				**on Hell Gate, p.56**													
1359	Cryders Point, 0.4 mile NNW of	14	40° 48.02'	73° 47.92'	–0 29	–0 43	–0 30	–1 00	0.4	0.2			1.3	110°			1.1	285°
1361	Bronx-Whitestone Bridge, East of		40° 48.1'	73° 49.6'	–0 34	–0 46	–0 10	–1 27	0.5	0.2			1.7	076°			1.0	247°
1363	College Point Reef, 0.25 n.mi. NW of	15d	40° 48.06'	73° 51.28'	–0 27	–0 47	–0 32	–1 00	0.4	0.3	0.1	351°	1.5	074°	0.1	350°	1.4	261°
1365	Flushing Creek entrance		40° 45.9'	73° 50.7'	Current weak and variable													
1367	Rikers I. chan., off La Guardia Field		40° 47'	73° 53'	+0 04	–0 04	+0 04	–0 08	0.3	0.3			1.1	088°			1.3	261°
1369	Bronx River (1 mile north of Hunts Pt.)		40° 48.9'	73° 52.5'	Current weak and variable													
1371	Hunts Point, southwest of		40° 48'	73° 53'	+0 01	–0 10	+0 01	–0 05	0.5	0.3			1.7	108°			1.3	280°
1373	South Brother Island, NW of	15	40° 47.8'	73° 54.1'	–0 17	+0 04	–0 06	–0 12	0.4	0.3			1.5	054°			1.2	252°
1375	Off Winthrop Ave., Astoria		40° 47.2'	73° 55.0'	+0 04	+0 02	–0 01	–0 11	1.0	0.5			3.4	040°			2.5	220°
1377	Mill Rock, northeast of		40° 46.9'	73° 56.2'	–0 23	+0 05	–0 29	–0 32	0.7	0.1			2.3	000°			0.6	288°
1379	Mill Rock, west of		40° 46.8'	73° 56.5'	–0 26	+0 08	–0 02	–0 17	0.4	0.2			1.2	000°			1.0	180°
1381	HELL GATE (off Mill Rock)		40° 46.7'	73° 56.3'	Daily predictions								3.4	050°			4.6	230°
	Roosevelt Island																	
1383	west of, off 75th Street		40° 46'	73° 57'	–0 02	–0 04	–0 08	+0 07	1.1	1.0			3.8	037°			4.7	215°
1385	east of, off 36th Avenue		40° 46'	73° 57'	–0 08	–0 04	–0 08	+0 11	1.0	0.7			3.5	030°			3.4	210°
1387	west of, off 67th Street		40° 45.74'	73° 57.24'	+0 13	–0 08	+0 06	+0 11	1.1	0.9			3.6	011°			4.0	230°
1389	west of, off 63rd Street		40° 45.58'	73° 57.27'	–0 10	–0 06	+0 00	+0 03	0.8	0.6			2.8	036°			2.9	223°
1391	east of		40° 45.49'	73° 57.08'	+0 09	–0 11	–0 02	+0 36	0.8	0.6			2.8	028°			2.6	200°
1393	Manhattan, off 31st Street		40° 44.38'	73° 58.17'	Current weak and variable				0.4	0.5			1.5	000°			2.1	175°
1395	Newtown Creek entrance		40° 44'	73° 57'														
1397	Pier 67, off 19th Street		40° 44'	73° 58'	–0 08	+0 08	–0 08	+0 07	0.5	0.4			1.8	355°			1.9	179°
1399	Williamsburg Bridge, 0.3 mile north of		40° 43.08'	73° 58.24'	–0 05	+0 12	–0 01	+0 10	0.8	0.6			2.7	020°			2.9	220°
1401	Manhattan Bridge, East of	15	40° 42.5'	73° 59.4'	–0 28	+0 19	–0 13	+0 03	0.7	0.5	0.1	161°	2.5	083°			2.2	259°
1403	Brooklyn Bridge, 0.1 mile southwest of		40° 42.2'	74° 00.0'	–0 18	+0 08	–0 04	–0 07	0.9	0.8			2.9	046°			3.5	222°
	HARLEM RIVER																	
1405	East 107th Street	15	40° 47.4'	73° 56.1'	–0 08	–0 03	–1 09	–1 39	0.2	0.2			0.8	206°			0.8	030°
1407	Willis Ave. Bridge, 0.1 mile NW of		40° 48.3'	73° 55.8'	–0 30	+0 00	–0 12	–0 13	0.4	0.3			1.2	140°			1.3	330°
1409	Madison Ave. Bridge		40° 48.8'	73° 56.1'	–0 20	+0 18	–0 21	–0 14	0.5	0.4			1.8	180°			1.7	000°
1411	Macombs Dam Bridge		40° 49.7'	73° 56.1'	–0 20	+0 14	–0 22	–0 11	0.5	0.3			1.7	180°			1.4	000°
1413	High Bridge		40° 50.5'	73° 55.9'	–0 20	+0 08	–0 23	–0 08	0.6	0.4			2.0	189°			2.0	015°
1415	West 207th Street Bridge		40° 51.8'	73° 54.9'	–0 22	+0 05	–0 22	–0 02	0.6	0.4			2.0	215°			2.3	035°
1417	Broadway Bridge		40° 52.4'	73° 54.7'	–0 23	+0 08	–0 20	+0 04	0.6	0.5			2.1	116°			2.0	299°
1419	Henry Hudson Bridge, 0.7 nmi. SE of	16	40° 52.6'	73° 55.3'	+0 12	+0 31	–0 31	+0 41	0.2	0.3			1.8	137°			1.3	326°
	LONG ISLAND, South Coast																	
1421	Fire Island Lighted Whistle Bouy 2Fl		40° 29'	73° 11'	on The Narrows, p.60													
1423	Fire Island Inlet, 22 miles S of		40° 16'	73° 16'	Current weak and variable													
1425	Shinnecock Canal, railroad bridge <16>		40° 53.2'	72° 30.1'	Current weak and variable			–0 42		0.8							1.5	180°
1427	Ponquogue bridge, Shinnecock Bay		40° 50.6'	72° 28.7'	+1 04	+0 34	+0 19	+0 30	0.5	0.3			0.8	250°			0.6	090°
1429	Shinnecock Inlet		40° 37.78'	72° 18.40'	+0 04	–0 22	–0 38	–0 50	1.6	1.2			2.5	350°			2.3	170°
1431	Fire I. Inlet, 0.5 mi. S of Oak Beach		40° 35.5'	73° 34.0'	+0 07	–0 02	+0 21	–0 08	1.5	1.3			2.4	082°			2.4	244°
1433	Jones Inlet		40° 35.7'	73° 39.6'	–1 15	–0 49	–0 48	–1 05	1.8	1.3			3.1	035°			2.6	217°
1435	Long Beach, inside, between bridges		40° 35.4'	73° 45.3'	–0 44	+0 22	+0 24	–0 07	0.3	0.3			0.5	076°			0.6	277°
1437	East Rockaway Inlet		40° 27'	73° 49'	–1 36	–1 36	–1 11	–1 45	1.4	1.2			2.2	042°			2.3	227°
1439	Ambrose Light		40° 27'	73° 55'	Current weak and variable													
1441	Sandy Hook App. Lighted Horn Bouy 2A				See table 5.													
	JAMAICA BAY																	
1443	Rockaway Point	15	40° 32.18'	73° 56.48'	–2 26	–2 35	–1 46	–3 09	1.2	0.6	0.2	228°	1.9	301°	0.2	217°	1.1	140°
1445	Rockaway Inlet entrance		40° 33.7'	73° 56.1'	–1 45	–2 21	–1 41	–2 18	1.1	1.4			1.8	085°			2.7	244°
1447	Rockaway Inlet	14	40° 34.12'	73° 53.48'	–1 43	–2 01	–1 23	–2 36	1.0	0.8			1.6	066°	0.1	344°	1.5	261°
1449	Barren Island, east of		40° 35.0'	73° 53.0'	–1 49	–2 29	–2 11	–2 26	0.8	0.9			1.2	004°			1.7	192°

Endnotes can be found at the end of table 2.

TABLE 2. – CURRENT DIFFERENCES AND OTHER CONSTANTS

No.	PLACE	Meter Depth (ft)	POSITION Latitude North	POSITION Longitude West	TIME DIFF. Min. before Flood (h m)	TIME DIFF. Flood (h m)	TIME DIFF. Min. before Ebb (h m)	TIME DIFF. Ebb (h m)	SPEED RATIO Flood	SPEED RATIO Ebb	Min. before Flood (knots)	Min. before Flood (Dir.)	Max. Flood (knots)	Max. Flood (Dir.)	Min. before Ebb (knots)	Min. before Ebb (Dir.)	Max. Ebb (knots)	Max. Ebb (Dir.)
	JAMAICA BAY Time meridian, 75°W				*on The Narrows, p.60*													
1451	Canarsie (midchannel, off pier)	15	40°37.6'	73°53.0'	−1 44	−1 39	−1 26	−2 13	0.3	0.4	—	—	0.5	045°	—	—	0.7	222°
1453	Beach Channel (bridge)	16	40°35.0'	73°49.0'	−1 38	−1 14	−1 05	−1 32	1.2	1.1	—	—	1.9	062°	—	—	2.0	225°
1455	Grass Hassock Channel	17	40°36.6'	73°47.1'	−1 11	−1 03	−1 05	−1 01	0.6	0.5	—	—	1.0	052°	—	—	1.0	228°
	NEW YORK HARBOR ENTRANCE																	
1457	Ambrose Channel	15	40°31.00'	73°58.48'	−0 47	−1 11	−0 33	−0 14	1.0	0.9	0.1	025°	1.6	303°	—	—	1.7	123°
1459	Norton Point, WSW of	16	40°33.30'	74°01.30'	−0 03	−1 02	+0 18	+0 20	0.6	0.7	0.3	263°	1.0	341°	0.1	071°	1.2	166°
1461	THE NARROWS, midchannel	17	40°36.56'	74°02.77'	*Daily predictions*						0.2	064°	1.6	336°	—	—	1.9	164°
	do.	30	40°36.56'	74°02.77'	−0 23	−0 07	+0 13	+0 14	1.1	0.9	—	—	1.7	332°	0.1	246°	1.7	160°
	do.	43	40°36.56'	74°02.77'	−0 44	−0 11	+0 17	+0 00	1.2	0.9	0.1	244°	1.8	332°	0.1	244°	1.6	156°
	do.	63	40°36.56'	74°02.77'	−1 10	−0 31	+0 10	−0 13	1.1	0.7	0.1	240°	1.7	331°	—	—	1.3	147°
	NEW YORK HARBOR, Upper Bay																	
1463	Bay Ridge, west of	22	40°37.54'	74°03.24'	−0 01	+0 19	+0 34	+0 52	0.9	0.8	0.1	104°	1.4	354°	0.1	125°	1.5	185°
1465	Bay Ridge Channel	15	40°39.18'	74°01.54'	−0 48	−1 27	−0 04	−1 24	0.7	0.4	—	—	1.0	032°	—	—	0.7	212°
	do.	36	40°39.18'	74°01.54'	−1 25	−2 37	−0 58	−0 16	0.4	0.2	—	—	0.6	037°	—	—	0.4	225°
1467	Red Hook Channel		40°40.0'	74°01.2'	−0 53	−0 45	−0 16	−0 37	0.6	0.4	—	—	1.3	353°	—	—	0.7	170°
1469	Robbins Reef Light, east of		40°39.45'	74°03.50'	+0 26	+0 15	−0 06	+0 17	0.8	0.9	—	—	1.3	016°	—	—	1.6	204°
1471	Red Hook, 1 mile west of		40°40.5'	74°02.5'	+0 51	+1 05	+0 39	+0 45	0.8	1.2	—	—	1.3	024°	—	—	2.3	206°
1473	Statue of Liberty, east of		40°41.4'	74°01.8'	+1 07	+0 57	+0 48	+0 52	0.9	1.0	—	—	1.4	031°	—	—	1.9	205°
	HUDSON RIVER, Midchannel <17>				*on George Washington Bridge, p.64*													
1475	Hudson River entrance	14	40°42.30'	74°01.12'	−0 28	−0 28	−0 25	−0 19	0.8	0.5	0.1	292°	1.4	009°	—	—	1.4	199°
1477	Grants Tomb	18	40°48.48'	73°58.06'	−0 13	−0 22	+0 11	−0 33	1.0	0.7	—	—	1.8	025°	—	—	1.8	208°
1479	GEORGE WASHINGTON BRIDGE	14d	40°50.97'	73°56.99'	*Daily predictions*						—	—	1.7	010°	0.1	289°	2.5	203°
	do.	40d	40°50.97'	73°56.99'	−0 35	−0 38	−0 04	−0 19	1.0	0.8	0.3	288°	1.3	012°	—	—	1.9	198°
	do.	63d	40°50.97'	73°56.99'	−0 56	−0 40	+0 04	−0 36	0.7	0.4	0.2	285°	1.6	355°	—	—	1.1	177°
1481	Spuyten Duyvil	15	40°53'	73°56'	−0 06	+0 28	+0 10	+0 24	0.9	0.8	0.1	266°	1.4	020°	—	—	2.1	200°
1483	Riverdale		40°54'	73°55'	+0 54	+0 27	+0 15	+0 32	0.8	0.8	—	—	1.5	015°	—	—	2.0	200°
1485	Mount St. Vincent College, SW of		40°54.42'	73°54.48'	+0 09	+0 20	+0 27	+0 29	0.8	0.5	—	—	1.1	007°	—	—	1.4	190°
1487	Dobbs Ferry	5d	41°01'	73°53'	+1 13	+0 53	+0 37	+0 49	0.7	0.7	—	—	1.1	010°	—	—	1.7	190°
1489	Tappan Zee Bridge	16d	41°04.00'	73°52.90'	+1 12	+0 55	+0 52	+1 06	0.6	0.8	—	—	1.2	356°	—	—	1.9	175°
	do.	35d	41°04.00'	73°52.90'	+0 50	+1 04	+1 04	+1 05	0.7	0.7	0.1	265°	0.8	354°	0.1	265°	1.6	174°
	do.		41°04.00'	73°52.90'	+0 14	+0 29	+1 05	+1 05	0.5	0.4	—	—	0.9	349°	—	—	0.9	178°
1491	Tarrytown		41°05'	73°53'	+1 20	+1 06	+0 53	+1 02	0.6	0.6	—	—	1.1	000°	—	—	1.5	180°
1493	Ossining		41°10'	73°54'	+1 33	+1 22	+1 16	+1 19	0.5	0.5	—	—	0.9	320°	—	—	1.5	165°
1495	Haverstraw	4d	41°12.55'	73°57.07'	+2 29	+2 11	+1 58	+1 45	0.4	0.6	—	—	0.8	348°	—	—	1.5	165°
	do.	12d	41°12.55'	73°57.07'	+2 04	+2 10	+2 14	+2 01	0.5	0.3	—	—	0.8	345°	—	—	1.1	166°
1497	Stony Point	20d	41°14.49'	73°58.00'	+1 26	+1 46	+2 14	+1 31	0.5	0.6	0.1	076°	0.8	344°	0.1	073°	1.5	162°
	do.	14d	41°14.49'	73°58.00'	+2 09	+1 55	+1 46	+2 00	0.6	0.5	0.1	069°	1.0	348°	0.1	250°	0.7	154°
	do.	50d	41°14.49'	73°58.00'	+1 26	+1 50	+2 21	+1 40	0.7	0.2	—	—	1.3	334°	—	—	1.5	165°
1499	Peekskill		41°17'	73°57'	+1 34	+1 57	+2 22	+1 42	0.5	0.5	—	—	1.3	338°	—	—	0.6	170°
1501	Bear Mountain Bridge	13d	41°18.95'	73°59.03'	+1 53	+1 44	+1 46	+1 46	0.4	0.6	—	—	0.6	000°	—	—	1.2	180°
	do.	52d	41°18.95'	73°59.03'	+2 18	+1 32	+1 40	+2 05	0.6	0.6	—	—	0.6	343°	—	—	1.4	180°
	do.	88d	41°18.95'	73°59.03'	+1 58	+1 46	+2 02	+2 07	0.6	0.4	—	—	1.0	339°	—	—	1.2	167°
1503	Highland Falls		41°22'	73°58'	+1 34	+1 38	+2 07	+2 02	0.6	0.5	—	—	1.0	005°	—	—	0.9	161°
1505	West Point, off Duck Island	4d	41°24'	73°57'	+2 07	+1 57	+1 57	+2 04	0.6	0.5	—	—	1.0	010°	—	—	1.2	185°
1507	Newburgh Beacon Bridge	17d	41°31.00'	73°59.50'	+2 15	+2 04	+2 04	+2 19	0.6	0.4	—	—	1.2	350°	—	—	1.1	190°
	do.	24d	41°31.00'	73°59.50'	+2 19	+2 19	+2 25	+2 18	0.5	0.3	—	—	1.0	346°	—	—	1.0	171°
1509	Roseton	5d	41°33.75'	73°58.23'	+2 15	+2 08	+2 23	+2 51	0.6	0.6	0.1	123°	0.9	345°	0.1	128°	0.9	169°
	do.	15d	41°33.75'	73°58.23'	+2 13	+2 07	+2 41	+2 50	0.6	0.5	—	—	1.1	039°	0.1	128°	1.3	213°
	do.	41d	41°33.75'	73°58.23'	+2 57	+2 36	+2 43	+3 01	0.5	0.4	—	—	0.9	038°	—	—	0.9	215°

Endnotes can be found at the end of table 2.

TABLE 2. – CURRENT DIFFERENCES AND OTHER CONSTANTS

No.	PLACE	Position Latitude North	Position Longitude West	Meter Depth (ft)	Time Diff. Min. before Flood (h m)	Time Diff. Flood (h m)	Time Diff. Min. before Ebb (h m)	Time Diff. Ebb (h m)	Speed Ratio Flood	Speed Ratio Ebb	Min. before Flood knots	Min. before Flood Dir.	Max. Flood knots	Max. Flood Dir.	Min. before Ebb knots	Min. before Ebb Dir.	Max. Ebb knots	Max. Ebb Dir.
	HUDSON RIVER, Midchannel <17> Time meridian, 75°W																	
1511	New Hamburg	41°35'	73°57'		+2 48	+2 40	+2 24	+2 33	0.6	0.4	--	--	1.0	005°	--	--	1.1	195°
1513	Mid–Hudson Suspension Bridge	41°42.10'	73°56.76'	16d	+3 15	+2 49	+2 54	+3 09	0.7	0.6	--	--	1.2	005°	--	--	1.5	188°
	do.	41°42.10'	73°56.76'	32d	+3 14	+2 47	+2 50	+3 08	0.6	0.5	--	--	1.1	005°	--	--	1.4	186°
	do.	41°42.10'	73°56.76'	48d	+3 12	+2 45	+2 46	+3 09	0.5	0.5	--	--	0.9	005°	--	--	1.2	185°
1515	Hyde Park	41°47'	73°57'		+3 25	+3 08	+2 43	+3 00	0.7	0.5	--	--	1.2	005°	--	--	1.3	185°
	on George Washington Bridge, p.64																	
1517	Kingston Point, south of	41°55.10'	73°57.57'	4d	-0 31	-0 09	-0 07	-0 24	1.2	1.1	0.1	090°	1.3	009°	0.1	095°	1.5	177°
	do.	41°55.10'	73°57.57'	17d	-0 30	-0 10	-0 10	-0 22	1.2	1.1	0.1	090°	1.2	010°	0.1	095°	1.4	177°
	do.	41°55.10'	73°57.57'	30d	-0 30	-0 07	-0 07	-0 25	1.0	0.9	0.1	090°	1.0	011°	0.1	095°	1.1	178°
	on Kingston–Rhinecliff Bridge, p.68																	
1519	KINGSTON–RHINECLIFF BRIDGE	41°58.63'	73°57.13'	14d		Daily predictions												
	do.	41°58.63'	73°57.13'	4d	+0 00	-0 01	-0 01	-0 01	1.1	1.1	--	--	1.1	011°	--	--	1.3	191°
	do.	41°58.63'	73°57.13'	27d	-0 02	-0 01	-0 05	-0 04	0.8	0.9	--	--	0.9	010°	--	--	1.4	192°
1521	Barrytown	42°00'	73°56'		+0 21	+0 24	+0 14	+0 06	1.1	1.3	--	--	1.4	010°	--	--	1.7	190°
1523	Saugerties	42°04'	73°56'		+0 38	+0 45	+0 41	+0 28	1.3	1.5	--	--	1.5	000°	--	--	1.9	180°
1525	Silver Point, south of	42°08.29'	73°54.51'	4d	+0 38	+0 54	+0 40	+0 29	1.3	1.2	--	--	1.4	025°	--	--	1.5	205°
	do.	42°08.29'	73°54.51'	14d	+0 38	+0 54	+0 37	+0 27	1.2	1.1	--	--	1.3	025°	--	--	1.5	205°
	do.	42°08.29'	73°54.51'	31d	+0 28	+0 54	+0 40	+0 27	1.0	0.8	--	--	1.0	024°	--	--	1.1	205°
1527	Catskill	42°13'	73°51'		+1 11	+1 30	+0 54	+0 36	1.5	1.5	--	--	1.6	355°	--	--	2.0	175°
1529	Hudson	42°14.88'	73°49.10'	14d	+1 22	+1 17	+0 44	+0 48	1.4	1.5	--	--	1.5	061°	--	--	1.9	242°
	do.	42°14.88'	73°49.10'	24d	+1 21	+1 14	+0 40	+0 47	1.0	1.4	--	--	1.4	060°	--	--	1.8	242°
	do.	42°14.88'	73°49.10'	40d	+1 31	+1 17	+1 01	+1 04	1.4	1.1	--	--	1.5	007°	--	--	1.4	238°
1531	Coxsackie	42°21.08'	73°47.40'	4d	+1 30	+1 16	+1 00	+1 04	1.3	1.1	--	--	1.4	007°	--	--	1.5	190°
	do.	42°21.08'	73°47.40'	14d	+1 28	+1 12	+0 58	+1 04	1.4	1.1	--	--	1.1	007°	--	--	1.4	189°
	do.	42°21.08'	73°47.40'	31d	+1 41	+1 12	+1 10	+1 12	1.3	0.8	--	--	1.2	000°	--	--	1.1	184°
1533	Houghtaling Island, south of	42°25.36'	73°46.80'	4d	+1 41	+1 09	+1 09	+1 15	1.1	0.9	--	--	1.0	359°	--	--	1.2	180°
	do.	42°25.36'	73°46.80'	14d	+1 40	+1 09	+1 07	+1 14	1.2	0.8	--	--	1.0	357°	--	--	1.1	181°
	do.	42°25.36'	73°46.80'	27d	+1 41	+1 12	+1 10	+1 12	0.9	0.7	--	--	1.3	355°	--	--	0.9	175°
1535	New Baltimore	42°27'	73°47'		+2 07	+2 07	+1 58	+1 58	1.2	1.1	--	--	1.3	355°	--	--	1.5	175°
1537	Castleton-on-Hudson Bridge	42°30.26'	73°46.64'	6d	+1 50	+1 10	+1 06	+1 23	1.0	0.7	--	--	1.0	051°	--	--	0.9	233°
	do.	42°30.26'	73°46.64'	16d	+1 48	+1 09	+1 04	+1 20	0.9	0.7	--	--	1.0	050°	--	--	0.9	232°
	do.	42°30.26'	73°46.64'	32d	+2 08	+1 09	+1 27	+1 16	0.8	0.6	0.2	270°	0.8	049°	0.2	068°	0.8	229°
1539	Port of Albany	42°37.39'	73°45.34'	7d	+2 17	+1 10	+1 26	+0 48	0.4	0.4	--	--	0.5	021°	--	--	0.5	198°
	do.	42°37.39'	73°45.34'	16d	+2 18	+1 11	+1 27	+2 14	0.4	0.4	--	--	0.4	020°	--	--	0.5	198°
	do.	42°37.39'	73°45.34'	30d	+2 17	+1 10	+1 27	+2 06	0.4	0.4	--	--	0.4	018°	--	--	0.5	200°
1541	Troy (below the locks) <19>	42°44'	73°42'		--	--	--	--	--	--	--	--	--	--	--	--	--	--
	NEW YORK HARBOR, Lower Bay on The Narrows, p.60																	
1543	Sandy Hook Channel	40°29.06'	74°00.06'	15	-1 23	-2 04	-1 14	-1 30	1.0	0.5	--	--	1.6	286°	--	--	1.9	094°
1545	Sandy Hook Chan., 0.4 mi. W of N. Tip	40°28.79'	74°01.30'		-1 41	-1 56	-1 38	-1 57	1.3	0.9	--	--	2.0	235°	--	--	1.6	050°
1547	Sandy Hook Pt., 2 mi. W of (channel)	40°28.8'	74°03.6'		-1 35	-2 01	-1 58	-1 49	0.4	0.3	--	--	0.6	263°	--	--	0.6	086°
1549	Chapel Hill South Channel	40°29.90'	74°03.8'		-2 02	-2 31	-1 48	-2 15	0.4	0.3	--	--	0.7	255°	--	--	0.6	075°
1551	New Dorp Beach, 1.2 miles south of	40°32.4'	74°05.8'		-4 09	-3 37	-4 43	-4 23	0.3	0.3	--	--	0.4	225°	--	--	0.5	030°
1553	Old Orchard Shoal Lt. 1.2 mi. ENE of	40°31.1'	74°04.4'		-2 09	-2 08	-1 31	-2 09	0.4	0.2	--	--	0.7	270°	--	--	0.4	085°
1555	New Dorp Beach, 1.2 mi. ENE of	40°32.9'	74°03.7'		---	+0 06	---	-0 06	0.5	0.7	--	--	0.5	045°	--	--	0.5	225°
1557	Midland Beach, 2.6 miles SE of <20>	40°32.8'	74°02.35'		-1 17	-1 57	-1 06	-1 00	0.5	0.7	0.2	270°	0.8	335°	0.2	068°	1.3	160°
1559	Coney Island Lt., 1.5 miles SSE of	40°33.1'	74°00.3'		-1 33	-1 49	-0 25	-0 57	0.7	0.7	--	--	1.1	310°	--	--	0.8	125°
1561	Hoffman Island, 0.2 mile west of	40°35.1'	74°04'		-2 06	-2 13	-1 36	-1 50	0.6	0.8	--	--	1.2	020°	--	--	1.4	210°
1563	Rockaway Inlet Jetty, 1 mile SW of	40°31.8'	73°57.2'		-1 14	-0 45	-0 32	-0 55	0.8	0.8	--	--	1.1	287°	--	--	1.2	102°
1565	Coney Island Channel, west end	40°34.2'	74°00.5'		---	---	---	---	0.7	0.6	--	--	1.1	293°	--	--	--	--
	SANDY HOOK BAY <22>																	
1567	Highlands Bridge, Shrewsbury River	40°23.8'	73°58.8'		+0 31	+0 35	+0 25	+0 12	1.7	1.3	--	--	2.6	170°	--	--	2.5	--
1569	Seabright Bridge, Shrewsbury River	40°21.9'	73°58.5'		+1 05	+1 05	+0 44	+0 44	0.9	0.9	--	--	1.4	185°	--	--	1.7	--

Endnotes can be found at the end of table 2.

TABLE 2. – CURRENT DIFFERENCES AND OTHER CONSTANTS

No.	PLACE	Meter Depth (ft)	Position Lat. North	Position Long. West	Time Diff. Min. before Flood (h m)	Time Diff. Flood (h m)	Time Diff. Min. before Ebb (h m)	Time Diff. Ebb (h m)	Speed Ratio Flood	Speed Ratio Ebb	Min. before Flood knots	Min. before Flood Dir.	Max. Flood knots	Max. Flood Dir.	Min. before Ebb knots	Min. before Ebb Dir.	Max. Ebb knots	Max. Ebb Dir.
	RARITAN BAY Time meridian, 75°W				on The Narrows, p.60													
1571	Raritan Bay Reach Channel	15	40°29.36'	74°07.06'	−1 55	−2 41	−0 46	−0 58	0.4	0.2	− −	− −	0.6	285°	− −	− −	0.4	094°
1573	Keyport Channel entrance		40°26.9'	74°11.9'	Current weak and variable				0.4	0.3	− −	− −	0.6	278°	− −	− −	0.5	079°
1575	Red Bank, 1.4 miles south of	14	40°28.9'	74°12.6'	−1 35	−2 13	−1 30	−1 51	0.4	0.2	− −	− −	0.5	281°	0.1	008°	0.3	079°
1577	Seguine Point	34	40°30.24'	74°11.12'	−1 52	−2 51	−0 56	−2 15	0.3	0.1	− −	− −	0.5	285°	− −	− −	0.2	105°
	. . . do.	14		74°11.12'	−3 28	−2 52	−0 21	−2 31										
1579	Ward Point, ESE		40°29.30'	74°13.48'	−1 45	−1 59	−0 19	−1 01	0.5	0.3	0.1	328°	0.7	244°	0.1	133°	0.5	048°
	RARITAN RIVER																	
1581	Railroad Bridge, Raritan River	15	40°29.54'	74°17.00'	−2 02	−2 26	−1 23	−2 08	0.6	0.4	− −	− −	0.9	326°	− −	− −	0.7	147°
1583	Washington Canal, north entrance		40°28.3'	74°22.1'	−1 02	−1 26	−1 38	−2 58	1.0	0.8	− −	− −	1.5	240°	− −	− −	1.5	060°
1585	South River entrance		40°28.7'	74°22.7'	−1 45	−2 15	−0 35	−1 51	0.7	0.5	− −	− −	1.1	180°	− −	− −	1.0	000°
	ARTHUR KILL																	
1587	Tottenville, Arthur Kill River	15	40°30.8'	74°15.3'	−1 04	−1 26	−0 41	−1 30	0.7	0.6	− −	− −	1.0	023°	− −	− −	1.1	211°
	. . . do.	32	40°30.8'	74°15.3'	−1 23	−1 06	−0 56	−1 10	0.4	0.3	− −	− −	0.6	026°	− −	− −	0.5	207°
1589	Tufts Point–Smoking Point		40°33.4'	74°13.4'	−0 38	−0 45	−0 32	−1 07	0.8	0.6	− −	− −	1.2	109°	− −	− −	1.2	267°
1591	Tremley Point Reach	21	40°35.18'	74°12.30'	−0 08	−0 55	+0 23	+0 22	0.6	0.4	− −	− −	0.9	015°	− −	− −	0.8	198°
1593	Elizabethport		40°38.8'	74°10.9'	+0 15	−0 10	+0 24	−0 03	0.9	0.6	− −	− −	1.4	090°	− −	− −	1.1	262°
	KILL VAN KULL				on Bergen Point Reach, p.72													
1595	BERGEN POINT REACH (BAYONNE BRIDGE)	16	40°38.5'	74°08.6'	−0 15	+0 02	+0 14	−0 04	0.8	0.9	0.1	346°	1.9	260°	− −	− −	1.4	078°
	. . . do.	29	40°38.5'	74°08.6'	Daily predictions						− −	− −	1.6	263°	− −	− −	1.3	079°
	NEWARK BAY				on The Narrows, p.60													
1597	Bergen Point, East Reach	15	40°38.42'	74°07.48'	−1 24	−2 14	−1 43	−1 51	0.7	0.6	− −	− −	1.1	274°	− −	− −	1.2	094°
1599	New Brighton	15	40°39.00'	74°05.06'	−1 34	−2 09	−1 32	−1 50	0.8	1.0	− −	− −	1.3	262°	− −	− −	1.9	072°
1601	South Reach, Newark Bay	15	40°39.36'	74°08.24'	−0 46	−1 46	−0 59	−1 13	0.4	0.4	− −	− −	0.7	031°	0.0	296°	0.7	218°
	HACKENSACK RIVER																	
1603	Lincoln Highway Bridge, north of		40°44'	74°06'	+0 04	+0 11	+0 39	−0 21	0.6	0.4	− −	− −	0.9	017°	− −	− −	0.8	181°
	PASSAIC RIVER																	
1605	Lincoln Highway Bridge		40°44'	74°07'	−0 21	−0 20	−0 20	−0 27	0.4	0.3	− −	− −	0.6	009°	− −	− −	0.5	180°
	NEW JERSEY COAST				on Delaware Bay Entrance, p.76													
1607	Shark River Entrance	5d	40°11.24'	74°00.76'	−2 26	−2 31	−2 33	−2 08	1.1	0.9	− −	− −	1.9	273°	− −	− −	1.5	098°
	. . . do.	15d	40°11.24'	74°00.76'	−2 27	−2 30	−2 33	−2 10	0.9	0.7	− −	− −	1.5	275°	− −	− −	1.2	097°
1609	Manasquan Inlet		40°06'	74°02'	−1 03	−1 09	−1 39	−1 53	1.0	1.1	− −	− −	1.7	300°	− −	− −	1.8	120°
1611	Manasquan R., hwy. bridge, main chan		40°06'	74°03'	−1 01	−1 29	−1 42	−0 46	1.3	1.2	− −	− −	2.2	230°	− −	− −	2.1	050°
1613	Point Pleasant Canal, north bridge <54>		40°05'	74°04'	+1 26	+0 49	+0 21	+1 14	1.0	1.2	− −	− −	1.8	170°	− −	− −	2.5	350°
1615	Barnegat Inlet		39°46'	74°07'	+0 41	+0 27	−0 12	−0 08	1.3	1.5	− −	− −	2.2	270°	− −	− −	0.9	090°
1617	Manahawkin Drawbridge		39°39'	74°11'	+2 13	+2 04	+1 58	+3 25	0.6	0.5	− −	− −	2.1	030°	− −	− −	2.0	210°
1619	Absecon Inlet	9d	39°22.59'	74°24.87'	−1 30	−1 30	−1 21	−2 14	1.3	1.1	0.1	055°	2.2	328°	− −	− −	2.0	147°
	. . . do.	42d	39°22.59'	74°24.87'	−1 22	−1 45	−1 23	−2 04	1.1	1.1	0.1	239°	1.9	327°	− −	− −	1.8	144°
1621	Corson's Inlet Entrance	15d	39°12.50'	74°39.11'	−1 53	−1 57	−2 04	−2 59	0.9	1.1	− −	− −	1.6	308°	− −	− −	1.8	129°
1623	Cape May, 72 miles east of		39°04'	73°25'	Current weak and variable													
1625	Five-Fathom Bank NE. Buoy 2 FB		38°58'	74°32'	Current weak and variable													

Endnotes can be found at the end of table 2.

TABLE 2. – CURRENT DIFFERENCES AND OTHER CONSTANTS

No.	PLACE	Meter Depth (ft)	Latitude North	Longitude West	Time Diff. Min. before Flood (h m)	Flood (h m)	Min. before Ebb (h m)	Ebb (h m)	Speed Ratio Flood	Speed Ratio Ebb	Min. before Flood knots	Dir.	Max. Flood knots	Dir.	Min. before Ebb knots	Dir.	Max. Ebb knots	Dir.
	NEW JERSEY COAST Time meridian, 75°W				on Delaware Bay Entrance, p.76													
1627	Five Fathom Bank Traffic Lane	35d	38°47.30'	74°42.68'	−2 10	−2 21	−1 27	−1 36	0.3	0.2	---	---	0.6	304°	---	---	0.4	121°
	...do...	50d	38°47.30'	74°42.68'	−2 45	−1 57	−1 48	−2 16	0.2	0.2	---	---	0.4	302°	---	---	0.3	128°
1629	McCrie Shoal		38°51'	74°51'	−0 54	−1 05	−1 10	−1 00	0.7	0.8	---	---	1.3	280°	---	---	1.4	100°
1631	Cape May Harbor entrance	5d	38°58.85'	74°52.36'	−2 02	−1 59	−2 01	−2 06	0.9	1.0	---	---	1.6	324°	---	---	1.7	142°
	...do...	15d	38°58.85'	74°52.36'	−1 42	−1 23	−1 34	−1 07	1.1	1.3	---	---	1.5	323°	---	---	1.7	142°
1633	Cape May Canal, east end	28d	38°57'	74°54'	−2 07	−2 01	−2 20	−2 01	1.1	1.1	---	---	1.9	310°	---	---	1.9	130°
1635	Cape May Canal, west end		38°58'	74°58'	−2 08	−2 27	−2 15	−2 12	0.5	0.5	---	---	0.9	264°	---	---	0.9	089°
	DELAWARE BAY and RIVER																	
1637	Cape May Channel	15d	38°54'	74°58'	−1 34	−2 09	−1 38	−1 41	0.9	1.4	---	---	1.5	306°	---	---	2.3	150°
1639	Cape May Point, 1.4 n.mi. SSW of	25d	38°54.37'	74°58.68'	−1 24	−1 57	−1 29	−1 43	0.8	1.1	0.1	030°	1.5	309°	0.1	214°	1.8	130°
	...do...	15d	38°54.37'	74°58.68'	−1 17	−1 44	−1 27	−1 27	0.6	0.7	0.1	038°	1.1	306°	0.1	223°	1.2	139°
1641	Cape May Point, 2.7 n.mi. SSW of	22	38°53.40'	74°59.13'	−1 50	−1 47	−1 14	−1 32	0.7	0.5	0.1	228°	1.2	299°	0.2	208°	0.9	146°
1643	DELAWARE BAY ENTRANCE	12d	38°51.22'	75°04.62'	Daily predictions						0.2	253°	1.8	342°	0.2	061°	1.7	152°
1645	Cape Henlopen, 0.7 n.mi. ESE of	70d	38°47.97'	75°04.90'	−0 25	−0 32	−1 07	−0 59	1.0	1.4	---	---	1.8	331°	---	---	2.4	139°
1647	Cape Henlopen, 2 miles northeast of	17d	38°49.2'	75°03.4'	−1 46	−0 35	−0 51	−0 40	0.7	0.4	0.1	042°	1.2	317°	0.1	232°	0.7	150°
1649	Cape Henlopen, 3.0 n.mi. NNE of	31d	38°51.22'	75°04.62'	+0 01	−0 18	−0 30	+0 03	1.1	1.4	0.2	252°	2.0	315°	0.2	062°	2.3	145°
	...do...	57d	38°51.22'	75°04.62'	−0 02	−0 01	−0 01	+0 02	1.0	0.9	0.1	250°	1.7	342°	0.1	065°	1.7	152°
	...do...	96d	38°51.22'	75°04.62'	−0 09	−0 12	+0 04	+0 08	1.1	0.8	---	---	1.9	338°	0.0	245°	1.5	152°
1651	Cape Henlopen, 4.8 n.mi. northeast of	18d	38°51.55'	75°01.47'	−0 18	−0 27	+0 17	+0 01	1.0	0.7	0.1	053°	1.9	334°	0.2	229°	1.3	154°
	...do...	28d	38°51.55'	75°01.47'	−0 30	−0 28	+0 11	−0 59	0.9	1.1	0.2	241°	1.8	333°	0.2	220°	1.2	149°
1653	Cape Henlopen, 5 miles north of		38°53.0'	75°05.3'	−0 43	−1 50	−1 09	−0 51	0.6	0.7	0.1	228°	1.5	322°	---	---	1.8	150°
1655	Breakwater Harbor		38°47.6'	75°06.5'	+0 02	+0 00	−1 11	+0 12	0.5	0.5	---	---	1.0	301°	---	---	1.2	154°
1657	Roosevelt Inlet (between jetties) <24>		38°47.5'	75°09.5'	−1 15	−1 29	−1 41	−1 10	0.4	0.7	---	---	2.0	344°	---	---	1.9	173°
1659	Broadkill Slough	14d	38°53.78'	75°12.63'	−0 56	−0 31	−0 30	−0 55	0.9	0.4	---	---	0.8	266°	---	---	0.9	078°
1661	Mispillion River mouth		38°56.8'	75°18.9'	+2 14	+1 50	+1 22	+1 18	0.5	0.6	---	---	0.7	206°	---	---	1.1	030°
1663	Bay Shore Channel (north)	13d	38°54.68'	74°58.88'	−0 49	−0 34	−0 24	−0 04	0.5	0.5	0.1	223°	0.8	314°	0.1	223°	0.6	132°
1665	Bay Shore Channel (city of Town Bank)	15d	38°59.08'	74°59.28'	−0 51	−1 30	−1 12	−0 21	0.9	0.6	0.1	093°	1.5	025°	0.1	275°	1.0	190°
1667	BRANDYWINE SHOAL LIGHT, 0.5nm west of	15d	38°59.26'	75°07.62'	Daily Predictions, p.80						---	---	0.9	006°	---	---	0.7	183°
1669	Brandywine Ra. (off Brandywine Shoal N)	40d	39°00.37'	75°08.38'	−0 30	−0 38	−0 25	−0 39	0.7	0.7	0.1	241°	0.9	006°	0.1	241°	1.0	183°
1671	Big Stone Beach, 2.8 miles southeast of		39°00.37'	75°08.38'	−0 56	−0 38	−0 32	−0 32	0.3	0.4	0.1	061°	1.5	330°	---	---	1.4	153°
1673	Big Stone Beach, 2.2 n.mi. ENE of	15d	38°58.7'	75°16.6'	−1 04	−1 30	−1 08	−1 07	0.4	0.5	---	---	1.2	339°	0.1	233°	1.1	164°
1675	Fourteen Ft. Bank Lt. 1.4 n.mi. SSE of	12d	39°00.48'	75°17.05'	−0 13	−0 26	−0 23	+0 04	0.3	0.4	0.1	071°	0.6	326°	---	---	0.6	153°
	...do...	30d	39°02.32'	75°09.48'	−0 10	−0 36	−0 14	+0 10	0.7	0.7	0.1	069°	0.7	344°	0.1	249°	0.9	145°
1677	Fourteen Ft. Bank Lt., 1.2 mi. east of		39°03.3'	75°09.5'	−0 40	−0 26	−0 17	−0 05	0.5	0.4	---	---	0.6	343°	---	---	0.7	155°
1679	Deadman Shoal, 3.1 n.mi. SW of	13d	39°04.00'	75°04.22'	−0 10	−0 35	+0 02	−0 19	0.7	0.9	0.1	085°	1.3	339°	0.1	263°	1.5	174°
1681	Egg Island Flats		39°06.4'	75°07.1'	−0 43	−1 05	−0 35	−1 26	0.5	0.4	---	---	0.7	352°	---	---	0.6	173°
1683	Brandywine Range at Miah Maull Range		39°04.97'	75°11.28'	−1 13	−0 36	−0 58	+0 44	0.4	0.4	0.1	067°	1.0	355°	---	---	1.2	159°
1685	Maurice River entrance	9d	39°13.0'	75°02.7'	+0 20	+0 06	−0 06	+0 39	0.6	0.7	---	---	1.0	341°	---	---	1.0	192°
1687	Mauricetown Bridge, Maurice River		39°23.7'	74°59.6'	+0 31	+0 48	+0 37	+0 33	0.6	0.6	---	---	2.4	012°	---	---	2.2	180°
1689	Millville Drawbridge, Maurice River <25>		39°04'	75°02.4'	+0 41		+0 27	+1 51	1.4	1.3	---	---	0.6	000°	---	---	0.4	180°
1691	St. Jones River ent., 1 mile east of		39°12.8'	75°23'	−0 20	−0 40	−0 16	−0 09	0.3	0.2	---	---	0.9	334°	---	---	0.7	122°
1693	Kelly Island, 1.5 miles east of		39°11.4'	75°21.7'	+0 31	+0 11	+0 17	+0 16	0.5	0.7	---	---	0.9	348°	---	---	1.2	164°
1695	Miah Maull Range at Cross Ledge Range	16d	39°10.72'	75°16.40'	+0 59	+0 02	+1 00	+1 31	0.9	1.1	0.2	254°	1.5	335°	0.1	241°	1.8	160°
1697	False Egg Island Point, 2 miles off		39°14.87'	75°12'	+0 07	−0 35	−0 14	+0 06	0.6	0.8	---	---	1.1	342°	---	---	1.3	158°
1699	Ben Davis Pt. Shoal, southwest of	15d	39°16.13'	75°18.93'	+1 27	+0 51	+1 03	+1 41	1.0	1.3	0.2	047°	1.8	321°	---	---	1.9	147°
1701	Ben Davis Point, 3.2 n.mi. SW of	12d	39°16.9'	75°20.88'	+1 46	+0 59	+1 24	+1 55	1.1	1.3	0.2	047°	1.9	328°	---	---	2.2	140°
1703	Ben Davis Point, 0.8 mile southwest of	43d	39°16.13'	75°20.88'	+0 41	+0 38	+1 48	+2 13	0.8	0.5	---	---	0.8	319°	---	---	2.4	136°
1705	Cohansey River, 0.5 mile above entrance <1>		39°20.9'	75°18.2'	+0 37	+0 41	+0 46	+0 25	0.7	0.8	---	---	1.2	308°	---	---	1.4	254°
1707	Bridgeton (Broad Street Bridge) <1>		39°25.6'	75°14.2'	+1 10	+1 48	+1 04	+1 56	0.1	0.2	---	---	0.2	000°	---	---	0.3	180°

Endnotes can be found at the end of table 2.

TABLE 2. – CURRENT DIFFERENCES AND OTHER CONSTANTS

No.	PLACE	Meter Depth (ft)	Position Lat. North	Position Long. West	Time Diff. Min. before Flood (h m)	Time Diff. Flood (h m)	Time Diff. Min. before Ebb (h m)	Time Diff. Ebb (h m)	Speed Ratio Flood	Speed Ratio Ebb	Min. before Flood knots	Min. before Flood Dir.	Max. Flood knots	Max. Flood Dir.	Min. before Ebb knots	Min. before Ebb Dir.	Max. Ebb knots	Max. Ebb Dir.
	DELAWARE BAY and RIVER Time meridian, 75°W				**on Delaware Bay Entrance, p.76**													
1709	Arnold Point, 2.2 n.mi. WSW of	14d	39° 22.67'	75° 28.07'	+2 03	+1 39	+2 00	+2 14	1.2	1.1	--	--	2.1	324°	0.1	047°	1.9	145°
	...do.	29d	39° 22.67'	75° 28.07'	+1 30	+1 29	+1 49	+1 34	0.9	0.8	0.1	225°	1.6	327°	0.1	055°	1.3	140°
1711	Smyrna River entrance		39° 21.9'	75° 30.8'	+1 29	+1 02	+1 30	+1 32	0.7	0.9	--	--	1.2	250°	--	--	1.5	070°
					on Reedy Point, p.84													
1713	Stony Point, channel west of		39° 27.1'	75° 33.8'	+0 03	+0 00	-0 25	-1 09	0.8	0.9	--	--	1.5	324°	--	--	1.9	151°
1715	Appoquinimink River entrance		39° 26.3'	75° 34.9'	-0 47	+0 05	-0 47	-1 41	0.6	0.5	--	--	1.0	231°	--	--	1.2	048°
1717	Artificial Island (Baker Range)	14d	39° 28.20'	75° 33.88'	-0 19	-0 11	-0 09	-0 30	1.2	1.2	0.2	267°	2.1	346°	--	--	2.7	175°
1719	Reedy Island (off end of pier)		39° 30.7'	75° 33.4'	-0 19	+0 11	-0 09	-0 52	1.3	1.2	--	--	2.4	027°	--	--	2.6	194°
1721	Alloway Creek ent., 0.2 mile above		39° 29.9'	75° 31.5'	-0 59	-0 08	-0 44	-2 19	1.2	0.9	--	--	2.1	129°	--	--	2.1	325°
1723	New Bridge, Alloway Creek		39° 31.6'	75° 27.1'	-0 17	+1 07	+0 33	-0 39	0.7	0.6	--	--	1.3	090°	--	--	1.4	270°
1725	Chesapeake and Delaware Canal Entrance	15d	39° 33.63'	75° 34.20'	+2 44	+2 41	+3 36	+1 40	0.8	0.9	--	--	1.4	264°	--	--	2.0	087°
1727	REEDY POINT, 0.3nm east of south jetty	15d	39° 33.51'	75° 33.10'	Daily predictions						0.1	074°	1.7	351°	0.1	260°	2.0	163°
1729	Reedy Point, 1.1 miles east of		39° 33.58'	75° 32.47'	-0 01	-0 21	+0 05	-0 39	1.0	0.8	--	--	1.8	354°	--	--	1.7	179°
1731	Reedy Point, 0.85 n.mi. northeast of	15d	39° 34.23'	75° 33.22'	+0 14	-0 14	-0 03	-0 45	0.9	1.0	--	--	1.6	341°	--	--	2.2	163°
1733	Salem River entrance	15d	39° 34.2'	75° 30.1'	+0 26	-0 43	+0 34	-0 06	0.8	0.7	--	--	1.5	062°	--	--	1.6	245°
1735	Bulkhead Shoal Channel, SE, Del. City		39° 34.58'	75° 34.52'	+0 04	-0 05	+0 06	-0 33	1.0	0.9	--	--	1.5	299°	--	--	2.1	118°
1737	Bulkhead Shoal Channel, off Del. City	14d	39° 35.0'	75° 35.2'	-0 04	+0 08	+0 00	-0 31	1.2	0.9	--	--	2.1	308°	--	--	2.1	138°
1739	Pea Patch Island, channel east of		39° 36.0'	75° 33.9'	+0 10	+0 23	+0 30	-0 06	1.3	1.0	--	--	2.3	319°	--	--	2.3	148°
1741	Finns Point, 0.60 n.mi. Northwest of	16d	39° 36.37'	75° 34.47'	+0 14	+0 18	+0 22	-0 22	1.2	1.0	--	--	2.1	332°	--	--	2.3	152°
1743	Penns Neck, 0.6 mile west of		39° 37.05'	75° 34.92'	+0 18	+0 48	+0 11	-0 44	0.9	0.8	--	--	1.7	002°	--	--	1.7	167°
1745	Penns Neck, 0.3 mile west of		39° 37.07'	75° 34.58'	+0 02	+0 17	+0 05	-0 42	1.0	0.8	--	--	1.8	339°	--	--	1.7	152°
1747	New Castle, channel abreast of		39° 39.1'	75° 33.2'	+0 16	+0 03	+0 03	-0 44	1.0	1.1	--	--	1.9	051°	--	--	2.4	230°
1749	Kelly Point, 0.2 mile northwest of		39° 38.9'	75° 32.8'	+0 23	+1 05	+0 21	-0 44	0.9	0.7	--	--	1.6	049°	--	--	1.5	230°
1751	Riverview Beach, 0.75 n.mi. west of		39° 39.40'	75° 32.38'	+0 31	+0 33	+0 36	-0 08	1.1	0.9	--	--	2.0	038°	--	--	1.9	225°
1753	Deepwater Point, channel northwest of	15d	39° 42.1'	75° 30.6'	+0 24	+1 04	+0 42	-0 20	1.7	1.2	--	--	3.0	029°	--	--	2.6	215°
1755	Christina River, 0.9 n.mi. above ent	15d	39° 43.30'	75° 31.77'	+0 32	+0 26	+0 22	-0 46	0.1	0.4	0.1	226°	0.2	303°	--	--	0.8	137°
1757	Cherry Island Flats, channel east of		39° 44.3'	75° 29.1'	+0 49	+1 18	+0 59	-0 18	0.9	0.6	--	--	1.6	027°	--	--	1.4	207°
1759	Oldsmans Point		39° 45.9'	75° 28.4'	+1 08	+0 52	+1 00	+0 25	0.9	0.7	--	--	1.6	027°	--	--	1.5	210°
					on Philadelphia, p.88													
1761	Marcus Hook Bar (north), Main Channel	15d	39° 47.70'	75° 26.08'	-1 25	-1 29	-0 22	-0 37	1.3	0.8	--	--	1.9	059°	--	--	1.7	246°
1763	Marcus Hook		39° 48.2'	75° 24.6'	-0 41	-0 37	-0 25	-0 14	1.1	0.8	--	--	1.7	061°	--	--	1.6	232°
1765	Eddystone		39° 50.8'	75° 20.5'	-0 14	-0 15	+0 04	-0 10	1.1	1.1	--	--	1.7	058°	--	--	2.2	242°
1767	Essington Harbor		39° 51.5'	75° 17.0'	-1 30	-1 02	-0 23	-1 09	0.9	0.6	--	--	1.4	096°	--	--	2.2	274°
1769	Crab Point, 0.5 mile east of		39° 50.8'	75° 18.3'	-0 51	-0 12	+0 17	-0 07	1.4	0.9	--	--	2.1	094°	--	--	1.9	268°
1771	Hog Island, channel southeast of		39° 52.0'	75° 12.9'	-0 49	-0 13	+0 15	-0 13	1.3	1.1	--	--	1.9	054°	--	--	2.2	231°
1773	Schuylkill River entrance <1>		39° 53.2'	75° 11.7'	--	-1 36	--	-0 57	0.3	0.2	--	--	0.5	356°	--	--	0.4	178°
1775	Schuylkill River <1>	12d	39° 54.23'	75° 12.90'	--	-1 24	--	-1 35	0.2	0.2	--	--	0.2	351°	--	--	0.3	172°
1777	Eagle Point, 0.2 n.mi. northwest of	17d	39° 52.82'	75° 10.38'	-0 27	-0 56	+0 08	-1 05	1.1	0.9	--	--	1.6	091°	--	--	1.8	271°
	...do.	40d	39° 52.82'	75° 10.38'	-0 33	-1 11	+0 03	-0 29	0.7	0.6	--	--	1.1	090°	--	--	1.3	274°
1779	Gloucester		39° 53.4'	75° 08.1'	-0 26	+0 06	+0 27	-0 05	1.5	1.0	--	--	2.2	020°	--	--	2.0	210°
1781	Greenwich Point, northeast of		39° 54.5'	75° 07.6'	-0 26	-0 03	+0 27	-0 04	1.1	0.8	--	--	1.6	002°	--	--	1.6	188°
1783	Camden Marine Terminals, E of Chan. <26>		39° 56.4'	75° 08.2'	+0 13	+0 17	+0 49	+0 02	0.9	0.6	--	--	1.3	005°	--	--	1.1	174°
1785	PHILADELPHIA, PENNS LANDING,	15d	39° 56.76'	75° 08.33'	Daily predictions						--	--	1.5	017°	--	--	2.0	201°
1787	Petty Island (west end), Main Channel	24d	39° 58.03'	75° 07.13'	-0 06	-0 06	+0 21	-0 26	1.0	0.9	--	--	1.8	066°	--	--	1.8	248°
1789	Fisher Point		39° 58.9'	75° 04.2'	-0 11	-0 03	+0 14	-1 06	1.0	0.7	--	--	1.4	041°	--	--	1.3	223°
1791	Fivemile Point Bridge, northeast of	35d	39° 59.18'	75° 03.75'	+0 28	+0 50	+0 56	+0 01	0.9	0.8	--	--	1.3	038°	--	--	1.3	214°
1793	Torresdale, west of channel		40° 02.4'	74° 59.4'	+1 15	+1 00	+0 32	+0 41	0.6	0.8	--	--	0.9	044°	--	--	1.6	223°
1795	Rancocas Creek, off Delanco		40° 02.6'	74° 57.6'	+0 57	-0 01	+1 24	-0 36	0.7	0.5	--	--	1.0	090°	--	--	0.9	272°
1797	College Point, 0.4 n.mi. east of	21d 8	40° 04.65'	74° 53.20'	+0 54	+0 42	+0 42	-1 03	0.8	0.6	--	--	1.2	084°	--	--	1.2	252°
1799	Bristol, south of		40° 05.3'	74° 51.6'	+1 16	+0 35	+0 30	+1 05	0.9	0.8	--	--	1.3	024°	--	--	1.8	200°
1801	Burlington Island, channel east of		40° 05.7'	74° 50.2'	+1 53	+0 50	-0 11	+1 42	0.6	0.8	--	--	0.9	018°	--	--	1.6	204°
1803	Newbold Island north of, Main Channel	15d	40° 08.03'	74° 45.38'	+0 47	-0 26	+0 09	-1 35	0.4	0.2	--	--	0.7	084°	--	--	0.5	250°
1805	Whitehill <27>		40° 08.2'	74° 44.2'	--	--	--	+2 02	--	0.7	--	--	--	--	--	--	1.4	233°

Endnotes can be found at the end of table 2.

TABLE 2. – CURRENT DIFFERENCES AND OTHER CONSTANTS

No.	PLACE	Meter Depth (ft)	POSITION Latitude North	POSITION Longitude West	TIME DIFFERENCES Min. before Flood (h m)	Flood (h m)	Min. before Ebb (h m)	Ebb (h m)	SPEED RATIOS Flood	Ebb	AVG — Minimum before Flood (knots)	Dir.	Maximum Flood (knots)	Dir.	Minimum before Ebb (knots)	Dir.	Maximum Ebb (knots)	Dir.
	DEL., MD. and VA. COAST Time meridian, 75°W																	
1807	Fenwick Shoal Lighted Whistle Buoy 2		38°25'	74°46'														
1809	Winter-Quarter Shoal Buoy 6WQS		37°55'	74°56'														
					on Chesapeake Bay Entrance, p.92 See table 5. Current weak and variable													
1811	Smith Island Shoal, southeast of		37°05.3'	75°43.5'	-1 41	-1 56	-2 15	-1 41	0.3	0.4	--	--	0.3	298°	--	--	0.4	068°
1813	Cape Henry Light, 2.2 miles southeast of	7	36°53.9'	75°58.7'	-1 21	-1 02	-2 50	-1 17	0.9	0.8	--	--	1.0	346°	--	--	0.9	165°
	CHESAPEAKE BAY																	
1815	Cape Henry Light, 3.4nm NNE of	7d	36°58.79'	75°58.85'	-0 08	-0 39	-0 31	-0 08	0.9	1.5	0.2	206°	1.0	287°	0.2	016°	1.6	116°
	…do.	15d	36°58.79'	75°58.85'	-0 19	-0 43	-0 29	-0 12	0.9	1.1	0.1	199°	1.0	284°	0.1	198°	1.2	112°
	…do.	30d	36°58.79'	75°58.85'	-0 54	-0 38	-0 43	-0 45	0.5	0.6	0.1	009°	0.6	277°	0.1	195°	0.6	104°
1817	Cape Henry Light, 2.35nm NNE of	15d	36°57.74'	75°59.14'	+0 12	-0 06	-0 22	+0 00	0.5	1.0	--	--	1.0	291°	0.1	029°	1.0	116°
	…do.	30d	36°57.74'	75°59.14'	-0 41	-0 39	-0 33	-0 32	1.1	0.9	--	--	1.4	294°	0.1	208°	1.0	123°
	…do.	45d	36°57.74'	75°59.14'	-1 10	-0 47	-0 30	-0 48	1.1	0.8	--	--	1.2	294°	0.1	205°	0.9	125°
	…do.	60d	36°57.74'	75°59.14'	-1 27	-0 57	-0 36	-1 03	1.1	0.7	--	--	1.2	294°	0.1	204°	0.7	124°
1819	Cape Henry Light, 1.4nm NE of	15d	36°56.73'	75°59.38'	+0 38	+0 05	-0 23	+0 14	0.8	1.4	0.1	205°	0.9	298°	--	--	1.5	117°
	…do.	30d	36°56.73'	75°59.38'	-0 05	-0 20	-0 15	+0 03	1.1	1.1	0.1	205°	1.2	298°	--	--	1.2	118°
	…do.	45d	36°56.73'	75°59.38'	-0 23	-0 30	-0 10	-0 08	1.1	1.1	0.1	203°	1.2	293°	0.1	199°	1.1	114°
	…do.	60d	36°56.73'	75°59.38'	-0 37	-0 32	-0 10	-0 18	0.9	0.9	--	--	1.0	282°	0.1	191°	1.0	107°
1821	Cape Henry Light, 0.8 n.mi. NNE of	15d	36°56.33'	75°59.98'	+0 21	-0 36	-0 44	+0 03	1.0	1.6	0.2	003°	1.0	298°	--	--	1.7	113°
	…do.	38d	36°56.33'	75°59.98'	+1 47	-2 20	-2 16	-1 59	1.1	1.1	0.1	210°	1.2	275°	0.2	189°	1.2	106°
1823	Cape Henry Light, 2.0 n.mi. north of	15d	36°57.53'	76°00.63'	+0 07	-0 14	+0 20	+0 13	1.1	1.0	0.1	012°	1.2	289°	--	--	1.1	110°
	…do.	39d	36°57.53'	76°00.63'	-0 28	-0 29	+0 15	-0 24	1.1	0.7	0.1	002°	0.9	277°	0.1	190°	0.7	110°
	…do.	54d	36°57.53'	76°00.63'	-1 08	-0 32	-0 06	-1 12	0.8	0.5	0.1	209°	1.1	263°	0.2	177°	0.5	111°
1825	CHESAPEAKE BAY ENTRANCE, buoy LB2CH	22d	36°57.54'	76°00.76'	*Daily predictions*				1.2	1.2	0.1	209°	1.1	297°	--	--	1.1	112°
1827	Cape Henry Light, 4.6 miles north of		37°00.1'	75°59.3'	-0 32	-0 30	-0 21	+0 16	1.2	0.7	--	--	1.3	294°	--	--	1.3	104°
1829	Cape Henry Light, 5.9 n.mi. north of	14d	37°01.24'	75°59.33'	-1 04	-0 48	-1 06	-0 43	0.5	1.0	0.1	228°	0.6	307°	--	--	0.7	140°
1831	Cape Henry Light, 8.3 mi. NW of	12	37°02.20'	76°06.60'	+0 11	+0 04	+0 05	+0 19	0.9	0.8	--	--	1.0	329°	--	--	1.1	133°
1833	Lynnhaven Roads		36°55.1'	76°04.9'	-0 25	-0 21	-0 25	-0 17	0.7	0.7	--	--	0.8	280°	--	--	0.9	070°
1835	Lynnhaven Inlet bridge		36°54.4'	76°05.6'	-1 23	-1 41	-2 23	-2 37	0.5	1.3	--	--	0.6	180°	--	--	1.4	000°
	Chesapeake Bay Bridge Tunnel																	
1837	Chesapeake Beach, 1.5 miles north of	6d	36°56.69'	76°07.33'	+0 24	+0 09	-0 34	-0 07	0.7	0.8	0.3	205°	0.8	305°	0.2	013°	0.9	100°
1839	0.75nm west, Thimble Shoal Channel	16d	36°58.64'	76°07.45'	-0 08	-0 21	-0 27	+0 01	1.1	1.0	0.1	200°	1.2	288°	0.1	017°	1.1	113°
	…do.	29d	36°58.64'	76°07.45'	-0 35	-0 20	+0 05	-0 05	1.0	0.8	0.1	008°	1.1	289°	--	--	0.8	111°
	…do.	39d	36°58.64'	76°07.45'	-0 47	-0 26	+0 25	+0 04	0.8	0.5	--	--	0.9	284°	--	--	0.5	101°
1841	Tail of the Horseshoe		36°58.64'	76°07.45'	-0 48	-0 20	+0 12	-0 06	0.8	0.5	--	--	0.6	281°	--	--	0.5	096°
1843	Chesapeake Channel (bridge tunnel)	13d	37°02.50'	76°06.20'	+0 00	-0 09	-0 24	+0 21	0.8	0.9	--	--	0.9	300°	--	--	1.0	110°
1845	Chesapeake Channel (Buoy '15')	34d	37°03.40'	76°04.33'	+0 00	-0 01	-0 08	+0 12	1.6	1.4	--	--	1.8	335°	--	--	1.5	145°
1847	Fishermans Island, 3.2 miles WSW of	20	37°03.40'	76°05.58'	-0 35	-0 06	+0 10	+0 31	0.5	0.4	0.2	037°	0.6	311°	0.1	229°	0.4	125°
1849	Fishermans Island, 1.4 miles WSW of	5d	37°04.78'	76°05.58'	-0 26	-0 12	+0 17	-0 14	0.5	0.4	0.2	032°	0.6	309°	0.1	232°	0.4	139°
1851	Fishermans Island, 2.45nm south of	6d	37°04.00'	76°02.25'	-0 27	-0 51	-0 52	-0 43	0.5	1.5	--	--	1.2	330°	--	--	1.6	135°
1853	Fishermans Island, 1.7 n.mi. south of	16d	37°02.64'	76°00.25'	-1 14	-0 41	-0 57	-1 09	1.6	1.7	--	--	1.8	330°	0.1	028°	1.8	140°
1855	Fishermans Island, 0.5 n.mi. SW of	6d	37°02.64'	75°57.77'	-0 22	-0 59	-0 54	-0 38	1.1	1.5	0.2	220°	1.2	301°	0.1	028°	1.6	126°
1857	Fishermans I., 0.4 mile west of	16d	37°02.64'	75°57.77'	-0 39	-1 07	-0 53	-0 40	1.1	1.7	0.1	213°	1.6	298°	--	--	1.1	127°
1859	Fishermans I., 1.4 n.mi. WNW of	31d	37°03.37'	75°58.33'	-1 06	-1 11	-0 55	-0 53	1.0	1.0	0.2	218°	1.0	298°	--	--	1.4	123°
1861	Fishermans I., 1.1 miles northwest of	16d	37°03.37'	75°58.33'	-0 24	-1 08	-0 56	-0 33	0.9	0.9	0.2	218°	1.0	297°	--	--	1.1	126°
1863	Cape Charles, off Wise Point	5	37°04.85'	75°58.83'	-0 42	-0 58	-1 04	-0 41	0.7	1.3	0.2	223°	0.8	290°	--	--	1.4	120°
1865	Little Creek, 0.2 n.mi. N of east jetty <63>	15d	37°05.57'	75°59.33'	-1 02	-0 54	-0 46	-0 42	1.4	1.8	0.2	218°	1.5	306°	0.1	218°	1.9	140°
1867	Butler Bluff, 2.1 n.mi. WSW of	16d	37°06.10'	76°00.33'	-0 26	-0 47	-0 28	-0 34	1.8	1.9	--	--	2.0	005°	0.1	247°	2.0	175°
1869	York Spit Channel, N of Buoy '26'		37°06.88'	76°00.00'	-0 33	-0 53	-0 17	-0 26	1.1	1.5	0.1	060°	1.2	333°	--	--	1.2	155°
1871	Old Plantation Flats Lt., 0.5 mi. W of	15d	37°06.05'	75°58.30'	-0 44	-0 19	+0 16	+1 13	1.6	0.2	--	--	1.6	355°	--	--	1.6	165°
1873	Cape Charles City, 3.3 n.mi. west of	14d	37°09.37'	76°01.60'	+0 04	-0 02	-1 19	-1 08	0.6	0.3	--	--	0.7	305°	--	--	0.2	075°
		7	37°12.90'	76°08.50'	-1 06	-1 57	-1 17	-1 05	0.3	0.3	--	--	0.3	278°	--	--	0.3	092°
			37°14.00'	76°04.10'	-0 03	-0 25	+0 17	+1 19	0.7	1.0	--	--	0.8	348°	--	--	0.8	164°
		15d	37°15.87'	76°05.62'	+1 28	+1 11	+0 44	+0 59	1.1	1.2	--	--	0.8	010°	--	--	1.1	195°
		40d	37°15.87'	76°05.62'	+0 33	+0 39	+1 15	+0 54	0.9	0.9	0.2	280°	1.2	355°	0.1	094°	1.3	175°
		95d	37°15.87'	76°05.62'	+0 11	+0 04	+0 30	+0 23	0.8	0.8	--	--	0.9	356°	0.1	284°	0.8	182°
					+0 24	+0 21	+0 57	+1 17	0.9	0.8	0.1	223°	1.0	322°	--	--	0.8	138°

Endnotes can be found at the end of table 2.

TABLE 2. – CURRENT DIFFERENCES AND OTHER CONSTANTS

No.	PLACE	Meter Depth (ft)	Position Lat. North	Position Long. West	Time Diff. Min. before Flood (h m)	Flood (h m)	Min. before Ebb (h m)	Ebb (h m)	Speed Ratios Flood	Ebb	Min. before Flood (knots)	Dir.	Maximum Flood (knots)	Dir.	Min. before Ebb (knots)	Dir.	Maximum Ebb (knots)	Dir.
	CHESAPEAKE BAY Time meridian, 75°W				on Chesapeake Bay Entrance, p.92													
1875	New Point Comfort, 4.1 n.mi. ESE of	15d	37° 17.40'	76° 11.45'	+1 02	+0 43	+0 06	+0 39	0.7	0.9	0.3	296°	0.8	018°	0.3	098°	1.0	202°
1877	Wolf Trap Light, 0.5 mile west of		37° 23.4'	76° 11.9'	+1 38	+1 21	+0 54	+1 29	0.9	1.1	—	—	1.0	015°	—	—	1.2	190°
1879	Wolf Trap Light, 5.8 miles east of		37° 23.1'	76° 04.3'	+2 18	+2 01	+1 34	+2 09	0.8	1.2	—	—	0.9	015°	—	—	1.3	175°
1881	Church Neck Point, 1.9 n.mi. W of	15d	37° 24.20'	76° 00.78'	+0 41	+0 58	+0 56	+0 43	1.2	0.4	0.2	275°	0.4	003°	0.2	098°	0.4	177°
1883	Wolf Trap Light, 6.1 n.mi. ENE of	14d	37° 24.50'	76° 03.83'	+1 35	+1 19	+1 48	+2 04	0.8	1.0	0.2	099°	1.3	006°	0.2	279°	1.1	191°
1885	Wolf Trap Light, 5.2 n.mi. ENE of	29d	37° 24.50'	76° 05.00'	+0 21	+0 16	+0 47	+1 00	1.2	0.7	0.2	283°	0.7	012°	0.2	098°	0.7	173°
	do.	15d	37° 24.50'	76° 05.00'	+1 30	+1 55	+2 01	+2 02	0.9	1.0	—	—	1.3	010°	0.2	266°	1.1	187°
	do.	40d	37° 24.50'	76° 05.00'	+1 02	+1 45	+2 03	+1 12	0.7	0.6	0.2	089°	1.0	352°	—	—	0.7	183°
1887	Wolf Trap Light, 1.4 n.mi. NNE of	63d	37° 24.67'	76° 10.57'	+0 19	+0 43	+1 25	+1 04	1.0	1.1	—	—	0.8	343°	0.2	088°	0.6	158°
1889	Wolf Trap Light, 2.0 n.mi. NW of	15d	37° 25.00'	76° 12.54'	+1 33	+1 37	+1 12	+1 12	0.5	0.6	—	—	1.1	005°	—	—	1.2	175°
1891	Nassawadox Point, 1.9 n.mi. NW of	14d	37° 29.97'	75° 59.37'	-0 02	-0 06	-0 25	+0 01	0.5	0.6	—	—	0.6	345°	0.1	270°	0.6	166°
1893	Gwynn Island, 8.0 n.mi. east of	13d	37° 29.70'	76° 06.50'	+1 11	+1 04	+2 08	+2 26	0.9	1.0	0.2	267°	0.6	352°	0.2	090°	0.6	178°
	do.	14d	37° 29.70'	76° 06.50'	+1 58	+2 24	+1 06	+0 16	1.0	0.5	0.2	102°	1.0	357°	0.3	281°	1.1	175°
1895	Gwynn Island, 1.5 n.mi. east of	28d	37° 30.03'	76° 14.70'	+0 28	+0 28	+0 14	+0 15	0.9	0.8	—	—	0.6	013°	0.1	227°	0.5	209°
1897	Stingray Point, 5.5 miles east of	16d	37° 35.0'	76° 10.4'	+0 54	+0 15	+2 41	+2 25	0.9	0.8	—	—	0.5	331°	—	—	0.9	159°
1899	Stingray Point, 12.5 miles east of		37° 33.8'	76° 02.3'	+2 23	+2 57	+1 29	+2 29	0.5	0.6	—	—	1.0	343°	—	—	0.9	179°
1901	Powells Bluff, 2.2 n.mi. NW of		37° 35.45'	75° 58.10'	+2 13	+2 21	+1 14	+1 16	0.8	0.8	0.1	101°	0.6	015°	0.1	284°	0.8	175°
1903	Windmill Point Light, 8.3 n.mi. ESE of	17d	37° 34.60'	76° 03.80'	+1 16	+0 50	+2 24	+2 39	0.5	0.4	0.1	270°	0.9	359°	0.1	095°	0.6	201°
	do.	14d	37° 34.60'	76° 11.50'	+2 13	+2 18	+2 27	+2 07	0.5	0.8	0.2	099°	0.5	017°	0.2	255°	0.8	182°
1905	Windmill Point Light, 2.2 n.mi. ESE of	33d	37° 35.30'	76° 11.50'	+1 01	+1 59	+1 41	+2 22	0.4	0.4	0.1	079°	0.6	001°	0.1	081°	0.4	172°
	do.	14d	37° 35.30'	76° 00.52'	+2 44	+0 56	+1 21	+1 37	0.5	0.7	—	—	0.6	342°	0.1	246°	0.9	169°
1907	Milby Point, 5.3 n.mi. WNW of	35d	37° 39.85'	76° 00.52'	+1 03	-0 27	+0 32	+2 25	0.4	0.4	0.1	120°	0.6	016°	0.2	297°	0.4	175°
1909	Bluff Point, 4.6 n.mi. east of	13d	37° 40.70'	76° 12.25'	+0 28	+2 46	+1 45	+2 39	0.7	0.7	—	—	0.5	043°	—	—	0.7	210°
	do.	38d	37° 40.70'	76° 12.25'	+3 05	+1 22	+1 52	+1 54	0.4	0.2	0.1	089°	0.4	003°	0.1	291°	0.4	197°
1911	Tangier Sound Light, 5.8 n.mi. west of	13d	37° 47.03'	76° 05.68'	+1 25	+3 30	+3 16	+3 19	0.4	0.7	—	—	0.5	013°	0.2	255°	0.7	185°
1913	Great Wicomico R. Lt., 3.8 n.mi. ESE of	33d	37° 47.00'	76° 11.50'	+3 29	+3 38	+3 14	+3 45	0.5	0.5	0.1	273°	0.5	344°	0.1	280°	0.5	196°
	do.	15d	37° 47.00'	76° 11.50'	+3 15	+2 48	+4 09	+3 15	0.5	0.3	—	—	0.4	355°	—	—	0.3	196°
1915	Smith Point Light, 6.7 n.mi. east of	14d	37° 52.83'	76° 02.65'	+2 06	+2 18	+2 05	+1 52	0.4	0.4	—	—	0.6	013°	0.1	249°	0.4	178°
1917	Smith Point Light, 4.5 n.mi. east of	39d	37° 52.67'	76° 05.30'	+2 24	+3 25	+3 09	+3 28	0.4	0.7	—	—	0.4	352°	0.1	256°	0.7	171°
	do.	9d	37° 52.67'	76° 05.30'	+3 22	+2 48	+2 29	+2 59	0.4	0.5	—	—	0.5	341°	—	—	0.5	168°
1919	Smith Point Light, 3.0 n.mi. east of	14d	37° 52.65'	76° 07.08'	+3 13	+4 15	+3 02	+3 25	0.4	0.4	0.1	080°	0.4	347°	0.1	272°	0.7	167°
	do.	24d	37° 52.65'	76° 07.08'	+4 24	+1 43	+2 36	+3 27	0.4	0.3	0.1	068°	0.4	342°	—	—	0.7	149°
1921	Smith Point Light, 1.5 n.mi. east of	15d	37° 52.75'	76° 09.12'	+2 10	+3 54	+3 04	+4 15	0.4	0.7	—	—	0.4	348°	0.1	098°	0.3	159°
	do.	34d	37° 52.75'	76° 09.12'	+4 21	+3 42	+3 49	+3 27	0.7	0.3	—	—	0.4	347°	0.1	243°	0.5	176°
	do.	14d	37° 52.75'	76° 09.12'	+2 44	+2 03	+3 29	+2 30	0.4	0.5	—	—	0.8	013°	0.3	097°	0.3	160°
1923	Smith Point Light, 0.8 n.mi. NW of	39d	37° 53.23'	76° 11.90'	+2 05	+2 06	+2 17	+2 20	0.8	0.8	0.2	079°	0.9	356°	—	—	0.8	150°
1925	Smith Point Light, 5.0 n.mi. NW of	68d	37° 56.19'	76° 15.68'	+2 23	+3 04	+2 47	+3 17	0.4	0.8	—	—	0.5	021°	0.1	209°	0.9	125°
	do.	8d	37° 56.19'	76° 15.68'	+3 46	+3 18	+3 39	+3 59	0.4	0.9	—	—	0.5	306°	—	—	0.7	135°
1927	Smith Point Light, 6 miles north of	5d	37° 58.9'	76° 11.4'	+3 38	+3 51	+2 59	+3 11	0.4	0.4	—	—	0.5	350°	—	—	1.0	187°
1929	Smith Island, 3.6 n.mi. northwest of	15d	38° 00.45'	76° 07.28'	+4 22	+2 33	+4 16	+4 07	0.4	0.7	0.1	096°	0.4	014°	—	—	0.4	161°
1931	Point Lookout, 5.9 n.mi. ESE of	15d	38° 00.53'	76° 12.07'	+2 43	+4 13	+4 23	+4 23	0.4	0.2	—	—	0.4	340°	—	—	0.2	167°
	do.	51d	38° 00.53'	76° 12.07'	+3 40	+3 51	+2 17	+4 30	0.4	0.5	—	—	0.4	330°	—	—	0.5	160°
1933	Point Lookout, 1.5 n.mi. east of	16d	38° 02.30'	76° 17.50'	+2 40	See Table 5.	+3 56	+3 25	0.4	0.5	—	—	0.4	010°	—	—	0.3	191°
1935	Point Lookin		38° 06.6'	76° 13.1'	+5 03	+5 31	+4 23	+4 38	—	—	—	—	—	—	—	—	—	—
1937	Adams Island, 1.1 n.mi. west of	12d	38° 08.67'	76° 06.87'	+4 29	+3 09	+2 17	+3 19	0.1	0.3	—	—	0.1	017°	0.1	257°	0.4	167°
1939	Adams Island, 3.4 n.mi. west of	16d	38° 08.38'	76° 09.80'	+4 52	+4 30	+3 23	+4 30	0.2	0.4	—	—	0.2	325°	—	—	0.2	170°
1941	Point No Point, 4.3 n.mi. east of	17d	38° 08.13'	76° 13.75'	+4 42	+4 53	+5 24	+5 38	0.3	0.2	—	—	0.3	340°	—	—	0.2	172°
1943	Point No Point, 2.8 n.mi. east of	15d	38° 08.38'	76° 15.67'	+5 16	+4 52	+4 04	+4 58	0.2	0.5	—	—	0.2	340°	—	—	0.2	162°
	do.	39d	38° 08.38'	76° 12.07'	+3 32	+4 20	+5 02	+4 46	0.4	0.2	—	—	0.4	347°	—	—	0.5	172°
1945	Point No Point, 1.0 n.mi. east of	17d	38° 08.43'	76° 18.13'	+4 36	+4 26	+3 51	+4 26	0.3	0.5	—	—	0.3	001°	—	—	0.6	233°
1947	Hooper Strait (west), at buoy '2'	15d	38° 13.25'	76° 06.20'	+2 00	+1 49	+1 53	+1 33	0.5	0.6	—	—	0.6	035°	0.2	304°	0.6	233°

Endnotes can be found at the end of table 2.

TABLE 2. – CURRENT DIFFERENCES AND OTHER CONSTANTS

No.	PLACE	Meter Depth (ft)	POSITION Latitude (North)	POSITION Longitude (West)	TIME DIFF. Min. before Flood (h m)	TIME DIFF. Flood (h m)	TIME DIFF. Min. before Ebb (h m)	TIME DIFF. Ebb (h m)	SPEED RATIOS Flood	SPEED RATIOS Ebb	Min. before Flood (knots)	Min. before Flood (Dir.)	Maximum Flood (knots)	Maximum Flood (Dir.)	Min. before Ebb (knots)	Min. before Ebb (Dir.)	Maximum Ebb (knots)	Maximum Ebb (Dir.)
	CHESAPEAKE BAY Time meridian, 75°W				on Baltimore Harbor Approach, p.96													
1949	Cedar Point, 4.7 n.mi. east of	5d	38° 17.92'	76° 16.38'	-3 29	-3 45	-4 07	-3 36	0.6	0.9	--	--	0.5	325°	--	--	0.7	145°
	...do.	15d	38° 17.92'	76° 16.38'	-3 54	-3 59	-4 04	-3 36	0.6	0.7	--	--	0.4	323°	--	--	0.6	144°
1951	Cedar Point, 2.9 n.mi. ENE of	16d	38° 18.65'	76° 18.80'	-2 35	-2 34	-3 16	-2 55	0.5	0.8	--	--	0.4	347°	--	--	0.7	164°
	...do.	50d	38° 18.65'	76° 18.65'	-4 08	-3 30	-3 05	-3 15	0.5	0.3	--	--	0.4	326°	--	--	0.3	141°
1953	Cedar Point, 1.1 miles ENE of	17d	38° 18.27'	76° 21.10'	-3 23	-2 50	-2 36	-3 42	0.5	0.8	--	--	0.4	010°	--	--	0.6	185°
1955	Drum Point, 2.8 miles northeast of		38° 20.18'	76° 21.95'		-3 12	-- --	-2 42	0.2	0.5	--	--	0.2	335°	--	--	0.4	185°
1957	Cove Point, 1.1 n.mi. east of	40d	38° 22.88'	76° 21.62'	-2 57	-2 42	-2 40	-2 14	0.9	0.9	--	--	0.7	342°	--	--	0.6	165°
	...do.	15d	38° 21.62'	76° 21.62'	-3 22	-3 19	-2 38	-3 26	0.5	0.7	--	--	0.4	343°	--	--	0.7	169°
1959	Cove Point, 2.7 n.mi. east of	98d	38° 22.80'	76° 19.52'	-3 15	-2 41	-2 59	-2 40	0.9	0.9	--	--	0.6	344°	0.1	246°	0.5	170°
	...do.	11d	38° 22.80'	76° 19.52'	-3 49	-4 02	-1 53	-2 40	0.5	0.6	--	--	0.4	347°	--	--	0.4	165°
	...do.	15d	38° 22.80'	76° 19.52'	-2 57	-3 36	-3 13	-3 36	0.7	0.7	--	--	0.6	341°	--	--	0.6	171°
1961	Cove Point, 3.9 n.mi. east of	40d	38° 22.52'	76° 17.92'	-3 23	-2 29	-4 08	-3 44	0.4	0.6	--	--	0.3	346°	--	--	0.6	159°
1963	Cove Point, 4.9 n.mi. NNE of	67d	38° 28.03'	76° 22.60'	-3 55	-2 47	-2 24	-2 26	0.7	0.6	--	--	0.6	333°	--	--	0.3	149°
	...do.		38° 28.03'	76° 22.60'	-3 27	-3 38	-2 26	-2 17	1.0	0.4	--	--	0.8	332°	--	--	0.3	135°
	...do.		38° 28.03'	76° 22.60'	-3 29	-2 41	-1 58	-2 58	0.6	0.4	--	--	0.2	321°	--	--	0.3	160°
	...do.		38° 28.03'	76° 22.60'	-2 16	-2 39	-2 14	-2 37	0.6	0.8	--	--	0.5	340°	--	--	0.6	165°
1965	Kenwood Beach, 1.5 miles northeast of	5d	38° 31.1'	76° 28.9'	-2 31	-1 37	-2 46	-3 41	0.2	0.7	--	--	0.2	352°	--	--	0.3	156°
1967	James Island, 1.6 n.mi. SW of	15d	38° 29.14'	76° 21.87'	-3 15	-1 36	-3 31	-3 27	0.6	0.5	0.1	077°	0.5	344°	0.1	251°	0.5	175°
1969	James Island, 3.4 miles west of	20d	38° 29.14'	76° 21.87'	-1 49	-1 41	-3 01	-2 02	0.5	0.4	0.1	068°	0.4	005°	--	--	0.6	175°
1971	James Island, 2.5 miles WNW of		38° 31.5'	76° 25.2'	-1 39	-2 23	-2 18	-2 36	0.5	0.5	--	--	0.2	000°	--	--	0.6	155°
1973	Plum Point, 1.4 miles ESE of		38° 32.0'	76° 23.6'	-2 34	-1 51	-2 20	-2 04	0.2	0.8	0.1	116°	0.7	037°	--	--	0.6	203°
1975	Sharp Island Lt., 2.3 n.mi. SE of	18d	38° 36.75'	76° 28.65'	-1 50	-1 26	-3 07	-2 54	0.8	0.7	--	--	0.7	357°	--	--	0.4	183°
1977	Sharp Island Lt., 2.1 n.mi. west of	18d	38° 36.43'	76° 20.88'	-0 44	-1 22	-1 33	-1 33	0.4	0.5	--	--	0.3	355°	--	--	0.6	186°
1979	Sharp Island Lt., 3.4 n.mi. west of	35d	38° 38.60'	76° 26.88'	-1 08	+1 21	-1 57	-1 43	0.4	0.5	--	--	0.3	353°	--	--	0.4	183°
1981	Plum Point, 2.1 n.mi. NNE of	15d	38° 38.63'	76° 25.77'	+0 58	-1 24	-2 23	-2 24	0.4	0.5	--	--	0.3	350°	0.1	272°	0.3	174°
1983	Poplar Island, 2.2 n.mi. WSW of	14d	38° 38.70'	76° 29.23'	-1 20	-1 04	-1 51	-2 01	0.4	0.9	--	--	0.5	359°	--	--	0.6	185°
1985	Poplar Island, 3.0 n.mi. WSW of	48d	38° 45.37'	76° 26.73'	-1 03	-3 38	-0 57	-0 49	0.5	0.4	--	--	0.4	355°	--	--	0.4	189°
1987	Holland Point, 2.0 n.mi. east of	15d	38° 44.98'	76° 26.73'	-3 27	-0 39	-0 59	-1 08	0.2	0.4	0.1	085°	0.2	350°	--	--	0.3	172°
1989	Kent Point, 4 miles southwest of		38° 45.10'	76° 29.93'	-0 52	-0 23	+2 01	+1 13	0.6	0.6	--	--	0.4	354°	--	--	0.3	180°
1991	Kent Point, 1.3 miles south of	19	38° 49.00'	76° 26.00'	-0 08	-2 27	-1 45	-1 39	0.6	0.5	--	--	0.2	025°	--	--	0.4	210°
1993	Horseshoe Point, 1.7 miles east of	22d	38° 50.30'	76° 21.85'	-2 24	-0 14	-1 11	-1 05	0.9	0.6	--	--	0.4	055°	--	--	0.5	235°
1995	Bloody Point Bar Light, 0.6 mi. NW of	16d	38° 50.37'	76° 27.20'	-1 05	-0 09	-3 53	-3 47	0.6	0.5	--	--	0.5	005°	--	--	0.5	200°
1997	Thomas Pt. Shoal Lt. 1.8 mi. SW of	33d	38° 52.50'	76° 24.17'	-0 25	-1 18	-0 49	-1 10	0.6	0.6	--	--	0.4	035°	--	--	0.3	190°
1999	Thomas Pt. Shoal Lt., 2.0 n.mi. east of		38° 53.75'	76° 27.70'	-0 54	-0 19	+0 02	-0 05	1.0	1.3	--	--	0.5	340°	--	--	0.5	190°
2001	Thomas Pt. Shoal Lt., 0.5 n.mi. SE of	15d	38° 53.46'	76° 23.21'	-0 03	+0 08	-1 43	-0 20	0.7	0.7	0.1	102°	0.5	007°	0.1	120°	0.5	186°
2003	Tolly Point, 1.6 miles east of	41d	38° 53.46'	76° 25.62'	+0 16	+0 15	-0 22	-0 41	0.6	0.9	--	--	0.8	033°	--	--	0.6	191°
2005	Chesapeake Bay Bridge, main channel	15d	38° 56.07'	76° 25.02'	-1 33	-1 14	-0 43	-1 20	0.9	1.1	--	--	0.6	018°	--	--	0.7	196°
2007	Sandy Point, 2.3 n.mi. east of	43d	38° 59.50'	76° 23.10'	-0 11	+0 24	-1 25	-0 24	1.1	0.9	--	--	0.7	355°	--	--	0.9	190°
2009	Sandy Point, 0.8 n.mi. ESE of	15d	39° 00.16'	76° 20.93'	-0 59	-1 10	-0 32	+0 13	1.2	1.5	0.1	116°	0.8	025°	--	--	0.7	230°
2011	BALTIMORE HBR. APP. (off Sandy Point)	38d	39° 00.24'	76° 22.80'	-0 04	+0 26	-0 17	-0 39	1.0	1.0	--	--	0.8	021°	0.1	276°	0.7	210°
						Daily predictions		+0 05					0.9	025°			1.2	199°
2013	Craighill Channel entrance, Buoy '2C'		39° 00.78'	76° 22.10'	+0 00	+0 01	-0 59	-1 02			0.1	116°	0.8	025°	0.1	276°	0.8	197°
					Current weak and variable													
2015	Love Point, 2.8 miles NNE of		39° 02.42'	76° 22.67'	-0 48	+0 19	-0 06	+0 09	1.0	0.9	--	--	0.8	353°	0.1	244°	0.7	189°
2017	Love Point, 2.5 miles north of		39° 02.42'	76° 22.67'	-1 33	-0 45	-0 48	+0 18	0.5	0.6	--	--	0.4	325°	--	--	0.5	147°
2019	Love Point, 2.0 nmi north of		39° 04.7'	76° 16.3'	-0 45	-0 05	-0 07	-0 07	0.8	0.5	--	--	0.6	055°	0.1	334°	0.4	240°
2021	Craighill Channel, NE of Mountain Pt	5d	39° 04.78'	76° 18.73'	+0 28	+0 40	-0 07	-0 38	0.5	0.6	0.1	146°	0.4	067°	0.1	325°	0.5	238°
2023	Craighill Channel, Belvidere Shoal	15d	39° 04.44'	76° 18.19'	+0 10	+0 46	+0 25	-0 35	0.8	0.5	--	--	0.6	055°	--	--	0.4	240°
2025	Craighill Angle, right outside quarter	18d	39° 04.88'	76° 23.67'	+0 12	+0 27	+0 33	+0 34	0.6	0.9	--	--	0.6	350°	0.1	270°	0.7	175°
2027	Swan Point, 2.7 n.mi. SW of	14d	39° 07.70'	76° 23.27'	+0 18	+0 42	+0 34	+0 19	0.6	0.6	0.1	078°	0.5	360°	--	--	0.5	186°
	...do.	27d	39° 06.48'	76° 18.32'	-0 27	+0 30	+0 38	+0 23	0.6	0.5	--	--	0.5	345°	--	--	0.5	170°
2029	Swan Point, 2.15 n.mi. west of	18d	39° 08.85'	76° 19.48'	+0 18	+0 50	+1 05	+1 06	0.6	0.7	--	--	0.7	008°	0.1	271°	0.5	203°

Endnotes can be found at the end of table 2.

TABLE 2. – CURRENT DIFFERENCES AND OTHER CONSTANTS

No.	PLACE	Meter Depth (ft)	POSITION Latitude North	POSITION Longitude West	TIME DIFFERENCES Min. before Flood (h m)	Flood (h m)	Min. before Ebb (h m)	Ebb (h m)	SPEED RATIOS Flood	Ebb	AVERAGE SPEEDS AND DIRECTIONS Minimum before Flood (knots)	Dir.	Maximum Flood (knots)	Dir.	Minimum before Ebb (knots)	Dir.	Maximum Ebb (knots)	Dir.
	CHESAPEAKE BAY Time meridian, 75°W				**on Baltimore Harbor Approach, p.96**													
2031	Swan Point, 1.6 miles northwest of	14d	39°09.75'	76°18.28'	+0 53	+0 44	+0 38	+0 57	0.8	0.9	--	--	0.6	020°	--	--	0.7	215°
2033	Brewerton Channel Eastern Ext., Buoy '7'	17d	39°09.78'	76°23.38'	+0 16	-0 02	-0 14	-0 05	0.5	0.4	0.2	080°	0.4	013°	--	--	0.3	175°
2035	Tolchester Channel, SW of Bouy '58B'	25d	39°10.95'	76°16.87'	+0 44	+0 20	+0 48	+0 54	1.1	1.1	0.2	302°	0.9	030°	--	--	0.9	229°
	....do.	15d	39°10.95'	76°16.87'	-0 09	+0 02	+0 38	-0 48	0.9	0.8	--	--	0.7	025°	--	--	0.5	217°
2037	Tolchester Channel, Buoy '22'	15d	39°11.47'	76°15.95'	+1 43	+1 10	+0 59	+1 23	0.9	0.8	--	--	0.7	061°	0.1	151°	0.7	231°
2039	Tolchester Channel, south of Buoy 38B	15d	39°11.57'	76°17.27'	+0 51	+1 08	+0 59	+0 50	0.7	0.8	--	--	0.5	028°	--	--	0.6	208°
2041	North Point, 2.5 miles northeast of	7	39°12.87'	76°23.72'	+1 25	+1 00	+0 53	+1 06	0.4	0.5	--	--	0.3	035°	--	--	0.4	225°
2043	Tolchester Beach, 0.33 n.mi. west of	15d	39°13.03'	76°14.90'	+0 49	+1 20	+1 22	+1 24	1.2	1.1	--	--	1.0	015°	--	--	0.8	201°
2045	Pooles Island, 4 miles southwest of		39°13.60'	76°19.88'	+0 59	+0 48	+0 56	+1 12	0.6	0.8	0.1	285°	0.6	025°	--	--	0.6	210°
2047	Pooles Island 2.0 n.mi. SSW of	15d	39°14.78'	76°17.80'	+1 01	+0 58	+1 03	+1 29	0.7	0.7	0.2	327°	0.6	038°	--	--	0.6	238°
2049	Pooles Island, 0.8 mile south of		39°15.7'	76°16.4'	+1 01	+1 24	+1 12	+1 20	0.9	1.2	--	--	0.7	060°	--	--	1.0	255°
2051	Miller Island, 1.5 miles ENE of		39°16.5'	76°19.9'	+0 11	+0 15	+0 37	+0 25	0.6	0.3	--	--	0.5	000°	--	--	0.8	185°
2053	Pooles Island, 1.6 n.mi. east of	16d	39°16.47'	76°13.57'	+1 28	+1 34	+1 45	+1 03	1.1	1.1	--	--	0.9	014°	0.1	289°	0.8	208°
2055	Robins Point, 0.7 mile ESE of	5	39°17.75'	76°16.10'	-0 03	-0 14	+0 37	-0 13	1.4	1.0	--	--	1.1	025°	--	--	0.8	210°
2057	Worton Point, 1.5 n.mi. WSW of	17d	39°18.70'	76°13.03'	+2 04	+1 45	+1 27	+1 36	1.0	1.1	--	--	1.1	023°	0.2	298°	0.9	211°
2059	Worton Point, 1.1 miles northwest of		39°19.9'	76°12.0'	+1 43	+1 43	+1 38	+1 32	1.4	1.5	--	--	0.8	040°	--	--	1.2	245°
2061	Howell Point, 0.8 n.mi. west of	15d	39°22.23'	76°07.80'	+2 30	+1 48	+1 19	+1 33	1.0	1.3	--	--	0.8	051°	--	--	1.0	235°
2063	Howell Point, 0.4 mile NNW of		39°22.6'	76°06.9'	+1 28	+1 24	+1 20	+1 18	1.1	1.1	--	--	0.9	080°	--	--	0.9	245°
2065	Grove Point, 0.7 n.mi.NW of	14d	39°23.78'	76°03.02'	+2 40	+2 01	+1 31	+2 03	0.6	1.0	0.1	131°	0.5	034°	--	--	0.8	211°
2067	Turkey Point, 1.2 n.mi. SW of	9d	39°26.60'	76°02.03'	+2 39	+1 30	+0 58	+1 00	0.6	0.8	0.2	101°	0.2	021°	--	--	0.5	193°
2069	Spesutie Island, channel north of	7	39°28.83'	76°04.90'	+1 42	+1 20	+1 49	+1 40	0.8	0.6	--	--	0.6	285°	--	--	0.5	100°
2071	Rocky Pt. (Elk Neck), 0.25 n.mi. SW of	9d	39°29.30'	75°59.85'	+1 42	+1 28	+1 14	+1 49	0.6	0.7	--	--	0.5	009°	--	--	0.6	196°
2073	Red Point, 0.2 mile W of, Northeast River	7	39°31.75'	76°05.08'	+1 42	+1 28	+1 57	+1 47	0.9	0.6	--	--	0.7	--	--	--	0.5	--
2075	Havre de Grace, Susquehanna River		39°33.13'		Current weak and variable													
	HAMPTON ROADS				**on Chesapeake Bay Entrance, p.92**													
2077	Thimble Shoal Channel (west end)	15d	37°00.32'	76°13.60'	-0 20	-0 27	-0 42	+0 24	0.8	1.1	0.3	204°	0.9	293°	0.2	018°	1.2	116°
2079	Hampton Roads entrance, midchannel	8d	36°59.66'	76°18.32'	-0 57	-1 10	-1 04	+0 24	1.5	1.8	--	--	1.7	243°	0.1	151°	1.9	059°
	....do.	15d	36°59.66'	76°18.32'	-1 04	-1 13	-1 06	-1 05	1.5	1.7	--	--	1.7	244°	--	--	1.8	062°
	....do.	31d	36°59.66'	76°18.32'	-1 23	-1 15	-1 17	-1 10	1.5	1.5	--	--	1.7	243°	--	--	1.6	065°
	....do.	44d	36°59.66'	76°18.32'	-1 55	-1 23	-1 17	-1 27	1.5	1.3	--	--	1.7	241°	--	--	1.4	059°
	....do.	61d	36°59.66'	76°18.32'	-2 26	-1 51	-1 32	-1 43	1.1	1.0	0.1	144°	1.2	229°	0.1	138°	1.1	055°
	Old Point Comfort																	
2081	0.55 n.mi. east of	48d	37°00.12'	76°17.72'	-3 07	-1 11	-0 23	-2 18	1.3	0.6	--	--	1.4	251°	--	--	0.6	060°
2083	0.2 mile south of		36°59.77'	76°18.88'	-0 42	-1 04	-1 33	-1 32	1.5	1.3	--	--	1.7	240°	--	--	1.4	075°
2085	0.9 mile southwest of		36°59.33'	76°19.57'	-0 58	-0 53	-0 41	-1 18	1.5	1.4	--	--	1.7	240°	--	--	1.5	050°
2087	Willoughby Spit, 0.8 mile northwest of		36°58.6'	76°18.4'	-1 37	-2 09	-2 21	-2 01	0.6	0.9	--	--	0.7	260°	--	--	1.0	040°
2089	Willoughby Bay entrance		36°57.7'	76°17.9'	-1 55	-2 34	-3 01	-2 26	0.3	0.4	--	--	0.3	135°	--	--	0.4	330°
2091	Sewells Point, channel west of		36°57.5'	76°20.4'	-0 46	-1 26	-2 03	-1 18	0.8	1.1	--	--	0.9	195°	--	--	1.2	000°
2093	Norfolk Harbor Reach (Buoy R '8')	13d	36°57.00'	76°20.37'	-0 23	-1 21	-2 16	-0 23	0.5	0.8	--	--	0.6	183°	0.1	094°	0.9	011°
	....do.	42d	36°57.00'	76°20.37'	-0 38	-1 02	-1 39	+0 57	0.4	0.3	--	--	0.3	152°	--	--	0.3	000°
2095	Sewells Point, pierhead	7	36°56.8'	76°20.1'	-0 57	-1 19	-1 41	-1 11	0.5	0.8	--	--	0.6	195°	--	--	0.8	010°
	Newport News																	
2097	Channel, middle	15	36°57.38'	76°22.90'	-0 48	-1 02	-0 52	-1 08	1.0	1.0	--	--	1.1	244°	--	--	1.1	076°
2099	Channel, west end <63>	15	36°57.20'	76°24.80'	-0 21	-0 59	-0 37	-0 16	0.6	0.6	--	--	0.7	280°	0.1	010°	0.6	092°
2101	Middle Ground, 1 mile south of	7	36°56.0'	76°23.2'	+0 28	+0 11	-0 16	+0 19	1.0	1.1	--	--	1.1	270°	--	--	1.2	100°
	ELIZABETH RIVER																	
2103	Craney Island	15	36°53.68'	76°20.15'	-1 22	-1 54	-2 33	-1 55	0.6	0.8	0.1	098°	0.7	177°	0.2	270°	0.9	001°
2105	Craney Island Reach	7d	36°53.43'	76°20.15'	-1 32	-1 47	-2 16	-1 46	0.5	0.7	--	--	0.6	184°	--	--	0.7	009°
	....do.	17d	36°53.43'	76°20.15'	-2 05	-2 03	-1 58	-1 53	0.5	0.6	--	--	0.6	184°	--	--	0.6	004°
	....do.	33d	36°53.43'	76°20.15'	-2 52	-1 24	-1 51	-2 07	0.6	0.5	--	--	0.7	185°	--	--	0.5	008°
	....do.	43d	36°53.43'	76°20.15'	-3 17	-2 56	-2 06	-2 30	0.6	0.5	--	--	0.7	182°	--	--	0.5	004°
2107	Lamberts Point	15	36°52.50'	76°19.95'	-2 08	-2 00	-2 34	-1 57	0.4	0.7	--	--	0.5	143°	--	--	0.7	328°
2109	West Norfolk Bridge, Western Branch		36°51.5'	76°20.6'	-2 06	-2 19	-2 46	-2 11	0.5	0.7	--	--	0.6	260°	--	--	0.7	080°

Endnotes can be found at the end of table 2.

TABLE 2. – CURRENT DIFFERENCES AND OTHER CONSTANTS

No.	PLACE	Latitude North	Longitude West	Meter Depth ft	Min. before Flood h m	Flood h m	Min. before Ebb h m	Ebb h m	Speed Ratios Flood	Speed Ratios Ebb	Min. before Flood knots	Min. before Flood Dir.	Maximum Flood knots	Maximum Flood Dir.	Min. before Ebb knots	Min. before Ebb Dir.	Maximum Ebb knots	Maximum Ebb Dir.
	ELIZABETH RIVER Time meridian, 75°W				**on Chesapeake Bay Entrance, p.92**													
2111	Seaboard Coast Line RR, Pinner Point	36° 51.6'	76° 19.0'		−2 13	−2 14	−2 11	−2 16	0.4	0.4	–	–	0.4	140°	–	–	0.4	290°
2113	Berkley Bridge, Eastern Branch	36° 50.5'	76° 17.0'		−2 30	−2 30	−2 16	−2 56	0.4	0.4	–	–	0.3	120°	–	–	0.4	295°
2115	Norfolk and Western RR. Bridge, E Branch	36° 50.2'	76° 14.7'		−1 37	−1 54	−2 21	−1 46	0.4	0.6	–	–	0.4	100°	–	–	0.6	280°
2117	Berkley, Southern Branch	36° 50.0'	76° 17.8'		−2 28	−1 56	−2 08	−2 34	0.3	0.3	–	–	0.3	215°	–	–	0.3	330°
2119	Chesapeake, Southern Branch	36° 48.5'	76° 17.4'		−2 03	−1 55	−2 10	−2 00	0.6	0.6	–	–	0.7	180°	–	–	0.6	360°
2121	Gilmerton Hwy. bridge, Southern Branch	36° 46.5'	76° 17.7'		−2 13	−1 58	−2 23	−2 10	0.5	0.7	–	–	0.6	180°	–	–	0.7	360°
2123	Money Point, Southern Branch	36° 46.44'	76° 18.13'	15d	−2 09	−1 27	−2 10	−2 28	0.4	0.3	–	–	0.4	088°	–	–	0.3	276°
	NANSEMOND RIVER																	
2125	Pig Point, 1.8 miles northeast of	36° 55.4'	76° 25.1'		−0 53	−0 46	−0 35	−0 48	0.7	0.9	–	–	0.8	285°	–	–	1.0	070°
2127	Town Point Bridge, 0.5 mile east of	36° 53.3'	76° 29.0'		−1 30	−1 38	−1 31	−1 14	0.8	0.8	–	–	0.9	265°	–	–	0.8	070°
2129	Dumpling Island	36° 48.5'	76° 33.5'		−1 22	−1 39	−2 06	−1 31	0.9	0.9	–	–	1.0	175°	–	–	1.0	345°
	JAMES RIVER																	
	Newport News																	
2131	0.15nm WSW of Pier No.2	36° 58.76'	76° 26.61'	6d	−0 01	−0 24	−0 21	−0 06	1.1	1.4	–	–	1.2	342°	–	–	1.5	161°
	...do.	36° 58.76'	76° 26.61'	15d	−0 19	−0 36	−0 15	−0 11	1.2	1.3	–	–	1.3	344°	–	–	1.4	161°
	...do.	36° 58.76'	76° 26.61'	29d	−0 37	−0 51	−0 16	−0 20	1.1	1.1	–	–	1.2	347°	–	–	1.2	162°
	...do.	36° 58.76'	76° 26.61'	42d	−0 53	−0 57	−0 26	−0 26	0.9	0.9	–	–	1.0	346°	–	–	1.0	165°
2133	0.8 mile SW of shipbuilding plant	36° 58.5'	76° 27.3'	6	−0 02	−0 21	−0 27	−0 03	0.9	1.1	–	–	1.0	325°	–	–	1.2	140°
2135	1.5 miles SW of shipbuilding plant	36° 58.1'	76° 28.2'		−0 41	−0 39	−0 43	−0 50	0.9	1.0	–	–	1.0	350°	–	–	1.1	140°
	Rocklanding Shoal Channel																	
2137	South end	37° 03.50'	76° 35.63'		+0 34	+0 22	+0 20	+1 07	0.7	1.0	–	–	0.8	310°	–	–	1.1	165°
2139	Middle	37° 05.20'	76° 36.83'		+0 44	+0 57	+1 03	+1 02	1.0	0.9	–	–	1.1	345°	–	–	1.0	155°
2141	North end	37° 06.60'	76° 37.95'		+0 55	+1 01	+1 07	+1 15	1.2	0.9	–	–	1.3	340°	–	–	1.0	145°
2143	Point of Shoals, west of	37° 08.6'	76° 39.6'		+2 23	+2 06	+1 39	+2 14	0.3	0.8	–	–	0.3	325°	–	–	0.9	195°
2145	Deepwater Shoals	37° 08.6'	76° 38.2'		+1 37	+1 33	+0 59	+0 50	1.1	0.8	–	–	1.2	353°	–	–	0.9	166°
2147	Hog Point	37° 12'	76° 41.5'		+2 23	+1 56	+1 39	+2 04	0.9	1.2	–	–	1.0	260°	–	–	1.3	070°
2149	Jamestown Island, Church Point	37° 12.2'	76° 47.0'		+2 19	+1 55	+2 02	+2 08	1.0	1.0	–	–	1.3	325°	–	–	1.2	145°
2151	Chickahominy River Bridge	37° 15.7'	76° 52.5'		+2 00	+1 50	+2 03	+1 52	1.2	1.1	–	–	1.3	332°	–	–	1.2	154°
2153	Caremont Landing	37° 14.0'	76° 57.2'		+3 38	+3 11	+2 54	+3 19	1.3	1.4	–	–	1.5	290°	–	–	1.5	125°
2155	Brandon Point, 0.3 mile northeast of	37° 16.5'	76° 59.2'		+3 51	+3 17	+2 57	+3 20	1.1	1.2	–	–	1.2	350°	–	–	1.3	170°
2157	Windmill Point	37° 18.7'	77° 05.7'		+4 25	+3 21	+3 24	+3 29	1.2	0.9	–	–	1.3	310°	–	–	1.0	065°
2159	Coggins Point, 0.5 mile north of	37° 18.4'	77° 10.0'		+4 40	+3 39	+3 27	+4 00	0.5	0.8	–	–	0.6	273°	–	–	0.9	088°
2161	City Point	37° 19.0'	77° 16.3'		+4 43	+3 56	+3 59	+4 04	1.2	1.1	–	–	1.3	320°	–	–	1.2	135°
2163	Appomattox River entrance	37° 18.7'	77° 16.2'		+5 19	+4 20	+3 57	+3 51	0.9	0.8	–	–	1.0	271°	–	–	0.8	080°
2165	Bermuda Hundred	37° 20.2'	77° 17.7'		+5 40	+4 13	+3 21	+4 19	0.8	1.2	–	–	0.9	019°	–	–	1.3	199°
2167	Dutch Gap Canal, 0.5 mile east of	37° 22.8'	77° 20.8'		+5 23	+4 41	+4 39	+4 49	0.7	0.8	–	–	0.8	270°	–	–	1.0	160°
2169	Rocketts <19>	37° 31.2'	77° 25.0'		–	–	–	–	–	–	–	–	–	–	–	–	–	–
	YORK RIVER																	
2171	York River Ent. Channel (SE end) <29>	37° 07.38'	76° 09.20'	13d	+0 45	+0 43	+0 52	+0 53	0.9	0.9	0.3	256°	1.0	342°	0.3	074°	1.0	162°
	...do.	37° 07.38'	76° 09.20'	32d	−0 50	+0 19	+0 24	−0 15	0.4	0.4	0.2	083°	0.5	329°	0.2	246°	0.4	174°
2173	York Spit Light, 0.8 mile southwest of	37° 12.0'	76° 16.0'		−0 42	−0 33	−0 16	−0 20	0.7	0.8	–	–	0.8	323°	–	–	0.8	145°
2175	York River Ent. Channel (NW end)	37° 13.55'	76° 18.47'	15d	−1 52	−0 45	+0 03	−0 26	0.6	0.5	0.2	200°	0.7	298°	–	–	0.9	128°
2177	Tue Marshes Light, 0.7 n.mi. north of	37° 14.80'	76° 23.28'	14d	+1 27	+1 26	+1 18	+1 18	0.9	0.8	–	–	1.0	265°	–	–	0.9	078°
	...do.	37° 14.80'	76° 23.28'	39d	+0 27	+0 24	+1 15	+0 55	0.4	0.6	–	–	0.5	247°	–	–	0.6	070°
	...do.	37° 14.80'	76° 23.28'	49d	−2 56	−2 11	−1 11	−1 48	0.4	0.3	–	–	0.5	249°	–	–	0.3	068°
2179	Tue Marshes Light, 0.9 n.mi. WNW of	37° 14.28'	76° 24.13'	14d	−0 21	−0 30	−0 30	−0 32	0.7	0.7	–	–	0.8	249°	–	–	0.7	069°
	...do.	37° 14.28'	76° 24.13'	28d	−1 20	−1 15	−0 46	−1 41	0.5	0.6	–	–	0.6	262°	–	–	0.6	064°
	Tue Marshes Light, 2.7 miles west of																	
2181	Midchannel	37° 14.0'	76° 26.6'		−0 18	−0 17	−0 22	−0 30	0.5	0.6	–	–	0.6	258°	–	–	0.6	072°
2183	North edge of channel	37° 14.2'	76° 26.6'		−0 53	−0 56	−1 16	−1 08	0.4	0.7	–	–	0.5	251°	–	–	0.7	074°
2185	South edge of channel	37° 13.6'	76° 26.5'		−0 31	−0 49	−1 02	−0 31	0.4	0.5	–	–	0.4	257°	–	–	0.5	095°

Endnotes can be found at the end of table 2.

TABLE 2. – CURRENT DIFFERENCES AND OTHER CONSTANTS

No.	PLACE	Meter Depth (ft)	Latitude North	Longitude West	Min. before Flood (h m)	Flood (h m)	Min. before Ebb (h m)	Ebb (h m)	Speed Ratio Flood	Speed Ratio Ebb	Min. before Flood knots	Min. before Flood Dir.	Max. Flood knots	Max. Flood Dir.	Min. before Ebb knots	Min. before Ebb Dir.	Max. Ebb knots	Max. Ebb Dir.
	YORK RIVER Time meridian, 75°W				on Chesapeake Bay Entrance, p.92													
2187	Yorktown		37° 14.5'	76° 30.5'	-0 35	-1 07	-0 59	-0 24	1.1	1.5	--	--	1.2	302°	--	--	1.6	124°
2189	Gloucester Point, 150 yds. southeast of		37° 14.55'	76° 30.10'	-0 40	-0 40	-0 24	-1 28	0.8	1.0	--	--	0.9	267°	--	--	1.1	090°
2191	Gloucester Point, 0.4 mile southwest of		37° 14.42'	76° 30.65'	-0 30	-0 39	-0 24	-0 51	1.0	0.9	--	--	1.1	294°	--	--	1.0	108°
2193	Pages Rock, 1 mile SSE of		37° 17.6'	76° 34.8'	-0 15	-0 15	-0 27	-0 29	0.9	0.9	--	--	1.0	303°	--	--	1.0	125°
2195	Blundering Point, 0.9 mile SSW of		37° 18.13'	76° 35.80'	-0 27	-0 26	-0 03	-0 23	0.9	1.0	--	--	1.1	293°	--	--	1.1	138°
2197	Clay Bank Pier, 100 yds. southwest of		37° 20.78'	76° 36.80'	-0 07	-0 25	-0 37	-0 12	1.0	1.0	--	--	1.1	311°	--	--	1.1	123°
2199	Allmondsville		37° 24.'	76° 40'	+0 43	+0 05	-0 01	+0 13	1.0	1.0	--	--	1.3	310°	--	--	1.1	105°
2201	Purtan Island, 0.2 mile southwest of		37° 24.88'	76° 41.22'	+0 44	+0 26	+0 18	+0 46	1.2	1.0	--	--	0.9	320°	--	--	1.1	104°
2203	Goff Point, 0.8 mile SSW of		37° 29.97'	76° 47.03'	+1 32	+0 57	+1 14	+1 47	0.8	0.9	--	--	1.1	340°	--	--	1.0	123°
2205	West Point, 0.8 mile below		37° 30.9'	76° 47.5'	+1 18	+0 41	+0 34	+0 59	0.7	1.4	--	--	0.8	350°	--	--	1.5	150°
2207	Lord Delaware Bridge, 100 yds. S of		37° 32.22'	76° 47.45'	+1 32	+0 51	+1 08	+1 39	0.7	0.5	--	--	1.4	260°	--	--	0.5	210°
2209	Wakema, Mattaponi River		37° 39.2'	76° 54.0'	+2 03	+1 26	+1 19	+1 34	1.3	1.6	--	--	0.9	275°	--	--	1.7	280°
2211	Walkerton, Mattaponi River		37° 43.4'	77° 01.5'	+3 24	+2 35	+2 10	+3 18	0.8	0.9	--	--	0.6	327°	--	--	0.9	095°
2213	Eltham Bridge, 100 yds. north of		37° 32.10'	76° 48.42'	+2 01	+1 54	+1 37	+2 07	0.5	0.8	--	--	1.2	235°	--	--	0.9	124°
2215	Lester Manor, Pamunkey River		37° 34.9'	76° 59.4'	+3 13	+2 51	+2 39	+2 59	1.1	0.9	--	--	0.5	290°	--	--	1.0	055°
2217	Northbury, Pamunkey River		37° 37.5'	77° 07.3'	+4 28	+4 11	+3 44	+4 19	0.4	1.2	--	--	--	--	--	--	1.3	100°
	MOBJACK BAY and PIANKATANK RIVER																	
2219	New Point Comfort, 2.0 n.mi. WSW of	16d	37° 17.70'	76° 19.25'	+0 58	+1 39	+1 12	+1 56	0.5	0.4	--	--	0.6	315°	--	--	0.4	129°
2221	Bland Point, Piankatank River		37° 31.8'	76° 21.9'	+0 03	-0 14	-0 41	-0 06	0.4	0.2	--	--	0.4	300°	--	--	0.2	125°
2223	Doctor Point, 0.4 mile west of		37° 31.1'	76° 27.0'	+0 05	-0 42	-1 28	-0 13	0.4	0.4	--	--	0.4	311°	--	--	0.4	142°
	RAPPAHANNOCK RIVER																	
2225	Stingray Point, 1.2 n.mi. NE of	28d	37° 34.53'	76° 17.08'	+1 01	-0 04	-0 51	+0 54	0.4	0.5	--	--	0.4	293°	0.1	188°	0.5	121°
2227	Windmill Point, 1.0 n.mi. SSW of	15d	37° 36.00'	76° 17.50'	+1 08	+1 14	+1 49	+1 24	0.6	0.5	--	--	0.7	286°	--	--	0.5	103°
	...do.	38d	37° 35.72'	76° 17.50'	+0 33	+1 18	+1 50	+1 05	0.5	0.3	--	--	0.6	269°	--	--	0.3	090°
2229	Mosquito Point, 0.9 mile SSE of		37° 37.97'	76° 21.08'	+1 22	+1 47	+1 27	+1 16	0.6	0.6	--	--	0.7	265°	--	--	0.6	090°
2231	Orchard Point, 1.0 mile south of		37° 37.8'	76° 27.45'	+1 39	+1 51	+1 39	+1 49	0.4	0.5	--	--	0.5	270°	--	--	0.6	085°
2233	Towles Point		37° 40.28'	76° 30.4'	- - -	+1 23	+1 59	+1 51	0.6	0.6	--	--	0.6	274°	--	--	0.5	103°
2235	Rogue Point, 0.8 mile WNW of		37° 40.95'	76° 33.20'	+2 14	+2 00	- - -	+1 51	0.5	0.6	--	--	0.6	000°	--	--	0.6	195°
2237	Waterview, 1.3 miles NNE of		37° 44.95'	76° 35.92'	+2 49	+2 15	+2 35	+2 34	0.6	0.6	--	--	0.7	340°	--	--	0.6	155°
2239	Tarpley Point, 1.5 miles south of		37° 46.15'	76° 39.12'	+2 37	+2 53	+3 09	+3 03	0.6	0.7	--	--	0.7	300°	--	--	0.7	105°
2241	Jones Point, 1.4 miles NNW of		37° 48.03'	76° 41.58'	+2 52	+2 39	+3 08	+2 51	1.0	0.8	--	--	1.1	315°	--	--	0.9	105°
2243	Sharps, 1.2 miles south of		37° 48.18'	76° 41.92'	+3 00	+3 02	+3 26	+3 25	0.8	0.8	--	--	0.9	290°	--	--	0.8	095°
2245	Bowlers Rock, 0.2 mile north of		37° 49.58'	76° 44.00'	+3 13	+3 04	+3 41	+3 14	0.9	0.9	--	--	1.0	315°	--	--	1.0	135°
2247	Accaceek Point, 0.3 mile southwest of		37° 52.52'	76° 46.40'	+3 51	+3 23	+3 16	+3 37	1.1	1.0	--	--	1.2	335°	--	--	1.2	150°
2249	Tappahannock Bridge, 1.8 miles SE of	9d	37° 55.10'	76° 49.27'	+3 51	+3 23	+3 45	+3 52	1.3	1.2	--	--	1.4	315°	--	--	1.3	150°
2251	Port Royal		38° 10.5'	77° 11.4'	+6 43	+6 26	+5 59	+6 34	0.6	0.7	--	--	0.7	310°	--	--	0.7	130°
	POCOMOKE SOUND																	
2253	Pocomoke Sound Approach		37° 38.00'	75° 57.90'	+1 09	+1 28	+2 00	+1 55	0.6	0.7	--	--	0.7	009°	--	--	0.7	196°
2255	Watts Island, 4 miles south of	7	37° 43.2'	75° 54.0'	+0 50	+0 17	+0 16	+0 20	0.5	0.6	--	--	0.6	027°	--	--	0.6	247°
2257	Watts Island, 2.3 n.mi. east of	13d	37° 47.62'	75° 50.83'	+1 53	+1 24	+1 20	+1 50	0.9	1.0	--	--	1.0	032°	--	--	1.1	208°
	...do.	48d	37° 47.62'	75° 50.83'	+1 26	+1 13	+1 30	+1 10	0.9	0.8	--	--	1.0	025°	--	--	0.9	209°
2259	Long Point, 2.0 n.mi. northeast of	9d	37° 47.90'	75° 47.90'	+1 24	+0 57	+1 03	+1 23	0.4	0.3	--	--	0.4	024°	--	--	0.3	211°
2261	Pocomoke R., 0.5 mile below Shelltown		37° 58.3'	75° 38.7'	+4 03	+3 16	+3 19	+3 24	1.0	0.8	--	--	1.1	045°	--	--	0.9	170°
	TANGIER SOUND																	
2263	Tangier Sound Light, 0.5 n.mi. east of	16d	37° 47.25'	75° 57.83'	+2 21	+1 59	+2 07	+2 28	0.8	0.8	0.1	115°	0.9	019°	--	--	0.9	195°
	...do.	41d	37° 47.25'	75° 57.83'	+2 20	+1 57	+2 14	+2 17	0.9	0.8	--	--	1.0	011°	--	--	0.9	189°
2265	Tangier Sound Light, 1.5 miles NE of		37° 48.5'	75° 57.4'	+2 03	+2 18	+2 04	+2 03	1.1	1.0	--	--	1.2	014°	--	--	1.1	220°
2267	Clump Island, 2.5 n.mi. west of	15d	37° 54.50'	75° 57.42'	+3 05	+3 04	+3 06	+3 16	0.7	0.6	--	--	0.8	348°	--	--	0.6	168°
	...do.	40d	37° 54.50'	75° 57.42'	+2 56	+2 45	+2 53	+3 09	0.7	0.6	--	--	0.8	342°	--	--	0.6	166°

Endnotes can be found at the end of table 2.

TABLE 2. – CURRENT DIFFERENCES AND OTHER CONSTANTS

No.	PLACE	Meter Depth (ft)	Latitude North	Longitude West	Min. before Flood (h m)	Flood (h m)	Min. before Ebb (h m)	Ebb (h m)	SR Flood	SR Ebb	Min. bef. Flood knots	Dir.	Max. Flood knots	Dir.	Min. bef. Ebb knots	Dir.	Max. Ebb knots	Dir.
	TANGIER SOUND Time meridian, 75°W				on Chesapeake Bay Entrance, p.92													
2269	Janes Island Light, 2.3 n.mi. NNE of	14d	38° 00.05'	75° 54.52'	+3 17	+3 14	+3 23	+3 09	0.6	0.7	–	–	0.7	001°	–	–	0.7	188°
	do.	39d	38° 00.05'	75° 54.52'	+3 28	+3 33	+3 40	+4 02	0.6	0.7	–	–	0.7	008°	–	–	0.7	174°
	do.	92d	38° 00.05'	75° 54.52'	+2 58	+3 39	+3 33	+3 28	0.5	0.4	–	–	0.6	348°	–	–	0.4	181°
2271	Big Annemessex River Entrance	12d	38° 02.56'	75° 51.27'	+2 07	+1 35	+1 36	+1 46	0.3	0.7	–	–	0.3	074°	–	–	0.2	258°
2273	Kedges Strait Buoy '4'	12d	38° 03.45'	76° 01.93'	+0 46	+0 49	+0 47	+0 57	0.7	0.7	–	–	0.8	091°	–	–	0.7	276°
2275	Manokin R. Ent., 1.1 n.mi. E of Drum Pt	20d	38° 05.82'	75° 53.48'	+2 18	+2 16	+2 32	+2 32	0.4	0.3	–	–	0.4	008°	–	–	0.3	197°
2277	Deal Is., 0.6 n.mi. W. of, at Buoy '14'	24d	38° 08.45'	75° 58.33'	+2 18	+2 13	+3 14	+3 03	0.6	0.6	–	–	0.7	000°	–	–	0.6	181°
	do.	41d	38° 08.45'	75° 58.33'	+2 51	+2 21	+3 24	+3 29	0.5	0.4	–	–	0.6	355°	–	–	0.4	175°
2279	Frog Point, 1.6 miles south of		38° 12.6'	75° 57.3'	+3 52	+3 16	+3 30	+3 55	0.9	1.0	–	–	1.0	048°	–	–	1.1	240°
	Wicomico River																	
2281	Long Point and Nanticoke Point, between	9d	38° 12.80'	75° 54.00'	+3 24	+2 53	+2 56	+3 36	0.4	0.7	–	–	0.5	063°	–	–	0.7	263°
2283	Victor Point, 0.8 mile southwest of		38° 14.3'	75° 51.8'	+3 43	+3 10	+3 38	+3 58	0.5	0.8	–	–	0.6	034°	–	–	0.9	242°
2285	Whitehaven		38° 15.9'	75° 47.5'	+3 29	+4 01	+3 51	+3 25	1.0	1.0	–	–	1.1	089°	–	–	1.1	284°
2287	Whitehaven, 2.5 miles above		38° 17.8'	75° 45.5'	+3 33	+3 29	+3 34	+3 19	0.9	1.0	–	–	1.0	006°	–	–	1.1	188°
2289	Salisbury, 2 miles below	4	38° 20.4'	75° 38.3'	+3 56	+3 47	+3 52	+3 52	0.5	0.8	–	–	0.6	085°	–	–	0.8	258°
2291	Sandy Point, Nanticoke River	4	38° 14.8'	75° 55.7'	+3 47	+3 52	+4 10	+4 03	1.1	1.0	–	–	1.2	000°	–	–	1.1	182°
2293	Roaring Point, WSW of Nanticoke River	18d	38° 15.80'	75° 55.40'	+3 50	+3 17	+4 06	+3 34	0.8	0.8	–	–	0.9	356°	–	–	0.9	181°
	do.	37d	38° 15.80'	75° 55.40'	+3 38	+3 15	+4 34	+3 36	0.5	0.5	–	–	0.6	350°	–	–	0.5	150°
2295	Chapter Point, Nanticoke River		38° 22.6'	75° 52.0'	+5 19	+3 59	+4 41	+5 42	1.3	1.1	–	–	1.5	014°	–	–	1.2	204°
2297	Fishing Bay Entrance, at Buoy '2'	15d	38° 13.48'	75° 59.37'	+3 47	+4 16	+4 02	+4 45	0.4	0.7	0.1	050°	0.8	311°	0.1	202°	0.7	139°
2299	Hooper Strait, at Buoy '4'	14d	38° 13.05'	76° 03.83'	+0 51	+0 48	+1 16	+1 07	0.7	0.7	–	–	0.8	097°	–	–	0.7	287°
2301	Honga River Entrance, at Buoy '1A'	26d	38° 14.80'	76° 07.00'	+2 52	+2 22	+3 17	+3 03	0.4	0.4	–	–	0.5	331°	0.1	078°	0.4	152°
	GREAT WICOMICO RIVER																	
2303	Sandy Point, east of		37° 49.30'	76° 18.00'	+0 58	+0 41	+0 14	+0 49	0.3	0.3	–	–	0.3	320°	–	–	0.3	140°
	POTOMAC RIVER																	
2305	Point Lookout, 5.2 n.mi. SW of	13d	37° 58.12'	76° 23.50'	+2 34	+1 37	+1 38	+1 16	0.1	0.1	–	–	0.1	294°	–	–	0.1	113°
2307	Point Lookout, 3.1 n.mi. SW of	15d	37° 59.87'	76° 21.75'	+3 34	+3 23	+3 20	+3 19	0.3	0.4	–	–	0.3	295°	–	–	0.4	116°
	...do.	34d	37° 59.87'	76° 21.75'	+2 44	+2 20	+2 50	+2 40	0.2	0.2	0.1	216°	0.2	303°	0.1	214°	0.2	126°
2309	Point Lookout, 1.8 n.mi. SW of	14d	38° 00.80'	76° 20.62'	+3 01	+3 01	+3 48	+3 31	0.4	0.4	–	–	0.5	297°	–	–	0.4	122°
	...do.	47d	38° 00.80'	76° 20.62'	+2 08	+2 31	+3 16	+3 13	0.3	0.1	–	–	0.3	309°	–	–	0.1	102°
	...do.	15d	38° 01.25'	76° 19.45'	+2 25	+2 48	+3 14	+2 48	0.6	0.5	0.2	211°	0.7	270°	0.1	197°	0.5	117°
2311	Point Lookout, 1.0 n.mi. south of	43d	38° 01.25'	76° 19.45'	+2 00	+2 31	+3 58	+3 04	0.5	0.3	–	–	0.6	271°	–	–	0.3	086°
	Cornfield Point																	
2313	1 mile south of		38° 02'	76° 21'	Current irregular						–	–	–	–	–	–	–	–
2315	midchannel		38° 01.1'	76° 21.3'	+4 33	+4 16	+3 49	+4 32	0.4	0.6	–	–	0.5	310°	–	–	0.5	130°
2317	3.8 miles south of		37° 59.4'	76° 21.5'	+4 18	+4 01	+3 34	+4 09	0.6	0.6	–	–	0.5	280°	–	–	0.6	110°
2319	Fort Point, St. Marys River		38° 07.8'	76° 26.9'	Current weak and variable						–	–	0.7	315°	–	–	0.6	100°
2321	Yeocomico River entrance		38° 02.1'	76° 31.2'	Current weak and variable						–	–	–	–	–	–	–	–
	Piney Point																	
2323	0.2 mile south of	15d	38° 07.8'	76° 32.0'	+3 33	+3 16	+2 49	+3 24	1.2	0.6	–	–	1.3	280°	–	–	0.6	145°
2325	1.06 n.mi. south of	31d	38° 06.95'	76° 31.84'	+4 17	+3 58	+3 34	+4 25	0.4	0.5	–	–	0.5	315°	–	–	0.5	128°
	do.		38° 06.95'	76° 31.84'	+3 45	+3 56	+4 20	+4 06	0.5	0.4	–	–	0.6	315°	0.1	044°	0.4	130°
2327	2.2 miles south of		38° 05.9'	76° 33.1'	+3 33	+3 16	+2 49	+3 24	0.4	0.5	–	–	0.5	280°	–	–	0.5	130°
2329	Lower Machodoc Creek entrance		38° 08.7'	76° 39.3'	Current weak and variable						–	–	–	–	–	–	–	–
2331	White Point, Nomini Creek entrance		38° 08.1'	76° 43.3'	Current weak and variable						–	–	–	–	–	–	–	–
2333	Breton Bay entrance		38° 14.5'	76° 41.7'	+4 08	+3 51	+3 24	+3 59	1.1	1.1	–	–	1.2	155°	–	–	1.2	335°
2335	St. Clements Bay entrance		38° 11.7'	76° 42.5'	+2 53	+2 36	+2 09	+2 44	0.5	0.4	–	–	0.6	030°	–	–	0.4	200°
2337	St. Clements I., 1.8 miles southeast of		38° 14.5'	76° 43.7'	+5 18	+5 01	+4 34	+5 09	0.4	0.8	–	–	0.4	250°	–	–	0.9	085°
2339	St. Clements I., 1.1 miles southwest of		38° 11.57'	76° 45.67'	+5 04	+5 04	+4 33	+4 58	0.5	0.8	–	–	0.6	281°	–	–	0.8	099°
2341	Rock Point, Wicomico River entrance		38° 16.4'	76° 49.3'	+3 42	+3 57	+3 42	+3 46	0.4	0.6	–	–	0.5	019°	–	–	0.6	174°

Endnotes can be found at the end of table 2.

TABLE 2. – CURRENT DIFFERENCES AND OTHER CONSTANTS

No.	PLACE	Meter Depth (ft)	POSITION Latitude North	POSITION Longitude West	TIME DIFFERENCES Min. before Flood (h m)	TIME DIFFERENCES Flood (h m)	TIME DIFFERENCES Min. before Ebb (h m)	TIME DIFFERENCES Ebb (h m)	SPEED RATIOS Flood	SPEED RATIOS Ebb	Minimum before Flood (knots)	Minimum before Flood (Dir.)	Maximum Flood (knots)	Maximum Flood (Dir.)	Minimum before Ebb (knots)	Minimum before Ebb (Dir.)	Maximum Ebb (knots)	Maximum Ebb (Dir.)
	POTOMAC RIVER Time meridian, 75°W				**on Baltimore Harbor Approach, p.96**													
2343	Swan Point		38°16.4'	76°56.7'	-1 54	-2 04	-2 32	-2 09	0.4	1.0			0.3	350°			0.8	140°
2345	Dahlgren Harbor Channel		38°18.90'	77°01.93'	Current weak and variable													
2347	Upper Machodoc Creek entrance		38°19.1'	77°02'	Current irregular													
2349	Persimmon Point		38°22.1'	76°59.4'	-1 09	-1 19	-1 47	-1 24	1.5	1.8			0.3	270°			0.3	090°
2351	Potomac River Bridge, 0.4 mile south of		38°21.38'	76°59.20'	-1 25	-1 28	-1 38	-1 17	1.1	1.8			1.2	325°			1.4	175°
2353	Chapel Point, Port Tobacco River		38°27.9'	77°02.2'	Current weak and variable								0.9	000°			1.4	165°
2355	Maryland Point		38°20.8'	77°11.8'	-1 04	-1 14	-1 42	-1 19	1.4	1.8			1.1	270°			1.4	080°
2357	Quantico		38°31.3'	77°16.6'	-0 54	-1 04	-1 32	-1 09	0.9	1.1			0.7	020°			0.9	200°
2359	Quantico Creek entrance		38°31.7'	77°17.3'	-1 19	-1 29	-1 57	-1 34	0.6	0.6			0.5	305°			0.5	115°
2361	Freestone Point, 2.3 miles east of		38°35.78'	77°11.88'	-0 03	-0 01	-0 28	-0 06	0.9	0.9			0.7	030°			0.7	229°
2363	Hallowing Point		38°38.70'	77°07.65'	+0 12	-0 05	-0 24	-0 15	1.4	1.4			1.1	345°			1.1	149°
2365	Jones Point, Alexandria		38°47.62'	77°02.23'	+0 36	+0 01	+0 09	+0 07	1.2	1.1			1.0	352°			0.9	171°
2367	Hains Point		38°51.08'	77°01.32'	+0 20	+0 31	+0 04	-0 18	0.8	0.4			0.6	359°			0.3	176°
2369	Anacostia River entrance		38°51.8'	77°00.6'	Current weak and variable													
2371	South Capitol Street Bridge		38°52.07'	77°00.38'	Current weak and variable													
2373	Washington Channel, Washington, D.C.		38°51.8'	77°01.2'	Current weak and variable													
2375	Virginia Channel, Washington, D.C. <13>		38°52'	77°02'	—	—	—	—	—	—			—	—			0.6	145°
	PATUXENT RIVER																	
2377	Hog Point, 0.6 n.mi. north of	13d	38°19.08'	76°24.07'	-4 45	-5 29	-5 59	-6 00	0.5	0.6			0.4	258°	0.1	358°	0.5	070°
	do.	41d	38°19.08'	76°24.07'	-6 24	-5 38	-5 36	-6 38	0.5	0.3			0.4	263°			0.2	061°
2379	Drum Point, 0.3 mile SSE of		38°18.93'	76°25.15'	-5 20	-5 20	-5 25	-5 16	0.5	0.5			0.4	245°			0.4	065°
2381	Sandy Point, 0.5 mile south of	15	38°18.50'	76°27.30'	-5 08	-5 49	-5 53	-4 55	0.6	0.6			0.4	300°			0.5	125°
2383	Point Patience, 0.1 mile southwest of		38°19.70'	76°29.20'	-5 07	-6 12	-6 46	-6 01	0.6	1.0			0.5	315°			0.8	145°
2385	Broomes Island, 0.4 mile south of <62>		38°23.70'	76°33.25'	-5 01	-5 16	-5 02	-5 02	0.5	0.6			0.4	290°			0.5	110°
2387	Sheridan Point, 0.1 mile southwest of		38°27.97'	76°38.88'	-4 33	-4 54	-4 38	-4 16	0.8	0.8			0.6	320°			0.6	135°
2389	Benedict, highway bridge		38°30.70'	76°40.33'	-4 45	-4 38	-4 09	-4 35	1.0	0.6			0.8	025°			0.5	190°
2391	Lyons Creek Wharf		38°44.8'	76°41.1'	-3 14	-3 24	-3 52	-3 29	1.4	1.1			1.1	315°			0.9	140°
	LITTLE CHOPTANK RIVER																	
2393	Hills Point, 1.0 mile south of		38°33.0'	76°18.7'	Current weak and variable													
2395	Ragged Point, 1.5 miles east of		38°31.80'	76°14.65'	-4 53	-5 15	-4 29	-4 57	0.5	0.2			0.4	045°			0.2	235°
	CHOPTANK RIVER																	
2397	Cook Point, 1.4 n.mi. NNW of	15d	38°38.83'	76°18.40'	-3 52	-4 06	-4 06	-4 24	0.8	0.7			0.6	049°			0.5	241°
	do.	45d	38°38.83'	76°18.40'	-4 09	-4 05	-4 03	-4 12	0.6	0.6	0.1	145°	0.5	068°			0.5	232°
2399	Holland Point, 2.0 n.mi. SSW of	14d	38°40.43'	76°15.45'	-3 54	-4 21	-3 26	-4 00	0.3	0.2			0.2	089°			0.2	262°
2401	Chlora Point, 0.5 n.mi. SSW of	17d	38°37.70'	76°09.10'	-3 45	-3 32	-3 13	-3 58	0.6	0.5			0.5	139°			0.4	332°
	do.	24d	38°37.70'	76°09.00'	-3 48	-3 33	-3 13	-3 42	0.4	0.4			0.4	143°			0.3	323°
2403	Martin Point, 0.6 n.mi. west of	18d	38°37.63'	76°08.15'	-3 18	-3 42	-3 22	-3 34	0.3	0.5			0.3	155°			0.2	341°
2405	Howell Point, 0.5 n.mi. south of	7d	38°36.23'	76°06.87'	-3 17	-4 04	-3 52	-3 42	0.4	0.5			0.4	122°			0.3	274°
2407	Cambridge hwy. bridge, W. of Swing Span	18d	38°34.78'	76°03.67'	-2 48	-3 05	-1 07	-2 13	0.6	0.3			0.4	132°			0.3	316°
2409	Off Jamaica Point		38°36.58'	75°58.97'	-2 13	-2 32	-2 44	-2 26	0.6	0.8			0.5	000°			0.6	205°
2411	Poplar Point, south of		38°40.52'	75°57.98'	-1 52	-2 05	-1 56	-2 15	1.0	1.0			0.8	305°			0.8	100°
2413	Dover Bridge		38°45.40'	75°59.92'	-1 19	-1 50	-1 25	-1 47	1.1	1.0			0.9	050°			0.8	235°
2415	Oxford, Tred Avon River		38°41.72'	76°10.67'	-4 05	-4 05		-4 03	0.4	0.2			0.3	040°			0.2	225°
2417	Easton Pt., 0.5 mi. below, Tred Avon River		38°45.8'	76°06.0'	Current weak and variable													
2419	Mulberry Pt., 0.6 mi. S of, Broad Creek		38°44.33'	76°14.95'	-4 07	-4 10		-4 18	0.4	0.2			0.3	350°			0.2	170°
2421	Bald Eagle Pt., east of, Harris Creek		38°43.75'	76°18.30'	-4 07	-4 27		-4 14	0.5	0.5			0.4	010°			0.4	175°

Endnotes can be found at the end of table 2.

TABLE 2. – CURRENT DIFFERENCES AND OTHER CONSTANTS

No.	PLACE	Meter Depth (ft)	POSITION Latitude (North)	POSITION Longitude (West)	TIME DIFFERENCES Min. before Flood (h m)	Flood (h m)	Min. before Ebb (h m)	Ebb (h m)	SPEED RATIOS Flood	Ebb	Minimum before Flood (knots)	(Dir.)	Maximum Flood (knots)	(Dir.)	Minimum before Ebb (knots)	(Dir.)	Maximum Ebb (knots)	(Dir.)
	EASTERN BAY Time meridian, 75°W				**on Baltimore Harbor Approach, p.96**													
2423	Poplar Island, east of south end	15d	38° 44.9'	76° 21.2'	−2 20	−2 20	−2 20	−2 20	1.2	0.8	— —	— —	1.0	000°	— —	— —	0.6	170°
2425	Kent Point, 1.4 n.mi. east of		38° 50.33'	76° 20.25'	−3 04	−3 18	−3 49	−3 12	0.5	0.4	— —	— —	0.4	043°	— —	— —	0.3	233°
2427	Long Point, 1 mile southeast of		38° 50.6'	76° 19.6'	−3 40	−3 40	−3 40	−3 40	0.6	0.5	— —	— —	0.5	040°	— —	— —	0.4	235°
2429	Turkey Point, 1.3 miles WSW of		38° 53.68'	76° 19.55'	Current weak and variable													
2431	Parson Island, 1.4 miles west of		38° 54.83'	76° 16.77'	Current weak and variable													
2433	Parson Island, 0.7 mile NNE of		38° 55.48'	76° 14.33'	— —	−2 45	— —	−2 50	0.2	0.2	— —	— —	0.2	305°	— —	— —	0.2	150°
2435	Tilghman Point, 1 mile north of		38° 52.78'	76° 15.18'	−3 15	−3 18	−3 15	−3 55	0.4	0.4	— —	— —	0.3	060°	— —	— —	0.3	265°
2437	Wye River, west of Bruffs Island	9	38° 51.28'	76° 11.88'	−2 33	−3 18	−3 17	−3 00	0.8	0.9	— —	— —	0.6	030°	— —	— —	0.7	190°
2439	Deepwater Point, Miles River		38° 48.33'	76° 12.55'	−3 48	−3 52	−3 43	−4 14	0.6	0.6	— —	— —	0.5	215°	— —	— —	0.5	025°
2441	Long Point, 0.8 mi. east of, Miles River		38° 46.43'	76° 09.32'	— —	−3 24	— —	−3 45	0.4	0.2	— —	— —	0.3	055°	— —	— —	0.2	245°
	WEST and SOUTH RIVERS																	
2443	Cheston Point, south of, West River		38° 51.33'	76° 31.43'	Current weak and variable													
2445	South River entrance		38° 54.77'	76° 29.43'	Current weak and variable													
	SEVERN and MAGOTHY RIVERS																	
2447	Greenbury Point, 1.8 miles east of	8	38° 58.40'	76° 25.00'	−0 57	−1 05	−0 51	−0 47	0.8	0.8	— —	— —	0.6	070°	— —	— —	0.6	245°
2449	Annapolis		38° 58.95'	76° 28.50'	— —	−3 35	— —	−2 26	0.5	0.4	— —	— —	0.4	320°	— —	— —	0.3	110°
2451	Brewer Point, Severn River		39° 01.83'	76° 31.73'	— —	−1 22	— —	−1 50	0.4	0.4	— —	— —	0.3	275°	— —	— —	0.3	155°
2453	Mountain Point, Magothy River entrance		39° 03.47'	76° 26.23'	−2 20	−2 00	−1 29	−2 04	0.8	0.4	— —	— —	0.6	315°	— —	— —	0.3	125°
	CHESTER RIVER																	
2455	Love Point, 1.6 n.mi. east of	16d	39° 02.05'	76° 16.07'	−1 42	−1 15	−0 47	−1 15	0.6	0.4	0.1	278°	0.4	202°	0.1	261°	0.4	341°
2457	Kent Island Narrows (highway bridge)	4	38° 58.23'	76° 14.83'	−2 07	−2 25	−2 11	−2 56	1.2	1.1	— —	— —	1.0	005°	— —	— —	0.9	190°
2459	Hail Point, 0.7 n.mi.east of	16d	39° 06.38'	76° 10.95'	−0 51	−1 08	−1 12	−0 37	0.5	0.6	— —	— —	0.4	002°	— —	— —	0.5	168°
2461	Deep Point		39° 00.63'	76° 07.23'	−0 31	−0 33	−0 32	−0 18	0.6	0.9	— —	— —	0.5	065°	— —	— —	0.7	260°
2463	Chestertown		39° 12.43'	76° 03.67'	−0 21	+0 05	−0 02	−0 17	0.8	0.6	— —	— —	0.6	025°	— —	— —	0.5	220°
	PATAPSCO RIVER																	
2465	North Point, Brewerton Channel	15d	39° 10.70'	76° 26.65'	Current weak and variable													
2467	Brewerton Angle		39° 12.08'	76° 30.78'	Current weak and variable													
2469	Fort McHenry Angle		39° 15.45'	76° 34.53'	Current weak and variable													
2471	Bear Creek entrance		39° 13.8'	76° 29.9'	Current weak and variable													
2473	Curtis Creek entrance		39° 13.1'	76° 34.6'	Current weak and variable													
2475	Fort McHenry, NW Harbor entrance		39° 15.8'	76° 34.5'	Current weak and variable													
2477	Middle Branch entrance		39° 15.4'	76° 37.0'	Current weak and variable													
	BACK, GUNPOWDER and BUSH RIVERS																	
2479	Lynch Point, Back River		39° 15.0'	76° 26.3'	+0 00	−0 10	+0 00	−0 10	0.7	0.5	— —	— —	0.6	310°	— —	— —	0.4	130°
2481	Gunpowder River entrance		39° 18.7'	76° 18.5'	−0 24	−0 41	+0 25	+0 05	0.5	0.4	— —	— —	0.4	040°	— —	— —	0.3	205°
2483	Bush River, 0.4 mi. SW of Bush Point		39° 21.4'	76° 15.4'	+0 07	−0 24	+0 21	+0 20	0.8	0.6	— —	— —	0.6	325°	— —	— —	0.5	165°
	SASSAFRAS RIVER																	
2485	Grove Point		39° 22.7'	76° 02.6'	+0 46	+0 46	+0 51	+0 44	0.5	0.4	— —	— —	0.4	095°	— —	— —	0.3	288°
2487	Ordinary Point, 0.4 mile west of		39° 22.45'	75° 59.25'	+0 50	+0 37	+1 17	+0 58	0.6	0.5	— —	— —	0.5	165°	— —	— —	0.4	345°
2489	Georgetown		39° 21.67'	75° 53.17'	+1 00	+0 25	+0 56	+1 25	0.4	0.5	— —	— —	0.3	090°	— —	— —	0.4	200°

Endnotes can be found at the end of table 2.

TABLE 2. – CURRENT DIFFERENCES AND OTHER CONSTANTS

No.	PLACE	Meter Depth (ft)	Latitude North	Longitude West	Min. before Flood	Flood	Min. before Ebb	Ebb	Ratio Flood	Ratio Ebb	Min. before Flood knots	Dir.	Max. Flood knots	Dir.	Min. before Ebb knots	Dir.	Max. Ebb knots	Dir.
	ELK RIVER Time meridian, 75°W				**on Baltimore Harbor Approach, p.96**													
2491	Arnold Point, 0.4 mile west of		39°27.83'	75°58.45'	+1 39	+1 45	+1 24	+1 32	1.0	1.0			0.8	040°			0.8	215°
2493	Old Town Point Wharf, northwest of	17d	39°30.23'	75°55.12'	+2 00	+1 53	+1 49	+1 45	1.3	1.6			1.1	054°			1.3	242°
	...do.	29d	39°30.23'	75°55.12'	+2 07	+2 04	+1 47	+1 45	1.2	1.4			0.9	055°			1.1	237°
2495	Hendersons Point		39°33.2'	75°51.6'	+2 05	+2 05	+2 05	+2 05	0.6	0.9			0.5	030°			0.7	210°
	CHESAPEAKE and DELAWARE CANAL				**on Ches. & Del. Canal, p.100**													
2497	Back Creek, 0.3 n.mi. W of Sandy Pt	14d	39°31.67'	75°51.97'	-0 06	-0 12	-0 10	-0 01	0.6	0.7			1.2	057°			1.4	244°
	...do.	31d	39°31.67'	75°51.97'	-0 04	-0 25	-0 00	+0 01	0.6	0.6			1.2	052°			1.2	240°
2499	C&D CANAL, Chesapeake City	9d	39°31.82'	75°49.58'	Daily predictions								2.0	097°			1.9	278°
2501	Chesapeake City Bridge, 0.45 n.mi. E of	26d	39°31.67'	75°48.43'	-0 27	-0 11	+0 08	-0 07	1.0	0.7			1.5	092°			1.4	273°
	...do.	37d	39°31.67'	75°48.43'	-0 31	-0 16	+0 11	-0 14	0.7	0.5			1.9	083°			0.9	275°
2503	Conrail Bridge, east of	17d	39°31.67'	75°42.15'	-0 35	-0 25	+0 02	-0 08	0.9	0.7			1.4	099°			1.3	278°
	...do.	34d	39°32.55'	75°42.15'	-0 40	-0 23	-0 01	-0 34	0.7	0.5			1.7	096°			1.0	281°
2505	St. George Bridge, 0.1 n.mi. ENE of	18d	39°33.17'	75°39.00'	-0 57	-1 08	-0 48	-1 08	0.9	0.7			1.7	064°			1.3	247°
2507	Reedy Point Radio Tower, south of	19d	39°33.62'	75°34.20'	-1 05	-0 55	-0 10	-0 16	1.0	0.7			1.9	078°			1.3	263°
	VIRGINIA, outer coast				**on Chesapeake Bay Entrance, p.92**													
2509	Cape Henry Light, 0.7 mile east of		36°55.70'	75°59.60'	-0 06	-0 23	-1 07	-0 06	0.9	1.8			1.0	320°			1.9	105°
2511	Virginia Beach, south end		36°33.00'	75°52.10'	-0 53	-0 20	-0 21	-0 09	0.4	0.4			0.5	350°			0.4	170°
	PAMLICO SOUND				**on Charleston Harbor, p.112**													
	Oregon Inlet																	
2513	Bodie Island–Pea Island, between	6	35°46.6'	75°32.1'	+2 38	+2 20	+2 03	+1 52	1.2	0.6			2.1	202°	0.1	113°	1.2	028°
	...do.	12	35°46.6'	75°32.1'	+2 49	+2 36	+2 02	+1 48	1.2	0.6			2.0	204°	0.1	113°	1.2	036°
2515	Coast Guard Tower, southwest of	6	35°45.7'	75°31.9'	+3 04	+2 30	+1 53	+2 18	0.8	0.8			1.4	205°			1.5	028°
	...do.	12	35°45.7'	75°31.9'	+3 01	+2 33	+1 57	+1 33	0.8	0.7			1.3	212°			1.4	033°
2517	Herbert C. Bonner Bridge, WSW of	6	35°46.2'	75°32.8'	+3 32	+2 55	+1 30	+1 46	0.6	0.9			1.0	280°			1.8	087°
2519	Hatteras Inlet		35°12'	75°45'	+2 42	+2 42	+2 18	+1 38	1.2	1.0			2.1	307°			2.0	148°
2521	Diamond Shoal Light, 3.9 miles SSW of		35°09'	75°18'	Current weak and variable													
	Ocracoke Inlet																	
2523	channel entrance		35°03.92'	76°01.13'	+2 48	+2 24	+1 43	+1 40	1.0	1.2			1.7	000°			2.4	145°
2525	Teaches Hole Channel	10	35°04.75'	76°00.28'	+2 49	+2 27	+1 42	+1 47	0.6	0.8			1.1	050°			1.6	195°
2527	Blair Channel	10	35°04.88'	76°02.03'	+2 52	+2 33	+1 48	+2 03	0.6	0.9			1.6	355°			1.7	140°
2529	Wallace Channel	9	35°04.78'	76°03.12'	+2 51	+2 57	+2 03	+2 13	0.6	0.9			1.6	305°			1.8	140°
2531	Sheep Island Slue		35°04'	76°06'	+3 18	+3 18	+1 35	+1 56	0.1	0.2			0.2	310°			0.3	095°
2533	Ocracoke Inlet, 3.5 miles SSE of		35°01'	76°00'	Current weak and variable													
	NORTH CAROLINA COAST																	
	Beaufort Inlet																	
2535	Shackleford Banks, 0.8 mile S of	6	34°39.98'	76°39.33'	+1 19	+1 16	+0 37	+0 57	0.8	0.7			1.4	314°			1.5	145°
2537	Approach		34°40.3'	76°40.2'	+2 03	+1 19	+0 57	+0 57	0.2	0.7			0.3	358°			1.4	161°
2539	Fort Macon, 0.6 mile SE of		34°41.15'	76°40.10'	+1 42	+1 47	+0 51	+0 38	0.7	0.9			1.2	332°			1.7	154°
2541	Fort Macon, 0.2 mile NE of		34°41.98'	76°40.52'	+1 12	+1 12	+0 36	+0 21	1.1	0.9			2.0	307°			1.8	151°
	...do.	10	34°41.98'	76°40.52'	+1 18	+1 18	+0 34	+0 39	0.9	0.9	0.1	232°	1.6	320°	0.1	232°	1.7	153°
2543	Tombstone Point, 0.1 mile E of	20	34°42.23'	76°41.17'	+1 13	+1 25	+0 25	+0 27	0.8	0.8	0.2	242°	1.6	305°	0.1	220°	1.7	128°
2545	Turning Basin	15	34°42.78'	76°41.65'	+1 11	+1 34	+0 50	+0 32	0.7	0.5	0.1	222°	1.2	327°	0.1	237°	1.0	144°
	...do.	15	34°42.78'	76°41.65'	+1 09	+1 39	+0 59	+0 32	0.7	0.8	0.4	048°	1.4	334°			1.0	138°
2547	Sugarloaf Island, 0.2 mile S of	15	34°42.75'	76°42.83'	+1 58	+1 47	+1 22	+1 14	0.8	0.7			1.2	266°			1.6	094°
2549	Morehead City, S of	6	34°43.00'	76°43.97'	+2 12	+1 42	+1 29	+1 42	0.6	0.5			1.4	293°			1.4	110°
2551	Morehead City, RR. bridge, N of	6	34°43.37'	76°41.63'	+0 44	+1 01	+0 09	-1 03	0.6	0.8	0.2	127°	1.0	054°			1.0	185°
2553	Newport Marshes, SE of	6	34°43.88'	76°41.00'	+0 57	+1 02	+0 18	-0 08	0.8	0.6	0.1	130°	1.0	044°	0.1	122°	1.8	215°
2555	Newport Marshes, E of	15	34°44.27'	76°40.83'	+0 53	+1 15	+0 21	-0 08	0.8	0.6			1.3	044°			1.2	226°
	...do.	6			+0 07	+0 11	-0 37	-0 09	0.6	0.5			1.0	040°			1.0	224°

Endnotes can be found at the end of table 2.

TABLE 2. – CURRENT DIFFERENCES AND OTHER CONSTANTS

No.	PLACE	POSITION Latitude North	POSITION Longitude West	Meter Depth (ft)	TIME DIFF. Min. before Flood (h m)	TIME DIFF. Flood (h m)	TIME DIFF. Min. before Ebb (h m)	TIME DIFF. Ebb (h m)	SPEED RATIOS Flood	SPEED RATIOS Ebb	Min. before Flood (knots)	Min. before Flood (Dir.)	Maximum Flood (knots)	Maximum Flood (Dir.)	Min. before Ebb (knots)	Min. before Ebb (Dir.)	Maximum Ebb (knots)	Maximum Ebb (Dir.)
	NORTH CAROLINA COAST Time meridian, 75°W																	
	Beaufort Inlet-cont.					on Charleston Harbor, p.112												
2557	Radio Island, E of	34°42.70'	76°40.78'	6	+0 55	+0 55	+0 20	+0 16	0.7	0.6	– –	– –	1.2	022°	– –	– –	1.2	202°
2559	Beaufort, off docks	34°43'	76°40'		Current irregular						– –	– –	0.5	310°	– –	– –	0.5	130°
2561	Bird Shoal, SE of	34°42.03'	76°39.23'	6	+1 40	+1 34	+1 10	+0 16	0.5	0.4	– –	– –	0.8	126°	0.1	217°	0.8	304°
2563	Shackleford Point, NE of	34°41.53'	76°39.13'	6	+1 32	+1 28	+1 10	+0 46	0.8	0.6	0.1	218°	1.3	135°	– –	– –	1.1	305°
2565	Carrot Island	34°42.13'	76°37.05'	6	+1 49	+1 34	+1 15	+1 49	0.5	0.7	0.1	359°	0.9	080°	0.1	181°	1.3	262°
2567	Middle Marshes, S of	34°40.70'	76°36.83'	6	+0 59	+1 04	+1 03	+0 18	0.8	0.5	0.1	197°	1.4	123°	– –	– –	1.1	275°
2569	Cape Lookout Shoals Ltd. Whistle Buoy 14	34°18'	76°24'		Current weak and variable													
	CAPE FEAR RIVER					on Southport, p.104												
2571	Bald Head Shoal	33°51.26'	78°01.63'	12d	–0 40	+0 07	–1 24	–0 49	0.3	0.5	0.2	291°	0.6	013°	0.3	095°	1.7	208°
	do.	33°51.26'	78°01.63'	28d	–2 01	–1 51	–0 44	–0 51	0.3	0.3	0.3	295°	0.6	013°	0.1	108°	1.0	203°
2573	Fort Caswell	33°53.30'	78°00.46'	12d	–0 22	+0 06	–0 24	–0 32	0.7	0.5	– –	– –	1.2	012°	0.1	119°	1.6	161°
	do.	33°53.30'	78°00.46'	18d	–0 32	–0 01	–0 21	–0 35	0.6	0.4	– –	– –	1.1	006°	0.1	254°	1.3	161°
	do.	33°53.30'	78°00.46'	28d	–0 40	+0 18	–0 06	–0 51	0.7	0.3	0.1	074°	1.3	347°	0.2	258°	0.9	162°
2575	SOUTHPORT	33°54.92'	78°00.73'	7d		Daily predictions			1.1	0.8	– –	– –	1.9	048°	0.1	142°	3.3	235°
	do.	33°54.92'	78°00.73'	20d					1.0	0.5	– –	– –	1.7	056°	– –	– –	2.5	231°
	do.	33°54.92'	78°00.73'	37d					0.4	0.2	– –	– –	0.7	060°	– –	– –	1.7	225°
2577	Southport, at Dutchman Creek, ICW	33°55.06'	78°02.58'	4d	–0 14	+0 01	+0 02	–0 06	0.3	0.3	– –	– –	0.6	295°	– –	– –	0.7	119°
	do.	33°55.06'	78°02.58'	12d	–0 30	–0 01	–0 01	–0 11	0.2	0.3	– –	– –	0.4	294°	– –	– –	0.7	117°
2579	Oak Island Bridge, ICW	33°55.30'	78°04.37'	11d	–1 11	–0 47	–0 58	–2 03	0.2	0.2	0.2	336°	0.4	270°	– –	– –	0.9	086°
2581	Snows Marsh Channel	33°56.23'	77°58.67'	12d	–0 58	+0 10	–0 49	–1 48	1.3	0.7	0.1	322°	2.2	049°	0.1	030°	2.1	262°
	do.	33°56.23'	77°58.67'	25d	–0 09	+0 18	–1 55	–2 07	1.1	0.5	0.1	330°	1.9	051°	0.1	335°	1.7	239°
	do.	33°56.23'	77°58.67'	38d	–0 14	+0 33	+0 18	–0 02	0.9	0.4	0.1	333°	1.6	054°	0.1	333°	1.4	247°
2583	Sunny Point, 0.5 nm southeast of	33°58.70'	77°57.00'	12d	+0 10	+0 12	+0 24	+0 03	1.0	0.3	0.1	209°	1.8	017°	– –	– –	1.3	190°
	do.	33°58.70'	77°57.00'	18d	–0 06	+0 00	+0 28	+0 06	0.9	0.2	0.1	097°	1.6	014°	0.1	090°	1.0	178°
	do.	33°58.70'	77°57.00'	35d	–0 35	+0 18	+0 34	–0 05	0.7	0.1	0.1	262°	1.2	000°	0.1	267°	0.8	178°
2585	Reaves Point, 0.3 mile east of	33°59.92'	77°56.97'	6	–0 21	–1 01	+0 47	–1 58	0.2	0.1	– –	– –	0.3	351°	0.1	251°	0.3	181°
	do.	33°59.92'	77°56.97'	16	–0 06	+0 37	+0 23	–0 56	0.4	0.1	– –	– –	0.7	332°	0.0	256°	0.2	159°
	do.	33°59.92'	77°56.97'	26	–0 39	+0 40	+1 00	+0 28	0.6	0.5	– –	– –	1.0	331°	– –	– –	1.6	195°
2587	Reaves Point Channel	33°59.08'	77°55.85'	6	+0 57	+2 05	+0 56	+2 05	0.8	0.5	– –	– –	1.3	009°	– –	– –	1.7	192°
	do.	33°59.08'	77°55.85'	16	+0 34	+0 04	+1 02	–0 04	0.9	0.3	– –	– –	1.5	013°	– –	– –	1.1	194°
	do.	33°59.08'	77°55.85'	26	+0 20	+1 02	+1 02	+0 43	0.6	0.4	0.1	105°	1.1	017°	– –	– –	1.1	191°
2589	Reaves Point, 0.9 nm northeast of	34°00.36'	77°56.41'	16	+0 16	+0 43	+1 03	+0 58	0.9	0.3	– –	– –	1.5	022°	– –	– –	1.2	191°
	do.	34°00.37'	77°56.41'	20d	+0 06	+0 17	+1 06	+0 37	0.8	0.4	– –	– –	1.3	019°	– –	– –	1.0	205°
2591	Reaves Point, 0.4 mile north of	34°00.37'	77°57.15'	10d	–0 11	+0 35	+1 15	+0 44	0.5	0.3	– –	– –	0.9	020°	– –	– –	0.9	198°
	do.	34°00.37'	77°57.15'	20d	+1 11	+1 34	+1 18	+1 10	0.5	0.2	– –	– –	0.8	027°	– –	– –	0.7	191°
	do.	34°00.37'	77°57.15'	33d	+0 51	+1 00	+1 37	+0 17	0.5	0.2	– –	– –	0.9	011°	0.1	117°	0.8	183°
2593	Orton Point, 0.5 nm south of	34°02.84'	77°56.46'	8d	–0 05	+0 20	+0 14	+0 21	0.9	0.7	– –	– –	1.5	050°	– –	– –	2.2	189°
	do.	34°02.84'	77°56.46'	15d	+0 03	–0 01	+0 21	+0 22	1.0	0.5	– –	– –	1.7	358°	– –	– –	1.7	181°
	do.	34°02.84'	77°56.46'	38d	–0 11	–1 01	+0 19	–0 29	0.7	0.5	– –	– –	1.3	359°	– –	– –	0.7	179°
	do.	34°04.73'	77°55.92'	6	–1 14	+5 19	+5 51	+4 22	0.8	0.2	– –	– –	1.3	001°	– –	– –	1.8	254°
	do.	34°04.73'	77°55.92'	16	+4 31	+5 59	+5 34	+4 12	0.4	0.1	– –	– –	0.7	073°	– –	– –	0.4	233°
	do.	34°04.73'	77°55.92'	26	+4 19	+0 35	+0 43	+0 53	0.6	0.6	– –	– –	1.1	045°	– –	– –	2.1	183°
2595	Snows Cut, Intracoastal Waterway	34°04.76'	77°53.94'	3d	+0 42	+0 34	+0 57	+0 46	0.6	0.4	0.1	098°	1.1	013°	– –	– –	1.6	188°
2597	Myrtle Sound, Intracoastal Waterway	34°01.74'	77°53.06'	16d	–0 12	+0 17	+1 09	+0 40	0.7	0.7	0.1	102°	1.3	011°	0.1	080°	2.4	166°
2599	Upper Midnight Channel	34°01.74'	77°56.45'	7d	+0 57	+1 08	+0 59	+1 01	0.9	0.6	– –	– –	1.5	359°	– –	– –	1.9	166°
	do.	34°01.74'	77°56.45'	20d	+0 47	+0 44	+1 13	+1 06	1.0	0.6	– –	– –	1.7	349°	– –	– –	1.1	163°
	do.	34°01.74'	77°56.45'	33d	+0 17	+0 16	+1 12	+0 51	0.8	0.4	– –	– –	1.3	348°	– –	– –	2.3	161°
2601	Doctor Point, 0.6 nm NNW of	34°04.73'	77°55.92'	6d	+1 06	+1 12	+1 05	+1 16	0.7	0.7	– –	– –	1.3	344°	– –	– –	2.1	167°
	do.	34°04.73'	77°55.92'	16d	+0 25	+0 22	+1 12	+0 40	0.7	0.4	– –	– –	1.2	344°	– –	– –	1.9	189°
	do.	34°04.73'	77°55.92'	32d	+1 09	+1 26	+1 24	+1 21	1.0	0.6	– –	– –	1.8	350°	– –	– –	1.9	185°
2603	Keg Island, west side	34°05.82'	77°56.08'	7d	+0 56	+1 14	+1 29	+1 19	1.1	0.6	0.1	037°	1.1	007°	– –	– –	1.1	187°
	do.	34°05.82'	77°56.08'	30d	+1 21	+1 33	+1 35	+0 57	0.8	0.3	– –	– –	1.4	007°	– –	– –	1.7	126°
2605	Campbell Island, east side	34°07.19'	77°56.11'	9d	+1 19	+1 43	+1 20	+1 03	0.9	0.5	– –	– –	1.4	004°	– –	– –	0.8	124°
	do.	34°07.19'	77°56.18'	15d	+0 25	+1 08	+1 44	+1 22	0.9	0.5	– –	– –	1.6	310°	– –	– –		136°
	do.	34°07.19'	77°56.18'	35d			+1 51	+1 27	0.8	0.3	– –	– –	1.4	309°	– –	– –		
2607	Upper Big I Range	34°08.13'	77°56.53'	7d									1.4	313°	– –	– –		
	do.	34°08.13'	77°56.53'	13d														
	do.	34°08.13'	77°56.53'	36d														

Endnotes can be found at the end of table 2.

TABLE 2. – CURRENT DIFFERENCES AND OTHER CONSTANTS

No.	PLACE	Meter Depth (ft)	Latitude North	Longitude West	Min. before Flood (h m)	Flood (h m)	Min. before Ebb (h m)	Ebb (h m)	Ratio Flood	Ratio Ebb	Min before Flood knots	Dir.	Max Flood knots	Dir.	Min before Ebb knots	Dir.	Max Ebb knots	Dir.
	CAPE FEAR RIVER Time meridian, 75°W																	
	on Southport, p.104																	
2609	Lower Brunswick Range	9d	34°09.36'	77°57.50'	+1 30	+1 57	+1 36	+1 35	0.9	0.5	---	---	1.5	322°	---	---	1.8	140°
	...do.	16d	34°09.36'	77°57.50'	+1 29	+1 47	+1 50	+1 49	0.9	0.5	---	---	1.6	322°	---	---	1.7	141°
	...do.	39d	34°09.36'	77°57.50'	+0 28	+1 24	+2 01	+1 22	0.7	0.3	---	---	1.2	324°	---	---	0.8	147°
2611	Port of Wilmington, south end shoals	14d	34°10.55'	77°57.42'	+1 15	+2 09	+1 24	+0 36	0.4	0.4	---	---	0.6	005°	0.1	083°	1.2	182°
2613	Port of Wilmington, south end, east of channel	14d	34°10.55'	77°57.45'	+1 27	+1 33	+1 03	+0 15	0.4	0.5	---	---	0.7	005°	---	---	1.5	174°
2615	Port of Wilmington, south end, mid-channel	14d	34°10.55'	77°57.45'	+1 22	+1 19	+1 00	+0 30	0.5	0.3	---	---	0.8	355°	---	---	1.1	173°
	Brunswick River																	
2617	0.4 mile north of	6	34°10.87'	77°57.95'	+1 42	+0 26	+1 12	+0 13	0.5	0.4	---	---	0.8	290°	0.1	200°	1.2	118°
	...do.	16	34°10.87'	77°57.95'	+1 34	+0 48	+1 14	+0 13	0.5	0.3	---	---	0.8	301°	---	---	1.0	127°
2619	1.8 miles north of mouth	6	34°12.33'	77°58.47'	+1 48	+1 30	+1 20	+1 43	0.3	0.3	---	---	0.5	354°	---	---	0.8	170°
	on Wilmington, p.108																	
2621	Dram Tree Point, 0.5 mile SSE of	6d	34°11.44'	77°57.46'	+0 09	-0 02	-0 24	-0 26	0.5	0.7	---	---	0.7	358°	---	---	1.3	181°
	...do.	32d	34°11.44'	77°57.46'	-0 34	-0 26	+0 38	+0 17	0.8	0.5	---	---	1.2	000°	---	---	1.0	178°
2623	State Pier, at the pier	15d	34°12.47'	77°57.33'	-2 59	-1 28	-0 16	-1 28	0.2	0.2	---	---	0.3	011°	---	---	0.5	192°
2625	State Pier, east of channel	15d	34°12.47'	77°57.36'	-0 33	+0 23	+0 19	-0 49	0.3	0.3	---	---	0.4	011°	---	---	0.7	185°
2627	State Pier, midchannel	15d	34°12.47'	77°57.39'	+0 23	+0 10	-0 09	+0 31	0.3	0.5	---	---	0.4	007°	---	---	1.1	185°
2629	WILMINGTON, USS North Carolina	5d	34°14.01'	77°57.02'	Daily predictions				1.1	0.9	---	---	1.6	000°	---	---	2.1	179°
	...do.	25d	34°14.01'	77°57.02'	-0 16	-0 07	+0 13	+0 22	0.8	0.7	---	---	1.4	000°	---	---	1.8	180°
2631	Wilmington, Northeast River	4d	34°14.52'	77°57.24'	-0 04	+0 13	+0 27	+0 30	0.8	0.6	---	---	1.3	336°	0.1	250°	1.4	171°
	...do.	14d	34°14.52'	77°57.24'	-0 01	+0 03	+0 29	+0 34	0.5	0.8	---	---	0.8	342°	---	---	1.3	169°
	...do.	34d	34°14.52'	77°57.24'	-0 14	+0 01	+0 37	+0 48	0.9	0.5	---	---	1.5	006°	---	---	0.7	161°
2633	Point Peter	5d	34°14.55'	77°57.46'	+0 19	+0 20	+0 05	-0 11	0.6	0.9	---	---	0.9	311°	---	---	1.6	132°
	...do.	23d	34°14.55'	77°57.46'	-0 17	-0 17	+0 08	+0 28	0.9	0.7	---	---	1.4	305°	---	---	1.1	133°
2635	Isabel Holmes Bridge	6d	34°14.55'	77°57.01'	+0 11	+0 23	+0 34	+0 41	0.9	0.5	---	---	1.1	036°	---	---	1.4	215°
	...do.	29d	34°15.14'	77°57.01'	+0 02	+0 01	+0 42	+1 17	0.7	0.5	---	---	0.4	037°	---	---	1.1	224°
2637	Hilton RR Bridge, 0.1nm north of	12d	34°15.55'	77°56.88'	+0 23	+0 19	+0 13	+0 34	0.3	0.6	---	---	0.5	344°	---	---	1.2	169°
	...do.	31d	34°15.55'	77°56.88'	+0 07	+0 07	+0 38	+0 38	0.3	0.5	---	---	0.5	002°	---	---	1.1	173°
	NORTH CAROLINA COAST																	
2639	Frying Pan Shoals, off Cape Fear		33°34'	77°49'	See table 5.													
2641	Frying Pan Shoals Light, 14.3 mi. NW of		33°28'	77°34'	Current weak and variable													
	on Charleston Harbor, p.112																	
	WINYAH BAY																	
2643	Winyah Bay entrance		33°12.43'	79°11.07'	+1 47	+1 35	+1 05	+1 20	1.1	1.0	---	---	1.9	320°	---	---	2.0	140°
2645	Range D, off Mosquito Creek		33°14.65'	79°12.35'	+2 00	+1 57	+1 13	+1 42	1.2	1.1	---	---	2.1	330°	---	---	2.2	130°
2647	Frazier Point, south of		33°17.70'	79°16.37'	+1 52	+1 52	+2 20	+1 59	1.1	0.5	---	---	1.8	000°	---	---	0.9	115°
2649	Frazier Point, west of		33°18.58'	79°17.20'	+2 23	+2 19	+2 01	+1 41	0.9	1.0	---	---	1.6	000°	---	---	2.0	170°
2651	Rabbit Island, northwest of		33°20.37'	79°16.82'	+2 39	+2 46	+2 14	+2 25	1.2	0.9	---	---	2.1	015°	---	---	1.8	215°
2653	Sampit River entrance		33°21.08'	79°17.25'	+1 33	+1 20	+1 39	+0 53	0.6	0.7	---	---	1.1	345°	---	---	1.3	135°
2655	Georgetown, Sampit River		33°21.55'	79°15.83'	+2 00	+1 18	+0 56	+0 52	0.5	0.6	---	---	0.7	275°	---	---	1.1	080°
2657	Pee Dee River, swing bridge		33°22.23'	79°15.12'	+3 03	+3 13	+1 57	+2 43	0.4	0.5	---	---	0.7	000°	---	---	0.9	210°
2659	Lafayette swing bridge, Waccamaw River		33°22.12'	79°15.12'	+3 23	+3 04	+1 56	+2 31	0.4	0.6	---	---	0.7	005°	---	---	1.2	200°
2661	Butler Island, 0.3 mile south of		33°25.00'	79°12.72'	+3 36	+3 34	+2 11	+2 55	0.4	0.5	---	---	0.6	030°	---	---	0.9	205°
	SOUTH CAROLINA COAST																	
2663	North Santee River entrance	6	33°08.15'	79°14.45'	+1 00	+0 33	+0 03	-0 01	0.9	0.9	---	---	1.5	010°	---	---	1.8	165°
2665	South Santee River entrance	5	33°07.2'	79°16.5'	+0 20	+0 38	+0 27	+0 15	0.9	0.8	---	---	1.5	045°	---	---	1.6	240°
2667	Cape Romain		---	---	See table 5.													
2669	Capers Inlet		---	---	Current weak and variable													
2671	Charleston Entrance, 37 miles east of		32°42'	79°06'	See table 5.													
2673	Charleston Lighted Whistle Buoy 2C		32°41'	79°43'	See table 5.													

Endnotes can be found at the end of table 2.

TABLE 2. – CURRENT DIFFERENCES AND OTHER CONSTANTS

CHARLESTON HARBOR — Time meridian, 75°W — on Charleston Harbor, p.112

No.	PLACE	Meter Depth (ft)	Lat. North	Long. West	Min. before Flood (h m)	Flood (h m)	Min. before Ebb (h m)	Ebb (h m)	Speed Ratio Flood	Speed Ratio Ebb	Min. bef. Flood (kn)	Dir.	Max. Flood (kn)	Dir.	Min. bef. Ebb (kn)	Dir.	Max. Ebb (kn)	Dir.
2675	Fort Sumter Range, Buoy '2'		32°40.98'	79°43.56'	−1 05	−0 51	−1 11	−1 03	0.2	0.2	0.2	194°	0.3	280°	0.2	023°	0.4	104°
2677	Fort Sumter Range, Buoy '4'		32°41.86'	79°45.34'	−0 49	−0 59	−1 10	−0 38	0.3	0.2	0.1	202°	0.5	289°	0.1	026°	0.4	117°
2679	Fort Sumter Range, Buoy '8'		32°42.90'	79°47.54'	−0 15	−0 16	+0 17	+0 24	0.4	0.5	0.2	204°	0.6	299°	0.1	038°	0.9	128°
2681	Fort Sumter Range, Buoy '14'		32°43.46'	79°48.60'	−0 10	−0 04	+0 16	+0 01	0.6	0.8	0.1	193°	1.1	287°	0.2	019°	1.5	116°
2683	North Jetty, 0.8 mile southeast of <30>		32°43.05'	79°48.00'	−0 06	−0 48	−1 09	−0 16	0.2	0.6	0.1	202°	0.4	295°	0.1	358°	1.1	110°
2685	Charleston Hbr. ent. (between jetties)		32°44.00'	79°50.00'	−0 01	+0 04	+0 05	+0 09	1.1	0.9			1.8	320°			1.8	121°
2687	Fort Sumter Range, Buoy '20'		32°44.43'	79°50.67'	−0 33	−0 15	−0 33	−0 51	0.9	0.9	0.1	230°	1.6	305°	0.1	040°	2.8	128°
2689	South Jetty, break in		32°43.87'	79°51.02'	+0 38	+0 31	−0 06	+0 22	0.7	1.4			1.6	002°			2.0	204°
2691	CHARLESTON HARBOR (off Fort Sumter)		32°45.36'	79°52.22'		Daily predictions							1.7	313°			1.7	127°
2693	Ft. Sumter, 0.6 n.mi. NW of		32°45.67'	79°52.03'	−0 05	−0 03	+0 01	−0 24	0.9	0.9	0.2	212°	1.6	322°	0.1	233°	2.6	138°
2695	South Chan., 0.8 mi. ENE of Ft. Johnson		32°45.52'	79°53.08'	+0 43	+0 11	−0 12	+0 13	0.5	1.3	0.1	220°	0.8	275°			1.9	115°
2697	South Chan., 0.4 mi. NW of Ft. Johnson		32°45.48'	79°54.38'	+0 17	+0 58	−0 16	+0 43	0.4	1.0			0.7	282°			1.5	104°
2699	Sullivans I., 0.7 mi. NE of Ft. Sumter		32°45.72'	79°52.05'	+0 17	+0 37	+0 01	−0 03	0.8	0.8			1.4	342°			1.7	132°
2701	Castle Pinckney, 0.4 mile south of		32°46.02'	79°54.70'	+0 40	+1 00	+0 14	+0 58	0.5	0.9	0.1	240°	0.8	304°			0.8	098°
2703	South Channel, Buoy '32'		32°45.73'	79°54.66'	−0 01	−0 04	+0 18	−0 02	0.5	0.5	0.1	219°	0.8	305°	0.1	026°	1.3	125°
2705	Castle Pinckney, 0.6 mile southwest of		32°45.98'	79°55.17'	+1 21	+1 20	+0 24	+0 40	0.4	0.7			0.7	318°			1.3	156°
2707	Shutes Folly Island, 0.4 mile west of		32°46.58'	79°55.25'	+0 53	+0 59	+0 20	+0 08	0.5	1.1			0.8	028°			2.2	164°
2709	Customhouse Reach, off Customhouse		32°46.77'	79°55.35'	+0 49	+1 03	+0 59	+0 23	0.6	0.7			1.0	009°			1.8	190°
2711	Customhouse Reach		32°46.95'	79°55.20'	+0 46	+0 37	+0 37	+0 15	0.6	0.9			1.0	005°	0.1	098°	2.2	153°
2713	Town Creek Lower Reach		32°47.55'	79°55.47'	+0 34	+0 24	+0 02	−0 07	0.6	1.1			1.1	335°			2.5	172°
2715	Town Creek, 0.2 mile above bridge		32°48.32'	79°55.90'	+1 06	+0 54	+0 03	+0 03	0.5	1.3			0.8	002°			0.9	166°
2717	Rebellion Reach, 0.8 n.mi. N. of Ft. Sumter		32°45.98'	79°52.40'	−0 06	+0 27	−0 25	−0 48	0.4	0.4	0.1	240°	0.7	329°			0.8	143°
2719	The Cove, entrance on the Cove Range		32°46.05'	79°52.32'	+0 28	+1 14	+0 06	+0 10	0.7	0.5			1.2	346°			1.1	151°
2721	Hog Island Channel		32°46.87'	79°52.58'	−0 39	−0 03	−0 29	−0 20	0.5	0.4			0.8	325°			1.6	125°
2723	Folly I. Channel, N of Ft. Johnson		32°46.18'	79°54.07'	−1 09	−0 03	−0 04	−0 59	0.7	0.6			1.2	301°			1.5	104°
2725	Folly Reach, Buoy '5'		32°46.58'	79°53.95'	+0 02	+0 35	+0 18	+0 13	0.7	0.8	0.1	205°	1.2	292°			1.9	110°
2727	Shutes Reach, Buoy '8'		32°46.93'	79°54.65'	+0 18	+0 22	+0 15	−0 25	0.7	0.8			1.3	315°	0.1	037°	1.3	136°
2729	Horse Reach		32°47.17'	79°54.90'	+0 36	+0 23	−0 12	−0 09	0.8	1.0			1.4	350°			1.8	146°
2731	Hog Island Reach, Buoy '12'		32°47.67'	79°55.25'	+0 13	+0 28	+0 14	−0 12	0.8	0.9			1.3	012°			2.0	193°
2733	Drum Island, 0.4 mile SSE of		32°47.67'	79°54.92'	+0 34	+0 53	+0 11	−0 02	0.7	0.9			1.2	011°	0.1	103°	1.8	155°
2735	Drum Island, east of (bridge)		32°48.27'	79°54.72'	+0 30	+0 42	+0 15	+0 06	0.8	0.7			1.2	020°			2.0	183°
2737	Hog Island Reach, SW of Remley Point		32°48.71'	79°55.37'	+0 30	+0 44	+0 43	+0 51	0.7	0.7			1.1	030°			2.0	210°
2739	Hog Island Reach, off Drum I., Buoy 45		32°48.97'		+0 26	+1 00	+1 06	+1 00	0.4	0.5			0.6	312°			1.0	133°
	Cooper River																	
2741	Drum Island, 0.2 mile above		32°49.18'	79°55.75'	+1 12	+1 09	+0 01	+0 37	0.6	1.2			1.1	332°			2.4	152°
2743	Daniel Island Reach, Buoy '48'		32°49.63'	79°55.73'	+1 01	+1 29	+0 53	+0 55	0.7	0.7			1.2	006°	0.1	278°	1.3	182°
2745	Shipyard Creek entrance <31>		32°49.80'	79°56.10'	+0 41	+1 06	−0 29	+0 09	0.3	0.8			0.5				1.5	197°
2747	Daniel Island Reach		32°49.97'	79°55.80'	+1 29	+1 49	+0 42	+0 51	0.8	1.2			1.3	352°			2.3	190°
2749	Daniel Island Bend		32°50.85'	79°55.75'	+0 55	+1 29	+0 55	+0 39	0.7	1.1			1.2	335°	0.1	260°	2.1	153°
2751	Daniel Island Bend, west side of <47>		32°51.82'	79°56.00'				−0 01									1.0	144°
2753	North Charleston		32°51.82'	79°57.53'	+1 26	+2 28	+1 04	+0 17	0.6	0.9			1.1	335°			1.7	142°
2755	Filbin Creek Reach		32°53.32'	79°57.92'	+1 31	+2 06	+1 08	+1 27	0.7	0.9			1.2	006°			1.4	180°
2757	Filbin Creek Reach, 0.2 mile east of		32°53.28'	79°57.63'	+1 16	+1 47	+0 32	+0 29	0.4	0.7			0.6	002°			1.4	197°
2759	Filbin Creek Reach, Buoy 58		32°53.78'	79°57.67'	+1 18	+2 04	+1 24	+1 09	0.6	0.7			1.1	031°			1.3	214°
2761	Ordnance Reach		32°54.38'	79°57.17'	+1 35	+2 34	+1 05	+1 07	0.6	0.6			1.0	062°			1.2	242°
2763	Yellow House Creek		32°54.53'	79°56.18'	+2 06	+2 41	+0 57	+1 12	0.4	0.7			0.7	088°			1.4	270°
2765	Yellow House Landing, 1 mile NW of		32°55.18'	79°55.83'	+2 26	+2 43	+0 58	+1 06	0.4	0.5			0.7	334°			1.8	170°
2767	Woods Point, SE of		32°55.55'	79°55.97'	+1 48	+1 55	+1 55	+2 09	0.5	0.5			0.8	002°	0.1	067°	1.0	157°
2769	Woods Point		32°55.90'	79°56.30'	+2 41	+3 02	+1 11	+1 43	0.9	0.7			0.9	010°			1.4	201°
2771	Snow Point, 0.5 mile north of		32°57.1'	79°55.8'	+2 15	+2 36	+1 48	+1 33	0.6	0.7			1.1	252°			1.2	210°
2773	Back River entrance		32°58.1'	79°56.0'	+0 46	+0 45	+0 48	+0 34	0.6	0.6			1.0	024°			0.9	067°
2775	Amoco Pier, off		32°57.55'	79°55.08'	+2 09	+2 49	+2 10	+1 48	0.4	0.5	0.1	292°	0.7	036°	0.1	297°	2.0	191°
2777	Moreland, 0.5 n.mi. below		33°00.03'	79°54.28'	+2 39	+2 58	+2 28	+2 19	1.1	1.0			1.9	308°			1.3	216°
2779	Hagan Island, 1 n.mi. below		33°02.00'	79°54.80'	+2 39	+3 52	+2 27	+1 37	0.8	0.7	0.1	048°	1.3	280°			1.4	134°
2781	The Tee, 0.4 mile southwest of		33°03.80'	79°55.78'	+4 22	+4 20	+2 29	+3 20	0.6	0.9			1.0	339°			1.7	098°
2783	The Tee		33°03.95'	79°55.38'	+3 00	+3 09	+2 36	+1 43	0.6	0.5	0.1	075°	0.9		0.1	253°	1.0	161°

Endnotes can be found at the end of table 2.

TABLE 2. – CURRENT DIFFERENCES AND OTHER CONSTANTS

No.	PLACE	Meter Depth (ft)	POSITION Latitude (North)	POSITION Longitude (West)	TIME DIFFERENCES Min. before Flood (h m)	Flood (h m)	Min. before Ebb (h m)	Ebb (h m)	SPEED RATIOS Flood	Ebb	Minimum before Flood (knots)	Dir.	Maximum Flood (knots)	Dir.	Minimum before Ebb (knots)	Dir.	Maximum Ebb (knots)	Dir.
	CHARLESTON HARBOR Time meridian, 75°W				**on Charleston Harbor, p.112**													
	Cooper River—cont.																	
2785	Childsbury, S.A.L. RR. bridge		33° 05.63'	79° 56.55'	+4 43	+4 27	+2 15	+3 34	0.4	0.9	--	--	0.7	309°	--	--	1.7	141°
2787	East Branch, 0.2 mile above entrance		33° 04.1'	79° 55.2'	+3 01	+3 07	+2 59	+3 06	1.1	0.9	--	--	1.8	084°	--	--	1.7	262°
2789	Bonneau Ferry, east of		33° 04.3'	79° 53.0'	+3 27	+3 10	+2 44	+3 36	0.4	0.4	--	--	0.7	022°	--	--	0.8	197°
	Wando River																	
2791	Remley Point, 0.2 mile northwest of		32° 48.97'	79° 54.57'	-0 14	+0 36	+0 20	-0 04	0.8	0.9	--	--	1.3	028°	--	--	1.8	191°
2793	Wando River Upper Reach, Turning Basin		32° 50.00'	79° 53.80'	-0 14	-0 12	-0 09	-0 09	0.6	0.6	--	--	1.0	012°	--	--	1.2	192°
2795	Rathall Creek entrance		32° 51.57'	79° 53.77'	+0 25	+0 35	+0 18	-0 18	0.6	0.9	--	--	1.3	030°	--	--	1.7	216°
2797	Horlbeck Creek, 0.2 mile above entrance		32° 53.1'	79° 50.7'	+0 28	+0 29	+0 31	+0 24	0.4	0.6	--	--	1.0	026°	--	--	0.9	218°
2799	Nowell Creek entrance		32° 52.5'	79° 52.5'	-0 02	+0 42	-0 12	-0 39	0.5	0.6	--	--	0.7	350°	--	--	1.1	171°
2801	Buoy '19', off Nowell Creek		32° 52.32'	79° 51.93'	-0 08	-0 06	+0 04	-0 19	0.5	0.5	--	--	0.8	080°	--	--	1.0	261°
2803	Horlbeck Creek, 2.5 miles north of		32° 55.1'	79° 50.3'	+0 30	+0 41	+0 26	+0 28	0.5	0.7	--	--	0.8	015°	--	--	1.3	207°
	Ashley River																	
2805	Battery, southwest of		32° 46.03'	79° 56.03'	+0 16	+0 09	-0 24	+0 03	0.7	0.9	--	--	1.2	303°	--	--	1.8	114°
2807	Wappoo Creek, off of		32° 46.38'	79° 57.00'	+0 07	-0 05	-0 06	-0 41	0.7	0.6	--	--	1.1	315°	--	--	1.2	136°
2809	Highway Bridge		32° 46.92'	79° 57.60'	-0 09	+0 30	-0 03	-0 18	0.6	0.6	--	--	1.2	321°	--	--	1.1	138°
2811	S.C.L. RR. bridge, 0.1 mile below		32° 47.73'	79° 58.40'	-0 06	+0 44	-0 12	-0 28	0.6	0.8	--	--	1.0	353°	--	--	1.1	150°
2813	S.C.L. RR. bridge, 1.5 miles above		32° 49.2'	79° 57.9'	+0 22	+0 19	+0 17	+0 09	0.7	0.5	--	--	1.2	351°	--	--	1.5	178°
2815	State Hwy. 7 bridge		32° 50.23'	79° 58.92'	+0 06	-0 04	+0 05	-0 05	0.6	0.5	--	--	1.0	293°	--	--	1.0	114°
2817	West Marsh Island, 0.1 mile east of		32° 49.7'	80° 00.5'	+0 23	+0 30	+0 14	+0 25	0.4	0.5	--	--	0.7	250°	--	--	1.0	086°
2819	Bees Ferry Bridge		32° 50.8'	80° 03.0'	+1 13	+0 44	+0 37	+0 22	1.1	1.2	--	--	1.9	310°	--	--	2.3	130°
	STONO RIVER																	
2821	Stono Inlet		32° 37.6'	79° 59.6'	-0 14	+0 44	-0 09	-0 45	1.1	1.4	--	--	1.9	315°	--	--	2.7	136°
2823	Snake Island	12	32° 38.4'	80° 01.2'	-0 44	-0 42	-0 30	-0 38	0.7	0.8	--	--	1.1	347°	--	--	1.1	179°
2825	Johns Island Airport, south of	12	32° 41.0'	80° 00.6'	-0 15	-0 46	-0 13	-0 34	0.9	0.8	--	--	1.5	007°	--	--	1.6	192°
2827	Johns Island Bridge	14	32° 45.2'	80° 00.0'	+0 40	-1 00	-0 46	+0 10	0.9	0.5	--	--	1.6	358°	--	--	1.9	182°
2829	Elliott Cut, west end		32° 46.0'	80° 00.0'	+0 10	+1 48	+0 29	+0 18	0.9	1.0	--	--	0.6	260°	--	--	0.8	080°
2831	Johns Island	12	32° 47.2'	80° 06.4'	-0 24	0 34		-0 32	0.3	0.4	--	--	0.4	249°	--	--	0.7	068°
2833	Pleasant Point	12	32° 45.0'	80° 08.0'	+2 04	+1 39	+3 54	+3 37	0.4	0.4	--	--	0.7	008°	--	--	0.7	196°
						+5 05					--	--	0.2	006°	--	--		
											--	--	0.7	011°	--	--		
	SOUTH CAROLINA COAST—cont.																	
2835	Folly Island, 3.5 miles east of		32° 38.4'	79° 50.5'	Current weak and variable													
2837	Folly Island, 2.0 miles east of		32° 39.4'	79° 52.1'	See table 5.													
2839	Deveaux Banks, off North Edisto River entrance	12	32° 32.7'	80° 09.4'	-0 16	-0 01	-0 04	-0 26	0.8	1.0	0.1	042°	1.4	306°	0.1	072°	2.0	126°
2841	North Edisto River entrance		32° 33.7'	80° 11.2'	+0 56	+1 10	+1 11	+0 43	1.7	1.9	--	--	2.9	332°	--	--	3.7	142°
2843	Wadmalaw Island, Wadmalaw River entrance	12	32° 39.9'	80° 14.1'	-1 02	+0 11	+0 06	-1 29	0.7	0.4	--	--	1.1	355°	--	--	0.7	165°
2845	Goshen Point, SE of, Wadmalaw River	12	32° 42.6'	80° 10.3'	+0 51	+2 18	+1 47	+1 48	0.5	0.5	--	--	0.6	059°	--	--	0.7	249°
2847	Goshen Point, south of, Wadmalaw River	12	32° 42.8'	80° 11.2'	+1 24	+2 03	+1 35	+1 53	0.4	0.5	--	--	0.6	048°	--	--	1.0	235°
2849	White Point, south of, Dawho River	12	32° 37.5'	80° 16.9'	+1 36	+0 02	+0 29	+1 37	0.5	0.3	--	--	0.8	234°	--	--	0.8	044°
2851	Whooping Island, Dawho River		32° 38.2'	80° 20.4'	+0 19	+0 36	-0 09	+0 24	1.1	1.1	--	--	1.8	246°	--	--	0.6	070°
2853	South Edisto River entrance		32° 29.3'	80° 20.9'	+0 00	-0 14	+0 12	+0 37	0.7	0.5	--	--	1.2	350°	--	--	2.2	146°
2855	Pine Island, South Edisto River	15	32° 30.4'	80° 21.7'	-2 43	-0 09	-3 20	-1 26	0.7	0.4	--	--	1.2	345°	--	--	1.0	163°
2857	Fenwick Island Cut, South Edisto River	15	32° 32.1'	80° 24.8'	+0 59	-0 55	+0 59	+0 52	0.4	0.8	--	--	0.8	220°	--	--	0.8	023°
2859	Sampson Island, S end, South Edisto River	15	32° 33.8'	80° 23.5'	+1 35	0 34	+1 02	+0 52	0.8	0.8	--	--	1.4	037°	--	--	1.5	244°
2861	Sampson Island, NE end, South Edisto River	15	32° 37.0'	80° 23.2'	+1 44	+1 15	+0 53	+0 05	0.7	0.7	--	--	1.2	334°	0.1	352°	1.4	156°
2863	Jehossee Island, S tip, South Edisto River	15	32° 36.2'	80° 25.2'	+2 26	+0 48	+1 01	+2 25	0.7	0.7	--	--	1.2	275°	--	--	1.4	069°
2865	Smuggedy Swamp, South Edisto River	6	32° 39.6'	80° 24.7'	+1 21	+1 14	+0 54	+0 56	0.6	0.7	--	--	1.1	349°	--	--	1.3	166°
2867	Hutchinson Island, Ashepoo River	6	32° 31.9'	80° 26.1'	+1 22	+0 36	+0 56	+1 12	0.5	0.6	0.1	349°	0.8	278°	--	--	1.2	068°
2869	Ashepoo Coosaw Cutoff	6	32° 31.5'	80° 27.2'	+1 05	-0 33	+0 17	-0 35	0.6	0.6	--	--	1.1	065°	--	--	1.6	265°
2871	Pelican Bank, St. Helena Sound	15	32° 27.3'	80° 25.7'	+1 04	+0 46	+1 00	+1 00	0.9	0.8	--	--	1.5	300°	--	--	1.5	118°
2873	Ashepoo River, off Jefford Creek entrance		32° 30.4'	80° 24.6'	+1 00	+1 04	+1 00	+0 43	0.9	0.8	--	--	1.5	016°	--	--	1.6	197°
2875	Egg Bank, St. Helena Sound	10	32° 26.1'	80° 26.6'	-0 12	-1 24	-0 06	-0 20	0.8	0.8	--	--	1.3	329°	0.1	053°	1.5	128°

Endnotes can be found at the end of table 2.

TABLE 2. – CURRENT DIFFERENCES AND OTHER CONSTANTS

No.	PLACE	POSITION Latitude North	POSITION Longitude West	Meter Depth (ft)	TIME DIFFERENCES Min. before Flood (h m)	Flood (h m)	Min. before Ebb (h m)	Ebb (h m)	SPEED RATIOS Flood	Ebb	AVG SPEEDS Min. before Flood (knots)	Dir.	Maximum Flood (knots)	Dir.	Minimum before Ebb (knots)	Dir.	Maximum Ebb (knots)	Dir.
	SOUTH CAROLINA COAST—cont. Time meridian, 75°W					*on Charleston Harbor, p.112*												
2877	Morgan Island, NE of, Coosaw River	32° 29.3'	80° 28.4'	15	+0 28	+0 27	+0 36	+0 19	0.8	1.0	—	—	1.4	303°	0.1	205°	1.8	125°
2879	Ashe Island Cut, SW of, Coosaw River	32° 30.6'	80° 30.3'	15	+0 32	-0 09	+0 43	+0 31	0.6	0.6	—	—	1.0	325°	—	—	1.2	134°
2881	Ashe Island Cut, St. Helena Sound	32° 31.2'	80° 29.3'	6	+0 31	+1 41	+1 01	-0 13	0.5	0.4	—	—	0.8	232°	—	—	0.8	034°
2883	Combahee River	32° 31.6'	80° 32.2'	8	+0 55	+0 59	+1 04	+0 53	0.6	0.8	—	—	1.0	335°	—	—	1.5	147°
2885	Combahee River	32° 33.0'	80° 33.8'	15	+1 36	+1 35	+1 33	+1 03	0.8	1.0	—	—	1.3	280°	—	—	2.0	073°
2887	Parrot Creek, Coosaw Island	32° 28.4'	80° 32.7'	15	+0 12	-0 48	+0 24	-0 54	0.7	0.6	—	—	1.2	355°	—	—	1.1	175°
2889	Morgan Island, North end, Coosaw River	32° 30.2'	80° 32.2'	15	+0 34	+0 41	+0 27	-0 30	0.8	0.9	—	—	1.4	271°	—	—	1.7	085°
2891	Williman Creek	32° 33.7'	80° 35.5'	10	+0 40	+1 27	+1 02	+0 04	0.6	0.8	—	—	1.1	343°	—	—	1.6	160°
2893	Coosaw Island, South of, Morgan River	32° 27.1'	80° 35.0'	10	+0 09	+0 55	+0 15	-0 03	0.7	0.7	—	—	1.2	252°	—	—	1.4	058°
2895	Sams Point, Northwest of, Coosaw River	32° 29.6'	80° 35.0'	10	+0 34	+0 36	+0 31	+0 24	0.5	0.6	—	—	0.8	292°	—	—	1.1	117°
2897	Whale Branch River	32° 31.6'	80° 41.5'	10	+1 12	-0 09	+0 51	-0 09	0.5	0.7	—	—	0.8	295°	—	—	1.3	111°
2899	Fripps Inlet, Fripps Island	32° 20.4'	80° 27.9'	15	-0 29	+1 12	-0 22	-1 29	0.7	0.6	—	—	1.2	299°	—	—	1.2	104°
2901	Martins Industry, 5 miles east of	32° 06'	80° 28'				See table 5.											
	PORT ROYAL SOUND																	
2903	Southeast Channel entrance	32° 08'	80° 35'	15	-0 30	-0 38	-0 09	-0 12	0.8	0.8	—	—	1.3	310°	0.2	071°	1.6	150°
2905	Port Royal Plantation Tower, east of	32° 13.4'	80° 39.4'	15	+0 33	-0 16	+0 19	+0 16	0.9	1.0	—	—	1.5	347°	—	—	1.9	147°
2907	Bay Point Island, S of, Broad River entrance	32° 14.0'	80° 37.8'	15	+0 39	-1 09	+0 06	+0 46	0.7	0.9	0.1	238°	1.2	320°	—	—	1.7	128°
2909	Broad River Entrance, Point Royal Sound	32° 13.9'	80° 38.4'	15	+0 36	+0 21	+0 32	-0 25	1.0	0.9	0.1	234°	1.7	324°	0.2	041°	1.7	138°
2911	Hilton Head	32° 15'	80° 40'	15	+0 16	+0 49	+0 32	+0 01	1.1	0.9	—	—	1.8	324°	—	—	1.8	146°
2913	Beaufort River Entrance	32° 17.3'	80° 39.1'	10	+0 19	+1 11	+0 20	-0 03	0.7	0.7	—	—	1.3	010°	—	—	1.4	195°
2915	Parris Island, Beaufort River	32° 19.6'	80° 39.4'	15	+0 29	+1 12	+0 11	+0 00	0.7	0.8	—	—	1.2	356°	—	—	1.5	175°
2917	Chowan Creek	32° 22.2'	80° 38.3'	15	+0 24	+1 53	+0 23	-0 34	0.6	0.6	—	—	0.9	039°	—	—	1.1	246°
2919	Parris Island, Beaufort River	32° 21.6'	80° 40.5'	15	+0 56	+1 19	+0 51	-0 22	0.7	0.7	—	—	1.2	341°	—	—	1.4	149°
2921	Beaufort River	32° 24.2'	80° 40.3'	12	+1 04	+1 19	+1 01	+0 33	0.5	0.5	0.1	286°	0.9	012°	—	—	1.0	200°
2923	Beaufort, Beaufort River	32° 25.8'	80° 40.6'	15	+0 55	+1 18	+1 21	+0 17	0.7	0.6	—	—	1.1	073°	—	—	1.1	257°
2925	Beaufort Airport, Beaufort River	32° 27.0'	80° 39.8'	15	+1 25	+1 39	+2 50	+1 08	0.5	0.4	—	—	0.9	333°	—	—	0.9	152°
2927	Brickyard Creek	32° 28.4'	80° 41.5'	10	+1 48	+0 30	-1 58	+2 58	0.5	0.6	—	—	0.8	351°	—	—	0.8	171°
2929	Skull Creek, north entrance	32° 15.8'	80° 44.5'	15	-1 50	-1 20	-1 58	-2 14	0.4	0.8	—	—	0.7	222°	—	—	1.2	035°
2931	Daws Island, SE of, Broad River	32° 18.1'	80° 43.5'	15	+0 46	+0 05	+0 29	+0 31	0.8	0.7	—	—	1.4	330°	0.1	048°	1.5	150°
2933	Parris Island Lookout Tower, Broad River	32° 18.7'	80° 42.4'	10	+0 39	-0 07	+0 34	+0 16	0.7	0.7	—	—	1.1	339°	—	—	1.4	152°
2935	Daws Island, south of, Chechessee River	32° 17.2'	80° 44.6'	15	+0 31	-0 22	+0 39	-0 02	0.6	0.7	0.1	232°	1.0	317°	0.1	048°	1.3	142°
2937	Lemon Island South, Chechessee River	32° 21.0'	80° 48.4'	12	+0 33	+1 19	+0 49	+0 31	0.6	0.7	—	—	0.9	359°	—	—	1.3	175°
2939	Broad River Bridge, S of, Broad River	32° 22.9'	80° 46.6'	15	+0 52	-0 15	+1 32	+0 07	0.6	0.8	—	—	1.1	341°	—	—	1.5	156°
2941	Byrd Creek Entrance, SE of, Broad River	32° 27.4'	80° 49.1'	12	+1 27	+0 51	+1 54	+0 52	0.6	0.5	—	—	0.9	354°	—	—	1.5	174°
2943	Little Barnwell I., E of, Whale Branch River	32° 30.1'	80° 47.2'	6	+1 41	+3 03		+0 40	0.6	0.4	—	—	1.0	354°	—	—	0.8	175°
	CALIBOGUE SOUND					*on Savannah River Entrance, p.116*												
2945	Braddock Point, SW of, Calibogue Sound	32° 06.3'	80° 50.2'	10	-0 15	+0 16	-0 04	-1 04	0.8	1.0	—	—	1.6	006°	0.1	095°	2.0	183°
2947	Haig Point Light, NW of, Cooper River	32° 08.9'	80° 50.5'	10	-0 51	-0 05	-0 40	-1 22	0.4	0.7	—	—	0.8	278°	—	—	1.4	094°
2949	Ramshorn Creek Light, E of, Cooper River	32° 07.8'	80° 52.9'	6	+0 06	-0 53	+0 15	-1 17	0.5	0.7	—	—	1.0	280°	—	—	1.3	098°
2951	Spanish Wells, Calibogue Sound	32° 11.2'	80° 47.1'	30	-0 14	+2 57	+1 23	-1 10	0.7	0.7	—	—	1.4	028°	—	—	1.5	204°
2953	Skull Creek, south entrance	32° 13.4'	80° 47.1'	10	+0 38	+1 23	+1 12	+0 55	0.4	0.4	—	—	0.7	053°	0.1	309°	0.9	231°
2955	MacKay Creek, south entrance	32° 13.2'	80° 47.4'	10	+0 06	+0 03	+0 12	-0 26	0.3	0.6	—	—	0.7	033°	—	—	1.2	212°
	NEW and WRIGHT RIVERS																	
2957	Bloody Pt., 0.5 mile north of, New River	32° 05.3'	80° 52.8'		-1 03	+0 00	-0 53	-2 13	0.6	0.6	—	—	1.2	332°	—	—	1.3	147°
2959	Bloody Pt., 0.5 mile west of, New River	32° 04.9'	80° 53.0'		-0 47	-0 21	-0 36	-1 26	0.9	0.9	—	—	1.7	267°	—	—	1.8	092°
2961	Wright R., 0.2 mile above Walls Cut	32° 05.1'	80° 55.3'		-0 38	-0 16	-0 38	-1 16	0.6	0.8	—	—	1.2	332°	—	—	1.6	142°
2963	Fields Cut <32>	32° 05'	80° 57'				-2 00	-1 51	—	0.9	—	—	—	—	—	—	1.9	042°
2965	Walls Cut, Turtle Island	32° 04.9'	80° 55.0'	6	-2 29	-0 57	-1 12	-3 05	0.5	0.5	0.2	087°	1.0	294°	0.1	060°	0.9	100°
2967	Daufuskie Landing Light, south of	32° 06.1'	80° 53.9'	10	+0 07	+1 04	+0 02	-1 45	0.7	0.8	—	—	1.5	043°	—	—	1.7	226°

Endnotes can be found at the end of table 2.

TABLE 2. – CURRENT DIFFERENCES AND OTHER CONSTANTS

No.	PLACE	Meter Depth (ft)	Lat. North	Long. West	TIME DIFF. Min. before Flood	TIME DIFF. Flood	TIME DIFF. Min. before Ebb	TIME DIFF. Ebb	SPEED RATIO Flood	SPEED RATIO Ebb	Min. before Flood (kn)	Dir.	Max. Flood (kn)	Dir.	Min. before Ebb (kn)	Dir.	Max. Ebb (kn)	Dir.
	SAVANNAH RIVER — Time meridian, 75°W																	
2969	Savannah Light, 1.2 miles southeast of		31° 57'	80° 40'							––	––	––	––	––	––	2.0	110°
2971	SAVANNAH RIVER ENT. (between jetties)	11	32° 02.14'	80° 53.42'	See table 5. Daily predictions on Savannah River Entrance, p.116						––	––	––	––	––	––	3.1	098°
2973	Fort Pulaski		32° 02.2'	80° 54.1'	+0 42	+0 51	+0 15	+0 09	0.9	1.5	––	––	2.0	286°	––	––	2.8	140°
2975	Fort Pulaski, 1.8 miles above		32° 02.7'	80° 55.9'	+0 25	+0 18	–0 01	+0 12	1.1	1.4	––	––	1.8	283°	––	––	3.0	116°
2977	Fort Pulaski, 4.8 miles above		32° 04.5'	80° 58.6'	+0 36	+0 31	+0 06	–0 16	1.1	1.5	––	––	2.2	316°	––	––	1.2	069°
2979	McQueen Island Cut	10	32° 03.9'	80° 59.2'	–2 39	–2 45	–1 04	–2 44	0.3	0.6	––	––	2.1	296°	––	––	2.6	104°
2981	Elba Island Cut, NE of, Savannah River	10	32° 04.4'	80° 57.9'	+0 26	+0 15	–0 37	–0 14	0.7	1.3	0.1	202°	0.7	251°	0.1	183°	2.5	149°
2983	Elba Island, NE of, Savannah River	10	32° 05.4'	80° 59.6'	+1 01	+0 40	–0 35	–0 27	0.6	1.2	––	––	1.4	288°	––	––	1.6	040°
2985	Elba Island, west of, Savannah River		32° 05.7'	81° 01.2'	+0 37	+0 52	–0 30	–0 53	0.5	0.8	––	––	1.1	329°	––	––	1.5	094°
2987	Fig Island, north of, Back River		32° 05.1'	81° 01.0'	+0 14	+0 18	–0 25	–1 00	0.5	0.7	––	––	0.9	219°	––	––	1.5	122°
2989	South Channel, western end		32° 05.3'	81° 00.1'	+0 42	–0 36	–0 33	–0 35	0.5	0.7	––	––	1.0	280°	––	––	1.6	206°
2991	Wilmington R. ent., south channel	10	32° 04.6'	81° 05.8'	+0 42	+0 41	+1 28	+1 05	0.6	1.3	––	––	1.0	300°	––	––	2.6	146°
2993	Savannah, southeast of highway bridge		32° 05.2'	81° 05'	+1 36	+0 45	–0 24	+0 18	0.8	1.1	––	––	1.0	032°	––	––	2.2	106°
2995	Savannah		32° 05'	81° 08.2'	+1 12	+0 45	+0 01	–0 21	0.8	1.7	––	––	1.1	319°	––	––	2.1	152°
2997	Kings Island Channel, Savannah River <58>	10	32° 07.6'	81° 07.1'	+1 21	+0 54	+0 06	+0 59	1.2	1.7	––	––	1.6	279°	––	––	1.5	150°
2999	Seaboard Coast Line Railroad		32° 06.2'	81° 08.1'	+1 06	+1 36	+0 29	+0 48	0.7	1.0	––	––	1.5	339°	––	––	3.5	160°
3001	King Island, west of		32° 07.4'	81° 08.4'	+1 21	+2 00	+0 33	+1 19	0.5	0.7	––	––	2.4	320°	––	––	2.0	210°
3003	Port Wentworth, 0.2 mile above		32° 08.8'	81° 08.7'	+2 00	+1 36	+0 24		––	––	––	––	1.4	337°	––	––	1.5	––
3005	Seaboard Coast Line Railroad		32° 13.9'						––	––	––	––	0.9	022°	––	––	1.9	––
3007	Wassaw Island, N of E end, Wassaw Sound	10	31° 54.9'	80° 56.3'	–0 48	–0 50	–0 45	–1 33	0.7	1.0	0.1	015°	1.4	292°	––	––	2.1	108°
	WASSAW SOUND																	
3009	Entrance, off Beach Hammock	10	31° 56.5'	80° 55.9'	–0 41	–1 00	–0 54	–1 44	0.9	1.1	––	––	1.7	352°	––	––	2.2	156°
3011	Wilmington Island, SSE of, Bull River	10	31° 58.0'	80° 55.8'	–0 35	+0 38	–0 40	–2 00	0.4	0.7	––	––	0.7	035°	––	––	1.5	218°
3013	Lazaretto Creek Entrance, N of, Bull River		32° 00.0'	80° 55.7'	–0 37	+0 00	–0 33	–2 04	0.5	0.7	––	––	1.0	015°	––	––	1.4	207°
3015	Bull River, 2 miles below hwy. bridge		32° 01.1'	80° 56.4'	–0 18	–0 18	–0 25	–1 57	0.6	0.8	––	––	1.4	327°	––	––	1.6	151°
3017	Entrance, off Wassaw Island	10	31° 55.0'	80° 56.8'	–0 46	–1 11	–0 42	–1 27	0.7	0.9	––	––	1.2	277°	––	––	1.7	105°
3019	Wilmington River ent. off Cabbage Island		31° 56.3'	80° 58.6'	–0 44	–0 36	–0 45	–1 51	0.6	0.8	0.1	208°	1.2	323°	––	––	2.1	138°
3021	Joe's Cut, Wilmington River		31° 56.6'	80° 59.1'	–0 54	–0 48	–0 34	–1 44	0.6	1.0	––	––	1.2	315°	––	––	1.4	123°
3023	Wilmington R., 0.5 mi. S of Turners Creek	10	32° 00.3'	81° 00.2'	–0 31	–0 10	–0 37	–1 51	0.5	0.7	––	––	0.8	344°	––	––	1.0	154°
3025	Thunderbolt, SE of, Wilmington River	10	32° 01.4'	81° 00.2'	–0 20	–1 04	+0 12	+0 25	0.4	0.5	––	––	0.8	298°	––	––	1.0	121°
3027	Oatland Island, north tip		32° 04.4'	81° 00.6'	–3 20	–2 14	–0 43	–2 32	0.3	0.5	––	––	0.6	317°	––	––	1.4	138°
3029	Skidaway River, north entrance	10	32° 00.5'	81° 00.5'	–0 46	–0 02	–0 49	–2 11	0.6	0.7	––	––	0.6	204°	––	––	1.9	016°
3031	Skidaway Island, N End, Wilmington River	10	32° 00.6'	81° 01.2'	–0 33	+0 16	–0 23	–1 49	0.6	0.9	0.1	225°	1.1	307°	––	––	1.2	119°
3033	Dutch Island, SE of, Skidaway River	10	31° 59.5'	81° 01.2'	–0 40	+0 16	–0 33	–2 02	0.5	0.6	––	––	0.5	245°	––	––	0.5	061°
3035	Isle of Hope City, SE of, Skidaway River	10	31° 58.6'	81° 02.8'	–0 17	–0 30	–0 32	–1 25	0.2	0.3	––	––	0.8	268°	––	––	0.6	072°
3037	Isle of Hope City, Skidaway River	6	31° 58.8'	81° 03.3'	–0 34	+0 00	–0 19	–1 03	0.4	0.3	––	––	0.8	212°	––	––	1.0	028°
3039	Burntpot Island, west of, Skidaway River		31° 58.1'	81° 03.2'	–0 27	–0 41	–0 13	–0 24	0.5	0.5	––	––	1.0	194°	––	––	1.1	018°
3041	Skidaway Narrows	6	31° 57.4'	81° 03.6'	+0 03	–0 24	+0 26	+0 17	0.5	0.4	––	––	0.9	218°	––	––	0.8	042°
3043	Long Island, NNE of, Skidaway River		31° 56.6'	81° 03.6'	–0 13	–1 09	+1 02	–8 05	0.4	0.4	––	––	0.8	226°	––	––	0.5	047°
3045	Long Island, south of, Skidaway River	10	31° 56.2'	81° 04.6'	–4 25	–4 43	–6 07	–2 16	0.2	0.3	––	––	0.5	075°	––	––	1.0	258°
3047	Pigeon Island, SSE of, Skidaway River	10	31° 55.3'	81° 04.8'	–2 37	–2 43	–0 56	–2 05	0.2	0.5	––	––	0.4	331°	––	––	1.5	150°
3049	Burnside Island, SE of, Burnside River	10	31° 52.2'	81° 04.4'	–0 40	+0 53	–0 20	–1 38	0.4	0.6	––	––	1.4	114°	0.1	234°	2.1	295°
3051	Little Don Island, east of, Vernon River	10	31° 53.3'	81° 05.9'	–0 17	–1 16	–0 03	–1 06	0.7	0.7	0.2	232°	1.3	316°	0.1	179°	1.1	153°
3053	Little Ogeechee River Entrance	20	31° 53.3'	81° 05.9'	–0 15	–0 59	–0 03	–0 57	0.7	1.0	––	––	1.3	259°	––	––	2.1	071°
	...do.	20			–0 30	–0 50	+0 05	–0 30	0.7	0.6	––	––	1.3	244°	––	––	1.1	073°
3055	Montgomery, Vernon River	6	31° 56.1'	81° 07.7'	–0 32	+0 00	–0 24	–1 30	0.3	0.6	––	––	0.6	267°	0.1	127°	1.8	089°
3057	Odingsell River Entrance	10	31° 52.1'	81° 00.0'	–0 54	+0 44	–0 48	–2 14	0.7	0.9	––	––	1.3	032°	––	––	1.6	212°
	...do.	20	31° 52.1'	81° 00.0'	–1 19	+0 42	–0 42	–2 12	0.6	0.8	––	––	1.3	030°	––	––	1.6	210°
	OSSABAW SOUND																	
3059	Wassaw Island, SSW of	10	31° 51.4'	81° 00.5'	–0 26	–1 04	–0 27	–1 01	0.8	1.1	0.1	034°	1.6	316°	––	––	2.3	123°
	...do.	20	31° 51.4'	81° 00.5'	–0 46	–0 58	–0 43	–1 01	0.7	0.9	0.1	209°	1.4	312°	––	––	1.8	132°
3061	Bradley Point, NNE of	10	31° 49.9'	81° 02.3'	–0 48	–0 58	–0 48	–1 12	0.6	0.8	0.1	033°	1.3	302°	0.1	198°	1.7	125°
3063	Raccoon Key	10	31° 51.7'	81° 03.3'	–0 45	–1 23	–0 36	–1 35	0.8	0.9	––	––	1.6	285°	0.1	198°	1.9	117°

Endnotes can be found at the end of table 2.

TABLE 2. – CURRENT DIFFERENCES AND OTHER CONSTANTS

No.	PLACE	Meter Depth (ft)	POSITION Latitude North	POSITION Longitude West	TIME DIFF. Min. before Flood (h m)	TIME DIFF. Flood (h m)	TIME DIFF. Min. before Ebb (h m)	TIME DIFF. Ebb (h m)	SPEED RATIO Flood	SPEED RATIO Ebb	Min. before Flood knots	Min. before Flood Dir.	Maximum Flood knots	Maximum Flood Dir.	Min. before Ebb knots	Min. before Ebb Dir.	Maximum Ebb knots	Maximum Ebb Dir.
	OSSABAW SOUND Time meridian, 75°W				on Savannah River Entrance, p.116													
3065	Little Wassaw Island, SW of	10	31°52.2'	81°03.0'	−1 05	−0 17	−0 21	−1 51	0.9	0.7	0.1	209°	1.7	282°	0.1	193°	1.4	116°
3067	Vernon R., 1.2 miles S of Possum Point		31°53.9'	81°05.9'	−0 24	+0 02	−0 12	−1 33	0.6	0.8	--	--	1.1	324°	--	--	1.7	166°
3069	Little Ogeechee River Entrance, north of		31°53.8'	81°05.7'	−0 41	+0 29	−0 30	−2 03	0.6	0.8	--	--	1.2	324°	0.1	239°	1.6	156°
3071	Raccoon Key & Egg Island Shoal, between	10d	31°50.57'	81°04.05'	+0 20	+0 17	−0 23	−0 57	0.8	1.0	0.2	274°	1.6	254°	0.2	197°	2.0	129°
3073	Florida Passage, N of, Ogeechee River	10	31°51.4'	81°08.6'	+0 10	+0 01	−0 01	−0 05	0.7	1.0	--	--	1.4	302°	--	--	2.1	127°
3075	Florida Passage (south)	6d	31°49.78'	81°09.47'	−1 48	−1 13	−0 23	−1 10	0.5	0.7	--	--	0.9	187°	0.3	191°	1.4	018°
	ST. CATHERINES SOUND																	
	Bear River																	
3077	610 Statute Mile Mark	6d	31°48.63'	81°10.60'	+0 20	+0 48	−0 05	−0 39	0.5	0.7	0.2	338°	1.0	357°	0.2	280°	1.5	175°
3079	North of Big Tom Creek Entrance	10d	31°47.00'	81°09.62'	−0 24	−0 13	−0 19	−1 25	0.6	0.7	--	--	1.2	011°	--	--	1.5	179°
3081	South of Kilkenny Creek Entrance		31°45.50'	81°10.40'	+0 26	+1 25	−0 02	−1 12	0.6	1.0	--	--	1.2	348°	--	--	2.0	190°
3083	Northwest of Newell Creek Entrance	10d	31°44.93'	81°09.93'	−0 11	+0 12	−0 16	−1 12	0.3	0.9	0.1	086°	1.1	349°	0.1	076°	1.8	149°
3085	Medway River at Marsh Island	10d	31°44.60'	81°13.20'	−0 39	−0 18	−0 15	−0 56	0.9	0.8	0.3	306°	0.6	313°	0.3	209°	1.6	117°
3087	St. Catherines Sound Entrance	10d	31°42.90'	81°08.43'	−0 40	−0 31	−0 13	−1 27	0.7	0.8	0.1	020°	1.8	291°	0.2	173°	1.7	126°
3089	Medway River, northwest of Cedar Point	10d	31°42.87'	81°11.45'	−0 34	−0 43	−0 23	−1 21	0.7	0.8	0.5	139°	1.5	304°	0.4	324°	1.7	146°
3091	N. Newport River, NE of Vandyke Creek	10d	31°41.47'	81°11.22'	−0 27	+0 12	+0 00	−1 21	0.6	0.8	0.2	011°	1.3	233°	--	--	1.7	045°
3093	N. Newport River, above Walburg Creek	6d	31°40.43'	81°11.72'	−0 34	+0 30	−0 39	−0 40	0.5	0.9	0.1	308°	1.0	195°	--	--	1.6	011°
3095	N. Newport River, NW of Johnson Creek	10d	31°39.78'	81°12.63'	−0 20	−1 01	−0 37	−0 27	0.5	0.7	0.1	210°	0.9	312°	--	--	1.8	138°
3097	N. Newport River, ESE of S. Newport Cut	6d	31°39.92'	81°15.87'	+0 32	−0 13	+0 27	+0 15	0.5	0.5	--	--	1.0	319°	--	--	1.4	147°
3099	S. Newport River, below S. Newport Cut	10d	31°39.02'	81°18.12'	+1 20	+1 30	+2 41	+2 15	0.5	0.5	0.2	128°	0.9	306°	0.1	042°	1.0	134°
3101	S. Newport River, above Swain River Ent	10d	31°37.47'	81°13.00'	−0 22	−1 13	+0 00	−0 43	0.6	0.6	0.1	156°	1.1	335°	0.1	075°	1.2	156°
	SAPELO SOUND																	
3103	Entrance	19d	31°32.4'	81°10.8'	−0 30	+0 28	−0 06	−0 59	0.9	1.1	0.1	212°	1.7	290°	0.1	194°	2.2	118°
3105	.....do.	29d	31°32.4'	81°10.8'	−0 48	−0 36	−0 17	−1 02	0.7	0.9	--	--	1.3	289°	0.1	189°	1.7	116°
3107	Johnson Creek, midway between ends	12d	31°37.6'	81°11.3'	−1 50	−1 08	−0 35	−1 59	0.4	0.4	--	--	0.8	015°	--	--	0.9	195°
3109	Cedar Hammock, south of	11d	31°32.7'	81°14.8'	−0 26	−1 00	−0 12	−1 38	0.7	0.6	--	--	1.4	277°	--	--	1.2	096°
3111	Sapelo River Entrance		31°32.1'	81°16.3'	−0 23	+0 10	−0 12	−0 43	0.6	0.6	--	--	1.1	234°	--	--	1.3	058°
3113	Sutherland Bluff, Sapelo River	13d	31°32.9'	81°17.9'	−0 33	+1 16	−0 25	−1 16	0.4	0.5	--	--	0.8	227°	--	--	1.0	056°
	Front River																	
3115	New Teakettle Cr., 0.8 mi. N of <35>		31°30.8'	81°17.4'	−0 54	−0 29	−1 08	−2 05	0.4	0.5	--	--	0.8	236°	0.1	203°	1.0	053°
	Mud River																	
3117	Crescent River	11d	31°29.2'	81°18.4'	−1 27	+1 07	−0 34	−2 11	0.2	0.5	--	--	0.5	293°	--	--	1.1	133°
3119	Old Teakettle Creek (north)	13d	31°28.7'	81°19.7'	−0 35	+0 01	+0 14	−1 21	0.5	0.6	--	--	0.9	078°	--	--	1.2	256°
	DOBOY SOUND																	
3121	Bar	14d	31°20.7'	81°14.1'	−0 29	−0 29	−0 09	−0 53	0.7	0.7	--	--	1.3	312°	--	--	1.4	114°
3123	Entrance	22d	31°20.5'	81°15.8'	−0 32	−0 10	−0 24	−1 49	0.8	0.9	--	--	1.6	289°	--	--	1.8	106°
3125	.....do.	15d	31°20.5'	81°15.8'	−0 56	−0 05	−0 20	−1 26	0.8	0.8	--	--	1.6	276°	--	--	1.7	099°
3127	Old Teakettle Creek, south of	13d	31°25.2'	81°18.9'	−0 45	−1 45	−2 16	−2 44	0.5	0.4	--	--	1.1	335°	--	--	1.1	159°
3129	Old Teakettle Creek (south)	10d	31°26.2'	81°18.5'	−3 12	−0 56	−0 16	−1 00	0.3	0.3	--	--	0.9	021°	--	--	0.7	207°
3131	Folly River and Cardigan River, between	13d	31°26.5'	81°20.2'	−0 55	−0 25	−0 32	−0 24	0.6	0.7	--	--	0.7	327°	--	--	0.6	150°
3133	South River	21d	31°22.0'	81°18.7'	−0 22	−0 33	−0 29	−0 24	0.5	0.4	--	--	1.1	282°	--	--	1.3	095°
3135	.....do.	9d	31°23.0'	81°20.1'	−0 41	−0 06	+0 08	+0 22	0.5	0.2	0.1	317°	1.0	286°	--	--	0.8	095°
3137	North River at Darien River	12d	31°23.0'	81°20.1'	−0 10	+0 36	+0 47	+0 13	0.6	0.5	--	--	0.5	247°	--	--	0.4	029°
3139	Doboy Island (North River)	20d	31°24.2'	81°19.7'	−0 14	+0 36	+0 46	+0 22	0.6	0.5	--	--	1.1	224°	--	--	1.1	037°
3141	.....do.	13d	31°24.2'	81°19.7'	−0 20	+0 12	+0 46	+0 22	0.5	0.3	--	--	0.9	225°	--	--	0.6	043°
3137	Buzzard Roost Creek	13d	31°24.9'	81°22.5'	+0 22	+0 12	+0 56	+0 28	0.3	0.2	--	--	0.7	177°	--	--	0.4	002°

Endnotes can be found at the end of table 2.

TABLE 2. – CURRENT DIFFERENCES AND OTHER CONSTANTS

No.	PLACE	Meter Depth (ft)	POSITION Latitude North	POSITION Longitude West	TIME DIFF Min. before Flood (h m)	TIME DIFF Flood (h m)	TIME DIFF Min. before Ebb (h m)	TIME DIFF Ebb (h m)	SPEED RATIOS Flood	SPEED RATIOS Ebb	Min before Flood knots	Min before Flood Dir.	Max Flood knots	Max Flood Dir.	Min before Ebb knots	Min before Ebb Dir.	Max Ebb knots	Max Ebb Dir.
	ALTAMAHA SOUND Time meridian, 75°W				on Savannah River Entrance, p.116													
3139	Little Egg Island, northwest of	12d	31°19.1'	81°18.3'	−0 33	−0 53	−0 25	−1 10	0.6	0.6	--	--	1.1	296°	--	--	1.2	110°
3141	Little Mud River Range	9d	31°19.6'	81°19.1'	−0 38	−1 05	−0 23	−0 06	0.3	0.5	--	--	0.6	304°	--	--	0.9	116°
3143	Little St. Simon Island (north)	11d	31°18.7'	81°21.2'	+0 10	+0 06	−0 15	−1 29	0.6	0.8	--	--	1.2	267°	--	--	1.6	089°
3145	Onemile Cut, 1 mile southeast of		31°18.8'	81°21.1'	+0 46	+0 03	−1 09	−0 32	0.5	0.9	--	--	1.0	272°	--	--	1.9	092°
	Buttermilk Sound																	
3147	Broughton Island (south)	9d	31°18.6'	81°24.8'	−2 06	+0 12	−0 01	−1 51	0.4	0.4	0.1	292°	0.9	222°	--	--	0.8	030°
	ST. SIMONS SOUND																	
3149	Bar Channel	12d	31°06.3'	81°20.3'	−0 13	−0 44	+0 09	−0 02	0.4	0.8	0.1	033°	0.8	308°	--	--	1.7	119°
3151	Entrance, north of channel	13d	31°08.01'	81°24.24'	−0 32	+0 18	+0 07	−1 11	0.9	0.6	--	--	1.7	290°	--	--	1.2	107°
3153	Entrance, south of channel	11d	31°07.6'	81°24.2'	−0 27	−0 03	−0 21	−0 59	0.8	1.1	--	--	1.6	262°	0.1	188°	2.2	080°
	do.	29d	31°07.6'	81°24.2'	−0 18	+0 06	+0 06	−0 21	0.6	0.8	--	--	1.2	257°	--	--	1.7	092°
3155	Back River entrance	10d	31°08.9'	81°26.5'	−0 37	+1 34	+0 08	−1 16	0.5	0.5	--	--	1.0	288°	--	--	1.1	111°
	do.	18d	31°08.9'	81°26.5'	−1 29	+1 36	+0 08	−1 15	0.5	0.4	--	--	0.9	280°	--	--	0.8	109°
3157	Mackay R., 0.5 mi. N of Troup Creek entrance		31°13.5'	81°26.0'	+0 56	+0 09	+0 35	+0 24	0.7	0.7	--	--	0.9	348°	--	--	1.5	166°
3159	Brunswick River, off Quarantine Dock		31°06.7'	81°28.4'	+0 10	−0 03	+0 11	−0 39	0.7	1.0	0.1	223°	1.3	300°	--	--	2.1	125°
3161	Brunswick River Bridge, southeast of	13d	31°06.9'	81°28.6'	−0 15	+0 42	+0 26	−1 09	0.5	0.7	0.1	226°	1.0	308°	--	--	1.4	132°
	do.	21d	31°06.9'	81°28.6'	+0 19	+0 55	+0 56	−0 02	0.5	0.7	--	--	1.0	306°	--	--	1.5	129°
3163	Brunswick, off Prince Street Dock		31°08.3'	81°29.8'	−0 01	+0 18	+0 06	−1 08	0.5	0.6	--	--	1.0	342°	--	--	1.3	166°
3165	Turtle River, off Allied Chemical Corp		31°10.6'	81°31.5'	+0 16	+0 18	+0 36	−0 33	0.7	0.8	--	--	1.3	348°	--	--	1.7	165°
3167	Turtle River, off Andrews Island	20d	31°08.6'	81°31.6'	−0 21	+0 40	+0 31	−0 23	0.5	0.7	--	--	1.1	339°	--	--	1.4	153°
	ST. ANDREWS SOUND																	
3169	Entrance		30°59.2'	81°24.3'	−0 18	+0 13	+0 02	−1 00	1.1	1.1	--	--	2.1	268°	--	--	2.2	103°
3171	Jekyll Creek, south entrance		31°02.1'	81°26.0'	−0 21	−0 21	−0 25	−1 20	0.5	0.7	--	--	1.0	060°	--	--	1.4	232°
3173	Cumberland River, north entrance		30°57.5'	81°25.9'	−0 29	+0 32	−0 17	−1 18	0.7	0.7	--	--	1.3	191°	--	--	1.5	018°
3175	Cabin Bluff, Cumberland River		30°52.9'	81°30.8'	+0 21	+1 29	+0 51	−0 45	0.7	0.6	--	--	1.3	171°	--	--	1.3	355°
	CUMBERLAND SOUND				on St. Marys River Entrance, p.120													
	St. Marys River																	
3177	south jetty	8d	30°42.42'	81°32.92'	−0 18	−1 16	−0 56	−0 27	0.3	0.6	0.5	038°	0.8	341°	0.1	225°	1.6	110°
	do.	18d	30°42.42'	81°32.92'	−0 19	−1 02	−0 54	−0 33	0.3	0.6	0.4	033°	0.7	329°	0.2	226°	1.5	112°
	do.	34d	30°42.42'	81°32.92'	−0 19	−0 55	−0 48	−0 32	0.3	0.5	0.2	024°	0.6	313°	0.2	225°	1.2	114°
3179	ST. MARYS RIVER ENTRANCE	8d	30°42.48'	81°26.68'			**Daily predictions**											
	do.	25d	30°42.48'	81°26.68'	−0 04	+0 00	+0 01	+0 02	0.9	0.9	0.1	183°	2.2	272°	--	--	2.8	093°
	do.	42d	30°42.48'	81°26.68'	−0 08	+0 01	+0 01	+0 02	0.8	0.7	--	--	1.9	271°	--	--	2.5	092°
3181	Fort Clinch, 0.3 n.mi. N of	50d	30°42.36'	81°27.14'	−0 36	−0 14	−0 23	−0 33	0.6	0.6	0.2	002°	1.4	275°	0.1	280°	1.6	087°
3183	Quarantine Reach, 0.4nm W of Fort Clinch	7d	30°42.28'	81°27.72'	−0 05	−0 19	−0 27	+0 00	0.5	0.6	0.1	226°	1.2	235°	0.1	318°	1.7	034°
	do.	27d	30°42.28'	81°27.72'	−0 09	+0 02	−0 18	−0 14	0.5	0.5	0.1	307°	1.1	232°	--	--	1.4	047°
	do.	46d	30°42.28'	81°27.72'	−0 11	+0 13	−0 12	−0 21	0.6	0.4	--	--	1.1	226°	--	--	1.2	065°
3185	Fort Clinch, 1.1 n.mi. NW of	14d	30°42.54'	81°28.36'	−0 01	−0 01	+0 10	+0 18	0.6	0.7	0.1	214°	1.3	309°	0.1	067°	1.9	133°
	do.	29d	30°42.54'	81°28.36'	−0 13	+0 02	+0 02	+0 08	0.5	0.5	0.1	010°	1.3	315°	0.1	032°	1.3	122°
3187	Cumberland Island, Range B Channel	22d	30°43.52'	81°29.04'	−0 18	−0 38	−0 06	+0 06	0.5	0.7	--	--	1.2	350°	--	--	1.8	170°
3189	Drum Point Island, Range D Channel	12d	30°45.54'	81°29.13'	−0 05	−0 11	+0 02	−0 03	0.4	0.6	0.1	165°	0.9	350°	0.1	154°	1.5	170°
	do.	22d	30°45.54'	81°29.12'	−0 10	−0 34	−0 08	−0 09	0.4	0.5	0.2	160°	0.9	351°	0.1	115°	1.3	170°
3191	Kings Bay, Lower Turning Basin	14d	30°47.56'	81°30.48'	−0 03	+0 38	−0 18	−1 04	0.1	0.1	0.1	282°	0.3	307°	0.1	316°	0.3	127°
3193	Stafford Island, west of		30°48.6'	81°29.5'	−0 25	−0 20	−0 27	−1 01	0.6	0.5	--	--	1.5	000°	--	--	1.6	180°
3195	Old Fernandina, Amelia River, Old Town Reach	4d	30°41.16'	81°27.64'	−0 03	+0 03	+0 03	−0 06	0.7	0.6	--	--	1.5	188°	--	--	1.6	018°
	do.	14d	30°41.16'	81°27.64'	−0 06	+0 28	+0 05	−0 03	0.6	0.5	--	--	1.4	189°	--	--	1.4	015°
	do.	24d	30°41.16'	81°27.64'	−0 12	+0 31	+0 06	−0 02	0.5	0.5	--	--	1.2	193°	--	--	1.2	010°
3197	Fernandina Beach, City Front Reach, Amelia River	5d	30°40.21'	81°28.07'	+0 24	−0 11	−0 12	+0 30	0.4	0.4	--	--	0.8	240°	--	--	1.0	068°
	do.	11d	30°40.21'	81°28.07'	+0 28	−0 05	−0 08	+0 33	0.3	0.3	--	--	0.6	239°	--	--	0.9	063°
	do.	29d	30°40.21'	81°28.07'	+0 29	−0 03	−0 07	+0 34	0.3	0.3	--	--	0.6	239°	0.1	146°	0.9	059°
3199	Kingsley Creek, highway bridge		30°37.7'	81°29.1'	+1 45	+1 17	+0 53	+1 25	0.5	0.6	--	--	1.1	150°	--	--	1.6	330°

Endnotes can be found at the end of table 2.

TABLE 2. – CURRENT DIFFERENCES AND OTHER CONSTANTS

No.	PLACE	Meter Depth (ft)	Latitude North	Longitude West	Min. before Flood (h m)	Flood (h m)	Min. before Ebb (h m)	Ebb (h m)	Flood Ratio	Ebb Ratio	Min. before Flood (knots)	Min. before Flood (Dir.)	Max. Flood (knots)	Max. Flood (Dir.)	Min. before Ebb (knots)	Min. before Ebb (Dir.)	Max. Ebb (knots)	Max. Ebb (Dir.)
	NASSAU SOUND — Time meridian, 75°W																	
	on Miami Harbor Entrance, p.140																	
3201	Midsound, 1 mi. N of Sawpit Creek entrance		30°31.4'	81°27.1'	+0 02	-0 12	-0 15	-0 21	0.8	0.7	--	--	1.7	312°	--	--	1.7	135°
3203	South Amelia River, off Walker Creek		30°32.2'	81°27.9'	-1 08	-0 09	-0 40	-1 57	0.6	0.6	--	--	1.4	341°	--	--	1.4	162°
3205	Nassau River, SW of Mesa Marsh		30°32.0'	81°28.8'	-1 08	-0 09	-0 01	-0 13	0.7	0.7	--	--	1.5	294°	--	--	1.7	129°
3207	Ft. George River		30°27.4'	81°27.1'	-1 35	-1 08	-1 26	-2 20	0.1	0.4	--	--	0.3	334°	--	--	0.9	162°
	ST. JOHNS RIVER																	
	on St. Johns River Entrance, p.124																	
3209	St. Johns Point, 5 miles east of	5d	30°23.5'	81°18.0'	*Current weak and variable*													
3211	St. Johns Bar Cut, 0.7 n.mi. east of jetties <64>	14d	30°23.88'	81°21.83'	+0 33	-1 19	-0 41	+1 04	0.3	0.8	0.5	021°	0.6	356°	0.2	045°	1.6	091°
3213	St. Johns Bar Cut 0.13 n.mi. ENE of south jetty	14d	30°23.88'	81°21.83'	-1 19	-2 43	-0 13	+0 13	0.3	0.6	0.6	040°	0.7	007°	--	--	1.2	095°
	...do.	31d	30°23.85'	81°22.45'	-2 20	-2 04	-1 17	-0 54	0.2	0.3	0.3	038°	0.4	318°	0.2	227°	0.6	122°
	...do.	33d	30°23.85'	81°22.45'	+0 11	+0 02	+0 10	+1 35	0.4	1.1	0.2	011°	0.9	317°	0.2	173°	2.2	094°
	...do.	46d	30°23.85'	81°22.45'	-1 03	+0 04	+0 21	-0 11	0.5	0.7	0.2	178°	1.0	298°	0.2	158°	1.4	095°
3215	ST. JOHNS RIVER ENT. (between jetties)	16d	30°24.02'	81°23.15'	-2 05	-0 03	+0 22	-0 25	0.5	0.5	0.2	176°	1.1	275°	0.1	144°	1.0	100°
	...do.	10d	30°24.02'	81°23.15'	+0 06	+0 13	-0 04	+0 07	1.0	1.2	--	--	2.0	262°	--	--	2.0	081°
	...do.	30d	30°24.02'	81°23.15'	-0 19	+0 01	-0 02	+0 07	0.9	0.9	--	--	1.9	262°	--	--	2.1	081°
3217	Mayport Basin Entrance	9d	30°23.82'	81°23.93'	-0 02	-0 08	+0 11	+0 33	0.6	0.7	--	--	1.2	255°	--	--	1.9	080°
	...do.	15d	30°23.82'	81°23.93'	-0 12	+0 17	+0 17	+0 07	0.7	0.6	0.1	179°	1.3	251°	0.1	166°	1.4	093°
	...do.	32d	30°23.82'	81°23.93'	+0 24	+0 48	+0 34	+0 34	0.7	0.3	--	--	1.3	247°	0.1	164°	1.2	087°
3219	Mayport	7d	30°23.6'	81°26.0'	-0 06	+1 02	-0 04	-0 04	1.1	1.6	0.1	333°	2.2	211°	--	--	0.6	069°
	...do.	17d	30°23.6'	81°26.0'	-0 03	+0 38	+0 15	+0 05	1.1	1.3	--	--	2.7	211°	--	--	3.3	026°
	...do.	27d	30°23.6'	81°26.0'	-0 27	+0 26	+0 12	+0 14	0.9	0.9	--	--	1.7	211°	--	--	1.8	026°
3221	Mile Point, southeast of	7d	30°22.9'	81°26.7'	+0 06	+0 38	+0 48	+0 44	1.5	1.6	--	--	3.0	241°	--	--	2.6	026°
	...do.	18d	30°22.9'	81°26.7'	-0 12	+0 38	+0 54	+0 56	1.2	1.2	--	--	2.5	241°	--	--	3.2	073°
	...do.	29d	30°22.9'	81°26.7'	-0 42	+1 00	+1 00	+0 38	1.1	0.9	--	--	2.3	241°	--	--	2.5	073°
3223	ICW Intersection	10d	30°23.02'	81°27.52'	+0 27	+0 29	+0 08	+0 58	0.8	1.3	0.2	217°	1.6	293°	0.4	003°	1.8	073°
	...do.	16d	30°23.02'	81°27.52'	-0 22	+0 31	+0 10	+0 49	0.8	1.2	0.2	213°	1.6	293°	0.3	007°	2.6	125°
	...do.	29d	30°23.02'	81°27.52'	+0 09	+0 35	+0 49	+0 21	0.8	1.0	0.1	200°	1.5	294°	0.2	020°	2.4	113°
3225	Pablo Creek bascule bridge <33>	3	30°19.4'	81°26.3'	-0 14	-0 18	-0 49	+0 59	1.7	2.5	--	--	3.4	180°	--	--	2.1	099°
3227	Sisters Creek entrance (bridge)	4d	30°23.4'	81°27.7'	-3 30	-3 14	-2 13	-2 34	0.6	0.6	--	--	1.6	000°	--	--	5.2	000°
	...do.	10d	30°23.4'	81°27.7'	-3 36	-3 04	-2 07	-2 34	0.9	1.2	--	--	1.6	000°	--	--	1.6	180°
3229	St. Johns Bluff	7d	30°23.4'	81°29.5'	+0 30	+1 21	-0 18	+1 02	0.8	1.0	--	--	1.7	244°	--	--	1.2	180°
	...do.	17d	30°23.4'	81°29.5'	+0 18	+1 03	+0 30	+1 02	0.9	0.8	--	--	1.6	244°	--	--	2.4	059°
	...do.	26d	30°23.4'	81°29.5'	-0 12	+0 33	+0 24	+1 14	0.8	0.8	--	--	1.6	244°	--	--	2.0	059°
3231	Blount Island, East of	16d	30°23.52'	81°30.51'	+1 21	+1 08	+0 49	+1 54	0.7	1.1	0.2	000°	1.5	275°	0.2	183°	1.6	059°
	...do.	30d	30°23.52'	81°30.51'	+0 54	+0 58	+1 04	+1 43	0.7	0.8	0.2	011°	1.4	270°	0.1	168°	2.3	079°
	...do.	5d	30°23.52'	81°30.51'	+0 33	+1 08	+1 12	+1 32	0.5	0.6	0.2	183°	1.1	264°	--	--	1.7	090°
3233	Dames Point, 0.23 n.mi. ESE of	14d	30°23.19'	81°33.23'	+1 58	+1 51	+1 40	+1 59	0.5	0.9	0.2	351°	1.0	244°	0.4	136°	1.3	099°
	...do.	31d	30°23.19'	81°33.23'	+1 26	+0 54	+1 19	+1 57	0.6	0.9	0.1	343°	1.1	256°	0.2	158°	1.7	066°
	...do.	5d	30°23.19'	81°33.23'	+0 33	+2 24	+2 04	+1 58	0.6	0.4	--	--	1.1	270°	0.1	000°	1.9	068°
3235	Dames Point, 0.25 n.mi. SE of	14d	30°23.08'	81°33.28'	+1 52	+1 39	+1 28	+2 14	0.6	0.9	--	--	1.2	254°	--	--	0.7	069°
	...do.	28d	30°23.08'	81°33.28'	+1 39	+1 29	+1 32	+2 07	0.6	0.9	0.1	345°	1.4	257°	0.2	155°	0.9	080°
	...do.	7d	30°23.08'	81°33.28'	+1 30	+2 00	+2 01	+2 14	0.7	0.7	0.1	343°	1.2	254°	--	--	1.8	073°
3237	Drummond Point, channel south of	7d	30°24.55'	81°36.17'	+1 15	+3 16	+2 44	+3 00	0.7	0.8	0.1	160°	1.4	241°	--	--	1.4	073°
	...do.	17d	30°24.55'	81°36.17'	+1 51	+3 06	+2 51	+3 01	0.6	0.7	--	--	1.3	222°	--	--	1.7	060°
	...do.	27d	30°24.55'	81°36.17'	+1 21	+3 28	+2 46	+2 51	0.6	0.5	--	--	1.2	243°	--	--	1.4	061°
3239	Trout River Cut	6d	30°23.03'	81°37.69'	+2 31	+3 28	+2 32	+2 52	0.6	0.5	--	--	1.3	193°	--	--	1.5	057°
	...do.	15d	30°23.03'	81°37.69'	+2 19	+3 13	+2 42	+2 58	0.6	0.6	0.1	277°	1.1	191°	0.1	280°	1.3	005°
	...do.	32d	30°23.03'	81°37.69'	+1 49	+2 30	+2 51	+2 27	0.7	0.5	--	--	1.1	205°	0.1	107°	1.0	025°
3241	Chaseville Turn	4d	30°22.71'	81°37.77'	+2 16	+2 39	+2 28	+2 27	0.7	0.7	--	--	1.4	165°	--	--	1.0	023°
	...do.	14d	30°22.71'	81°37.77'	+2 10	+2 29	+2 25	+2 28	0.6	0.5	0.1	089°	1.3	166°	0.1	082°	1.0	339°
	...do.	30d	30°22.71'	81°37.77'	+1 48	+2 25	+2 55	+2 25	0.5	0.6	0.1	279°	1.2	186°	--	--	1.1	003°
3243	Terminal Channel (north end)	7d	30°21.42'	81°37.08'	+2 39	+3 16	+3 02	+2 43	0.5	0.6	--	--	1.0	225°	--	--	1.1	017°
	...do.	17d	30°21.42'	81°37.08'	+2 16	+3 06	+3 22	+3 38	0.6	0.3	--	--	1.2	183°	--	--	1.3	001°
	...do.	27d	30°21.42'	81°37.08'	+1 51	+3 28	+3 16	+3 33	0.5	0.6	--	--	1.0	185°	--	--	1.3	001°
3245	Commodore Point, terminal channel	7d	30°19.05'	81°37.58'	+2 39	+3 13	+3 10	+3 37	0.5	0.4	--	--	0.9	197°	--	--	0.7	072°
	...do.	17d	30°19.05'	81°37.58'	+2 12	+3 13	+3 23	+3 25	0.5	0.4	--	--	1.0	221°	--	--	1.0	051°
	...do.	27d	30°19.05'	81°37.58'	+1 43	+2 30	+3 38	+3 08	0.6	0.4	--	--	1.1	221°	--	--	0.8	035°

Daily predictions

Endnotes can be found at the end of table 2.

TABLE 2. – CURRENT DIFFERENCES AND OTHER CONSTANTS

No.	PLACE	POSITION Latitude North	POSITION Longitude West	Meter Depth (ft)	TIME DIFF Min. before Flood (h m)	TIME DIFF Flood (h m)	TIME DIFF Min. before Ebb (h m)	TIME DIFF Ebb (h m)	SPEED RATIO Flood	SPEED RATIO Ebb	Min. before Flood (knots)	Min. before Flood (Dir.)	Maximum Flood (knots)	Maximum Flood (Dir.)	Min. before Ebb (knots)	Min. before Ebb (Dir.)	Maximum Ebb (knots)	Maximum Ebb (Dir.)
	ST. JOHNS RIVER Time meridian, 75°W				*on St. Johns River Entrance, p.124*													
3247	Jacksonville, off Washington St	30°19.3'	81°39.2'		+2 59	+3 10	+2 54	+3 23	0.9	0.9	—	—	1.8	281°	—	—	1.9	118°
3249	Jacksonville, F.E.C. RR. bridge	30°19.3'	81°39.9'		+2 59	+3 24	+2 59	+3 39	0.8	0.8	—	—	1.8	240°	—	—	1.7	060°
3251	Winter Point	30°18.5'	81°40.5'		+2 59	+3 22	+4 04	+3 59	0.6	0.5	—	—	1.1	200°	—	—	1.1	015°
3253	Mandarin Point	30°09.3'	81°41.1'		+3 07	+3 39	+3 24	+3 38	0.3	0.4	—	—	0.6	179°	—	—	0.8	013°
	...do.	30°09.3'	81°41.1'	6d	+3 13	+3 33	+3 24	+3 38	0.3	0.3	—	—	0.6	179°	—	—	0.7	013°
	...do.	30°09.3'	81°41.1'	15d	+2 48	+3 33	+3 24	+3 32	0.3	0.3	—	—	0.5	179°	—	—	0.5	013°
3255	Red Bay Point, draw bridge	29°59.1'	81°37.8'	24d	+2 48	+3 57	+5 24	+4 02	0.5	0.3	—	—	0.9	115°	—	—	0.6	300°
	...do.	29°59.1'	81°37.8'	6d	+2 42	+3 57	+5 18	+4 08	0.5	0.3	—	—	0.9	115°	—	—	0.5	300°
	...do.	29°59.1'	81°37.8'	14d	+2 48	+3 57	+5 30	+4 08	0.4	0.2	—	—	0.8	115°	—	—	0.4	300°
3257	Tocoi to Lake George	- -	- -		*Current weak and variable*													
	FORT PIERCE INLET				*on Fort Pierce Inlet, p.128*													
3259	FORT PIERCE INLET ENTRANCE	27°28.27'	80°17.55'	16d	*Daily predictions*				1.1	1.1	—	—	2.7	258°	—	—	2.8	080°
	...do.	27°28.27'	80°17.55'	6d	+0 02	+0 02	-0 01	+0 01	1.1	1.0	—	—	2.8	258°	—	—	3.1	081°
	...do.	27°28.27'	80°17.55'	23d	-0 02	+0 00	+0 00	-0 01	1.0	0.9	—	—	2.6	259°	—	—	2.6	079°
	...do.	27°28.27'	80°17.55'	33d	-0 03	-0 01	-0 06	-0 03	0.8	0.8	—	—	2.2	260°	—	—	2.3	077°
3261	Inner Range, north of USCG station	27°27.98'	80°18.49'	5d	-0 05	-0 00	-0 06	-0 06	0.8	0.6	—	—	2.1	242°	0.1	159°	1.6	076°
	...do.	27°27.98'	80°18.49'	14d	+0 01	-0 01	+0 05	+0 08	0.7	0.6	—	—	2.0	243°	—	—	1.6	065°
	...do.	27°27.98'	80°18.49'	21d	+0 01	-0 01	+0 05	+0 08	0.6	0.5	—	—	1.7	243°	—	—	1.4	061°
3263	Turning Basin	27°27.61'	80°19.26'	6d	+0 06	-0 18	+0 14	+0 23	0.2	0.2	0.1	303°	0.6	218°	0.1	298°	0.6	020°
	...do.	27°27.61'	80°19.26'	16d	+0 05	-0 21	+0 17	+0 26	0.2	0.2	0.1	302°	0.7	219°	0.1	297°	0.5	022°
	...do.	27°27.61'	80°19.26'	19d	+0 06	-0 20	+0 16	+0 28	0.2	0.2	—	—	0.6	218°	0.1	296°	0.5	023°
3265	South Bridge (ICW)	27°27.60'	80°19.15'	3d	-0 06	+0 12	-0 10	+0 00	0.6	0.5	—	—	1.6	238°	0.2	315°	1.3	031°
	...do.	27°27.60'	80°19.15'	9d	+0 00	+0 09	-0 11	+0 03	0.5	0.4	—	—	1.4	236°	0.2	317°	1.2	036°
	...do.	27°27.60'	80°19.15'	16d	+0 00	+0 09	-0 14	+0 06	0.5	0.3	—	—	1.3	232°	0.1	325°	0.9	053°
	LAKE WORTH INLET				*on Lake Worth Inlet, p.132*													
3267	LAKE WORTH INLET ENTRANCE	26°46.38'	80°02.17'	15d	*Daily predictions*				1.1	0.9	—	—	1.6	267°	—	—	1.3	086°
	...do.	26°46.38'	80°02.17'	5d	+0 04	+0 02	+0 02	+0 05	0.7	0.9	—	—	1.8	267°	—	—	1.2	092°
	...do.	26°46.38'	80°02.17'	28d	-0 04	-0 01	-0 03	-0 04			—	—	1.2	268°	—	—	1.1	085°
3269	Pier 13	26°46.02'	80°03.04'	6d	See Table 5.						—	—			—	—		
	...do.	26°46.02'	80°03.04'	15d	See Table 5.						—	—			—	—		
	...do.	26°46.02'	80°03.04'	19d	See Table 5.						—	—			—	—		
3271	North Turning Basin	26°46.28'	80°03.02'	3d	-0 02	-0 26	-0 05	+0 33	0.6	0.9	—	—	0.9	356°	—	—	1.1	170°
	...do.	26°46.28'	80°03.02'	8d	+0 00	-0 25	-0 04	+0 35	0.6	0.8	—	—	0.9	356°	0.1	254°	1.0	168°
	PORT EVERGLADES				*on Port Everglades, p.136*													
3273	Pier 2, 1.3 miles east of <34>	26°05.63'	80°05.78'	16d	*Current weak and variable*						—	—	—	—	—	—	0.4	— —
3275	PORT EVERGLADES ENTRANCE	26°05.59'	80°06.33'	9d	*Daily predictions*				1.1	1.1	—	—	0.6	257°	—	—	0.6	075°
	...do.	26°05.59'	80°06.33'	22d	+0 24	-0 09	-0 09	-0 07	1.0	0.9	—	—	0.5	259°	—	—	0.7	077°
	...do.	26°05.59'	80°06.33'	35d	-0 01	+0 06	+0 01	-0 07	1.0	0.7	—	—	0.6	255°	—	—	0.6	075°
	...do.	26°05.59'	80°06.33'	4d	-1 03	-0 04	+0 08	-0 13	0.3	0.8	—	—	0.1	251°	—	—	0.4	077°
3277	Turning Basin	26°05.69'	80°07.04'	14d	*Current weak and variable*						—	—	0.1	358°	—	—	0.5	173°
	...do.	26°05.69'	80°07.04'	34d	*Current weak and variable*						—	—	—	—	—	—	—	—
3279	17th Street Bridge, 0.1mile south of	26°05.98'	80°07.15'	6d	-0 20	-0 12	-0 09	-0 18	1.6	1.2	0.1	100°	0.9	022°	0.1	101°	0.8	184°
	...do.	26°05.98'	80°07.15'	9d	-0 29	-0 10	-0 14	-0 24	1.6	1.1	—	—	0.9	021°	0.1	102°	0.7	184°
	...do.	26°05.98'	80°07.15'	12d	-0 38	-0 12	-0 09	-0 27	1.5	1.1	—	—	0.9	024°	0.1	103°	0.7	184°
3281	Fort Lauderdale, New River	26°06.73'	80°07.18'		-0 14	-0 01	-0 28	+0 52	1.4	0.8	—	—	0.2	005°	—	—	0.5	130°
3283	South Entrance (ICW)	26°05.24'	80°06.79'	5d	+0 34	-0 06	-0 38	-0 22	0.3	0.7	—	—	0.2	173°	—	—	0.4	353°
	...do.	26°05.24'	80°06.79'	15d	+0 37	+0 15	-0 21	-0 06	0.3	0.6	—	—	0.2	171°	—	—	0.4	350°
	...do.	26°05.24'	80°06.79'	31d	-0 14	+0 11	+0 20	-0 03	0.4	0.3	—	—	0.2	168°	—	—	0.2	351°

Endnotes can be found at the end of table 2.

TABLE 2. – CURRENT DIFFERENCES AND OTHER CONSTANTS

No.	PLACE	Meter Depth (ft)	POSITION Latitude (North)	POSITION Longitude (West)	TIME DIFF. Min. before Flood (h m)	TIME DIFF. Flood (h m)	TIME DIFF. Min. before Ebb (h m)	TIME DIFF. Ebb (h m)	SPEED RATIO Flood	SPEED RATIO Ebb	Min. before Flood (knots)	Min. before Flood (Dir.)	Maximum Flood (knots)	Maximum Flood (Dir.)	Min. before Ebb (knots)	Min. before Ebb (Dir.)	Maximum Ebb (knots)	Maximum Ebb (Dir.)
	PORT EVERGLADES Time meridian, 75°W				*on Port Everglades, p.136*													
3285	South Port, at the terminals	6d	26°04.46'	80°06.83'	+0 26	+0 20	-0 05	-0 03	0.5	0.5	--	--	0.3	175°	--	--	0.3	356°
	...do.	16d	26°04.46'	80°06.83'	+0 18	+0 29	+0 09	-0 09	0.5	0.4	--	--	0.3	175°	--	--	0.3	356°
	...do.	26d	26°04.46'	80°06.83'	+0 28	+0 36	+0 12	-0 39	0.5	0.4	--	--	0.3	175°	--	--	0.3	355°
	MIAMI HARBOR				*on Miami Harbor Entrance, p.140*													
3287	Bakers Haulover Cut		25°54.0'	80°07.4'	+0 00	+0 19	+0 13	-0 08	1.3	1.0	--	--	2.9	270°	--	--	2.5	090°
	Government Cut																	
3289	South Jetty	9d	25°45.63'	80°07.61'	-0 03	-0 01	-0 05	-0 12	0.7	0.8	0.1	040°	1.6	317°	0.1	041°	1.8	118°
	...do.	15d	25°45.63'	80°07.61'	-0 06	-0 03	-0 05	-0 10	0.7	0.7	0.1	039°	1.6	319°	0.1	042°	1.7	117°
	...do.	38d	25°45.63'	80°07.61'	-0 15	-0 01	-0 02	-0 14	0.6	0.5	0.2	044°	1.4	321°	0.1	041°	1.2	115°
3291	MIAMI HARBOR ENTRANCE	15d	25°45.84'	80°08.04'	+0 00	*Daily predictions*	-0 01	-0 01	1.0	1.0	--	--	2.2	293°	--	--	2.4	113°
	...do.	8d	25°45.84'	80°08.04'	-0 01		+0 00	-0 01	1.0	1.0	--	--	2.3	293°	--	--	2.4	114°
	...do.	22d	25°45.84'	80°08.04'	-0 04		+0 00	-0 02	0.8	0.8	--	--	2.2	292°	--	--	2.3	113°
	...do.	35d	25°45.84'	80°08.04'	-0 06	+0 03	-0 02	-0 11	0.5	0.8	--	--	1.8	292°	--	--	1.9	115°
3293	West entrance, south side	4d	25°45.88'	80°08.25'	-0 09	-0 09	-0 27	-0 01	0.4	0.8	0.1	015°	1.0	290°	0.1	015°	2.0	097°
	...do.	14d	25°45.88'	80°08.25'	-0 16	-0 36	-0 29	-0 05	0.4	0.8	0.1	015°	0.9	289°	0.1	015°	2.0	094°
	...do.	34d	25°45.80'	80°08.25'			-0 28	-0 08	0.3	0.6	--	--	0.7	262°	--	--	1.4	090°
	Main Channel																	
3295	Fisher Island Turning Basin	9d	25°46.07'	80°08.61'	+0 00	+0 34	+0 34	-0 01	0.6	0.3	0.1	038°	1.4	293°	--	--	0.8	123°
	...do.	16d	25°46.07'	80°08.61'	+0 08	+0 34	+0 36	+0 09	0.6	0.3	0.1	033°	1.4	293°	--	--	0.9	119°
3297	Main Ship Channel	36d	25°46.40'	80°09.42'	+0 17	+0 33	+0 38	+0 07	0.5	0.3	--	--	1.1	291°	--	--	0.7	111°
	...do.	16d	25°46.40'	80°09.42'	+0 04	+0 22	+0 19	+0 13	0.5	0.4	--	--	1.2	295°	--	--	1.0	110°
	...do.	33d	25°46.40'	80°09.42'	-0 28	+0 16	+0 21	+0 15	0.4	0.3	--	--	0.9	294°	--	--	0.9	112°
3299	Dodge Island, SE Turning Basin	4d	25°46.91'	80°10.84'	+0 41	+0 28	+0 22	-0 06	0.2	0.1	0.2	027°	0.4	305°	--	--	0.6	116°
	...do.	14d	25°46.91'	80°10.84'	+0 27	+0 06	-0 36	+0 07	0.2	0.1	0.1	028°	0.4	305°	--	--	0.3	118°
	...do.	30d	25°46.91'	80°10.84'	+0 02	-0 48	+0 19	+0 12	0.1	0.2	0.1	032°	0.5	307°	--	--	0.4	119°
3301	Dodge Island, NW Turning Basin	7d	25°47.13'	80°11.04'	-0 03	+0 00	+0 43	+0 17	0.1	0.2	--	--	0.3	304°	--	--	0.3	104°
	...do.	17d	25°47.13'	80°11.04'	+0 14	+0 14	-0 15	+0 43	0.1	0.1	--	--	0.3	334°	--	--	0.5	173°
	...do.	30d	25°47.13'	80°11.04'	-0 38	+0 18	+0 06	-0 31	0.1	0.1	--	--	0.3	317°	--	--	0.3	163°
	Fishermans Channel																	
3303	Pilot House	5d	25°45.95'	80°08.75'	-0 02	-1 37	-1 36	-0 02	0.2	0.3	--	--	0.3	255°	--	--	0.7	086°
	...do.	14d	25°45.95'	80°08.75'	-0 07	-1 00	-1 05	+0 19	0.2	0.2	--	--	0.4	255°	--	--	0.6	086°
	...do.	31d	25°45.95'	80°09.07'	+0 06	-0 38	-0 38	+0 07	0.3	0.2	--	--	0.6	258°	--	--	0.4	085°
3305	Norris Cut	7d	25°45.90'	80°09.07'	-0 03	+0 15	-0 05	-0 20	0.4	0.4	--	--	0.8	294°	0.1	018°	1.1	089°
	...do.	14d	25°45.90'	80°09.07'	+0 06	+0 07	-0 01	-0 09	0.4	0.4	--	--	0.6	286°	--	--	0.8	088°
	...do.	34d	25°45.90'	80°09.69'	+0 02	+0 10	-0 08	+0 00	0.3	0.3	--	--	0.6	276°	--	--	0.8	092°
3307	Lummus Island, SW corner	4d	25°45.91'	80°09.69'	+0 18	-0 12	-0 04	+0 13	0.3	0.3	--	--	0.5	268°	--	--	0.6	091°
	...do.	14d	25°45.91'	80°10.06'	+0 06	-0 02	-0 51	+0 01	0.2	0.3	--	--	0.5	269°	--	--	0.7	089°
3309	Lummus Island Turning Basin	7d	25°46.06'	80°10.06'	--	-0 26	-0 13	+0 41	0.2	0.1	--	--	0.3	293°	--	--	0.3	121°
	...do.	14d	25°46.06'	80°10.06'	+0 44	-0 32	--	+0 45	0.1	0.1	--	--	0.3	291°	--	--	0.3	099°
	...do.	34d	25°46.06'	80°10.06'	+0 32	--	-0 05	+1 43	0.1	0.1	--	--	0.3	--	--	--	0.3	060°
3311	Dodge Island Cut, west end	5d	25°46.38'	80°10.71'	-0 08	+0 31	+0 37	+0 04	0.1	0.1	0.1	012°	0.1	253°	--	--	0.2	085°
	...do.	15d	25°46.38'	80°10.71'	-0 30	+0 31	+0 18	+0 43	--	0.1	--	--	0.2	271°	--	--	0.2	089°
	...do.	28d	25°46.38'	80°10.71'	-0 06	-0 48	-0 08	+1 04	0.1	0.2	--	--	0.3	266°	--	--	0.3	077°
3313	Miami River Entrance	2d	25°46.22'	80°11.25'		-0 05	+0 24	+0 48	0.2	0.2	--	--	0.3	267°	--	--	0.5	090°
	...do.	12d	25°46.22'	80°11.25'		-0 46		+0 51	0.2	0.2	--	--	0.3	263°	--	--	0.4	051°
3315	Fowey Rocks Light, 1.5 miles SW of		25°35'	80°07'	*Current weak and variable*													
	FLORIDA REEFS to BLACKBURN BAY				*on Key West, p.144*													
3317	Caesar Creek, Biscayne Bay		25°23.2'	80°13.6'	+0 09	+0 03	-0 21	-0 23	0.9	1.0	--	--	1.2	316°	--	--	1.8	123°
3319	Long Key, drawbridge east of		24°50.4'	80°46.2'	+1 00	+1 38	+2 14	+1 15	0.8	0.7	--	--	1.1	000°	--	--	1.2	202°
3321	Long Key Viaduct		24°48.1'	80°51.9'	+1 36	+1 39	+1 55	+1 39	0.7	0.7	--	--	0.9	349°	--	--	1.6	170°
3323	Moser Channel, between Molasses and Pigeon Keys	3d	24°41.89'	81°10.15'	+1 21	+1 19	+1 16	+1 15	0.9	0.9	--	--	1.2	346°	--	--	1.6	164°
	...do.	9d	24°41.89'	81°10.15'	+1 21	+1 17	+1 16	+1 16	0.7	0.8	--	--	0.9	345°	--	--	1.3	163°

Endnotes can be found at the end of table 2.

TABLE 2. – CURRENT DIFFERENCES AND OTHER CONSTANTS

No.	PLACE	Meter Depth (ft)	POSITION Latitude North	POSITION Longitude West	TIME DIFFERENCES Min. before Flood (h m)	TIME DIFFERENCES Flood (h m)	TIME DIFFERENCES Min. before Ebb (h m)	TIME DIFFERENCES Ebb (h m)	SPEED RATIOS Flood	SPEED RATIOS Ebb	Minimum before Flood (knots)	Minimum before Flood (Dir.)	Maximum Flood (knots)	Maximum Flood (Dir.)	Minimum before Ebb (knots)	Minimum before Ebb (Dir.)	Maximum Ebb (knots)	Maximum Ebb (Dir.)
	FLORIDA REEFS to BLACKBURN BAY Time meridian, 75°W																	
	on Key West, p.144																	
3325	Bahia Honda Harbor	4d	24°39.38'	81°17.31'	+1 15	+1 09	+1 07	+1 17	1.0	0.9	--	--	1.3	007°	--	--	1.5	183°
3327	Loggerhead Key, East of	2d	24°36.97'	81°27.19'	+0 03	+0 10	+0 10	+0 06	0.2	0.2	--	--	0.2	322°	--	--	0.3	158°
	do.	8d	24°36.97'	81°27.19'	+0 27	+0 14	-0 06	+0 29	0.1	0.1	--	--	0.2	330°	--	--	0.2	154°
3329	Safe Harbor Entrance, Stock Island	11d	24°33.35'	81°44.07'	+0 57	+1 35	+1 13	+0 35	0.5	0.5	--	--	0.7	312°	--	--	0.9	142°
3331	No Name Key, northeast of		24°42.3'	81°18.8'	*Current weak and variable*													
	Key West																	
3333	Main Ship Channel entrance	4d	24°28.24'	81°48.71'	-0 22	-0 48	-0 12	-0 10	0.2	0.2	0.1	260°	0.3	339°	0.1	263°	0.3	187°
	do.	17d	24°28.24'	81°48.71'	-0 10	-0 06	-0 39	-0 29	0.1	0.2	0.1	258°	0.2	331°	0.1	265°	0.3	182°
3335	Key West Channel, Cut–A Cut–B Turn	6d	24°31.56'	81°49.09'	+0 27	-0 04	+0 20	+0 52	0.4	0.5	0.3	248°	0.5	309°	0.2	237°	0.8	164°
	do.	26d	24°31.56'	81°49.09'	+0 32	-0 03	+0 06	+0 56	0.3	0.4	0.1	249°	0.4	324°	0.1	241°	0.7	161°
3337	Southwest channel	3d	24°32.05'	81°49.93'	+0 33	+0 35	+0 01	+0 16	0.4	0.5	0.1	279°	0.5	355°	0.1	282°	0.8	202°
	do.	20d	24°32.05'	81°49.93'	+0 31	+0 25	-0 03	+0 19	0.3	0.4	0.1	283°	0.5	004°	0.1	286°	0.7	202°
3339	KEY WEST, 0.3 mi. W of Ft. Taylor	4d	24°32.88'	81°49.01'	*Daily predictions*								1.3	007°			1.7	187°
	do.	14d	24°32.88'	81°49.01'	-0 02	+0 01	-0 02	-0 01	0.8	0.9	0.1	278°	1.1	009°	0.1	096°	1.4	186°
3341	Ft. Taylor, 0.6 mile N of	6d	24°33.5'	81°48.6'	-0 02	+0 24	-0 18	-0 05	0.4	0.7	--	--	0.6	042°	--	--	1.2	202°
3343	Key West Harbor Range channel	6d	24°33.78'	81°48.56'	+0 18	+0 25	+0 10	+0 09	0.8	0.8	0.1	304°	1.1	035°	0.1	126°	1.4	215°
	do.	19d	24°33.78'	81°48.56'	+0 15	+0 26	+0 08	+0 05	0.7	0.7	--	--	0.9	032°	--	--	1.1	212°
3345	Turning Basin	6d	24°33.83'	81°48.37'	+0 23	+0 27	+0 19	+0 16	0.9	0.7	0.1	115°	1.2	024°	0.1	299°	1.2	210°
	do.	23d	24°33.83'	81°48.37'	+0 18	+0 31	+0 16	+0 10	0.7	0.7	0.1	120°	0.9	026°	0.1	304°	0.9	214°
3347	Northwest Channel, W of Middle Ground	4d	24°34.10'	81°50.10'	-0 07	-0 19	+0 01	-0 04	0.7	0.6	--	--	1.2	353°	--	--	1.4	162°
	do.	17d	24°34.10'	81°50.10'	-0 08	-0 18	+0 00	-0 04	1.2	0.8	--	--	1.3	313°	--	--	1.4	140°
3349	Northwest Channel, W of Calda Bank	5d	24°36.92'	81°52.29'	-0 19	-0 22	+0 03	-0 07	1.0	0.8	--	--	1.2	321°	0.1	227°	1.0	145°
	do.	22d	24°36.92'	81°52.29'	-0 19	-0 21	-0 01	-0 10	0.8	0.6	--	--	1.1		--	--	0.8	144°
3351	Fleming Key Cut	4d	24°34.09'	81°48.11'	+1 27	+0 23	-0 02	+0 56	0.4	0.5	0.3	003°	0.5	068°	--	--	1.7	279°
	do.	17d	24°34.09'	81°48.11'	+1 19	+0 09	-0 11	+1 00	0.4	1.0	0.3	000°	0.5	064°	--	--	1.4	274°
3353	Man of War Harbor	3d	24°35.22'	81°48.37'	+0 28	+0 45	+0 21	+0 01	0.7	0.8	0.2	289°	0.9	002°	--	--	0.9	187°
	do.	16d	24°35.22'	81°48.37'	+1 03	+0 45	+0 18	+0 00	0.5	0.5	0.2	293°	0.7	006°	--	--	0.8	182°
3355	Fleming Key, North of	2d	24°35.80'	81°47.92'	+1 30	+1 17	+0 48	+1 07	1.1	1.1	--	--	1.4	059°	--	--	1.9	242°
	do.	9d	24°35.80'	81°47.92'	+1 28	+1 17	+0 49	+1 08	1.1	0.8	--	--	1.1	061°	--	--	1.4	241°
3357	Boca Grande Channel	2d	24°33.99'	82°04.01'	-0 10	-0 18	-0 11	-0 11	0.9	0.7	--	--	1.2	013°	--	--	1.3	190°
	do.	12d	24°33.99'	82°04.01'	-0 12	-0 21	-0 13	-0 11	0.7	0.6	--	--	0.9	013°	--	--	1.0	191°
3359	New Ground	6d	24°39.04'	82°24.97'	+1 41	+1 08	+1 04	+1 46	0.5	0.5	0.3	305°	0.6	064°	0.2	154°	0.9	260°
	do.	32d	24°39.04'	82°24.97'	+1 38	+1 04	+1 01	+1 43	0.4	0.4	0.3	351°	0.6	066°	0.1	152°	0.7	259°
3361	Isaac Shoal		24°33.5'	82°32.2'	+1 02	+1 05	+1 45	+1 37	0.8	0.4	--	--	1.0	002°	--	--	0.6	181°
3363	Southeast Channel, 1.1 miles E of Garden Key		24°37.60'	82°51.10'	-0 25	+0 05	+0 30	+0 18	0.5	0.4	--	--	0.6	004°	--	--	0.6	172°
3365	Southwest Channel		24°36.92'	82°54.70'	+0 47	+0 25	+1 18	+1 46	0.3	0.5	--	--	0.4	001°	--	--	0.6	209°
	on Tampa Bay Entrance, p.148																	
3367	Point Ybel, 0.4 mile northwest of		26°27.40'	82°01.12'	-0 25	-0 52	+0 17	+0 35	0.8	0.7	--	--	1.0	255°	--	--	0.9	080°
3369	Captiva Pass <37>		26°36.56'	82°13.34'	-0 53	-1 29	-1 14	-0 23	1.4	0.9	--	--	1.8	067°	--	--	1.9	251°
3371	Boca Grande Pass, Charlotte Harbor		26°42.86'	82°15.40'	-0 15	-0 37	-0 15	+0 05	1.7	1.3	--	--	2.2	057°	--	--	1.8	251°
3373	Pine Island Sound		26°40.90'	82°11.87'	---	---	---	---			--	--	0.5	011°	--	--	0.5	191°
3375	Little Pine I. bridge, Mattacha Pass		26°37.9'	82°04.1'	---	-0 19	---	---	0.4	0.4	--	--	0.6	132°	--	--	--	--
3377	Cape Haze, 2.3 mi. S of, Charlotte Hbr		26°44.7'	82°09.1'	+0 30	+0 41	-0 20	+1 18	0.4	0.4	--	--	0.5	080°	--	--	0.5	268°
3379	Punta Gorda, Peace River Bridge		26°56.7'	82°03.4'	---	---	---	---	0.3	0.2	--	--	0.4	047°	--	--	0.3	230°
3381	Myakka River bridge <45>		26°57.5'	82°12.8'	+1 48	+1 18	+1 47	---	0.8	0.8	--	--	0.5	304°	--	--	--	--
3383	Gasparilla Pass		26°48.74'	82°16.86'	-1 15	-1 13	-0 35	-0 41	0.8	0.8	--	--	1.0	066°	--	--	1.1	236°
3385	Venice Inlet		27°06.8'	82°28.0'	-2 05	-2 08	-1 57	-1 59	0.8	0.7	--	--	1.1	087°	--	--	0.9	262°
3387	Blackburn Bay, south end, bridge		27°07.4'	82°28.2'	-0 55	-1 20	-1 28	-0 10	0.7	0.5	--	--	0.9	357°	--	--	0.7	180°

Endnotes can be found at the end of table 2.

TABLE 2. – CURRENT DIFFERENCES AND OTHER CONSTANTS

No.	PLACE	Meter Depth (ft)	Lat. North	Long. West	Min. before Flood	Flood	Min. before Ebb	Ebb	SR Flood	SR Ebb	Min. bef. Flood knots	Dir.	Max. Flood knots	Dir.	Min. bef. Ebb knots	Dir.	Max. Ebb knots	Dir.
	SARASOTA BAY Time meridian, 75°W				**on Tampa Bay Entrance, p.148**													
3389	Big Sarasota Pass		27°18.0'	82°33.8'	-1 54	-1 49	-1 34	-2 03	1.2	0.8	—	—	1.5	006°	—	—	1.0	183°
3391	Sarasota Bay, south end, bridge		27°18.1'	82°32.8'	-1 25	-1 39	-1 13	-0 32	0.2	0.2	—	—	0.3	196°	—	—	0.3	013°
3393	New Pass		27°19.9'	82°34.9'	-2 06	-2 48	-1 18	-1 25	1.2	0.8	—	—	1.6	046°	—	—	1.0	231°
3395	Golden Gate Point, off		27°19.7'	82°33.4'	-1 38	-1 57	-1 25	-1 19	0.3	0.2	—	—	0.4	344°	—	—	0.3	159°
3397	Longboat Pass		27°26.5'	82°41.4'	-2 32	-2 42	-1 51	-1 56	1.4	1.2	—	—	1.8	088°	—	—	1.6	267°
3399	Cortez, north of bridge		27°28.2'	82°41.6'	-1 47	-1 10	-0 25	-1 11	0.5	0.1	—	—	0.6	346°	—	—	0.1	162°
	TAMPA BAY																	
3401	Egmont Channel, marker '10'	15d	27°36.03'	82°52.06'	-2 04	-3 17	-2 22	-1 31	0.2	0.2	0.2	319°	0.2	018°	0.1	139°	0.3	259°
3403	Egmont Channel (3 mi. W of Egmont Key Lt.)		27°36.5'	82°49.1'	-0 30	-0 28	-0 30	-0 29	0.4	0.5	—	—	0.5	065°	0.1	032°	0.7	260°
3405	TAMPA BAY ENTRANCE (Egmont Channel)	15d	27°36.26'	82°45.62'	**Daily predictions**						—	—	1.3	120°	—	—	1.3	298°
3407	Southwest Channel (S of Egmont Key)	15d	27°33.70'	82°46.04'	-0 46	-0 53	-0 40	-0 30	0.6	0.9	0.1	357°	0.8	087°	—	—	1.2	269°
3409	Mullet Key Channel entrance		27°36.27'	82°43.43'	-0 03	-0 01	-0 23	+0 08	0.8	0.8	—	—	1.1	055°	—	—	1.1	255°
3411	Passage Key Inlet (off Bean Pt.)	15d	27°32.36'	82°44.86'	-1 29	-1 50	-1 13	+1 08	0.6	0.7	—	—	0.8	081°	—	—	0.9	247°
3413	Rattlesnake Key, 3.1 miles west of		27°33.20'	82°41.30'	+0 20	-0 05	-0 51	+0 04	0.3	0.4	—	—	0.4	065°	—	—	0.6	250°
3415	Rattlesnake Key, 1.1 miles northwest of		27°34.25'	82°38.63'	-0 28	-0 34	-0 34	-0 09	0.2	0.1	—	—	0.3	035°	—	—	0.2	210°
3417	Mullet Key Channel, marker '24'	15d	27°36.50'	82°41.64'	-0 14	-0 07	-0 06	-0 06	0.7	0.7	—	—	0.9	073°	—	—	1.0	255°
3419	Bunces Pass (West of Bayway bridge)		27°38.82'	82°44.37'	-0 47	-0 46	-1 07	-1 02	0.8	0.7	—	—	1.0	125°	—	—	0.8	315°
3421	Pine Key (Pinellas Bayway bridge)		27°41.55'	82°43.03'	-0 32	-0 29	-1 07	-1 00	0.3	0.6	—	—	0.4	100°	—	—	0.8	280°
3423	Cats Point (bridge west of)	15d	27°42.50'	82°43.48'	-1 27	-2 41	-2 12	-1 23	0.5	0.5	—	—	0.6	015°	—	—	0.7	150°
3425	SUNSHINE SKYWAY BRIDGE		27°37.22'	82°39.32'	**Daily predictions, p.152**						—	—	1.3	060°	—	—	1.1	235°
3427	Cut A & B, Channel Junction		27°38.33'	82°37.53'	+0 25	+0 07	+0 23	+0 46	0.8	0.7	—	—	1.0	045°	—	—	1.0	225°
3429	Joe Island, 1.8 miles northwest of		27°36.75'	82°37.50'	+0 03	-0 07	-0 24	-0 02	0.5	0.7	—	—	0.7	070°	—	—	0.9	245°
3431	Harbor Key, 1.3 miles west of	15d	27°36.67'	82°35.67'	-0 50	-0 56	-1 06	-0 38	0.2	0.3	—	—	0.3	020°	—	—	0.4	160°
	Pinellas Point																	
3433	2 miles southwest of		27°40.55'	82°39.53'	Current weak and variable						—	—	—	—	—	—	—	—
3435	2.6 miles south of		27°39.63'	82°38.50'	-0 46	-0 23	-0 16	-0 34	0.6	0.7	—	—	0.8	030°	—	—	0.9	210°
3437	0.5 mile southeast of		27°41.82'	82°37.95'	-1 28	-1 19	-1 53	-0 57	0.2	0.2	—	—	0.3	045°	—	—	0.3	220°
3439	1.9 miles SE of		27°41.08'	82°36.58'	+0 29	-0 32	-0 06	+0 20	0.5	0.6	—	—	0.7	020°	—	—	0.8	180°
3441	3 miles southeast of		27°40.38'	82°35.58'	+0 29	+0 23	+0 20	+0 47	0.6	0.6	—	—	0.8	025°	—	—	0.8	200°
3443	Port Manatee Channel entrance	15d	27°39.72'	82°35.95'	-0 01	+0 08	+0 24	+0 23	0.6	0.6	—	—	0.8	033°	—	—	0.8	216°
3445	Port Manatee Channel, marker '4'	15d	27°39.21'	82°35.39'	-0 34	-0 11	-0 22	+0 01	0.2	0.3	—	—	0.2	056°	—	—	0.4	242°
3447	Piney Point, 0.6 mile NNW of		27°39.22'	82°33.73'	+0 12	-0 29	-0 45	+0 01	0.3	0.4	—	—	0.4	355°	—	—	0.5	215°
					on Old Tampa Bay Ent., p.156													
3449	Lewis Island, 0.9 mile east of	14	27°43.47'	82°36.58'	+0 03	-0 52	-0 47	-0 23	0.9	0.7	—	—	0.8	022°	—	—	0.7	143°
3451	Camp Key, 1.9 miles northwest of	15	27°42.47'	82°33.00'	+0 02	-0 27	-0 35	-0 27	0.7	0.5	—	—	0.6	036°	—	—	0.5	223°
3453	Shell Point, 1.1 miles west of		27°43.28'	82°30.22'	Current weak and variable						—	—	0.3	065°	—	—	0.3	235°
3455	Port of St. Petersburg approach, marker 'S'	12	27°45.55'	82°36.61'	Current weak and variable						0.1	274°	0.3	344°	0.1	277°	0.3	203°
3457	Snell Isle, 1.8 miles east of	14	27°47.62'	82°34.33'	+0 45	-0 03	-0 43	-0 12	0.3	0.4	—	—	0.3	353°	—	—	0.4	158°
3459	Ross Island, 1 mile east of, marker '4'	15d	27°59.90'	82°34.20'	+0 34	+0 34	+0 07	+0 25	0.9	0.7	—	—	0.9	358°	—	—	0.7	179°
3461	OLD TAMPA BAY ENTRANCE (Port Tampa)	15d	27°51.80'	82°33.22'	**Daily predictions**						0.1	297°	0.9	025°	—	—	0.8	211°
3463	Gandy Bridge, west channel	15	27°52.75'	82°34.83'	+0 07	-0 46	-0 38	-0 38	1.0	0.9	—	—	0.9	000°	—	—	0.9	155°
3465	Gandy Bridge, east channel	6d	27°53.17'	82°33.08'	+0 31	-0 01	-0 15	+0 23	0.6	0.5	—	—	0.5	014°	—	—	0.5	166°
3467	W Howard Frankland Bridge	7	27°55.55'	82°35.17'	+0 18	+0 27	+0 03	+0 10	0.3	0.2	—	—	0.3	285°	—	—	0.2	138°
3469	Courtney Campbell Parkway	7	27°58.08'	82°37.45'	+0 36	+0 03	-0 20	+0 10	0.6	0.6	—	—	0.5	338°	—	—	0.6	138°
3471	Gadsden Pt. Cut-Cut G Channel junction	15d	27°47.16'	82°31.32'	Current weak and variable						—	—	0.2	030°	0.1	312°	0.2	241°
3473	Alafia River Ent., 1.2 miles west of		27°50.97'	82°25.28'	Current weak and variable						—	—	0.2	060°	—	—	0.2	215°

Endnotes can be found at the end of table 2.

TABLE 2. – CURRENT DIFFERENCES AND OTHER CONSTANTS

No.	PLACE	Meter Depth (ft)	Latitude (North)	Longitude (West)	Min. before Flood (h m)	Flood (h m)	Min. before Ebb (h m)	Ebb (h m)	Speed Ratio Flood	Speed Ratio Ebb	Min. before Flood knots	Dir.	Max Flood knots	Dir.	Min. before Ebb knots	Dir.	Max Ebb knots	Dir.
	BOCA CIEGA BAY and ST. JOSEPH SOUND Time meridian, 75°W																	
	on Tampa Bay Entrance, p.148																	
3475	Pass-a-Grille Channel		27°41.1'	82°44.1'	-0 30	-0 43	-0 30	-0 17	0.9	1.0	--	--	1.2	357°	--	--	1.4	186°
3477	Bridge, 0.8 mi. south of Maximo Pt. <39>		27°41.6'	82°40.8'	-1 05	-1 22	-1 05	-0 50	0.9	1.0	--	--	1.2	078°	--	--	1.4	255°
3479	Gulfport, south of		27°43.7'	82°42.4'	Current weak and variable													
3481	Blind Pass (north end)		27°45.4'	82°45.7'	-1 20	-1 25	-1 20	-1 12	0.5	0.3	--	--	0.6	000°	--	--	0.4	180°
3483	Treasure Island Causeway		27°46.2'	82°45.3'	Current weak and variable													
	JOHNS PASS ENTRANCE																	
	on Johns Pass Entrance, p.160 — Daily predictions																	
3485	JOHNS PASS ENTRANCE	2d	27°46.69'	82°47.23'	+0 01	-0 05	-0 03	+0 02	0.9	0.9	--	--	0.4	053°	0.1	137°	1.1	222°
	...do...	8d	27°46.69'	82°47.23'	-0 30	-0 08	+0 04	-0 27	2.3	1.4	--	--	0.4	051°	0.1	135°	0.9	223°
3487	Johns Pass Bridge, north span	3d	27°47.00'	82°46.93'	-0 37	-0 11	+0 09	-0 23	2.7	1.2	--	--	1.0	034°	--	--	1.5	209°
	...do...	16d	27°47.00'	82°46.93'	-0 39	-0 11	+0 31	-0 32	3.3	0.7	--	--	1.1	039°	--	--	1.2	209°
3489	Johns Pass Bridge, 0.3nm north of	3d	27°47.10'	82°46.79'	-0 39	+0 09	+0 27	-0 33	2.8	0.6	0.1	135°	1.4	045°	--	--	0.8	228°
	...do...	11d	27°47.10'	82°46.79'	--	--	--	--	--	--	0.1	322°	1.2	047°	--	--	0.7	235°
	on Tampa Bay Entrance, p.148 — Current weak and variable																	
3491	Treasure Island, 3.5 miles southwest of		27°45.0'	82°50.0'	-0 23	-0 25	-1 17	-0 54	0.5	0.1	--	--	0.6	180°	--	--	0.2	000°
3493	The Narrows (Indian Rocks Beach Bridge)		27°52.6'	82°51.0'	-2 24	-2 49	-2 18	-1 50	1.0	0.8	--	--	1.3	179°	--	--	1.1	348°
3495	Clearwater Pass, 0.2 mi. NE of Sand Key		27°57.4'	82°49.4'	--	--	--	--	--	--	--	--	0.4	018°	--	--	0.6	195°
3497	St. Joseph Sound, off		28°05.0'	82°55.0'														
	APALACHEE BAY																	
3499	St. Marks River approach		30°02.8'	84°10.8'	-0 57	-0 46	-0 10	-0 08	0.5	0.4	--	--	0.6	339°	--	--	0.5	170°
3501	Four Mile Point, St. Marks River		30°06.7'	84°12.2'	-0 13	-0 14	+0 24	-0 26	0.3	0.3	--	--	0.4	358°	--	--	0.4	187°
3503	St. Marks, St. Marks River		30°09.3'	84°12.1'	+1 38	+1 10	-0 23	+0 23	0.2	0.3	--	--	0.3	067°	--	--	0.4	247°
	ST. ANDREW BAY Time meridian, 90°W																	
	on St. Andrew Bay Entrance, p.164 — Daily predictions																	
3505	ST. ANDREW BAY ENTRANCE	18d	30°07.31'	85°43.78'	+0 45	+0 07	-0 14	-0 16	1.0	1.4	--	--	1.3	045°	--	--	1.6	225°
	...do...	5d	30°07.31'	85°43.78'	-0 32	-0 09	+0 02	+0 00	0.8	0.8	--	--	1.2	044°	--	--	1.8	230°
	...do...	31d	30°07.31'	85°43.78'	+2 10	+0 32	+0 03	+0 29	0.2	0.4	--	--	1.1	047°	--	--	1.3	221°
3507	Courtney Point, 0.75mi. SE of	7d	30°08.32'	85°41.95'	-0 47	+1 49	+1 31	+0 23	0.4	0.2	--	--	0.3	069°	--	--	0.6	210°
	...do...	20d	30°08.32'	85°41.95'	-0 49	+2 07	+1 39	+0 20	0.3	0.4	--	--	0.4	065°	--	--	0.3	256°
	...do...	30d	30°08.32'	85°41.95'	--	--	--	-0 04	--	0.2	--	--	0.4	068°	--	--	0.3	273°
3509	Courtney Point, 0.4mi. ESE of	4d	30°08.65'	85°42.20'	--	--	--	-1 05	--	--	--	--	--	--	--	--	0.7	174°
	...do...	11d	30°08.65'	85°42.20'	--	--	--	--	--	--	--	--	--	--	--	--	0.4	190°
	...do...	17d	30°08.65'	85°42.20'	--	--	--	--	--	--	--	--	--	--	--	--	--	--
	Current weak and variable																	
3511	Redfish Point	5d	30°08.64'	85°40.01'	+1 20	-0 02	-0 49	-0 17	0.2	0.4	--	--	0.4	101°	--	--	0.6	319°
	...do...	19d	30°08.64'	85°40.01'	-1 03	-0 05	+0 36	-0 14	0.3	0.3	--	--	0.4	118°	--	--	0.4	310°
	...do...	32d	30°08.64'	85°40.01'	-1 11	+0 26	+1 04	-0 50	0.4	0.2	--	--	0.4	129°	--	--	0.3	303°
3513	Paper Mill	3d	30°07.83'	85°37.90'	+0 44	+0 28	-0 41	+0 58	0.3	0.4	--	--	--	--	--	--	0.7	249°
	...do...	16d	30°07.83'	85°37.90'	-0 46	--	+0 19	+1 08	0.3	0.3	--	--	0.3	086°	--	--	0.5	245°
	...do...	27d	30°07.83'	85°37.90'	+2 59	+0 41	+0 40	+0 05	0.3	0.2	--	--	--	--	--	--	0.3	238°
3515	Bear Point, 0.6nm E of	4d	30°09.86'	85°42.81'	-0 05	+0 44	-0 20	+0 41	0.2	0.4	--	--	0.2	297°	--	--	0.6	120°
	...do...	14d	30°09.86'	85°42.81'	-2 13	+1 13	+1 13	-0 38	0.4	0.2	--	--	0.5	312°	--	--	0.3	137°
	...do...	27d	30°09.86'	85°42.81'	+0 52	+2 40	+2 40	+0 31	0.5	--	--	--	0.6	334°	--	--	--	--
3517	Long Point, West Bay	4d	30°14.35'	85°44.99'	--	+0 04	+0 11	--	0.2	0.2	--	--	0.2	005°	--	--	0.3	173°
	PENSACOLA BAY																	
	on Mobile Bay Entrance, p.168																	
3519	Pensacola Bay entrance, midchannel		30°20.1'	87°18.0'	-1 13	-1 01	+0 06	-0 49	1.1	1.3	--	--	1.6	074°	--	--	1.8	256°

Endnotes can be found at the end of table 2.

TABLE 2. – CURRENT DIFFERENCES AND OTHER CONSTANTS

No.	PLACE	Meter Depth (ft)	POSITION Latitude North	POSITION Longitude West	TIME DIFF. Min. before Flood (h m)	TIME DIFF. Flood (h m)	TIME DIFF. Min. before Ebb (h m)	TIME DIFF. Ebb (h m)	SPEED RATIOS Flood	SPEED RATIOS Ebb	Min. before Flood knots	Min. before Flood Dir.	Maximum Flood knots	Maximum Flood Dir.	Min. before Ebb knots	Min. before Ebb Dir.	Maximum Ebb knots	Maximum Ebb Dir.
	MOBILE BAY Time meridian, 90°W				*on Mobile Bay Entrance, p.168*													
3521	Main Ship Channel entrance	11d	30° 09.2'	88° 03.2'	---	+0 20	---	+1 16	0.4	0.7	---	---	0.7	344°	0.0	175°	1.0	182°
3523	MOBILE BAY ENTRANCE, off Mobile Point	25d	30° 13.62'	88° 02.07'	Daily predictions						0.1	285°	1.4	014°	---	---	1.4	201°
	...do.	41d	30° 13.62'	88° 02.07'	-0 19	-0 01	+0 08	+0 01	0.8	0.7	0.1	285°	1.2	007°	0.1	282°	1.0	198°
	...do.		30° 13.62'	88° 02.07'	-0 38	-0 01	+0 08	+0 16	0.6	0.5	0.2	279°	0.9	357°	0.1	280°	0.8	205°
3525	Channel, 6 miles N of Mobile Point		30° 19.8'	88° 01.7'	-0 10	+0 46	+1 14	+1 09	0.4	0.4	---	---	0.6	032°	---	---	0.5	208°
3527	Great Point Clear, channel west of		30° 29.4'	88° 01.1'	Current weak and variable						---	---			---	---		
3529	Mobile River entrance		30° 40.2'	88° 02.0'	+5 11	+4 24	+2 32	+3 11	0.2	0.5	---	---	0.3	333°	---	---	0.7	151°
3531	Tensaw River entrance (bridge)		30° 40.9'	88° 00.7'	+1 39	+1 05	-1 12	+0 05	0.3	0.7	---	---	0.4	029°	---	---	1.0	222°
3533	Dauphin Island Causeway	7d	30° 17.36'	88° 07.72'	+0 44	+4 50	+1 50	+1 26	0.9	0.9	---	---	1.2	061°	---	---	1.2	242°
	MISSISSIPPI SOUND																	
3535	Petit Bois Island, Dauphin Island, between	5d	30° 13.31'	88° 22.25'	-3 31	-2 12	-2 06	-1 02	0.3	0.4	0.1	268°	0.4	349°	---	---	0.6	172°
3537	Horn Island Pass (LB 17)	12d	30° 12.90'	88° 30.65'	-2 04	+3 08	-1 09	-0 40	0.5	1.0	---	---	0.6	024°	---	---	1.4	228°
	...do.	25d	30° 12.90'	88° 30.65'	-2 49	+3 02	-0 20	-0 35	0.5	0.5	---	---	0.7	024°	---	---	0.9	222°
3539	Horn Island, Petit Bois Island, between	7d	30° 13.54'	88° 32.40'	-2 38	-1 23	-0 58	-0 36	0.4	0.6	---	---	0.6	048°	0.1	134°	0.7	172°
3541	Pascagoula River highway bridge <24>		30° 22.3'	88° 33.8'	---	+0 18	---	-0 36	0.9	0.9	---	---	1.2	016°	---	---	1.2	201°
	Gulfport Ship Channel																	
3543	Ship Island, 1.0nm S of, (LB 22)	11d	30° 11.64'	88° 59.35'	-2 09	+3 28	+0 43	+0 56	0.2	0.3	---	---	0.3	308°	---	---	0.5	113°
3545	Ship Island, 0.5nm NW of, (LB 26)	15d	30° 12.96'	88° 59.68'	-0 05	+3 50	+2 05	+1 41	0.3	0.4	---	---	0.5	008°	---	---	0.5	141°
3547	Ship Island, 1.8nm NW of, (DM 32)	10d	30° 14.35'	89° 00.00'	+2 49	+5 04	+2 22	+2 29	0.3	0.4	---	---	0.4	029°	---	---	0.6	184°
	LOUISIANA COAST																	
3549	Quatre Bayoux Pass, Barataria Bay		29° 18.6'	89° 51.1'	+1 12	+0 34	+0 31	+0 32	0.6	0.9	---	---	1.2	288°	---	---	1.3	103°
3551	Pass Abel, Barataria Bay		29° 17.7'	89° 54.2'	+0 28	+0 30	+0 01	+0 23	0.6	1.1	---	---	0.9	317°	---	---	1.6	143°
3553	Barataria Pass, Barataria Bay		29° 16.3'	89° 56.9'	+2 04	+0 53	+0 49	+0 45	1.1	0.9	---	---	1.5	315°	---	---	1.3	120°
3555	Barataria Bay, 1.1 mi. NE of Manilla		29° 26.2'	89° 57.6'	+4 16	+3 05	+2 58	+4 38	0.3	0.3	---	---	0.4	356°	---	---	0.5	118°
3557	Caminada Pass, Barataria Bay		29° 11.9'	90° 02.8'	+1 19	+1 57	+0 44	+1 04	1.1	1.1	---	---	1.5	297°	---	---	1.5	118°
3559	Seabrook Bridge, New Orleans <1>		30° 01.9'	90° 02.1'	---	-2 54	---	-4 02	0.9	0.6	---	---	1.2	350°	---	---	0.9	170°
3561	Cat Island Pass, Terrebonne Bay	6	29° 04.8'	90° 34.4'	-2 32	-1 57	-1 05	-2 59	0.8	1.2	---	---	1.1	013°	---	---	1.5	195°
3563	Wine Island Pass		29° 04.2'	90° 38.0'	-4 33	-5 03	-3 38	-4 17	1.2	1.5	---	---	1.7	325°	---	---	1.9	160°
3565	Caillou Boca, Caillou Bay	4	29° 03.5'	90° 48.5'	-0 33	-0 41	+2 59	-0 05	0.9	0.6	---	---	1.3	095°	---	---	0.7	264°
3567	Calcasieu Pass, Cameron Fishing Pier	6d	29° 45.85'	93° 20.58'	Daily predictions *on Galveston Bay Entrance, p.180*						---	---	1.5	356°	---	---	1.8	175°
3569	Calcasieu Pass, 35 miles south of		29° 10.15'	93° 19.23'	Current weak and variable						---	---			---	---		
3571	Calcasieu Pass, 67 miles south of <41>		28° 39.80'	93° 19.95'	Current weak and variable						---	---			---	---		
	TEXAS																	
	Sabine Pass				*on Sabine Pass, p.176*													
3573	Texas Point, 1.7 miles SSE of	4d	29° 39.0'	93° 49.6'	+0 33	-0 08	-0 50	-0 17	1.0	1.6	---	---	1.1	335°	---	---	1.6	145°
3575	SABINE PASS, USCG STATION	3d	29° 43.72'	93° 52.20'	Daily predictions						---	---	1.1	321°	---	---	1.0	143°
3577	Sabine Front Range		29° 45.48'	93° 53.41'	+0 19	+0 10	+0 36	+0 26	1.2	1.2	---	---	1.3	335°	0.1	248°	1.2	166°
3579	Rainbow Bridge, Sabine Lake	13	29° 58.78'	93° 52.29'	+1 14	+2 01	+4 40	+2 40	0.7	0.6	---	---	0.8	285°	---	---	0.7	108°
3581	GALVESTON BAY ENT. (between jetties)	15d	29° 20.92'	94° 42.85'	Daily predictions *on Galveston Bay Entrance, p.180*						---	---	1.4	277°	0.1	004°	1.2	088°
	...do.	5d	29° 20.92'	94° 42.85'	+0 17	+0 15	+0 02	+0 05	1.0	1.1	0.1	179°	1.4	272°	---	---	1.3	091°
	...do.	34d	29° 20.92'	94° 42.85'	-0 18	-0 01	-0 03	-0 13	0.8	0.9	0.1	188°	1.1	274°	---	---	1.1	094°

Endnotes can be found at the end of table 2.

TABLE 2. – CURRENT DIFFERENCES AND OTHER CONSTANTS

No.	PLACE	Meter Depth (ft)	Latitude North	Longitude West	Min. before Flood (h m)	Flood (h m)	Min. before Ebb (h m)	Ebb (h m)	Speed Ratio Flood	Speed Ratio Ebb	Min before Flood knots	Min before Flood Dir.	Max Flood knots	Max Flood Dir.	Min before Ebb knots	Min before Ebb Dir.	Max Ebb knots	Max Ebb Dir.
	GALVESTON BAY Time meridian, 90°W				*on Bolivar Roads, p.184*													
3583	Galveston Bay Entr. Channel, LB11	13	29° 20.55'	94° 44.46'	+0 04	-0 02	+0 37	+0 24	0.8	1.0	0.1	000°	1.3	282°	0.1	359°	1.3	077°
	...do.	26	29° 20.55'	94° 44.46'	-0 25	-0 13	-0 34	-0 44	0.8	0.9	0.1	346°	1.3	267°	0.1	344°	1.2	065°
3585	BOLIVAR ROADS	14d	29° 20.60'	94° 46.88'	Daily predictions						0.1	210°	1.6	296°	0.1	210°	1.3	123°
	...do.	8d	29° 20.60'	94° 46.88'	+0 09	+0 07	-0 16	-0 01	1.0	1.1	0.1	213°	1.6	295°	0.1	033°	1.5	125°
	...do.	31d	29° 20.60'	94° 46.88'	-0 32	-0 11	+0 17	-0 08	0.8	0.6	--	--	1.2	306°	--	--	1.0	115°
3587	Quarantine Station, 0.3 mile S of <24>	16d	29° 19.8'	94° 46.7'	--	+2 16	-2 30	-1 53	0.7	0.6	--	--	1.1	196°	--	--	0.8	009°
3589	Galveston Channel, west end <24>	3d	29° 18.6'	94° 49.2'	-0 30	-0 54	-3 49	-1 11	1.0	1.2	--	--	1.6	272°	0.1	182°	1.6	103°
3591	Galveston Causeway RR. bridge	14d	29° 17.85'	94° 53.15'	-0 12	-0 22	-2 14	-1 21	0.4	0.8	--	--	0.6	266°	0.1	052°	1.1	099°
3593	Houston Channel, W of Port Bolivar	26d	29° 21.88'	94° 47.80'	-0 05	-0 18	-2 15	-1 41	1.1	1.0	--	--	1.7	313°	--	--	1.3	135°
	...do.		29° 21.88'	94° 47.80'	-0 03	-0 11	-2 12	-1 55	1.0	0.9	--	--	1.5	312°	--	--	1.2	133°
	...do.		29° 21.88'	94° 47.80'	-0 06	-0 14	-2 12	-1 41	0.9	0.8	--	--	1.4	312°	--	--	1.0	133°
3595	Houston Ship Channel (Red Fish Bar)	7d	29° 30.44'	94° 52.48'	+0 41	+1 13	+1 17	+0 50	0.5	0.5	0.1	069°	0.7	341°	--	--	0.7	154°
	...do.	14d	29° 30.44'	94° 52.48'	+0 45	+1 28	+1 20	+1 10	0.7	0.7	0.1	064°	1.0	331°	--	--	0.9	148°
	...do.	24d	29° 30.44'	94° 52.48'	+0 48	+1 15	+1 05	+1 42	0.5	0.5	0.1	065°	0.8	323°	--	--	0.7	144°
3597	Morgans Point	6d	29° 40.79'	94° 58.90'	+2 15	+1 43	-0 50	+1 16	0.3	0.5	--	--	0.5	336°	--	--	0.5	163°
	...do.	15d	29° 40.79'	94° 58.90'	+1 44	+1 23	+1 02	+1 11	0.2	0.4	--	--	0.5	341°	--	--	0.5	159°
	...do.	25d	29° 40.79'	94° 58.90'	+0 47	+0 58	--	+1 20	--	0.3	--	--	0.4	340°	--	--	0.4	160°
	TEXAS COAST				*on Galveston Bay Entrance, p.180*													
3599	Matagorda Channel (entrance jetty)	15	28° 25.3'	96° 19.4'	-0 40	-0 27	-1 14	-1 25	1.4	1.5	--	--	2.0	317°	--	--	1.9	142°
					on Aransas Pass, p.188													
3601	ARANSAS PASS	35d	27° 50.03'	97° 02.65'	Daily predictions				1.1	1.5	--	--	1.6	300°	--	--	1.5	118°
	...do.	15d	27° 50.03'	97° 02.65'	+0 00	+0 00	+0 00	+0 00	0.9	0.8	--	--	1.9	300°	--	--	2.0	118°
	...do.	50d	27° 50.03'	97° 02.65'	+0 24	+1 48	+2 11	+1 09	0.7	0.5	--	--	1.0	300°	--	--	0.7	118°
3603	Port Ingleside	5d	27° 48.90'	97° 13.80'	--	--	--	--	--	--	--	--	0.7	286°	--	--	0.5	102°
3605	Sabine Bank <46>		29° 18.20'	94° 00.20'	--	--	--	--	--	--	--	--	--	--	--	--	--	--
3607	Heald Bank, 28 miles SSE of <46>		28° 40.17'	93° 59.60'	--	--	--	--	--	--	--	--	--	--	--	--	--	--
	PUERTO RICO Time meridian, 60°W				*on Vieques Passage, p.192*													
3609	Las Mareas		17° 55.41'	66° 09.70'	Current weak and variable						--	--	0.3	256°	--	--	0.4	095°
3611	Punta Ostiones, 1.5 miles west of		18° 05.2'	67° 13.6'	-0 26	-0 52	-0 04	-0 35	1.7	1.3	--	--	1.0	187°	--	--	0.9	001°
3613	VIEQUES PASSAGE		18° 11.3'	65° 37.1'	Daily predictions						--	--	0.6	250°	--	--	0.7	057°
3615	Vieques Sound		18° 15.87'	65° 34.20'	-0 44	-1 16	-1 28	-1 05	0.7	0.9	--	--	0.4	180°	--	--	0.6	355°
3617	Largo Shoals, west of		18° 19'	65° 35'	-0 52	-1 28	-1 33	-1 08	0.7	1.0	--	--	0.4	186°	--	--	0.7	330°
3619	Ramos Cay, 0.3 mile SE of <1>		18° 18.6'	65° 36.4'	--	-0 42	--	-0 44	0.3	0.1	--	--	0.2	120°	--	--	0.1	284°
3621	Palominos Island, 0.9 mile SW of <13>		18° 20.1'	65° 34.8'	-1 13	-1 52	-2 27	-0 48	0.5	1.6	--	--	0.3	162°	--	--	0.5	307°
3623	Fajardo Harbor (channel)		18° 20.1'	65° 37'	--	--	--	-1 45	--	--	--	--	--	--	--	--	--	--
3625	Isla Marina, 0.2 mile west of <1> <13>		18° 20.50'	65° 37.38'	--	--	--	-2 06	--	1.0	--	--	--	--	--	--	1.1	339°
3627	Coronala Laja, 0.4 mile NW of <1> <13>		18° 21.6'	65° 37.3'	--	--	--	-1 33	--	0.4	--	--	--	--	--	--	0.7	335°
3629	Pasaje de San Juan <1> <13>		18° 23.9'	65° 36.9'	--	--	--	-1 15	--	1.7	--	--	--	--	--	--	0.3	000°
3631	Bahia de San Juan		18° 27.23'	66° 06.6'	Current weak and variable						--	--	--	--	--	--	1.2	310°
3633	Bahia de San Juan entrance <42>		18° 28.3'	66° 07.6'	Current weak and variable						--	--	--	--	--	--	--	--

ENDNOTES

<1> The times of minimum before flood and minimum before ebb are indefinite.

< 2> Current speeds up to 9.0 knots have been observed in the vicinity of the Boilers.

< 6> Current is variable; current speeds are usually less than 1 knot. Currents are strong in the entrance to Menemsha Pond.

< 7> In the open waters of Buzzards Bay, except in the entrance and off Penikese Island and West Island, the current is too weak and variable to be predicted.

< 8> The currents in Narragansett Bay have a pronounced irregularity which is evidenced at times during the month by a long period of approximate slack water preceding the flood, and at other times by a double flood of two distinct maximums of speed separated by a period of lesser speed. These peculiarities appear to be somewhat unstable, consequently, flood currents differing from those predicted should be expected. The ebb current is fairly regular and the predictions for maximum ebb will usually agree closely with the current encountered.

< 9> At minimum flood, current sometimes ebbs for a short period.

<10> At minimum flood, current frequently ebbs for a short period.

<11> Flood is too weak to be predicted. Time difference gives mid-point of 4 hour stand of weak and variable current and time of maximum ebb.

<13> Current seldom floods.

<16> For maximum southward current only, the gates of the lock being closed to prevent northward flow. Apply difference and ratio to maximum ebb at The Narrows.

<17> Spring freshwater flow tends to decrease flood speeds and increase ebb speeds by approximately 0.25knots. This also has the effect of delaying the slack before flood and advancing the slack before ebb by 15 to 45 minutes.

<19> Current always ebbs. Ebb speeds vary depending on freshwater flow and average 1.5 knots in the spring and 0.5 knots in the fall.

<20> Current is rotary, turning clockwise. It flows northwest at times of "minimum before flood" at The Narrows; northeast 1 hour after maximum flood; southeast 1 1/2 hours after "minimum before ebb"; and southwest 2 hours after maximum ebb.

<21> Current is rotary, turning clockwise. Minimum current of 0.2 knot sets west about the time of "minimum before flood" at The Narrows. Minimum current of 0.2 knot sets ENE about the time of "minimum before ebb" at The Narrows.

<22> In Sandy Hook Bay (except in southern extremity) the current is weak.

<24> The times of minimum before flood and ebb are variable.

<25> Current usually ebbs during the period 3 hours before to 3 hours after maximum ebb. Flood is weak and variable.

<26> Station is east of channel. Velocities in mid-channel are approximately 40% greater.

<27> Flood is usually weak and of short duration. A weak ebb or flood current occurs about 6 hours after maximum flood at Delaware Bay Entrance.

<29> Current tends to rotate clockwise. At times of "minimum before flood" there may be a weak current flowing WSW while at times of "minimum before ebb" there may be a weak current flowing ENE.

<30> Current tends to rotate clockwise. At times of "minimum before flood" there may be a weak current flowing southwest, while at times of "minimum before ebb" there may be a weak current flowing north.

<31> Flood usually flows northward, however, direction is variable.

<32> Flood is variable, current sometimes changes to ebb for a short time during the flood period.

<33> Due to changes in the waterway, average speed values given are probably too large.

<34> Flood usually occurs in a southerly direction and the ebb in a northeastwardly direction.

<35> Flood is weak and variable.

<37> For greater ebb only.

<39> For greater ebb. Lesser ebb is almost equal to greater ebb.

ENDNOTES

<41> Current is weak and variable. Current is somewhat rotary turning clockwise.

<42> Current is normally weak and variable, but winds may cause heavy swells.

<43> Minimum ebb is extremely weak, possibly flooding for a short period.

<44> Every other ebb phase exhibits a double ebb pattern. For single ebb phases use time differences and speed ratios of the first ebb.

<45> Ebb is weak and variable.

<46> Current is somewhat rotary, speed seldom exceeds 0.3 knot.

<47> Flood is weak and variable with speeds less than or equal to 0.2 knot. Minimums are indefinite.

<49> During period observed, the current flow was nearly continuous in a southwesterly direction with an average speed of about 0.4 knot.

<51> Observations were made in the summer months when the freshwater discharge was at a minimum. Periods of heavier discharge will increase ebb current speeds and decrease flood current speeds.

<52> Observations were made in the spring during period of heavy freshwater discharge. Periods of lesser discharge will decrease ebb current speeds and increase flood current speeds.

<53> Observations at this location showed long periods of minimum currents and short durations of flood and ebb currents.

<54> Turbulence with hazardous current speeds of 6 to 7 knots have been reported near the bridges in the canal. Extreme caution should be exercised.

<55> The time of minimum before flood is indefinite.

<58> It has been reported that under conditions of extreme river discharge, the currents can reach 7 or 8 knots. Caution should be exercised when docking and undocking vessels.

<59> Flood currents are defined as flowing out of Buzzards Bay into Vineyard Sound.

<62> Short term observational data taken by United States Power Squadrons (USPS) as part of the NOS/USPS Tidal Current Predictions Quality Assurance Program has shown that predictions at this location are accurate.

<63> Short term observational data taken by United States Power Squadrons (USPS) as part of the NOS/USPS Tidal Current Predictions Quality Assurance Program have shown predictions at these locations to be inaccurate.

- Observed speeds at "Little Creek" were approximately twice the predicted values.

- Observations at "Newport News Channel, west end" showed both time and speed of the currents were altered by the Monitor-Merrimac Tunnel. Predictions should be used with caution.

- Observations at "Lake Worth Inlet" showed that maximum currents occurred up to 2 hours earlier than predicted, and speeds were decreased by at least 25%.

- Observations at "Fort Pierce Inlet" showed that maximum currents occurred up to 1 hours earlier than predicted, and speeds were decreased by at least 25%.

CAUTION—During the first 2 hours of flood in the channel north of Governers Island, the current in the Hudson River is still ebbing while during the first 1 1/2 hours of ebb in this channel, the current in the Hudson River is still flooding. At such times, special care must be taken by large ships in navigating this channel.

<64> At times of slack before flood there is a non-tidal current flowing NE at speeds of approximately 0.5 knots.

TABLE 3.—SPEED OF CURRENT AT ANY TIME

EXPLANATION

Though the predictions in this publication give only the slacks and maximum currents, the speed of the current at any intermediate time can be obtained approximately by the use of this table. Directions for its use are given below the table.

Before using the table for a place listed in Table 2, the predictions for the day in question should be first obtained by means of the differences and ratios given in Table 2.

The examples below follow the numbered steps in the directions.

Example 1.—Find the speed of the current in The Race at 6:00 on a day when the predictions which immediately precede and follow 6:00 are as follows:

(1)	Slack Water	Maximum (Flood)	
	Time	Time	Speed
	4:18	7:36	3.2 knots

Directions under the table indicate Table A is to be used for this station.

(2) Interval between slack and maximum flood is 7:36 − 4:18 = 3^h18^m. Column heading nearest to 3^h18^m is 3^h20^m.

(3) Interval between slack and time desired is 6:00 − 4:18 = 1^h42^m. Line labeled 1^h40^m is nearest to 1^h42^m.

(4) Factor in column 3^h20^m and on line 1^h40^m is 0.7. The above flood speed of 3.2 knots multiplied by 0.7 gives a flood speed of 2.24 knots (or 2.2 knots, since one decimal is sufficient) for the time desired.

Example 2.—Find the speed of the current in the Harlem River at Broadway Bridge at 16:30 on a day when the predictions (obtained using the difference and ratio in table 2) which immediately precede and follow 16:30 are as follows:

(1)	Maximum (Ebb)		Slack Water
	Time	Speed	Time
	13:49	2.5 knots	17:25

Directions under the table indicate Table B is to be used, since this station in Table 2 is referred to Hell Gate.

(2) Interval between slack and maximum ebb is 17:25 − 13:49 = 3^h36^m. Hence, use column headed 3^h40^m.

(3) Interval between slack and time desired is 17:25 − 16:30 = 0^h55^m. Hence, use line labeled 1^h00^m.

(4) Factor in column 3^h40^m and on line 1^h00^m is 0.5. The above ebb speed of 2.5 knots multiplied by 0.5 gives an ebb speed of 1.2 knots for the desired time.

When the interval between slack and maximum current is greater than 5^h40^m, enter the table with one-half the interval between slack and maximum current and one-half the interval between slack and the desired time and use the factor thus found.

TABLE 3.—SPEED OF CURRENT AT ANY TIME

TABLE A

Interval between slack and desired time	Interval between slack and maximum current													
	h. m. 1 20	h. m. 1 40	h. m. 2 00	h. m. 2 20	h. m. 2 40	h. m. 3 00	h.m. 3 20	h.m. 3 40	h.m. 4 00	h.m. 4 20	h.m. 4 40	h.m. 5 00	h.m. 5 20	h.m. 5 40
h. m.	knots	knots	knots	knots	knots	knots	knots	knots	knots	knots	knots	knots	knots	knots
0 20	0.4	0.3	0.3	0.2	0.2	0.2	0.2	0.1	0.1	0.1	0.1	0.1	0.1	0.1
0 40	0.7	0.6	0.5	0.4	0.4	0.3	0.3	0.3	0.3	0.2	0.2	0.2	0.2	0.2
1 00	0.9	0.8	0.7	0.6	0.6	0.5	0.5	0.4	0.4	0.4	0.3	0.3	0.3	0.3
1 20	1.0	1.0	0.9	0.8	0.7	0.6	0.6	0.5	0.5	0.5	0.4	0.4	0.4	0.4
1 40	----	1.0	1.0	0.9	0.8	0.8	0.7	0.7	0.6	0.6	0.5	0.5	0.5	0.4
2 00	----	----	1.0	1.0	0.9	0.9	0.8	0.8	0.7	0.7	0.6	0.6	0.6	0.5
2 20	----	----	----	1.0	1.0	0.9	0.9	0.8	0.8	0.7	0.7	0.7	0.6	0.6
2 40	----	----	----	----	1.0	1.0	1.0	0.9	0.9	0.8	0.8	0.7	0.7	0.7
3 00	----	----	----	----	----	1.0	1.0	1.0	0.9	0.9	0.8	0.8	0.8	0.7
3 20	----	----	----	----	----	----	1.0	1.0	1.0	0.9	0.9	0.9	0.8	0.8
3 40	----	----	----	----	----	----	----	1.0	1.0	1.0	0.9	0.9	0.9	0.9
4 00	----	----	----	----	----	----	----	----	1.0	1.0	1.0	1.0	0.9	0.9
4 20	----	----	----	----	----	----	----	----	----	1.0	1.0	1.0	1.0	0.9
4 40	----	----	----	----	----	----	----	----	----	----	1.0	1.0	1.0	1.0
5 00	----	----	----	----	----	----	----	----	----	----	----	1.0	1.0	1.0
5 20	----	----	----	----	----	----	----	----	----	----	----	----	1.0	1.0
5 40	----	----	----	----	----	----	----	----	----	----	----	----	----	1.0

TABLE B

Interval between slack and desired time	Interval between slack and maximum current													
	h. m. 1 20	h. m. 1 40	h. m. 2 00	h. m. 2 20	h. m. 2 40	h. m. 3 00	h. m. 3 20	h. m. 3 40	h. m. 4 00	h. m. 4 20	h. m. 4 40	h. m. 5 00	h. m. 5 20	h. m. 5 40
h. m.	knots	knots	knots	knots	knots	knots	knots	knots	knots	knots	knots	knots	knots	knots
0 20	0.5	0.4	0.4	0.3	0.3	0.3	0.3	0.3	0.2	0.2	0.2	0.2	0.2	0.2
0 40	0.8	0.7	0.6	0.5	0.5	0.5	0.4	0.4	0.4	0.4	0.3	0.3	0.3	0.3
1 00	0.9	0.8	0.8	0.7	0.7	0.6	0.6	0.5	0.5	0.5	0.4	0.4	0.4	0.4
1 20	1.0	1.0	0.9	0.8	0.8	0.7	0.7	0.6	0.6	0.6	0.5	0.5	0.5	0.5
1 40	----	1.0	1.0	0.9	0.9	0.8	0.8	0.7	0.7	0.7	0.6	0.6	0.6	0.6
2 00	----	----	1.0	1.0	0.9	0.9	0.9	0.8	0.8	0.7	0.7	0.7	0.7	0.6
2 20	----	----	----	1.0	1.0	1.0	0.9	0.9	0.8	0.8	0.8	0.7	0.7	0.7
2 40	----	----	----	----	1.0	1.0	1.0	0.9	0.9	0.9	0.8	0.8	0.8	0.7
3 00	----	----	----	----	----	1.0	1.0	1.0	0.9	0.9	0.9	0.9	0.8	0.8
3 20	----	----	----	----	----	----	1.0	1.0	1.0	1.0	0.9	0.9	0.9	0.9
3 40	----	----	----	----	----	----	----	1.0	1.0	1.0	1.0	0.9	0.9	0.9
4 00	----	----	----	----	----	----	----	----	1.0	1.0	1.0	1.0	0.9	0.9
4 20	----	----	----	----	----	----	----	----	----	1.0	1.0	1.0	1.0	0.9
4 40	----	----	----	----	----	----	----	----	----	----	1.0	1.0	1.0	1.0
5 00	----	----	----	----	----	----	----	----	----	----	----	1.0	1.0	1.0
5 20	----	----	----	----	----	----	----	----	----	----	----	----	1.0	1.0
5 40	----	----	----	----	----	----	----	----	----	----	----	----	----	1.0

Use **Table A** for all places except those listed below for Table B.

Use **Table B** for Cape Code Canal, Hell Gate, Chesapeake and Delaware Canal, and all stations in table 2 which are referred to them.

1. From predictions find the time of slack water and the time and velocity of maximum current (flood or ebb), one of which is immediately before and the other after the time for which the velocity is desired.

2. Find the interval of time between the above slack and maximum current, and enter the top of Table A or B with the interval which most nearly agrees with this value.

3. Find the interval of time between the above slack and the time desired, and enter the side of Table A or B with the interval which most nearly agrees with this value.

4. Find, in the Table, the factor corresponding to the above two intervals, and multiply the maximum velocity by this factor. The result will be the approximate velocity at the time desired.

TABLE 4.—DURATION OF SLACK

The predicted times of slack water given in this publication indicate the instant of zero speed, which is only momentary. There is a period on each side of the slack water, however, during which the current is so weak that for practical purposes it may be considered negligible.

The following tables give, for various maximum currents, the approximate period of time during which weak currents not exceeding 0.1 to 0.5 knot will be encountered. This duration includes the last of the flood or ebb and the beginning of the following ebb or flood, that is, half of the duration will be before and half after the time of slack water.

Table A should be used for all places except those listed below for Table B.

Table B should be used for Cape Cod Canal, Hell Gate, Chesapeake and Delaware Canal, and all stations in Table 2 which are referred to them.

Duration of weak current near time of slack water

Maximum current	Period with a speed not more than -				
	0.1 knot	0.2 knot	0.3 knot	0.4 knot	0.5 knot
Knots	Minutes	Minutes	Minutes	Minutes	Minutes
1.0	23	46	70	94	120
1.5	15	31	46	62	78
2.0	11	23	35	46	58
3.0	8	15	23	31	38
4.0	6	11	17	23	29
5.0	5	9	14	18	23
6.0	4	8	11	15	19
7.0	3	7	10	13	16
8.0	3	6	9	11	14
9.0	3	5	8	10	13
10.0	2	5	7	9	11

TABLE B

Maximum current	Period with a speed not more than -				
	0.1 knot	0.2 knot	0.3 knot	0.4 knot	0.5 knot
Knots	Minutes	Minutes	Minutes	Minutes	Minutes
1.0	13	28	46	66	89
1.5	8	18	28	39	52
2.0	6	13	20	28	36
3.0	4	8	13	18	22
4.0	3	6	9	13	17
5.0	3	5	8	10	13
6.0	2	4	6	8	11
7.0	2	4	5	7	9
8.0	2	3	5	6	8

When there is a difference between the speeds of the maximum flood and ebb preceding and following the slack for which the duration is desired, it will be sufficiently accurate for practical purposes to find a separate duration for each maximum speed and take the average of the two as the duration of the weak current.

TABLE 5.—ROTARY TIDAL CURRENTS

EXPLANATION

Offshore and in some of the wider indentations of the coast, the tidal current is quite different from that found in the more protected bays and rivers. In these inside waters the tidal current is of the reversing type. The current sets in one direction for a period of 6 hours after which is ceases to flow momentarily and then sets in the opposite direction during the following 6 hours. The offshore tidal current, not being confined to a definite channel, changes its direction continually and never slows to a true slack water. Thus in a tidal cycle of 12 ½ hours it will have set in all directions of the compass. This type of current is referred to as a rotary current.

A characteristic feature of the rotary current is the absence of slack water. Although the current generally varies from hour to hour, this variation from greatest current to least current and back again to greatest does not give rise to a period of slack water. When the speed of the rotary tidal current is least, it is known as the minimum current, and when it is greatest it is known as the maximum current. The minimum and maximum speeds of the rotary current are related to each other in the same way as slack and strength of current. A minimum speed of the current follows a maximum speed by an interval of approximately 3 hours and followed in turn by another maximum after a further interval of 3 hours.

The following table provides the direction and speed of the rotary current for each hour at a number of offshore stations. The times and speeds are referred to predictions for a reference station in Table 1. All times are in local standard time for the secondary station.

The speeds given in the table are the average speeds for the station. The Moon when new, full, or at perigee tends to increase the speeds 15 to 20 percent above average. When perigee occurs at or near the time of new or full Moon, the current speeds will be 30 to 40 percent above average. The Moon when at first and third quarter or at apogee tend to decrease the current speeds below average by 15 to 20 percent. When apogee occurs at or near the first or third quarter Moon, the currents will be 30 to 40 percent below average. The speeds will be about average when apogee occurs at or near the time of the new or full Moon and also when perigee occurs at or near the first or third quarter Moon. (See table of astronomical data for dates of Moon phases and other data.)

The direction of the current is given in degrees, true, reading clockwise from 0° at north, and is the direction toward which the water is flowing.

The speeds and directions are for tidal current only and do not include the effect of the wind. When a wind is blowing, a wind-driven current will be set up as is superimposed on the normal tidal current. The actual current encountered will thus be a combination of the wind-driven current and the tidal current. See the chapters on "Wind-Driven Currents" and "The Combination of Currents".

As an example, in the following table the current at Nantucket Shoals is given for each hour after maximum flood at Pollock Rip Channel. Suppose it is desired to find the direction and speed of the current at Nantucket Shoals at 3:15 p.m. (15:15) on a day when the maximum flood at Pollock Rip Channel is predicted in Table 1 to occur at 13:20. The desired time is therefore 2 hours after the maximum flood at Pollock Rip Channel. From the table the tidal current at Nantucket Shoals at 2 hours is setting 015E true with an average speed of 0.8 knots. If this day is near the time of new Moon and about half way between apogee and perigee, then the distance effect of the moon will be nil and the phase effect alone will increase the speed by about 15 percent, to 0.9 knots.

Caution - Speeds from 1 ½ to 3 knots have been observed at most of the stations in this table. Near Diamond Shoal Light a speed of 4 knots has occurred.

At some offshore stations, such as those near the entrance to Chesapeake Bay, the tidal current is directed alternately toward and away from the bay entrance with intervening periods of slack water. At these stations the current is essentially a reversing current. For such places, differences for predicting the current are given in Table 2.

TABLE 5.—ROTARY TIDAL CURRENTS

262

Station Name	Depth		Hourly time increments											
			0	1	2	3	4	5	6	7	8	9	10	11
after Maximum Flood at BAY OF FUNDY ENTRANCE (Add time increment to the time of maximum flood, then subtract 1 hour to correct to standard time at the subordinate station.)														
Horse Head Island, 0.2nm ENE of	14	knots	0.13	0.19	0.20	0.17	0.16	0.18	0.20	0.15	0.12	0.19	0.23	0.21
		degrees	106	298	340	133	198	184	174	121	084	054	036	083
Pickering Island, north of	14	knots	0.23	0.20	0.21	0.31	0.29	0.27	0.22	0.23	0.24	0.20	0.24	0.24
		degrees	296	278	281	283	256	254	237	200	198	171	088	087
Swains Ledge, WSW of	14	knots	0.39	0.36	0.39	0.35	0.29	0.30	0.38	0.36	0.37	0.27	0.27	0.24
		degrees	029	040	313	296	275	141	163	171	172	034	038	035
Isleboro Harbor, Penobscot Bay	14	knots	0.30	0.29	0.22	0.32	0.31	0.32	0.43	0.42	0.25	0.24	0.25	0.20
		degrees	342	348	336	348	210	205	188	177	139	090	069	063
Mark Island, 0.3 nm North of	14	knots	0.33	0.19	0.17	0.18	0.28	0.23	0.20	0.21	0.23	0.25	0.28	0.32
		degrees	044	088	171	244	235	204	329	294	308	312	022	037
After Maximum Flood at BUCKSPORT														
Islesboro Ledge, PEB0612 Bin 8	51	knots	0.24	0.12	0.04	0.19	0.32	0.37	0.34	0.26	0.13	0.06	0.18	0.26
		degrees	035	037	116	203	204	196	182	168	155	074	040	039
Islesboro Ledge, PEB0612 Bin 13	18.5	knots	0.17	0.08	0.06	0.14	0.28	0.43	0.48	0.46	0.37	0.21	0.06	0.17
		degrees	013	354	276	215	192	183	189	205	216	223	287	002
After Minimum Before Flood at BOSTON HARBOR														
Ram Island, 0.2nm NNE of	10	knots	0.03	0.23	0.23	0.25	0.32	0.33	0.31	0.29	0.27	0.28	0.26	0.23
		degrees	265	265	270	282	319	333	357	067	070	073	076	073
Ram Island, 0.2nm southeast of	10	knots	0.30	0.45	0.46	0.50	0.51	0.50	0.51	0.49	0.48	0.49	0.46	0.40
		degrees	210	258	248	262	280	340	009	049	068	074	082	090
Great Pig Rocks, southeast of	10	knots	0.29	0.30	0.32	0.34	0.37	0.35	0.34	0.34	0.34	0.35	0.36	0.34
		degrees	200	212	229	247	265	284	002	042	058	065	080	086
Galloupes Point, 0.4nm south of	10	knots	0.50	0.52	0.56	0.54	0.55	0.55	0.52	0.52	0.49	0.51	0.50	0.49
		degrees	138	220	284	252	250	240	211	078	081	085	091	095

TABLE 5.—ROTARY TIDAL CURRENTS

Station Name	Depth	Hourly time increments												
		0	1	2	3	4	5	6	7	8	9	10	11	
		After Minimum Before Flood at BOSTON HARBOR												
Little Hahant 0.9nm northeast of	10	0.20	0.21	0.24	0.25	0.26	0.26	0.24	0.23	0.23	0.21	0.21	0.20	knots
		306	340	228	223	200	216	290	357	059	045	037	028	degrees
Egg Rock, southwest of	10	0.42	0.45	0.47	0.46	0.45	0.44	0.45	0.44	0.47	0.42	0.43	0.40	knots
		213	193	175	178	222	267	330	328	335	334	337	306	degrees
Egg Rock, 0.2nm north of	10	0.42	0.43	0.46	0.46	0.48	0.49	0.48	0.50	0.49	0.47	0.47	0.45	knots
		221	215	213	215	219	235	221	019	009	052	055	135	degrees
Bass Point, 0.5nm SSW of	15	0.11	0.51	0.55	0.50	0.47	0.46	0.46	0.48	0.57	0.66	0.64	0.51	knots
		191	295	303	308	313	354	010	046	089	109	121	132	degrees
Bass Point, 0.7nm west of	10	0.30	0.38	0.38	0.37	0.36	0.35	0.30	0.19	0.30	0.35	0.38	0.36	knots
		251	331	332	343	343	347	029	144	146	165	173	190	degrees
Deer Island Light, 1.3nm NW of	10	0.33	0.36	0.36	0.40	0.40	0.45	0.35	0.35	0.34	0.35	0.34	0.29	knots
		007	024	060	348	063	095	081	102	104	135	158	339	degrees
Georges Island, 0.2nm WSW of	10	0.22	0.29	0.37	0.44	0.44	0.44	0.50	0.47	0.39	0.37	0.36	0.30	knots
		217	209	052	074	066	032	029	061	082	071	070	069	degrees
Georges Island, 0.2nm WSW of	20	0.15	0.24	0.28	0.31	0.34	0.35	0.40	0.39	0.28	0.35	0.32	0.23	knots
		271	231	030	076	064	029	021	049	067	056	050	044	degrees
Peddocks Island, east of	10	0.20	0.27	0.41	0.35	0.28	0.34	0.33	0.29	0.33	0.33	0.32	0.26	knots
		246	282	019	024	355	338	345	013	002	345	333	331	degrees
Peddocks island, east of	20	0.15	0.20	0.34	0.24	0.22	0.31	0.32	0.26	0.28	0.31	0.26	0.17	knots
		220	232	020	024	345	333	331	009	003	339	329	322	degrees
		After Maximum Flood at POLLOCK RIP CHANNEL												
Georges Bank 41°50'N 66°37'W		0.9	1.1	1.2	1.1	1.0	0.9	1.0	1.3	1.6	1.4	0.9	0.8	knots
		285	304	324	341	010	043	089	127	147	172	197	232	degrees

TABLE 5. – ROTARY TIDAL CURRENTS

Station Name	Depth		0	1	2	3	4	5	6	7	8	9	10	11	
			After Maximum Flood at POLLOCK RIP CHANNEL												
Georges Bank 41°48'N 67°34'W		knots	1.5	2.1	2.0	1.3	0.7	0.8	1.3	2.0	1.9	1.7	1.2	0.9	knots
		degrees	325	332	342	358	035	099	126	150	159	169	197	275	degrees
Georges Bank 41°42'N 67°37'W		knots	1.1	1.3	1.0	0.8	0.6	0.8	1.0	1.1	1.1	1.0	1.0	0.9	knots
		degrees	316	341	356	016	043	092	122	146	170	195	215	272	degrees
Georges Bank 41°54'N 67°08'W		knots	1.1	1.4	1.5	1.2	0.7	0.8	1.1	1.5	1.2	1.1	0.9	0.8	knots
		degrees	298	325	344	000	033	082	118	138	153	178	208	236	degrees
Georges Bank 41°41'N 67°49'W		knots	1.6	1.8	1.4	0.8	0.3	0.9	1.5	1.7	1.7	1.1	0.8	1.2	knots
		degrees	318	320	325	330	067	111	117	126	144	160	242	292	degrees
Georges Bank 41°30'N 68°07'W		knots	1.5	1.7	1.5	1.1	0.9	0.9	1.3	1.7	1.6	1.3	1.0	1.1	knots
		degrees	312	338	346	014	059	099	123	144	160	187	244	274	degrees
Georges Bank 41°29'N 67°04'W		knots	1.0	1.2	1.4	1.3	1.2	1.1	1.2	1.4	1.5	1.3	1.2	1.1	knots
		degrees	277	302	329	348	015	048	085	122	145	166	194	223	degrees
Georges Bank 41°14'N 67°38'W		knots	1.4	1.6	1.6	1.4	1.1	0.9	1.2	1.6	1.6	1.5	1.4	1.2	knots
		degrees	305	332	355	015	038	077	112	141	162	187	214	252	degrees
Georges Bank 41°13'N 68°20'W		knots	1.5	2.0	1.4	0.8	0.6	0.7	1.0	1.3	1.4	1.5	1.3	0.9	knots
		degrees	319	332	345	009	042	080	118	138	154	169	188	236	degrees
Georges Bank 40°48'N 67°40'W		knots	0.9	0.9	0.8	0.6	0.6	0.6	0.9	1.0	1.0	0.9	0.8	0.8	knots
		degrees	304	340	353	029	056	083	107	140	156	175	202	245	degrees
Georges Bank 40°49'N 68°34'W		knots	1.2	1.5	1.4	1.1	0.8	0.8	1.0	1.4	1.5	1.4	1.1	0.9	knots
		degrees	301	326	345	008	036	069	106	139	153	175	201	237	degrees
Great South Channel, Georges Bank 41°10'N 68°56'W		knots	0.5	0.7	1.1	1.0	0.7	0.4	0.4	0.7	1.0	1.0	0.8	0.6	knots
		degrees	318	349	352	356	359	018	106	157	165	173	180	204	degrees
Nantucket Shoals		knots	0.6	0.7	0.8	0.8	0.8	0.7	0.6	0.7	0.8	0.8	0.8	0.7	knots
		degrees	323	355	015	038	055	085	125	162	192	212	232	257	degrees
Davis Bank, Nantucket Shoals		knots	1.5	2.1	2.4	2.1	1.1	0.4	1.2	1.9	2.2	2.2	1.6	0.7	knots
		degrees	015	028	032	035	037	128	197	204	205	206	213	307	degrees

TABLE 5. — ROTARY TIDAL CURRENTS

Station Name	Depth		0	1	2	3	4	5	6	7	8	9	10	11
			After Maximum Flood at POLLOCK RIP CHANNEL											
Davis Bank, Nantucket Shoals, 15 miles SE of Nantucket Island		knots	0.9	1.2	1.3	1.1	0.8	0.9	0.8	1.2	1.1	0.9	0.7	0.7
		degrees	346	028	047	073	103	132	182	215	240	251	267	302
Davis Bank, Nantucket Shoals, 17.5 miles SE of Nantucket Island		knots	0.8	1.5	1.9	1.8	1.1	0.4	1.2	1.9	1.7	1.5	0.9	0.2
		degrees	023	027	028	029	046	115	191	202	215	225	233	270
Great South Channel, Georges Bank 40°31'N 68°47'W		knots	0.7	0.9	1.1	1.0	0.8	0.4	0.7	0.9	1.0	1.0	0.8	0.6
		degrees	320	331	342	003	023	063	129	140	164	179	190	221
Davis Bank, Nantucket Shoals, 18.5 miles SE of Nantucket Island		knots	0.6	1.3	1.5	1.4	1.1	0.8	0.6	1.3	1.7	1.4	1.0	0.3
		degrees	030	036	038	050	080	105	178	230	235	238	241	265
Nantucket Island, 28 miles east of		knots	0.9	1.3	1.4	1.1	0.5	0.3	0.8	1.1	1.1	0.9	0.7	0.1
		degrees	019	007	359	351	334	221	198	185	184	184	183	060
Monomoy Point, 23 miles east of		knots	0.7	1.0	0.9	0.7	0.3	0.1	0.5	0.8	0.9	0.8	0.5	0.1
		degrees	320	324	326	330	334	144	145	146	147	148	150	230
Nauset Beach Light, 5 miles NE		knots	0.5	0.6	0.5	0.2	0.1	0.2	0.4	0.6	0.6	0.4	0.2	0.2
		degrees	315	327	340	357	016	124	132	135	139	145	269	297
Great Round Shoal Channel entrance		knots	1.6	1.4	1.3	1.1	0.8	1.2	1.5	1.5	1.2	0.9	0.8	1.2
		degrees	032	045	068	095	140	192	210	220	235	264	303	350
Great Round Shoal Channel, 4 miles NE of Great Point		knots	0.8	1.1	1.3	1.0	0.5	0.5	1.1	1.4	1.2	0.7	0.2	0.4
		degrees	080	088	096	104	129	213	267	275	280	284	328	042
Cuttyhunk Island, 3.25 miles SW		knots	0.4	0.3	0.2	0.3	0.5	0.5	0.4	0.3	0.2	0.3	0.3	0.4
		degrees	356	015	080	123	146	158	173	208	267	306	322	335
Gooseberry Neck, 2 miles SSE of		knots	0.6	0.4	0.2	0.3	0.4	0.5	0.5	0.3	0.2	0.2	0.3	0.5
		degrees	052	065	108	168	210	223	232	249	274	321	016	038
Browns Ledge, Massachusetts		knots	0.3	0.3	0.3	0.4	0.4	0.4	0.3	0.2	0.3	0.3	0.4	0.5
		degrees	330	012	028	104	118	123	168	205	201	270	282	318
			After Maximum Flood at THE RACE											
Point Judith, Harbor of Refuge		knots	0.2	0.2	0.4	0.5	0.5	0.5	0.4	0.2	0.1	0.1	0.1	0.1
		degrees	197	160	151	159	146	124	109	104	090	030	336	209

Hourly time increments

TABLE 5.—ROTARY TIDAL CURRENTS

Station Name	Depth	0	1	2	3	4	5	6	7	8	9	10	11	
							Hourly time increments							
After Maximum Flood at THE RACE														
Point Judith, 4.5 miles SW of		0.6	0.6	0.5	0.2	0.2	0.6	0.7	0.5	0.3	0.1	0.1	0.3	knots
		264	270	270	280	062	070	078	095	105	120	286	277	degrees
Grace Point, 2 miles NW of		0.2	0.2	0.4	0.6	0.7	0.6	0.6	0.4	0.2	0.1	0.1	0.1	knots
		304	002	028	028	037	071	086	126	137	213	256	267	degrees
Little Gull Island, 3.7 miles ESE		0.8	0.5	0.2	0.2	0.7	1.1	1.6	1.2	0.6	0.2	0.4	0.7	knots
		271	284	320	068	077	095	118	128	150	171	221	228	degrees
Great Round Shoal Channel		1.0	1.3	1.3	0.8	0.5	0.7	0.9	1.3	1.1	0.9	0.3	0.4	knots
		047	060	070	091	153	211	234	247	252	260	305	035	degrees
After Maximum Flood at THE NARROWS, NEW YORK														
Sandy Hook Approach Lighted Horn Bouy 2A, 0.2 miles W		0.4	0.3	0.2	0.2	0.3	0.4	0.6	0.5	0.2	0.2	0.3	0.4	knots
		313	325	356	055	094	118	136	147	177	256	290	298	degrees
After Maximum Flood at DELAWARE BAY ENTRANCE														
Fenwick Shoal Lighted Whistle Bouy 2		0.2	0.2	0.1	0.1	0.1	0.3	0.3	0.3	0.2	0.1	0.1	0.2	knots
		342	349	357	043	110	135	150	165	185	226	282	318	degrees
After Maximum Flood at CHESAPEAKE BAY ENTRANCE														
Point Lookout, 1.5nm east of	16	0.31	0.26	0.24	0.24	0.22	0.22	0.18	0.10	0.09	0.13	0.20	0.29	knots
		197	217	242	266	290	311	330	358	073	113	152	179	degrees
After Maximum Flood at CHARLESTON HARBOR														
Frying Pan Shoals, off Cape Fear		0.3	0.2	0.2	0.3	0.3	0.3	0.3	0.2	0.2	0.3	0.3	0.3	knots
		335	010	050	090	110	128	150	188	235	268	290	305	degrees
Cape Romain, 5 miles SE		0.2	0.2	0.3	0.3	0.3	0.3	0.2	0.2	0.3	0.4	0.3	0.3	knots
		006	038	055	067	093	114	167	212	242	244	262	292	degrees
Cape Romain, 6.9 miles SW		0.3	0.2	0.2	0.3	0.3	0.3	0.2	0.2	0.2	0.2	0.3	0.3	knots
		317	350	019	071	115	111	132	160	216	251	266	303	degrees
Capers Inlet, 1.9 miles east of		0.1	0.1	0.2	0.2	0.1	0.1	0.1	0.1	0.2	0.2	0.1	0.1	knots
		012	058	052	053	067	098	129	214	222	254	246	247	degrees

TABLE 5.—ROTARY TIDAL CURRENTS

Station Name	Depth		0	1	2	3	4	5	6	7	8	9	10	11	
															Hourly time increments
After Maximum Flood at CHARLESTON HARBOR															
Capers Inlet, 3.6 miles SE of			0.2	0.1	0.2	0.2	0.2	0.2	0.2	0.1	0.1	0.2	0.2	0.2	knots
			302	357	034	017	089	094	112	116	189	249	268	282	degrees
Charleston Entrance, 37 miles E			0.3	0.3	0.2	0.2	0.3	0.3	0.3	0.3	0.2	0.2	0.2	0.3	knots
			328	350	020	065	095	118	140	163	195	235	268	295	degrees
Charleston Lighted Whistle Buoy 2C			0.2	0.2	0.1	0.2	0.3	0.3	0.2	0.2	0.2	0.2	0.3	0.3	knots
			300	332	017	055	077	093	117	153	207	242	260	275	degrees
Folly Island, 2 miles east of			0.1	0.2	0.3	0.3	0.2	0.2	0.1	0.2	0.2	0.3	0.3	0.2	knots
			346	024	058	076	102	121	164	222	256	256	271	290	degrees
Folly Island, 3.5 miles east of			0.1	0.2	0.2	0.2	0.2	0.2	0.1	0.1	0.2	0.2	0.2	0.1	knots
			322	047	069	086	096	115	148	215	256	260	265	285	degrees
Martins Industry, 5 miles east of			0.4	0.3	0.1	0.3	0.3	0.4	0.5	0.4	0.2	0.2	0.3	0.4	knots
			282	293	330	030	075	092	102	110	140	200	250	271	degrees
After Maximum Flood at SAVANNAH RIVER ENTRANCE															
Savannah Light, 1.2 miles SE			0.3	0.2	0.1	0.1	0.2	0.3	0.3	0.3	0.2	0.1	0.2	0.3	knots
			296	308	326	045	090	107	114	123	145	213	267	283	degrees
After Maximum Flood at Port Everglades Entrance															
Port Everglades Turning Basin	33.7		0.8	0.12	0.14	0.16	0.15	0.07	0.05	0.6	0.4	0.3	0.2	0.1	knots
			198	193	180	160	144	114	35	353	329	310	309	267	degrees
Port Everglades Turning Basin	14.0		0.02	0.03	0.07	0.09	0.12	0.13	0.11	0.06	0.03	0.12	0.15	0.11	knots
			327	219	202	173	154	148	148	135	29	337	330	332	degrees
After Maximum Flood at Lake Worth Inlet Entrance															
Pier 13, Lake Worth Inlet	18.7		0.23	0.44	0.47	0.33	0.33	0.12	0.06	0.04	0.02	0.01	0.03	0.04	knots
			314	349	351	350	342	205	183	177	168	138	162	203	degrees
Pier 13, Lake Worth Inlet	15.4		0.23	0.44	0.47	0.33	0.33	0.03	0.06	0.04	0.03	0.02	0.04	0.04	knots
			339	347	349	348	339	213	188	190	190	169	172	209	degrees
Pier 13, Lake Worth Inlet	5.5		0.21	0.40	0.43	0.31	0.11	0.02	0.05	0.03	0.02	0.00	0.04	0.04	knots
			347	349	350	351	347	207	190	224	289	282	176	188	degrees

Tabular values are mean current speed and direction at specific intervals relative to the reference station.

THE GULF STREAM

The region where the Gulf of Mexico narrows to form the channel between Florida Keys and Cuba may be regarded as the head of the Gulf Stream. From this region the stream sets eastward and northward through the Straits of Florida, and after passing Little Bahama Bank it continues northward and then northeastward, following the general direction of the 100-fathom curve as far as Cape Hatteras. The flow in the Straits is frequently referred to as the Florida Current.

Shortly after emerging from the Straits of Florida, the stream is joined by the Antilles Current, which flows northwesterly along the open ocean side of the West Indies before uniting with the water which has passed through the straits. Beyond Cape Hatteras the combined current turns more and more eastward under the combined effects of the deflecting force of the Earth's rotation and the eastwardly trending coastline, until the region of the Grand Banks of Newfoundland is reached.

Eastward of the Grand Banks the whole surface is slowly driven eastward and northeastward by the prevailing westerly winds to the coastal waters of northwestern Europe. For distinction, this broad and variable wind-driven surface movement is sometimes referred to as the North Atlantic Drift or Gulf Stream Drift.

In general, the Gulf Stream as it issues into the sea through the Straits of Florida may be characterized as a swift, highly saline current of blue water whose upper stratum is composed of warm water.

On its western or inner side, the Gulf Stream is separated from the coastal waters by a zone of rapidly falling temperature, to which the term "cold wall" has been applied. It is most clearly marked north of Cape Hatteras but extends, more or less well defined, from the Straits to Grand Banks.

Throughout the whole stretch of 400 miles in the Straits of Florida, the stream flows with considerable speed. Abreast of Havana, the average surface speed in the axis of the stream is about 2 1/2 knots. As the cross-sectional area of the stream decreases, the speed increases gradually, until abreast of Cape Florida it becomes about 3 1/2 knots. From this point within the narrows of the straits, the speed along the axis gradually decreases to about 2 1/2 knots off Cape Hatteras, N.C. These values are for the axis of the stream where the current is a maximum, the speed of the stream decreasing gradually from the axis as the edges of the stream are approached. The speed of the stream, furthermore, is subject to fluctuations brought about by variations in winds and barometric pressure.

The following tables give the mean surface speed of the Gulf Stream in two cross sections in the Straits of Florida:

Between Rebecca Shoal and Cuba		Between Fowey Rocks and Gun Cay	
Distance south of Rebecca Shoal	Mean surface speed observed	Distance east of Fowey Rocks	Mean Surface Speed observe
Nautical miles	Knots	Nautical miles	Knots
20	0.3	8	2.7
35	0.7	11 1/2	3.5
50	2.2	15	3.2
68	2.2	22	2.7
86	0.8	29	2.1
		36	1.7

Crossing the Gulf Stream at Jupiter or Fowey Rocks, an average allowance of 2.5 knots in a northerly direction should be made for the current.

Crossing the stream from Havana, a fair allowance for the average current between 100-fathoms curves is 1.1 knots in an east-north-easterly direction.

THE GULF STREAM

From within the straits, the axis of the Gulf Stream runs approximately parallel with the 100-fathom curve as far as Cape Hatteras. Since this stretch of coast line sweeps northward in a sharper curve than does the 100-fathom line, the stream lies at varying distances from the shore. The lateral boundaries of the current within the straits are fairly well fixed, but when the stream flows into the sea the eastern boundary becomes somewhat vague. On the western side, the limits can be defined approximately since the waters of the stream differ in color, temperature, salinity, and flow from the inshore coastal waters. On the east, however, the Antilles Current combines with the Gulf Stream, so that its waters here merge gradually with the waters of the open Atlantic. Observation of the National Ocean Service indicate that, in general, the average position of the inner edge of the Gulf Stream as far as Cape Hatteras lies inside the 50-fathom curve. The Gulf Stream, however, shifts somewhat with the seasons, and is considerably influenced by the winds which cause fluctuations in its position, direction, and speed; consequently, any limits which are assigned refer to mean or average positions.

The approximate mean positions of the inner edge and axis (point where greatest speed may be found) are indicated in the following table:

Approximate mean position of the Gulf Stream

Locality	Inner Edge	Axis
North of Havana, Cuba		25
Southeast of Key West, Florida		45
East of Fowey Rocks, Florida		10
East of Miami Beach, Florida		15
East of Palm Beach, Florida		15
East of Jupiter Inlet, Florida		20
East of Cape Canaveral, Florida	10	45
East of Daytona Beach, Florida	25	75
East of Ormond Beach, Florida	25	75
East of St. Augustine, Florida. (coast line)	40	85
East of Jacksonville, Florida. (coast line)	55	90
Southeast of Savannah, Georgia. (coast line)	65	95
Southeast of Charleston, South Carolina. (coast line)	55	90
Southeast of Myrtle Beach, South Carolina.	60	100
Southeast of Cape Fear, North Carolina (light)	35	75
Southeast of Cape Lookout, North Carolina (light)	20	50
Southeast of Cape Hatteras, North Carolina.	10	35
Southeast of Virginia Beach, Virginia.	85	115
Southeast of Atlantic City, New Jersey	120	
Southeast of Sandy Hook, New Jersey.	150	

At the western end of the Straits of Florida the limits of the Gulf Stream are not well defined, and for this reason the location of the inner edge has been omitted for Havana, Cuba, and Key West, Florida., in the above table. Between Fowey Rocks and Jupiter Inlet the inner edge is deflected westward and lies very close to the shore line.

Along the Florida Reefs between Alligator Reef and Dry Tortugas the distance of the northerly edge of the Gulf Stream from the edge of the reefs gradually increases toward the west. Off Alligator Reef it is quite close inshore, while off Rebecca Shoal and Dry Tortugas it is possibly 15 to 20 miles south of the 100-fathom curve. Between the reefs and the northern edge of the Gulf Stream the currents are ordinarily tidal and are subject at all times to considerable modification by local winds and barometric conditions. This neutral zone varies in both length and breadth; it may extend along the reefs a greater or lesser distance than stated, and its width varies as the northern edge of the Gulf Stream approaches or recedes from the reefs.

The approximate position of the axis of the Gulf Stream for various regions is shown on the following National Ocean Service Charts: No. 11013, Straits of Florida; No. 411, South Carolina to Cuba; No.11460, Cape Canaveral to Key West; No. 11420, Alligator Reef to Havana. Chart No. 11009 show the axis and the position of the inner edge of the Gulf Stream from Cape Hatteras to Straits of Florida.

WIND-DRIVEN CURRENTS

A wind continuing for some time will produce a current the speed of which depends on the speed of the wind, and unless the current is by some other cause, the deflective force of the Earth's rotation will cause it to set to the right of the direction of the wind in the northern hemisphere and to the left in the southern hemisphere.

The current produced at off-shore locations by local winds of various strengths and directions have been investigated from observations made at 20 lightships (some of which have since been moved) from Portland, Maine to St. John's River, Florida. The observations were made hourly and varied in length from 1 to 2 years at most of the locations to 5 years at Nantucket Shoals and 9 years at Diamond Shoal. The averages obtained are given below and may prove helpful in estimating the probable current that may result from various winds at the several locations.

Caution.—There were of course many departures from these averages of speed and direction, for the wind-driven current often depends not only on the length of time the wind blows but also on factors other than the local wind at the time and place of the current. The mariner must not, therefore, assume that the given wind will always produce the indicated current.

It should be remembered, too, that the current which a vessel experiences at any time is the resultant of the combined actions of the tidal current, the wind-driven current, and any other currents such as the Gulf Stream or currents due to river discharge.

Speed.—The table below shows the average speed of the current due to winds of various strengths.

Wind speed (mile per hour)	10	20	30	40	50
Average current speed (knots) due to wind at following lightship stations:					
Boston and Barnegat	0.1	0.1	0.2	0.3	0.3
Diamond Shoal and Cape Lookout Shoals	0.5	0.6	0.7	0.8	1.0
All other locations	0.2	0.3	0.4	0.5	0.6

Direction.—The position of the shore line with respect to the station influences considerably the direction of the currents due to certain winds. The following table shows for each station the average number of degrees by which the wind-driven current is deflected to the right or left (—) of the wind. Thus, at Cape Lookout Shoals the table indicates that with a north wind the wind-driven current flows on the average 030° west of south, and with an east wind it flows 029° south of west.

WIND-DRIVEN CURRENTS

Average deviation of current to right of wind direction

[A minus sign (—) indicates that the current sets to the left of the wind]

Wind from _____ Old Lightship Stations	Lat.	Long.	N	NNE	NE	ENE	E	ESE	SE	SSE	S	SSW	SW	WSW	W	WNW	NW	NNW
Portland	43 32	70 06	24	14	9	8	-2	-14	0	26	15	18	18	24	15	34	13	18
Boston	42 20	70 45	--	-1	--	21	--	32	--	29	--	20	--	2	--	19	--	15
Pollock Rip Slue	41 37	69 54	6	5	48	-38	30	-53	-24	-75	-25	167	70	59	36	53	20	19
Nantucket Shoals	40 37	69 37	44	46	28	24	9	16	12	3	25	0	6	18	30	39	41	48
Hen and Chickens	41 27	71 01	16	14	-7	-1	-14	3	-39	-36	25	55	35	30	20	16	16	8
Brenton Reef	41 26	71 23	34	25	22	19	25	1	-7	8	27	48	23	41	41	31	21	24
Fire Island	40 29	73 11	35	23	15	8	2	-17	31	55	40	41	31	14	-2	0	25	37
Ambrose Channel	40 27	73 49	36	40	21	11	18	72	27	112	82	70	63	46	37	22	23	21
Scotland	40 27	73 55	16	-12	-26	-36	-61	-36	-92	-150	90	33	77	44	15	30	27	13
Barnegat	39 46	73 56	6	5	-13	-9	-16	-7	33	54	55	30	14	8	0	-5	21	29
Northeast End	38 58	74 30	30	14	-3	-11	-20	-31	-42	-28	37	44	25	18	7	16	25	18
Overfalls	38 48	75 01	28	-6	-1	2	-40	-56	-78	-22	68	28	55	54	32	31	32	45
Winter-Quarter Shoal	37 55	74 56	18	-1	-5	-21	-27	-35	-19	31	23	20	4	14	9	8	28	27
Chesapeake	36 59	75 42	18	-2	-4	5	-6	23	73	71	57	38	27	26	22	18	15	22
Diamond Shoal	35 05	75 20	11	3	-3	36	65	88	74	52	40	22	7	-10	-13	-17	-25	-4
Cape Lookout Shoals	34 18	76 24	30	24	2	2	-29	--	21	80	54	31	32	21	2	18	5	-5
Frying Pan Shoals	33 34	77 49	34	34	18	6	2	9	48	55	48	38	26	14	-7	-12	-27	-6
Savannah	31 57	80 40	12	12	-9	-18	-23	-46	17	50	43	17	7	-8	-10	7	15	33
Brunswick	31 00	81 10	17	-2	-10	-28	-18	-21	37	29	23	2	6	-21	-21	-26	16	18
St. Johns	30 23	81 18	3	-12	-27	-47	-84	30	35	26	26	27	1	16	-8	-17	6	8

THE COMBINATION OF CURRENTS

In determining from the current tables the speed and direction of the current at any time, it is frequently necessary to combine the tidal current with the wind-driven current. The following methods indicate how the resultant of two or more currents may be easily determined.

Currents in the same direction.—When two or more currents set in the same direction it is a simple matter to combine them. The resultant current will have a speed which is equal to the sum of all the currents and it will set in the same direction.

For example, a vessel is near the Nantucket Shoals station at a time when the tidal current is setting 120° with a speed of 0.6 knot, and at the same time a wind of 40 miles per hour is blowing from the west; What current will the vessel be subject to at that time? Since a wind of 40 miles per hour from the west will give rise to a current setting 120° with a speed of 0.5 knot, the combined tidal and wind-driven currents will set in the same direction (120°) with a speed of 0.6 + 0.5 = 1.1 knots.

Currents in opposite directions.—The combination of currents setting in opposite directions is likewise a simple matter. The speed of the resultant current is the difference between the opposite setting currents, and the direction of the resultant current is the same as that of the greater current.

As an example, let it be required to determine the speed of the current at the Nantucket Shoals station when the tidal current is setting 205° with a speed of 0.8 knot, and when a wind of 40 miles per hour is blowing from the south. The current produced by a wind of 40 miles per hour from the south would set 025° with a speed of 0.5 knot. The tidal and wind-driven currents, therefore, set in opposite directions, the tidal current being the stronger. Hence, the resultant current will set in the direction of the tidal current (205°) with a speed of 0.8 - 0.5 = 0.3 knot.

THE COMBINATION OF CURRENTS

Currents in different directions.—The combination of currents setting at arbitrary angles is best solved by a graphical method. Taking the combination of two currents as the simplest case, draw a line whose direction and length (to a suitable scale) represent the direction and speed of one of the currents to be combined. From this line draw another (to the same scale) representing the direction and speed of the second current. The line joining the origin of the first line with the end of the second line represents the direction and speed of the combined current.

As an example, take Nantucket Shoals station at a time when the tidal current is 0.7 knot setting 355° and a wind of 50 miles per hour is blowing from the west-southwest. The wind-driven current, according to the preceding chapter, would therefore be about 0.6 knot setting 085°.

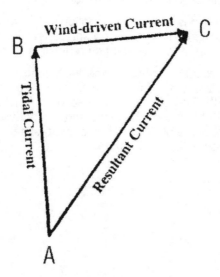

Combination of tidal current and wind-driven current

Using a scale of 2 inches to represent 1 knot, draw from point *A*, the origin in the diagram above, the line *AB* 1.4 inches in length directed 355° to represent the tidal current. From point *B* draw the line *BC* 1.2 inches in length directed 085° to represent the wind-driven current. The line *AC* represents the resultant current, which on being measured, is found to be about 1.8 inches in length directed 035°. Hence, the combined current sets 35° with a speed of 0.9 knot.

The combination of three or more currents is made in the same way as above, for example, the third current to be combined being drawn from the point *C*. The resultant current is given by joining the origin with the end of the last line. For drawing the lines, a parallel rule and compass rose will be found convenient. A protractor or polar coordinate paper may also be used.

CURRENT DIAGRAMS

EXPLANATION

"Current diagram" is a graphic table that shows the velocities of the flood and ebb currents and the times of slack and strength over a considerable stretch of the channel of a tidal waterway. At definite intervals along the channel the velocities of the current are shown with reference to the times of turning of the current at some reference station. This make it a simple matter to determine the approximate velocity of the current along the channel for any desired time.

In using the diagrams, the desired time should be converted to hours before or after the time of the nearest predicted slack water at the reference station.

Besides showing in compact form the velocities of the current and their changes through the flood and ebb cycles, the current diagram serves two other useful purposes. By its use the mariner can determine the most advantageous time to pass through the waterway to carry the most favorable current and also the speed and direction of the current that will be encountered in the channel at any time.

Each diagram represents average durations and average velocities of flood and ebb. The durations and velocities of flood and ebb vary from day to day. Therefore predictions for the reference station at times will differ from average conditions and when precise results are desired the diagrams should be modified to represent conditions at such particular times. This can be done by changing the width of the shaded and unshaded portions of the diagram to agree in hours with the durations of flood and ebb, respectively, as given by the predictions for that time. The speeds in the shaded area should then be multiplied by the ratio of the predicted flood speed to the average flood speed (maximum flood speed given opposite the name of the reference station on the diagram) and the speeds in the unshaded area by the ratio of the predicted ebb speed to the average ebb speed.

In a number of cases approximate results can be obtained by using the diagram as drawn and modifying the final result by the ratio of speeds as mentioned above. Thus, if the diagram in a particular case gives a favorable flood speed averaging about 1.0 knot and the ratio of the predicted flood speed to the average flood speed is 0.5 the approximate favorable current for the particular time would be 1.0 x 0.5 = 0.5 knot.

CURRENT DIAGRAMS

VINEYARD AND NANTUCKET SOUNDS
EXPLANATION OF CURRENT DIAGRAM

The current diagram on the opposite page represents average conditions of the surface currents along the middle of the channel from Gay Head to the east end of Pollock Rip Channel, the scale being too small to show details.

Easterly streams are designated "Flood" and westerly streams "Ebb." The small figures in the diagram denote the speed of the current in knots and tenths. The times are referred to slack waters at Pollock Rip Channel (Butler Hole), daily predictions for which are given in Table 1 of these current tables.

The speed lines are directly related to the diagram. By transferring to the diagram the direction of the speed line which corresponds to the ship's speed, the diagram will show the general direction and speed of the current encountered by the vessel in passing through the sounds or the most favorable time, with respect to currents, for leaving any place shown on the left margin.

To determine speed and direction of current.—With parallel rulers transfer to the diagram the direction of the speed line corresponding to normal speed of vessel, moving edge of ruler to the point where the horizontal line representing place of departure intersects the vertical line representing the time of day in question. If the ruler's edge lies within the shaded portion of the diagram, a flood current will be encountered; if within the unshaded, an ebb current; and if along the boundary of both, slack water. The figures on the diagram along the edge of the rule will show the speed of the current encountered at any place indicated on the left margin of the diagram.

Example.—A 12-knot vessel bound westward enters Pollock Rip Channel at 0700 of a given day, and it is desired to ascertain the speed and direction of the current which will be encountered on its passage through the sounds. Assuming that on the given day ebb begins at Pollock Rip Channel at 0508 and flood begins at 1120, the time 0700 will be about 2 hours after ebb begins. With parallel rulers transfer to the diagram the 12-knot speed line "Westbound," placing edge of rule on the point where the vertical line "2 hours after ebb begins at Pollock Rip Channel" intersects the horizontal 47-mile line which is the starting point. It will be found that the edge of the ruler passes through the unshaded portion of the diagram, the speeds along the edge averaging about 1.4 knots. The vessel will, therefore, have a favorable ebb current averaging about 1.4 knots all the way to Gay Head. It will also be seen that the edge of the ruler crosses the horizontal 16-mile line (at East Chop) about halfway between the figures 1.6 and 2.2. Therefore, when passing the vicinity of East Chop she will have a favorable current of almost 2 knots.

To determine the time of a favorable current for passing through the sounds.—With parallel rulers transfer to the diagram the direction of the speed line corresponding to normal speed of vessel, moving the ruler over the diagram until its edge runs as nearly as possible through the general line of largest speeds of shaded portion if eastbound and unshaded portion if westbound, giving consideration only to that part of the diagram which lies between place of departure and destination. An average of the figures along the edge of the ruler will give the average strength of current. The time (before or after flood begins or ebb begins at Pollock Rip Channel) for leaving any place shown on the left margin will be indicated vertically above the point where the ruler cuts a line drawn horizontally through the name of the place in question.

Example.—A 12-knot vessel will leave Gay Head for Pollock Rip Channel on a day when flood begins at Pollock Rip Channel at 0454 and ebb begins at 1104. At what time should she get under way so as to carry the most favorable current all the way through the sounds?

Place parallel rulers along the 12-knot speed line "Eastbound." Transfer the direction to the shaded portion of the diagram and as near as possible to the axis so as to include the greatest possible number of larger current speeds. It will be found that the edge of the ruler cuts the horizontal line at Gay Head at the point representing "3 hours after flood begins at Pollock Rip Channel," and that the average of the currents along the edge of rulers is about 0.8 knot in a favorable direction. For the given day flood begins at Pollock Rip Channel at 0454; hence, if the vessel leaves Gay Head 3 hours later, or about 0754, she will average a favorable current of almost 1 knot all the way.

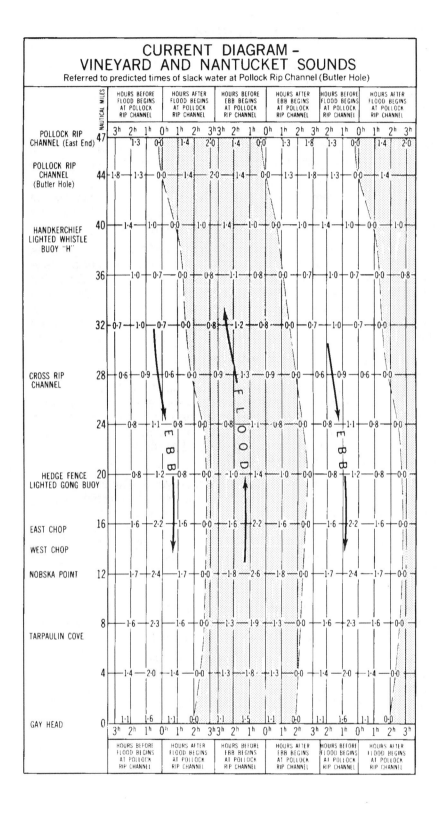

CURRENT DIAGRAM –
VINEYARD AND NANTUCKET SOUNDS
Referred to predicted times of slack water at Pollock Rip Channel (Butler Hole)

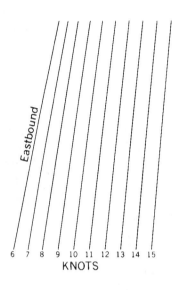

SPEED LINES

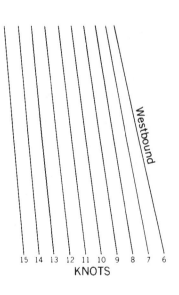

CURRENT DIAGRAMS

EAST RIVER, NEW YORK
EXPLANATION OF CURRENT DIAGRAM

The current diagram on the opposite page represents average conditions of the surface currents along the middle of the channel between Governors Island and Throgs Neck, the scale being too small to show details. Eddies, of more or less violence, occur in numerous localities in the East River, but as a general rule the currents follow the channels.

On the diagram northerly and easterly streams are designated as "Flood" currents and westerly and southerly streams as "Ebb" currents. The small figures on the diagram denote the speed of the current in knots and tenths. The times are referred to slack waters at Hell Gate, daily predictions for which are given in Table 1 of these current tables.

The speed lines are directly related to the diagram. By their use the speed and general direction of the current encountered by a vessel passing through the river may be determined; also the time of a favorable current for leaving any place shown on the left margin of the diagram may be found.

To determine the speed and direction of the current.—With parallel rulers transfer to the diagram the direction of the speed line corresponding to the normal speed of vessel, placing edge of ruler opposite the place of departure on the time before or after flood begins or ebb begins at Hell Gate that corresponds to the time of day desired. If the ruler's edge lies along the shaded portion of the diagram, a flood current will be encountered; if along the unshaded, an ebb current; and if along the boundary of both, slack water. The figures on the diagram along the edge of the ruler will show the speed of the current encountered at any place along the course indicated by the names on the left margin of diagram.

Example.—A 12-knot vessel passes Throgs Neck for Governors Island at 0820 of a given day and it is desired to ascertain the speed and direction of the current which will be encountered in passing through East River. Assuming that on the given day ebb begins at Hell Gate at 0614 and flood begins at 1245, the time 0820 will be about 2 hours after ebb begins. With parallel rulers transfer to the diagram the 12-knot speed line "Southbound", placing edge of ruler at the top in the column "Hours after ebb begins at Hell Gate" and intersecting 2h. It will be found that the edge of the ruler passes through strength of current in the unshaded portion of diagram averaging about 2.4 knots. The vessel will, therefore, have a favorable current averaging about 2.4 knots all the way.

To determine the time of a favorable current for passing through the East River.—With parallel rulers transfer to the diagram the direction of the speed line corresponding to normal speed of vessel, moving the ruler over the diagram until its edge runs as nearly as possible through the general line of greatest current of unshaded portion if bound westward and southward,and shaded portion if bound northward and eastward. An average of the figures along edge of ruler will give average strength of current. The time (before or after flood begins or ebb begins at Hell Gate) for leaving any place on the left margin of diagram will be found vertically above the point where the parallel ruler cuts the horizontal line opposite the name of the place in question.

Example.—A 12-knot vessel in New York Harbor desires to pass through the East River in the afternoon of a day when flood begins at Hell Gate at 1404 and ebb begins at 1934. At what time should she get under way as to carry the most favorable current all the way to Throgs Neck?

Place parallel rulers along the 12-knot speed line "Northbound." Transfer this direction to the shaded portion of diagram so as to include the greatest number of larger current speeds. It will be found that the ruler's edge cuts the horizontal line at Governors Island about vertically under "2 1/2 hours after flood begins at Hell Gate", and the average of the speeds along the edge of the ruler is about 2.3 knots. For the given day flood begins in Hell Gate at 1404 hence, if the vessel leaves Governors Island about 2 1/2 hours later, or 1630 on that day, she will have a favorable current, averaging about 2.3 knots all the way.

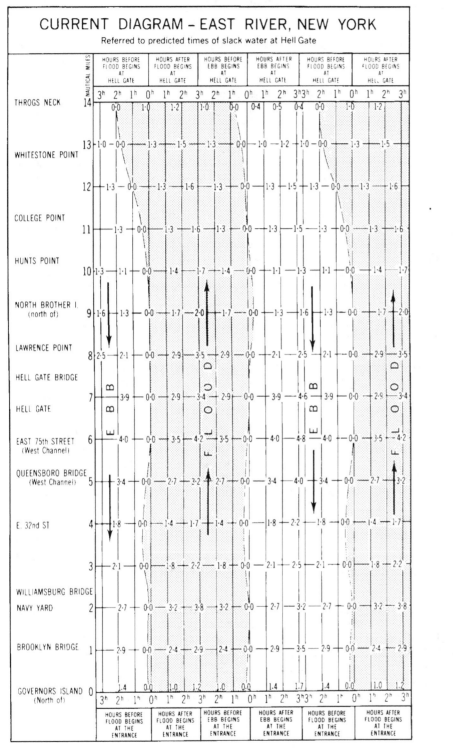

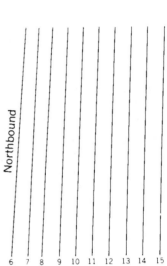

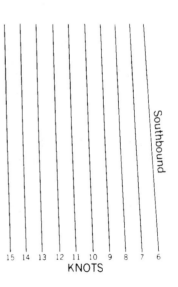

CURRENT DIAGRAMS

NEW YORK HARBOR VIA AMBROSE CHANNEL
EXPLANATION OF CURRENT DIAGRAM

The current diagram on the opposite page represents average conditions of the surface currents along the middle of the channel from Ambrose Channel entrance to Spuyten Duyvil, the scale being too small to show details.

Northerly streams are designated "Flood" and southerly streams "Ebb." The small figures in the diagram denote the speed of the current in knots and tenths. The times are referred to slack waters at The Narrows, daily predictions for which are given in Table 1 of these current tables.

The speed lines are directly related to the diagram. By transferring to the diagram the direction of the speed line which corresponds to the ship's speed, the diagram will show the general direction and speed of the current encountered by the vessel on entering or leaving the harbor or the most favorable time, with respect to currents, for leaving any place shown on the left margin.

To determine speed and direction of current.—With parallel rulers transfer to the diagram the direction of the speed line corresponding to normal speed of vessel, moving edge of ruler to the point where the horizontal line representing place of departure intersects the vertical line representing the time of day in question. If the ruler's edge lies within the shaded portion of the diagram, a flood current will be encountered; if within the unshaded, an ebb current; and if along the boundary of both, slack water. The figures on the diagram along the edge of the ruler will show the speed of the current encountered at any place indicated on the left margin of the diagram.

Example.—A 10-knot vessel enters Ambrose Channel about 1040 of a given day. Flood begins at The Narrows at 0835 and ebb begins at 1420. The time 1040 will be about 2 hours after flood begins. With parallel rulers transfer to the diagram the 10-knot speed line "Northbound," placing edge of ruler on the point where the vertical line "2 hours after flood begins" intersects the horizontal 0-mile line which is the starting point. It will be found that the edge of the ruler passes through the shaded portion of the diagram, the speeds along the edge of the ruler from Ambrose Channel entrance to Chelsea Docks averaging about 1.4 knots. The vessel will, therefore, have a favorable flood current averaging about 1.4 knots all the way to Chelsea Docks.

To determine the time of a favorable current for leaving or entering the harbor.—With parallel rulers transfer to the diagram the direction of the speed line corresponding to normal speed of vessel, moving the ruler over the diagram until its edge runs as nearly as possible through the general line of largest speeds of shaded portion if northbound and unshaded portion if southbound, giving consideration only to that part of the diagram which lies between place of departure and destination. An average of the figures along the edge of the ruler will give the average strength of current. The time (before or after flood or ebb begins at The Narrows) for leaving any place shown on the left margin will be indicated vertically above the point where the ruler cuts a line drawn horizontally through the name of the place in question.

Example.—A 10-knot vessel will leave Chelsea Docks on a day when flood begins at The Narrows at 0804 and ebb begins at 1338. At what time should she get under way so as to carry the most favorable current all the way to Ambrose Channel entrance?

Place parallel rulers along the 10-knot speed line "Southbound." Transfer the direction to the unshaded portion of the diagram as near as possible to the axis so as to include the greatest possible number of larger current speeds on the portion of the chart below Chelsea Docks. It will be found that the edge of the ruler cuts the horizontal line at Chelsea Docks at the point representing "2 hours after ebb begins at The Narrows," and that the average of the currents along the edge of the ruler is about 1.5 knots in a favorable direction. For the given day, ebb begins at The Narrows at 1338; hence, if the vessel leaves Chelsea Docks 2 hours later, or about 1608, she will average a favorable current of about 1.5 knots all the way to Ambrose Channel entrance.

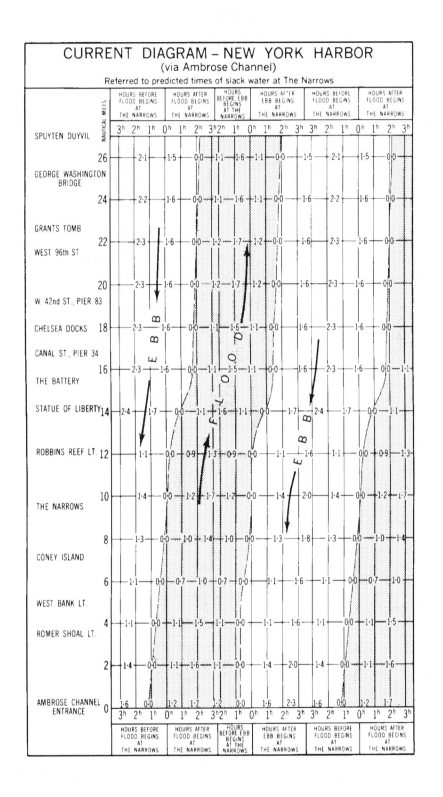

CURRENT DIAGRAM – NEW YORK HARBOR
(via Ambrose Channel)
Referred to predicted times of slack water at The Narrows

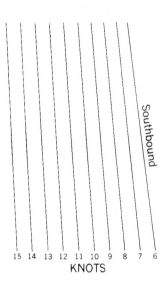

SPEED LINES

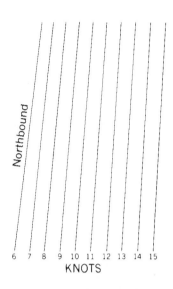

Northbound

6 7 8 9 10 11 12 13 14 15
KNOTS

Southbound

15 14 13 12 11 10 9 8 7 6
KNOTS

CURRENT DIAGRAMS

DELAWARE BAY AND RIVER
EXPLANATION OF CURRENT DIAGRAM

This current diagram represents average conditions of the surface currents along the middle of the channel between Bristol and Delaware Bay Entrance, the scale being too small to show details.

Northerly streams are designated "Flood" and Southerly streams "Ebb." The small figures in the diagram denote the speed of the current in knots and tenths. The times are referred to slack waters at Delaware Bay Entrance, daily predictions for which are given in Table 1 of these current tables.

The speed lines are directly related to the diagram. By transferring to the diagram the direction of the speed line which corresponds to the ship's speed, the diagram will show the general direction and speed of the current encountered by the vessel in passing up or down the bay and river or the most favorable time, with respect to currents, for leaving any place shown in the left margin.

To determine speed and direction of current.—With parallel rulers transfer to the diagram the direction of the speed line corresponding to the normal speed of vessel, moving edge of ruler to the point where the horizontal line representing place of departure intersects the vertical line representing the time in question. If the ruler's edge lies within the shaded portion of the diagram, a flood current will be encountered; if within the unshaded, an ebb current, and if along the boundary of both, slack water. The figures in the diagram along the edge of the ruler will show the speed of the current encountered at any place indicated in the left margin of the diagram.

Example.—A 15-knot vessel bound southward leaves Philadelphia (Chestnut Street) at 0330 of a given day and it is desired to ascertain the speed and direction of the current which will be encountered between Philadelphia and Delaware Bay Entrance. Assuming that on the given day flood begins at Delaware Bay Entrance at 0436 and ebb begins at 1038, the time 0330 will be about 1 hour before flood begins. With parallel rulers transfer to the diagram the 15-knot speed line "Southbound" placing the edge of ruler on the intersection of the vertical line "1 hour before flood begins at Delaware Bay Entrance" and a horizontal line through Philadelphia (Chestnut Street) which is the starting point. It will be found that the edge of the ruler passes through an unshaded (ebb) portion with an average speed of about 1.3 knots from Philadelphia to the vicinity of Arnold Point, and the rest of the way through a shaded (flood) portion with an average speed of about 0.8 knot. The vessel will, therefore, have a favorable current averaging about 1.3 knots to the vicinity of Arnold Point and an unfavorable current averaging about 0.8 knot the rest of the way to Delaware Bay Entrance.

To determine the time of a favorable current for passing up or down the bay and river.—With parallel rulers transfer to the diagram the direction of the speed line corresponding to normal speed of vessel, moving the ruler over the diagram until its edge runs as nearly as possible through the general line of largest speeds of shaded portion if northbound or unshaded portion if southbound giving consideration only to that part of the diagram which lies between places of departure and destination. An average of the figures along edge of ruler will give the average speed of current. The time (before or after flood begins or ebb begins at Delaware Bay Entrance) for leaving any place shown in the left margin will be indicated vertically above or below the point where the ruler cuts a line drawn horizontally through the place in question.

Example.—A 12-knot vessel will leave Delaware Bay Entrance on a day when flood begins at 0505 and ebb begins at 1112. At what time should she get under way so as to carry the most favorable current all the way to Philadelphia? With parallel rulers transfer the direction of 12-knot speed line "Northbound" to the shaded portion of diagram and as near as possible to the axis so as to include the greatest number of larger speeds. The edge of the ruler will cut the horizontal line at Delaware Bay Entrance near the vertical line "2 hours after flood begins at Delaware Bay Entrance" and the speeds along the ruler's edge will average about 1.7 knots. On the given day flood begins at Delaware Bay Entrance at 0505, hence, if the vessel leaves about 2 hours later, i.e., about 0700, she will have a favorable current averaging about 1.7 knots all the way.

Note.—It is readily seen by transferring southbound speed lines to this diagram that southbound vessels can carry a favorable current for about 50 miles only.

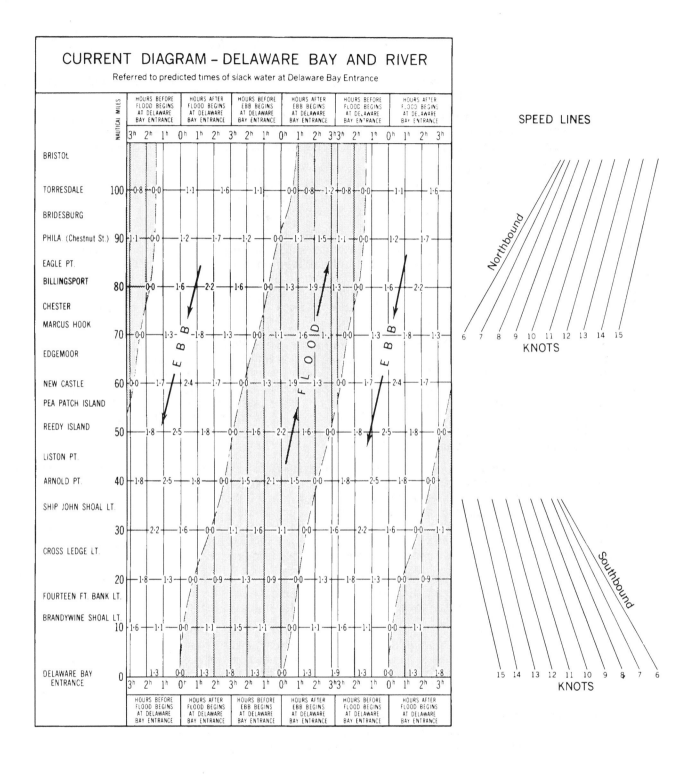

CURRENT DIAGRAM – DELAWARE BAY AND RIVER
Referred to predicted times of slack water at Delaware Bay Entrance

SPEED LINES

Northbound

KNOTS

Southbound

KNOTS

CURRENT DIAGRAMS

CHESAPEAKE BAY
EXPLANATION OF CURRENT DIAGRAM

This current diagram represents average conditions of the surface currents along the middle of the channel from Cape Henry Light to Baltimore, the scale being too small to show details.

Northerly streams are designated "Flood" and southerly streams "Ebb." The small figures in the diagram denote the speed of the current in knots and tenths. The times are referred to slack waters at Chesapeake Bay Entrance, daily predictions for which are given in Table 1 of these current tables.

The speed lines are directly related to the diagram. By transferring to the diagram the direction of the speed line which corresponds to the ship's speed, the diagram will show the general direction and speed of the current encountered by the vessel in passing up or down the bay or the most favorable time, with respect to currents, for leaving any place shown in the left margin.

To determine speed and direction of current.—With parallel rulers transfer to the diagram the direction of the speed line corresponding to the normal speed of vessel, moving edge of ruler to the point where the horizontal line representing place of departure intersects the vertical line representing the time in question. If the ruler's edge lies within the shaded portion of the diagram, a flood current will be encountered; if within the unshaded, an ebb current, and if along the boundary of both, slack water. The figures in the diagram along the edge of the ruler will show the speed of the current encountered at any place indicated in the left margin of the diagram.

Example.—A 12-knot vessel bound for Baltimore passes Cape Henry Light at 1430 of a given day, and it is desired to ascertain the speed and direction of the current which will be encountered. Assuming that on the given day flood begins at Chesapeake Bay entrance at 1256 and ebb begins at 1803, the time 1430 will be about 1 hours after flood begins. With parallel rulers transfer to the diagram the 12-knot speed line "Northbound," placing edge of ruler so that it will cross the horizontal line opposite Cape Henry at a point "1 hours after flood begins at the entrance." It will be found that the edge of the ruler passes through strength of current in the shaded portion of the diagram averaging about 0.7 knot. The vessel will, therefore, have a favorable current averaging about 0.7 knot all the way to Baltimore.

To determine the time of a favorable current for passing through the bay.—With parallel rulers transfer to the diagram the direction of the speed line corresponding to normal speed of vessel, moving the ruler over the diagram until its edge runs approximately through the general line of greatest current of unshaded portion if southbound and shaded portion if northbound. An average of the figures along edge of ruler will give average strength of current. The time (before or after ebb or flood begins at the entrance) for leaving any place in the left margin of diagram will be found vertically above the point where the parallel ruler cuts the horizontal line opposite the place in question.

Example.—A 12-knot vessel in Baltimore Harbor desires to leave for Cape Henry Light on the afternoon of a day when flood begins at Chesapeake Bay Entrance at 1148 and ebb begins at 1718. At what time should she get under way so as to carry the most favorable current?

Place parallel rulers along the 12-knot speed line "Southbound." Transfer this direction to the diagram and move it along so as to include the greatest possible number of larger current speeds in the unshaded portion of the diagram. The most favorable time for leaving Baltimore thus found is about 1 hour after flood begins at the entrance, or about 1248. There will be an unfavorable current of about 0.2 knot as far as Seven Foot Knoll Light; after passing this light there will be an average favorable current of about 0.3 knot as far as Cove Point Light; from Cove Point Light to Bluff Point a contrary current averaging about 0.3 knot will be encountered; from Bluff Point to Tail of the Horseshoe there will be an average favorable current of about 0.9 knot; and from Tail of the Horseshoe to Cape Henry an average contrary current of about 0.2 knot will again be encountered.

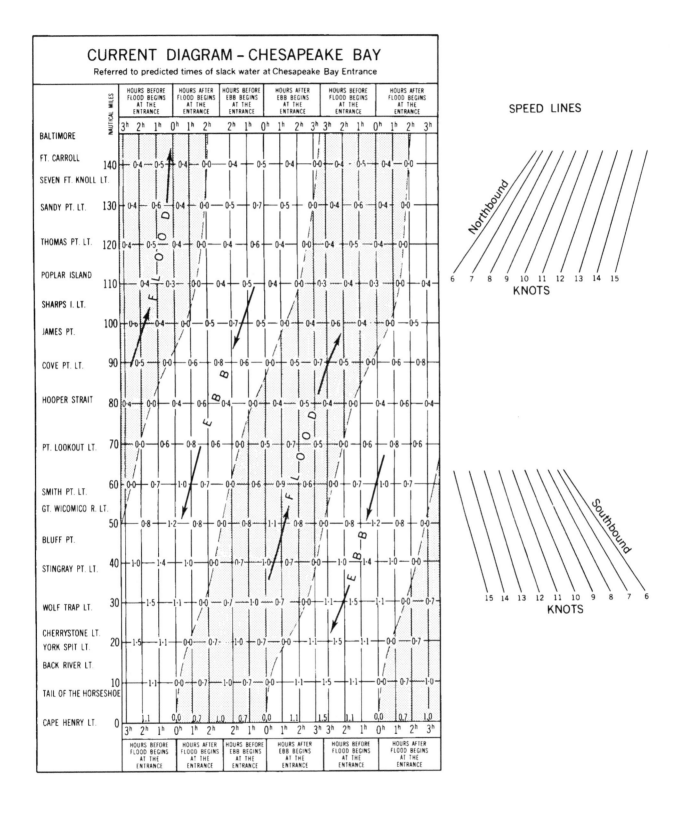

PUBLICATIONS RELATING TO TIDES AND TIDAL CURRENTS

TIDE TABLES

Advance information relative to the rise and fall of the tide is given in annual tide tables. These tables include the predicted times and heights of high and low waters for every day in the year for a number of reference stations and differences for obtaining similar predictions for numerous other places.

Tide Tables, Central and Western Pacific Ocean and Indian Ocean
Tide Tables, East Coast of North and South America (Including Greenland)
Tide Tables, Europe and West Coast of Africa (Including the Mediterranean Sea)
Tide Tables, West Coast of North and South America (Including the Hawaiian Islands)

TIDAL CURRENT TABLES

Accompanying the rise and fall of the tide is a periodic horizontal flow of the water known as the tidal current. Advance information relative to these currents is made available in annual tidal current tables which include daily predictions of the times of slack water and the times and velocities of strength of flood and ebb currents for a number of waterways together with differences for obtaining predictions for numerous other places.

Tidal Current Tables, Atlantic Coast of North America
Tidal Current Tables, Pacific Coast of North America and Asia

OFFICIAL U.S. DATUMS

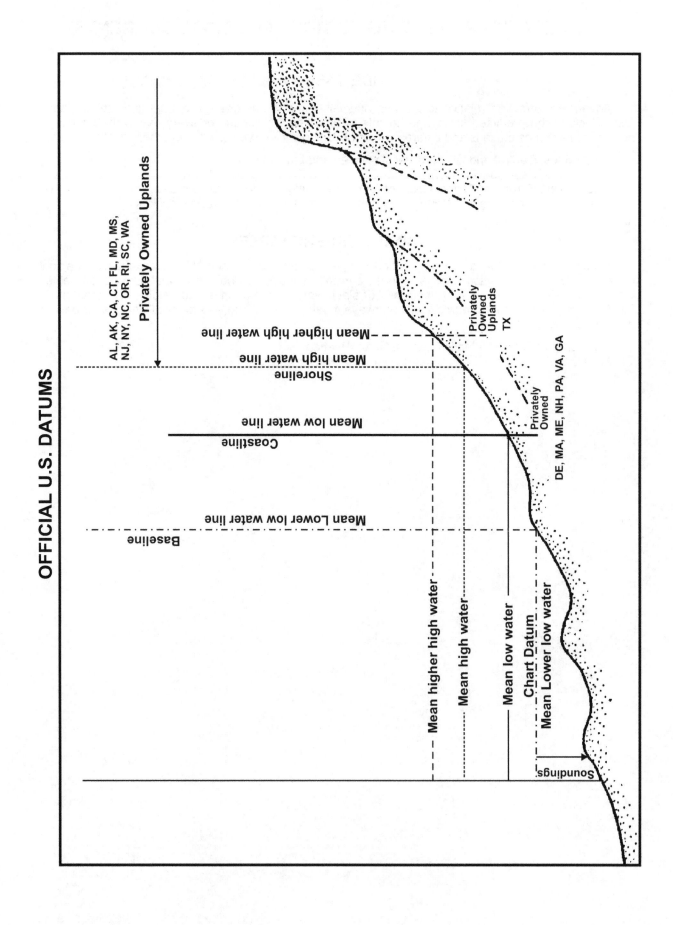

GLOSSARY OF TERMS

ANNUAL INEQUALITY—Seasonal variation in the water level or current, more or less periodic, due chiefly to meteorological causes.

APOGEAN TIDES OR TIDAL CURRENTS—Tides of decreased range or currents of decreased speed occurring monthly as the result of the Moon being in apogee (farthest from the Earth).

AUTOMATIC TIDE GAGE—An instrument that automatically registers the rise and fall of the tide. In some instruments, the registration is accomplished by recording the heights at regular intervals in digital format, in others by a continuous graph in which the height versus corresponding time of the tide is recorded.

BENCH MARK (BM)—A fixed physical object or marks used as reference for a vertical datum. A *tidal bench mark is* one near a tide station to which the tide staff and tidal datums are referred. A *Geodetic bench mark* identifies a surveyed point in the National Geodetic Vertical Network.

CHART DATUM—The tidal datum to which soundings on a chart are referred. It is usually taken to correspond to low water elevation of the tide, and its depression below mean sea level is represented by the symbol Zo.

CURRENT—Generally, a horizontal movement of water. Currents may be classified as *tidal* and *nontidal*. Tidal currents are caused by gravitational interactions between the Sun, Moon, and Earth and are a part of the same general movement of the sea that is manifested in the vertical rise and fall, called *tide*. Nontidal currents include the permanent currents in the general circulatory systems of the sea as well as temporary currents arising from more pronounced meteorological variability.

CURRENT DIFFERENCE—Difference between the time of slack water (or minimum current) or strength of current in any locality and the time of the corresponding phase of the tidal current at a reference station, for which predictions are given in the *Tidal Current Tables*.

CURRENT ELLIPSE—A graphic representation of a rotary current in which the velocity of the current at different hours of the tidal cycle is represented by radius vectors and vectorial angles. A line joining the extremities of the radius vectors will form a curve roughly approximating an ellipse. The cycle is completed in one-half tidal day or in a whole tidal day according to whether the tidal current is of the semidiurnal or the diurnal type. A current of the mixed type will give a curve of two unequal loops each tidal day.

CURRENT METER—An instrument for measuring the speed and direction or just the speed of a current. The measurements are usually Eulerian since the meter is most often fixed or moored at a specific location.

DATUM (vertical)—For marine applications, a base elevation used as a reference from which to reckon heights or depths. It is called a *tidal datum* when defined by a certain phase of the tide. Tidal datums are local datums and should not be extended into areas which have differing topographic features without substantiating measurements. In order that they may be recovered when needed, such datums are referenced to fixed points known as *bench marks.*

DAYLIGHT SAVING TIME—A time used during the summer in some localities in which clocks are advanced 1 hour from the usual standard time.

DIURNAL—Having a period or cycle of approximately 1 tidal day. Thus, the tide is said to be diurnal when only one high water and one low water occur during a tidal day, and the tidal current is said to be diurnal when there is a single flood and single ebb period in the tidal day. A rotary current is diurnal if it changes its direction through all points of the compass once each tidal day.

DIURNAL INEQUALITY—The difference in height of the two high waters or of the two low waters of each day; also the difference in speed between the two flood tidal currents or the two ebb tidal currents of each day. The difference changes with the declination of the Moon and to a lesser extent with the declination of the Sun. In general, the inequality tends to increase with an increasing declination, either north or south, and to diminish as the Moon approaches the Equator. *Mean diurnal high water inequality* (DHQ) is one-half the average difference between the two high waters of each day observed over a specific 19-year Metonic cycle (the National Tidal Datum Epoch). It is obtained by subtracting the mean of all high waters from the mean of the higher high waters. *Mean diurnal low water inequality* (DLQ) is one-half the average difference between the two low waters of each day observed over a specific 19-year Metonic cycle (the National Tidal Datum Epoch). It is obtained by subtracting the mean of the lower low waters from the mean of all low waters. *Tropic high water inequality* (HWQ) is the average difference between the two high waters of the day at the times of the tropic tides. *Tropic low water inequality* (LWQ) is the average difference between the two low waters of the day at the times of the tropic tides. Mean and tropic inequalities as defined above are applicable only when the type of tide is either semidiurnal or mixed. Diurnal inequality is sometimes called *declinational inequality.*

DOUBLE EBB—An ebb tidal current where, after ebb begins, the speed increases to a maximum called *first ebb*; it then decreases, reaching a *minimum ebb* near the middle of the ebb period (and at some places it may actually run in a flood direction for a short period); it then again ebbs to a maximum speed called second ebb after which it decreases to slack water.

DOUBLE FLOOD—A flood tidal current where, after flood begins, the speed increases to a maximum called first flood; it then decreases, reaching a minimum flood near the middle of the flood period (and at some places it may actually run in an ebb direction for a short period); it then again floods to a maximum speed called second flood after which it decreases to slack water.

DOUBLE TIDE—A double-headed tide, that is, a high water consisting of two maxima of nearly the same height separated by a relatively small depression, or a low water consisting of two minima separated by a relatively small elevation. Sometimes, it is called an agger.

DURATION OF FLOOD AND DURATION OF EBB—Duration of flood is the interval of time in which a tidal current is flooding, and the *duration of ebb* is the interval in which it is ebbing. Together they cover, on an average, a period of 12.42 hours for a semidiurnal tidal current or a period of 24.84 hours for a diurnal current. In a normal semidiurnal tidal current, the duration of flood and duration of ebb will each be approximately equal to 6.21 hours, but the times may be modified greatly by the presence of a nontidal flow. In a river the duration of ebb is usually longer than the duration of flood because of the freshwater discharge, especially during the spring when snow and ice melt are the predominant influences.

DURATION OF RISE AND DURATION OF FALL—*Duration of rise* is the interval from low water to high water, and *duration of fall* is the interval from high water to low water. Together they cover, on an average, a period of 12.42 hours for a semidiurnal tide or a period of 24.84 hours for a diurnal tide. In a normal semidiurnal tide, the duration of rise and duration of fall will each be approximately equal to 6.21 hours, but in shallow waters and in rivers there is a tendency for a decrease in the duration of rise and a corresponding increase in the duration of fall.

EBB CURRENT—The movement of a tidal current away from shore or down a tidal river or estuary. In the mixed type of reversing tidal current, the terms *greater ebb* and *lesser ebb* are applied respectively to the ebb tidal currents of greater and lesser speed of each day. The terms *maximum ebb* and *minimum ebb* are applied to the maximum and minimum speeds of a current running continuously ebb, the speed alternately increasing and decreasing without coming to a slack or reversing. The expression maximum ebb is also applicable to any ebb current at the time of greatest speed.

EQUATORIAL TIDAL CURRENTS—Tidal currents occurring semimonthly as a result of the Moon being over the Equator. At these times the tendency of the Moon to produce a diurnal inequality in the tidal current is at a minimum.

EQUATORIAL TIDES—Tides occurring semi monthly as the result of the Moon being over the Equator. At these times the tendency of the Moon to produce a diurnal inequality in the tide is at a minimum.

FLOOD CURRENT—The movement of a tidal current toward the shore or up a tidal river or estuary. In the mixed type of reversing current, the terms *greater flood* and *lesser flood* are applied respectively to the flood currents of greater and lesser speed of each day. The terms *maximum flood* and *minimum flood* are applied to the maximum and minimum speeds of a flood current, the speed of which alternately increases and decreases without coming to a slack or reversing. The expression maximum flood is also applicable to any flood current at the time of greatest speed.

GREAT DIURNAL RANGE (Gt)—The difference in height between mean higher high water and mean lower low water. The expression may also be used in its contracted form, *diurnal range.*

GREENWICH INTERVAL—An interval referred to the transit of the Moon over the meridian of Greenwich as distinguished from the local interval which is referred to the Moon's transit over the local meri-dian. The relation in hours between Greenwich and local intervals may be expressed by the formula:

Greenwich interval = local interval +0.069 L where L is the west longitude of the local meridan in degrees. For east longitude, L is to be considered negative.

GULF COAST LOW WATER DATUM—A chart datum. Specifically, the tidal datum formerly designated for the coastal waters of the Gulf Coast of the United States. It was defined as *mean lower low water* when the type of tide was mixed and *mean low water* when the type of tide was diurnal.

HALF-TIDE LEVEL—See *mean tide level.*

GLOSSARY OF TERMS

HARMONIC ANALYSIS—The mathematical process by which the observed tide or tidal current at any place is separated into basic harmonic constituents.

HARMONIC CONSTANTS—The amplitudes and epochs of the harmonic constituents of the tide or tidal current at any place.

HARMONIC CONSTITUENT—One of the harmonic elements in a mathematical expression for the tide-producing force and in corresponding formulas for the tide or tidal current. Each constituent represents a periodic change or variation in the relative positions of the Earth, Moon, and Sun. A single constituent is usually written in the form $y = A \cos(at + \alpha)$, in which y is a function of time as expressed by the symbol t and is reckoned from a specific origin. The coefficient A is called the amplitude of the constituent and is a measure of its relative importance. The angle $(at + \alpha)$ changes uniformly and its value at any time is called the phase of the constituent. The speed of the constituent is the rate of change in its phase and is represented by the symbol a in the formula. The quantity α is the phase of the constituent at the initial instant from which the time is reckoned. The period of the constituent is the time required for the phase to change through 360° and is the cycle of the astronomical condition represented by the constituent.

HIGH WATER (HW)—The maximum height reached by a rising tide. The height may be due solely to the periodic tidal forces or it may have superimposed upon it the effects of prevailing meteorological conditions. Use of the synonymous term, *high tide*, is discouraged.

HIGHER HIGH WATER (HHW)—The higher of the two high waters of any tidal day.

HIGHER LOW WATER (HLW)—The higher of the two low waters of any tidal day.

HYDRAULIC CURRENT—A current in a channel caused by a difference in the surface level at the two ends. Such a current may be expected in a strait connecting two bodies of water in which the tides differ in time or range. The current in the East River, N.Y., connecting Long Island Sound and New York Harbor, is an example.

KNOT—A unit of speed, one international nautical mile (1,852.0 meters or 6,076.11549 international feet) per hour.

LOW WATER (LW)—The minimum height reached by a falling tide. The height may be due solely to the periodic tidal forces or it may have superimposed upon it the effects of meteorological conditions. Use of the synonymous term, *low tide*, is discouraged.

LOWER HIGH WATER (LHW)—The lower of the two high waters of any tidal day.

LOWER LOW WATER (LLW)—The lower of the two low waters of any tidal day.

LUNAR DAY—The time of the rotation of the Earth with respect to the Moon, or the interval between two successive upper transits of the Moon over the meridian of a place. The mean lunar day is approximately 24.84 solar hours long, or 1.035 times as long as the mean solar day.

LUNAR INTERVAL—The difference in time between the transit of the Moon over the meridian of Greenwich and over a local meridian. The average value of this interval expressed in hours is 0.069 L, in which L is the local longitude in degrees, positive for west longitude and negative for east longitude. The lunar interval equals the difference between the local and Greenwich interval of a tide or current phase.

LUNICURRENT INTERVAL—The interval between the Moon's transit (upper or lower) over the local or Greenwich meridian and a specified phase of the tidal current following the transit. Examples: *strength of flood interval and strength of ebb interval,* which may be abbreviated to *flood interval and ebb interval,* respectively. The interval is described as local or Greenwich according to whether the reference is to the Moon's transit over the local or Greenwich meridian. When not otherwise specified, the reference is assumed to be local.

LUNITIDAL INTERVAL—The interval between the Moon's transit (upper or lower) over the local or Greenwich meridian and the following high or low water. The average of all high water intervals for all phases of the Moon is known as *mean high water lunitidal interval* and is abbreviated to high water interval (HWI). Similarly the *mean low water lunitidal interval* is abbreviated to *low water interval* (LWI). The interval is described as local or Greenwich according to whether the reference is to the transit over the local or Greenwich meridian. When not otherwise specified, the reference is assumed to be local.

MEAN HIGH WATER (MHW)—A tidal datum. The arithmetic mean of the high water heights observed over a specific 19-year Metonic cycle (the National Tidal Datum Epoch). For stations with shorter series, simultaneous observational comparisons are made with a primary control tide station in order to derive the equivalent of a 19-year value.

MEAN HIGHER HIGH WATER (MHHW)—A tidal datum. The arithmetic mean of the higher high water heights of a mixed tide observed over a specific 19-year Metonic cycle (the National Tidal Datum Epoch). Only the higher high water of each pair of high waters, or the only high water of a tidal day is included in the mean.

MEAN HIGHER HIGH WATER LINE (MHHWL)—The intersection of the land with the water surface at the elevation of mean higher high water.

MEAN LOW WATER (MLW)—A tidal datum. The arithmetic mean of the low water heights observed over a specific 19-year Metonic cycle (the National Tidal Datum Epoch). For stations with shorter series, simultaneous observational comparisons are made with a primary control tide station in order to derive the equivalent of a 19-year value.

MEAN LOW WATER SPRINGS (MLWS)—A tidal datum. Frequently abbreviated spring low water. The arithmetic mean of the low water heights occurring at the time of the spring tides observed over a specific 19-year Metonic cycle (the National Tidal Datum Epoch).

MEAN LOWER LOW WATER (MLLW)—A tidal datum. The arithmetic mean of the lower low water heights of a mixed tide observed over a specific 19-year Metonic cycle (the National Tidal Datum Epoch). Only the lower low water of each pair of low waters, or the only low water of a tidal day is included in the mean.

MEAN RANGE OF TIDE (Mn)—The difference in height between mean high water and mean low water.

MEAN RIVER LEVEL—A tidal datum. The average height of the surface of a tidal river at any point for all stages of the tide observed over a 19-year Metonic cycle (the National Tidal Datum Epoch), usually determined from hourly height readings. In rivers subject to occasional freshets the river level may undergo wide variations, and for practical purposes certain months of the year may be excluded in the determination of tidal datums. For charting purposes, tidal datums for rivers are usually based on observations during selected periods when the river is at or near low water stage.

MEAN SEA LEVEL (MSL)—A tidal datum. The arithmetic mean of hourly water elevations observed over a specific 19-year Metonic cycle (the National Tidal Datum Epoch). Shorter series are specified in the name; e.g., monthly mean sea level and yearly mean sea level.

MEAN TIDE LEVEL (MTL)—Also called half-tide level. A tidal datum midway between mean high water and mean low water.

MIXED TIDE—Type of tide with a large inequality in the high and/or low water heights, with two high waters and two low waters usually occurring each tidal day. In strictness, all tides are mixed but the name is usually applied to the tides intermediate to those predominantly semidiurnal and those predominantly diurnal.

NATIONAL TIDAL DATUM EPOCH—The specific 19-year period adopted by the National Ocean Service as the official time segment over which tide observations are taken and reduced to obtain mean values (e.g., mean lower low water, etc.) for tidal datums. It is necessary for standardization because of periodic and apparent secular trends in sea level. The present National Tidal Datum Epoch is 1960 through 1978. It is reviewed annually for possible revision and must be actively considered for revision every 25 years.

NEAP TIDES OR TIDAL CURRENTS—Tides of decreased range or tidal currents of decreased speed occurring semimonthly as the result of the Moon being in quadrature. The neap range (Np) of the tide is the average semidiurnal range occurring at the time of neap tides and is most conveniently computed from the harmonic constants. It is smaller than the mean range where the type of tide is either semidiurnal or mixed and is of no practical significance where the type of tide is diurnal. The average height of the high waters of the neap tides is called neap high water or high water neaps (MHWN) and the average height of the corresponding low waters is called neap low water or low water neaps (MLWN).

PERIGEAN TIDES OR TIDAL CURRENTS—Tides of increased range or tidal currents of increased speed occurring monthly as the result of the Moon being in perigee or nearest the Earth. The perigean range (Pn) of tide is the average semidiurnal range occurring at the time of perigean tides and is most conveniently computed from the harmonic constants. It is larger than the mean range where the type of tide is either semidiurnal or mixed, and is of no practical significance where the type of tide is diurnal.

RANGE OF TIDE—The difference in height between consecutive high and low waters, the mean range is the difference in height between mean high water and mean low water. Where the type of tide is diurnal the mean range is the same as the diurnal range.

For other ranges, see great diurnal, spring, neap, perigean, apogean, and tropic tides.

REFERENCE STATION—A tide or current station for which independent daily predictions are given in the *Tide Tables and Tidal Current Tables,* and from which corresponding predictions are obtained for subordinate stations by means of differences and ratios.

REVERSING CURRENT—A tidal current which flows alternately in approximately opposite directions with a slack water at each reversal of direction. Currents of this type usually occur in rivers and straits where the direction of flow is more or less restricted to certain channels. When the movement is towards the shore or up a stream, the current is said to be flooding, and when in the opposite direction it is said to be ebbing. The combined flood and ebb movement including the slack water covers, on an average, 12.42 hours for the semidiurnal current. If unaffected by a nontidal flow, the flood and ebb movements will each last about 6 hours, but when combined with such a flow, the durations of flood and ebb may be quite unequal. During the flow in each direction the speed of the current will vary from zero at the time of slack water to a maximum about midway between the slacks.

ROTARY CURRENT—A tidal current that flows continually with the direction of flow changing through all points of the compass during the tidal period. Rotary currents are usually found offshore where the direction of flow is not restricted by any barriers. The tendency for the rotation in direction has its origin in the Coriolis force and, unless modified by local conditions, the change is clockwise in the Northern Hemisphere and counterclockwise in the Southern. The speed of the current usually varies throughout the tidal cycle, passing through the two maxima in approximately opposite directions and the two minima with the direction of the current at approximately 90° from the direction at time of maximum speed.

SEMIDIURNAL—Having a period or cycle of approximately one-half of a tidal day. The predominating type of tide throughout the world is semidiurnal, with two high waters and two low waters each tidal day. The tidal current is said to be semidiurnal when there are two flood and two ebb periods each day.

SET (OF CURRENT)—The direction *towards* which the current flows.

SLACK WATER—The state of a tidal current when its speed is near zero, especially the moment when a reversing current changes direction and its speed is zero. The term is also applied to the entire period of low speed near the time of turning of the current when it is too weak to be of any practical importance in navigation. The relation of the time of slack water to the tidal phases varies in different localities. For standing tidal waves, slack water occurs near the times of high and low water, while for progressive tidal waves, slack water occurs midway between high and low water.

SPRING TIDES OR TIDAL CURRENTS—Tides of increased range or tidal currents of increased speed occurring semimonthly as the result of the Moon being new or full. The *spring range* (Sg) of tide is the average semidiurnal range occurring at the time of spring tides and is most conveniently computed from the harmonic constants. It is larger than the mean range where the type of tide is either semidiurnal or mixed, and is of no practical significance where the type of tide is diurnal. The mean of the high waters of the spring tide is called *spring high water or mean high water springs* (MHWS), and the average height of the corresponding low waters is called *spring low water or mean low water springs* (MLWS).

STAND OF TIDE—Sometimes called a platform tide. An interval at high or low water when there is no sensible change in the height of the tide. The water level is stationary at high and low water for only an instant, but the change in level near these times is so slow that it is not usually perceptible. In general, the duration of the apparent stand will depend upon the range of tide, being longer for a small range than for a large range, but where there is a tendency for a double tide the stand may last for several hours even with a large range of tide.

STANDARD TIME—A kind of time based upon the transit of the Sun over a certain specified meridian, called the *time meridian,* and adopted for use over a considerable area. With a few exceptions, standard time is based upon some meridian which differs by a multiple of 15° from the meridian of Greenwich.

STRENGTH OF CURRENT—Phase of tidal current in which the speed is a maximum; also the speed at this time. Beginning with slack before flood in the period of a reversing tidal current (or minimum before flood in a rotary current), the speed gradually increases to flood strength and then diminishes to slack before ebb (or minimum before ebb in a rotary current), after which the current turns in direction, the speed increases to ebb strength and then diminishes to slack before flood completing the cycle. If it is assumed that the speed throughout the cycle varies as the ordinates of a cosine curve, it can be shown that the average speed for an entire flood or ebb period is equal to $2/\pi$ or 0.6366 of the speed of the corresponding strength of current.

SUBORDINATE CURRENT STATION—(1) A current station from which a relatively short series of observations is reduced by comparison with simultaneous observations from a control current station. (2) A station listed in the *Tidal Current Tables* for which predictions are to be obtained by means of differences and ratios applied to the full predictions at a reference station .

SUBORDINATE TIDE STATION—(1) A tide station from which a relatively short series of observations is reduced by comparison with simultaneous observations from a tide station with a relatively long series of observations. (2) A station listed in the *Tide Tables* for which predictions are to be obtained by means of differences and ratios applied to the full predictions at a reference station.

TIDAL CURRENT TABLES—Tables which give daily predictions of the times and speeds of the tidal currents. These predictions are usually supplemented by current differences and constants through which additional predictions can be obtained for numerous other places.

TIDAL DIFFERENCE—Difference in time or height of a high or low water at a subordinate station and at a reference station for which predictions are given in the *Tide Tables*. The difference, when applied according to sign to the prediction at the reference station, gives the corresponding time or height for the subordinate station .

TIDE—The periodic rise and fall of the water resulting from gravitational interactions between the Sun, Moon, and Earth. The vertical component of the particulate motion of a tidal wave. Although the accompanying horizontal movement of the water is part of the same phenomenon, it is preferable to designate the motion as tidal current.

TIDE TABLES—Tables which give daily predictions of the times and heights of high and low waters. These predictions are usually supplemented by tidal differences and constants through which additional predictions can be obtained for numerous other places.

TIME MERIDIAN—A meridian used as a reference for time.

TROPIC CURRENTS—Tidal currents occurring semimonthly when the effect of the Moon's maximum declination is greatest. At these times the tendency of the Moon to produce a diurnal inequality in the current is at a maximum.

TROPIC RANGES—The *great tropic range* (Gc), or *tropic range*, is the difference in height between tropic higher high water and tropic lower low water. The *small tropic range* (Sc) is the difference in height between tropic lower high water and tropic higher low water. The *mean tropic range* (Mc) is the mean between the great tropic range and the small tropic range. The small tropic range and the mean tropic range are applicable only when the type of tide is semidiurnal or mixed. Tropic ranges are most conveniently computed from the harmonic constants.

TROPIC TIDES—Tides occurring semimonthly when the effect of the Moon's maximum declination is greatest. At these times there is a tendency for an increase in the diurnal range. The tidal datums pertaining to the tropic tides are designated as *tropic higher high water* (TcHHW), *tropic lower high water* (TcLHW), *tropic higher low water* (TcHLW), and *tropic lower low water* (TcLLW).

TYPE OF TIDE—A classification based on characteristic forms of a tide curve. Qualitatively, when the two high waters and two low waters of each tidal day are approximately equal in height, the tide is said to be *semidiurnal*; when there is a relatively large diurnal inequality in the high or low waters or both, it is said to be *mixed*; and when there is only one high water and one low water in each tidal day, it is said to be *diurnal*.

VANISHING TIDE—In a mixed tide with very large diurnal inequality, the lower high water (or higher low water) frequently becomes indistinct (or vanishes) at time of extreme declinations. During these periods the diurnal tide has such overriding dominance that the semidiurnal tide, although still present, cannot be readily seen on the tide curve.

[Stations marked with an asterisk (*) are reference stations for which daily predictions are given in table 1. Page numbers of reference stations are given in parentheses.]

ASTRONOMICAL DATA, 2019

January

	d	h	m
S	5	19	..
●	6	01	28
A	9	04	..
E	13	08	..
◐	14	06	46
N	20	00	..
O	21	05	16
P	21	20	..
E	26	01	..
◑	27	21	10

February

	d	h	m
S	2	01	..
●	4	21	04
A	5	09	..
E	9	15	..
◐	12	22	26
N	16	10	..
P	19	09	..
O	19	15	54
E	22	10	..
◑	26	11	28

March

	d	h	m
S	1	07	..
A	4	11	..
●	6	16	04
E	8	20	..
◐	14	10	27
N	15	19	..
P	19	20	..
☉m	20	21	58
O	21	01	43
E	21	20	..
◑	28	04	10
S	28	13	..

April

	d	h	m
A	1	00	..
E	5	02	..
●	5	08	50
N	12	00	..
◐	12	19	06
P	16	22	..
E	18	07	..
O	19	11	12
S	24	22	..
◑	26	22	18
A	28	18	..

May

	d	h	m
E	2	10	..
●	4	22	45
N	9	06	..
◐	12	01	12
P	13	22	..
E	15	15	..
O	18	21	11
S	22	07	..
A	26	13	..
◑	26	16	34
E	29	19	..

June

	d	h	m
●	3	10	02
N	5	13	..
P	7	23	..
◐	10	05	59
E	11	22	..
O	17	08	31
S	18	16	..
☉j	21	15	54
A	23	08	..
◑	25	09	46
E	26	04	..

July

	d	h	m
●	2	19	16
N	2	23	..
P	5	05	..
E	9	03	..
◐	9	10	55
S	15	23	..
O	16	21	38
A	21	00	..
E	23	11	..
◑	25	01	18
N	30	09	..

August

	d	h	m
●	1	03	12
P	2	07	..
E	5	10	..
◐	7	17	31
S	12	05	..
O	15	12	29
A	17	11	..
E	19	17	..
◑	23	14	56
N	26	18	..
●	30	10	37
P	30	16	..

September

	d	h	m
E	1	18	..
◐	6	03	10
S	8	10	..
A	13	14	..
O	14	04	33
E	15	23	..
◑	22	02	41
N	23	02	..
☉s	23	07	50
P	28	02	..
●	28	18	26
E	29	05	..

October

	d	h	m
◐	5	16	47
S	5	17	..
A	10	18	..
E	13	05	..
O	13	21	08
N	20	09	..
◑	21	12	39
P	26	11	..
E	26	16	..
●	28	03	38

November

	d	h	m
S	2	01	..
◐	4	10	23
A	7	09	..
E	9	12	..
O	12	13	34
N	16	14	..
◑	19	21	11
E	23	01	..
P	23	08	..
●	26	15	06
S	29	11	..

December

	d	h	m
◐	4	06	58
A	5	04	..
E	6	21	..
O	12	05	12
N	13	21	..
P	18	20	..
◑	19	04	57
E	20	07	..
☉d	22	04	19
●	26	05	13
S	26	21	..
P	31	23	..

LUNAR DATA

- ● -- new Moon
- ◐ -- first quarter
- ○ -- full Moon
- ◑ -- last quarter

- A -- Moon in apogee
- P -- Moon in perigee
- N -- Moon farthest north of Equator
- E -- Moon on Equator
- S -- Moon farthest south of Equator

SOLAR DATA

- ☉m -- March equinox
- ☉j -- June solstice
- ☉s -- September equinox
- ☉d -- December solstice

Greenwich mean time (GMT) or universal time (UT) is the mean solar time on the Greenwich meridian reckoned in days of 24 mean solar hours written as 00^h at midnight and 12^h at noon. To convert the above times to those of other standard time meridians, add 1 hour for each 15° of east longitude of the desired meridian and subtract 1 hour for each 15° of west longitude.

This table was compiled from data supplied by the Nautical Almanac Office, United States Naval Observatory.